What Can You Do?

Case Studies

CENGAGENOW

Just What You Need To Know and Do NOW!

CengageNOW™ is an online teaching and learning resource that provides more control in less time and delivers better student outcomes.

▶ **Teaching and Learning Resource**—Create assignments, grade, quiz, and track student outcomes.

▶ **More Control in Less Time**—Use flexible assignment and grade book options to best suit your overall course plan.

▶ **Better Student Outcomes**—A diagnostic Personalized Study Plan empowers students to master concepts, prepare for exams, and get a better grade.

Archipoch/Shutterstock

Over 550,000 students have already taken advantage of CengageNOW, and here is what students and instructors are saying...

According to a survey of over 1300 student users:		According to a survey of over 250 instructors:	
80%	believe using CengageNOW helped them better understand key concepts in the course	**91%**	believe using CengageNOW helps students better understand key concepts
75%	believe using CengageNOW helped them be more prepared for exams	**86%**	believe using CengageNOW helps students be more prepared for exams
77%	believe using CengageNOW helped them get a better grade	**84%**	believe using CengageNOW helps students get a better grade
75%	would recommend CengageNOW to a friend	**76%**	would recommend CengageNOW to a colleague

Go to www.nelsonbrain.com to take a tour and learn more.

Living in the Environment

THIRD CANADIAN EDITION

Living in the Environment

THIRD CANADIAN EDITION

G. Tyler Miller, Jr.

President, Earth Education and Research

Dave Hackett

Nipissing University

NELSON / EDUCATION

NELSON / EDUCATION

Living in the Environment, **Third Canadian Edition**
by G. Tyler Miller, Jr., and Dave Hackett

**Vice President, Editorial
Higher Education:**
Anne Williams

Publisher:
Paul Fam

Marketing Manager:
Leanne Newell

Senior Developmental Editor:
Mark Grzeskowiak

Photo Researcher:
Kristiina Paul

Permissions Coordinator:
Kristiina Paul

Content Production Manager:
Claire Horsnell

Production Service:
Integra Software Services

Copy Editor:
Marcia Gallego

Proofreader:
Integra Software Services

Indexer:
Integra Software Services

Senior Production Coordinator:
Ferial Suleman

Design Director:
Ken Phipps

Managing Designer:
Franca Amore

Interior Design:
Dianna Little

Cover Design:
Sharon Lucas

Cover Image:
Peter Nosko

Compositor:
Integra Software Services

Printer:
R. R. Donnelley

Library and Archives Canada Cataloguing in Publication

Miller, G. Tyler (George Tyler), 1931– Living in the environment/ G. Tyler Miller, Scott E. Spoolman, Dave Hackett.—3rd Canadian ed. Includes index.
ISBN 978-0-17-651013-8

1. Environmental sciences— Textbooks. 2. Human ecology— Textbooks. 3. Environmental policy—Textbooks. 4. Environmental sciences—Canada—Textbooks. I. Hackett, David F. (David Franklin), 1953– II. Spoolman, Scott III. Title.

GE105.M54 2013   333.7
C2012-906046-1

ISBN-13: 978-0-17-651013-8
ISBN-10: 0-17-651013-3

Brief Contents

Detailed Contents

NASA

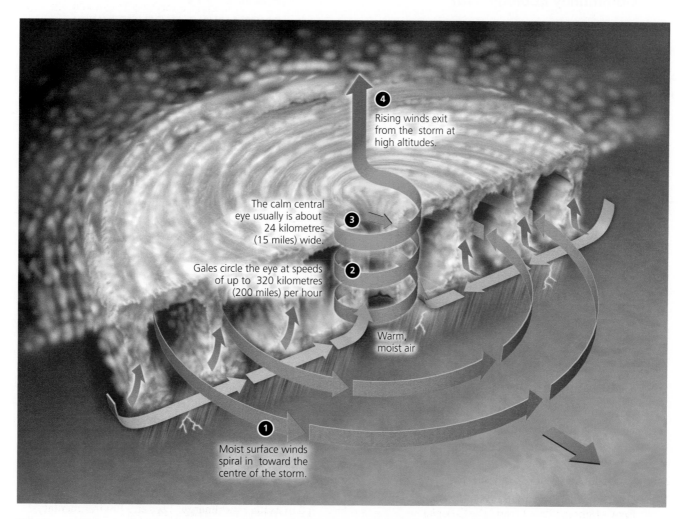

This diagram illustrates the formation of a *tropical cyclone*. Those forming in the Atlantic Ocean are called *hurricanes*; those forming in the Pacific Ocean are called *typhoons*.

Bleached coral

Stephen Mcsweeny/Shutterstock.com

Owls may hoot or even approach when participants in the Nocturnal Owl Survey broadcast owl calls into the forest at night. This great grey owl is curious and territorial.

12 Sustaining Biodiversity: The Species Approach 249

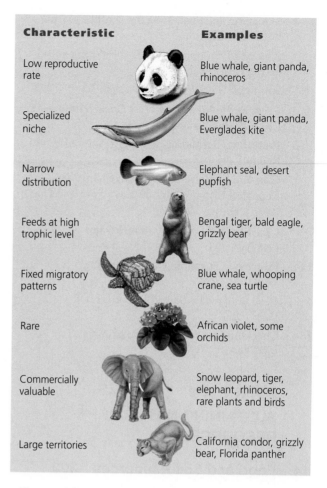

Characteristic		Examples
Low reproductive rate		Blue whale, giant panda, rhinoceros
Specialized niche		Blue whale, giant panda, Everglades kite
Narrow distribution		Elephant seal, desert pupfish
Feeds at high trophic level		Bengal tiger, bald eagle, grizzly bear
Fixed migratory patterns		Blue whale, whooping crane, sea turtle
Rare		African violet, some orchids
Commercially valuable		Snow leopard, tiger, elephant, rhinoceros, rare plants and birds
Large territories		California condor, grizzly bear, Florida panther

Characteristics of species that are prone to ecological and biological extinction.

13 Sustaining Aquatic Biodiversity 278

PART IV

SUSTAINING NATURAL RESOURCES

Natural landscaping or xeriscaping can reduce water use by as much as 85% by using rocks and plants that need little water and are adapted to local growing conditions.

© canadabrian/Alamy

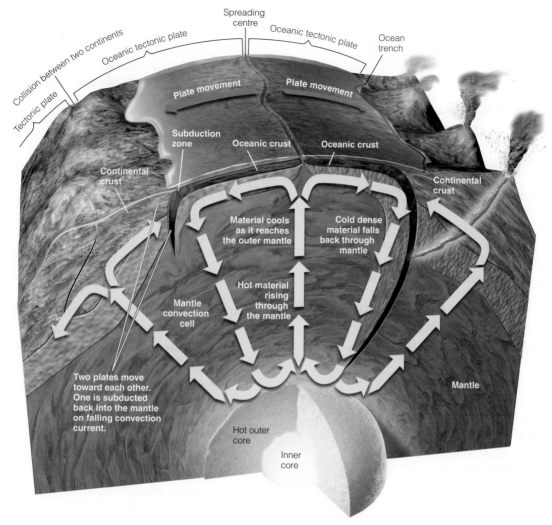

The Earth's crust is made up of a series of rigid plates, called *tectonic plates*, which move around in response to forces in the mantle.

Predatory insects can be bought by the thousands and released to control pests.

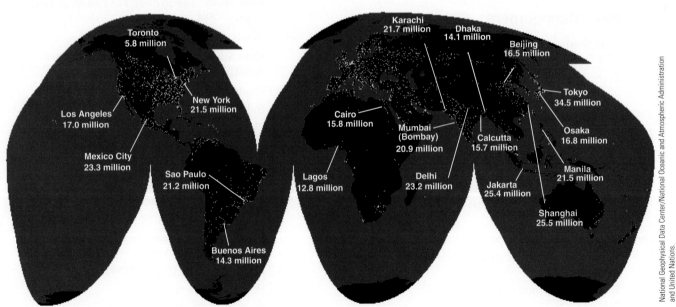

Major urban areas throughout the world based on satellite images of the Earth at night that show city lights.

National Geophysical Data Center/National Oceanic and Atmospheric Administration and United Nations.

Preface for Instructors

What Are the Major Features of This Book?
Science Based, Solutions Oriented, and Flexible Use

This book is designed to support introductory courses about environmental science. It is an *interdisciplinary* study of how nature works and how things in nature are interconnected. About 40% of the book is devoted to providing a scientific base needed to understand environmental problems and to evaluate possible solutions, 30% presents environmental problems, and another 30% presents and evaluates solutions to these problems.

This book is *science based, solutions oriented*, and *flexible*. It is divided into six major parts (see Brief Contents, p. v). A highly flexible format allows instructors to use almost any course outline. We suggest that instructors use Chapter 1 to provide an overview of environmental problems and solutions and Chapters 3 through 9 to provide a base of scientific principles and concepts. The remaining chapters—2 and 10 through 28—can be used in virtually any order or omitted as desired. In addition, sections within chapters can be omitted or rearranged to meet instructor needs.

Each chapter begins with a brief *Case Study* designed to capture interest and set the stage for the material that follows. In addition to these 28 Case Studies, many other Case Studies are found throughout the book; they provide a more in-depth look at specific environmental problems and their possible solutions.

This book is an integrated study of environmental problems, connections, and solutions. The seven integrative themes are *natural capital, sustainability, pollution prevention and waste reduction, population and exponential growth, energy and energy efficiency, solutions to environmental problems, and the importance of individuals working together to bring about environmental change.*

To get an overview of this book, we urge you to look at the Brief Contents.

This book has more than 560 illustrations (many of them new to this edition) designed to present complex ideas in understandable ways and to relate learning to the real world.

We have usually not cited specific sources of information within the text to avoid interrupting the flow of the material. Instead, on the website you will find readings. Placing references on the website allows us to update them regularly and keep links current.

To help ensure that the material is accurate and up to date, we have consulted more than 10 000 research sources in the professional literature and about the same number of Internet sites. We have also benefited from numerous experts and teachers who have provided detailed reviews.

How Is the Presentation of Views Balanced?
Trade-Offs

There are always *trade-offs* involved in making and implementing environmental decisions. The challenge for an author is to give a fair and balanced presentation of opposing viewpoints, advantages and disadvantages of various technologies and proposed solutions to environmental problems, and good and bad news about environmental problems without injecting personal bias. This allows readers to make up their own minds about important environmental issues. To study a subject as important as environmental science and end up with no conclusions, opinions, and beliefs would mean that both the teacher and student have failed. However, students should reach their own conclusions by using critical thinking to evaluate opposing ideas and to understand the trade-offs involved.

A few examples of our efforts to provide a balanced presentation are (1) the advantages and disadvantages of reducing birth rates (pp. 206–210), (2) Case Study: Should Commercial Whaling Be Resumed? (p. 286), (3) advantages and disadvantages of pesticides (pp. 572–575), and (4) 45 trade-offs diagrams that give the advantages and disadvantages of various environmental technologies and solutions to environmental problems.

Why Was This Order of Chapters Chosen?
Satisfying Text Users

There are hundreds of different ways to organize the chapters in this book to fit the needs of different instructors. That is why one of the key features of this book is the *flexibility* for changing the order of chapters once the basic science has been covered.

We have decided to put the three chapters on biodiversity (Chapters 11, 12, and 13) after the chapters in Part II on Science and Ecological Principles for two reasons. *First*, the loss and degradation of biodiversity is one of the most serious environmental problems. *Second*, the majority of instructors using this book prefer that we put all of the biology together (Chapters 4 through 13).

There is no best chapter order, but this one makes sense to most text users. Because of the book's flexibility, anyone who wants to use a different order can easily do so.

What Are the Major Features of the Third Canadian Edition? Above All, a Canadian Perspective

A Canadian perspective considers global as well as specifically Canadian environmental issues, such as the development of Alberta's oil sands and Canada's reaction to the Kyoto accord. Such a perspective is strongly informed by an awareness of the environmental problems and solutions associated with our powerful neighbour to the south.

Comparisons and contrasts between Canada and the United States—and other countries such as China, India, Russia, Brazil, Nigeria, and the Netherlands—continue to be an important aspect of the third Canadian edition.

Major features emphasized in the new edition include the following:

- The UN Millennium Development Goals, and progress toward the 2015 deadline, are placed in context with appropriate chapters of the book; updates to this material will be posted on the website.
- A Review section at the end of each chapter.
- Ecological Footprint Analysis and Data Analysis features.
- New online Web Resources sections where material that is introduced in the textbook can be expanded at greater depth and updated. Go to http://www.nelson.com/livingintheenvironment3e.

Selected highlights of the new edition listed by chapter:

Chapter 1—Environmental Problems: An Introduction and Overview

- Spotlights about the World Wildlife Fund's *Living Planet Report 2012* and the ecological footprint of Calgary, Alberta, plus further explanation and analysis of the concept of the "ecological footprint."

Chapter 3—Science, Systems, Matter, and Energy

- More details about the chemicals of life and more opportunities for students to interact with the material.

Chapter 4—Ecosystems: What Are They and How Do They Work?

- A Spotlight about Canadian geospatial technologies, and new information about remote sensing, satellites, GIS, and landscape ecology.

Chapter 6—Climate and Terrestrial Biodiversity

- More information about factors that influence weather and climate, including new material about greenhouse gases, the jet stream, tropical cyclones, and urban effects.

Chapter 8—Community Ecology

- New information on the use of indicator species for ecological purposes.

Chapter 10—Applying Population Ecology: The Human Population

- New information about human population growth in Canada, the world, and selected countries, plus an update on Millennium Development Goals that relate to population topics.

Chapter 11—Sustaining Terrestrial Biodiversity: Managing and Protecting Ecosystems

- A Case Study about Clayoquot Sound and a Spotlight on the Boreal Forest Agreement, plus further information about silvicultural systems.

Chapter 12—Sustaining Biodiversity: The Species Approach

- A Spotlight on white nose syndrome in bats.

Chapter 13—Sustaining Aquatic Biodiversity

- A Spotlight on diversifying the East Coast fishery, updates on the cod and salmon fisheries, and new figures about fish and shellfish.

Chapter 14—Food and Soil Resources

- New information about food resources, a Spotlight on problems with sea lice, and an update on Millennium Development Goals that relate to food.

Chapter 16—Geology and Nonrenewable Mineral Resources

- An update on Canadian diamonds and a Spotlight on potentially conflicting uses of the Niagara Escarpment.

Chapter 17—Nonrenewable Energy Resources

- Spotlights on making decisions about energy, on pros and cons of developing shale gas, and on the disaster at the Fukushima nuclear power plant.

Chapter 18—Energy Efficiency and Renewable Energy

- A Case Study about tidal power in the Bay of Fundy and new information about biodiesel fuel.

Chapter 21—Climate Change and Ozone Loss

- A Connections box about special properties of the global warming and ozone loss problems, an update about climate change, and new opportunities for students to interact with the material.

Chapter 22—Water Pollution

- Spotlights about the Deepwater Horizon oil disaster and Canada's drinking water report card.

Chapter 23—Pest Management

- A Spotlight about the mountain pine beetle infestation of western Canada.

Chapter 26—Economics, Environment, and Sustainability

- Updates about green businesses, progress indicators, and Millennium Development Goals related to poverty.

Chapter 27—Politics, Environment, and Sustainability

- A Spotlight on the UN Rio + 20 Summit and an update on environmental leadership.

As well, a host of other Canadian environmental topics are described and explained, with links to further print and web resources.

What In-Text Study Aids Are Provided? Tried and True Tools Plus Some New Ones

Each chapter begins with a few general questions to reveal how it is organized and what students will be learning. When a new term is introduced and defined, it is printed in boldface type. A glossary of all key terms is located on the website.

Questions are used as titles for all subsections so readers know the focus of the material that follows. In effect, this is a built-in set of learning objectives. A brief attention-grabbing headline follows each subsection question to give students a general idea of the content of the subsection. This is followed by a single sentence that summarizes the key material in each subsection. In effect, this provides readers with a built-in running summary of the material. We believe this is a more effective learning tool than providing a summary of the entire chapter at the end of each chapter.

Each chapter ends with a set of *Review* questions, a *Critical Thinking* section, and a list of *Projects*, and many include an *Ecological Footprint Analysis*. All have an online list of *Further Readings*.

The *Data Analysis* and *Ecological Footprint Analysis* exercises in the third Canadian edition of *Living in the Environment* were adapted from the U.S. 16th edition. Contributions to the quantitative exercises in the U.S. 16th edition of *Living in the Environment* were provided by Dr. Dean Goodwin and his colleagues, Berry Cobb, Deborah Stevens, Jeannette Adkins, Jim Lehner, Judy Treharne, Lonnie Miller, and Tom Mowbray.

What Internet and Online Study Aids Are Available?

Qualified users of this textbook have free access to the student website. Access the online resource material for this book by logging on at

http://www.nelson.com/livingintheenvironment3e

At this website you will find the following material for each chapter:

- Flash Cards, which allow you to test your mastery of the Terms and Concepts to Remember for each chapter.
- Chapter Overview Questions, which provide quick-answer questions that students can complete and submit to their instructor for review.
- Chapter Review Questions, which provide a multiple-choice practice quiz.
- Student Guide to InfoTrac® College Edition, which will lead you to Critical Thinking Projects that use InfoTrac® College Edition as a research tool.
- References, which lists the major books and articles consulted in writing this chapter.
- A brief What You Can Do list addressing key environmental problems.
- Weblinks, which take you to a list of websites with news, research, and images related to individual sections of the chapter.

Teachers and students using *new* copies of this textbook also have free and unlimited access to *InfoTrac® College Edition*. This fully searchable online library gives users access to complete environmental articles from several hundred periodicals dating back over the past 25 years.

Also available with this edition is *CengageNOW*, an online learning tool that helps students access their unique study needs. The CNOW was prepared by Stephen Turnbull of the University of New Brunswick. Students take a pre-test, and a personalized study plan provides them with specific resources for review. A post-test then identifies content that might require further study. *How Do I Prepare* tutorials, another feature of *CengageNOW*, walk students through basic math, chemistry, and study skills to help them brush up quickly and be ready to succeed in their course.

What Instructor Resources Are Available?

 The **Nelson Education Teaching Advantage (NETA)** program delivers research-based instructor resources that promote student engagement and higher-order thinking to enable the success of Canadian students and educators.

Instructors today face many challenges. Resources are limited, time is scarce, and a new kind of student has emerged: one who is juggling school with work, has gaps in his or her basic knowledge, and is immersed in technology in a way that has led to a completely new style of learning. In response, Nelson Education has gathered a group of dedicated instructors to advise us on the creation of richer and more flexible ancillaries and online learning platforms that respond to the needs of today's teaching environments. Whether your course is offered in-class, online, or both, Nelson is pleased to provide pedagogically driven, research-based resources to support you.

The members of our editorial advisory board have experience across a variety of disciplines and are recognized for their commitment to teaching. They include:

Norman Althouse, Haskayne School of Business, University of Calgary

Brenda Chant-Smith, Department of Psychology, Trent University

Scott Follows, Manning School of Business Administration, Acadia University

Jon Houseman, Department of Biology, University of Ottawa

Glen Loppnow, Department of Chemistry, University of Alberta

Tanya Noel, Department of Biology, York University

Gary Poole, Senior Scholar, Centre for Health Education Scholarship, and Associate Director, School of Population and Public Health, University of British Columbia

Dan Pratt, Department of Educational Studies, University of British Columbia

Mercedes Rowinsky-Geurts, Department of Languages and Literatures, Wilfrid Laurier University

David DiBattista, Department of Psychology, Brock University

Roger Fisher, PhD

In consultation with the editorial advisory board, Nelson Education has completely rethought the structure, approaches, and formats of our key textbook ancillaries and online learning platforms. We've also increased our investment in editorial support for our ancillary and digital authors. The result is the Nelson Education Teaching Advantage and its key

components: *NETA Engagement, NETA Assessment, NETA Presentation,* and *NETA Digital.* Each component includes one or more ancillaries prepared according to our best practices and may also be accompanied by documentation explaining the theory behind the practices.

NETA Engagement presents materials that help instructors deliver engaging content and activities to their classes. Instead of Instructor's Manuals that regurgitate chapter outlines and key terms from the text, NETA Enriched Instructor's Manuals (EIMs) provide genuine assistance to teachers. The EIMs answer questions like *What should students learn?, Why should students care?,* and *What are some common student misconceptions and stumbling blocks?* EIMs not only identify the topics that cause students the most difficulty, but also describe techniques and resources to help students master these concepts. Dr. Roger Fisher's *Instructor's Guide to Classroom Engagement (IGCE)* accompanies every Enriched Instructor's Manual. (Information about the NETA Enriched Instructor's Manual prepared for *Living in the Environment* is included in the description of the IRCD below.)

NETA Assessment relates to testing materials. Under *NETA Assessment,* Nelson's authors create multiple-choice questions that reflect research-based best practices for constructing effective questions and testing not just recall but also higher-order thinking. Our guidelines were developed by David DiBattista, a 3M National Teaching Fellow whose recent research as a professor of psychology at Brock University has focused on multiple-choice testing. All Test Bank authors receive training at workshops conducted by Prof. DiBattista, as do the copyeditors assigned to each Test Bank. A copy of *Multiple Choice Tests: Getting Beyond Remembering,* Prof. DiBattista's guide to writing effective tests, is included with every Nelson Test Bank/Computerized Test Bank package. (Information about the NETA Test Bank prepared for *Living in the Environment* is included in the description of the IRCD below.)

NETA Presentation has been developed to help instructors make the best use of PowerPoint® in their classrooms. With a clean and uncluttered design developed by Maureen Stone of StoneSoup Consulting, NETA Presentation features slides with improved readability, more multi-media and graphic materials, activities to use in class, and tips for instructors on the Notes page. A copy of *NETA Guidelines for Classroom Presentations* by Maureen Stone is included with each set of PowerPoint slides. (Information about the NETA PowerPoint® prepared for *Living in the Environment* is included in the description of the IRCD below.)

NETA Digital is a framework based on Arthur Chickering and Zelda Gamson's seminal work "Seven Principles of Good Practice In Undergraduate

Education" (AAHE Bulletin, 1987) and the follow-up work by Chickering and Stephen C. Ehrmann, "Implementing the Seven Principles: Technology as Lever"(AAHE Bulletin, 1996). This aspect of the NETA program guides the writing and development of our digital products to ensure that they appropriately reflect the core goals of contact, collaboration, multimodal learning, time on task, prompt feedback, active learning, and high expectations. The resulting focus on pedagogical utility, rather than technological wizardry, ensures that all of our technology supports better outcomes for students.

IRCD

Key instructor ancillaries are provided on the *Instructor's Resource CD* (ISBN 0176661662), giving instructors the ultimate tool for customizing lectures and presentations. (Downloadable web versions are also available at www.nelson.com/livinginthe-environment3e.) The IRCD includes:

- **NETA Engagement:** The Enriched Instructor's Manual was written by Monika Havelka of the University of Toronto at Mississauga. It is organized according to the textbook chapters and addresses eight key educational concerns, such as typical stumbling blocks student face and how to address them.

- **NETA Assessment:** The Test Bank was written by Peter Bush of Saint Mary's University. It includes over 1700 multiple-choice questions written according to NETA guidelines for effective construction and development of higher-order questions. Also included are over 500 True/False questions, 450 Completion questions, and approximately 250 Short Answer questions. Test Bank files are provided in Word format for easy editing and in PDF format for convenient printing whatever your system.

 The Computerized Test Bank by ExamView® includes all the questions from the Test Bank. The easy-to-use ExamView software is compatible with Microsoft Windows and Mac OS. Create tests by selecting questions from the question bank, modifying these questions as desired, and adding new questions you write yourself. You can administer quizzes online and export tests to WebCT, Blackboard, and other formats.

- **NETA Presentation:** Microsoft® PowerPoint® lecture slides for every chapter have been created by Yuen-ying Carpenter, of the University of Calgary, many featuring key figures, tables, and photographs from NETA principles of clear design and engaging content have been incorporated throughout.

- **Image Library:** This resource consists of digital copies of figures, short tables, and photographs used in the book. Instructors may use these jpegs to create their own PowerPoint presentations.

- **DayOne:** Day One—Prof InClass is a PowerPoint presentation that you can customize to orient your students to the class and their text at the beginning of the course.

- **TurningPoint®:** Another valuable resource for instructors is **TurningPoint® classroom response software** customized for *Living in the Environment*. Now you can author, deliver, show, access, and grade, all in PowerPoint…with no toggling back and forth between screens! JoinIn on Turning Point is the only classroom response software tool that gives you true PowerPoint integration. With JoinIn, you are no longer tied to your computer. You can walk about your classroom as you lecture, showing slides and collecting and displaying responses with ease. There is simply no easier or more effective way to turn your lecture hall into a personal, fully interactive experience for your students. If you can use PowerPoint, you can use JoinIn on TurningPoint! (Contact your Nelson publishing representative for details.)

Student Ancillaries
Living in the Environment Classroom Video

Nelson has partnered with the Canadian Broadcasting Corporation to offer uniquely Canadian videos for this edition of *Living in the Environment*. Many chapters are supported by a carefully selected clip from the CBC archives focusing on newsworthy and relevant environmental issues and topics. Free with adoption. (ISBN: 0-17-647950-3)

Help Us Improve This Book

Let us know how you think this book can be improved; if you find any errors, bias, or confusing explanations, please e-mail Dave Hackett about them at

daveh@nipissingu.ca

Most errors can be corrected in subsequent printings of this edition rather than waiting for a new edition.

U.S. Acknowledgments

We wish to thank the many students and teachers who have responded so favorably to the 16 previous editions of *Living in the Environment*, the 13 editions of *Environmental Science*, the nine editions of *Sustaining the Earth*, and the five editions of *Essentials of Ecology*, and who have corrected errors and offered many helpful suggestions for improvement. We are also deeply indebted to the more than 295 reviewers, who pointed out errors and suggested many important improvements in the various editions of these three books.

It takes a village to produce a textbook, and the members of the talented production team, listed on the copyright page, have made vital contributions. Our special thanks go to development editor Christopher Delgado, who patiently and expertly keeps us on track, production editors Hal Humphrey and Nicole Barone, copy editor Deborah Thompson, layout expert Judy Maenle, photo researcher Abigail Reip, artist Patrick Lane, media editor Alexandria Brady, assistant editor Alexis Glubka, editorial assistants Brandusa Radoias and Joshua Taylor, and Brooks/Cole's hard-working sales staff. Finally, we are fortunate and delighted to be working with Yolanda Cossio, the Biology publisher at Brooks/Cole. We thank her for her inspiring leadership and for her many insights and questions that have helped us to improve this book.

We also thank Ed Wells and the team who developed the *Laboratory Manual* to accompany this book, and the people who have translated it into eight languages for use throughout much of the world.

G. Tyler Miller, Jr.
Scott Spoolman

Canadian Acknowledgments

I am deeply indebted to my student researchers—Michelle Rondeau, Sonje Bols, and Andrew Lamar—who not only found Canadian material for the book but also identified material that would be especially interesting and relevant from a student's perspective. I am also indebted to members of my family—Lloyd, Lisa, Marilyn, and Sean Hackett—for assistance and feedback throughout the writing process.

I would like to acknowledge the contributions of my colleagues—especially Rebecca Barker, Alex Berry, Peter Bush, Jacqueline Chalifoux, Kevan Cowcill, Jessica Crain, Joe Crowley, Carolyn Deloyde, Natasha Dombrowski, Mike Gemmell, Carly Dokis, Terry Dokis, Mike Grandmaison, David Hunt, Corina Irwin, Victoria Jackson, Shannon Langlois, John MacLachlan, Eric Mattson, David McRobert, Gord Miller, Sue Miller, Reehan Mirza, James Murton, Brian Naylor, Peter Nosko, Fred Pinto, Oriana Pokorny, Dan Reeves, Richard Rowe, Ursina Rusch, Paul Smylie, Melissa Stacey, Martee Storms, Merilyn Twiss, Dave Vadnais, Sharlene Waugh, and Carl Wolfe. I am also grateful to the students in my environmental science and animal ecology courses who researched and brainstormed some of the ideas developed in the book; their enthusiasm for all aspects of the environment was contagious.

I thank my Publisher, Paul Fam, and my Developmental Editor, Mark Grzeskowiak, for guiding me through all the stages of the production process.

I dedicate this book to my son, Sean; to my parents, Lloyd and Marilyn Hackett; and to the Canadian students who will help shape our country's environmental future.

Dave Hackett

Reviewers

Nelson would like to thank the reviewers for their contributions to the text:

David M. Atkinson, Ryerson University

Peter Bush, Saint Mary's University

Leslie Goodman, University of Manitoba

Lorelei Hanson, Athabasca University

Stephen Donald Turnbull, University of New Brunswick – Saint John

Carl Wolfe, York University

HOW TO USE THIS TEXT

The third Canadian edition of *Living in the Environment* is designed to meet the needs of introduction to the environment courses, and boasts a wealth of Canadian and international examples, issues, cases, photographs, and environmental personalities throughout the text. The following will help guide you through *Living in the Environment*'s many features.

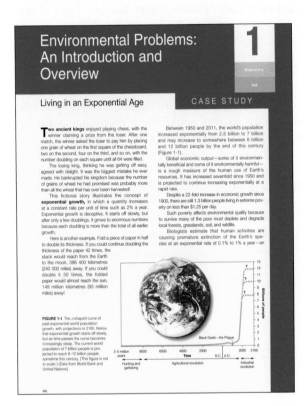

CHAPTER OPENER CASE STUDY

Each chapter begins with a case study designed to capture interest and set the stage for the material that follows.

CHAPTER PURPOSE AND QUESTIONS

Chapter 1 presents an overview of environmental problems, their causes, and their solutions. The chapter addresses the following questions:

1-1 What keeps us alive? What is an environmentally sustainable society?

1-2 How fast is the human population increasing? What are economic growth, economic development, and globalization?

1-3 What are the Earth's main types of resources? How can they be depleted or degraded?

1-4 What are the principal types of pollution? What can we do about pollution?

1-5 What are the basic causes of today's environmental problems? How are these causes connected?

1-6 Is our current course sustainable? What is environmentally sustainable development?

CHAPTER PURPOSE AND QUESTIONS

These questions reveal how each chapter is organized and what students will be learning.

INDIVIDUALS MATTER

Killing Invader Species and Saving Shipping Companies Money

A large cargo ship typically has a dozen or more ballast tanks below deck. Each tank is the size of a high-school gymnasium and holds millions of litres of water.

When a ship takes on cargo and leaves port it pumps water into the ballast tanks to keep it low in the water, submerge its rudder, and help maintain stability. This water also contains large numbers of fish, crabs, clams, and other species (many of them microscopic) found in the port's local waters.

When the ship's cargo is removed at its destination its ballast water is released until the ship is loaded again. This dumps millions of foreign organisms into rivers and bays. Thus cargo ships moving about 80% of the goods traded internationally play the primary role in the release of nonnative aquatic organisms into various parts of the world.

In 2002, researchers Mario Tamburri and Kerstin Wasson found that pumping nitrogen gas into ballast tanks while a ship is at sea virtually eliminates dissolved oxygen in the ballast water. This saves the shipping industry money by reducing corrosion of a ship's steel compartments. In addition, within three days it kills most fish, crabs, clams, and other potential invader species lurking in the ballast tanks.

INDIVIDUALS MATTER

Profiles of individuals who have made important contributions to environmental science and to the advancement of environmental goals are featured. More can be found on the website.

SPOTLIGHT

The Canadian Boreal Forest Agreement

The boreal forest is a vast green coniferous forest that stretches across northern Canada from Newfoundland to British Columbia (pp. 123, 133, 228). It is home to Aboriginal people and to many species of plants and animals, including species at risk such as woodland caribou (*Rangifer tarandus*, p. 267). It is also an area containing many different resources such as wood, minerals, diamonds, and fossil fuels, which companies have been trying to develop. The boreal forest has been negatively impacted by logging, development, fragmentation, disturbance, invasive species, and climate change. According to the David Suzuki Foundation (http://www

a plan that will conserve large areas of Canada's boreal forest, protect threatened woodland caribou, and provide a competitive edge for the timber companies involved, on the 72 million hectares (178 million acres) of boreal forest that are licensed to the FPAC members.

The foresters have agreed to suspend new logging operations on 29 million hectares (72 million acres) of boreal forest until plans for protected areas can be finalized. They will put in place sustainable forestry practices and will conduct their operations in accordance with conservation plans aimed at aiding threatened caribou. The conservation groups will commit to supporting the efforts made

their resources to promote global recognition of the sustainable forestry being practised, and they will stop boycotting products of these companies.

The success of this agreement also depends on the support and involvement of First Nations people since much of the boreal forest is in traditional First Nations territory. The boreal forest has been home to some of Canada's Aboriginal people for thousands of years, and they have developed much traditional knowledge of how to sustainably use the resources of the boreal forest (Karst, 2010). You can learn more about the Canadian Boreal Forest Agreement at http://www

SPOTLIGHT

The people and environmental issues that are making a difference to Canada and the world are highlighted.

Natural Capital

Forests

Ecological Services	Economic Services
Support energy flow and chemical cycling	Fuelwood
Reduce soil erosion	Lumber
Absorb and release water	Pulp to make paper
Purify water	Biomass
Purify air	Non-wood forest products
Influence local and regional climate	Ecotourism
Store atmospheric carbon	Recreation
Provide habitats supporting biodiversity	Many different jobs

NATURAL CAPITAL AND NATURAL CAPITAL DEGRADATION

Natural resources and services, as well as the human activities that can degrade natural capital, are illustrated in these diagrams.

Trade-Offs

Clear-Cutting Forests

Advantages	Disadvantages
Higher timber yields	Reduces biodiversity
Maximum economic return in shortest time	Disrupts ecosystem processes
Can reforest with genetically improved fast-growing trees	Destroys and fragments some wildlife habitats
Short time to establish new stand of trees	Leaves moderate to large openings
Needs less skill and planning	Increases soil erosion
Best way to harvest tree plantations	Increases sediment water pollution and flooding when done on steep slopes
Good for tree species needing full or moderate sunlight for growth	Eliminates most recreational value for several decades

TRADE-OFFS

The advantages and disadvantages of various environmental technologies and solutions to environmental problems are presented.

Solutions

Sustainable Forestry

- Grow more timber on long rotations
- Rely more on selection cutting and strip cutting
- No clear-cutting, seed-tree, or shelterwood cutting on steeply sloped land
- No fragmentation of remaining large blocks of forest
- Sharply reduce road building into uncut forest areas
- Leave most standing dead trees and fallen timber for wildlife habitat and nutrient recycling
- Certify timber grown by sustainable methods
- Include ecological services of trees and forests in estimating economic value

SOLUTIONS

Proposed solutions are presented in a balanced manner and challenge students to think critically about them.

CONSIDER, DISCUSS, OR DEBATE

Individual reflection on and/or classroom discussion of environmental issues covered in the text is facilitated by this feature.

CONSIDER, DISCUSS, OR DEBATE

Should there be a global effort to reduce the cutting of old-growth forests? Give reasons for your answer. How would this global effort be accomplished in Canada? In tropical countries?

CONNECTIONS

The Interdisciplinary Nature of Environmental Science

Environmental science draws on all relevant sciences and social sciences that can shed light on a given topic. For example, an understanding of SOUND POLLUTION draws on: (1) *physics* in terms of the production and propagation of sound waves, (2) *biology* in terms of how sound is received and processed by our bodies, (3) *medical science* in terms of physical damage resulting from too much sound, (4) *psychology* in terms of harmful psychological effects of sound, (5) *geography* in terms of planning sound zones around airports and hospitals, and (6) *engineering* in terms of creating buildings and devices that minimize the effects of sound pollution. Knowledge gained from the synergy of these and other disciplines is applied to human society through many diverse laws and guidelines that affect sound pollution in our homes, workplaces, and public environments.

For more information about sound pollution, see Chapter 25.

CONNECTIONS

The interdisciplinary nature of environmental science is highlighted.

DID YOU KNOW?

Environmental facts (usually with a Canadian connection) are highlighted.

DID YOU KNOW

The world's first national park service was established in Canada! Sir Wilfred Laurier's government passed the Dominion Forest Reserves and Parks Act on May 19, 1911. James Harkin (see p. 27) was appointed commissioner of the Dominion Parks Branch and guided the expansion of Canada's national park system between 1911 and 1936.

SELF CHECK

Opportunities are provided for students to assess their own knowledge.

SELF CHECK

See Clayoquot Sound with your own eyes! If you enter words such as "Clayoquot AND tour AND video" into a search engine, you will find many short, entertaining videos that illustrate some of the exciting and beautiful features of Clayoquot Sound. You can also find many photo sites featuring Clayoquot Sound and the biosphere reserve, such as the one at http://www.oceanlight.com/lightbox.php.

CRITICAL THINKING AND PROJECTS

Encourage students to think critically and apply what they have learned to their lives.

QUANTITATIVE DATA ANALYSIS OR ECOLOGICAL FOOTPRINT ANALYSIS

Questions designed to test students' ability to quantitatively analyze their ecological footprint and concepts covered in each chapter are presented here.

REVIEW QUESTIONS

A detailed set of review questions is presented here that includes chapter key terms in italics.

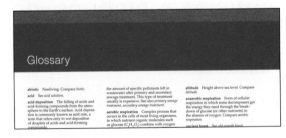

GLOSSARY

A glossary of key terms is presented on the text's website.

For more information, go to **http://www.nelson.com/ livingintheenvironment3e**

Student Resources available on the website for
Living in the Environment, **Third Canadian Edition**

- Test Yourself
  —Chapter Overview Questions, which provide quick-answer questions that students can complete and submit to their instructor for review.
  —Chapter Review Questions, which provide a multiple-choice practice quiz.

- Flash Cards
  —Flash Cards, which allow you to test your mastery of the Terms and Concepts to Remember for each chapter.

- Weblinks

  —Weblinks, which take you to a list of websites with news, research, and images related to individual sections of the chapter.

- Learning Objectives
- Glossary
- Further Readings
- What Can You Do?
- Canada's National Parks
- Degree Programs
- Environmental Organizations
- About the Book
- Features about unfolding environmental topics that can best be tracked online.

CENGAGENOW™

CengageNOW™ is an online learning and homework assessment program created in concert with *Living in the Environment* to present a seamless, integrated learning tool.

With CengageNOW™, instructors can dramatically affect student success. Assigning text-specific tutorials requires no instructor set-up. Or, faculty can use the same system to create tailored homework assignments, quizzes, and tests that auto-grade and flow directly into your gradebook! This capability means that you can assign marks to homework assignments, motivating students to study the material and come to class prepared.

Students can improve their grades and save study time with CengageNOW™, too. It isn't just reading—

it provides a customized study plan that lets students master what they need to know without wasting time on what they already know! The study plan provides a road map to interactive exercises, videos, e-books, and other resources that will help students master the subject.

Pre-tests and post-tests allow students to monitor their progress, and focused studying via CengageNOW™ will minimize student efforts and yet maximize results.

CENGAGENOW ACTIVE FIGURES

This online visual learning supplement allows students to enhance their scientific understanding by viewing animations, many of them interactive.

Introduction: Learning Skills

Students who can begin early in their lives to think of things as connected, even if they revise their views every year, have begun the life of learning.

Mark Van Doren

Why Is It Important to Study Environmental Science? Learning How the Earth Works

Environmental science may be the most important course you will ever take.

Welcome to *environmental science*—an *interdisciplinary* study of how nature works and how things in nature are interconnected. This book is an integrated and science-based study of environmental problems, connections, and solutions.

Environmental issues affect every part of your life and are an important part of the news stories presented on television and in newspapers and magazines. Thus, the concepts, information, and issues discussed in this book and the course you are taking should be useful to you now and in the future.

Understandably, we are biased. But *we strongly believe that environmental science is the single most important course in your education.* What could be more important than learning how the Earth works, how we are affecting its life-support system, and how we can reduce our environmental impact? In India, every college student must take an introductory course in environmental science.

We live in an incredibly challenging era. There is a growing awareness that during this century we need to make a new cultural transition in which we learn how to live more sustainably by not degrading our life support system.

We hope that this book and the course you are taking will help you to learn about the exciting challenges we face. More importantly, we hope that it will stimulate you to become involved in thinking about, and taking actions to address, environmental issues.

How Did We Become Involved with Environmental Problems? Individuals and Events Matter

We became involved after our eyes were opened to the environmental problems affecting our world.

G. Tyler Miller, Jr. In 1966, I heard Dean Cowie, a physicist with the U.S. Geological Survey, give a lecture on the problems of population growth and pollution. After six months of study, I was convinced of the seriousness of these and other environmental problems. Since then, I have been studying, teaching, and writing about them. This book summarizes what I have learned in more than three decades of trying to understand environmental principles, problems, connections, and solutions.

Dave Hackett. In 1986, I was studying Columbian ground squirrels in the Rocky Mountains of Alberta when the world's most serious nuclear power plant accident occurred in Chernobyl, Ukraine (Case Study, p. 382). As the massive radioactive cloud spread out and encircled the globe, I realized that no place on Earth is immune to the effects of such catastrophic events. To protect the people and places I care about, I resolved to become part of the solution to the world's environmental problems.

How Can You Improve Your Study and Learning Skills? Becoming an Efficient and Effective Learner

Learning how to learn is life's most important skill.

Maximizing your ability to learn should be one of your most important lifetime educational goals. This involves continually trying to *improve your study and learning skills.*

This has a number of payoffs. You can learn more and do this more efficiently. You will also have more time to pursue other interests besides studying without feeling guilty about always being behind. It can also help you get better grades and live a more fruitful and rewarding life.

Here are some *general study and learning skills.*

Get organized. Becoming more efficient at studying gives you more time for other interests.

Make daily to-do lists. Put items in order of importance, focus on the most important tasks, and assign a time to work on these items. Because life is full of uncertainties, you will be lucky to accomplish half of the items on your daily list. Shift your schedule as needed to accomplish the most important items.

Set up a study routine in a distraction-free environment. Develop a realistic daily study schedule and stick to it. Study in a quiet, well-lighted space. Work sitting at a desk or table—not lying down on a couch or bed. Take breaks every hour or so. During each break, take several deep breaths and move around to help yourself stay more alert and focused.

Avoid procrastination—putting work off until another time. Do not fall behind on your reading and other assignments. Accomplish this by setting aside a particular time for studying each day and making it a part of your daily routine.

Do not eat dessert first. Otherwise, you may never get to the main meal (studying). When you have accomplished your study goals, reward yourself with play (dessert).

Make hills out of mountains. It is psychologically difficult to climb a mountain such as reading an entire book, reading a chapter in a book, writing a paper, or cramming to study for a test. Instead, break such large tasks (mountains) down into a series of small tasks (hills). Each day read a few pages of a book or chapter, write a few paragraphs of a paper, and review what you have studied and learned. As Henry Ford put it, "Nothing is particularly hard if you divide it into small jobs."

Look at the big picture first. Get an overview of an assigned reading by looking at the main headings or chapter outline. In this textbook, we provide a list of the main questions that are the focus of each chapter.

Ask and answer questions as you read. For example, what is the main point of this section or paragraph? To help you do this we start each subsection with a question that the material is designed to answer. Then, to help you further, we follow this question with a brief headline to give you an idea of how the question will be answered. Then we provide a one-sentence summary of the key material in the subsection. This provides you with a running summary of the text. Our goal is to present the material in more manageable bites. You can also use the one-sentence summaries as a way to review what you have learned. Putting them all together gives you a summary of the chapter.

Focus on key terms. Use the glossary on the text's website to look up the meaning of terms or words you do not understand. Make flash cards for learning key terms and concepts and review them frequently. This book shows all key terms in **boldfaced** type and lesser but still important terms in *italicized type.* Flash cards for testing your mastery of key terms for each chapter are available on the website for this book.

Interact with what you read. We do this by marking key sentences and paragraphs with a highlighter or pen. We write comments in the margins. We fold down the top corner of pages with highlighted passages and the top and bottom corners of especially important pages. This way, we can flip through a chapter or book and quickly review the key ideas.

Review to reinforce learning. Before each class, review the material you learned in the previous class and read the assigned material. Review, fill in, and organize your notes as soon as possible after each class.

Become a better note taker. Do not try to take down everything your instructor says. Instead, take down main points and key facts using your own shorthand system. Fill in and organize your notes after class.

Write out answers to questions to focus and reinforce learning. Answer questions at the end of each chapter or those assigned to you and the review questions on the website for each chapter. Do this in writing as if you were turning them in for a grade. Save your answers for review and preparation for tests.

Use the buddy system. Study with a friend or become a member of a study group to compare notes, review material, and prepare for tests. Explaining something to someone else is a great way to focus your thoughts and reinforce your learning. Attend any review sessions offered by instructors or teaching assistants.

Learn your instructor's test style. Does your instructor emphasize multiple-choice, fill-in-the-blank, true-or-false, factual, thought, or essay questions? How much of the test will come from the textbook and how much from lecture material? Adapt your learning and studying methods to this style. You may disagree with this style and feel that it does not adequately reflect what you know. But the reality is that your instructor is in charge.

Become a better test taker. Avoid cramming. Eat well and get plenty of sleep before a test. Arrive on time or early. Calm yourself and increase your oxygen intake by taking several deep breaths. Do this about every 10–15 minutes. Look over the test and answer the questions you know well first. Then work on the harder ones. Use the process of elimination to narrow down the choices for multiple-choice questions. Getting it down to two choices gives you a 50% chance of picking the right answer. For essay questions, organize your thoughts before you start writing. If you have no idea what a question means, make an educated guess. You might get some partial credit and avoid a zero. Another strategy for getting some credit is to show your knowledge and reasoning by writing: "If this question means so and so, then my answer is _____."

Develop an optimistic outlook. Try to be a "glass is half-full" rather than a "glass is half-empty" person. Pessimism, fear, anxiety, and excessive worrying (especially over things that you cannot control) are destructive and lead to inaction. Try to keep your energizing feelings of optimism ahead of your immobilizing feelings of pessimism. Then you will always be moving forward.

Take time to enjoy life. Every day take time to laugh and enjoy nature, beauty, and friendship. Becoming an effective and efficient learner is the best way to do this without getting behind and living under a cloud of guilt and anxiety.

How Can You Improve Your Critical Thinking Skills? Detecting Baloney

Learning how to think critically is a skill you will need throughout your life.

Every day we are exposed to a sea of information, ideas, and opinions. How do we know what to believe and why? Do the claims seem reasonable or exaggerated?

Critical thinking involves developing skills to help you analyze and evaluate the validity of information and ideas you are exposed to as well as to make decisions. Critical thinking skills help you decide rationally what to believe or what to do. This involves examining information and conclusions or beliefs in terms of the evidence and the chain of logical reasoning that supports them. Critical thinking helps you distinguish between facts and opinions, evaluate evidence and arguments, take and defend an informed position on issues, integrate information and see relationships, and apply your knowledge to dealing with new and different problems. Here are some basic strategies for learning how to think more critically.

Question everything and everybody. Be skeptical, as any good scientist is. Do not believe everything you hear or read, including the content of this textbook. Evaluate all information you receive. Seek other sources and opinions. As Albert Einstein put it, "The important thing is not to stop questioning."

Do not believe everything you read on the Internet. The Internet is a wonderful and easily accessible source of information. It is also a useful way to find alternative information and opinions on almost any subject or issue—much of it not available in the mainstream media and scholarly articles. However, because the Internet is so open, anyone can write anything they want with no editorial control or peer evaluation—the method in which scientific or other experts in an area review and comment on an article before it is accepted for publication in a scholarly journal. As a result,

evaluating information on the Internet is one of the best ways to put into practice the principles of critical thinking discussed here. Use and enjoy the Internet, but think critically and proceed with caution.

Identify and evaluate your personal biases and beliefs. Each of us has biases and beliefs taught to us by sources such as parents, teachers, friends, role models, and experience. What are your basic beliefs and biases? Where did they come from? What assumptions are they based on? How sure are you that your beliefs and assumptions are right, and why? According to William James, "A great many people think they are thinking when they are merely rearranging their prejudices."

Be open-minded, flexible, and humble. Be open to considering different points of view, suspend judgment until you gather more evidence, and be capable of changing your mind. Recognize that there may be a number of useful and acceptable solutions to a problem and that very few issues are black or white. There are usually valid points on both (or many) sides of an issue. One way to evaluate divergent views is to get into another person's head or walk in his or her shoes. How does he or she see or view the world? What are his or her basic assumptions and beliefs? Is his or her position logically consistent with his or her assumptions and beliefs? And be humble about what you know. According to Will Durant, "Education is a progressive discovery of our own ignorance."

Evaluate how the information related to an issue was obtained. Are the statements made based on firsthand knowledge or research or on hearsay? Are unnamed sources used? Is the information based on reproducible and widely accepted scientific studies (*sound* or *consensus science*, p. 37) or preliminary scientific results that may be valid but need further testing (*frontier science*, p. 37)? Is the information based on a few isolated stories or experiences (*anecdotal information*) instead of carefully controlled studies? Is it based on unsubstantiated and widely doubted scientific information or beliefs (*junk science* or *pseudoscience*)? You need to know how to detect junk science, as discussed on p. 37.

Question the evidence and conclusions presented. What are the conclusions or claims? What evidence is presented to support them? Does the evidence support them? Is there a need to gather further evidence to test the conclusions? Are there other, more reasonable conclusions?

Try to identify and assess the assumptions and beliefs of those presenting evidence and drawing conclusions. What is their expertise in this area? Do they have any unstated assumptions, beliefs, biases, or values? Do they have a personal agenda? Can they benefit financially or politically from acceptance of their evidence and conclusions? Would investigators with different basic assumptions or beliefs take the same data and come to different conclusions?

Do the arguments used involve common logical fallacies or debating tricks? Here are six examples of logical fallacies or debating tricks that often confuse issues. *First,* attack the presenter of an argument rather than the argument itself. *Second,* appeal to emotion rather than facts and logic. *Third,* claim that if one piece of evidence or one conclusion is false, then all other pieces of evidence and conclusions are false. *Fourth,* say that a conclusion is false because it has not been scientifically proven (scientists can never prove anything absolutely, but they can establish degrees of reliability, as discussed on p. 37). *Fifth,* inject irrelevant or misleading information to divert attention from important points. *Sixth,* present only either/or alternatives when in fact a greater number of alternatives is available.

Now that you know about these tricks, realize what others are doing when they try to use these tricks on you!

Become a seeker of wisdom, not a vessel of information. Develop a written list of principles, concepts, and rules to serve as guidelines in evaluating evidence and claims and making decisions. Continually evaluate and modify this list on the basis of experience. Many people believe that the main goal of education is to learn as much as you can by concentrating on gathering more and more information—much of it useless or misleading. We believe that the primary goal is to focus on the most important information. This is done by learning how to sift through mountains of facts and ideas to find the few *nuggets of wisdom* that are the most useful in understanding the world and in making decisions. This takes a firm commitment to learning how to think logically and critically and continually flushing less valuable and thought-clogging information from our minds. This book is full of facts and numbers, but they are useful only to the extent that they lead to an understanding of key and useful ideas, scientific laws, concepts, principles, and connections. A major goal of the study of environmental science is to find out how nature works and sustains itself (*environmental wisdom*) and to use *principles of environmental wisdom* to help make our human societies and economies more sustainable and thus more beneficial and enjoyable. As Sandra Carey put it, "Never mistake knowledge for wisdom. One helps you make a living; the other helps you make a life."

How Have We Attempted to Achieve Balance? Evaluate Trade-Offs

There are no simple answers to the environmental problems we face.

There are always *trade-offs* involved in making and implementing environmental decisions. Our challenge is to give a balanced presentation of different viewpoints, to outline advantages and disadvantages of various technologies, to describe proposed solutions to environmental problems, and to report recent news about environmental problems, without injecting personal bias.

Studying a subject as important as environmental science and ending up with no conclusions, opinions, and beliefs means that both the teacher and student have failed. However, such conclusions should be based on using critical thinking to evaluate different ideas and to understand the trade-offs involved.

How Can You Improve This Book? Keep Those Ideas Coming

We welcome your help in improving this book.

Researching and writing a book that covers and connects ideas in such a wide variety of disciplines is a challenging and exciting task. Almost every day we learn about some new connection in nature.

In a book this complex, there are bound to be some errors—some typographical mistakes that slip through and some statements that you might question based on your knowledge and research. Our goal is to provide you with an interesting, accurate, balanced, and challenging book that furthers your understanding of this vital subject. We have also attempted to provide balance in presenting various sides of key environmental issues.

We invite you to point out any remaining biases, to correct any errors you find, and to suggest ways to improve this book. Over decades of teaching, some of our best teachers have been students taking our classes and reading our textbooks. Please e-mail your suggestions to

daveh@nipissingu.ca

Now start your journey into this fascinating and important study of how the Earth works and how we can leave the planet in at least as good a shape as we found it. Have fun.

Study nature, love nature, stay close to nature. It will never fail you.
FRANK LLOYD WRIGHT

Environmental Problems: An Introduction and Overview

1

Soil

Biodiversity

Living in an Exponential Age

CASE STUDY

Two ancient kings enjoyed playing chess, with the winner claiming a prize from the loser. After one match, the winner asked the loser to pay him by placing one grain of wheat on the first square of the chessboard, two on the second, four on the third, and so on, with the number doubling on each square until all 64 were filled.

The losing king, thinking he was getting off easy, agreed with delight. It was the biggest mistake he ever made. He bankrupted his kingdom because the number of grains of wheat he had promised was probably more than all the wheat that has ever been harvested!

This fictional story illustrates the concept of **exponential growth,** in which a quantity increases at a constant rate per unit of time such as 2% a year. Exponential growth is deceptive. It starts off slowly, but after only a few doublings, it grows to enormous numbers because each doubling is more than the total of all earlier growth.

Here is another example. Fold a piece of paper in half to double its thickness. If you could continue doubling the thickness of the paper 42 times, the stack would reach from the Earth to the moon, 386 400 kilometres (240 000 miles) away. If you could double it 50 times, the folded paper would almost reach the sun, 149 million kilometres (93 million miles) away!

Between 1950 and 2011, the world's population increased exponentially from 2.5 billion to 7 billion and may increase to somewhere between 8 billion and 12 billion people by the end of this century (Figure 1-1).

Global economic output—some of it environmentally beneficial and some of it environmentally harmful—is a rough measure of the human use of Earth's resources. It has increased sevenfold since 1950 and is projected to continue increasing exponentially at a rapid rate.

Despite a 22-fold increase in economic growth since 1900, there are still 1.3 billion people living in extreme poverty on less than $1.25 per day.

Such poverty affects environmental quality because to survive many of the poor must deplete and degrade local forests, grasslands, soil, and wildlife.

Biologists estimate that human activities are causing premature extinction of the Earth's species at an exponential rate of 0.1% to 1% a year—an

(continued)

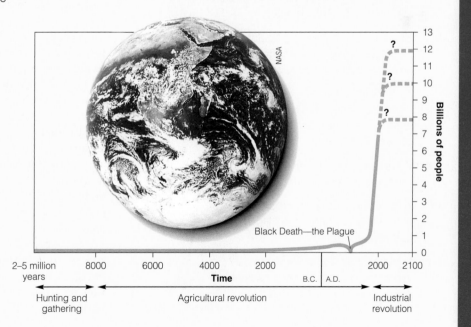

FIGURE 1-1 The *J*-shaped curve of past exponential world population growth, with projections to 2100. Notice that exponential growth starts off slowly, but as time passes the curve becomes increasingly steep. The current world population of 7 billion people is projected to reach 8–12 billion people sometime this century. (This figure is not to scale.) (Data from World Bank and United Nations)

Black Death—the Plague

2–5 million years | 8000 | 6000 | 4000 | 2000 | | 2000 | 2100
Time | B.C. | A.D.

Hunting and gathering | Agricultural revolution | Industrial revolution

Billions of people

irreversible loss of Earth's great variety of life forms, or *biodiversity*. In various parts of the world, forests, grasslands, **wetlands,** and coral reefs continue to disappear or become degraded as the human ecological footprint continues to spread exponentially across the globe.

There is growing concern that exponential growth in human activities such as burning fossil fuels and clearing forests will change the Earth's climate during this century. This could ruin some areas for farming, shift water supplies, alter and reduce biodiversity, and disrupt economies in various parts of the world.

Exponential growth plays a key role in five important and interconnected environmental issues: *population growth, resource use and waste, poverty, loss of biological diversity,* and *global climate change. Great news.* We have solutions to these problems that we should implement as quickly as possible, as you will learn in this book.

Alone in space, alone in its life-supporting systems, powered by inconceivable energies, mediating them to us through the most delicate adjustments, wayward, unlikely, unpredictable, but nourishing, enlivening, and enriching in the largest degree—is this not a precious home for all of us? Is it not worth our love?

Barbara Ward and René Dubos

CHAPTER PURPOSE AND QUESTIONS

Chapter 1 presents an overview of environmental problems, their causes, and their solutions. The chapter addresses the following questions:

1-1   What keeps us alive? What is an environmentally sustainable society?

1-2   How fast is the human population increasing? What are economic growth, economic development, and globalization?

1-3   What are the Earth's main types of resources? How can they be depleted or degraded?

1-4   What are the principal types of pollution? What can we do about pollution?

1-5   What are the basic causes of today's environmental problems? How are these causes connected?

1-6   Is our current course sustainable? What is environmentally sustainable development?

LIVING MORE SUSTAINABLY

What Is the Difference between Environment, Ecology, and Environmental Science? Defining Some Basic Terms

Environmental science is a study of how the Earth works, how we interact with the Earth, and how to deal with environmental problems.

Environment is everything that affects a living organism (any unique form of life). **Ecology** is a biological science that studies the relationships between living organisms and their environment.

This textbook is an introduction to **environmental science,** an interdisciplinary study that uses information from the physical sciences and social sciences to learn how the Earth works, how we interact with the Earth, and how to deal with environmental problems. Environmental science involves integrating ideas from the *natural world* (*biosphere*) and our *cultural world* (*culturesphere*).

Environmentalism is a social movement dedicated to protecting the Earth's life support systems for us and other species. Members of the environmental community include **ecologists, environmental scientists, conservation biologists, conservationists, preservationists, restorationists,** and **environmentalists.** The ideas and accomplishments of some of these key people will be noted throughout this book.

What Keeps Us Alive? The Sun and the Earth's Natural Capital

All life and economies depend on energy from the sun (solar capital) and the Earth's resources and ecological services (natural capital).

Our existence, lifestyles, and economies depend completely on the sun and the Earth, a blue and white island in the black void of space (Figure 1-1). To economists, *capital* is wealth used to sustain a business and to generate more wealth. For example, suppose you invest $100 000 of capital and get a 10% return on your money. In a year you get $10 000 in income from interest and increase your wealth to $110 000.

By analogy, we can think of energy from the sun as **solar capital. Solar energy** includes direct sunlight and indirect forms of renewable solar energy such as *wind power, hydropower* (energy from flowing water), and *biomass* (direct solar energy converted to chemical energy and stored in biological sources of energy such as wood).

Similarly, we can think of the planet's air, water, soil, wildlife, forest, rangeland, fishery, mineral, and energy resources and the processes of natural purification, recycling, and pest control as **natural resources** or **natural capital** (Figure 1-2).

The Interdisciplinary Nature of Environmental Science

Environmental science draws on all relevant sciences and social sciences that can shed light on a given topic. For example, an understanding of **sound pollution** draws on: (1) *physics* in terms of the production and propagation of sound waves, (2) *biology* in terms of how sound is received and processed by our bodies, (3) *medical science* in terms of physical damage resulting from too much sound, (4) *psychology* in terms of harmful psychological effects of sound, (5) *geography* in terms of planning sound zones around airports and hospitals, and (6) *engineering* in terms of creating buildings and devices that minimize the effects of sound pollution. Knowledge gained from the synergy of these and other disciplines is applied to human society through many diverse laws and guidelines that affect sound pollution in our homes, workplaces, and public environments.

For more information about sound pollution, see Chapter 25.

Natural capital consists of *resources* (orange in Figure 1-2) and *ecological services* (bluish green in Figure 1-2) that support and sustain the Earth's life and economies. This priceless natural capital that nature provides at no cost to us plus the natural biological income it supplies can sustain the planet and our economies indefinitely as long as we do not deplete them. Examples of *biological income* are renewable supplies of wood, fish, grassland for grazing, and underground water for drinking and irrigation.

What Are Carrying Capacity and Sustainability? Numbers of Organisms and Duration of a System

Carrying capacity is a reflection of how many organisms can be supported in an area. Sustainability refers to how long a system or activity will last.

Carrying capacity refers to the maximum number of organisms that can be maintained in an area without degrading the environment. The term is used in managing wild species such as deer or salmon (Chapter 9). It is also used to refer to the maximum numbers of people who can live in an area, at a very basic level of existence, without degrading the environment. In the case of people, if they have cultural amenities such as luxuries and technologies that raise their impact beyond basic levels, then the term **cultural carrying capacity** is used (Chapter 10).

Sustainability refers to the ability of a system to survive for an extended period of time. For example, if we manage natural resources such as fish or forests well, they should be available to us for as long as we need them; this would be a sustainable resource, and we might think in terms of the sustainable harvest that we could remove from that resource without jeopardizing it for future use or viability. The term can also be applied to human systems and activities (next section).

Dr. David Suzuki

David Suzuki has been called the face of environmental science in Canada. For over three decades, he has used intellect, communication skills, and passion to make his chosen field both understandable and compelling to audiences throughout the world.

After receiving his Ph.D. in zoology from the University of Chicago in 1961, Suzuki joined the University of British Columbia and gained worldwide recognition for his expertise in fruit fly genetics. Inspired by his growing interest in educating the public about science and environmental issues, he went on to produce and host radio and television shows, including *Quirks and Quarks* and *The Nature of Things*. He has written more than 50 books (among them a textbook on genetics), delivered more than 500 lectures, and contributed numerous articles on environmental topics.

Dr. Suzuki has received many accolades for his distinguished career as a scientist, broadcaster, writer, and champion of environmental and humanitarian causes. In 1990, he founded the David Suzuki Foundation, which is committed to developing "a world vision of sustainable communities within the planet's carrying capacity." To learn more about the foundation and its activities, visit http://www.davidsuzuki.org.

The Canadian Press/Jeff McIntosh

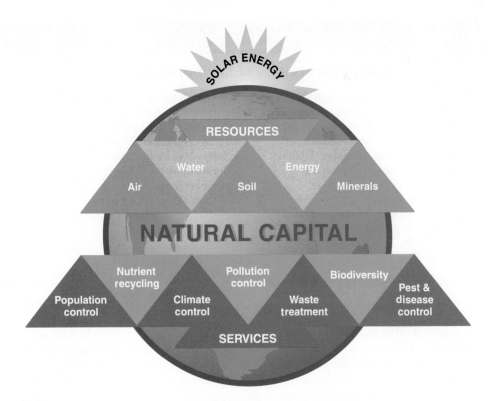

FIGURE 1-2 The Earth's *natural capital.* Energy from the sun (solar capital) and the Earth's natural capital provides resources (orange) and ecological services (bluish green) that support and sustain the Earth's life and economies. Wedges from this diagram will be used near the titles of various chapters to indicate the components of natural capital that are the primary focus of such chapters.

Carrying capacity and sustainability are related. A sustainable population of wildlife, or humans, would not overwhelm the carrying capacity of the environment that supports it.

What Is an Environmentally Sustainable Society? One That Preserves Natural Capital and Lives Off Its Income

An environmentally sustainable society meets the basic resource needs of its people indefinitely without degrading or depleting the natural capital that supplies these resources.

An **environmentally sustainable society** meets the current needs of its people for food, clean water, clean air, shelter, and other basic resources without compromising the ability of future generations to meet their needs. *Living sustainably* means living off natural income replenished by soils, plants, air, and water and not depleting or degrading the Earth's natural capital that supplies this biological income.

Imagine you win $1 million in a lottery. Invest this capital at 10% interest per year, and you will have a sustainable annual income of $100 000 without depleting your capital. If you spend $200 000 a year, your $1 million will be gone early in the 7th year and even if you spend only $110 000 a year, you will be bankrupt early in the 18th year.

The lesson here is an old one: *protect your capital and live off the income it provides.* Deplete, waste, or squander your capital, and you move from a sustainable to an unsustainable lifestyle.

The same lesson applies to the Earth's natural capital. According to many environmentalists and leading scientists, we are living unsustainably by wasting, depleting, and degrading the Earth's natural capital at an accelerating rate.

Some people disagree. They contend that environmentalists have exaggerated the seriousness of population, resource, and environmental problems. They also believe we can overcome these problems by human ingenuity, economic growth, and technological advances.

1-2 POPULATION GROWTH, ECONOMIC GROWTH, ECONOMIC DEVELOPMENT, AND GLOBALIZATION

How Rapidly Is the Human Population Growing? Pretty Fast

The rate at which the world's population is growing has slowed but it is still growing quite rapidly.

Currently, the world's population is growing exponentially at a rate of about 1.18% a year. This does not seem like a very fast rate. But it added about 83 million people (7.0 billion × 1.18 = 83 million) to the world's population in 2011, an average increase of 227 000 people a day, or 9 460 an hour. At this rate it would take only 152 days to completely repopulate Canada, or 12 days to repopulate Toronto or the entire Maritimes. Cities the size of Ottawa, Edmonton, or Calgary could be repopulated within about five days each!

How much is 83 million? Suppose you spend 1 second saying hello to each of the 83 million new people added this year for 24 hours a day—no sleeping, eating, or anything else allowed. How long would this handshaking marathon take? Answer: 2.6 years. By then there would be more than 255 million new people to shake hands with. Exponential growth is astonishing!

SELF CHECK

Are you having difficulty visualizing the 7 billion people who inhabit our planet? Go to http://www.7billionworld.com/ to see 7 billion little people on your screen. If you scroll to the extreme bottom right-hand corner of your screen and click on the arrow, you will be led to the worldometers webpage, where numbers depicting world population growth and resource consumption change before your eyes!

What Is the Difference between Economic Growth and Economic Development? More Stuff and Better Living Standards

Economic growth provides people with more goods and services and economic development uses economic growth to improve living standards.

Economic growth is an increase in the capacity of a country to provide people with goods and services. Accomplishing this increase requires population growth (more producers and consumers), more production and consumption per person, or both.

Economic growth is usually measured by the percentage change in a country's **gross domestic product (GDP):** the annual market value of all goods and services produced by all firms and organizations, foreign and domestic, operating within a country. Changes in a country's standard of living are measured by **per capita GDP:** the GDP divided by the total population at midyear.

Economic development is the improvement of living standards by economic growth. The United Nations (UN) classifies the world's countries as economically developed or developing based primarily on their degree of industrialization and their per capita GDP.

The **developed countries** (with 1.3 billion people) include Canada, the United States, Japan, Australia, New Zealand, and most European countries. Most are highly industrialized and have high average per capita GDP. All other nations (with 5.7 billion people) are classified as **developing countries,** most of them in Africa, Asia, and Latin America. Some are *middle-income, moderately developed countries,* such as China, India, Brazil, and Mexico, and others are *low-income countries*, such as Haiti, Nicaragua, and Nigeria.

Figure 1-3 compares some key characteristics of developed and developing countries. About 97%

of the projected increase in the world's population is expected to take place in developing countries (Figure 1-4).

Figure 1-5 summarizes some of the benefits (*good news*) and harm (*bad news*) caused mostly by economic development. It shows effects of the wide and increasing gap between the world's haves and have-nots.

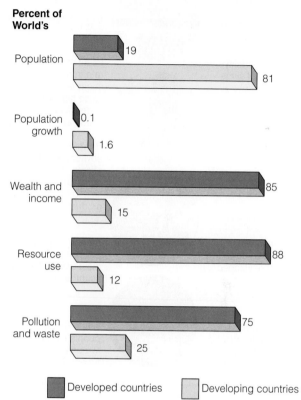

FIGURE 1-3 Comparison of developed and developing countries. (Data from United Nations and the World Bank)

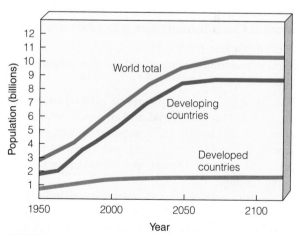

FIGURE 1-4 Past and projected population size for developed countries, developing countries, and the world, 1950–2100. Developing countries are expected to account for 97% of the 2.5 billion people projected to be added to the world's population between 2004 and 2050. (Data from United Nations)

Trade-Offs

Economic Development

Good News	Bad News
Global life expectancy doubled since 1950	Life expectancy 11 years less in developing countries than in developed countries
Infant mortality cut in half since 1955	Infant mortality rate in developing countries over 8 times higher than in developed countries
Food production ahead of population growth since 1978	Harmful environmental effects of agriculture may limit future food production
Air and water pollution down in most developed countries since 1970	Air and water pollution levels in most developing countries too high
Number of people living in poverty dropped 6% since 1990	Half of world's people trying to live on less than $4 per day

FIGURE 1-5 Trade-offs: good and bad news about economic development. Pick the single pieces of *good news* and *bad news* that you believe are the most important. (Data from United Nations and World Health Organization)

What Is Globalization? Being Connected

We live in a world that is increasingly interconnected through economic, cultural, and environmental interdependence.

You have probably heard about **globalization:** the process of social, economic, and environmental global changes that leads to an increasingly interconnected world. It involves increasing exchanges of people, products, services, capital, and ideas across international borders.

Factors accelerating globalization include information and communication technologies, human mobility, and international trade and investment. Modern communication via cell phones and the Internet also allows powerless people throughout the world to share ideas and to band together to bring about change from the bottom up.

This decentralized network, where everyone has access to everyone else, represents a *democratization of learning and communication* that is unprecedented in human history. A sustainable community or country recognizes that it is part of a larger global economic and ecological system and that it cannot be sustainable unless these larger systems are also sustainable.

1-3 RESOURCES

What Is a Resource? Something We Need or Want

We obtain resources from the environment to meet our needs and wants.

From a human standpoint, a **resource** is anything obtained from the environment to meet our needs and wants. Examples include food, water, shelter, manufactured goods, transportation, communication, and recreation. On our short human time scale, we classify the material resources we get from the environment as *perpetual, renewable,* or *nonrenewable,* as shown in Figure 1-6.

Some resources, such as solar energy, fresh air, wind, fresh surface water, fertile soil, and wild edible plants, are directly available for use. Other resources, such as petroleum (oil), iron, groundwater (water found underground), and modern crops, are not directly available. They become useful to us only with some effort and technological ingenuity. For example, petroleum was a mysterious fluid until we learned how to find and extract it and refine it into gasoline, heating oil, and other products that we could sell at affordable prices.

What Are Perpetual and Renewable Resources? Resources That Can Last

Resources renewed by natural processes are sustainable if we do not use them faster than they are replenished.

Solar energy is called a **perpetual resource** because on a human time scale it is renewed continuously. It is expected to last at least 6 billion years as the sun completes its life cycle as a star.

On a human time scale, a **renewable resource** can be replenished fairly rapidly (from hours to several decades) through natural processes. But this works only as long as the resource is not used up faster than it is replaced. Examples of renewable resources are forests, grasslands, wild animals, fresh water, fresh air, and fertile soil.

Renewable resources can be depleted or degraded. The highest rate at which a renewable resource can be

NEL

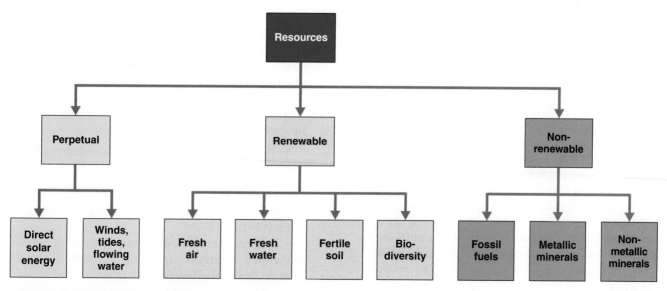

FIGURE 1-6 Natural capital: major types of material resources. This scheme is not fixed; renewable resources can become **nonrenewable resources** if used for a prolonged period at a faster rate than natural processes renew them.

used *indefinitely* without reducing its available supply is called its **sustainable yield.**

When we exceed a renewable resource's natural replacement rate, the available supply begins to shrink, a process known as **environmental degradation.** Examples include urbanization of productive land, excessive topsoil erosion, pollution, deforestation (temporary or permanent removal of large expanses of forest for agriculture or other uses), groundwater depletion, overgrazing of grasslands by livestock, and reduction in the Earth's forms of wildlife (biodiversity) by elimination of habitats and species.

Case Study: The Tragedy of the Commons— Degrading Free Renewable Resources

Renewable resources that are freely available to everyone can be degraded.

One cause of environmental degradation of renewable resources is the overuse of **common-property** or **free-access resources.** No individual owns these resources, and they are available to users at little or no charge.

Examples include clean air, the open ocean and its fish, migratory birds, **wildlife species,** publicly owned lands (such as provincial and national parks), gases of the lower atmosphere, and space.

In 1968, biologist Garrett Hardin (1915–2003) called the degradation of renewable free-access resources the **tragedy of the commons** (Spotlight, p. 9). It happens because each user reasons, "If I do not use this resource, someone else will. The little bit I use or pollute is not enough to matter, and such resources are renewable."

With only a few users, this logic works. But the cumulative effect of many people trying to exploit a free-access resource eventually exhausts or ruins it. Then no one can benefit from it, and that is the tragedy.

One solution is to use free-access resources at rates well below their estimated sustainable yields by reducing population, regulating access to the resources, or both. Some communities have established rules and traditions to regulate and share their access to common-property resources such as ocean fisheries, grazing lands, and forests. Governments have also enacted laws and international treaties to regulate access to commonly owned resources such as forests, national parks, rangelands, and fisheries in coastal waters.

Another potential solution is to *convert free-access resources to private ownership.* The reasoning is that if you own something, you are more likely to protect your investment.

This sounds good, but private ownership is not always the answer. One problem is private owners do not always protect natural resources they own when this conflicts with protecting their financial capital or increasing their profits. For example, some private forest owners can make more money by clear-cutting the timber, selling the degraded land, and investing their profits in other timberlands or businesses.

A second problem is that this approach is not practical for global common resources—such as the atmosphere, the open ocean, most wildlife species, and migratory birds—that cannot be divided up and converted to private property.

What Is Our Ecological Footprint? Our Growing Environmental Impact

Supplying each person with renewable resources and absorbing the wastes from such resource use creates a large ecological footprint or environmental impact.

The **per capita ecological footprint** is the amount of biologically productive land and water needed to supply each person in a population with the renewable resources they use and to absorb or dispose of the wastes from such resource use. It measures the average environmental impact of individuals in different countries and areas. In other words, it is a measure of how much of the Earth's natural capital and biological income each of us uses. The units used are *global hectares* (gha); each gha is a hectare of biologically productive land with average world productivity.

Biological capacity, or **biocapacity,** is the area of land that is actually available to produce renewable resources and to absorb wastes. It is also measured in terms of global hectares (gha).

Bad news. Humanity's **ecological footprint** exceeded the Earth's biological capacity to replenish renewable resources and absorb wastes by 30% in 2005 and by 50% in 2008 (Figure 1-7). The diagram playfully suggests that we need the capacity of an extra half-planet to remedy our current situation, and we will need the capacity of three extra planets by 2050 if we continue using resources and producing wastes at ongoing rates. Clearly, the "extra-planet" solution is not a realistic option. We are going to have to learn rapidly how to reduce our impact and live sustainably within the biological capacity of planet Earth (Global Footprint Network, 2012; WWF, 2012).

The ecological footprint of each person in a **more-developed country** is large compared to those of individuals from **less-developed countries** (Figure 1-7, right side). For example, the *per capita* ecological footprint of Canada is nearly as large as that of the United States, and much larger than that of countries like China or India. This part of the diagram reflects

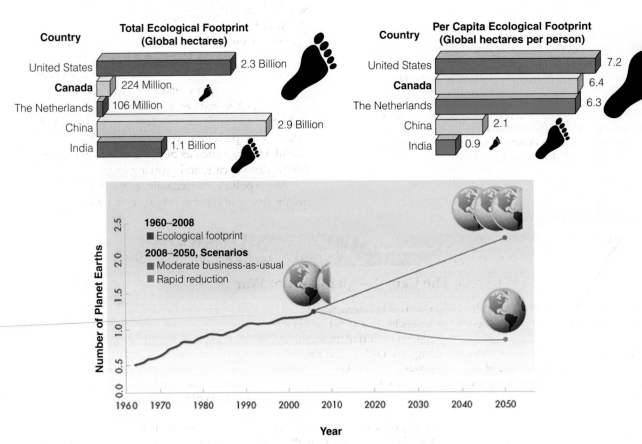

FIGURE 1-7 Natural capital use and degradation: total and per capita ecological footprints of Canada and four other countries (top). In 2008, humanity's ecological footprint was 50% higher than the Earth's carrying capacity (bottom; note the need for an extra "half-planet" to balance our impact). According to UN projections, if current trends continue we will need "two planet Earths" by the mid-2030s and "three planet Earths" by the mid-2050s, or we can choose a more sustainable path (the lower curve in the bottom diagram). (Global Footprint Network, 2012. Available at http://www.footprintnetwork.org)

the role that affluence and resource consumption per individual play in contributing to human impact on our planet.

However, population size becomes important when considering the *total* ecological footprint of each country. The relatively small populations of Canada (35 million) and the Netherlands (17 million) result in these countries each having a relatively small total ecological footprint (Figure 1-7, left side). In contrast, countries such as China and India have a larger total ecological footprint owing to their much larger populations of 1.3 billion people and 1.2 billion people, respectively. Population numbers and growth will be considered more fully in Chapter 10.

In addition to concerns about overconsumption of resources in more-developed countries and rapid population growth in less-developed countries, there is the impending pressure of future development as countries with large populations such as China and India become more industrialized and affluent, thereby increasing the size and impact of their ecological footprints.

1-4 POLLUTION

Where Do Pollutants Come from, and What Are Their Harmful Effects? Threats to Health and Survival

Pollutants are chemicals found at high enough levels in the environment to cause harm to people or other organisms.

Pollution is the presence of substances at high enough levels in air, water, soil, or food to threaten the health, survival, or activities of humans or other organisms. **Pollutants** can enter the environment naturally (for example, from volcanic eruptions) or through human or anthropogenic activities (for example, from burning coal). Most pollution from human activities occurs in or near urban and industrial areas, where pollution sources such as cars and factories are concentrated. Industrialized agriculture is also a major source of pollution. Most pollutants are unintended by-products of useful activities such as burning coal to generate electricity, driving cars, and growing crops.

Some pollutants contaminate the areas where they are produced and some are carried by wind or flowing

SPOTLIGHT

A Tragedy of the Commons: The Canada–Spain Turbot War

The Turbot War of 1995—in which a Spanish trawler fishing with illegal nets was seized by Canadian patrol ships—was a "tragedy of the commons" that arose because of differing views about declining fish stocks in international waters.

In brief, cod, redfish, and flounder populations had been all but fished out on the Grand Banks east of Newfoundland. Part of this famous fishing area was within Canada's 320-kilometre (200-mile) Exclusive Economic Zone, but part was in international waters accessible to any nation. As the remaining turbot populations began to rapidly decline, the federal government declared a moratorium on turbot fishing throughout the Grand Banks.

This conservation measure prompted many foreign fishing vessels to withdraw from the area, but Spain threatened to send warships to protect its fleet. Six days later, Canadian patrol boats seized a Spanish trawler that was fishing for turbot using illegal fine-mesh nets. Spain dispatched naval vessels to protect the remainder of its fishing fleet on the Grand Banks. The federal government responded by authorizing its navy to fire if the Spanish vessels uncovered their guns. Two peace-loving nations were on the verge of going to war over fish!

Further details about developments at the Grand Banks fishery can be found in Chapter 13.

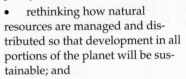

WWF'S *Living Planet Report 2012*

WWF—the global conservation organization—released their latest *Living Planet Report* in May 2012. The report makes the point that we are currently using 50% more resources than the Earth can provide and that we are on an unsustainable path toward a future where two planets would be required to fulfill our needs by 2030. It argues that we need to wake up to this reality and adopt a "One Planet" perspective (WWF, 2012).

The report calls our attention to some important facts:

• The Living Planet Index (an indicator of biodiversity health based on trends in 9, 014 populations of 2, 688 animal species in various habitats all over the planet) has shown a global decline of 28% between 1970 and 2008, with a decline of 70% observed in tropical areas.

• The global ecological footprint has increased in response to overconsumption and population growth, and has surpassed the global biocapacity (the area of land available to produce renewable resources and to absorb our wastes such as CO_2 emissions). For example, in 2008 the world's total ecological footprint was 18.2 billion global hectares (gha) compared to a total biocapacity of 12.0 billion gha. This is an overshoot

of 50% beyond the total biocapacity, leading to analogies about another half-planet being required to handle our demands.

• There are important linkages between biodiversity, the natural services of ecosystems, and the demands of people that must be understood. The report details the products and natural services that are provided by healthy and interconnected forest, freshwater, and ocean ecosystems, and illustrates that as these ecosystems are degraded and uncoupled by human impact, the ability of the planet to renew itself becomes impaired.

The report argues that the situation is extremely serious but can still be remedied if we adopt a One Planet perspective. This would involve changes to our economies and lifestyles such as the following:

• greater protection of natural ecosystems that provide us with biodiversity, resources, and services;

• more efficient and innovative management of our production systems so that our needs can be met while lowering human impact;

• changes in consumption rates and patterns so that our demands on the environment align with the

biocapacity of the Earth to provide resources and purify wastes;

• rethinking how natural resources are managed and distributed so that development in all portions of the planet will be sustainable; and

• redirecting financial flows away from technologies and practices that are destructive, toward those that will allow us to meet our needs indefinitely within the bounds of our one planet.

The full report, describing these points in much greater detail, can be found online at http://wwf .panda.org/about_our_earth/ all_publications/living_planet_ report/2012_lpr/.

Courtesy of the WWF

---

water to other areas. Pollution does not respect the neat territorial political lines we draw on maps.

The pollutants we produce come from two types of sources. **Point sources** of pollutants are single, identifiable sources. Examples are the smokestack of a coal-burning power plant, the drainpipe of a factory, and the exhaust pipe of an automobile. **Nonpoint sources** of pollutants are dispersed and often difficult to identify. Examples are pesticides sprayed into the air or blown by the wind into the atmosphere and runoff of fertilizers and pesticides from farmlands, golf courses, and suburban lawns and gardens into streams and lakes. It is much easier and cheaper to identify and control pollution from point sources than from widely dispersed nonpoint sources.

Pollutants can have three types of unwanted effects. *First*, they can disrupt or degrade life-support systems for humans and other species. *Second*, they can damage wildlife, human health, and property. *Third*, they can be nuisances such as noise and unpleasant smells, tastes, and sights.

Solutions: What Can We Do about Pollution? Prevention Pays

We can try to clean up pollutants in the environment or prevent them from entering the environment.

We use two basic approaches to deal with pollution. One is **pollution prevention,** or **input pollution control,** which reduces or eliminates the production of

The Ecological Footprint of Calgary, Alberta

The idea of the ecological footprint is not restricted to global or per capita perspectives. Cities can use the concept to address their environmental problems and to plan their development. When Calgary was identified as a municipality with environmental problems, City officials agreed to undertake an ecological footprint analysis. The 2005 study resulted in a number of documents, including *Toward a Preferred Future: Understanding Calgary's Ecological Footprint* (City of Calgary, 2007) and *Calgary's Ecological Footprint Baseline Report 2008* (City of Calgary, 2009).

The baseline report showed that each citizen of Calgary had an ecological footprint of 9.4 gha per person, compared to the Canadian average of 7.1 gha. The problem was that Calgarians were being par-

ticularly extravagant in their use of energy, their consumption of goods and services, and various aspects of their housing.

The City took action in a number of ways, including taking steps to protect green spaces, powering its light rail system with 100% wind-generated energy, and organizing the transition toward providing renewable energy sources throughout Calgary. The City also developed a user-friendly web page with a wealth of information and some interactive features to inform and involve the citizens.

In 2010, a follow-up report showed that the City had already made some progress. The ecological footprint was now 8.6 gha, down 8.6% since 2008. The progress was due to greater efficiency in

crop production and consumption of more local foods. The energy component of the footprint had actually increased, and City officials realized that energy demands were coupled to aspects of the built environment, such as a large amount of low-density housing that was wasteful of heat energy and caused people to make their daily commute by car. The City began to focus on a municipal development plan and a transportation plan to help solve these problems.

Calgary has been progressive in adopting its Ecological Footprint Project and other initiatives that will allow it to mitigate its potential environmental problems through informed planning and intelligent urban design.

---

pollutants. The other is **pollution cleanup,** or **output pollution control,** which involves cleaning up or diluting pollutants after they have been produced.

Environmentalists have identified three problems with relying primarily on pollution cleanup. *First,* it is only a temporary bandage as long as population and consumption levels grow without corresponding improvements in pollution control technology. For example, adding catalytic converters to car exhaust systems has reduced some forms of air pollution. But increases in the number of cars and in the distance each travels have reduced the effectiveness of this approach.

Second, cleanup often removes a pollutant from one part of the environment only to cause pollution in another. For example, we can collect garbage, but the garbage may then be *burned* (causing air pollution and leaving toxic ash that must be put somewhere); *dumped* into streams, lakes, and oceans (causing water pollution); or *buried* (causing soil and groundwater pollution).

Third, once pollutants have entered and become dispersed into the environment at harmful levels, it usually costs too much to reduce them to acceptable levels.

Both pollution prevention (front-of-the-pipe) and pollution cleanup (end-of-the-pipe) solutions are

needed. But environmentalists and some economists urge us to put more emphasis on prevention because it works better and is cheaper than cleanup. As Benjamin Franklin observed long ago, "An ounce of prevention is worth a pound of cure."

1-5 ENVIRONMENTAL AND RESOURCE PROBLEMS: CAUSES AND CONNECTIONS

What Are Key Environmental Problems and Their Basic Causes? The Big Five

The major causes of environmental problems are population growth, poverty, wasteful resource use, poor environmental accounting, and ecological ignorance.

We face a number of interconnected environmental and resource problems, as listed in Figure 1-8. The first step in dealing with these problems is to identify their underlying causes, listed in Figure 1-9 (p. 12) and sometimes known as the *big five.*

Three of these causes are rapid population growth (p. 4 and Chapter 10), poverty (below and in Chapter 26), and excessive and wasteful use of resources (p. 13 and Chapters 17, 18, and 24). The fourth cause is failure to include the harmful environmental

FIGURE 1-8 Natural capital degradation: major environmental and resource problems.

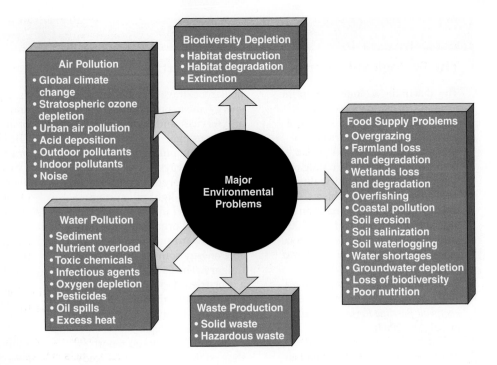

Air Pollution
• Global climate change
• Stratospheric ozone depletion
• Urban air pollution
• Acid deposition
• Outdoor pollutants
• Indoor pollutants
• Noise

Biodiversity Depletion
• Habitat destruction
• Habitat degradation
• Extinction

Major Environmental Problems

Food Supply Problems
• Overgrazing
• Farmland loss and degradation
• Wetlands loss and degradation
• Overfishing
• Coastal pollution
• Soil erosion
• Soil salinization
• Soil waterlogging
• Water shortages
• Groundwater depletion
• Loss of biodiversity
• Poor nutrition

Water Pollution
• Sediment
• Nutrient overload
• Toxic chemicals
• Infectious agents
• Oxygen depletion
• Pesticides
• Oil spills
• Excess heat

Waste Production
• Solid waste
• Hazardous waste

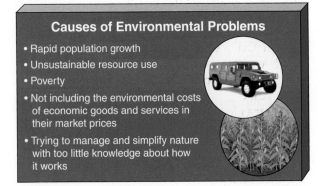

Causes of Environmental Problems

• Rapid population growth
• Unsustainable resource use
• Poverty
• Not including the environmental costs of economic goods and services in their market prices
• Trying to manage and simplify nature with too little knowledge about how it works

FIGURE 1-9 Environmentalists have identified five basic causes of the environmental problems we face.

costs of items in their market prices, discussed in Chapter 26. This in turn is a policy and political failure to address this issue (Chapter 27). The fifth cause, inadequate understanding of how the Earth works, is discussed throughout this book.

What Is the Relationship between Poverty and Environmental Problems? Being Poor Is Bad for People and the Earth

Poverty is a major threat to human health and the environment.

Many of the world's poor do not have access to the basic necessities for a healthy, productive, and decent life, as listed in Figure 1-10. Their daily lives are focused on getting enough food, water, and fuel (for cooking and heat) to survive. Desperate for land to grow enough food, many of the world's poor people

deplete and degrade forests, soil, grasslands, and wildlife for short-term survival. They do not have the luxury of worrying about long-term environmental quality or sustainability.

Another problem for the poor is living in areas with high levels of air and water pollution and with a great risk of natural disasters such as floods, earthquakes, hurricanes, and volcanic eruptions. And they usually must take jobs—if they can find them—with unhealthy and unsafe working conditions at very low pay.

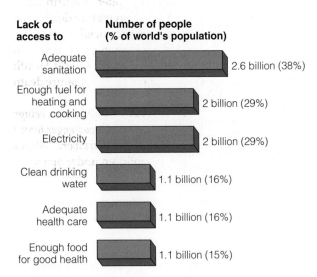

Lack of access to	Number of people (% of world's population)
Adequate sanitation	2.6 billion (38%)
Enough fuel for heating and cooking	2 billion (29%)
Electricity	2 billion (29%)
Clean drinking water	1.1 billion (16%)
Adequate health care	1.1 billion (16%)
Enough food for good health	1.1 billion (15%)

FIGURE 1-10 Natural capital degradation: some harmful effects of poverty. Which two of these effects do you believe are the most harmful? (Data from United Nations, World Bank, and World Health Organization)

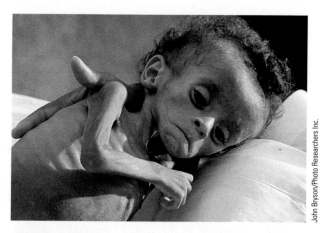

FIGURE 1-11 One in every three children under age 5, such as this Brazilian child, suffers from malnutrition. According to the World Health Organization, each day at least 12 000 children under age 5 die prematurely from malnutrition and infectious diseases from drinking contaminated water and other causes.

Poverty also affects population growth. Poor people often have many children as a form of economic security. Their children help them grow food, gather fuel (mostly wood and dung), haul drinking water, tend livestock, work, and beg in the streets. The children also help their parents survive in their old age before they die, typically in their 50s in the poorest countries. The poor do not have retirement plans, social security, or government-sponsored health plans.

Many of the world's desperately poor die prematurely from four preventable health problems. One is *malnutrition* from a lack of protein and other **nutrients** needed for good health (Figure 1-11). The second is increased susceptibility to normally nonfatal infectious diseases, such as diarrhea and measles, because of their weakened condition from malnutrition. A third factor is lack of access to clean drinking water. A fourth factor is severe respiratory disease and premature death from inhaling indoor air pollutants produced by burning wood or coal for heat and cooking in open fires or in poorly vented stoves. According to the World Health Organization, these four factors cause premature death for at least 7 million of the poor a year.

This premature death of about 19 200 human beings per day is equivalent to 48 fully loaded 400-passenger jumbo jet planes crashing every day with no survivors! About two-thirds of those dying are children under age 5.

What Is the Relationship between Resource Consumption and Environmental Problems? Affluenza

Many consumers in developed countries have become addicted to buying more and more stuff in their search for fulfillment and happiness.

Affluenza ("af-loo-EN-zuh") is a term used to describe the unsustainable addiction to overconsumption and materialism exhibited in the lifestyles of affluent consumers in Canada, the United States, and other developed countries. It is based on the assumption that buying more and more things can, should, and does buy happiness.

Most people infected with this contagious *shop-till-you-drop virus* have some telltale symptoms. They feel overworked, have high levels of debt and bankruptcy, suffer from increasing stress and anxiety, have declining health, and feel unfulfilled in their quest to accumulate more and more stuff. As humorist Will Rogers said, "Too many people spend money they haven't earned to buy things they don't want, to impress people they don't like." For some, shopping until you drop means shopping until you go bankrupt.

Globalization and global advertising are now spreading the virus throughout much of the world. This, in combination with population growth, will greatly increase the impact that humans have on the planet.

What can we do about affluenza? The first step for addicts is to admit they have a problem. Then they begin steps to kick their addiction by going on a stuff diet. For example, before buying anything a person with the affluenza addiction should ask: Do I really need this or merely want it? Can I buy it secondhand (reuse)? Can I borrow it from a friend or relative? Another withdrawal strategy: Do not hang out with other addicts. Shopaholics should avoid malls as much as they can.

After a lifetime of studying the growth and decline of the world's human civilizations, historian Arnold Toynbee (1987) summarized the true measure of a civilization's growth in what he called the *law of progressive simplification:* "True growth occurs as civilizations transfer an increasing proportion of energy and attention from the material side of life to the nonmaterial side and thereby develop their culture, capacity for compassion, sense of community, and strength of democracy."

How Can Affluence Help Increase Environmental Quality? Another Side of the Story

Affluent countries have more money for improving environmental quality.

Some analysts point out that affluence need not lead to environmental degradation. Instead, it can lead people to become more concerned about environmental quality, and it provides money for developing technologies to reduce pollution, environmental degradation, and resource waste. This explains why most of the important environmental progress made since 1970 has taken place in developed countries.

In Canada and the United States, in many ways the air is cleaner, drinking water is purer, most rivers and lakes are cleaner, and the food supply is more abundant and safer than in 1970. Also, most energy and material resources are used more efficiently. Similar advances have been made in most other affluent countries. Affluence financed these improvements in environmental quality.

How Are Environmental Problems and Their Causes Connected? Exploring Connections

Environmental quality is affected by interactions among population size, resource consumption, and technology.

Once we have identified environmental problems and their root causes, the next step is to understand how they are connected to one another. The three-factor model in Figure 1-12 is a starting point.

According to this simple model, the environmental impact (I) of a population on a given area depends on three factors: the number of people (P), the average resource use per person (affluence, A), and the beneficial and harmful environmental effects of the technologies (T) used to provide and consume each unit of resource and to control or prevent the resulting pollution and environmental degradation.

In developing countries, population size and the resulting degradation of renewable resources as the poor struggle to stay alive tend to be the key factors in total environmental impact (Figure 1-12, top). In such countries per capita resource use is low.

In developed countries, high rates of per capita resource use and the resulting high levels of pollution and environmental degradation per person usually are the key factors determining overall environmental impact (Figure 1-12, bottom) and a country's ecological footprint per person (Figure 1-7). For example, the average North American citizen consumes about 35 times as much as the average citizen of India and 100 times as much as the average person in the world's poorest countries. *Thus poor parents in a developing country would need 70 to 200 children to have the same lifetime resource consumption as 2 children in a typical North American family.*

Some forms of technology, such as polluting factories, motor vehicles, and energy-wasting devices, increase environmental impact by raising the T factor in the equation. But other technologies, such as pollution control and prevention, solar cells, and energy-saving devices, lower environmental impact by decreasing the T factor. In other words, some forms of technology are *environmentally harmful* and some are *environmentally beneficial*.

Developing Countries

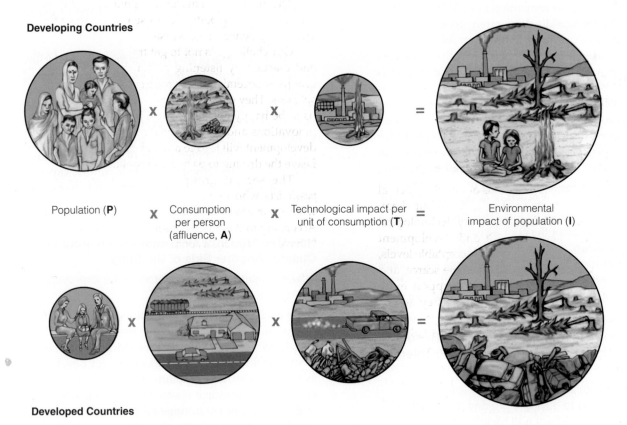

Population (**P**) X Consumption per person (affluence, **A**) X Technological impact per unit of consumption (**T**) = Environmental impact of population (**I**)

Developed Countries

FIGURE 1-12 Connections: simplified model of how three factors—number of people, affluence, and technology—affect the environmental impact of the population in developing countries (top) and developed countries (bottom).

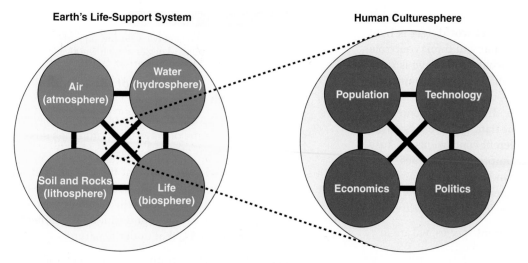

Earth's Life-Support System

Air (atmosphere)

Water (hydrosphere)

Soil and Rocks (lithosphere)

Life (biosphere)

Human Culturesphere

Population

Technology

Economics

Politics

FIGURE 1-13 Connections: the human culturesphere involves a number of connections among its human-created components. These, in turn, have multiple connections with each of the much larger components of the Earth's life-support system. The goal of environmental science is to learn as much as possible about the complex interactions of all these components.

The three-factor model in Figure 1-12 can help us understand how key environmental problems and some of their causes are connected. It can also guide us in seeking solutions. However, these problems involve a number of poorly understood interactions between many more factors than those in this simplified model, as outlined in Figure 1-13. Look at the interactions shown in this figure.

1-6 IS OUR PRESENT COURSE SUSTAINABLE?

Are Things Getting Better or Worse? The Answer Is Both

There is good and bad environmental news.

Experts disagree about how serious our environmental problems are and what we should do about them. Some analysts believe human ingenuity, technological advances, and economic growth and development will allow us to clean up pollution to acceptable levels, find substitutes for resources that become scarce, and keep expanding the Earth's ability to support more humans, as we have done in the past. They accuse many scientists and environmentalists of exaggerating the seriousness of the problems we face and failing to appreciate the progress we have made in improving quality of life and protecting the environment.

Environmentalists and many leading scientists disagree with this view. They cite evidence that we are degrading and disrupting many of the world's life-support systems for us and other species at an accelerating rate. They are greatly encouraged by the progress we have made in increasing average life expectancy,

reducing infant mortality, increasing food supplies, and reducing many forms of pollution—especially in developed countries. But they point out that we need to use the Earth in a way that is more sustainable for present and future human generations and other species that support us and other forms of life.

The most useful answer to the question of whether things are getting better or worse is *both*. Some things are getting better, some worse.

Our challenge is not to get trapped into confusion and inaction by listening primarily to either of two groups of extremists. One group consists of *technological optimists*. They tend to overstate the situation by telling us to be happy and not worry, because technological innovations and conventional economic growth and development will lead to a wonderworld for everyone. Leave the driving to us because we know best.

The second group consists of *environmental pessimists* who overstate the problems to the point where our environmental situation seems hopeless. According to the noted conservationist Aldo Leopold, "I have no hope for a conservation based on fear."

> **CONSIDER, DISCUSS, OR DEBATE**
>
> Is the society you live in on an unsustainable path? What are the most important changes that should be made?

How Should We Live? A Clash of Environmental Worldviews

The way we view the seriousness of environmental problems and how to solve them depends on our environmental worldview.

The differing views about how serious our environmental problems are and what we should do about them arise mostly out of differing environmental worldviews. Your **environmental worldview** is how you think the world works, what you think your role in the world should be, and what you believe is right and wrong environmental behaviour (**environmental ethics**).

People who have widely differing environmental worldviews can take the same data, be logically consistent, and arrive at quite different conclusions because they start with different assumptions and values.

Some people in today's industrial consumer societies have a **planetary management worldview.** Here are the basic environmental beliefs of this worldview:

- As the planet's most important species, we are in charge of nature.

- We will not run out of resources because of our ability to develop and find new ones.

- The potential for global economic growth is essentially unlimited.

- Our success depends on how well we manage the Earth's life-support systems, mostly for our own benefit.

A second environmental worldview, known as the **stewardship worldview,** consists of the following major beliefs:

- We are the planet's most important species, but we have an ethical responsibility to care for the rest of nature.

- We will probably not run out of resources, but they should not be wasted.

- We should encourage environmentally beneficial forms of economic growth and discourage environmentally harmful forms of economic growth.

- Our success depends on how well we can manage the Earth's life-support systems for our benefit and for the rest of nature.

Another environmental worldview, known as the **environmental wisdom worldview,** is based on the following major beliefs, which are the opposite of those making up the planetary management worldview:

- Nature exists for all species, not just for us, and we are not in charge of the Earth.

- The Earth's resources are limited, should not be wasted, and are not all for us.

- We should encourage Earth-sustaining forms of economic growth and discourage Earth-degrading forms.

- Our success depends on learning how the Earth sustains itself and integrating such lessons from nature (environmental wisdom) into the ways we think and act.

CONSIDER, DISCUSS, OR DEBATE

Which environmental worldview do you support? What are the strengths and weaknesses of each worldview?

What Are the Principles of Sustainability? Emulate Nature

We should develop our strategies of sustainability by mimicking the four major ways that nature has sustained itself for several billion years.

Environmental scientists say that the information we need to design sustainable human systems, and to live within the capacities of the Earth's life-support systems (Figure 1-13), can be found in four fundamental principles (Figure 1-14) that underlie nature:

- Natural systems are primarily based on various forms of solar energy, such as the energy captured by plants during photosynthesis and passed along food chains (p. 71).

- Matter is continuously recycled in natural systems; the wastes of one organism become the resources of another organism.

- Biodiversity is a thriving consequence of organisms responding to ecological opportunities provided by abundant resources and suitable environments in which to live.

- Yet natural populations do not rise without limit; there are natural processes of population regulation that adjust populations to the carrying capacity of the environment that supports them.

Our lack of attention to these principles is often at the root of our environmental problems, but happily the application of these principles can be part of the environmental solutions we need. This idea will be discussed at greater depth in the chapters that follow.

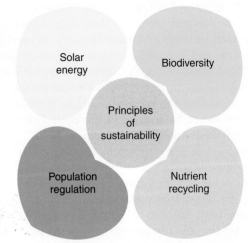

FIGURE 1-14 Sustaining natural capital: four interconnected principles overlap as the principles of sustainability that have maintained nature for billions of years.

A point to make here is that if we emulate the tried-and-true principles that have sustained nature for billions of years, we will be well on our way to designing sustainable human systems that do not overwhelm the carrying capacity of the Earth.

What Is Environmentally Sustainable Economic Development? Rewarding Environmentally Beneficial Activities

Environmentally sustainable economic development rewards environmentally beneficial and sustainable activities and discourages environmentally harmful and unsustainable activities.

During this century, many analysts call for us to put much greater emphasis on **environmentally sustainable economic development.** This would involve making development choices and supporting economic activities that are compatible with the principles of sustainability described above. Changes would be accomplished by means such as environmental education, economic rewards (government subsidies and tax breaks) that *encourage* sustainable activities, and economic penalties (government taxes and regulations) that *discourage* unsustainable activities. The result would be a shift to different choices (Figure 1-15) more compatible with a sustainable future.

Throughout this book, we try to give you a balanced view of good and bad environmental news. Try not to be overwhelmed or immobilized by the bad environmental news, because there is also some *great environmental news.* An example of *great news* is that politicians are rising to the challenge and being proactive about sustainable economic development. At the UN Millennium Summit of 2000, world leaders gathered to create eight Millennium Development Goals (Figure 1-16). These goals are aimed at solving eight major aspects of sustainable development by the year 2015, with specific targets to accomplish along the way. In various chapters that follow, we will look more closely at the eight Millennium Development Goals, at the targets they identify, and at some of the progress that has been made.

The challenge is to make creative use of our economic and political systems to apply the solutions that we discover through scientific research and technological innovation. One key is to recognize that most economic and political change comes about as a result of individuals, or small groups of individuals, working to bring about change by grassroots action from the bottom up. *More great news.* Social scientists suggest that it takes only about 5–10% of the

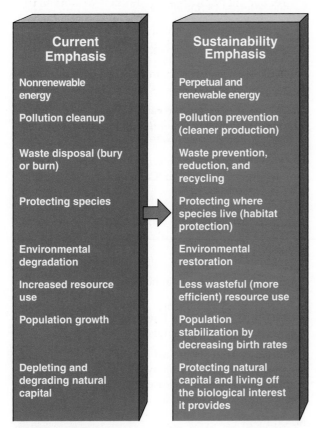

FIGURE 1-15 Solutions: some shifts involved in designing a more sustainable future.

FIGURE 1-16 A global initiative: the United Nations has identified eight Millennium Development Goals to be accomplished by 2015. We will examine these goals further in subsequent chapters. (http://www.unmillenniumproject.org/goals/index.htm)

Environmental Problems: An Introduction and Overview **17**

population of a country or of the world to bring about major social change. Anthropologist Margaret Mead summarized our potential for change: "Never doubt that a small group of thoughtful, committed citizens can change the world. Indeed, it is the only thing that ever has."

We live in exciting times during what might be called a *hinge of cultural history*. Indeed, if we had to pick an important time in which to live, it would be the next 50 years as we face the challenge of developing more environmentally sustainable societies.

What's the use of a house if you don't have a decent planet to put it on?

HENRY DAVID THOREAU

CHAPTER REVIEW

1. Review the Key Questions for this chapter on p. 2. What is *exponential growth*? Why is living in an exponential age a cause for concern for everyone living on the planet?

2. Define *environment*. Distinguish among *environmental science, ecology,* and *environmentalism*. Distinguish between an *organism* and a *species*. What is an *ecosystem*? What is *sustainability*? Explain the terms *natural capital, natural resources, solar capital, solar energy,* and *natural capital degradation*. What is *nutrient cycling* and why is it important? Describe the ultimate goal of an *environmentally sustainable society*.

3. What is the difference between *economic growth* and *economic development*? Distinguish between *gross domestic product (GDP)* and *per capita GDP*. Distinguish between *developed countries* and *developing countries* and describe their key characteristics. What is *globalization*?

4. What is a *resource*? What is *conservation*? Distinguish among a *renewable resource, nonrenewable resource,* and *perpetual resource* and give an example of each. What is *sustainable yield*? Define and give three examples of *environmental degradation*.

5. What is the *tragedy of the commons*? What is an *ecological footprint*? What is a *per capita ecological footprint*?

Compare the total and per capita ecological footprints of Canada, the United States, and China.

6. Define *pollution*. Distinguish between *point sources* and *nonpoint sources* of pollution. Distinguish between *pollution cleanup* and *pollution prevention* and give an example of each. Describe three problems with solutions that rely mostly on pollution cleanup.

7. Identify five basic causes of the environmental problems that we face today. What is *poverty*? In what ways do poverty and affluence affect the environment? Explain the problems we face by not including the harmful environmental costs in the prices of goods and services. Define *affluenza*.

8. What is an *environmental worldview*? What is *environmental ethics*? Distinguish among the *planetary management, stewardship,* and *environmental wisdom worldviews*. What is *environmentally sustainable economic development*?

9. Discuss the lessons we can learn from the Canada–Spain Turbot War (Spotlight, p. 9). How was this a tragedy of the commons?

10. What are four *scientific principles of sustainability*? Explain how exponential growth (**Case Study**) affects them.

CRITICAL THINKING

1. Do you favour instituting policies designed to reduce population growth and stabilize **(a)** the size of the world's population as soon as possible and **(b)** the size of Canada's population as soon as possible? Explain. If you agree that population stabilization is desirable, what three major policies would you implement to accomplish this goal?

2. List **(a)** three forms of economic growth you believe are environmentally unsustainable and

(b) three forms you believe are environmentally sustainable.

3. Give three examples of how environmental degradation can result from the tragedy of the commons.

4. When you read about vast numbers of human beings dying prematurely each day from preventable malnutrition and infectious disease, do you **(a)** doubt whether it is true, **(b)** not want to think about it, **(c)** feel hopeless,

(d) feel sad, **(e)** feel guilty, or **(f)** want to do something about this problem?

5. What is your reaction when you read that **(1)** the average North American consumes about 35 times more resources than the average Indian citizen, **(2)** human activities lead to the premature extinction of at least 10 species per day, and **(3)** human activities are projected to make the Earth's climate warmer: **(a)** skeptical about their accuracy, **(b)** indifferent, **(c)** sad, **(d)** helpless, **(e)** guilty, **(f)** concerned, or **(g)** outraged? Which of these reactions help to perpetuate such problems, and which can help to alleviate them?

6. See if you are infected by the affluenza bug by indicating whether you agree or disagree with the following statements.

   a. I am willing to work at a job I despise so I can buy lots of stuff.
   b. When I am feeling down, I like to go shopping to make myself feel better.
   c. I would rather be shopping right now.
   d. I owe more than $1 000 on my credit cards.
   e. I usually make only the minimum payment on my monthly credit-card bills.
   f. I am running out of room to store my stuff.

If you agree with three of these statements, you are infected with affluenza. If you agree with more than three, you have a serious case of affluenza. Compare your answers with those of your classmates and discuss the effects of the results on the environment and your feelings of happiness.

7. Explain why you agree or disagree with each of the following statements: **(a)** humans are superior to other forms of life, **(b)** humans are in charge of the Earth, **(c)** all economic growth is good, **(d)** the value of other species depends only on whether they are useful to us, **(e)** because all species eventually become extinct we should not worry about whether our activities cause the premature extinction of a species, **(f)** all species have an inherent right to exist, **(g)** nature has an almost unlimited storehouse of resources for human use, **(h)** technology can solve our environmental problems, **(i)** I do not believe I have any obligation to future generations, and **(j)** I do not believe I have any obligation to other species.

8. What are the basic beliefs of your environmental worldview? Are the beliefs of your environmental worldview consistent with your answers to question 7? Are your environmental actions consistent with your environmental worldview?

PROJECTS

1. What are the major resource and environmental problems where you live? Which of these problems affect you directly? Have these problems become better or worse during the last 10 years?

2. Write two-page scenarios describing what your life and that of any children you may have might be like 50 years from now if **(a)** we continue on our present path; or **(b)** we shift to more sustainable societies throughout most of the world.

3. Make a list of the resources you truly need. Then make another list of the resources you use each day only because you want them. Finally, make a third list of resources you want and hope to use in the future.

Compare your lists with those compiled by other members of your class, and relate the overall result to the tragedy of the commons (pp. 7 and 9).

4. Use the library or the Internet to find out bibliographic information about at least two of the following people mentioned in the chapter: *René Dubos, Garret Hardin, Aldo Leopold, Margaret Mead, William Rees, David Suzuki, Henry David Thoreau, Mathis Wackernagel,* and *Barbara Ward.*

5. Visit some online sites and answer the questions that allow you to calculate ecological footprints for yourself and for different lifestyles, types of accommodation, and regions. Reach conclusions about how to strive for smaller ecological footprints.

ECOLOGICAL FOOTPRINT ANALYSIS

If a country's or the world's *ecological footprint per person* (Figure 1-7, p. 8) is larger than its *biological capacity per person* to replenish its renewable resources and to absorb the resulting waste products and pollution, it is said to have an *ecological deficit*. If the reverse is true, it has an *ecological credit* or *reserve*. Use the data below to calculate the ecological deficit or credit for various countries.

Environmental Problems: An Introduction and Overview

Place	Per Capita Ecological Footprint (global hectares per person)*	Per Capita Biocapacity (global hectares per person)	Ecological Credit (+) or Debit (–) Place (global hectares per person)
World	2.7	1.8	–0.9
Canada	**6.4**	**15.0**	
United States	7.2	3.9	
United Kingdom	4.7	1.3	
Mexico	3.3	1.4	
Russia	4.4	6.6	
China	2.1	0.9	
India	0.9	0.5	
Germany	4.6	2.0	
Japan	4.2	0.6	
Brazil	2.9	9.6	

Source: Data from *WWF Living Planet Report 2012*.
*1 hectare = 2.47 acres

1. Which two countries have the largest ecological deficits?

2. Which countries have an ecological credit?

3. Rank the countries in order from the largest to the smallest per capita footprint.

Environmental History: Learning from the Past

2

Near Extinction of North American Bison

In 1500, before Europeans settled North America, 30–60 million North American plains bison—commonly known as the buffalo (*Bison bison bison*)—grazed the plains, prairies, and woodlands over much of the continent.

These animals were once so numerous that in 1832 a traveller wrote, "As far as my eye could reach the country seemed absolutely blackened by innumerable herds." A single herd on the move might thunder past for hours.

For centuries, Plains Native peoples depended heavily on bison. Typically they killed only enough animals to meet their needs for food, clothing, and shelter. They also burned dried feces of these animals, known as "buffalo chips," to cook food and provide heat.

By 1906, the once vast range of the bison had shrunk to a tiny area, and the species had been driven nearly to extinction (Figure 2-1). How did this happen? It began when settlers moving west after the U.S. Civil War upset the sustainable balance between Plains Native people and bison. Plains people traded bison skins to settlers for steel knives and firearms, which allowed them to kill more bison.

But it was the new settlers who caused the most relentless slaughter. As railroads spread westward starting in the late 1860s, railroad companies hired professional bison hunters—including Buffalo Bill Cody—to supply construction crews with meat. Passengers also gunned down bison from train windows for sport, leaving the carcasses to rot.

Commercial hunters shot millions of bison for their hides and tongues (considered a delicacy), leaving most of the meat to rot. "Bone pickers" collected the bleached bones that whitened the prairies and shipped them east to be ground up as fertilizer.

Farmers shot bison because they damaged crops, fences, telegraph poles, and sod houses. Ranchers killed them because they competed with cattle and sheep for pasture. The U.S. Army killed at least 12 million bison as part of its campaign to subdue the Plains tribes by killing off their primary source of food.

FIGURE 2-1 The historical range of the bison shrank severely between 1500 and 1906, mostly because of unregulated and deliberate overhunting.

Between 1870 and 1875, at least 2.5 million bison were slaughtered each year. An estimated 85 of the small number of wild plains bison that remained were given refuge in Yellowstone National Park. In 1906, the Canadian government purchased 700 plains bison, largely from an American rancher. These animals were moved to Buffalo Park near Wainwright, Alberta. As well, 250 wood bison (*Bison bison athabascae*), a northern subspecies of bison that once numbered 17 000 animals, survived in northern Alberta and in the Northwest Territories; they were protected by the establishment of Wood Buffalo Park in 1922. Today an estimated 150 000 plains bison reside in national parks, in wildlife refuge areas, and on private ranches in Canada and the United States. There are about 5 000 wood bison, most in Wood Buffalo National Park and in parts of northern Alberta and the Northwest Territories.

The history of humanity's relationships to the environment provides many important lessons that can help us deal with today's environmental problems and avoid repeating past mistakes.

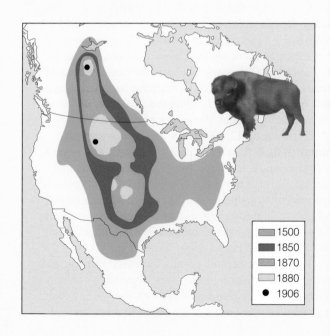

▢	1500
▢	1850
▢	1870
▢	1880
●	1906

A continent ages quickly once we come.

ERNEST HEMINGWAY

2-1 CULTURAL CHANGES AND THE ENVIRONMENT

What Major Human Cultural Changes Have Taken Place? Agriculture, Industrialization, and Globalization

Since our hunter-gatherer days we have undergone three major cultural changes that have increased our impact on the environment.

Evidence from fossils, DNA analysis, and studies of ancient cultures suggests that the earliest form of the human (*Homo sapiens*) species was *Homo sapiens idaltu*, which existed about 160 000 years ago. The latest version of our species, *Homo sapiens sapiens,* has been around for only about 60 000 years. Thus the various versions of *Homo sapiens* have walked the Earth for less than an eye blink of the estimated 3.7-billion-year existence of life on this marvellous planet. We are the planet's new infants.

Until about 12 000 years ago, we were mostly hunter-gatherers who typically moved as needed to find enough food for survival. Since then, three major cultural changes have occurred: the *agricultural revolution* (which began 10 000–12 000 years ago), the *industrial-medical revolution* (which began about 275 years ago), and the *information and globalization revolution* (which began about 50 years ago).

These changes have greatly increased our impact on the environment in three ways. They have given us much more energy and new technologies with which to alter and control more of the planet to meet our basic needs and increasing wants. They have also allowed expansion of the human population, mostly because of increased food supplies and longer life spans. In addition, they have greatly increased our resource use, pollution, and environmental degradation.

How Did Ancient Hunting-and-Gathering Societies Affect the Environment? Living Lightly on the Earth

Hunter-gatherers had a fairly small impact on their environment.

During most of their 60 000-year existence, *Homo sapiens sapiens* have been **hunter-gatherers.** They survived by collecting edible wild plant parts, hunting, fishing, and scavenging meat from animals killed by other predators. Our hunter-gatherer ancestors typically lived in small bands of fewer than 50 people who worked together to get enough food to survive. Many groups were nomadic, picking up their few possessions and moving seasonally from place to place to find enough food.

The earliest hunter-gatherers (and those still living this way today) survived through expert knowledge and understanding of their natural surroundings. Because of high infant mortality and an estimated average life span of 30–40 years, hunter-gatherer populations grew very slowly.

Advanced hunter-gatherers had greater environmental impacts than those of early hunter-gatherers. They used more advanced tools and fire to convert forests into grasslands. There is also some evidence that they probably contributed to the extinction of some large animals. They also altered the distribution of plants (and animals feeding on such plants) as they carried seeds and plants to new areas.

Early and advanced hunter-gatherers exploited their environment to survive. But their environmental impact usually was limited and local because of their small populations, low resource use per person, migration that allowed natural processes to repair most of the damage they caused, and lack of technology that could have expanded their impact.

CONSIDER, DISCUSS, OR DEBATE

What impacts did hunter-gatherers have on their environment? Compare this impact with the disturbances caused by other creatures such as beavers, seed-spreading birds, and herbivorous insects such as tent caterpillars.

What Was the Agricultural Revolution? More Food, More People, Longer Lives, and an Increasing Ecological Footprint

Agriculture provided more food for more people who lived longer and in better health but also greatly increased environmental degradation.

Some 10 000–12 000 years ago, a cultural shift known as the **agricultural revolution** began in several regions of the world. It involved a gradual move from usually nomadic hunting-and-gathering groups to settled agricultural communities in which people domesticated wild animals and cultivated wild plants.

Plant cultivation probably developed in many areas, some including tropical forests of Southeast Asia, northeast Africa, and Mexico. People discovered how to grow various wild food plants from roots or tubers (fleshy underground stems). To prepare the land for planting, they cleared small patches of tropical forests by cutting down trees and other vegetation and then burning the underbrush (Figure 2-2). The ashes fertilized the often nutrient-poor tropical forest soils in this **slash-and-burn cultivation.**

Early growers also used various forms of **shifting cultivation** (Figure 2-2), primarily in tropical regions. After a plot had been used for several years, the soil became depleted of nutrients or reinvaded by the forest. Then the growers cleared a new plot. They learned that each abandoned patch normally had to be left fallow (unplanted) for 10–30 years before the soil became fertile enough to grow crops again. While patches were regenerating, growers used them for tree crops, medicines, fuelwood, and other purposes. In this manner, most early growers practised *sustainable cultivation*.

These early farmers had fairly little impact on the environment. Their dependence mostly on human muscle power and crude stone or stick tools meant they could cultivate only small plots, and their population size and density were low. In addition, normally enough land was available so they could move to other

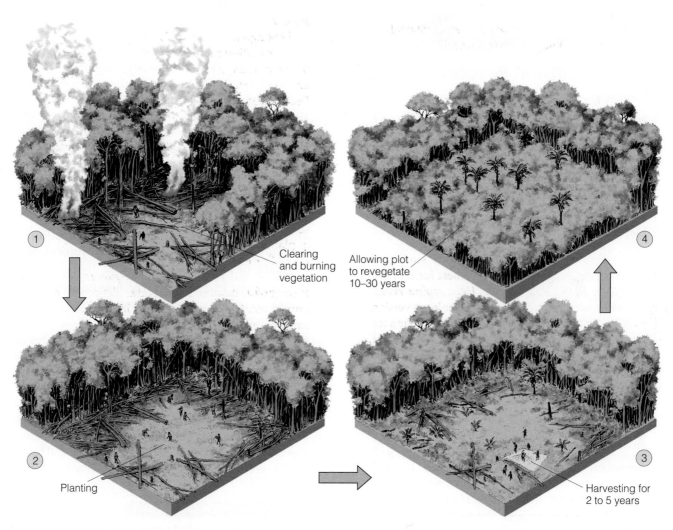

Clearing and burning vegetation

Allowing plot to revegetate 10–30 years

Planting

Harvesting for 2 to 5 years

FIGURE 2-2 The first crop-growing technique may have been a combination of slash-and-burn and shifting cultivation in tropical forests. This method is sustainable only if small plots of the forest are cleared, cultivated for no more than five years, and then allowed to regenerate for 10–30 years to renew soil fertility. Indigenous cultures have developed many variations of this technique and have found ways to use some former plots nondestructively while they are being regenerated.

areas and leave abandoned plots unplanted for the several decades needed to restore soil fertility.

As more intensive forms of agriculture developed and spread, this led to various beneficial and harmful effects (Figure 2-3).

CONSIDER, DISCUSS, OR DEBATE

Under what conditions were slash-and-burn cultivation and shifting cultivation sustainable? Do you think that these forms of agriculture limited human populations?

What Is the Industrial-Medical Revolution? More People, Longer Lives, More Production, and an Even Larger Ecological Footprint

As a result of the industrial-medical revolution, more people have lived longer and healthier lives at a higher standard of living, but pollution, resource

Trade-Offs

Agricultural Revolution

Good News	Bad News
More food	Destruction of wildlife habitats from clearing forests and grasslands
Supported a larger population	Killing of wild animals feeding on grass or crops
Longer life expectancy	Fertile land turned into desert by livestock overgrazing
Higher standard of living for many people	Soil eroded into streams and lakes
Formation of villages, towns, and cities	Towns and cities concentrated wastes and pollution and increased spread of diseases
Towns and cities served as centres for trade, government, and religion	Increase in armed conflict and slavery over ownership of land and water resources

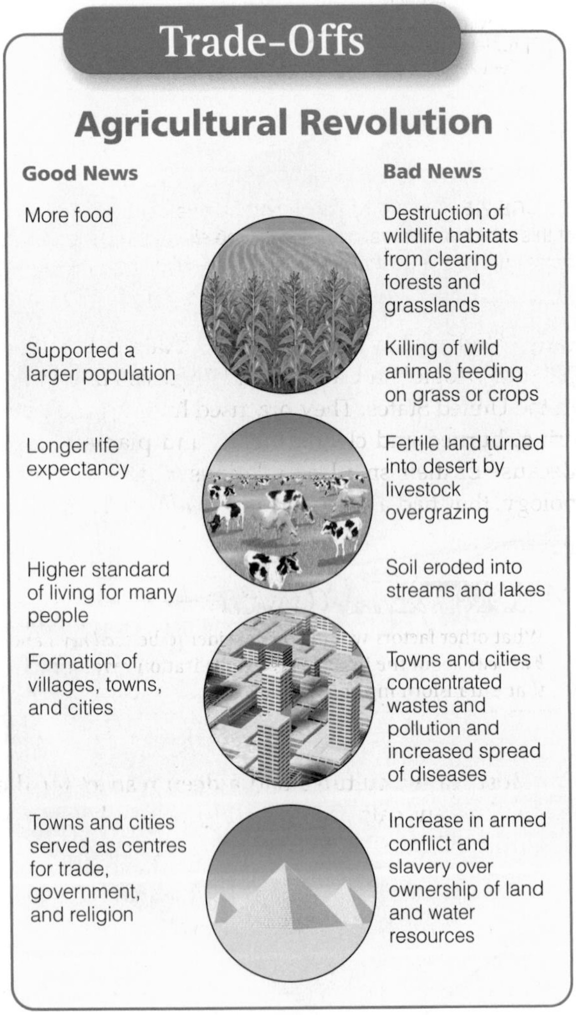

FIGURE 2-3 Trade-offs: good and bad news about the shift from hunting and gathering to agriculture. Pick the single pieces of *good news* and *bad news* that you think are the most important.

waste, and environmental degradation have increased.

The next cultural shift, the **industrial-medical revolution,** began in England in the mid-1700s, spread to the United States in the 1800s, and reached Canada in the latter half of the 19th century. It involved a shift from dependence on *renewable* wood (with supplies dwindling in some areas because of unsustainable cutting) and flowing water to dependence on machines running on *nonrenewable* fossil fuels (first coal and later oil and natural gas). This led to a switch from small-scale, localized production of handmade goods to large-scale production of machine-made goods in centralized factories.

Factory towns grew into cities as rural people came to the factories for employment. There they worked long hours under noisy, dirty, and hazardous conditions. Other workers toiled in dangerous coal mines.

In early industrial cities, coal smoke belching from chimneys was so heavy that many people died of lung ailments. Ash and soot covered everything, and some days the smoke was thick enough to blot out the sun.

Fossil fuel–powered farm machinery, commercial fertilizers, and new plant-breeding techniques increased crop yields per hectare. This helped protect biodiversity by reducing the need to expand the area of cropland. Because fewer farmers were needed, more people migrated to cities. With a larger and more reliable food supply and longer life spans, the human population began the sharp increase that continues today.

Figure 2-4 lists some of the beneficial (*good news*) and harmful (*bad news*) effects of the advanced industrial-medical revolution.

How Might the Information and Globalization Revolution Affect the Environment? Information Blessing or Information Overload

Global access to information can help us understand and respond to environmental problems but can lead to confusion from information overload.

Since 1950, and especially since 1970, we have begun making a new cultural shift called the **information and globalization revolution.** It is based on using new technologies for gaining rapid access to much more information on a global scale. These technologies include the telephone, radio, television, computers, the Internet, automated databases, and remote-sensing satellites. Figure 2-5 lists some of the possible beneficial and harmful effects of the information and globalization revolution.

CONSIDER, DISCUSS, OR DEBATE

In your view, what are the most important environmental impacts and environmental benefits of (a) the industrial-medical revolution and (b) the information and globalization revolution?

Trade-Offs

Industrial-Medical Revolution

Good News	Bad News
Mass production of useful and affordable products	Increased air pollution
Higher standard of living for many	Increased water pollution
Greatly increased agricultural production	Increased waste production
	Soil depletion and degradation
Lower infant mortality	Groundwater depletion
Longer life expectancy	
Increased urbanization	Habitat destruction and degradation
Increased education	Biodiversity depletion

FIGURE 2-4 Trade-offs: good and bad news about the effects of the advanced industrial revolution. Pick the single pieces of *good news* and *bad news* that you think are the most important.

Trade-Offs

Information-Globalization Revolution

Good News	Bad News
Computer-generated models and maps of the Earth's environmental systems	Information overload can cause confusion and sense of hopelessness
Remote-sensing satellite surveys of the world's environmental systems	Globalized economy can increase environmental degradation by homogenizing the Earth's surface
Ability to respond to environmental problems more effectively and rapidly	Globalized economy can decrease cultural diversity

FIGURE 2-5 Trade-offs: good and bad news about the effects of this latest cultural revolution. Pick the single pieces of *good news* and *bad news* that you think are the most important.

2-2 ENVIRONMENTAL HISTORY OF NORTH AMERICA: PRE-COLUMBIAN PEOPLES AND THE COLONIAL SETTLEMENT ERA

What Happened during the Pre-Columbian Era? Sustainable Living

Native people living in North America for at least 10 000 years had a fairly low environmental impact.

According to James Murton, a professor of environmental history at Nipissing University, the environmental history of North America can be divided into four eras: *pre-Columbian, colonial settlement, conservation,* and *environmental*.

During the *pre-Columbian era*, North America was occupied by 5–10 million tribal people for at least 10 000 years before European settlers began arriving in the early 1600s. These indigenous people were called "Indians" by the Europeans, "Natives" or "First Nations people" in Canada, and "Native Americans" in the United States. They practised hunting and gathering, burned and cleared fields, and planted crops. Because of their small populations and simple technology, they had a fairly low environmental impact.

> **CONSIDER, DISCUSS, OR DEBATE**
>
> What other factors would you consider to be *good news* and *bad news* about the information-globalization revolution that is transforming your world?

Most Native cultures had a deep respect for the land and its animals and did not believe in land ownership, as indicated by the following quotation:

> *My people, the Blackfeet Indians, have always had a sense of reverence for nature that made us want to move through the world carefully, leaving as little mark behind as possible. (Jamake Highwater, Blackfoot)*

Terry Dokis, a Native studies professor at Nipissing University, notes that although there were differences among groups of First Nations people, all saw nature as cyclic and renewable, and all had a great knowledge of the relationships among living organisms. They did not see themselves as owning the land; they were part of it. They did not see themselves as having dominion over nature; again, they were part of it. They had management strategies that allowed them to use wild resources without depleting them. All of this was necessary for a lifestyle that depended on the sustainable use of wild resources.

What Happened during the Colonial Settlement Era (1607–1890)? Taking Over a Continent

European settlers saw the continent as a vast frontier to conquer and settle.

The *colonial settlement era* began in the early 1600s when European colonists began settling North America. The early colonists developed a **myth of superabundance**. They viewed most of the continent as having vast and seemingly inexhaustible resources; at the same time, they saw it as a hostile and dangerous **wilderness** to be conquered and managed for human use.

The governments set up by European settlers conquered groups of Native people, took over the land, and urged people to spread across the continent. Settlement was much more widespread, and relations with Native people correspondingly more tense, in the English colonies (now the northeastern United States) than in New France (now Quebec and the Maritime provinces). With the defeat of New France in 1760, large numbers of settlers moved north. The transfer of vast areas of public land to private interests accelerated the settling of the continent.

This frontier environmental view prevailed for more than 280 years. By 1885, the Canadian government had completed its transcontinental railway and imposed its authority by defeating an uprising of Cree and Métis in the Northwest Rebellion. In the United States, the government declared the frontier officially closed in 1890.

2-3 ENVIRONMENTAL HISTORY OF NORTH AMERICA: THE EARLY CONSERVATION ERA (1832–1960)

What Happened between 1832 and 1870? Ignored Warnings

As conservation was slowly emerging in Canada, Americans largely ignored warnings that they were degrading their resource base.

In Canada, the myth of superabundance was still held by many people because there were large tracts of unexplored wilderness. However, there were some signs of conservation problems near the areas that were most densely settled; for instance, beavers had been trapped to the edge of extinction in some regions

by the 1820s and 1830s. The first Upper Canada game laws were established in 1839 to protect game birds. Fur-bearers were included with game birds in 1856. Small birds were protected by law in 1864 because they were believed to help protect crops by eating insects.

Between 1832 and 1870, a number of Americans became alarmed at the scope of resource depletion and degradation in the United States. They urged that part of the unspoiled wilderness on public lands—owned jointly by all people but managed by the government—be protected as a legacy to future generations.

Two early conservationists were *Henry David Thoreau* (Figure 2-6) and *George Perkins Marsh* (1801–82). Thoreau was alarmed at the loss of numerous wild species from his native eastern Massachusetts. To gain a better understanding of nature, he built a cabin in the woods on Walden Pond near Concord, Massachusetts, lived there alone for two years, and wrote *Life in the Woods*, an environmental classic.

In 1864, George Perkins Marsh, a scientist and member of Congress from Vermont, published *Man and Nature*, which helped legislators and citizens see the need for resource conservation. Marsh questioned the idea that the country's resources were inexhaustible. He also used scientific studies and case studies to show how the rise and fall of past civilizations were linked to the use and misuse of their resource base. Most of these warnings were not taken seriously.

> **CONSIDER, DISCUSS, OR DEBATE**
>
> Why was the myth of superabundance believed for so long? Could a myth last for so long in modern times? Why was this belief so destructive?

FIGURE 2-6 *Henry David Thoreau* (1817–62) was an American writer and naturalist who kept journals about his excursions into wild nature throughout parts of the northeastern United States and Canada and at Walden Pond in Massachusetts. He sought self-sufficiency, a simple lifestyle, and a harmonious coexistence with nature.

What Happened between 1870 and 1930? Government and Citizen Involvement

Canadian civil servants, and subsequently the federal government, began to focus on conservation. In the United States, the federal government tried to protect more of the nation's natural resources.

In Canada, the British North America Act of 1867 placed wildlife in the hands of the provinces. The federal government had been focused on economic and political issues, such as the transcontinental expansion of the railroad and the Confederation of Canada (1867). Banff was established in 1885 not for the sake of wildlife, but rather to promote the Canadian Pacific Railway. In 1886, Yoho and Glacier parks were similarly established as attractions for the CPR.

In 1887, the first bird sanctuary was established in Saskatchewan, but relatively little attention was paid to conservation until a group of civil servants began advancing the cause of wildlife. These individuals included *Howard Douglas*, who was appointed superintendent of Rocky Mountains Park; *Robert Campbell*, director of the forestry branch of the Department of the Interior, who advocated the protection of forest reserves; *Maxwell Graham*, chief of parks, who focused on preserving pronghorn antelope and bison; and Dominion entomologist *Gordon Hewitt*, who was instrumental in shaping the International Migratory Bird Treaty, the Migratory Birds Convention Act, and the Northwest Game Act.

Clifford Sifton (Figure 2-7) has been called the father of conservation in Canada. In 1896, upon his appointment as minister of the interior, he placed

FIGURE 2-8 *James Harkin* (1875–1955) served as Canada's first commissioner of national parks from 1911 to 1936. He is often called the father of national parks in Canada.

forests under federal control and organized the Canadian Forestry Association. As chair of the Commission of Conservation (1909–18), he promoted conservation measures and urged Canadians to take steps to avoid the misuse of resources taking place in the United States.

James Harkin (Figure 2-8), the first commissioner of national parks (1911–36), was similarly concerned about the conservation problems that the Americans were experiencing and worked to ensure that Canadian wildlife would be protected. Often called the father of national parks, Harkin played a critical role in the development of the National Parks Act and was instrumental in organizing Canada's parks into a cohesive system.

> **DID YOU KNOW**
>
> Ernest Thompson Seton (1860–1946) was born in England but moved to Canada at the age of five. He is renowned for his writings about nature; famous examples include *Wild Animals I Have Known* (1898) and *Lives of Game Animals* (4 volumes; 1925–7). He also wrote the first Scout Manual and helped to found the Boy Scout movement in North America.

In the United States, nature preservationist and activist *John Muir* (Figure 2-9) founded the Sierra Club in 1892. He became the leader of the *preservationist movement* that called for protecting large areas of wilderness on public lands from human exploitation, except for low-impact recreational activities such as hiking and camping. Muir also proposed and lobbied for creation of a national park system on public lands.

FIGURE 2-7 *Clifford Sifton* (1861–1929) was the first chair of the Commission of Conservation (est. 1909). He has been called the father of conservation in Canada.

FIGURE 2-9 *John Muir* (1838–1914) was a geologist, explorer, and naturalist. He spent six years studying, writing journals, and making sketches in the wilderness of California's Yosemite Valley and then went on to explore wilderness areas in Utah, Nevada, the Northwest, and Alaska. He was largely responsible for establishing Yosemite National Park in 1890. He also founded the Sierra Club and spent 22 years lobbying actively for conservation laws.

In 1905, Congress created the U.S. Forest Service to manage and protect the forest reserves. President Theodore Roosevelt appointed *Gifford Pinchot* (1865–1946) as its first chief. Pinchot pioneered scientific management of forest resources on public lands. In 1906, Congress passed the Antiquities Act, which allows the president to protect areas of scientific or historical interest on federal lands as national monuments. Roosevelt used this act to protect the Grand Canyon and other areas that would later become national parks.

In 1916, Congress passed the National Park Service Act. It declared that parks are to be maintained in a manner that leaves them unimpaired for future generations. The act also established the National Park Service (within the Department of the Interior) to manage the system.

After World War I, the country entered a new era of economic growth and expansion. During the Harding, Coolidge, and Hoover administrations, the federal government promoted increased resource removal from public lands at low prices to stimulate economic growth.

What Happened between 1930 and 1960? Depression and War

Governments focused on recovering from the Depression, the dust bowl, and war.

Like the U.S. National Park Service Act of 1916, Canada's National Parks Act (1930) incorporated the idea that parks were to be "left unimpaired for future generations." Up until 1945, when the emphasis shifted to developing more parks for recreational purposes, the government focused on the establishment of national and provincial parks in remote and beautiful areas.

In the 1930s, farmers confronted a drought that turned much of the Prairie provinces and the American Midwest into a dust bowl. Prime Minister *Mackenzie King*'s government responded with the Prairie Farm Rehabilitation Program, which led to improvements in soil conservation practices (Chapter 14).

Environmental influences during this period included *Archibald Belaney* (alias "Grey Owl"), who emigrated from England to Canada at age 18, adopted a Native persona, and wrote a number of influential books in which he made a passionate case for conservation. The Group of Seven, an unconventional group of Canadian painters, broke from staid artistic traditions of the time with their bold depictions of Canada's rugged beauty. Their art is considered to have played a role in helping Canadians visualize their national identity and in increasing our appreciation of wilderness (O'Brian and White, 2007).

SELF CHECK

Visit http://www.group-of-seven.org or other online galleries that feature Group of Seven art. Do these images "speak to you" on any emotional, artistic, or intellectual levels? Do the paintings help you to value the beauty of wild northern landscapes?

A second wave of American resource conservation and improvements in public health began in the early 1930s as President *Franklin D. Roosevelt* (1882–1945) strove to bring the country out of the Great Depression. The government purchased large tracts of land from cash-poor landowners, and the Civilian Conservation Corps (CCC) was established in 1933. It put 2 million unemployed people to work planting trees and developing and maintaining parks and recreation areas. The CCC also restored silted waterways and built levees and dams for flood control.

Aldo Leopold (1887–1948) worked for the U.S. Forest Service, and became alarmed about how fast wilderness was disappearing. He became a professor at the University of Wisconsin in 1933, and wrote extensively about game management and land ethics. He saw humans as a part of nature, and he argued that we have an ethical responsibility to preserve nature. Many of his ideas can be found in his most famous book, *A Sand County Almanac,* which was published the year after he died.

ENVIRONMENTAL HISTORY OF NORTH AMERICA: THE ENVIRONMENTAL ERA (1960 TO THE PRESENT)

What Happened during the 1960s? An Environmental Awakening

The modern environmental movement began, and more citizens urged government to improve environmental quality.

In the 1960s, concerns about water pollution, air pollution, hazardous waste, and pesticide use led to the emergence of a number of environmental groups in Canada, including Pollution Probe (in Ontario), the Ecology Action Centre (in the Maritimes), and the Society for the Promotion of Environmental Conservation (in Western Canada). In 1962, American biologist *Rachel Carson* (1907–64) published *Silent Spring*, which documented the pollution of air, water, and wildlife from pesticides such as DDT. This influential book, which generated considerable interest in the United States and Canada, helped broaden the concept of resource conservation to include preservation of wildlife and the *quality* of the air, water, and soil.

Many historians mark Carson's wake-up call as the beginning of the modern **environmental movement**. It flourished when a growing number of citizens organized to demand that political leaders enact laws and develop policies to curtail pollution, clean up polluted environments, and protect unspoiled areas from environmental degradation.

Between 1965 and 1970, the emerging science of *ecology* received widespread media attention in Canada and the United States. At the same time, the popular writings of biologists such as *Paul Ehrlich, Barry Commoner,* and *Garrett Hardin* awakened people to the interlocking relationships among population growth, resource use, and pollution.

The public also became aware that pollution and loss of habitat were endangering well-known wildlife species such as the North American bald eagle, grizzly bear, whooping crane, and peregrine falcon.

During the 1969 U.S. *Apollo* mission to the moon, astronauts photographed the Earth from space. The image of the Earth as a tiny blue and white planet in the black void of space united people all over the world and it led to the development of the *spaceship-Earth environmental worldview*. It reminded us that we live on a marvellous planetary spaceship (*Terra I*) that we should not harm because it is the only home we have.

What Happened during the 1970s? The Environmental Decade

Increased awareness and public concern led governments in Canada and the United States to pass a number of laws to improve environmental quality and conserve more natural resources.

The first annual *Earth Day* was held on April 20, 1970. During this event, some 20 million people took to the streets to heighten awareness and to demand improvements in environmental quality.

In Canada, the public became increasingly vocal about the need for wildlife and wilderness protection. Four key environmental groups—Greenpeace, the Sierra Club of Canada, the Canadian Audubon Society, and the Canadian Nature Federation—were established in the early 1970s. For their part, the federal and provincial governments established departments or ministries that focused on the environment, and passed environmental protection and environmental assessment laws, including the Arctic Waters Pollution Act (1970), the Clean Air Act (1971), and the Canadian Wildlife Act (1973). At the international level, Canada participated in the United Nations–sponsored 1972 Stockholm Conference on the Human Environment and the 1975 Convention on International Trade in Endangered Species (CITES). In 1978, the Committee on the Status of Endangered Wildlife in Canada (COSEWIC) began to research and publish its list of species at risk.

In the United States, Republican President *Richard Nixon* (1913–94) responded to the rapidly growing environmental movement. He established the Environmental Protection Agency (EPA) in 1970 and supported passage of the Endangered Species Act of 1973. This greatly strengthened the role of the federal government in protecting endangered species and their habitats.

Jimmy Carter (a Democrat, born 1924), president between 1977 and 1981, was very responsive to environmental concerns. He persuaded Congress to create the Department of Energy to develop a long-range energy strategy to reduce the country's heavy dependence on imported oil. Carter also used the Antiquities Act of 1906 to triple the amount of land in the National Wilderness System and double the area in the National Park System (primarily by adding vast tracts in Alaska).

What Happened during the 1980s? Two Different Experiences

While Canadians worked together to solve the problem of acid rain, an anti-environmental movement eroded past progress in the United States.

In Canada, *acid rain* was a pressing issue (Chapter 20). Prime Minister Brian Mulroney and President Ronald Reagan were at loggerheads over this issue of international pollution. Meanwhile, unprecedented levels of cooperation were seen in Canada as politicians, industry leaders, academics, environmentalists, and average citizens sat at roundtables brainstorming solutions. As the authors of the 1987 book *Our Common*

Future (also known as *The Brundtland Report*) discovered, Canadian politicians were more receptive than the U.S. government to the idea of sustainable development advanced in the book. In 1987, the *Montreal Protocol*, signed by 24 nations in Montreal, was the first international effort to protect the environment from a global threat—in this case, depletion of the ozone layer. Two years later, *Endangered Spaces: The Future for Canada's Wilderness*, a book edited by Monte Hummel, alerted Canadians to the growing threat to special habitats. In the United States, farmers and ranchers and leaders of the oil, automobile, mining, and timber industries strongly opposed many of the environmental laws and regulations developed in the 1960s and 1970s. They organized and funded a strong *anti-environmental movement* that persists today.

In 1981, *Ronald Reagan* (a Republican, 1911–2004), an advocate of less federal control, became president. Reagan greatly increased private energy and mineral development and timber cutting on public lands. He also drastically cut federal funding for research on energy conservation and renewable energy resources and eliminated tax incentives for residential solar energy and energy conservation enacted during the Carter administration. In addition, he lowered automobile gas mileage standards and relaxed federal air and water quality pollution standards.

In 1988, an industry-backed anti-environmental coalition called the *wise-use movement* was formed. Its major goals were to weaken or repeal most of the country's environmental laws and regulations and destroy the effectiveness of the environmental movement in the United States. Politically powerful coal, oil, mining, automobile, timber, and ranching interests helped back this movement.

Upon his election in 1989, *George H. W. Bush* (a Republican, born 1924) promised to be "the environmental president." He received criticism from environmentalists for not providing leadership on such key environmental issues as population growth, global warming, and loss of biodiversity. However, his revision of the U.S. Clean Air Act helped to solve acid precipitation problems in Canada.

What Happened from 1990 until Recent Times?

Canada has seen some changes in environmental leadership. American environmentalists are fighting to keep anti-environmentalists from undoing past progress.

In 1992, Canadian environmentalist and diplomat Maurice Strong chaired the historic Earth Summit held in Rio de Janeiro. Prime Minister Brian Mulroney and David Suzuki were among the participants at this historic and widely televised event.

In 1997, Canada was one of more than 160 countries represented at Kyoto, Japan. Prime Minister Jean Chrétien signed the Kyoto Protocol, committing Canada to reducing its greenhouse gas emissions to 6% below our 1990 emissions by 2008–12. Canada agreed to be legally bound by the treaty when Chrétien ratified the Kyoto Protocol in December 2002. The protocol itself did not come into force as an international treaty until it was ratified by 55 nations, accounting for at least 55% of greenhouse gas emissions; in February 2005, three months after Russia became the 55th nation to ratify, the Kyoto Protocol came into full force for the signing countries.

Prime Minister *Paul Martin*'s government (2003–6) continued to respond to the Kyoto Protocol. This government created a plan, "Moving Forward with Climate Change: A Plan for Honouring Our Kyoto Commitment," and promised to spend $10 billion to meet Kyoto targets by 2012.

In contrast, the government of Prime Minister *Stephen Harper* (elected in 2006) marked a radical departure from Canada's previous climate change policies. The Harper government ignored the Kyoto Protocol and instead promoted a controversial "made-in-Canada" Clean Air Act (discussed further in Chapters 21 and 27).

In the United States, *Bill Clinton* (a Democrat, born 1946) became president in 1993 and promised to provide national and global environmental leadership. During his eight years in office he appointed respected environmentalists to key positions in environmental and resource agencies and consulted with environmentalists about environmental policy, as Carter did.

Clinton vetoed most of the anti-environmental bills (or other bills passed with anti-environmental riders attached) passed by a Republican-dominated Congress between 1995 and 2000. He also used executive orders to make forest health the primary priority in managing national forests and to declare many roadless areas in national forests off limits to roads and logging. Despite these measures, environmentalists criticized Clinton for failing to push hard enough on key environmental issues such as global warming and global and national biodiversity protection.

Since 1990 environmentalists have had to spend much of their time and funds fighting efforts by the anti-environmental movement to discredit the environmental movement and weaken or eliminate most environmental laws passed during the 1960s and 1970s. They also had to counter claims by anti-environmental groups that problems such as global warming and ozone depletion are hoaxes or not very serious.

In 2001, *George W. Bush* (a Republican, born 1946) became president. Like Reagan in the 1980s, he appointed to key federal positions people who opposed or wanted to weaken many existing environmental and public land use laws and policies. Also like Reagan, he did not consult with environmental groups and leaders in developing environmental policies, and he greatly increased private energy and mineral development and timber cutting on public lands.

Bush opposed increasing automobile gas mileage standards as a way to save energy and reduce dependence on oil imports, and he supported relaxation of various federal air and water quality pollution standards. Like Reagan, he advanced an energy policy that placed much greater emphasis on use of fossil fuels and nuclear power, rather than on reducing energy waste and developing renewable energy resources.

In addition, he withdrew the United States from participation in the international Kyoto treaty designed to help reduce carbon dioxide emissions that can promote global warming. He also repealed or tried to weaken most of the pro-environmental measures established by Clinton.

CONSIDER, DISCUSS, OR DEBATE

How have attitudes toward the environment differed on either side of the Canada–U.S. border over the past 30 years? Why would governments carry out policies that appear to be destructive to their environments?

2-5 WHERE DO WE STAND NOW?

Where Do We Stand at Present? Poised to Make Some New Environmental History

We are now set to launch into the book, and into the world of environmental science, with some appreciation of how we came to this moment in history.

The purpose of Chapter 2 is to acquaint students with past people and events that help to explain *how*

things came to be as they are. We briefly summarized the time from hunter-gatherer days in North America, through colonial settlement and increasing urbanization in Canada and the United States, *to almost the current moment.* Along the way, we witnessed evidence of increases in human settlement density, changes in technology, and increases in environmental impact. We discovered that some resource and wildlife issues go back to the early days of North America. We learned of the development of new ideas, such as setting aside publicly owned land for **conservation** or preservation. We noted some individuals who made a difference, witnessed the births of some early environmental groups, and heard about the first legal acts designed to protect various aspects of the environment. We met some key politicians who helped to create a somewhat different environmental history on either side of the Canada–U.S. border. We have, however, paused just before the brink of *now*. We have saved discussions of *the present and the future* for all the chapters that follow. For example, we are now entering a time when the governments of Stephen Harper and Barack Obama are having increasing impacts in Canada and the United States; Chapter 27 on environmental politics will pursue such themes through the present and into the future.

Are there useful links to be made with the past? We think so. You might take a moment to read the Spotlight about traditional ecological knowledge (TEK) and consider how ancient wisdom might be used to inform the future. Applications of TEK will be pointed out in subsequent chapters.

The basic premise of studying environmental history is the thought that knowledge of the past can help to prevent future mistakes. What mistakes have we

---

SPOTLIGHT

Traditional Ecological Knowledge

Scientists and anthropologists have been paying increasing attention to the traditional ecological knowledge (TEK) of Native peoples. Broadly defined as a vast body of local ecological knowledge that has been built up over generations, TEK is transmitted orally and through experience. It involves a means of identifying and classifying local organisms, a set of observations about ecological relationships and cycles, and methods of self-management so that hunting and fishing grounds are not depleted of wildlife. For example,

Native people monitor natural signs in the environment and, when appropriate, rotate hunting and fishing grounds to allow these areas to renew.

Both the 1980 World Conservation Strategy (WCS) and the authors of *Our Common Future (The Brundtland Report)* have endorsed TEK as a means of involving Native people in the effective management of natural resources. The Mackenzie Valley Resource Management Act made extensive use of TEK when addressing the environmental and

social issues of the Mackenzie Valley Pipeline Inquiry (Bocking, 2007; Christensen and Grant, 2006).

TEK is being used increasingly to help settle land claims, guide projects, manage resources, and inform environmental assessments in Canada (CEAA, 2012; Manseau et al., 2005).

Note that some documents use slightly different terms, such as Aboriginal traditional knowledge (ATK) or traditional knowledge (TK), in place of TEK.

made? Could we have foreseen them? Are there ways to correct the future on the basis of what we have now learned? These and other topics will be discussed in the remaining 26 chapters of this book.

Thank God, they cannot cut down the clouds!

HENRY DAVID THOREAU

CHAPTER REVIEW

1. Review the Key Questions for this chapter on p. 22.

2. Find the *Consider, Discuss, or Debate* boxes sprinkled throughout Chapter 2 and answer the questions they pose, preferably through dialogue with other people.

3. Did *hunter-gatherers* have any significant environmental impact? Why did some early peoples practise *slash-and-burn cultivation* and *shifting cultivation*? Why did they not simply enrich their soils with nutrients? Why are we not using slash-and-burn cultivation in Canada?

4. What were the key traits of the *pre-Columbian era,* the *colonial settlement era,* the *conservation era,* and the *environmental era*? Differentiate among the *agricultural revolution*, the *industrial-medical revolution*, and the *information and globalization revolution*. What environmental problems and potential solutions were introduced with each of these revolutions?

5. At what stage, and in approximately which years, did a transition from *renewable fuels* to *nonrenewable fuels* begin? Why did this occur? How hard would it be to reverse this trend in modern times?

6. Why do we still have bison, and why do we have large park systems of public lands that have been set aside? Name some of the people from both sides of the Canada–U.S. border whose ideas led to these outcomes. What was the *myth of superabundance* and why did it pose environmental problems?

7. When were the first and subsequent acts established to protect Canadian wildlife and other resources? Name these acts and specify what they were intended to protect.

8. Which Canadian individuals and which American individuals made the most significant environmental contributions during each of the following periods: **(a)** 1870 to 1930, **(b)** 1930 to 1960, and **(c)** 1960 to now? Justify your answers.

9. When were environmental groups established in Canada and in the United States? By whom? Which of these groups have become the most important in modern times?

10. Group Canadian and U.S. politicians according to their apparent attitudes toward the environment. Justify the groups you have created and why you have included each politician in a particular group.

CRITICAL THINKING

1. What three major things would you do to reduce the harmful environmental impacts of advanced industrial societies?

2. Which one person do you believe has made the greatest and longest lasting contribution to the conservation and environmental movements in Canada? In the United States? Explain.

3. Public forests, grasslands, wildlife reserves, parks, and wilderness areas are owned by all citizens and managed for them by governments. In terms of the management policies for most of these lands, would you classify yourself as **(a)** a preservationist, **(b)** a conservationist,

or **(c)** an advocate of opening most lands to private enterprise? Explain.

4. Do you favour or oppose efforts to greatly weaken or repeal most environmental laws? Explain.

5. Some analysts believe the world's remaining hunter-gatherer societies should be given title to the land on which they and their ancestors have lived for centuries and should be left alone by modern civilization. They contend that we have created protected reserves for endangered wild species, so why not create reserves for these endangered human cultures? What do you think? Explain.

PROJECTS

1. What major changes (such as a change from agricultural to industrial, from rural to urban, or changes in population size, pollution, and environmental degradation) have taken place in your locale during the past

50 years? On balance, have these changes improved or decreased (a) the quality of your life and (b) the quality of life for members of your community as a whole?

2. Use the library or Internet to summarize the major accomplishments of the conservation and environmental movements in Canada and the United States. Compare and contrast the experience of the two countries.

3. Use the library or Internet to learn more about Archibald Belaney ("Grey Owl"), Rachel Carson, James Harkin, Aldo Leopold, and Clifford Sifton.

4. Use the library or Internet to learn more about traditional ecological knowledge. Compare and contrast TEK with ecological science. How can the two be combined to solve environmental and resource problems?

ECOLOGICAL FOOTPRINT ANALYSIS

Read about the environmental impacts of various groups of people described in Chapter 2, focusing on (a) hunter-gatherers, (b) farmers who use their own muscles and animal power (but not machinery) to practise agriculture, and (c) modern industrial people such as yourself. Armed with this information, go to a website such as http://www.myfootprint.org and answer the questions as if you were a person from each of those groups. Compare the resulting ecological footprints and draw a bar chart. Of course, modern footprint-calculating software is not designed for historical groups, and you will have to use your judgment in answering the questions and interpreting the results, but you should still see some interesting differences.

Researchers estimate that individuals in hunter-gatherer societies consumed natural resources such as food and wood at a rate of about 3 kilograms (7 pounds) per day; individuals from agricultural societies who used animals for food and power consumed resources at a rate of about 11 kilograms (24 pounds) per day; and modern industrial societies consume resources at a per capita rate of 15–35 kilograms (33–77 pounds) per day (SERI, 2009). How do these results compare with the ecological footprints you produced for the three groups?

Note that although the above stages reflect "history" in more-developed countries, people still farm by means of animal power many parts of the world, and hunter-gatherer societies still exist in places such as the Amazonian rain forests and Papua New Guinea!

3

Science, Systems, Matter, and Energy

Air
Water
Soil
Energy
Minerals

CASE STUDY

Environmental Lessons from Easter Island

Easter Island (Rapa Nui) is a small, isolated island in the great expanse of the South Pacific. According to anthropologist Terry Hunt, Polynesians used double-hulled sea-going canoes to colonize this island about 800 years ago. They brought along their pigs, chickens, dogs, stow-away rats, taro roots, yams, bananas, and sugarcane.

Evidence from pollen grains found in the soil and lake sediments and in artifacts shows that the island was abundantly forested with a variety of trees, including bass-woods (called hauhau) and giant palms. The Polynesians developed a civilization based on the island's trees. The towering palm trees were used for shelter, tools, and fishing boats. Hauhau trees were felled and burned to cook and to keep warm in the island's cool winters, and rope was made from the trees' fibres. Land was also cleared of trees to plant taro, sugarcane, bananas, and yams.

Using these abundant tree resources, the Polynesians developed an impressive civilization. They also developed a technology capable of making and moving large stone structures, including their famous statues (Figure 3-1). The people flourished, with the population peaking at some-where around 3 000 people. However, they used up the island's precious trees faster than they were regener-ated—an example of the tragedy of the commons.

New evidence collected by Terry Hunt (2006) suggests that rats, an invasive species introduced by the Polynesians, ate the seeds that would have regenerated the forests.

By 1600, only a few small trees were left. Without large trees, the islanders could not build their traditional

big canoes for hunting porpoises and catching fish in deeper offshore waters, and no one could escape the island by boat. Without the once-great forests to absorb and slowly release water, springs and streams dried up, exposed soils eroded, crop yields plummeted, and famine struck. There was no firewood for cooking or keeping warm. The hungry islanders ate all of the island's birds. Then they began eating the rats, descendants of hitch-hikers on the first canoes.

Both the population and the civilization collapsed as gangs fought one another for dwindling food supplies. Bone evidence indicates that the islanders began hunting and eating one another.

Dutch explorers reached the island on Easter Day, 1722. They found about 2 000 hungry Polynesians, living in caves on a shrubby grassland. According to Hunt, the Polynesian population was then decimated to about 100 people by a number of factors, including infectious dis-eases that the Europeans brought with them.

To what extent was the environmental disaster that took place at Easter Island similar to problems now faced by humans on a global scale? As on Easter Island, our population and our resource consumption are growing, and our resources are finite. We are having problems controlling invasive species (Chapters 12 and 13), and many people worry about new types of infectious diseases

(continued)

FIGURE 3-1 These massive stone figures on Easter Island are the remains of the technology created by an ancient civilization of Polynesians. Their civilization collapsed for a number of reasons: they used up the trees that were the basis of their livelihood; their ecosystems were drastically changed by the effects of an invasive species (rats); and they were unprepared to cope with new types of infectious diseases. No one knows how the early islanders (with no wheels, no draft animals, and no sources of energy other than their own muscles) transported these gigantic structures for great distances before erecting them. We presume they accom-plished it by felling large trees and using them to roll and erect the statues. To read more of the fascinating and controversial ideas about Easter Island, see Diamond (2005) and Hunt (2006).

modestlife/Shutterstock.com

such as avian flu and H1N1 flu (Chapter 19). What lessons can we learn from Easter Island? What constructive steps should we take to avoid a similar fate? Scientific knowledge is a key to learning how to live more sustainably. Thus we need to know what science is, understand the behaviour of complex systems studied by scientists, and have a basic knowledge of the nature of the matter and energy that make up the Earth's living and nonliving resources, as discussed in this chapter.

Science is an adventure of the human spirit. It is essentially an artistic enterprise, stimulated largely by curiosity, served largely by disciplined imagination, and based largely on faith in the reasonableness, order, and beauty of the universe.

WARREN WEAVER

CHAPTER PURPOSE AND QUESTIONS

Chapter 3 introduces the key scientific principles that will support later chapters. The chapter addresses the following questions:

3-1   What is science, and what do scientists do?

3-2   What are major components and behaviours of complex systems? Why are models useful?

3-3   What are the basic forms of matter? What makes matter useful to us as a resource?

3-4   What are the major forms of energy? What makes energy useful to us as a resource?

3-5   What scientific law governs changes of matter from one physical or chemical form to another?

3-6   What three main types of nuclear changes can matter undergo?

3-7   What are two scientific laws governing changes of energy from one form to another?

3-8   How are the scientific laws governing changes of matter and energy from one form to another related to resource use and environmental degradation?

3-1   THE NATURE OF SCIENCE

What Is Science, and What Do Scientists Do? Searching for Order in Nature

Scientists collect data, form hypotheses, and develop theories, models, and laws about how nature works.

Science is an attempt to discover order in the natural world and to use that knowledge to describe what is likely to happen in nature. Its goal is to increase our understanding of the natural world. Science is based on the fundamental assumption that events in the natural world follow orderly patterns that can be understood through careful observation and experimentation. Figure 3-2 summarizes the scientific process.

The first thing scientists do is ask a question or identify a problem to be investigated. Then they collect **scientific data,** or facts, related to the problem or question, by making observations and measurements. They often conduct **experiments** to study some phenomenon under controlled conditions. The resulting scientific data or facts must be confirmed by repeated observations and measurements, ideally by several different investigators.

The primary goal of science is not the data or facts themselves. Instead science seeks new ideas, principles, or models that connect and explain certain scientific data and descriptions of what is likely to happen in nature. Scientists working on a particular problem try to come up with a variety of possible explanations, or **scientific hypotheses,** of what they (or other scientists) observe in nature. A scientific hypothesis is an unconfirmed explanation of an observed phenomenon that can be tested by further research.

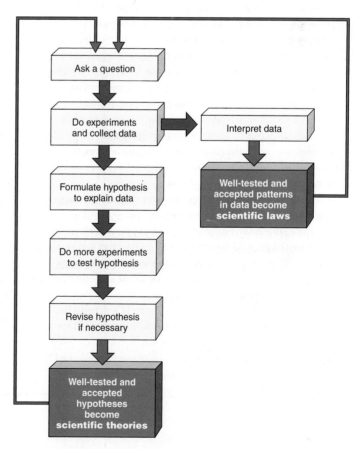

FIGURE 3-2 Scientists are involved in a never-ending cycle of asking questions and trying to answer them, in a logical and unbiased manner, using the sequence shown above.

One method scientists use to test a hypothesis is to develop a **model**, an approximate or simplified representation or simulation of a system being studied. It may be an actual working model, a mental model, a pictorial model, a computer model, or a mathematical model.

Three important features of the scientific process are *skepticism, reproducibility,* and *peer review* of results by other scientists. Scientists tend to be highly skeptical of any new data or hypotheses until they can be verified repeatedly.

Peers, or scientists working in the same field, check for reproducibility by repeating and checking one another's work to see if the data can be reproduced and whether proposed hypotheses are reasonable and useful.

Peer review happens when scientists openly publish details of the methods they used, the results of their experiments, and the reasoning behind their hypotheses. This process of publishing one's work for other scientists to examine and criticize helps keep scientists honest and reduces bias.

If repeated observations and measurements or tests using models support a particular hypothesis or a group of related hypotheses, the hypothesis becomes a **scientific theory.** In other words, a *scientific theory* is a verified, credible, and widely accepted scientific hypothesis or a related group of scientific hypotheses.

To scientists, scientific theories are not to be taken lightly. They are not guesses, speculations, or suggestions. Instead, they are useful explanations of processes or natural phenomena that have a high degree of certainty because they are supported by extensive evidence.

New evidence or a better explanation may modify, or in rare cases overturn, a particular scientific theory. But unless or until this happens, a scientific theory is the best and most reliable knowledge we have about how nature works.

Nonscientists often use the word *theory* incorrectly when they mean to refer to a *scientific hypothesis,* a tentative explanation or educated guess that needs further evaluation. The statement, "Oh, that's just a theory," made in everyday conversation, implies a lack of knowledge and careful testing—the opposite of the scientific meaning of the word.

Another important result of science is a **scientific,** or **natural, law:** a description of what we find happening in nature over and over in the same way. For example, after making thousands of observations and measurements over many decades, scientists formulated the *second law of thermodynamics.* Simply stated, this law says that heat always flows spontaneously from hot to cold—something you learned the first time you touched a hot object. A scientific law is no better than the accuracy of the observations or measurements upon which it is based. But if the data are accurate, a scientific law cannot be broken.

How Do Scientists Learn about Nature? Follow Many Paths

There are many scientific methods.

We often hear about *the* scientific method. In reality, many **scientific methods** exist: they are ways in which scientists gather data and formulate and test scientific hypotheses, models, theories, and laws.

Here is an example of applying the scientific process to an everyday situation:

Observation: You switch on your trusty flashlight and nothing happens.

Question: Why did the light not come on?

Hypothesis: Maybe the batteries are bad.

Test the hypothesis: Put in new batteries and switch on the flashlight.

Result: Flashlight still does not work.

New hypothesis: Maybe the bulb is burned out.

Experiment: Replace bulb with a new bulb.

Result: Flashlight works when switched on.

Conclusion: Second hypothesis is verified.

Situations in nature are usually much more complicated than this. Many *variables* or *factors* influence most processes or parts of nature that scientists seek to understand. Ideally, scientists conduct a *controlled experiment* to isolate and study the effect of a single variable. To do such *single-variable analysis,* scientists set up two groups. One is an *experimental group* in which the chosen variable is changed in a known way. The other is a *control group* in which the chosen variable is not changed. If the experiment is designed properly, any difference between the two groups should result from the variable that was changed in the experimental group.

A basic problem is that many of the problems environmental scientists investigate involve a huge number of interacting variables. This limitation is sometimes overcome by using *multivariable analysis*—running mathematical models on high-speed computers to analyze the interactions of many variables without having to carry out traditional controlled experiments.

What Types of Reasoning Do Scientists Use? Bottom-Up and Top-Down Reasoning

Scientists use inductive reasoning to convert observations and measurements to a general conclusion and deductive reasoning to convert a generalization to a specific conclusion.

Scientists arrive at certain conclusions with varying degrees of certainty by using inductive and deductive reasoning. **Inductive reasoning** involves using specific observations and measurements to arrive at a general conclusion or hypothesis. It is a form of *"bottom-up" reasoning* that involves going from the specific to the general. For example, suppose we observe that a variety of different objects fall to the ground when we drop them from various heights. We might then use inductive reasoning to conclude that *all objects fall to the Earth's surface when dropped.* Depending on the number of observations made, there may be a high degree of certainty in this conclusion. However, what we are really saying is that "all objects that we or other observers have dropped from various heights fall to the Earth's surface." Although it is extremely unlikely, we cannot be *absolutely sure* someone will drop an object that does not fall to the Earth's surface.

Deductive reasoning involves using logic to arrive at a specific conclusion based on a generalization or premise. It is a form of *"top-down" reasoning* that goes from the general to the specific. For example:

Generalization or premise: All birds have feathers.

Example: Eagles are birds.

Deductive conclusion: All eagles have feathers.

The conclusion of this *syllogism* (a series of logically connected statements) is valid as long as the premise is correct and we do not use faulty logic to arrive at the conclusion.

Deductive and inductive reasoning and critical thinking skills (pp. 57, 58) are important scientific tools. But scientists also try to come up with new or creative ideas to explain some of the things they observe in nature. Often such ideas defy conventional logic and current scientific knowledge. According to physicist Albert Einstein, "There is no completely logical way to a new scientific idea." Intuition, imagination, and creativity are as important in science as they are in poetry, art, music, and other great adventures of the human spirit, as reflected in scientist Warren Weaver's quotation found at the opening of this chapter.

One of the exciting things about science is that it is never complete. Each discovery unearths new unanswered questions in an ongoing quest for knowledge about how the natural world works. This is one reason why people choose this profession.

How Valid Are the Results of Science? Very Reliable, but Not Perfect

Scientists try to establish that a particular model, theory, or law has a very high probability of being true.

Scientists can do two major things. *First,* they can disprove things. *Second,* they can establish that a particular model, theory, or law has a very high probability or degree of certainty of being true. However, like scholars in any field, scientists cannot prove that their theories, models, and laws are *absolutely true.*

Although it may be extremely low, some degree of uncertainty is always involved in any scientific theory, model, or law. Most scientists rarely say something like, "Cigarettes cause lung cancer." Rather, the statement might be phrased, "There is overwhelming evidence from thousands of studies that indicate a significant relationship between cigarette smoking and lung cancer."

Most scientists also rarely use the word *proof.* When scientists hear someone say we should not take a scientific finding seriously because it has not been absolutely proven, they know that this person either knows little about the nature of science or is using a debating or advertising trick to cast doubt on a widely accepted scientific finding. Scientists tend to use words like *projections* and *scenarios* to describe what is *likely* to happen in nature instead of making *predictions* or *forecasts* about what *will* happen.

What Is the Difference between Frontier Science and Sound Science? Preliminary and Well-Tested Results

Scientific results fall into those that have not been confirmed (frontier science) and those that have been well tested and widely accepted (sound science).

News reports about science often focus on two things: new so-called scientific breakthroughs, and disputes between scientists over the validity of preliminary and untested data, hypotheses, and models. These preliminary results, called **frontier science,** are often controversial because they have not been widely tested and accepted. At the frontier stage, it is normal and healthy for reputable scientists to disagree about the meaning and accuracy of data and the validity of various hypotheses.

By contrast, **sound science,** or **consensus science,** consists of data, theories, and laws that are widely accepted by scientists who are considered experts in the field involved. The results of sound science are based on a self-correcting process of open peer review. One way to find out what scientists generally agree on is to seek out reports by scientific bodies such as the Royal Society of Canada, the U.S. National Academy of Sciences, and the British Royal Society, which attempt to summarize consensus among experts in key areas of science.

What Is Junk Science, and How Can We Detect It? Look Out for Baloney

Junk science is untested or biased ideas presented as sound science.

Junk science consists of scientific results or hypotheses presented as sound science but not having undergone the rigours of the peer review process. Note that frontier science is not necessarily junk science. Instead, it represents tentative results or hypotheses that are in the process of being validated or rejected by peer review.

There are two problems in uncovering junk science. One is that some scientists, politicians, and other analysts label as junk science any science that does not support or further their particular agenda. The other is that reporters and journalists sometimes mislead us in presenting sound or consensus science along with a quote from a scientist in the field who disagrees with the consensus view or from one who is not an expert in the field being discussed. Such attempts to give a false sense of balance or fairness can mislead the public into distrusting well-established sound science.

Here are some critical-thinking questions you can use to uncover junk science.

- How reliable are the sources making a particular claim? Do they have a hidden agenda? Are they experts in this field? What is their source of funding?

- Do the conclusions follow logically from the observations?

- Has the claim been verified by impartial peer review?

- How does the claim compare with the consensus view of experts in this field?

3-2 MODELS AND BEHAVIOUR OF SYSTEMS

Why Are Models of Complex Systems Useful? Using Inputs, Throughputs, and Outputs to Make Projections

Scientists project the behaviour of a complex system by developing a model of its inputs, throughputs (flows), and outputs of matter, energy, and information.

A **system** is a set of components that function and interact in some regular and theoretically understandable manner. Most *systems* have the following key components: **inputs** from the environment, **flows** or **throughputs** within the system at certain rates, and **outputs** to the environment (Figure 3-3).

Scientists use *models* or approximate representations or simulations to find out how systems work and to evaluate ideas or hypotheses. Some of the most powerful and useful technologies invented by humans are mathematical models, which are used

to supplement our mental models. *Mathematical models* consist of one or more equations used to describe or predict the behaviour of a system.

Making a mathematical model usually requires going many times through three steps. *First*, make an educated guess and write down some equations. *Second*, compute the likely behaviour of the system implied by the equations. *Third*, compare the system's projected behaviour with observations and behaviour projected by mental models, existing experimental data, and scientific hypotheses, laws, and theories.

Mathematical models are important because they can give us improved perceptions and projections, especially in situations where our mental models are weak and unreliable. They are particularly useful when there are many interacting variables, when the time frame is long, and when controlled experiments are impossible, too slow, or too expensive to conduct.

After building and testing a mathematical model, scientists use it to project what is *likely* to happen under a variety of conditions. In effect, they use mathematical models to answer *if–then* questions: "*If* we do such and such, *then* what is likely to happen now and in the future?" This process can give us a variety of projections or scenarios of possible futures or outcomes based on different assumptions.

Despite its usefulness, a mathematical model is nothing more than a set of hypotheses or assumptions about how we think a certain system works. Mathematical models (like all other models) are no better than the assumptions on which they are built and the data fed into them.

How Do Feedback Loops Affect Systems? Changing Direction

Outputs of matter, energy, or information fed back into a system can cause the system to do more of what it was doing (positive feedback) or less (negative feedback).

When someone asks you for feedback, they are asking for information that they can feed back into their mental processes to help them make a decision or carry out

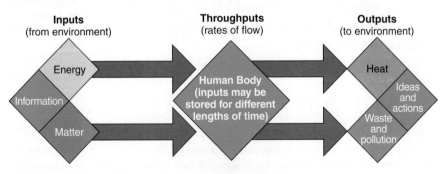

FIGURE 3-3 Major components of a *system* such as your body.

some action. All systems undergo change as a result of feedback loops. A **feedback loop** occurs when an output of matter, energy, or information is fed back into the system as an input and leads to changes in that system.

A **positive feedback loop** causes a system to change further in the same direction. For example, an atmosphere that was slightly warmer than normal would melt more snow and ice than usual at the poles of the Earth. The newly exposed land and sea would absorb more sunlight than the highly reflective snow and ice had done, thus leading to more warming of the atmosphere and more melting of snow and ice, and so on. Further details of factors affecting climate change can be found in Chapter 21.

A **negative,** or **corrective, feedback loop** causes a system to change in the opposite direction. An example is recycling aluminum cans. This involves melting aluminum and feeding it back into an economic system to make new aluminum products. This negative feedback loop of matter reduces the need to find, extract, and process virgin aluminum ore. It also reduces the flow of waste matter (discarded aluminum cans) into the environment.

The temperature-regulating system of your body is an example of a system governed by feedback. Normally a negative feedback loop prevents your body temperature from going too high. If you get hot, your brain receives this information and causes your body to sweat. The evaporation of sweat on your skin removes heat and cools your body. However, if your body temperature exceeds 42°C (108°F), your temperature control system breaks down as your body produces more heat than your sweat-dampened skin can get rid of. Then a positive feedback loop caused by overloading the system overwhelms the negative feedback loop. These conditions produce a net gain in body heat, which produces even more body heat, and so on, until you die from heatstroke.

The tragedy on Easter Island discussed at the beginning of the chapter also involved the coupling of positive and negative feedback loops. For example, as the abundance of trees turned to a shortage of trees, a positive feedback loop (more births than deaths) became weaker as death rates rose. Eventually a negative feedback loop (more deaths than births) dominated and caused a dieback of the island's human population.

How Do Time Delays Affect Complex Systems? Waiting for Something to Kick In

Sometimes corrective feedback takes so long to work that a system can cross a threshold and change its normal behaviour.

Complex systems often show a **time delay** between the input of a stimulus and the system's response to it. For example, scientists could plant trees in an attempt to restore the habitat of a community of endangered forest animals. However, trees take a long time to grow. By the time a suitable forest habitat had been re-established, the animals might have died out or dispersed.

Time delays can allow an environmental problem to build slowly, perhaps with few apparent changes in the complex system, until a *threshold level* or **tipping point** is reached; then the system might react in a sudden large-amplitude change. For example, a fishery might be harvested heavily for many years with no visible problem; then the fish population might suddenly collapse, leaving fish stocks at the level of commercial extinction.

What Is Synergy, and How Can It Affect Complex Systems? One Plus One Can Be Greater Than Two

Sometimes processes and feedbacks in a system can interact to amplify the results.

In arithmetic, 1 plus 1 always equals 2. However, in some of the complex systems found in nature, 1 plus 1 may add up to more than 2 because of synergistic interactions. A **synergistic interaction,** or **synergy,** occurs when two or more processes interact so that the combined effect is greater than the sum of their separate effects.

Synergy can result when two people work together to accomplish a task. For example, suppose you and I need to move a 140-kilogram (300-pound) tree that has fallen across the road. By ourselves, each of us can lift only, say, 45 kilograms (100 pounds). But if we work together and use our muscles properly, we can move the tree out of the way. That is using synergy to solve a problem. Research in the social sciences suggests that most political changes or changes in cultural beliefs are brought about by only about 5% (and rarely more than 10%) of a population working together (synergizing) and expanding their efforts to influence other people.

How Can We Anticipate Environmental Surprises? We Can Never Do Just One Thing

Because any action in a complex system has multiple and often unpredictable results, we should try to anticipate and plan for unintended results and surprises.

One basic principle of environmental science is *we can never do just one thing*. Any action in a complex system has multiple, unintended, and often unpredictable effects. Indeed, most of the harmful environmental problems we face today are unintended results of other activities that were designed to increase the quality of human life (Figure 3-4).

One factor that can lead to an environmental surprise is a *discontinuity* or abrupt change in a previously stable system when some *environmental threshold* is

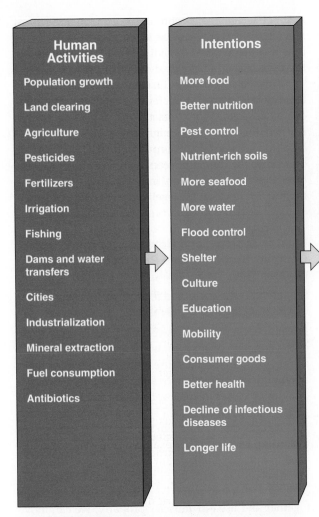

Human Activities	Intentions	Unintended Results
Population growth	More food	Too many people in some areas
Land clearing	Better nutrition	Deforestation
Agriculture	Pest control	Soil erosion and degradation
Pesticides	Nutrient-rich soils	Desertification
Fertilizers	More seafood	Water deficits
Irrigation	More water	Air pollution
Fishing	Flood control	Water pollution
Dams and water transfers	Shelter	Solid waste
Cities	Culture	Toxic waste
Industrialization	Education	Loss of biodiversity
Mineral extraction	Mobility	Fisheries depletion
Fuel consumption	Consumer goods	Climate change
Antibiotics	Better health	Ozone depletion
	Decline of infectious diseases	Genetic resistance to pesticides
	Longer life	Genetic resistance to antibiotics

FIGURE 3-4 Natural capital degradation: human activities designed to improve the quality of life have had a number of unintended harmful environmental effects.

crossed. For example, you may be able to lean back in a chair and balance yourself on two of its legs for a long time with only minor adjustments. But if you pass a certain threshold of movement, your balanced system suffers a discontinuity, or sudden shift, and you may find yourself on the floor. A similar change can happen when many trees in a forest start dying after being weakened and depleted of soil nutrients after decades of exposure to a cocktail of air pollutants.

3-3 MATTER

What Types of Matter Do We Find in Nature? Getting to the Bottom of Things

Matter exists in chemical forms as elements and compounds.

We are going to give you a brief introduction to some chemistry—a discussion of matter and energy. Some of you are saying "I hate chemistry. Why do I need to

know this stuff?" The answer is that you and every other material thing on this planet are made up of chemicals and energy. To understand life and environmental problems, you need to know some basic chemistry. We will try to make this journey as interesting and painless as possible. For those of you who have studied chemistry, this material will be a breeze.

Matter is anything that has **mass** (the amount of material in an object) and takes up space. Matter is found in two chemical forms. One is **elements**: the distinctive building blocks of matter that make up every material substance. The other consists of **compounds**: two or more different elements held together in fixed proportions by attractive forces called *chemical bonds*.

To simplify things, chemists represent each element by a one- or two-letter symbol. Examples used in this book are hydrogen (H), carbon (C), oxygen (O), nitrogen (N), phosphorus (P), sulphur (S), chlorine (Cl), fluorine (F), bromine (Br), sodium (Na), calcium (Ca), lead (Pb), mercury (Hg), arsenic (As), and uranium (U). Chemists have developed a way to classify elements in terms of their chemical behaviour by arranging them in a *periodic table of elements,* as discussed in Appendix 3. *Good news.* The elements previously listed are the only ones you need to know to understand the material in this book.

From a chemical standpoint, how much are you worth? Not much. If we add up the market price per kilogram for each element in someone weighing 70 kilograms (154 pounds), the total value comes to about $120. Not very uplifting, is it?

But of course you are worth much more because your body is not just a bunch of chemicals enclosed in a bag of skin. Instead you are an incredibly complex system of air, water, soil nutrients, energy-storing chemicals, and food chemicals interacting in millions of ways to keep you alive and healthy. Feel better now?

What Are Nature's Building Blocks? Matter's Bricks

Atoms, ions, and molecules are the building blocks of matter.

If you had a supermicroscope capable of looking at individual elements and compounds, you could see

they are made up of three types of building blocks. The first is an **atom:** the smallest unit of matter that exhibits the characteristics of an element. The second is an **ion:** an electrically charged atom or combination of atoms. A third building block is a **molecule:** a combination of two or more atoms of the same or different elements held together by chemical bonds.

Some elements are found in nature as molecules. Examples are nitrogen and oxygen, which together make up about 99% of the volume of air you just inhaled. Two atoms of nitrogen (N) combine to form a gaseous molecule, with the shorthand formula N_2 (read as "N-two"). The subscript after the element's symbol indicates the number of atoms of that element in a molecule. Similarly, most of the oxygen gas in the atmosphere exists as O_2 (read as "O-two") molecules. A small amount of oxygen, found mostly in the second layer of the atmosphere (stratosphere), exists as O_3 (read as "O-three") molecules, a gaseous form of oxygen called *ozone*.

What Are Atoms Made of? Looking Inside

Each atom has a tiny nucleus containing protons, and in most cases neutrons, and one or more electrons whizzing around somewhere outside the nucleus.

If you increased the magnification of your super-microscope, you would find that each different type of atom contains a certain number of *subatomic particles.* There are three types of these atomic building blocks:

positively charged **protons** (p), uncharged **neutrons** (n), and negatively charged **electrons** (e). Actually, there are other particles, but they need not concern us at this introductory level.

Each atom consists of an extremely small centre, or **nucleus,** surrounded by a diffuse cloud of electrons. The nucleus contains at least one proton and in most cases neutrons. Atoms are incredibly small. More than 3 million hydrogen atoms could sit side by side on the period at the end of this sentence. And the nucleus is some 10 000 times smaller than its accompanying cloud of electrons. Now that is tiny.

Each atom has a certain number of positively charged protons inside its nucleus and an equal number of negatively charged electrons outside its nucleus. Because these electrical charges cancel one another, *the atom as a whole has no net electrical charge.*

Each element has its own specific **atomic number,** equal to the number of protons in the nucleus of each of its atoms. The simplest element, hydrogen (H), has only 1 proton in its nucleus, so its atomic number is 1. Carbon (C), with 6 protons, has an atomic number of 6. Uranium (U), a much larger atom, has 92 protons and an atomic number of 92.

Because atoms are electrically neutral, the atomic number of an atom tells us the number of positively charged protons in its nucleus and the equal number of negatively charged electrons outside its nucleus. For example, an atom of uranium with an atomic number of 92 has 92 protons in its nucleus and 92 electrons outside, and thus no net electrical charge.

INDIVIDUALS MATTER

Ernest Rutherford: A Canadian Connection

Many people are aware that Ernest Rutherford (1871–1937) is widely regarded as the father of modern nuclear physics (Einstein reportedly called him "a second Newton"). Less well known is the fact that some of Rutherford's greatest achievements took place in Canada.

Rutherford was born near Nelson, New Zealand. He was educated at Nelson College and subsequently at Canterbury College at the University of New Zealand. In 1895, he won a scholarship to study at Cambridge University in England with J. J. Thomson, who discovered electrons in 1897. While working with J. J. Thomson, Rutherford experimented with

wireless signalling, electrical conduction of gases, and radioactivity.

In 1898, Rutherford became professor of physics at McGill University in Montreal. At McGill, he painstakingly demonstrated that atoms of radioactive elements (such as uranium) spontaneously decay into atoms of *different* elements (such as barium and krypton). Most scientists of the day believed that atoms were unchangeable, but Rutherford's 1904 book *Radioactivity* and his many papers on the topic silenced his critics and earned him worldwide acclaim.

In 1907, Rutherford accepted a position at Manchester University in England. A year later, he was awarded the Nobel Prize for his

investigations into the chemistry of radioactive substances. At Manchester, Rutherford conducted his famous experiments in which he fired alpha particles at gold foil and arrived at the conclusion that atoms are mostly space with a small, dense nucleus at the centre—the basis of our modern understanding of atoms. In 1919, he became the first person to split the atom and transmute an element when he bombarded nitrogen atoms with alpha particles and detected oxygen atoms.

To learn more about Rutherford's accomplishments, visit http://www.rutherford.org.nz/biography.htm.

Because electrons have so little mass compared with the mass of a proton or a neutron, *most of an atom's mass is concentrated in its nucleus*. The mass of an atom is described in terms of its **mass number:** the total number of neutrons and protons in its nucleus. For example, a hydrogen atom with 1 proton and no neutrons in its nucleus has a mass number of 1, and an atom of uranium with 92 protons and 143 neutrons in its nucleus has a mass number of 235 (92 + 143 = 235).

All atoms of an element have the same number of protons in their nuclei. But they may have different numbers of uncharged neutrons in their nuclei, and thus may have different mass numbers. Various forms of an element having the same atomic number but a different mass number are called **isotopes** of that element. Scientists identify isotopes by attaching their mass numbers to the name or symbol of the element. For example, hydrogen has three isotopes: hydrogen-1 (H-1), hydrogen-2 (H-2, common name *deuterium*), and hydrogen-3 (H-3, common name *tritium*). A natural sample of an element contains a **mixture** of its isotopes in a fixed proportion, or percentage abundance by weight (Figure 3-5).

What Are Ions? Getting Charged Up

Atoms of some elements can lose or gain one or more electrons to form ions with positive or negative electrical charges.

Ions form when an atom of an element loses or gains one or more electrons. Thus an *ion* is an atom or groups of atoms with one or more net positive (+) or negative (−) electrical charges, one for each electron lost or gained. Atoms are neutral but ions are all charged up.

Some elements, known as *metals*, tend to lose one or more of their electrons and form positively charged ions. Like a quarterback passing a football, they are *electron givers*. For example, an atom of the metallic element sodium (Na, atomic number 11) with 11 positively charged protons and 11 negatively charged electrons can lose one of its electrons. It then becomes a sodium ion with a positive charge of 1 (Na^+) because it now has 11 positive charges (protons) but only 10 negative charges (electrons).

Other atoms, known as *nonmetals*, tend to gain one or more electrons and form negatively charged ions. Like a tight end waiting for a pass from a quarterback, they are *electron receivers*. For example, an atom of the nonmetallic element chlorine (Cl, with an atomic number of 17) can gain an electron and become a chlorine ion. The ion has a negative charge of 1 (Cl^-) because it has 17 positively charged protons and 18 negatively charged electrons.

The number of positive or negative charges on an ion is shown as a superscript after the symbol for an atom or a group of atoms. Examples of ions encountered in this book are positive ions such as hydrogen ions (H^+), calcium ions (Ca^{2+}), and ammonium ions (NH_4^+), and negative ions such as nitrate ions (NO_3^-), sulphate ions (SO_4^{2-}), and phosphate ions (PO_4^{3-}).

The amount of a substance in a unit volume of air, water, or other medium is called its **concentration.** To help you picture this, if you added 10 times the amount of a substance (let's say sugar) to the same volume of liquid (let's say coffee), you would have 10 times the concentration of sugar in that coffee.

The concentration of hydrogen ions (H^+) in a water solution is a measure of its acidity or alkalinity, represented by a value called **pH.** On a *pH scale* of 0 to 14, *acids* have a pH less than 7, *bases* have a pH greater than 7, and a *neutral solution* has a pH of 7 (Figure 3-6).

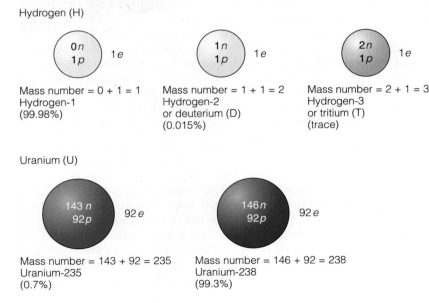

Hydrogen (H)

Mass number = 0 + 1 = 1
Hydrogen-1
(99.98%)

Mass number = 1 + 1 = 2
Hydrogen-2
or deuterium (D)
(0.015%)

Mass number = 2 + 1 = 3
Hydrogen-3
or tritium (T)
(trace)

Uranium (U)

Mass number = 143 + 92 = 235
Uranium-235
(0.7%)

Mass number = 146 + 92 = 238
Uranium-238
(99.3%)

FIGURE 3-5 Isotopes of hydrogen and uranium. All isotopes of hydrogen have an atomic number of 1 because each has one proton in its nucleus; similarly, all uranium isotopes have an atomic number of 92. However, each isotope of these elements has a different mass number because its nucleus contains a different number of neutrons. Figures in parentheses indicate the percentage abundance by weight of each isotope in a natural sample of the element.

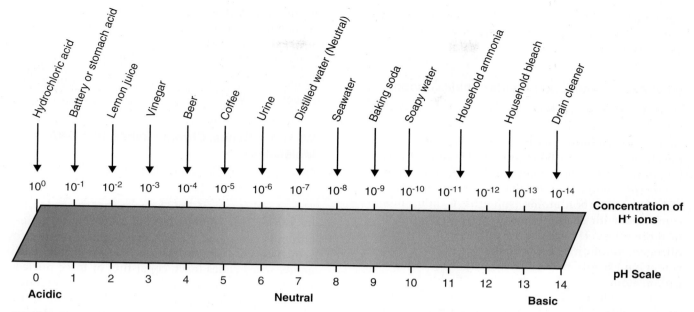

FIGURE 3-6 A pH value is a measure of the concentration of hydrogen ions (H^+) in a water solution. A solution with a pH less than 7 is acidic; a neutral solution has a pH of 7; and one with a pH greater than 7 is basic. Each whole-number drop in pH represents a tenfold increase in acidity. Here are some examples to compare with the pH scale. The pH of distilled water is 7. The pH of natural rainwater is 5.6, since some carbonic acid is formed as the raindrop absorbs extra CO_2 while falling through the atmosphere. Acid rain that has been created by human processes is often in the range of pH 4 to pH 5, although there are records of acid rain with a pH of 3 or less. You will read more about acid rain in Chapter 20. (From STARR. *Biology: Concepts and Applications* w/ CD-ROM + InfoTrac, 4E. © 2000 Cengage Learning. Reproduced by permission. www.cengage.com/permissions)

Each step along the pH scale involves changing the concentration of hydrogen ions (H^+) by a factor of 10. In other words, there are 10 times the number of H^+ ions in a solution with a pH of 6, compared to a solution with a pH of 7.

What Holds the Atoms and Ions in Compounds Together? Giving, Receiving, and Sharing Electrons

Some compounds are made up of oppositely charged ions and others are made up of molecules.

Most matter exists as *compounds,* substances containing atoms or ions of more than one element that are held together by chemical bonds. Chemists use a shorthand **chemical formula** to show the number of atoms or ions of each type in a compound. The formula contains the symbols for each of the elements present and uses subscripts to represent the number of atoms or ions of each element in the compound's basic structural unit.

Some compounds are made up of oppositely charged ions and are called *ionic compounds.* Those made up of molecules of uncharged atoms are called *covalent* or *molecular compounds.*

Sodium chloride (table salt) is an *ionic compound* represented by the chemical formula NaCl. It consists of a three-dimensional array of oppositely charged *ions* (Na^+ and Cl^-). The forces of attraction between these oppositely charged ions are called *ionic bonds,* as discussed in more detail in Appendix 3. They are formed when a metal atom (a giver) gives one or more electrons to a nonmetal atom (a receiver). Then the resulting positively and negatively charged ions attract one another. The result of this electron dating game, involving giving, receiving, and attraction between opposites, is an ionic compound.

Water, a *covalent* or *molecular compound,* consists of molecules made up of uncharged atoms of hydrogen (H) and oxygen (O). Each water molecule consists of two hydrogen atoms chemically bonded to an oxygen atom, yielding H_2O (read as "H-two-O") molecules. The bonds between the atoms in such molecules are called *covalent bonds,* as discussed in Appendix 3.

Covalent compounds form when atoms of various elements share one or more electrons. It is electron dating by sharing.

What Are Organic Compounds? Think Carbon

Organic compounds, based on Carbon, are the chemicals of life.

Table sugar, vitamins, plastics, penicillin, and most of the chemicals in your body are **organic compounds.** If you could view these compounds with your super-microscope, you would see that all (except one) have at least two carbon atoms (some have thousands) combined with each other and with atoms of one or more other elements such as hydrogen, oxygen, nitrogen, sulphur, phosphorus, chlorine, and fluorine. One exception, methane (CH_4), has only one carbon atom.

Almost all organic compounds are molecular compounds held together by covalent bonds. Organic compounds can be either *natural* (such as carbohydrates, proteins, and fats in natural foods) or *synthetic* (such as plastics and many drugs made by humans).

The millions of known organic (carbon-based) compounds include the following:

- *Hydrocarbons:* compounds of carbon and hydrogen atoms. An example is methane (CH_4), the main component of natural gas, and the simplest organic compound.

- *Chlorinated hydrocarbons:* compounds of carbon, hydrogen, and chlorine atoms. An example is the insecticide DDT ($C_{14}H_9Cl_5$).

- *Simple carbohydrates (simple sugars):* certain types of compounds of carbon, hydrogen, and oxygen atoms. An example is glucose ($C_6H_{12}O_6$), which most plants and animals break down in their cells to obtain energy.

What Can Molecules Do? Get Together

Simple organic molecules can link together to form more complex organic compounds.

Larger and more complex organic compounds, essential to life, are composed of *macromolecules.* Some of these molecules are called *polymers,* formed when a number of simple organic molecules (called *monomers*) are linked together like boxcars on a freight train. The three major types of organic molecules are:

- *complex carbohydrates* such as cellulose and starch, both of which consist of monomers of simple sugars such as glucose linked together;

- *proteins* formed by linkages of monomers called *amino acids;* and

- *nucleic acids* (DNA and RNA) formed by linkages of monomers called *nucleotides* (see Figures 5 and 6 in Appendix 3).

Lipids, which include fats and waxes, are not made of monomers but are a fourth type of macromolecule essential for life.

What Are Genes, Chromosomes, and DNA Molecules?

Genes, chromosomes, and DNA convey information to code for genetic traits.

The genetic traits of living organisms are coded for by the organic molecules associated with genes, chromosomes, and **DNA. Genes** consist of specific sequences of nucleotides in a DNA molecule. Each gene carries codes (each consisting of three nucleotides) needed to make various proteins. These coded units of genetic information about specific traits are passed on from parents to offspring during reproduction.

Chromosomes are combinations of genes that make up a single DNA molecule, together with a number of proteins. Each chromosome typically contains thousands of genes. Genetic information coded in your chromosomal DNA is what makes you different from an oak leaf, an alligator, a flea, or even from your parents. The relationships of genetic material to cells are depicted in Figure 3-7, which you may find useful in getting genetic terms straight.

The total weight of the DNA needed to reproduce the world's 7 billion people is only about 50 milligrams—the weight of a small match. If the DNA coiled in your body were unwound, it would stretch about 960 million kilometres (600 million miles)—more than six times the distance between the sun and the Earth.

The different molecules of DNA that make up the millions of species found on the Earth are like a vast and diverse genetic library. Each species is a unique book in that library.

The *genome* of a species is made up of the entire sequence of DNA "letters" or base pairs that combine to "spell out" the chromosomes in typical members of each species. In 2002, scientists were able to map out the genome for the human species.

What Are Inorganic Compounds? The Rest of the World's Compounds

Compounds without carbon–carbon and carbon–hydrogen bonds are called inorganic compounds.

Inorganic compounds do not have carbon–carbon or carbon–hydrogen bonds. Some of the inorganic compounds discussed in this book are sodium chloride

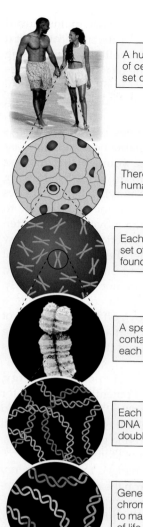

A human body contains trillions of cells, each with an identical set of genes.

There is a nucleus inside each human cell (except red blood cells).

Each cell nucleus has an identical set of chromosomes, which are found in pairs.

A specific pair of chromosomes contains one chromosome from each parent.

Each chromosome contains a long DNA molecule in the form of a coiled double helix.

Genes are segments of DNA on chromosomes that contain instructions to make proteins—the building blocks of life.

The genes in each cell are coded by sequences of nucleotides in their DNA molecules.

FIGURE 3-7 Relationships among cells, nuclei, chromosomes, DNA, genes, and nucleotides.

(NaCl), water (H_2O), nitrous oxide (N_2O), nitric oxide (NO), carbon monoxide (CO), carbon dioxide (CO_2), nitrogen dioxide (NO_2), sulphur dioxide (SO_2), ammonia (NH_3), hydrogen sulphide (H_2S), sulphuric acid (H_2SO_4), and nitric acid (HNO_3). *Good news.* These are the only inorganic compounds you need to know to understand the material in this book.

Now you know about the fairly small cast of chemicals (atoms, ions, molecules, and compounds) you will encounter in this book.

What Are Four States of Matter? Let's Get Physical

Matter exists in solid, liquid, and gaseous physical states, and in a fourth state known as plasma.

The atoms, ions, and molecules that make up matter are found in three *physical states:* solid, liquid, and gas. For example, water exists as ice, liquid, or water vapour depending on its temperature and the surrounding air pressure. The three physical states of any sample of matter differ in the spacing and orderliness of its atoms, ions, or molecules. A solid has the most compact and orderly arrangement and a gas the least compact and orderly arrangement. Liquids are somewhere in between.

A fourth state of matter is called **plasma.** It is a high-energy mixture of roughly equal numbers of positively charged ions and negatively charged electrons. A plasma forms when enough energy is applied to strip electrons away from the nuclei of atoms—somewhat like a blast of wind blowing the leaves off a tree.

Plasma is the most abundant form of matter in the universe. The sun and all stars consist mostly of plasma. There is little natural plasma on the Earth, with most of it found in lightning bolts and flames.

But scientists have learned how to make artificial plasmas in fluorescent lights, arc lamps, neon signs, gas discharge lasers, and TV and computer screens. They do this by running a high-voltage electric current through a gas. Scientists hope to be able to develop affordable plasma torches and use them to destroy toxic wastes, sterilize and clean water, remove soot from exhaust gases, and produce clean-burning hydrogen gas from diesel fuel, gasoline, or methane for use in fuel cells. Great stuff if we can do it.

What Is Matter Quality? Matter Usefulness

Matter can be classified as having high or low quality depending on how useful it is to us as a resource.

Matter quality is a measure of how useful a form of matter is to us as a resource, based on its availability and concentration, as shown in Figure 3-8. **High-quality matter** is concentrated, usually is found near the Earth's surface, and has great potential for use as a material resource. **Low-quality matter** is dilute, often is deep underground or dispersed in the ocean or the atmosphere, and usually has little potential for use as a material resource.

An aluminum can is a more concentrated, higher-quality form of aluminum than aluminum ore containing the same amount of aluminum. That is why it takes less energy, water, and money to recycle an aluminum can than to make a new can from aluminum ore.

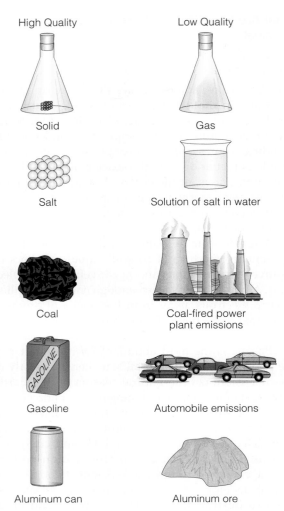

High Quality   Low Quality

Solid   Gas

Salt   Solution of salt in water

Coal   Coal-fired power plant emissions

Gasoline   Automobile emissions

Aluminum can   Aluminum ore

FIGURE 3-8 Examples of differences in matter quality. *High-quality matter* (left-hand column) is fairly easy to extract and concentrated; *low-quality matter* (right-hand column) is more difficult to extract and more dispersed than high-quality matter.

Material efficiency, or **resource productivity,** is the total amount of material needed to produce each unit of goods or services. *Great news.* Business expert Paul Hawken and physicist Amory Lovins contend that resource productivity in developed countries could be improved by 75–90% within two decades using existing technologies.

3-4 ENERGY

What Is Energy? Doing Work and Transferring Heat

Energy is the work needed to move matter and the heat that flows from hot to cooler samples of matter.

Energy is the capacity to do work and transfer heat. Work is performed when an object such as a grain of

sand, this book, a giant boulder, or an atom is moved over some distance as a result of the application of a force. Work is also performed in boiling water, heating a house, and cooking food. The heat of a hot object is energy, because if a hot object is placed in physical contact with a cold object, work is done in increasing the latter's temperature.

There are three major types of energy. One is **kinetic energy,** possessed by matter because of its mass and speed. You can convince yourself that moving matter carries the capacity to do work by thinking about what happens when a moving object collides with a stationary one. The result may be damage to either object, resulting from the movement of matter. That faster objects carry more kinetic energy than slow ones is evident if you consider the damage potential of two golf balls, one slow and one fast. Obviously, the faster-moving object can do more work. Similarly, more work can be obtained (in a collision) using a real golf ball than a hollow toy golf ball. Examples of kinetic energy in the environment are wind (a moving mass of air), flowing streams, and the flow of electrons in an electrical current.

The second type of energy is **potential energy,** which is stored in a system and potentially available for use. Examples of such stored energy include a rock held in your hand, an unlit match, still water held behind a dam, the chemical energy stored in gasoline molecules, and the nuclear energy stored in atomic nuclei.

Potential energy can be changed to kinetic energy under the right conditions. Drop the rock and its potential energy becomes kinetic energy (until it does work on your foot). Burn the gasoline in your car's engine, and the potential energy stored in the chemical bonds of its molecules changes into heat and kinetic energy that propels the car.

What Is Electromagnetic Radiation? Think Waves

Some energy travels in waves at the speed of light.

The third major type of energy is **electromagnetic energy.** It is carried by electromagnetic radiation consisting of oscillating electric and magnetic fields, which propagate in space as a *wave.*

Electromagnetic waves travel in vacuum at the speed of light, which is roughly 300 000 kilometres (186 000 miles) per second. Like any wave, **electromagnetic radiation** is characterized by the distance between successive peaks (or troughs), or *wavelength.* The wide range of electromagnetic wavelengths, known as the EM spectrum and shown in Figure 3-9, is divided into many parts based on the energy carried by the waves. Waves with a shorter wavelength carry more energy than longer-wavelength radiation.

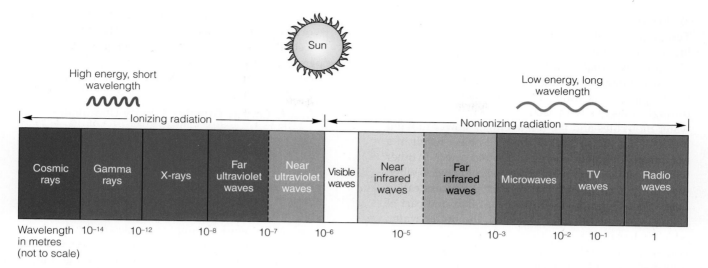

FIGURE 3-9 **The electromagnetic spectrum:** the range of electromagnetic waves, which differ in wavelength (distance between successive peaks or troughs) and energy content.

Cosmic rays, gamma rays, X-rays, and ultraviolet radiation (Figure 3-9, left side) are called **ionizing radiation** because they carry enough energy to knock electrons from atoms and change them to positively charged ions. The resulting highly reactive electrons and ions can disrupt living cells, interfere with body processes, and cause many types of sickness, including various cancers. Electromagnetic radiation in the other parts of the spectrum (Figure 3-9, right side) does not carry enough energy to form ions and is called **nonionizing radiation**. No scientific consensus exists on whether long-wavelength nonionizing radiation produced when an electrical current passes through a wire or motor is harmful to humans.

The portion of the electromagnetic spectrum to which our eyes are sensitive is actually only a small fraction of the nonionizing part of the spectrum. However, it is the part in which most of the Sun's emission of electromagnetic radiation is concentrated (Figure 3-10). That's convenient. But we are energy challenged because our senses can detect only a tiny amount of the electromagnetic radiation around us.

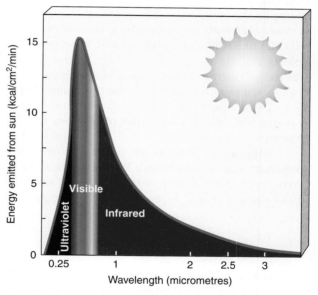

CENGAGENOW™ **ACTIVE FIGURE 3-10 Solar capital:** the spectrum of electromagnetic radiation released by the sun consists mostly of visible light. *See an animation based on this figure at* CengageNOW.

What Is Heat, and How Is It Transferred? Three Ways to Tango

Heat is the total kinetic energy of all the parts of a sample of matter and is transferred from one place to another by convection, conduction, and radiation.

Heat is the total kinetic energy associated with the random disordered movement of all the atoms, ions, or molecules within a given object. Any energy associated with the overall movement of that object does not

count toward its heat content. For example, a glass of water consists of at least 10 000 000 000 000 000 000 000 molecules in constant motion. The heat stored in this sample of water is the sum of the kinetic energy of all of these molecules, regardless of whether the glass is moving or not. Within the sample of water above, molecules continually collide with each other changing the speed (and kinetic energy) of each molecule many, many times every second. As a result, every molecule

Science, Systems, Matter, and Energy   **47**

in the sample has the same time-averaged speed. **Temperature** is a measure of that average speed, with higher temperatures corresponding to greater overall kinetic energy, that is, heat content.

Now imagine placing a cold object in a glass of hot water. Just as water molecules exchange energy through collisions with each other, collisions between water molecules and the (on average) slower-moving molecules at the surface of the cold object result in a net transfer of kinetic energy to the cold object. In other words, heat flows from hot objects to cold objects when they are placed in physical contact, a process called *conduction* (Figure 3-11). In the event that one part of a single volume of water is heated, the hotter water, which is less dense, rises to meet cold water and heat is again transferred from hot to cold. This kind of heat transport is called *convection*.

Heat can also be transferred through *radiation*. The random motion of the atoms or molecules in an object causes the emission of electromagnetic radiation characteristic of the object's temperature. For example, the sun's emission spectrum (Figure 3-10) is consistent with its surface temperature of nearly 6 000°C (10 800°F). On the other hand, most everyday objects radiate energy dominantly in the longer-wavelength infrared part of the EM spectrum. As an object's temperature increases, the dominant part of its emission spectrum shifts to shorter and shorter wavelengths, which is why hot iron glows red, for example.

At the same time as an object "glows" and loses heat, it may also absorb EM radiation from its environment, thus gaining heat. If the rate at which an object absorbs energy exceeds its rate of energy loss, the net result is an increase in heat content, in other words, an increase in temperature. If the rates are balanced, the object is in thermal equilibrium and its temperature remains constant.

What Is Energy Quality? Energy Usefulness

Energy can be classified as having high or low quality depending on how useful it is to us as a resource.

Energy quality is a measure of an energy source's ability to do useful work, as seen in Figure 3-12 (p. 49). **High-quality energy** is concentrated and can perform much useful work. Examples are electricity, the chemical energy stored in coal and gasoline, concentrated sunlight, and nuclei of uranium-235 used as fuel in nuclear power plants.

By contrast, **low-quality energy** is dispersed and has little ability to do useful work. An example of low-quality energy is heat dispersed in the moving molecules of a large amount of matter (such as the atmosphere or a large body of water) so that its temperature is low.

For example, the total amount of heat stored in the Atlantic Ocean is greater than the amount of high-quality chemical energy stored in all the oil deposits of Saudi Arabia. Yet the ocean's heat is so widely dispersed, it cannot be used to move things or to heat things to high temperatures.

It makes sense to match the quality of an energy source with the quality of energy needed to perform a particular task (Figure 3-12) because doing so saves energy and usually money.

Convection

Heating water in the bottom of a pan causes some of the water to vaporize into bubbles. Because they are lighter than the surrounding water, they rise. Water then sinks from the top to replace the rising bubbles. This up and down movement (convection) eventually heats all of the water.

Conduction

Heat from a stove burner causes atoms or molecules in the pan's bottom to vibrate faster. The vibrating atoms or molecules then collide with nearby atoms or molecules, causing them to vibrate faster. Eventually, molecules or atoms in the pan's handle are vibrating so fast it becomes too hot to touch.

Radiation

As the water boils, heat from the hot stove burner and pan radiate into the surrounding air, even though air conducts very little heat.

FIGURE 3-11 Three ways in which heat can be transferred from one place to another.

FIGURE 3-12 Categories of energy quality. *High-quality energy* is concentrated and has great ability to perform useful work. *Low-quality energy* is dispersed and has little ability to do useful work. To avoid unnecessary energy waste, it is best to match the quality of an energy source with the quality of energy needed to perform a task.

Source of Energy	Relative Energy Quality (usefulness)	Energy Tasks
Electricity Very high temperature heat (greater than 2 500°C) Nuclear fission (uranium) Nuclear fusion (deuterium) Concentrated sunlight High-velocity wind	Very high	Very high temperature heat (greater than 2 500°C) for industrial processes and producing electricity to run electrical devices (lights, motors)
High-temperature heat (1 000–2 500°C) Hydrogen gas Natural gas Gasoline Coal Food	High	Mechanical motion (to move vehicles and other things) High-temperature heat (1 000–2 500°C) for industrial processes and producing electricity
Normal sunlight Moderate-velocity wind High-velocity water flow Concentrated geothermal energy Moderate-temperature heat (100–1 000°C) Wood and crop wastes	Moderate	Moderate-temperature heat (100–1 000°C) for industrial processes, cooking, producing steam, electricity, and hot water
Dispersed geothermal energy Low-temperature heat (100°C or lower)	Low	Low-temperature heat (100°C or lower) for space heating

THE LAW OF CONSERVATION OF MATTER: A RULE WE CANNOT BREAK

What Is the Difference between a Physical and a Chemical Change? Changes in Form and in Chemical Makeup

Matter can change from one physical form to another or change its chemical composition.

When a sample of matter undergoes a **physical change,** its chemical composition is not changed. A piece of aluminum foil cut into small pieces is still aluminum foil. When solid water (ice) is melted or liquid water is boiled, none of the H_2O molecules involved are altered; instead, the molecules are organized in different spatial (physical) patterns.

In a **chemical change,** or **chemical reaction,** there is a change in the chemical composition of the elements or compounds. Chemists use shorthand chemical equations to represent what happens in a chemical reaction. For example, when coal burns completely, the solid carbon (C) it contains combines with oxygen gas (O_2) from the atmosphere to form the gaseous compound carbon dioxide (CO_2):

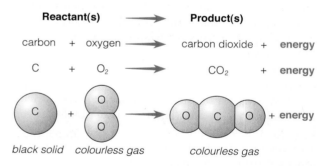

Reactant(s)	⟶	Product(s)
carbon + oxygen	⟶	carbon dioxide + **energy**
C + O_2	⟶	CO_2 + **energy**
black solid colourless gas		colourless gas

Energy is given off in this reaction, making coal a useful fuel. The reaction also shows how the complete burning of coal (or any of the carbon-containing compounds in wood, natural gas, oil, and gasoline) gives off carbon dioxide gas. This is a key gas that helps warm the lower atmosphere (troposphere).

The Law of Conservation of Matter: Why There Is No "Away"?

When a physical or chemical change occurs, no atoms are created or destroyed.

In a physical or chemical change, none of the atoms involved are either created or destroyed. They are simply rearranged into different spatial patterns (physical changes) or different combinations (chemical changes). This statement, based on many thousands of measurements, is known as the **law of conservation of matter.**

The law of conservation of matter means there is no "away" as in "to throw away." *Everything we think we have thrown away is still here somewhere on the planet with us in one form or another.* Dust and soot from the smokestacks of industrial plants, substances removed from polluted water at sewage treatment plants, and banned chemicals like DDT all have to go somewhere and can come back around to haunt us. For example, selling DDT abroad means it can return as residues in imported coffee, fruit, and other foods, or as fallout from air masses moved long distances by winds.

As well, many resources are limited. It makes sense to reuse and recycle matter for further useful purposes rather than allowing it to be converted from a valuable material to a waste-disposal problem after a single use. More details of reusing and recycling matter are given in Chapter 17.

How Do Chemists Keep Track of Atoms? Balancing Equations = Atomic Bookkeeping

Chemical equations are used as an accounting system to verify that no atoms are created or destroyed in a chemical reaction.

In keeping with the law of conservation of matter, each side of a chemical equation must have the same number of atoms of each element involved. Minding this law leads to what chemists call a *balanced chemical equation.*

The equation for the burning of carbon (C + O$_2$ → CO$_2$) is balanced because one atom of carbon and two atoms of oxygen are on both sides of the equation. That is an easy one.

Now we try a slightly harder one. When electricity is passed through water (H$_2$O), the water molecule can be broken down into hydrogen (H$_2$) and oxygen (O$_2$). This chemical reaction can be represented by the following shorthand chemical equation:

$$H_2O \quad \rightarrow \quad H_2 \quad + \quad O_2$$
2 H atoms   2 H atoms   2 O atoms
1 O atom

This equation is unbalanced because one atom of oxygen is on the left but two atoms are on the right.

We cannot change the subscripts of any of the formulas to balance this equation because that would make the substances different from those actually involved. That is a no-no according to the law of conservation of matter. Instead, we could use different numbers of the *molecules* involved to balance the equation. For example, we could use two water molecules:

$$2 H_2O \quad \rightarrow \quad H_2 \quad + \quad O_2$$
4 H atoms   2 H atoms   2 O atoms
2 O atoms

This equation is still unbalanced because although the numbers of oxygen atoms on both sides are now equal, the numbers of hydrogen atoms are not.

We can correct this by having the reaction produce two hydrogen molecules:

$$2 H_2O \quad \rightarrow \quad 2 H_2 \quad + \quad O_2$$
4 H atoms   4 H atoms   2 O atoms
2 O atoms

Now the equation is balanced, and the law of conservation of matter has been observed. We see that for every two molecules of water through which we pass electricity, two hydrogen molecules and one oxygen molecule are produced. By the way, this equation may change your life. It represents how we could use heat or electricity to decompose water and produce hydrogen gas that someday may replace oil as a means of powering our societies—more on this hydrogen revolution in Chapter 18.

SELF CHECK

Balance the Atoms Ready for more practice? Balance the chemical equation for the reaction of nitrogen gas (N$_2$) with hydrogen gas (H$_2$) to form ammonia gas (NH$_3$).

(Note that once the equation has been balanced, there are 2 N atoms and 6 H atoms on each side: N$_2$ + 3 H$_2$ → 2 NH$_3$.)

How Harmful Are Pollutants? Too Much of Bad Things

The law of conservation of matter tells us that we will always produce some pollutants, but we can produce much less and clean up some of what we do produce.

We can make the environment cleaner and convert some potentially harmful chemicals into less harmful physical or chemical forms. But *the law of conservation of matter means we will always face the problem of what to do with some quantity of wastes and pollutants.*

Three factors determining the severity of a pollutant's harmful effects are its *chemical nature,* its *concentration,* and its *persistence.*

The second of these factors, *concentration,* is sometimes expressed in **parts per million (ppm)**; 1 ppm corresponds to 1 part pollutant per million parts of the gas, liquid, or solid mixture in which the pollutant is found. Smaller concentration units are **parts per billion (ppb)** and **parts per trillion (ppt).**

We can reduce the concentration of a pollutant by dumping it into the air or a large volume of water, but there are limits to the effectiveness of this dilution approach. For example, the water flowing in a river can dilute or disperse some of the wastes we dump into the river. But if we dump in too much waste, this natural cleansing process does not work.

The third factor, **persistence,** is a measure of how long the pollutant stays in the air, water, soil, or body. Pollutants can be classified into four categories based on their persistence. **Degradable,** or **nonpersistent, pollutants** are broken down completely or reduced to acceptable levels by natural physical, chemical, and biological processes. Complex chemical pollutants that living organisms (usually specialized bacteria) break down into simpler chemicals are called **biodegradable pollutants.** Human sewage in a river, for example, is biodegraded fairly quickly by bacteria if the sewage is not added faster than it can be broken down.

Slowly degradable, or **persistent, pollutants** take decades or longer to degrade. Examples include the insecticide DDT and most plastics.

Nondegradable pollutants are chemicals that natural processes cannot break down. Examples include the toxic elements lead, mercury, and arsenic. Ideally, we should try not to use these chemicals, but if we do, we should figure out ways to keep them from getting into the environment. Further details of hazardous chemicals and toxicology can be found in Chapter 19.

3-6 NUCLEAR CHANGES

What Is Natural Radioactivity? Nuclei Losing Particles or Radiation

An atom can change from one isotope to another when its nucleus loses particles or gives off high-energy electromagnetic radiation.

In addition to physical and chemical changes, matter can undergo a third type of change known as a **nuclear change.** This occurs when nuclei of certain isotopes spontaneously change or are made to change into nuclei of different isotopes.

There are three types of nuclear change: radioactivity, nuclear fission, and nuclear fusion. **Radioactive decay** is a nuclear change in which unstable isotopes spontaneously emit fast-moving chunks of matter (called particles), high-energy electromagnetic radiation, or both at a fixed rate. Unstable isotopes are called **radioactive isotopes** or **radioisotopes,** and only decays yielding an isotope that is more stable than the original one occur spontaneously.

The **radiation** emitted by radioisotopes is damaging ionizing radiation. The most common form is high-energy electromagnetic radiation known as **gamma rays.** This radiation is highly penetrating, which makes it very useful in cancer therapy, but it is otherwise best avoided.

High-speed ionizing particles emitted from the nuclei of radioactive isotopes are most commonly of two types: **alpha particles** (fast-moving, positively charged chunks of matter that consist of two protons and two neutrons) and **beta particles** (high-speed electrons).

The decay of a given radioisotope into another specified isotope occurs at a fixed and unique characteristic rate. This rate of decay can be expressed in terms of the radioisotope's **half-life:** the time needed for *one-half* of the nuclei in a given quantity of the radioisotope to decay and emit radiation. Often, the product of the decay is another radioactive isotope. It too then decays with some characteristic half-life. The process continues until a nonradioactive (stable) isotope is produced. For example, the decay of uranium-238 proceeds through 14 different decay steps, which end with the formation of stable lead-206.

The characteristic half-life of an isotope may range from a few millionths of a second to several billion years (Table 3-1, right). An isotope's half-life cannot be changed by temperature, pressure, chemical reactions, or any other known factor.

Half-life can be used to estimate how long a sample of a radioisotope must be stored in a safe container before it decays to what is considered a safe level. A general rule is that such decay takes about 10 half-lives. Thus people must be protected from radioactive waste containing iodine-131 (which concentrates in the thyroid gland and has a half-life of 8 days) for 80 days (10 × 8 days). Plutonium-239, which is produced in nuclear reactors and used as the explosive in some nuclear weapons, can cause lung cancer

Table 3-1 Half-Lives of Selected Radioisotopes

Isotope	Half-Life	Radiation Emitted
Potassium-42	12.4 hours	Alpha, beta
Iodine-131	8 days	Beta, gamma
Cobalt-60	5.27 years	Beta, gamma
Hydrogen-3 (tritium)	12.5 years	Beta
Strontium-90	28 years	Beta
Carbon-14	5 370 years	Beta
Plutonium-239	24 000 years	Alpha, gamma
Uranium-235	710 million years	Alpha, gamma
Uranium-238	4.5 billion years	Alpha, gamma

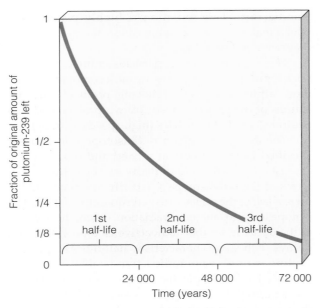

FIGURE 3-13 *Half-life.* The radioactive decay of pluto-nium-239, which is produced in nuclear reactors and used as the explosive in some nuclear weapons, has a half-life of 24 000 years. The amount of radioactivity emitted by a radioactive iso-tope decreases by one-half for each half-life that passes. Thus, after three half-lives, amounting to 72 000 years, one-eighth of a sample of plutonium-239 would still be radioactive.

when its particles are inhaled in minute amounts. Its half-life is 24 000 years (see Figure 3-13). Thus it must be stored safely for 240 000 years (10 × 24 000 years)—about four times longer than the latest version of our species (*Homo sapiens sapiens*) has existed. Chapter 17 has more on the problem of what to do with the nuclear wastes we have created.

Exposure to ionizing radiation from alpha parti-cles, beta particles, and gamma rays can damage cells in two ways. One is *genetic damage* from mutations or changes in DNA molecules that alter genes and chro-mosomes. If the mutation is harmful, it can lead to genetic defects in the next generation of offspring or several generations later.

The other is *somatic damage* to tissues, which causes harm during the victim's lifetime. Examples include burns, miscarriages, eye cataracts, and certain cancers.

According to Health Canada, exposure over an average lifetime to average levels of ionizing radiation from natural and human sources causes about 2.5% of all fatal cancers in the Canadian population.

What Is Nuclear Fission? Splitting Heavy Nuclei

Neutrons can split apart the nuclei of certain isotopes with large mass numbers and release a large amount of energy.

Nuclear fission is a nuclear change in which nuclei of certain isotopes with large mass numbers (such

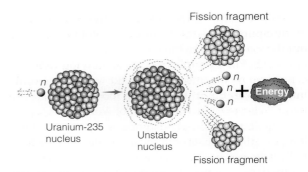

FIGURE 3-14 Fission of a uranium-235 nucleus by a neutron *(n)*.

as uranium-235) are split apart into lighter nuclei when struck by neutrons; each fission releases two or three more neutrons and energy (Figure 3-14). Each of these neutrons, in turn, can cause an additional fission. For these multiple fissions to take place, enough fissionable nuclei must be present to provide the **critical mass** needed for efficient capture of these neutrons.

Multiple fissions within a critical mass form a **chain reaction,** which releases an enormous amount of energy (Figure 3-15). This is somewhat like a room in which the floor is covered with spring-loaded mousetraps, each topped by a Ping-Pong ball. Open the door, throw in a single Ping-Pong ball, and

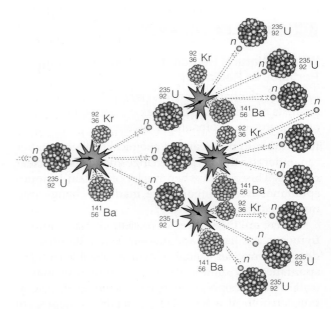

FIGURE 3-15 A *nuclear chain reaction* initiated by one neutron triggering fission in a single uranium-235 nucleus. This figure illustrates only a few of the trillions of fissions caused when a single uranium-235 nucleus is split within a critical mass of uranium-235 nuclei. The elements krypton (Kr) and barium (Ba), shown here as fission fragments, are only two of many possibilities.

watch the action in this simulated chain reaction of snapping mousetraps and balls flying around in every direction.

In an atomic bomb, an enormous amount of energy is released in a fraction of a second in an uncontrolled nuclear fission chain reaction. This reaction is initiated by an explosive charge, which pushes two masses of fissionable fuel together. This causes the fuel to reach the critical mass needed for a chain reaction and to give off a tremendous amount of energy in a gigantic explosion.

In the reactor of a nuclear power plant, the rate at which the nuclear fission chain reaction takes place is controlled so that under normal operation only one of every two or three neutrons released is used to split another nucleus. In conventional nuclear fission reactors, the splitting of uranium-235 nuclei releases heat, which produces high-pressure steam to spin turbines and thus generate electricity.

What Is Nuclear Fusion? Forcing Light Nuclei to Combine

Extremely high temperatures can force the nuclei of isotopes of some lightweight atoms to fuse together and release large amounts of energy.

Nuclear fusion is a nuclear change in which two isotopes of light elements, such as hydrogen, are forced together at extremely high temperatures until they fuse to form a heavier nucleus. Lots of energy is released when this happens. Temperatures of at least 100 million °C are needed to force the positively charged nuclei (which strongly repel one another) to fuse.

Nuclear fusion is much more difficult to initiate than nuclear fission, but once started it releases far more energy per unit of fuel than does fission. You would not be alive without nuclear fusion. Fusion of hydrogen nuclei to form helium nuclei is the source of energy in the sun and other stars.

After World War II, the principle of *uncontrolled nuclear fusion* was used to develop extremely powerful hydrogen, or thermonuclear, weapons. These weapons use the D–T fusion reaction, in which a hydrogen-2, or deuterium (D), nucleus and a hydrogen-3 (tritium, T) nucleus are fused to form a larger, helium-4 nucleus, a neutron, and energy, as shown in Figure 3-16.

Scientists have also tried to develop *controlled nuclear fusion,* in which the D–T reaction is used to produce heat that can be converted into electricity. After more than 50 years of research, this process is still in the laboratory stage. Even if it becomes technologically and economically feasible, many energy experts do not expect it to be a practical source of energy until after 2030, if then.

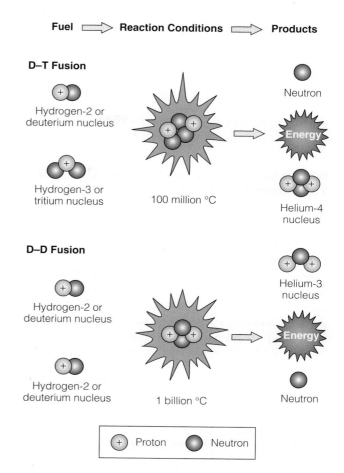

FIGURE 3-16 The deuterium–tritium (D–T) and deuterium–deuterium (D–D) *nuclear fusion* reactions, which take place at extremely high temperatures.

3-7 ENERGY LAWS: TWO RULES WE CANNOT BREAK

What Is the First Law of Thermodynamics? You Cannot Get Something for Nothing

In a physical or chemical change, we can change energy from one form to another but we can never create or destroy any of the energy involved.

Scientists have observed energy being changed from one form to another in millions of physical and chemical changes. But they have never been able to detect the creation or destruction of any energy. (In nuclear changes, the apparent creation of energy out of nothing is explained by a slight reduction in the total mass of the matter involved, matter and energy being equivalent as postulated by Einstein in 1905.) The results of these countless experiments have been summarized in the **law of conservation of energy,** also known as the **first law of thermodynamics:** *in all physical and chemical changes, energy is neither created nor destroyed, but it may be converted from one form to another.*

This scientific law tells us that when one form of energy is converted to another form in any physical or chemical change, *energy input always equals energy output*. No matter how hard we try or how clever we are, we cannot get more energy out of a system than we put in; in other words, *we cannot get something for nothing in terms of energy quantity*. This is one of Mother Nature's basic rules that we have to live with.

What Is the Second Law of Thermodynamics? You Cannot Even Break Even

Whenever energy is changed from one form to another we always end up with less usable energy than we started with.

Because the first law of thermodynamics states that energy can be neither created nor destroyed, we may be tempted to think we will always have enough energy. Yet if we fill a car's tank with gasoline and drive around or use a flashlight battery until it is dead, something has been lost. If it is not energy, what is it? The answer is *energy quality* (Figure 3-12), the amount of energy available that can perform useful work.

Countless experiments have shown that when energy is changed from one form to another, a decrease in energy quality always occurs. The results of these experiments have been summarized in what is called the **second law of thermodynamics:** *when energy is changed from one form to another, some of the useful energy is always degraded to lower quality, more dispersed, less useful energy*. This degraded energy usually takes the form of heat given off at a low temperature to the surroundings (environment). There it is dispersed by the random motion of air or water molecules and becomes even less useful as a resource.

In other words, *we cannot even break even in terms of energy quality because energy always goes from a more useful to a less useful form when energy is changed from one form to another*. No one has ever found a violation of this fundamental scientific law. It is another one of Mother Nature's basic rules that we have to live with. In fact, according to the late James Kay of the University of Waterloo and his colleagues, the second law of thermodynamics underlies the functioning of ecosystems, biological complexity, the inevitability of life itself, and even the solutions to environmental problems (http://www.jameskay.ca/about/ecosys.html).

Consider three examples of the second law of thermodynamics in action. *First*, when a car is driven, only about 20–25% of the high-quality chemical energy available in its gasoline fuel is converted into mechanical energy (to propel the vehicle) and electrical energy (to run its electrical systems). The remaining 75–80% is degraded to low-quality heat that is released into the environment and eventually lost into space.

Thus, most of the money you spend for gasoline is not used to get you anywhere.

Second, when electrical energy flows through filament wires in an incandescent lightbulb, it is changed into about 5% useful light and 95% low-quality heat that flows into the environment. In other words, this so-called *light bulb* is really a *heat bulb*. Good news. Scientists have developed compact fluorescent bulbs that are four times more efficient, and even more efficient bulbs are on the way. Do you use compact fluorescent bulbs?

Third, in living systems, solar energy is converted into chemical energy (food molecules) and then into mechanical energy (moving, thinking, and living). During each of these conversions, high-quality energy is degraded and flows into the environment as low-quality heat (Figure 3-17). Trace the flows and energy conversions in this diagram.

The second law of thermodynamics also means that *we can never recycle or reuse high-quality energy to perform useful work*. Once the concentrated energy in a serving of food, a litre of gasoline, a lump of coal, or a chunk of uranium is released, it is degraded to low-quality heat that is dispersed into the environment.

> **DID YOU KNOW**
>
> Two Canadians, Henry Woodward and Mathew Evans, patented a glass light bulb with a carbon filament in 1874. However, Woodward (a medical student) and Evans (an innkeeper) couldn't afford to mass-produce and market the light bulb. They sold their patent to American inventor Thomas Edison, who unveiled his version of glass light bulbs with carbon filaments in 1879.

Energy efficiency, or **energy productivity,** is a measure of how much useful work is accomplished by a particular input of energy into a system. *Good news.* There is plenty of room for improving energy efficiency. Scientists estimate that only about 16% of the energy we use ends up performing useful work. The remaining 84% is either unavoidably wasted because of the second law of thermodynamics (41%) or unnecessarily wasted (43%).

Here is a lesson from thermodynamics. The cheapest and quickest way for us to get more energy is to stop unnecessarily wasting almost half of the energy we use. We can do this by not driving gas-guzzling motor vehicles and by not living in poorly insulated and leaky houses. What are you doing to reduce your unnecessary waste of energy?

> **CONSIDER, DISCUSS, OR DEBATE**
>
> List several ways in which Canadians could reduce the amount of energy they consume. Which of the energy-reducing strategies in your list would have the greatest impact? The least impact? Which strategy or strategies are you most likely to apply in your own life?

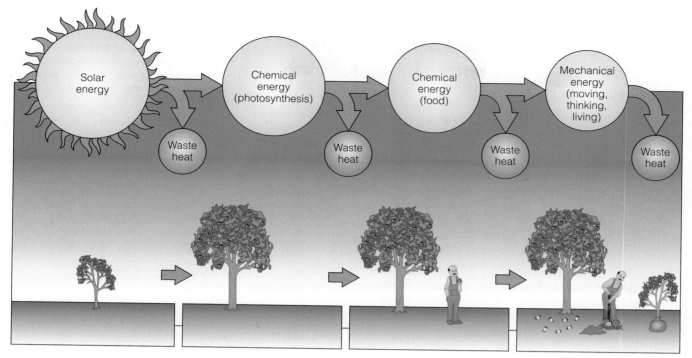

CENGAGENOW™ **ACTIVE FIGURE 3-17** The second law of thermodynamics in action in living systems. Each time energy is changed from one form to another, some of the initial input of high-quality energy is degraded, usually to low-quality heat that is dispersed into the environment. Note that the "waste heat" balloons above would be much larger than can be shown in this diagram. Find out why by reading Section 3-7 carefully. *See an animation based on this figure at* CengageNOW.

3-8 MATTER AND ENERGY LAWS AND ENVIRONMENTAL PROBLEMS

What Is a High-Throughput Economy? An Accelerating Treadmill

Most of today's economies increase economic growth by converting the world's resources to goods and services in ways that add large amounts of waste, pollution, and low-quality heat to the environment.

As a result of the law of conservation of matter and the second law of thermodynamics, individual resource use automatically adds some waste heat and waste matter to the environment. Most of today's advanced industrialized countries have **high-throughput (high-waste) economies** that attempt to sustain ever-increasing economic growth by increasing the one-way flow of matter and energy resources through their economic systems (Figure 3-18). These resources flow through their economies into planetary *sinks* (air, water, soil, organisms), where pollutants and wastes end up and can accumulate to harmful levels.

What happens if more and more people continue to use and waste more and more energy and matter resources at an increasing rate? In other words, what happens if most of the world's people get infected with the affluenza virus?

The law of conservation of matter and the two laws of thermodynamics discussed in this chapter tell us that eventually this consumption will exceed the capacity of the environment to dilute and degrade waste matter and absorb waste heat. However, they do not tell us how close we are to reaching such limits.

CONSIDER, DISCUSS, OR DEBATE

China, the world's most populous country, has the world's fastest economic growth rate. If China continues to develop at its present rate, what problems do you anticipate? How can these problems be avoided?

What Is a Matter-Recycling-and-Reuse Economy? Go in Circles Instead of Straight Lines

Recycling and reusing more of the Earth's matter resources slows down depletion of nonrenewable matter resources and reduces our environmental impact.

There is a way to slow down resource use and reduce the environmental impact of a high-throughput

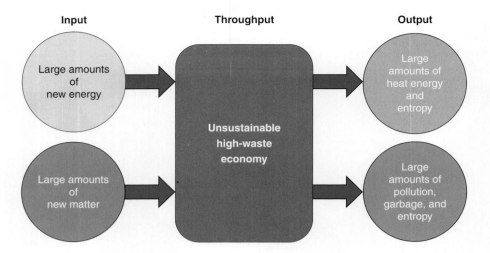

Input — **Throughput** — **Output**

Large amounts of new energy → Unsustainable high-waste economy → Large amounts of heat energy and entropy

Large amounts of new matter → → Large amounts of pollution, garbage, and entropy

FIGURE 3-18 Problem: the high-waste economies of many developed countries depend on a continuously increasing flow of energy and matter. This is unsustainable in terms of resources and creates undesirable consequences such as large amounts of garbage and pollution.

economy. We can convert such a linear high-throughput economy into a circular **matter-recycling-and-reuse economy** that recycles and reuses our matter outputs instead of dumping them into the environment.

Changing to a matter-recycling-and-reuse economy is an important way to buy some time. But this does not allow more and more people to use more and more resources indefinitely, even if all of those resources were somehow perfectly recycled and reused. The reason is that the two laws of thermodynamics tell us that recycling and reusing matter resources always requires using high-quality energy (which cannot be recycled) and adds waste heat to the environment.

What Is a Low-Throughput Economy? Learning from Nature

We can live more sustainably by reducing the throughput of matter and energy in our economies, not wasting matter and energy resources, recycling and reusing most of the matter resources we use, and stabilizing the size of our population.

Is there a better way out of the environmental situation that we have gotten ourselves into? You bet. The three scientific laws governing matter and energy changes suggest that the best long-term solution to our environmental and resource problems is to shift from an economy based on increasing matter and energy flow (throughput) to a more sustainable **low-throughput (low-waste) economy,** as summarized in Figure 3-19.

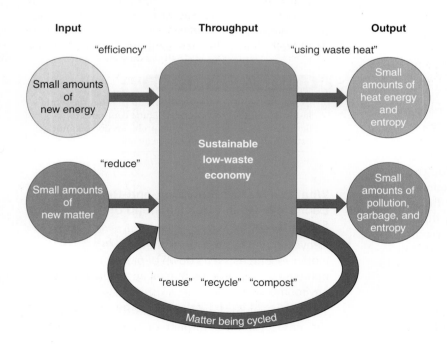

Input — **Throughput** — **Output**

"efficiency" — "using waste heat"

Small amounts of new energy → Sustainable low-waste economy → Small amounts of heat energy and entropy

Small amounts of new matter "reduce" → → Small amounts of pollution, garbage, and entropy

"reuse" "recycle" "compost"

Matter being cycled

FIGURE 3-19 Solution: a low-waste economy based on energy efficiency, matter recycling, and reduced use of new matter requires fewer resources and creates fewer environmental problems. Innovative new technologies and high-quality durable products would be features of this step toward a sustainable future.

This can be done by wasting less matter and energy, living more simply to decrease resource use per person, and slowing population growth to reduce the number of resource users. In other words, we can learn to live more sustainably by heeding the *lessons from nature* revealed by the law of conservation of mass and the two laws of thermodynamics.

The next five chapters apply the three basic scientific laws of matter and thermodynamics to living systems and look at some *biological principles* that can also teach us how to live more sustainably by working with nature.

The second law of thermodynamics holds, I think, the supreme position among laws of nature…. If your theory is found to be against the second law of thermodynamics, I can give you no hope.

ARTHUR S. EDDINGTON

CHAPTER REVIEW

1. Review the Key Questions for this chapter on p. 35. What is *science*? Describe the steps involved in the scientific process. What are *data*? What is an *experiment*? What is a *model*? Distinguish among a *scientific hypothesis*, *scientific theory*, and *scientific law (law of nature)*. What is *peer review* and why is it important? Explain why scientific theories are not to be taken lightly and why people often use the term *theory* incorrectly.

2. Distinguish between *inductive reasoning* and *deductive reasoning* and give an example of each. Explain why scientific theories and laws are the most important results of science.

3. Distinguish between *frontier science* and *consensus science*. What is *junk science*?

4. Define and give an example of a *system*. Distinguish among the *input*, *flow (throughput)*, and *output* of a system. Why are scientific models useful? What is *feedback*? What is a *feedback loop*? Distinguish between a *positive feedback loop* and a *negative (corrective) feedback loop* in a system, and give an example of each. Distinguish between a *time delay* and a *synergistic interaction (synergy)* in a system and give an example of each.

5. What is *matter*? Distinguish between an *element* and a *compound* and give an example of each. Distinguish among *atoms*, *ions*, and *molecules* and give an example of each. What is the *atomic theory*? Distinguish among *protons*, *neutrons*, and *electrons*. What is the *nucleus* of an atom? Distinguish between the *atomic number* and the *mass number* of an element. What is an *isotope*? What is *acidity*? What is *pH*?

6. What is a *chemical formula*? Distinguish between *organic compounds* and *inorganic compounds* and give an example of each. Distinguish among complex carbohydrates, proteins, nucleic acids, and lipids. Distinguish between *genes* and *chromosomes*. What is *matter quality*? Distinguish between *high-quality matter* and *low-quality matter* and give an example of each.

7. What is *energy*? Distinguish between *kinetic energy* and *potential energy* and give an example of each. What is *heat*? Define and give two examples of *electromagnetic radiation*. What is *energy quality*? Distinguish between *high-quality energy* and *low-quality energy* and give an example of each.

8. Distinguish between a *physical change* and a *chemical change (chemical reaction)* and give an example of each. What is a *nuclear change*? Explain the differences among *natural radioactive decay, nuclear fission*, and *nuclear fusion*. What is a *radioactive isotope (radioisotope)*? What is a *chain reaction*? What is the *law of conservation of matter* and why is it important?

9. What is the *law of conservation of energy (first law of thermodynamics)* and why is it important? What is the *second law of thermodynamics* and why is it important? Explain why this law means that we can never recycle or reuse high-quality energy. What is *energy efficiency (energy productivity)* and why is it important?

10. Explain how human activities can have unintended harmful environmental results. Relate the four *scientific principles of sustainability* (Chapter 1) to what went wrong on Easter Island (**Core Case Study**).

CRITICAL THINKING

1. Respond to the following statements:

   a. Scientists have not absolutely proven that anyone has ever died from smoking cigarettes.
   b. The greenhouse theory—that certain gases (such as water vapour and carbon dioxide) warm the atmosphere—is not a reliable idea because it is only a scientific theory.

2. See whether you can find an advertisement or an article describing some aspect of science in which

(a) the concept of scientific proof is misused, (b) the term *theory* is used when it should have been *hypothesis*, and (c) a consensus scientific finding is dismissed or downplayed because it is "only a theory" or is not viewed as sound science.

3. How does a scientific law (such as the law of conservation of matter) differ from a societal law (such as maximum speed limits for vehicles)? Can each be broken? Explain.

4. A tree grows and increases its mass. Explain why this is not a violation of the law of conservation of matter.

5. If there is no "away," why is the world not filled with waste matter?

6. Methane (CH_4) gas is the major component of natural gas. Write and balance the chemical equation for the burning of methane when it combines with oxygen gas in the atmosphere to form carbon dioxide and water.

7. Suppose you have 100 grams of radioactive plutonium-239 with a half-life of 24 000 years. How many grams of plutonium-239 will remain after **(a)** 12 000 years, **(b)** 24 000 years, and **(c)** 96 000 years?

8. Someone wants you to invest money in an automobile engine that will produce more energy than the energy in the fuel (such as gasoline or electricity) you use to run the motor. What is your response? Explain.

9. Use the second law of thermodynamics to explain why a barrel of oil can be used only once as a fuel.

PROJECTS

1. Use the library or Internet to find an example of junk science and explain why it is junk science. Compare your findings with those of your classmates.

2. **(a)** List two examples of negative feedback loops not discussed in this chapter, one that is beneficial and one that is detrimental. Compare your examples with those of your classmates. **(b)** Give two examples of positive feedback loops not discussed in this chapter. Include one that is beneficial and one that is detrimental. Compare your examples with those of your classmates.

3. If you have the use of a sensitive balance, try to demonstrate the law of conservation of mass in a physical change. Weigh a container with a lid (a glass jar will do), add an ice cube and weigh it again, and then allow the ice to melt and weigh it again. Explain how your results obey the law of conservation of matter.

4. Use the library or the Internet to find bibliographic information about at least two of the following people mentioned in the chapter: *Jared Diamond, Arthur Eddington, Thomas Edison, Albert Einstein, Mathew Evans, Paul Hawkin, Terry Hunt, James Kay, Amory Lovins, Ernest Rutherford, Warren Weaver, Henry Woodward.*

Ecosystems: What Are They, and How Do They Work?

Have You Thanked the Insects Today?

Insects have a bad reputation. We classify many as *pests* because they compete with us for food; spread human diseases such as malaria; and invade our lawns, gardens, and houses. Some people have "bugitis," a fear of all insects, and think the only good bug is a dead bug. This view fails to recognize the vital roles insects play in helping sustain life on Earth.

A large proportion of the Earth's plant species (including many trees) depends on insects to pollinate their flowers. Without pollinating insects, we would have few fruits and vegetables to enjoy.

Insects that eat other insects help control the populations of at least half the species of insects we call pests. An example is the praying mantis (Figure 4-1). This free pest-control service is an important part of the natural capital that helps sustain us.

Insects have been around for at least 400 million years and are phenomenally successful forms of life. An estimated 10 quintillion (10 followed by 18 zeros) insects live with us on the Earth—about 1.6 million insects for each one of us.

Some insects can reproduce at an astounding rate. For example, a single female housefly and her offspring can theoretically produce about 5.6 trillion houseflies in only one year.

Insects can rapidly evolve new genetic traits, such as resistance to pesticides. They also have an exceptional ability to evolve into new species when faced with new environmental conditions, and they are quite resistant to extinction.

For example, we can apply chemical pesticides to protect crops from pests. This can help grow more food. But there is a downside to pesticides. They can harm beneficial insects and other organisms that help protect crops from other insects. Widespread use of chemical pesticides can also accelerate the natural ability of rapidly reproducing insect pests to develop genetic resistance (immunity) to such chemicals. Thus, in the long run, chemical pesticides can backfire and become less effective in reducing crop losses from insect pests—a glaring example of unintended consequences.

The environmental lesson is that although insects can thrive without newcomers such as us, we and most other land organisms would perish quickly without them. Learning about the roles insects play in nature requires us to understand how insects and other organisms living in a *biological community* such as a forest or pond interact with one another and with the nonliving environment. Ecology is the science that studies such relationships and interactions in nature, as discussed in this and the following six chapters.

Doug Lemke/Shutterstock.com

FIGURE 4-1 Insects play important roles in helping sustain life on Earth. Some insects pollinate plants or break down wastes, whereas predatory insects such as the praying mantis help to control the populations of at least half of the insect species we classify as pests.

The Earth's thin film of living matter is sustained by grand-scale cycles of energy and chemical elements.

G. EVELYN HUTCHINSON

CHAPTER PURPOSE AND QUESTIONS

Chapter 4 examines the connections, cycles, relationships, terms, and principles that are central to the science of ecology and that underlie many of the environmental problems we face today. The chapter addresses the following questions:

4-1 What is ecology?

4-2 What are the major parts of Earth's life-support systems?

4-3 What are biomes and aquatic life zones?

4-4 What are food chains and food webs?

4-5 How fast can producers produce biomass?

4-6 What is soil and why is it important?

4-7 What are biogeochemical cycles?

4-8 How do ecologists learn about ecosystems?

4-1 THE NATURE OF ECOLOGY

What Is Ecology? Understanding Connections

Ecology is a study of connections in nature.

Ecology (from the Greek words *oikos*, "house" or "place to live," and *logos*, "study of") is the study of how organisms interact with one another and with their nonliving environment. In effect, it is a study of *connections in nature*—the house for the Earth's life. Ecologists focus on trying to understand the interactions among organisms, populations, communities, ecosystems, and the biosphere (Figure 4-2).

An **organism** is any form of life. The **cell** is the basic unit of life in organisms. Organisms may consist of a single cell (bacteria, for instance) or many cells. Look in the mirror. What you see is about 10 trillion cells divided into about 200 different types.

On the basis of their cell structure, organisms can be classified as either *eukaryotic* or *prokaryotic*. Each cell of a **eukaryotic** organism is surrounded by a membrane and has a distinct *nucleus* (a membrane-bounded structure containing genetic material in the form of DNA) and several other internal parts called *organelles* (Figure 4-3a, p. 62). All organisms except bacteria and some algae are eukaryotic.

A membrane surrounds the cell of a **prokaryotic** organism, but the cell contains no distinct nucleus or other internal parts enclosed by membranes (Figure 4-3b, p. 62). All **bacteria** are single-celled prokaryotic organisms. Most familiar organisms are eukaryotic, but they could not exist without hordes of prokaryotic organisms called *microbes* that can be seen only with the aid of a microscope (see Case Study below).

Organisms can be classified into a series of hierarchical categories (taxa) such as **kingdoms, phyla, classes, orders, families,** and **genera.** Ecologists often work at the level of **species,** groups of organisms that resemble one another in appearance, behaviour, chemistry, and genetic makeup. Scientists use a special system to name each species. (See Appendix 4 to learn more about how organisms are classified and named.)

Organisms that reproduce sexually by combining cells from both parents are classified as members of the same species if, under natural conditions, they can potentially breed with one another and produce live, fertile offspring.

How many species are on the Earth? We do not know. Estimates range from 3.6 million to 100 million, many of them in tropical forests. Most are insects and **microorganisms** too small to be seen with the naked eye. A conservative guess is that we share the planet with 10 million to 14 million other species.

So far biologists have identified, named, and briefly described about 1.4 million species, most of them are insects (Figure 4-4, p. 62).

Case Study: What Species Rule the World? Small Matters!

Multitudes of tiny microbes such as bacteria, protozoa, fungi, and yeast help keep us alive.

They are everywhere and there are trillions of them. Billions are found inside your body, on your body, in a handful of soil, and in a cup of river water.

These mostly invisible rulers of the Earth are *microbes*, a catchall term for many thousands of species of bacteria, protozoa, fungi, and yeasts—most too small to be seen with the naked eye.

Microbes do not get the respect they deserve. Most of us think of them as threats to our health in the form of infectious bacteria or "germs," fungi that cause athlete's foot and other skin diseases, and protozoa that cause diseases such as malaria. But these harmful microbes are in the minority.

You are alive because of multitudes of microbes toiling away, mostly out of sight. You can thank microbes for providing you with food by converting nitrogen gas in the atmosphere into forms that plants can take up from the soil as nutrients that keep you alive and well. Microbes also help produce foods such as bread, cheese, yogurt, vinegar, tofu, soy sauce, beer, and wine. You should also thank bacteria and fungi in the soil that decompose organic wastes into nutrients

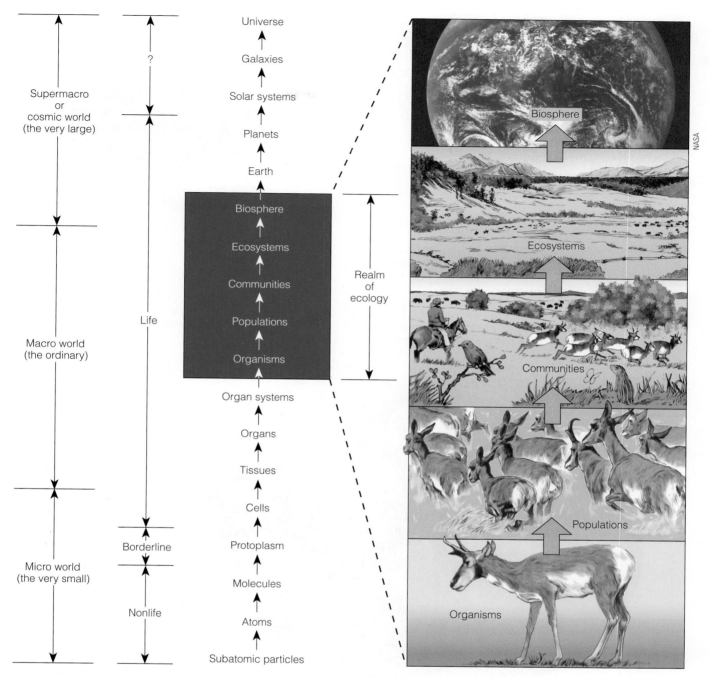

CENGAGENOW™ **ACTIVE FIGURE 4-2 Natural capital:** levels of organization of matter in nature. Note the five levels that ecology focuses on (in the blue box). *See an animation based on this figure at* CengageNOW.

that can be taken up by plants that we and most other animals eat. Without these microscopic creatures we would be up to our eyeballs in waste matter.

Microbes, especially bacteria, help purify the water you drink by breaking down wastes. Bacteria in your intestinal tract break down the food you eat. Some microbes in your nose prevent harmful bacteria from reaching your lungs. Others are the source of disease-fighting

antibiotics, including penicillin, erythromycin, and streptomycin. Genetic engineers are developing microbes that can extract metals from ores, break down various pollutants, and help clean up toxic waste sites.

Some microbes help control plant diseases and populations of insect species that attack our food crops. Relying more on these microbes for pest control can reduce the use of potentially harmful chemical pesticides.

Ecosystems: What Are They, and How Do They Work?

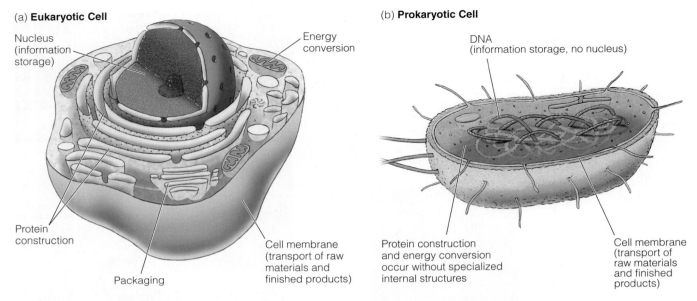

(a) Eukaryotic Cell

Nucleus (information storage)

Energy conversion

Protein construction

Packaging

Cell membrane (transport of raw materials and finished products)

(b) Prokaryotic Cell

DNA (information storage, no nucleus)

Protein construction and energy conversion occur without specialized internal structures

Cell membrane (transport of raw materials and finished products)

FIGURE 4-3 (a) Generalized structure of a eukaryotic cell. The parts and internal structure of cells in various types of organisms such as plants and animals differ somewhat from this generalized model. (b) Generalized structure of a prokaryotic cell. (Note that prokaryotic cells lack a distinct nucleus.)

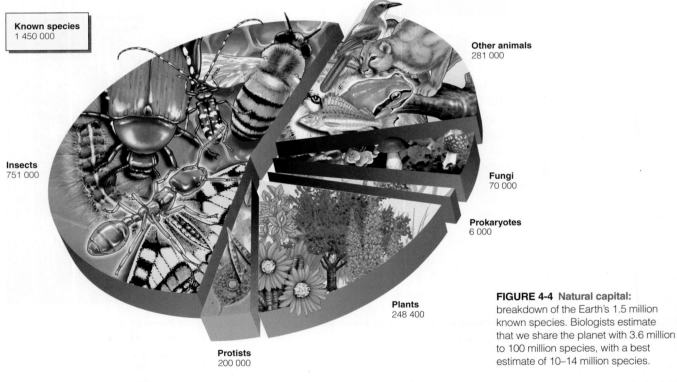

Known species
1 450 000

Other animals
281 000

Insects
751 000

Fungi
70 000

Prokaryotes
6 000

Plants
248 400

Protists
200 000

FIGURE 4-4 Natural capital: breakdown of the Earth's 1.5 million known species. Biologists estimate that we share the planet with 3.6 million to 100 million species, with a best estimate of 10–14 million species.

What Is a Population? Life in a Group

Members of a species interact in groups called populations that live together in a particular place or habitat.

A **population** is a group of interacting individuals of the same species occupying a specific area (Figure 4-5). Examples are sunfish in a pond, white oak trees in a forest, and people in a country. In most natural populations, individuals vary slightly in their genetic makeup, which is why they do not all look or act alike. This is called a population's *genetic diversity* (Figure 4-6).

The place or environment where a population (or an individual organism) normally lives is its **habitat.** It may be as large as an ocean or as small as the intestine of a termite.

FIGURE 4-5 A population of monarch butterflies. The geographic distribution of this butterfly coincides with that of the milkweed plant, on which monarch larvae and caterpillars feed.

FIGURE 4-6 The *genetic diversity* among individuals of one species of the Caribbean snail is reflected in the variations in shell colour and banding patterns.

The area over which we can find a species is called its **distribution** or **range.** Many species, such as some tropical plants, have a small range and may be found on a single hillside. Other species, such as the grizzly bear, have large ranges.

What Are Communities and Ecosystems? Interactions in Nature

A community consists of populations of different species living and interacting in an area, and an ecosystem is a community interacting with its physical environment of matter and energy.

A **community,** or **biological community,** consists of all the populations of the different species living and interacting in an area. It is a complex and interacting network of plants, animals, and microorganisms.

An **ecosystem** is a community of different species interacting with one another and with their physical environment of matter and energy. Ecosystems can range in size from a puddle of water to a **stream,** a patch of woods, an entire forest, or a desert. Ecosystems can be natural or artificial (human created). Examples of artificial ecosystems are crop fields, farm ponds, and reservoirs. All of the Earth's ecosystems together make up what we call the *biosphere.*

Scientists studying ecosystems seek answers to several questions. *First,* how many members of each species are present? *Second,* how do these organisms capture energy and matter (nutrients) from their environment? *Third,* how do they transfer energy and matter among themselves and to other ecosystems? *Fourth,* how do they release energy into the environment and return nutrients to the environment for recycling?

4-2 THE EARTH'S LIFE-SUPPORT SYSTEMS

What Are the Major Parts of the Earth's Life-Support Systems? The Spheres of Life

The Earth is made up of interconnected spherical layers that contain air, water, soil, minerals, and life.

We can think of the Earth as being made up of several spherical layers, as diagrammed in Figure 4-7. Study this figure carefully. The **atmosphere** is a thin envelope or membrane of air around the planet. Its inner layer, the **troposphere,** extends only about 17 kilometres (11 miles) above sea level. It contains most of the planet's air, mostly nitrogen (78%) and oxygen (21%). The next layer, stretching 17–48 kilometres (11–30 miles) above the Earth's surface, is the **stratosphere.** Its lower portion contains enough ozone (O_3) to filter out most of the sun's harmful ultraviolet radiation. This allows life to exist on land and in the surface layers of bodies of water.

The **hydrosphere** consists of the Earth's water. It is found as *liquid water* (both surface and underground), *ice* (polar ice, icebergs, and ice in frozen soil layers called *permafrost*), and *water vapour* in the atmosphere. The **lithosphere** is the Earth's crust and upper mantle; the crust contains nonrenewable fossil fuels (created from ancient fossils that were buried and subjected to intense pressure and heat) and minerals, and renewable soil chemicals (nutrients) needed for plant life.

The **biosphere** is the portion of the Earth in which living (biotic) organisms exist and interact with one another and with their nonliving (abiotic) environment. The biosphere includes most of the hydrosphere and

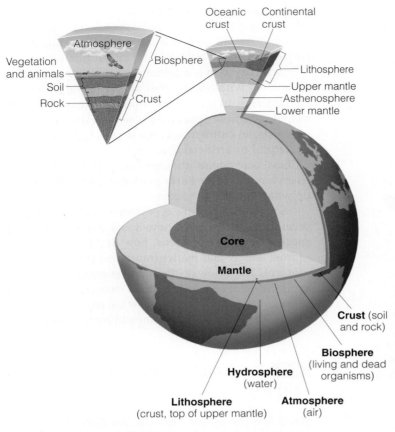

FIGURE 4-7 Natural capital: general structure of the Earth. The Earth's surface consists of a crust of rock floating on a mantle of solid and partly melted rock, which surrounds an intensely hot core.

parts of the lower atmosphere and upper lithosphere. It reaches from the deepest ocean floor, 20 kilometres (12 miles) below sea level, to the tops of the highest mountains.

All parts of the biosphere are interconnected. If the Earth were an apple, the biosphere would be no thicker than the apple's skin. *The goal of ecology is to understand the interactions in this thin, life-supporting global membrane of air, water, soil, and organisms.*

What Sustains Life on Earth? Sun, Cycles, and Gravity

Solar energy, the cycling of matter, and gravity sustain the Earth's life.

Life on the Earth depends on three interconnected factors, shown in Figure 4-8.

- The *one-way flow of high-quality energy* from the sun, through materials and living things in their feeding interactions, into the environment as low-quality energy (mostly heat dispersed into air or water molecules at a low temperature), and eventually back

into space as heat. No round-trips are allowed because energy cannot be recycled.

- The *cycling of matter* (the atoms, ions, or molecules needed for survival by living organisms) through parts of the biosphere. Because the Earth is closed to significant inputs of matter from space, the Earth's essentially fixed supply of nutrients must be recycled again and again for life to continue. Nutrient trips in ecosystems are round-trips.

- *Gravity,* which allows the planet to hold onto its atmosphere and causes the downward movement of chemicals in the matter cycles.

How Does the Sun Help Sustain Life on Earth? A Distant Nuclear Fusion Reactor

Energy released by the gigantic nuclear fusion reactor we call the sun provides the light and heat needed to sustain the Earth's life.

Energy from the sun supports most life on the Earth by lighting and warming the planet. It supports *photosynthesis,* the process in which green plants and some bacteria make compounds such as carbohydrates that keep them alive and feed most other organisms. And it powers the cycling of matter and drives the climate and weather systems that distribute heat and fresh water over the Earth's surface.

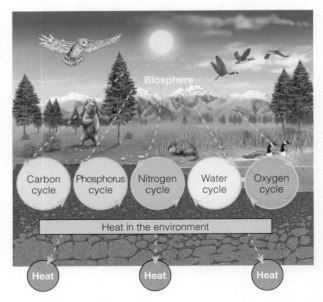

FIGURE 4-8 Natural capital: life on Earth depends on the *one-way flow of energy* (dashed lines) from the sun through the biosphere; the *cycling of crucial elements* (solid lines around circles); and *gravity,* which keeps atmospheric gases from escaping into space and draws chemicals downward in the matter cycles. This simplified model depicts only a few of the many cycling elements.

About one-billionth of the sun's output of energy reaches the Earth—a tiny sphere in the vastness of space—in the form of electromagnetic waves (Figure 3-10, p. 47). The amount of energy reaching the Earth from the sun equals the amount of heat energy the Earth reflects or radiates back into space. Otherwise, the Earth would heat up to temperatures too hot for life as we know it.

Much of the sun's incoming energy is reflected away or absorbed by chemicals, dust, and clouds in the atmosphere, as shown in Figure 4-9. About 80% of the energy that gets through warms the troposphere and evaporates and cycles water through the biosphere. About 1% of this incoming energy generates winds, and green plants, algae, and bacteria use less than 0.1% to fuel photosynthesis.

Most of the solar radiation making it through the atmosphere hits the surface of the Earth and is degraded into longer-wavelength infrared radiation. This infrared radiation interacts with so-called *greenhouse gases* (such as water vapour, carbon dioxide, methane, nitrous oxide, and ozone) in the troposphere. The radiation causes these gaseous molecules to vibrate and release infrared radiation with even longer wavelengths into the troposphere. As this radiation interacts with molecules in the air, it increases their kinetic energy, helping warm the troposphere and the Earth's surface. Without this **natural greenhouse effect,** the Earth would be too cold for life as we know it to exist.

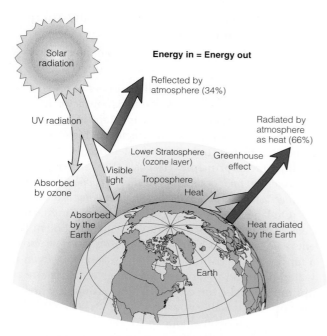

CENGAGENOW™ **ACTIVE FIGURE 4-9 Solar capital:** flow of energy to and from the Earth. *See an animation based on this figure at CengageNOW.*

4-3 ECOSYSTEM COMPONENTS

What Are Biomes and Aquatic Life Zones? Life on Land and at Sea

Life exists on land systems called biomes and in freshwater and ocean aquatic life zones.

Viewed from outer space, the Earth resembles an enormous jigsaw puzzle consisting of large masses of land and vast expanses of ocean.

Biologists have classified the terrestrial (land) portion of the biosphere into **biomes** ("BY-ohms"). They are large regions such as forests, deserts, and grasslands characterized by a distinct climate and specific species (especially vegetation) adapted to it (Figure 4-10, p. 66).

Scientists divide the watery parts of the biosphere into **aquatic life zones,** each containing numerous ecosystems. Examples include *freshwater life zones* (such as lakes and streams) and *ocean* or *marine life zones* (such as coral reefs, coastal estuaries, and the deep ocean).

What Are the Major Components of Ecosystems? Matter, Energy, Life

Ecosystems consist of nonliving (abiotic) and living (biotic) components.

Two types of components make up the biosphere and its ecosystems. One type, called **abiotic,** consists of nonliving components such as water, air, nutrients, and solar energy. The other type, called **biotic,** consists of biological components—plants, animals, and microbes.

Figures 4-11 (p. 67) and 4-12 (p. 67) are greatly simplified diagrams of some of the biotic and abiotic components in a freshwater aquatic ecosystem and a terrestrial ecosystem.

How Tolerant Are Organisms to Environmental Conditions? Tolerance Limits

Organisms differ in their responses to environmental factors.

Population of different species thrive under different physical conditions. Some need bright sunlight, and others thrive better in shade. Some need a hot environment and others a cool or cold one. Some do best under wet conditions and others under dry conditions.

Each population in an ecosystem has a **range of tolerance** to variations in its physical and chemical environment (Figure 4-13, p. 68). Individuals within a population may also have slightly different tolerance ranges for temperature or other factors because of small differences in genetic makeup, health, and age. For example, a trout population may do best within a narrow band of temperatures (*optimum level* or *range*),

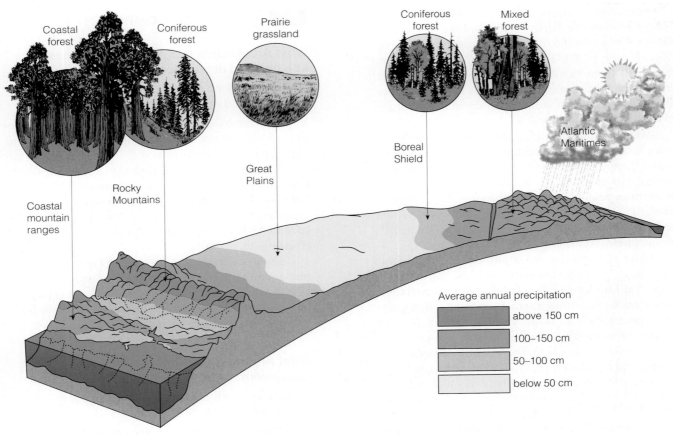

FIGURE 4-10 Natural capital: major biomes found along the 49th parallel across Canada. The differences reflect changes in climate, mainly differences in average annual precipitation and temperature (not shown).

Coastal forest
Coniferous forest
Prairie grassland
Coniferous forest
Mixed forest
Atlantic Maritimes
Boreal Shield
Great Plains
Rocky Mountains
Coastal mountain ranges

Average annual precipitation
above 150 cm
100–150 cm
50–100 cm
below 50 cm

but a few individuals can survive above and below that band (Figure 4-13, p. 68). However, if the water becomes too hot or too cold, none of the trout can survive.

These observations are summarized in the **law of tolerance:** *The existence, abundance, and distribution of a species in an ecosystem are determined by whether the levels of one or more physical or chemical factors fall within the range tolerated by that species.* A species may have a wide range of tolerance to some factors and a narrow range of tolerance to others. Most organisms are least tolerant during juvenile or reproductive stages of their life cycles. Highly tolerant species can live in a variety of habitats with widely different conditions. Figure 4-14 (p. 68) shows how environmental physical conditions can limit the distribution of a particular species.

SELF CHECK

Range of Tolerance Consider your own optimal range, zone of physiological stress, and zone of intolerance for an environmental factor such as temperature. How would the temperatures of these zones differ if you were wearing (a) a bathing suit, (b) normal clothes, or (c) a snowsuit? Devise a self-study that will let you test and verify your predictions at home!

What Factors Limit Population Growth? There Are Always Limits in Nature

Availability of matter and energy resources can limit the number of organisms in a population.

A variety of factors can affect the number of organisms in a population. However, sometimes one factor, known as a **limiting factor,** is more important in regulating population growth than other factors. This ecological principle, related to the law of tolerance, is called the **limiting factor principle:** *Too much or too little of any abiotic factor can limit or prevent growth of a population, even if all other factors are at or near the optimum range of tolerance.*

On land, **precipitation** often is the limiting factor. Lack of water in a desert limits plant growth. Soil nutrients also can act as a limiting factor on land. Suppose a farmer plants corn in phosphorus-poor soil. Even if water, nitrogen, potassium, and other nutrients are at optimum levels, the corn will stop growing when it uses up the available phosphorus.

Too much of an abiotic factor can also be limiting. For example, too much water or too much fertilizer can kill plants, a common mistake of many beginning gardeners.

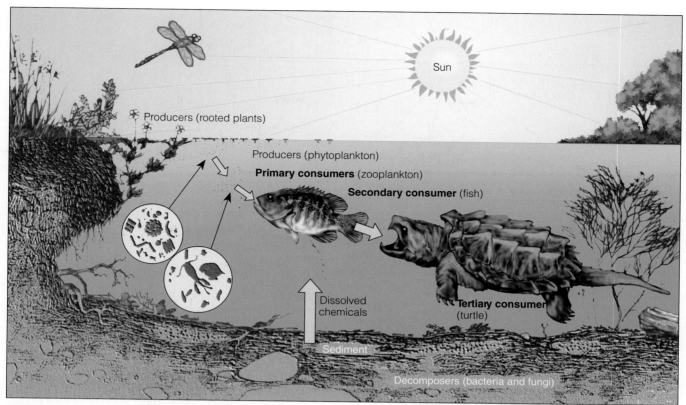

FIGURE 4-11 Major components of a freshwater ecosystem.

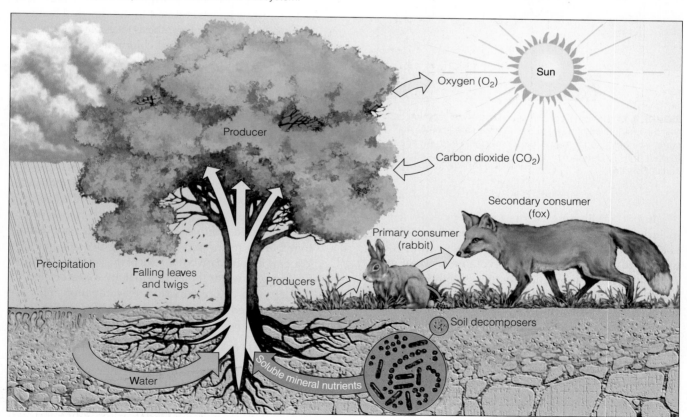

CENGAGENOW™ **ACTIVE FIGURE 4-12** Major components of an ecosystem in a field. *See an animation based on this figure at* CengageNOW.

Ecosystems: What Are They, and How Do They Work?

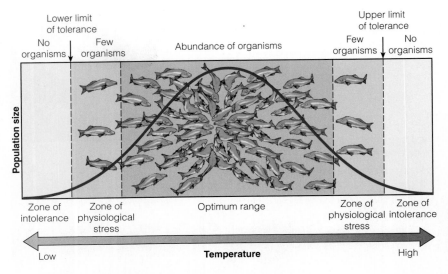

FIGURE 4-13 Range of tolerance for a population of organisms, such as fish, to an abiotic environmental factor—in this case, temperature.

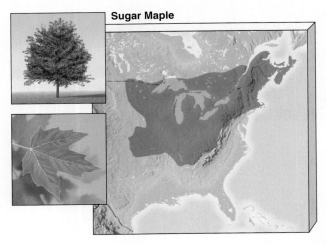

FIGURE 4-14 The physical conditions of the environment can limit the distribution of a species. The green area shows the current range of sugar maple trees in eastern North America. (Data from U.S. Department of Agriculture and the Canadian Forest Service)

Important limiting factors for aquatic ecosystems include temperature, sunlight, nutrient availability, and **dissolved oxygen (DO) content**—the amount of oxygen gas dissolved in a given volume of water at a particular temperature and pressure. Another limiting factor in aquatic ecosystems is **salinity**—the amounts of various inorganic minerals or salts dissolved in a given volume of water.

What Are the Major Biological Components of Ecosystems? Producers and Consumers

Some organisms in ecosystems produce food, and others consume food.

The Earth's organisms either produce or consume food. **Producers,** sometimes called **autotrophs** (self-feeders),

make their own food from compounds obtained from their environment.

On land, most producers are green plants. In fresh-water and marine ecosystems, algae and plants are the major producers near shorelines. In open water, the dominant producers are *phytoplankton*—mostly microscopic organisms that float or drift in the water.

Most producers make use of **photosynthesis** to capture **solar energy** from the sun and transform it into chemical energy such as that found in the chemical bonds of glucose ($C_6H_{12}O_6$). Photosynthesis takes place within specialized cell organelles called **chloroplasts** (Figure 4-15). Here the light-absorbing pigment chlorophyll is involved in a series of light-dependent chemical reactions that split water molecules (H_2O), resulting in hydrogen ions (H^+) and oxygen molecules (O_2) being produced. As part of this process, high-energy ATP (adenine triphosphate) molecules and NADPH (nicotinamide adenine dinucleotide phosphate) molecules are also formed. This is known as the *light reactions* stage of photosynthesis.

The ATP molecules and the NADPH molecules produced above power reactions in the Calvin cycle (light-independent reactions), causing carbon atoms to be released from carbon dioxide (CO_2) and linked together to form sugars such as glucose ($C_6H_{12}O_6$). Water is involved on both sides of the equation because for every 12 water molecules that are disassociated on the left side of the equation, 6 water molecules are newly formed on the right side of the equation. The reaction can be summarized as:

$$6\,CO_2 + 12\,H_2O + \text{Solar Energy} \rightarrow C_6H_{12}O_6 + 6\,O_2 + 6\,H_2O$$

This equation is often further simplified by removing water from both sides of the equation until only the net difference of 6 water molecules is shown. This simple form of the equation is handy because it illustrates that photosynthesis (shown just below) and aerobic respiration (shown on p. 71) are opposites.

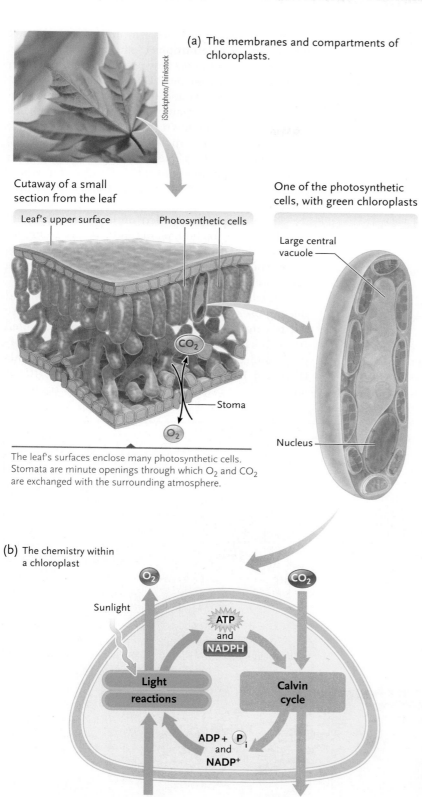

(a) The membranes and compartments of chloroplasts.

Cutaway of a small section from the leaf

One of the photosynthetic cells, with green chloroplasts

Leaf's upper surface

Photosynthetic cells

Large central vacuole

CO_2

Stoma

O_2

Nucleus

The leaf's surfaces enclose many photosynthetic cells. Stomata are minute openings through which O_2 and CO_2 are exchanged with the surrounding atmosphere.

(b) The chemistry within a chloroplast

O_2

CO_2

Sunlight

ATP and NADPH

Light reactions

Calvin cycle

$ADP + P_i$ and $NADP^+$

H_2O

Sugars

Carbohydrates and other organic substances

FIGURE 4-15 Natural capital: producers such as plants use solar energy to transform carbon dioxide and water to sugars and oxygen within the chloroplasts of a leaf. There are light reactions that result in the disassociation of water (H_2O) and the formation of oxygen (O_2) and high-energy molecules (ATP and NADPH). There is also a Calvin cycle, powered by ATP and NADPH, in which carbon dioxide (CO_2) is converted into sugars. Molecules of ADP, $NADP^+$, and inorganic phosphate from the Calvin cycle are then used in the light reactions. (From RUSSELL/ WOLFE/HERTZ/STARR. Biology, 1E. © 2010 Nelson Education Ltd. Reproduced by permission. www.cengage.com/permissions)

$$6\ CO_2 + 6\ H_2O + \text{Solar Energy} \rightarrow C_6H_{12}O_6 + 6\ O_2$$

As you will see, photosynthesis by producers and aerobic respiration by consumers have much to do with the cycling of carbon, hydrogen, and oxygen through food chains (p. 72), food webs (p. 72), and biogeochemical cycles (p. 80).

SELF CHECK

Balance the Atoms According to the law of conservation of matter (p. 49), no atoms should be created or destroyed in the chemical changes described above. For the simpler of the two equations about photosynthesis, can you see that there are 6 atoms of carbon (C), 12 atoms of oxygen (O), and 12 atoms of hydrogen (H) on both sides of the equation? Test yourself by counting the atoms in the slightly more complicated equation about photosynthesis. Is there still the same number of atoms on both sides of that equation? Why should there be?

(There should be 6 C atoms, 24 H atoms, and 24 O atoms on both sides of the equation. Law of conservation of matter.)

A few producers, mostly specialized bacteria, can convert simple compounds from their environment into more complex nutrient compounds *without sunlight.* This process is called **chemosynthesis.**

All other organisms in an ecosystem are **consumers,** or **heterotrophs** ("other feeders") that get the energy and nutrients they need by feeding on other organisms or their remains. **Decomposers** (mostly certain types of bacteria and fungi) are specialized consumers that recycle organic matter in ecosystems. They do this by breaking down (*biodegrading*) dead organic material or **detritus** ("di-TRI-tus," meaning "debris") to get nutrients. This releases the resulting simpler inorganic compounds into the soil and water, where producers can take them up as nutrients. Life works in circles.

Some consumers, called **omnivores,** play dual roles by feeding on both plants and animals. Examples are pigs, rats, foxes, bears, cockroaches, and humans. When you had lunch today were you an herbivore, a carnivore, or an omnivore?

Detritivores consist of **detritus feeders** and decomposers that feed on detritus. Hordes of these waste eaters and degraders can transform a fallen tree trunk into a powder and finally into simple inorganic molecules that plants can absorb as nutrients (Figure 4-16). *In natural ecosystems, there is little or no waste.* One organism's wastes serve as resources

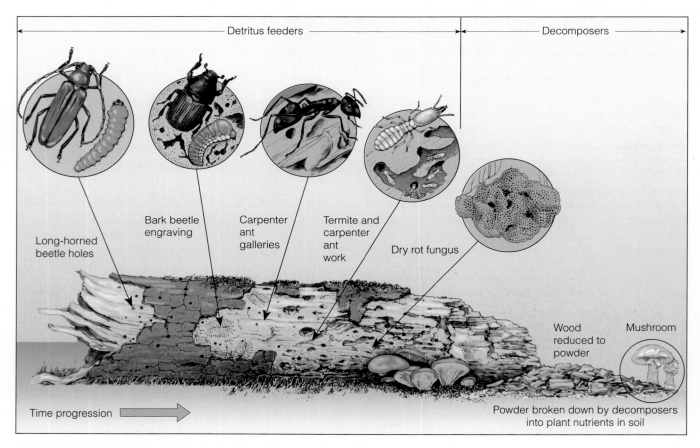

FIGURE 4-16 Natural capital: some detritivores, called *detritus feeders*, directly consume tiny fragments of this log. Other detritivores, called *decomposers* (mostly fungi and bacteria), digest complex organic chemicals in fragments of the log into simpler inorganic nutrients that can be used again by producers.

for others, as the nutrients that make life possible are recycled again and again. In nature *waste becomes food.*

Producers, consumers, and decomposers use the chemical energy stored in glucose and other organic compounds to fuel their life processes. In most cells this energy is released by **aerobic respiration,** which uses oxygen to convert organic nutrients back into carbon dioxide and water. The net effect of the hundreds of steps in this complex process is represented by the following chemical reaction:

glucose + oxygen → carbon dioxide + water + **energy**

$$C_6H_{12}O_6 + 6\,O_2 \rightarrow 6\,CO_2 + 6\,H_2O + \textbf{energy}$$

Although the detailed steps differ, the net chemical change for aerobic respiration is the opposite of that for photosynthesis (p. 68). Note that both processes combine to cycle atoms to and from the atmosphere.

Some decomposers get the energy they need by breaking down glucose (or other organic compounds) in the absence of oxygen. This form of cellular respiration is called **anaerobic respiration,** or **fermentation.** Instead of carbon dioxide and water, the end products of this process are compounds such as methane gas (CH_4, the main component of natural gas), ethyl alcohol (C_2H_6O), acetic acid ($C_2H_4O_2$, the key component of vinegar), and hydrogen sulphide (H_2S, when sulphur compounds are broken down). Have you ever smelled this form of cellular respiration?

The survival of any individual organism depends on the *flow of matter and energy* through its body. However, an ecosystem as a whole survives primarily through a combination of *matter recycling* (rather than one-way flow) and *one-way energy flow* (Figure 4-17).

Decomposers complete the cycle of matter by breaking down detritus into inorganic nutrients that can be reused by producers. Without decomposers, the entire world would be knee-deep in plant litter, dead animal bodies, animal wastes, and garbage, and most life as we know it would no longer exist. Have you thanked a decomposer today?

What Is Biodiversity? Variety Is the Spice of Life

A vital renewable resource is the biodiversity found in the Earth's variety of genes, species, ecosystems, and ecosystem processes.

Biological diversity, or **biodiversity,** is one of the Earth's most important renewable resources. Kinds of biodiversity include the following:

- **Genetic diversity:** the variety of genetic material within a species or a population.

- **Species diversity:** the number of species present in different habitats.

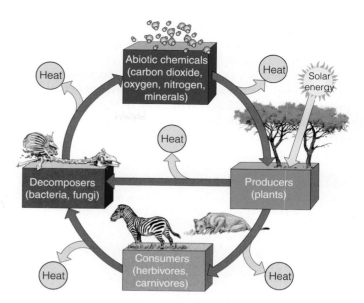

CENGAGENOW **ACTIVE FIGURE 4-17 Natural capital:** the main structural components of an ecosystem (energy, chemicals, and organisms). Matter recycling and the flow of energy from the sun, through organisms, and then into the environment as low-quality heat, link these components. *See an animation based on this figure at CengageNOW.*

- **Ecological diversity:** the variety of terrestrial and aquatic ecosystems found in an area or on the Earth.

- **Functional diversity:** the biological and chemical processes such as energy flow and matter recycling needed for the survival of species, communities, and ecosystems (Figure 4-17).

- **Structural diversity:** the range of variation in the physical characteristics of habitat; in general, a more heterogeneous habitat provides more opportunities for a wide range of organisms.

Some people also include *human cultural diversity* as part of the Earth's biodiversity. Each human culture has developed various ways to deal with changing environmental conditions.

The Earth's biodiversity is the biological wealth or capital that helps keep us alive and supports our economies. Biologist Edward O. Wilson describes the Earth's biodiversity as a "natural or biological Internet" that all living things are part of.

The Earth's biodiversity supplies us with food, wood, fibres, energy, raw materials, industrial chemicals, and medicines—all of which pour hundreds of billions of dollars into the world economy each year. It also helps preserve the quality of the air and water, maintain the fertility of soils, dispose of wastes, and control populations of pests that attack crops and forests.

Biodiversity is a renewable resource as long we live off the biological income it provides instead of the natural capital that supplies this income.

Some scientists say that the loss and degradation of biodiversity is the most important environmental problem we face. This is why understanding, protecting, and sustaining biodiversity is a major theme of ecology and of this book.

4-4 ENERGY FLOW IN ECOSYSTEMS

What Are Food Chains and Food Webs? Maps of Ecological Interdependence

Food chains and webs show how eaters, the eaten, and the decomposed are connected to one another in an ecosystem.

All organisms, whether dead or alive, are potential sources of food for other organisms. A caterpillar eats a leaf, a robin eats the caterpillar, and a hawk eats the robin. Decomposers consume the leaf, caterpillar, robin, and hawk after they die. As a result, *there is little matter waste in natural ecosystems.*

The sequence of organisms, each of which is a source of food for the next, is called a **food chain.** It determines how energy and nutrients move from one organism to another through an ecosystem (Figure 4-18).

Ecologists assign each organism in an ecosystem to a feeding level, also called a **trophic level,** depending on whether it is a producer or a consumer and on what it eats or decomposes. Producers belong to the first trophic level, primary consumers to the second trophic level, secondary consumers to the third, and so on. Detritivores and decomposers process detritus from all trophic levels.

Real ecosystems are more complex than this. Most consumers feed on more than one type of organism, and most organisms are eaten or decomposed by more than one type of consumer. Because most species participate in several different food chains, the organisms in most ecosystems form a complex network of interconnected food chains called a **food web.** Trace the flows of matter and energy within the simplified food web in Figure 4-19 (p. 73). Trophic levels can be

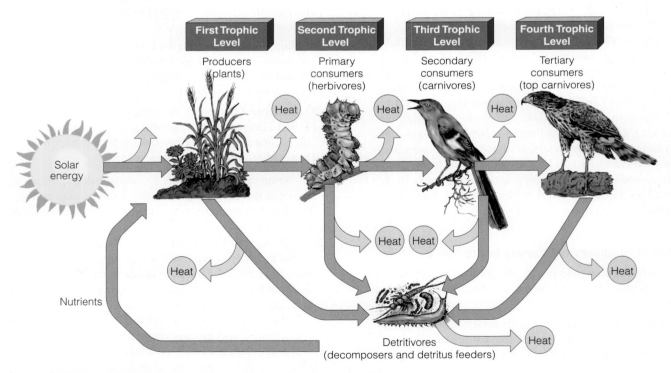

First Trophic Level	Second Trophic Level	Third Trophic Level	Fourth Trophic Level
Producers (plants)	Primary consumers (herbivores)	Secondary consumers (carnivores)	Tertiary consumers (top carnivores)

CENGAGENOW **ACTIVE FIGURE 4-18** Model of a *food chain*. The arrows show how chemical energy in food flows through various *trophic levels* in energy transfers; most of the energy is degraded to heat, in accordance with the second law of thermodynamics. Matter cycles from producers through consumers and detritivores, then back to producers. *See an animation based on this figure at* CengageNOW.

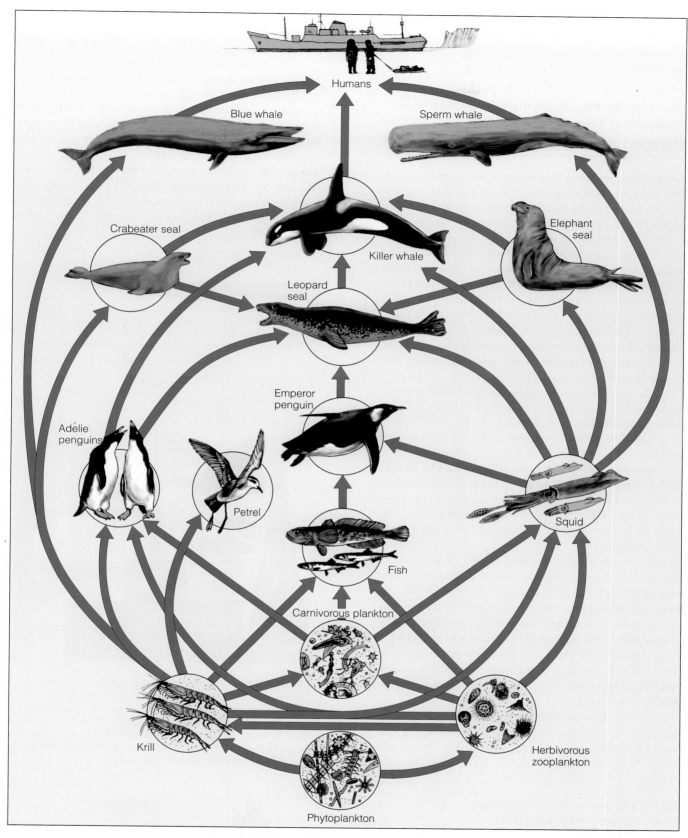

FIGURE 4-19 Greatly simplified *food web* in the Antarctic. Many more participants in the web, including an array of decomposer organisms, are not depicted here. This is part of life's Internet.

assigned in food webs just as in food chains. A food web shows how eaters, the eaten, and the decomposed are connected to one another. It is a map of life's interdependence.

How Can We Represent the Energy Flow in an Ecosystem? Think Pyramid

There is a decrease in the amount of energy available to each succeeding organism in a food chain or web.

Each trophic level in a food chain or web contains a certain amount of **biomass,** the dry weight of all organic matter contained in its organisms. In a food chain or web, chemical energy stored in biomass is transferred from one trophic level to another.

Energy transfer through food chains and food webs is not very efficient. The reason is that with each transfer some usable energy is degraded and lost to the environment as low-quality heat, in accordance with the second law of thermodynamics. Thus only a small portion of what is eaten and digested is actually converted into an organism's bodily material or biomass, and the amount of usable energy available to each successive trophic level declines.

The percentage of usable energy transferred as biomass from one trophic level to the next is called **ecological efficiency.** It ranges from 2% to 40% (that is, a loss of 60–98%) depending on the types of species and the ecosystem involved, but 10% is typical.

Assuming 10% ecological efficiency (90% loss) at each trophic transfer, if green plants in an area manage to capture 10 000 units of energy from the sun, then only about 1 000 units of energy will be available to support herbivores and only about 100 units to support carnivores.

The more trophic levels in a food chain or web, the greater the cumulative loss of usable energy as energy flows through the various trophic levels. The **pyramid of energy flow** in Figure 4-20 illustrates this energy loss for a simple food chain, assuming a 90% energy loss with each transfer. How does this diagram help explain why there are not very many tigers in the world? Figure 4-21 shows the pyramid of energy flow during one year for an aquatic ecosystem in Silver Springs, Florida.

Energy flow pyramids explain why the Earth can support more people if they eat at lower trophic levels by consuming grains, vegetables, and fruits directly rather than passing such crops through another trophic level and eating grain eaters such as cattle.

The large loss in energy between successive trophic levels also explains why food chains and webs rarely have more than four or five trophic levels. In most cases, too little energy is left after four or five transfers to support organisms feeding at these high trophic levels. This explains why there are so few top carnivores such as eagles, hawks, tigers, and white sharks. It also explains why such species usually are the first to suffer when the ecosystems supporting them are disrupted, and why these species are so vulnerable to extinction. Do you think we are on this list?

> **CONSIDER, DISCUSS, OR DEBATE**
>
> Aquatic food webs often have more trophic levels than terrestrial food webs (compare Figures 4-11 and 4-12). Why is this so? Give at least six different explanations.

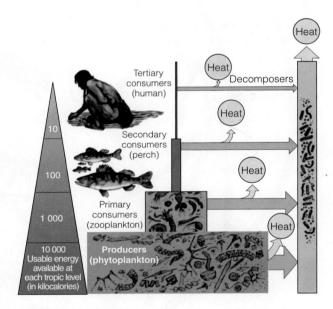

FIGURE 4-20 Generalized *pyramid of energy flow* showing the decrease in usable energy available at each succeeding trophic level in a food chain or web. In nature, ecological efficiency varies from 2% to 40%, with 10% efficiency being common. This model assumes a 10% ecological efficiency (90% loss of usable energy to the environment, in the form of low-quality heat) with each transfer from one trophic level to another.

FIGURE 4-21 Annual energy flow (in kilocalories per square metre per year) for an aquatic ecosystem in Silver Springs, Florida. (From STARR. *Biology: Concepts and Applications* w/CD-ROM + InfoTrac, 4E. © 2000 Cengage Learning. Reproduced by permission. www.cengage.com/permissions)

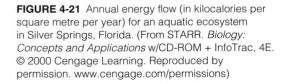
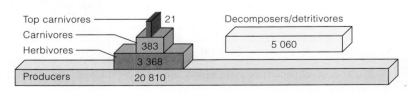

4-5 PRIMARY PRODUCTIVITY OF ECOSYSTEMS

How Fast Can Producers Produce Biomass? A Very Important Rate

Different ecosystems use solar energy to produce and use biomass at different rates.

The *rate* at which an ecosystem's producers convert solar energy into chemical energy as biomass is the ecosystem's **gross primary productivity (GPP).** However, to stay alive, grow, and reproduce, an ecosystem's producers must use some of the biomass they produce for their own respiration. **Net primary productivity (NPP)** is the *rate* at which producers use photosynthesis to store energy *minus* the *rate* at which they use some of this stored energy through aerobic respiration, as shown in Figure 4-22. In other words, NPP = GPP 2 − R, where R is energy used in respiration. NPP is a measure of how fast producers can provide the food needed by consumers in an ecosystem.

Various ecosystems and life zones differ in their NPP, as graphed in Figure 4-23. Looking at this graph, what are the three most productive and the three least productive systems? Generally, would you expect NPP to be higher at the equator than at the Earth's poles?

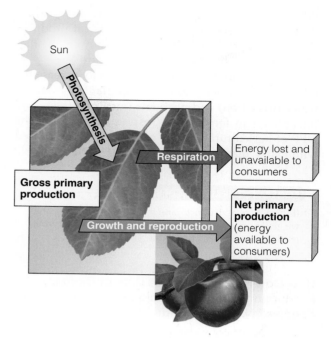

FIGURE 4-22 Distinction between gross primary productivity and net primary productivity. A plant uses some of its gross primary productivity to survive through respiration. The remaining energy is available to consumers.

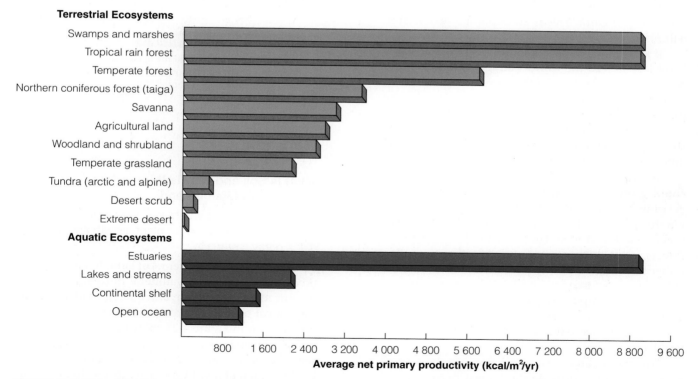

FIGURE 4-23 Natural capital: estimated annual average *net primary productivity* (NPP) per unit of area in major life zones and ecosystems, expressed as kilocalories of energy produced per square metre per year (kcal/m²/yr). (Data from *Communities and Ecosystems*, 2nd ed., by R. H. Whittaker, 1975. New York: Macmillan)

Why or why not? Despite its low net **primary productivity,** there is so much open ocean that it produces more of the Earth's NPP per year than any of the other ecosystems and life zones shown in Figure 4-23.

In agricultural systems, the goal is to increase the NPP and biomass of selected crop plants by adding water (irrigation) and nutrients (mostly nitrates and phosphates in fertilizers). Despite such inputs, the NPP of agricultural land is not very high compared with that of many other ecosystems (Figure 4-23).

> **CONSIDER, DISCUSS, OR DEBATE**
>
> If the NPP of agricultural land is not very high, why aren't we getting our food from the vast open oceans? Or from productive marshes, rain forests, and estuaries?

How Does the World's Net Rate of Biomass Production Limit the Populations of Consumer Species? Nature's Limits

The number of consumer organisms the Earth can support is determined by how fast producers can supply them with energy found in biomass.

As we have seen, producers are the source of all food in an ecosystem. Only the biomass represented by NPP is available as food for consumers, and they use only a portion of this. Thus *the planet's NPP ultimately limits the number of consumers (including humans) that can survive on the Earth.* This is an important lesson from nature.

It is tempting to conclude from Figure 4-23 that a good way to feed the world's hungry millions would be to harvest plants in highly productive estuaries, swamps, and marshes. But people cannot eat most plants in these areas. In addition, these plants provide vital food sources (and spawning areas) for fish, shrimp, and other aquatic species that provide us and other consumers with protein.

We might also conclude from Figure 4-23 that we could grow more food for human consumption by clearing highly productive tropical rain forests and planting food crops. According to most ecologists, this is also a bad idea. Here is why. In tropical rain forests, most nutrients are stored in the vegetation rather than in the soil, where they need to be to grow crops. When the trees are removed, frequent rains and growing crops rapidly deplete the nutrient-poor soils. Thus crops can be grown for only a short time without massive and expensive applications of commercial fertilizers.

Are the oceans a way out? Because the Earth's vast open oceans provide the largest percentage of the Earth's net primary productivity, why not harvest its primary producers (floating and drifting phytoplankton) to help feed the rapidly growing human population? The problem is that harvesting the widely dispersed, tiny floating producers in the open ocean would take much more fossil fuel and other types of energy than the food energy we would get. In addition, this would disrupt the food webs of the open ocean that provide us and other consumer organisms with important sources of energy and protein from fish and shellfish.

How Much of the World's Net Rate of Biomass Production Do We Use? Let Them Eat Crumbs

Humans are using, wasting, or destroying a significant amount of the world's biomass faster than producers can make it.

Peter Vitousek, Stuart Roystaczer, and other ecologists estimate that humans now use, waste, or destroy about 27% of the Earth's total potential NPP and 10%–55% of the NPP of the planet's terrestrial ecosystems.

These scientists contend that this is the main reason we are crowding out or eliminating the habitats and food supplies of a growing number of other species. What might happen to us and to other consumer species if the human population doubles over the next 40 to 50 years and per capita consumption of resources such as food, timber, and grassland rises sharply? This is an important question!

> **CONSIDER, DISCUSS, OR DEBATE**
>
> What can be done to avoid the apparently inevitable clash between human population growth, increasing affluence, and the planet's total potential NPP?

4-6 SOILS

What Is Soil and Why Is It Important? The Base of Life on Land

Soil is a slowly renewed resource that provides most of the nutrients needed for plant growth and also helps purify water.

Soil is a thin covering over most land that is a complex mixture of eroded rock, mineral nutrients, decaying organic matter, water, air, and billions of living organisms, most of them microscopic decomposers. Study the diagram in Figure 4-24 showing the profile of different aged soils. Soil is a renewable resource, but it is renewed very slowly. Depending mostly on climate, the formation of just 1 centimetre (0.4 inch) of soil can take from 15 years to hundreds of years.

Soil is the base of life on land because it provides most of the nutrients needed for plant growth. Indeed, you are largely a collection of soil nutrients imported into your body by the food you eat. Soil is also the Earth's primary filter that cleanses water as it passes through. It is also a major component of the Earth's water recycling and water storage processes. You can thank soil every time you drink a glass of water.

What Major Layers Are Found in Mature Soils? Layers Count

Most soils developed over a long time consist of several layers containing different materials.

Mature soils, or soils that have developed over a long time, are arranged in a series of horizontal layers called **soil horizons,** each with a distinct texture and composition that varies with different types of soils. A cross-sectional view of the horizons in a soil is called a **soil profile.** Most mature soils have at least three of the possible horizons (Figure 4-24). Think of them as floors in the building of life underneath your feet.

The top layer is the *surface litter layer,* or *O horizon.* It consists mostly of freshly fallen undecomposed

or partially decomposed leaves, twigs, crop wastes, animal wastes, fungi, and other organic materials. Normally, it is brown or black.

The *topsoil layer,* or *A horizon,* is a porous mixture of partially decomposed organic matter, called **humus,** and some inorganic mineral particles. It is usually darker and looser than deeper layers. A fertile soil that produces high crop yields has a thick topsoil layer with lots of humus. This helps topsoil hold water and nutrients taken up by plant roots.

The roots of most plants and most of a soil's organic matter are concentrated in a soil's two upper layers. As long as vegetation anchors these layers, soil stores water and releases it in a nourishing trickle.

The two top layers of most well-developed soils teem with bacteria, fungi, earthworms, and small insects that interact in complex food webs such as the one shown in Figure 4-25 (p. 78). Bacteria and other decomposer microorganisms found by the billions in every handful of topsoil break down some of its complex organic compounds into simpler inorganic

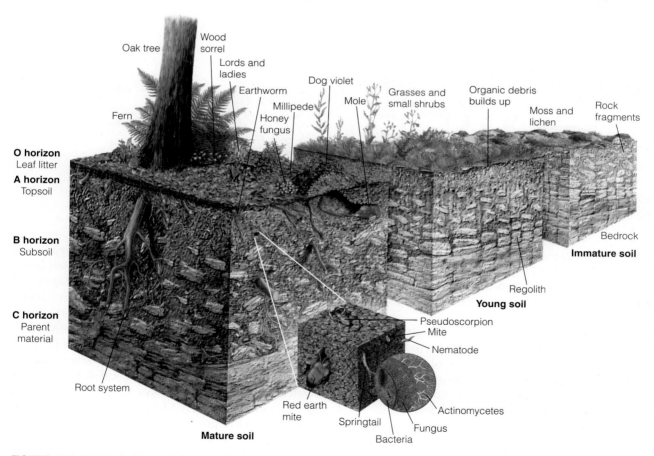

FIGURE 4-24 Natural capital: soil formation and generalized soil profile. Horizons, or layers, vary in number, composition, and thickness, depending on the type of soil. Soil is the base of life that provides the food you need to stay alive and healthy. (From Derek Elsom, *Earth: The Making, Shaping and Workings of a Planet,* 1992. Copyright © 1992 by Marshall Editions Developments Limited. New York: Macmillan. Used by permission.)

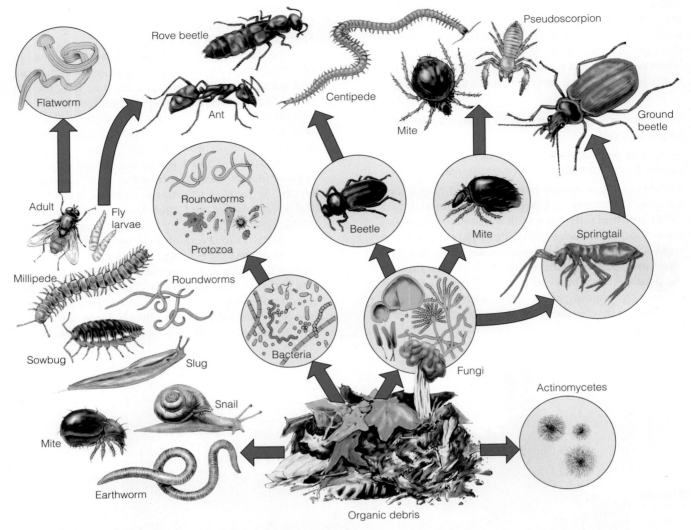

FIGURE 4-25 Natural capital: greatly simplified food web of living organisms found in soil or in a compost heap.

compounds soluble in water. Soil moisture carrying these dissolved nutrients is drawn up by the roots of plants and transported through stems and into leaves as part of the Earth's chemical cycling processes.

The colour of its topsoil tells us a lot about how useful a soil is for growing crops. Dark-brown or black topsoil is nitrogen-rich and high in organic matter. Grey, bright yellow, or red topsoils are low in organic matter and need nitrogen enrichment to support most crops. Pick up a handful of soil and look at its colour. What did you learn?

The *B horizon (subsoil)* and the *C horizon (parent material)* contain most of a soil's inorganic matter, mostly broken-down rock consisting of varying mixtures of sand, silt, clay, and gravel. The C horizon lies on a base of unweathered parent rock called *bedrock*.

The spaces, or pores, between the solid organic and inorganic particles in the upper and lower soil layers contain varying amounts of air (mostly nitrogen and oxygen gas) and water. Plant roots need the oxygen for cellular respiration.

Some of the precipitation that reaches the soil percolates through the soil layers and occupies many of the soil's open spaces or pores. This downward movement of water through soil is called **infiltration.** As the water seeps down, it dissolves various minerals and organic matter in upper layers and carries them to lower layers in a process called **leaching.**

Most of the world's crops are grown on soils exposed when grasslands and deciduous (leaf-shedding) forests are cleared. Worldwide there are many thousands of different soil types. Six important soil types, each with a distinct profile, are shown in Figure 4-26 (p. 79).

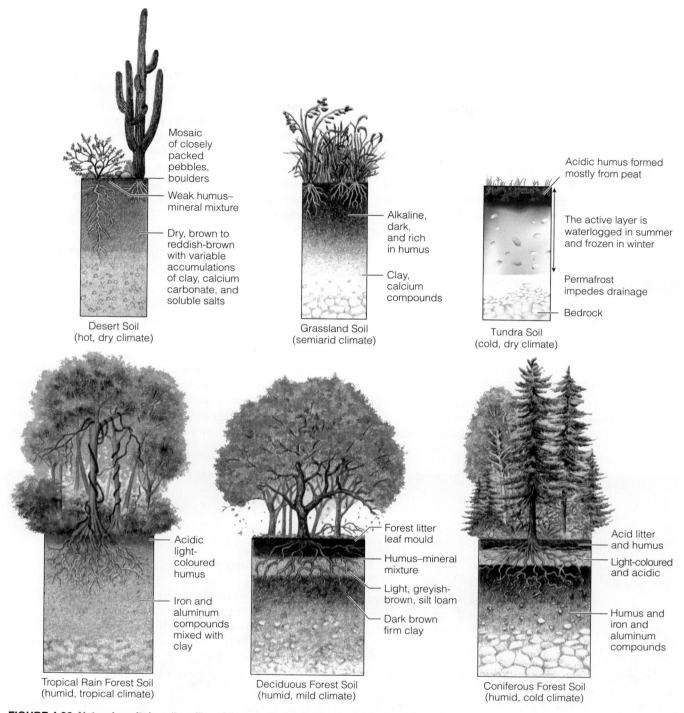

Desert Soil
(hot, dry climate)

Mosaic
of closely
packed
pebbles,
boulders

Weak humus–
mineral mixture

Dry, brown to
reddish-brown
with variable
accumulations
of clay, calcium
carbonate, and
soluble salts

Grassland Soil
(semiarid climate)

Alkaline,
dark,
and rich
in humus

Clay,
calcium
compounds

Tundra Soil
(cold, dry climate)

Acidic humus formed
mostly from peat

The active layer is
waterlogged in summer
and frozen in winter

Permafrost
impedes drainage

Bedrock

Tropical Rain Forest Soil
(humid, tropical climate)

Acidic
light-
coloured
humus

Iron and
aluminum
compounds
mixed with
clay

Deciduous Forest Soil
(humid, mild climate)

Forest litter
leaf mould

Humus–mineral
mixture

Light, greyish-
brown, silt loam

Dark brown
firm clay

Coniferous Forest Soil
(humid, cold climate)

Acid litter
and humus

Light-coloured
and acidic

Humus and
iron and
aluminum
compounds

FIGURE 4-26 Natural capital: soil profiles of the principal soil types typically found in six different biomes. The Tundra soil is from Arctic conditions; it features permafrost, waterlogging, few soil organisms, and poorly developed horizons.

How Do Soils Differ in Texture and Porosity? Composition and Spaces Are Important

Soils vary in the size of the particles they contain and the amount of space between these particles.

Soils vary in their content of *clay* (very fine particles), *silt* (fine particles), *sand* (medium-sized particles), and *gravel* (coarse to very coarse particles). The relative amounts of the different sizes and types of these mineral particles determine **soil texture**.

To get an idea of a soil's texture, take a small amount of topsoil, moisten it, and rub it between your fingers and thumb. A gritty feel means it contains a lot of sand. A sticky feel means a high clay content, and you should be able to roll it into a clump. Silt-laden soil feels smooth, like flour. A **loam** topsoil is best suited for plant growth. It has a texture between these extremes—a crumbly, spongy feeling—with many of its particles clumped loosely together.

Soil texture helps determine **soil porosity,** a measure of the volume of pores or spaces per volume of soil and of the average distances between those spaces. Fine particles are needed for water retention and coarse ones for air spaces. A porous soil has many pores and can hold more water and air than a less porous soil. The average size of the spaces or pores in a soil determines **soil permeability:** the rate at which water and air move from upper to lower soil layers.

4-7   MATTER CYCLING IN ECOSYSTEMS

What Are Biogeochemical Cycles? Going in Circles

Global cycles recycle nutrients through the Earth's air, land, water, and living organisms and, in the process, connect past, present, and future forms of life.

All organisms are interconnected by vast global recycling systems made up of **nutrient cycles,** or **biogeochemical cycles** (literally, life–earth–chemical

cycles). In these cycles, nutrient atoms, ions, and molecules that organisms need to live, grow, and reproduce are continuously cycled among air, water, soil, rock, and living organisms. These cycles, driven directly or indirectly by incoming solar energy and gravity, include the carbon, oxygen, nitrogen, phosphorus, and hydrologic (water) cycles (Figure 4-8, p. 64).

The Earth's chemical cycles connect past, present, and future forms of life. Some of the carbon atoms in your skin may once have been part of a leaf, a dinosaur's skin, or a layer of limestone rock. Your grandmother, Plato, or a hunter-gatherer who lived 25 000 years ago may have inhaled some of the oxygen molecules you just inhaled.

How Is Water Cycled in the Biosphere? The Water Cycle

A vast global cycle collects, purifies, distributes, and recycles the Earth's fixed supply of water.

The **hydrologic cycle,** or **water cycle,** recycles the Earth's fixed supply of water, as shown in Figure 4-27. Trace the flows and paths in this diagram. Solar energy evaporates water found on the Earth's surface into the atmosphere. Some of this water returns to the ground as rain or snow, passes through living organisms, flows into bodies of water, and eventually is evaporated again to continue the cycle. The water cycle

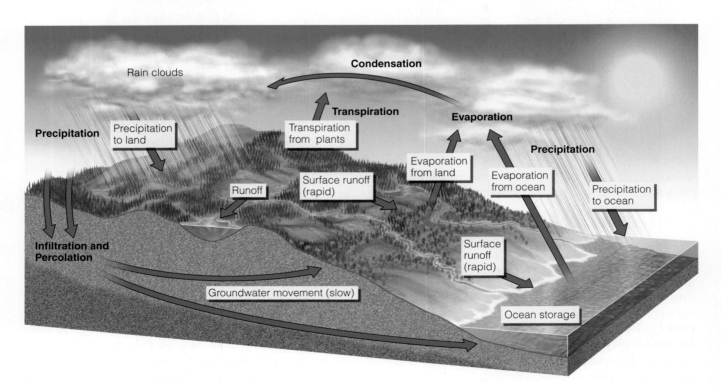

CENGAGENOW™ **ACTIVE FIGURE 4-27 Natural capital:** simplified model of the global *hydrologic cycle* that helps keep you alive. *See an animation based on this figure at* CengageNOW.

differs from most other nutrient cycles in that most of the water remains chemically unchanged and is transformed from one physical state to another.

The main processes in this water recycling and purifying cycle are *evaporation* (conversion of water into water vapour), *transpiration* (evaporation from plant leaves after water is extracted from soil by roots and transported throughout the plant), *condensation* (conversion of water vapour into droplets of liquid water), *precipitation* (rain, sleet, hail, and snow), *infiltration* (movement of water into soil), *percolation* (downward flow of water through soil and permeable rock formations to groundwater storage areas called aquifers), and *runoff* (surface movement down slopes to the sea to resume the cycle).

The water cycle is powered by energy from the sun, which evaporates water into the atmosphere, and by gravity, which draws the water back to the Earth's surface as precipitation. About 84% of water vapour in the atmosphere comes from the oceans, and the rest comes from land. This should not surprise you since almost three-fourths of the Earth is covered with water.

Winds and air masses transport water vapour over various parts of the Earth's surface, often over long distances. Falling temperatures cause the water vapour to condense into tiny droplets that form clouds in the sky or fog near the surface. For precipitation to occur, air must contain **condensation nuclei:** tiny particles on which droplets of water vapour can collect. Sources of such particles include volcanic ash, soil dust, smoke, sea salts, and particulate matter emitted by factories, coal-burning power plants, and motor vehicles.

Currently about one-tenth of the fresh water returning to the Earth's surface as precipitation becomes locked up in slowly flowing ice and snow called *glaciers.* But most precipitation falling on terrestrial ecosystems becomes *surface runoff.* This water flows into streams and lakes, which eventually carry water back to the oceans, where it can evaporate and cycle again.

Besides replenishing streams, lakes, and wetlands, surface runoff also causes soil erosion, which moves soil and weathered rock fragments from one place to another. Water is thus the primary sculptor of the Earth's landscape. Because water dissolves many nutrient compounds, it is also a major medium for transporting nutrients within and between ecosystems and for removing and diluting wastes.

Throughout the hydrologic cycle, many natural processes purify water. Evaporation and subsequent precipitation act as a natural distillation process that removes impurities dissolved in water. Water flowing above ground through streams and lakes and below ground in aquifers is naturally filtered and purified by chemical and biological processes, mostly by the actions of decomposer bacteria. Thus *the hydrologic cycle can also be viewed as a cycle of natural renewal of water quality.*

How Are Human Activities Affecting the Water Cycle? Messing with Nature

We alter the water cycle by withdrawing large amounts of fresh water, clearing vegetation, eroding soils, polluting surface and underground water, and contributing to climate change.

During the past 100 years, we have been intervening in the Earth's current water cycle in four major ways. *First,* we withdraw large quantities of fresh water from streams, lakes, and underground sources. In some heavily populated or heavily irrigated areas, withdrawals have led to groundwater depletion or intrusion of ocean salt water into underground water supplies.

Second, we clear vegetation from land for agriculture, mining, road and building construction, and other activities; sometimes we cover the land with buildings, concrete, or asphalt. This increases runoff, reduces infiltration that recharges groundwater supplies, increases the risk of flooding, and accelerates soil erosion and landslides. We also increase flooding by destroying wetlands, which act like sponges to absorb and hold overflows of water.

Third, we modify water quality by adding nutrients (such as phosphates and nitrates found in fertilizers) and other pollutants. *Fourth,* according to a 2003 study by Ruth Curry and her colleagues, the Earth's water cycle is speeding up as a result of a warmer climate caused partially by human inputs of carbon dioxide and other greenhouse gases into the atmosphere. This could change global precipitation patterns that affect the severity and frequency of droughts, floods, and storms. It can also intensify global warming by speeding up the input of water vapour—a powerful greenhouse gas—into the troposphere.

CONSIDER, DISCUSS, OR DEBATE

Exactly how can we solve the main problems stemming from human influences on the Earth's water cycle?

How Is Carbon Cycled in the Biosphere? Carbon Dioxide in Action

Carbon, the basic building block of organic compounds, recycles through the Earth's air, water, soil, and living organisms.

Carbon is the basic building block of the carbohydrates, fats, proteins, DNA, and other organic compounds necessary for life. It is circulated through the biosphere by the **carbon cycle,** as shown in Figure 4-28. Trace the flows and paths in this diagram.

This cycle is based on carbon dioxide gas, which makes up about 0.038% of the volume of

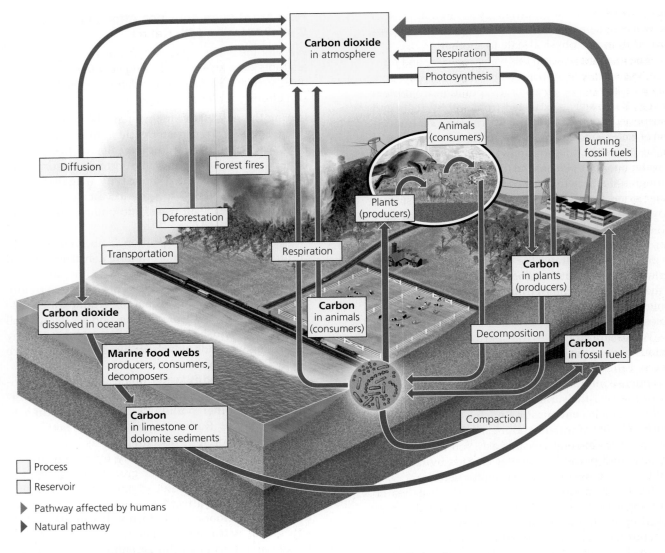

Process

Reservoir

▶ Pathway affected by humans

▶ Natural pathway

CENGAGENOW **ACTIVE FIGURE 4-28 Natural capital:** simplified model of the global *carbon cycle* that helps keep you alive.

the troposphere and is also dissolved in water. The aerobic respiration of organisms, volcanic eruptions, the weathering of carbonate rocks, and the burning of carbon-containing compounds found in wood, grasses, and fossil fuels add carbon dioxide to the troposphere. *Aerobic respiration* in the cells of oxygen-using producers, consumers, and decomposers breaks down glucose and other complex organic compounds and converts the carbon back to CO_2, which is released into the troposphere and in water for reuse by producers.

Carbon dioxide is removed from the troposphere by terrestrial and aquatic producers, which use *photosynthesis* to convert it into complex carbohydrates such as glucose ($C_6H_{12}O_6$).

This linkage between *photosynthesis* in producers and *aerobic respiration* in producers, consumers, and decomposers circulates carbon in the biosphere and is

a major part of the global carbon cycle. Oxygen and hydrogen, the other elements in carbohydrates, cycle almost in step with carbon.

Carbon dioxide, a *greenhouse gas*, is a key component of nature's thermostat. If the carbon cycle removes too much CO_2 from the atmosphere, the atmosphere will cool; if the cycle generates too much, the atmosphere will get warmer. Thus even slight changes in the carbon cycle can affect climate and ultimately the types of life that can exist on various parts of the planet.

Some carbon atoms normally take a long time to recycle. Over millions of years, buried deposits of dead plant matter and bacteria have been compressed between layers of sediment, where they form carbon-containing *fossil fuels* such as coal and oil (Figure 4-28). This carbon is not released to the atmosphere as CO_2 for recycling until long-term geological processes expose these deposits to air, or until these fuels are extracted and burned. In only a few hundred years, we have extracted and burned huge quantities of fossil fuels that took millions of years to form. This is why fossil fuels are nonrenewable resources on a human time scale.

Oceans play important roles in the carbon cycle. Some of the atmosphere's carbon dioxide dissolves in ocean water, and the ocean's photosynthesizing producers remove some. On the other hand, as ocean water warms, some of its dissolved CO_2 returns to the atmosphere, just as carbon dioxide fizzes out of a carbonated beverage when it warms. The balance between these two processes plays a role in the Earth's average temperature.

Some ocean organisms build their shells and skeletons by using dissolved CO_2 molecules in seawater to form carbonate compounds such as calcium carbonate ($CaCO_3$). When these organisms die, tiny particles of their shells and bone drift slowly to the ocean depths. There they are buried for eons (as long as 400 million years) in deep bottom sediments (Figure 4-28), where under immense pressure they are converted into limestone rock. Geological processes may eventually expose the limestone to the atmosphere and acidic precipitation and make its carbon available to living organisms once again.

How Are Human Activities Affecting the Carbon Cycle? Messing with Nature's Thermostat

Carbon dioxide produced by burning fossil fuels and clearing photosynthesizing vegetation faster than it is replaced can increase the average temperature of the troposphere.

Since 1800 and especially since 1950, we have been intervening in the Earth's carbon cycle in two ways that add carbon dioxide to the atmosphere. *First*, in some areas we clear trees and other plants that absorb CO_2 through photosynthesis faster than they can grow back. *Second*, we add large amounts of CO_2 by burning fossil fuels (Figure 4-29) and wood.

Computer models of the Earth's climate systems suggest that increased concentrations of atmospheric CO_2 and other gases we are adding to the atmosphere could enhance the planet's *natural greenhouse effect* that helps warm the lower atmosphere (troposphere) and the Earth's surface (Figure 4-9, p. 65). The resulting *global warming* could disrupt global food production and wildlife habitats, alter temperature and precipitation patterns, and raise the average sea level in various parts of the world—more about this in Chapter 21.

> **CONSIDER, DISCUSS, OR DEBATE**
>
> Does *global warming* seem like a wild idea to you? Do you think you have seen evidence of global warming in your lifetime?

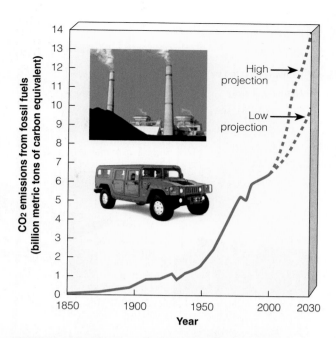

FIGURE 4-29 Natural capital degradation: human interference in the global carbon cycle from carbon dioxide emissions when fossil fuels are burned, 1850 to 2001, and projections to 2030 (dashed lines). (Data from UN Environment Programme, British Petroleum, International Energy Agency, and U.S. Department of Energy)

How Is Nitrogen Cycled in the Biosphere? Bacteria in Action

Different types of bacteria help recycle nitrogen through the Earth's air, water, soil, and living organisms.

Nitrogen is the atmosphere's most abundant element, with chemically unreactive nitrogen gas (N_2) making up about 78% of the volume of the troposphere. Nitrogen is a crucial component of proteins, many vitamins, and the nucleic acids DNA and RNA. However, N_2 cannot be absorbed and used (metabolized) directly as a nutrient by multicellular plants or animals.

Fortunately, two natural processes convert N_2 gas in the atmosphere into compounds that can enter food webs as part of the **nitrogen cycle,** depicted in Figure 4-30. Trace the flows and paths in this diagram. One of these processes is atmospheric electrical discharge in the form of lightning. This causes nitrogen (N_2) and oxygen (O_2) in the atmosphere to react and produce nitrogen oxide (NO). Try to write and balance the chemical equation for this reaction.

The other process is carried out by certain types of bacteria in aquatic systems, in the soil, and in the roots of some plants that can convert or "fix" N_2 into compounds useful as nutrients for plants and animals.

The nitrogen cycle consists of several major steps. In *nitrogen fixation*, specialized bacteria in the soil convert

Ecosystems: What Are They, and How Do They Work?

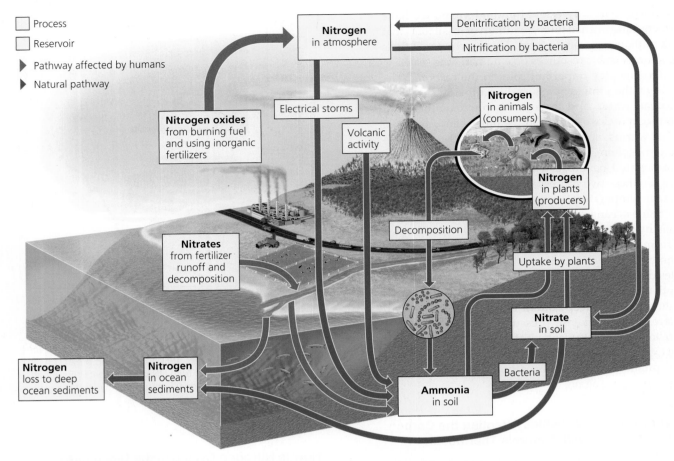

Legend:
- Process
- Reservoir
- Pathway affected by humans
- Natural pathway

Nitrogen in atmosphere

Denitrification by bacteria

Nitrification by bacteria

Nitrogen oxides from burning fuel and using inorganic fertilizers

Electrical storms

Volcanic activity

Nitrogen in animals (consumers)

Nitrogen in plants (producers)

Decomposition

Nitrates from fertilizer runoff and decomposition

Uptake by plants

Nitrate in soil

Nitrogen loss to deep ocean sediments

Nitrogen in ocean sediments

Bacteria

Ammonia in soil

CENGAGENOW˘ **ACTIVE FIGURE 4-30 Natural capital:** simplified model of the *nitrogen cycle* in a terrestrial ecosystem. This cycle helps keep you alive. *See an animation based on this figure at* CengageNOW.

("fix") gaseous nitrogen (N_2) to ammonia (NH_3) that can be used by plants. See if you can write a balanced chemical equation for the reaction of N_2 with H_2 to form NH_3.

Ammonia not taken up by plants may undergo *nitrification*. In this process, specialized aerobic bacteria convert most of the ammonia in soil to *nitrite ions* (NO_2^-), which are toxic to plants, and *nitrate ions* (NO_3^-), which are easily taken up by plants as a nutrient.

Nitrogen fixation and nitrification add inorganic ammonia, ammonium ions (NH_4^+), and nitrate ions to soil water. Then plant roots can absorb these dissolved substances in a step called *assimilation*. Plants use these ions to make nitrogen-containing organic molecules such as DNA, amino acids, and proteins. Animals, in turn, get their nitrogen by eating plants or plant-eating animals.

Plants and animals return nitrogen-rich organic compounds to the environment as wastes, cast-off particles, and dead bodies. In the *ammonification* step, vast armies of specialized decomposer bacteria convert this detritus into simpler nitrogen-containing inorganic compounds such as ammonia and water-soluble salts containing ammonium ions.

Nitrogen leaves the soil in the *denitrification* step in which other specialized anaerobic bacteria in water-logged soil and in the bottom sediments of lakes, oceans, swamps, and bogs convert NH_3 and NH_4^+ back into nitrite and nitrate ions and then into nitrogen gas (N_2) and nitrous oxide gas (N_2O). These gases are released to the atmosphere to begin the cycle again.

CONSIDER, DISCUSS, OR DEBATE

What would the nitrogen cycle (Figure 4-30) look like if there were no bacteria? Could we compensate somehow? How would farmland and natural ecosystems be affected?

How Are Human Activities Affecting the Nitrogen Cycle? Altering Nature

Excessive inputs of various nitrogen-containing compounds into the environment from human activities is becoming a major regional and global environmental problem.

In the past 100 years, human activities have had several effects on the Earth's current nitrogen cycle.

First, we add large amounts of nitric oxide (NO) to the atmosphere when we burn any fuel. In the atmosphere, this gas can be converted to nitrogen dioxide gas (NO_2) and nitric acid (HNO_3), which can return to the Earth's surface as damaging *acid deposition,* commonly called *acid rain*—more on this in Chapter 20.

Second, we add nitrous oxide (N_2O) to the atmosphere through the action of anaerobic bacteria on livestock wastes and commercial **inorganic fertilizers** applied to the soil. This gas can warm the troposphere and deplete ozone in the stratosphere.

Third, we release large quantities of nitrogen stored in soils and plants as gaseous compounds into the troposphere through destruction of forests, grasslands, and wetlands. *Fourth,* we upset aquatic ecosystems by adding excess nitrates in agricultural runoff and discharges from municipal sewage systems—more on this in Chapter 22.

Fifth, we remove nitrogen from topsoil when we harvest nitrogen-rich crops, irrigate crops, and burn or clear grasslands and forests before planting crops.

Sixth, inputs of nitrogen into the air, soil, and water mostly from our activities is beginning to affect the biodiversity of terrestrial and aquatic systems by shifting their species composition toward species that can thrive on increased supplies of nitrogen nutrients.

Since 1950, human activities have more than doubled the annual release of nitrogen from the terrestrial portion of the Earth into the rest of the environment. These excessive inputs of nitrogen into the air and water are a serious local, regional, and global environmental problem that so far has attracted fairly little attention compared to global environmental problems such as global warming and depletion of ozone in the stratosphere.

How Is Phosphorus Naturally Cycled in the Biosphere? Slow Cycling without Using the Atmosphere

Phosphorus cycles fairly slowly through the Earth's water, soil, and living organisms.

Phosphorus circulates through water, the Earth's crust, and living organisms in the **phosphorus cycle,** depicted in Figure 4-31. Trace the flows and paths in

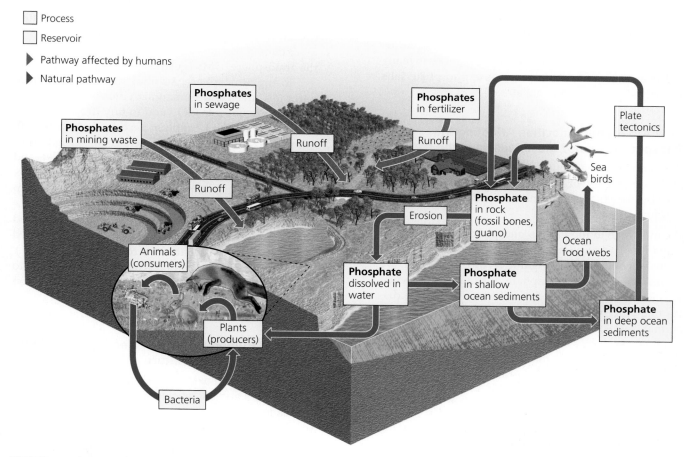

FIGURE 4-31 Natural capital: simplified model of the *phosphorus cycle*. This cycle helps keep you alive.

this diagram. With the exception of small particles of phosphate in dust, very little phosphorus circulates in the atmosphere because soil conditions do not allow bacteria to convert chemical forms of phosphorus to gaseous forms of phosphorus.

Phosphorus is typically found as phosphate salts containing phosphate ions (PO_4^{3-}) in terrestrial rock formations and ocean bottom sediments. The slow weathering and erosion of phosphorus-containing rocks releases phosphorus into soil water, lakes, and rivers as phosphate ions, which are taken up by plant roots. Animals get most of the phosphorus they need from the food they eat. Decomposers break down organic phosphorus compounds in dead organisms into the soil, where it can be reused by plants.

Phosphate can be lost from the cycle for long periods when it washes from the land into streams and rivers and is carried to the ocean. There it can be deposited as sediment on the sea floor and remain for millions of years. Someday geological uplift processes may expose these seafloor deposits from which phosphate can be eroded to start the cyclical process again.

Because most soils contain little phosphate, it is often the *limiting factor* for plant growth on land unless phosphorus (as phosphate salts mined from the ground) is applied to the soil as a fertilizer. Phosphorus also limits the growth of producer populations in many freshwater streams and lakes because phosphate salts are only slightly soluble in water.

How Are Human Activities Affecting the Phosphorus Cycle? More Messing with Nature

We remove large amounts of phosphate from the Earth to make fertilizer, reduce phosphorus in tropical soils by clearing forests, and add excess phosphates to aquatic systems.

We intervene in the Earth's phosphorus cycle in three ways. *First,* we mine large quantities of phosphate rock to make commercial inorganic fertilizers. *Second,* we reduce the available phosphate in tropical soils when we cut down areas of tropical forests. *Third,* we disrupt aquatic systems with phosphates from runoff of animal wastes, fertilizers, and discharges from sewage treatment systems—more on this in Chapter 22.

Scientists estimate that since 1900, human activities have increased the natural rate of phosphorus release into the environment about 3.7-fold.

CONSIDER, DISCUSS, OR DEBATE

Which of the steps depicted in Figure 4-31 are accelerated by human activities? Why is this a problem?

How Is Sulphur Cycled in the Biosphere? The Sulphur Cycle

Sulphur cycles through the Earth's air, water, soil, and living organisms.

Sulphur circulates through the biosphere in the **sulphur cycle,** shown in Figure 4-32 (p. 87). Trace the flows and paths in this diagram. Much of the Earth's sulphur is stored underground in rocks and minerals, including sulphate (SO_4^{2-}) salts buried deep under ocean sediments.

Sulphur also enters the atmosphere from several natural sources. Hydrogen sulphide (H_2S)—a colourless, highly poisonous gas with a rotten-egg smell—is released from active volcanoes and from organic matter in swamps, bogs, and tidal flats broken down by anaerobic decomposers.

Sulphur dioxide (SO_2), a colourless, suffocating gas, also comes from volcanoes. Particles of sulphate (SO_4^{2-}) salts, such as ammonium sulphate, enter the atmosphere from sea spray, dust storms, and forest fires. Plant roots absorb sulphate ions and incorporate the sulphur as an essential component of many proteins.

Certain marine algae produce large amounts of volatile dimethyl sulphide, or DMS (CH_3SCH_3). Tiny droplets of DMS serve as nuclei for the condensation of water into droplets found in clouds. Thus changes in DMS emissions can affect cloud cover and climate. In the atmosphere, DMS is converted to sulphur dioxide.

In the atmosphere, sulphur dioxide (SO_2) from natural sources and human activities is converted to sulphur trioxide gas (SO_3) and to tiny droplets of sulphuric acid (H_2SO_4). Sulphur dioxide also reacts with other atmospheric chemicals such as ammonia to produce tiny particles of sulphate salts. These droplets and particles fall to the Earth as components of *acid deposition,* which along with other air pollutants can harm trees and aquatic life—more on this in Chapter 20.

In the oxygen-deficient environments of flooded soils, freshwater wetlands, and tidal flats, specialized bacteria convert sulphate ions to sulphide ions (S^{2-}). The sulphide ions can then react with metal ions to form insoluble metallic sulphides, which are deposited as rock, and the cycle continues.

How Are Human Activities Affecting the Sulphur Cycle? Overloading Nature

We add sulphur dioxide to the atmosphere by burning coal and oil, refining oil, and producing some metals from ores.

We add sulphur dioxide to the atmosphere in three ways. *First,* we burn sulphur-containing coal and oil to produce electric power. *Second,* we refine sulphur-containing petroleum to make gasoline, heating

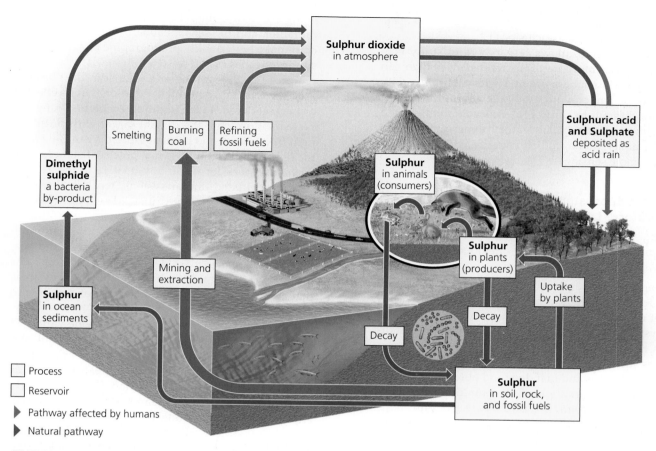

Smelting

Burning coal

Refining fossil fuels

Sulphur dioxide in atmosphere

Sulphuric acid and Sulphate deposited as acid rain

Dimethyl sulphide a bacteria by-product

Sulphur in animals (consumers)

Sulphur in plants (producers)

Uptake by plants

Mining and extraction

Sulphur in ocean sediments

Decay

Decay

Decay

Sulphur in soil, rock, and fossil fuels

☐ Process
☐ Reservoir
▶ Pathway affected by humans
▶ Natural pathway

CENGAGENOW™ **ACTIVE FIGURE 4-32 Natural capital:** simplified model of the *sulphur cycle*. See *an animation based on this figure at* CengageNOW.

oil, and other useful products. *Third*, we convert sulphur-containing metallic mineral ores into metals such as copper, lead, and zinc.

4-8 HOW DO ECOLOGISTS LEARN ABOUT ECOSYSTEMS?

What Is Field Research? Muddy Boots Ecology

Ecologists go into ecosystems ranging from tide pools to treetops to learn what organisms live there and how they interact.

Field research involves going into nature and observing and measuring the structure of ecosystems and what happens in them. Most of what we know about the structure and functioning of ecosystems described in this chapter has come from such research.

Ecologists trek through forests, deserts, and grasslands and wade or boat through wetlands, lakes, and streams collecting and observing species. Sometimes the methods they use involve very basic equipment such as rubber boots, nets, binoculars, plant presses, and simple pollution-monitoring instruments (Figure 4-33).

Increasingly, ecologists are going to the field with higher levels of technology such as computers, telemetry receivers, night vision, electronic data recorders, and sophisticated pollution-monitoring equipment.

Sometimes ecologists do field experiments in which they change one or more variables on some of their study sites and make comparisons with unmanipulated study sites. There is often very little control over all the variables that exist in the complexity

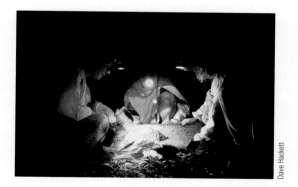

Dave Hackett

FIGURE 4-33 Three field researchers monitoring salamander populations on their study sites.

of natural ecosystems; however, with clever experimental design and large sample sizes, field ecologists can arrive at valuable conclusions.

Field research allows researchers to study ecosystems under more natural circumstances than can be achieved in a laboratory and with more proximity than can be gained with remote sensing. However, it is more difficult to control relevant variables in field experiments than in laboratory experiments, and smaller areas can be studied using field research than using remote sensing.

How Are Ecosystems Studied in the Laboratory? Life under Glass

Ecologists use aquarium tanks, greenhouses, and controlled indoor and outdoor chambers to study ecosystems.

During the past 50 years, ecologists have increasingly supplemented field research by using *laboratory research* to set up, observe, and make measurements of model ecosystems and populations under laboratory conditions. Such simplified systems have been set up in containers such as culture tubes, bottles, aquarium tanks, and greenhouses and in indoor and outdoor chambers where temperature, light, CO_2, humidity, and other variables can be controlled carefully (see p. 540).

Such systems make it easier for scientists to carry out controlled experiments. In addition, such laboratory experiments often are quicker and cheaper than similar experiments in the field.

But there is a catch. We must consider whether what scientists observe and measure in a simplified, controlled system under laboratory conditions takes place in the same way in the more complex and dynamic conditions found in nature. Thus the results of laboratory research must be coupled with and supported by other forms of research.

What Is Remote Sensing? Collecting Information from Above

Remote sensing is the acquisition of information from a distance.

In contrast to the close and controlled circumstances of laboratory research, remote sensing involves collecting data from an aerial view high above the Earth's surface. Initially, balloons and airplanes were used to take high-quality aerial photographs for analysis. Now satellites such as Landsat, Nimbus, RADARSAT, IKONOS, and UARS play an important role, and the information collected by remote sensing has become increasingly sophisticated.

There are two main types of data collecting. *Passive collection* involves monitoring radiation that is emitted or reflected by the object or area that is being studied. Commonly, sunlight is the source of radiation, and the sensors aboard the satellite or aircraft make high-quality photographic images or measure properties of the reflected light. *Active collection* requires that energy be emitted to scan the object or area; sensors then detect the radiation that is reflected or backscattered. **Lidar** (light detection and ranging) systems illuminate the distant target with pulses of light from a laser and then measure the time taken for the light to return; in this way, precise distances such as the height of forest canopy relative to the ground can be calculated. Radar systems work in the same way but use radio waves instead of light (Jensen, 2006; Popescu, 2012).

Remote sensing allows large amounts of information to be collected quickly from vast areas of land, sea, or atmosphere. Since the data are collected from afar using aircraft or satellites, it is possible to study areas that are extremely remote, dangerous, or sensitive to disturbance.

Remote sensing can be used for a wide variety of applications, such as measuring the height, extent, and biomass of forests; accurately mapping topographic features; or studying atmospheric features such as weather and pollution. The technology is constantly improving and provides researchers with new ways to answer important questions.

For example, Paul Treitz of Queen's University and his colleagues use remote-sensing data from satellites to estimate the percentage of cover, above ground biomass, and leaf area of plant communities in Arctic and boreal ecosystems. Without setting foot in these distant locations, they can learn about the plant community structure and probable biodiversity in these areas. They can use biomass information gathered over vast expanses of Arctic tundra and boreal forests to gain insights into the carbon stocks stored in plants; this information is key to understanding changes in plant productivity and carbon dioxide exchange that may be linked to global climate change (see http://www.geog.queensu.ca/larsees/research.htm).

What Are Geographic Information Systems? Specialized Computer Software

Geographic information systems are used to store, manipulate, and analyze spatial information.

A **geographic information system (GIS)** is specialized computer software that can combine different types of information, including data from remote sensing and from field studies, in a database using the same set of geographic coordinates. The data can be stored as layers; for example, Figure 4-34 shows four layers of

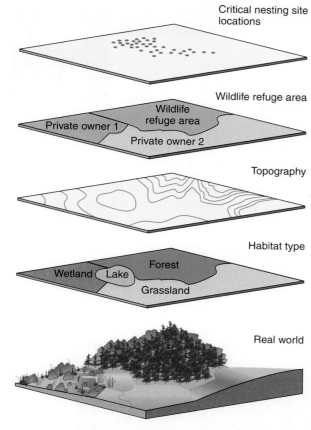

Critical nesting site
locations

Wildlife refuge area

Private owner 1 · Wildlife refuge area · Private owner 2

Topography

Habitat type

Wetland · Lake · Forest · Grassland

Real world

FIGURE 4-34 Geographic information systems (GIS) provide the computer technology for organizing, storing, and analyzing complex data collected over broad geographic areas. GIS enable scientists to overlay many layers of data (such as soils, topography, distribution of endangered populations, and land protection status).

information that represent important aspects about the "real-world" site shown at the bottom of the diagram. If the information is gathered over several years, time can become a factor in the GIS. Researchers can choose which types of data to analyze, combine, or track through time. GIS can be a potent tool for discovering relationships among variables, for understanding spatial relationships, and for making predictions about the future.

GIS has many applications in environmental science. For example, natural resource management, climate change, efforts to protect species at risk, and pollution control all have aspects that vary in time and space, making them prime candidates for the application of GIS. GIS is often an important tool in landscape ecology, described in the next section. For more information, see introductory textbooks about GIS such as those by Shellito (2011) and Chang (2012).

What Is Landscape Ecology? The Study of Spatial Patterns

Landscape ecology combines elements of ecology and geography to analyze the structure and function of an area of land.

Landscape ecology is the scientific study of how spatial patterns in the environment affect the abundance, distribution, and interaction of organisms. A **landscape** is an arbitrarily defined area of land that generally is larger than a single ecosystem but smaller than a biome. Landscape ecologists view the landscape as a *mosaic* of recognizably distinct *patches* that differ from their surroundings. Depending on the scale and the research question, these patches may be ecosystems, communities, or areas of habitat for a given organism.

Landscape ecology is an important component of environmental science and draws upon ecology and geography to develop a broad-scale understanding of how several ecosystems, communities, or habitat patches relate to each other and how they are changing through time. For example, landscape ecologists study the size, number, and isolation of the patches within the landscape. They monitor factors such as land-use changes, fragmentation of habitat, relationships between patch sizes and ecological processes, connectivity among the patches, and disturbance by humans and other organisms. As a result, landscape ecologists can provide important information to conservation biologists who are attempting to prevent the loss of species at risk or to protect the biodiversity of an area. Information from landscape ecology can also be used for planning purposes, such as providing principles for effective design of wildlife refuge areas or minimizing the impact of urban development on its surrounding landscape.

The study of landscape ecology has been facilitated by advances in remote sensing, which allows large areas of land to be monitored by increasingly sophisticated satellite technology, and by the development of GIS, which facilitates the analysis and interpretation of spatial data. For more information about landscape ecology, see Li et al. (2011) and Thornton et al. (2011).

What Is Systems Analysis? Simulating Ecosystems

Ecologists develop mathematical and other models to simulate the behaviour of ecosystems.

Since the late 1960s, ecologists have made increasing use of *systems analysis* to develop mathematical and other models that simulate ecosystems. Computer simulation of such models can help us understand large and very complex systems (such as rivers, oceans, forests, grasslands, cities, and climate) that cannot be adequately studied and modelled in field and laboratory

Canadian Geospatial Technologies

Geospatial technologies such as remote sensing and geographic information systems are changing the way we view and comprehend the world. Canada has been actively involved in developing these technologies.

Canada's first satellite, Alouette 1, was launched in 1962 to study the ionosphere. With the launch of Anik A-1 in 1972, Canada became the first country in the world with its own network of geostationary communication satellites. Other well-known Canadian satellites include RADARSAT-1, launched in 1995, and RADARSAT-2, launched in 2007. These two satellites are noteworthy in their use of a microwave radar system called *synthetic aperture radar* (SAR), which results in images of extremely high clarity, even when taken through dense atmospheric conditions or at night. The SCISAT satellite, launched in 2003, specializes in studying chemicals that affect the ozone layer over Canada and the Arctic. In 2014–2015, the three satellites of RADARSAT Constellation will be launched and will provide a daily scan of Canada and much of the world. As well as focusing on Canadian satellites, the *Canadian Space Agency* cooperates in projects involving the satellites and spacecraft of other countries (see http://www.asc-csa.gc.ca/eng/satellites/default.asp).

The world's first computerized GIS was developed in the 1960s by Roger Tomlinson and his colleagues at the federal Department of Forestry and Rural Development in Ottawa. It was called the *Canada Geographic Information System (CGIS)* and was used to store, manipulate, and analyze vast volumes of information about soils, agriculture, forests, wildlife, and many other factors for the *Canada Land Inventory*. The CGIS was used for 30 years to support the resource management and planning of the federal and provincial governments in Canada; however, the CGIS was developed for large-scale tasks on a mainframe computer and was never commercialized.

Many commercial geospatial products that you can use on your own computer are now available. For example, three Canadian GIS products are CARIS, FME, and uDig. A Canadian company that is gaining much attention for its powerful yet user-friendly software products is PCI Geomatics of Richmond Hill, Ontario. This company produces a desktop remote-sensing software package called Geomatica that uses satellite data, some of which can be downloaded for free, to perform analyses and make maps (see http://www.pcigeomatics.com/pdf/Geomatica2012/Geomatica_2012_Flyer.pdf). Increasingly, information from satellites is coming within reach of ordinary citizens.

For more information about Canadian geospatial technologies, and to view images captured by RADARSAT satellites, visit the Canadian Centre for Remote Sensing at Natural Resources Canada (http://www.nrcan.gc.ca/earth-sciences/geography-boundary/remote-sensing/11691).

research. Figure 4-35 outlines the major stages of systems analysis.

Researchers can change values of the variables in their computer models to project possible changes in environmental conditions, help anticipate environmental surprises, and analyze the effectiveness of various alternative solutions to environmental problems.

However, simulations and projections made using ecosystem models are no better than the data and assumptions used to develop the models. Thus careful field and laboratory ecological research must be used to provide the baseline data and determine the causal relationships between key variables needed to develop and test ecosystem models (Ford, 2010).

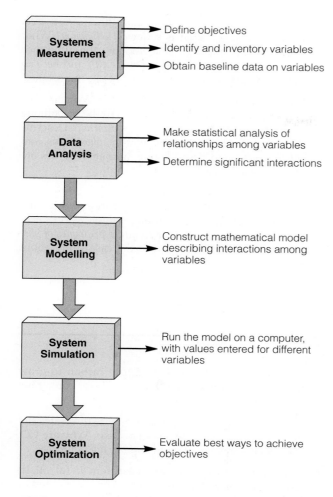

FIGURE 4-35 Major stages of systems analysis. (Modified data from Charles Southwick)

Why Do We Need Baseline Ecological Data? Understanding What We Have

We need baseline data about the world's ecosystems so we can see how they are changing and develop effective strategies for preventing or slowing their degradation.

Before we can understand what is happening to an ecosystem, community, or population, and how best to prevent harmful environmental changes, we need

to know its current condition. In other words, we need *baseline data* about its components, physical and chemical conditions, and how well it is functioning.

By analogy your doctor would like to have baseline data on your blood pressure, weight, and how well your organs and other systems are functioning as revealed by blood and other basic tests. Then when something happens to your health the doctor can run new tests and compare the results with the baseline data to determine what has changed and use this to come up with a treatment.

Ecologists call for a massive program to develop baseline data for the world's ecosystems. If we do not know how many elephants are in Africa, we cannot determine whether their populations are declining or increasing.

If we could see the bounty and beauty of nature the way it was 100 or 200 years ago, we would be outraged at what we have lost. But it is easy for us not to miss what we never saw or experienced.

For example, people visit degraded coastal environments such as a coral reef and call it beautiful because they are unaware how it used to look. Veteran divers say, "You should have seen it in the old days."

In this chapter, we have seen that almost all natural ecosystems and the biosphere itself achieve *long-term* sustainability in two ways. *First,* they use *solar energy* as their energy source. *Second,* they *recycle the chemical nutrients* their organisms need for survival, growth, and reproduction.

These two sustainability principles arise from the structure and function of natural ecosystems (Figures 4-8 and 4-17), the law of conservation of matter (p. 49), and the two laws of thermodynamics (p. 53). Thus the results of basic research in both the physical and biological sciences provide us with the same guidelines or lessons from nature on how we can live more sustainably on the Earth, as summarized in Figure 3-19 (p. 56).

All things come from earth, and to earth they all return.

MENANDER (342–290 B.C.)

CHAPTER REVIEW

1. Review the Key Questions for this chapter on p. 60. List as many benefits as possible that are provided to humans, and to natural ecosystems, by insects.

2. What is a *cell*? What is the *cell theory*? Distinguish between a *eukaryotic cell* and a *prokaryotic cell*. What is a *species*? Explain the importance of insects. Define *ecology*. What is *genetic diversity*? Distinguish among a *species, population, community (biological community), habitat, ecosystem,* and the *biosphere*.

3. Distinguish among the *atmosphere, troposphere, stratosphere, greenhouse gases, hydrosphere,* and *geosphere*. Distinguish between *biomes* and *aquatic life zones* and give an example of each. What three interconnected factors sustain life on Earth?

4. Describe what happens to solar energy as it flows to and from the Earth. What is the *natural greenhouse effect* and why is it important for life on Earth?

5. Distinguish between the *abiotic* and *biotic components* in ecosystems and give two examples of each. What is the *range of tolerance* for an abiotic factor? Define and give an example of a *limiting factor*. What is the *limiting factor principle*?

6. What is a *trophic level*? Distinguish among *producers (autotrophs)*, *consumers (heterotrophs)*, and *decomposers* and give an example of each in an ecosystem. Distinguish among *primary consumers (herbivores)*, *secondary consumers (carnivores)*, *high-level (third-level) consumers*, *omnivores*, *decomposers*, and *detritus feeders (detritivores)*, and give an example of each.

7. Distinguish among *photosynthesis, chemosynthesis, aerobic respiration*, and *anaerobic respiration (fermentation)*. What two processes sustain ecosystems and the biosphere and how are they linked? Explain the importance of microbes.

8. Explain what happens to energy as it flows through the food chains and food webs of an ecosystem. Distinguish between a *food chain* and a *food web*. What is *biomass*? What is *ecological efficiency*? What is the *pyramid of energy flow*? Discuss the difference between *gross primary productivity (GPP)* and *net primary productivity (NPP)* and explain their importance.

9. What happens to matter in an ecosystem? What is a *biogeochemical cycle (nutrient cycle)*? Describe the unique properties of water. What is *transpiration*? Describe the *hydrologic (water), carbon, nitrogen, phosphorus*, and *sulphur cycles* and describe how human activities are affecting each cycle.

10. Describe three ways in which scientists study ecosystems. Explain why we need much more basic data about the structure and condition of the world's ecosystems. How can the four *scientific principles of sustainability* (p. 16) be related to the case study about insects on page 59?

CRITICAL THINKING

1. Explain why microbes are the real rulers of the Earth.

2. **(a)** How would you set up a self-sustaining aquarium for tropical fish? **(b)** Suppose you have a balanced aquarium sealed with a clear glass top. Can life continue in the aquarium indefinitely as long as the sun shines regularly on it? **(c)** A friend cleans out your aquarium and removes all the soil and plants, leaving only the fish and water. What will happen? Explain.

3. Use the second law of thermodynamics (p. 54) to explain why there is such a sharp decrease in usable energy as energy flows through a food chain or web. Does an energy loss at each step violate the first law of thermodynamics (p. 53)? Explain.

4. Why do farmers not need to apply carbon to grow their crops but often need to add fertilizer containing nitrogen and phosphorus?

5. Carbon dioxide (CO_2) in the atmosphere fluctuates significantly on a daily and seasonal basis. Why are CO_2 levels relatively high at night and during winter?

6. What would happen to an ecosystem if **(a)** all its decomposers and detritus feeders were eliminated or **(b)** all its producers were eliminated? Are we necessary for the functioning of any natural ecosystem? Explain.

PROJECTS

1. Visit several types of nearby aquatic life zones and terrestrial ecosystems. For each site, try to determine the major producers, consumers, detritivores, and decomposers.

2. Write a brief scenario describing the sequence of consequences to us and to other forms of life if each of the following nutrient cycles stopped functioning: **(a)** carbon, **(b)** nitrogen, **(c)** phosphorus, and **(d)** water.

3. Use the library or the Internet to find out bibliographic information about at least two of the following people mentioned in the chapter: *Ruth Curry, Pierre Dansereau, G. Evelyn Hutchinson, Menander, Stuart Roystaczer, Peter Vitousek, Edward O. Wilson.*

ECOLOGICAL FOOTPRINT ANALYSIS

Based on the following carbon dioxide emissions data and population data estimated for July 2012, answer the questions below.

Country	Total Carbon Footprint—Carbon Dioxide Emissions (in metric gigatons per year*)	Population (in billions, July 2012)	Per Capita Carbon Footprint per Year (carbon dioxide emissions per year)
Canada	0.6	0.03	
China	5.0	1.34	
India	1.3	1.21	
Japan	1.3	0.13	
Russia	1.5	0.14	
United States	6.0	0.31	
WORLD	29	7.02	

Source: Data from World Resources Institute and International Energy Agency
***The prefix giga stands for "1 billion."**

1. Calculate the per capita carbon footprint for each country and the world and complete the table.

2. It has been suggested that a sustainable average world-wide carbon footprint per person should be no more than 2 metric tons per person per year. How does the Canadian carbon footprint per person compare with (a) the sustainable level and (b) the world average?

3. By what percentage will Canada, China, Japan, Russia, the United States, and the world each have to reduce their carbon footprints per person to achieve the estimated maximum sustainable carbon footprint per person of 2 metric tons per person per year?

Evolution and Biodiversity

Earth: The Just-Right, Resilient Planet

Life on the Earth (Figure 5-1) as we know it needs a certain temperature range: Venus is much too hot and Mars is much too cold, but the Earth is *just right.*

Life as we know it depends on the liquid water that dominates the Earth's surface. Temperature is crucial because most life on the Earth needs average temperatures between the freezing and boiling points of water.

The Earth's orbit is the right distance from the sun to provide these conditions. If the Earth were much closer, it would be too hot—like Venus—for water vapour to condense to form rain. If it were much farther away, its surface would be so cold—like Mars—that its water would exist only as ice. The Earth also spins; if it did not, the side facing the sun would be too hot and the other side too cold for water-based life to exist.

The Earth is also the right size: it has enough gravitational mass to keep its iron and nickel core molten and to keep the light gaseous molecules in its atmosphere (such as N_2, O_2, CO_2, and H_2O) from flying off into space.

On a time scale of millions of years, the Earth is enormously resilient and adaptive. During the 3.7 billion years since life arose, the average surface temperature of the Earth has remained within the narrow range of 10–20°C (50–68°F), even with a 30–40% increase in the sun's energy output. What a great temperature control system.

For several hundred million years, oxygen has made up about 21% of the volume of Earth's atmosphere. This is fortunate for us and most other forms of life. If the atmosphere's oxygen content dropped to about 15%, this would be lethal for most forms of life. If it increased to about 25%, oxygen in the atmosphere would probably ignite into a giant fireball. And thanks to the development of photosynthesizing bacteria more than 2 billion years ago, an ozone sunscreen protects us and many other

forms of life from an overdose of ultraviolet radiation. In short, this remarkable planet we live on is just right for life as we know it.

We can summarize the 3.7-billion-year biological history of the Earth in one sentence: *organisms convert solar energy to food, chemicals cycle, and a variety of species with different biological roles (niches) has evolved in response to changing environmental conditions.* Perhaps the two most astounding features of the planet are its incredibly rich diversity of life and its inherent ability to sustain life.

Here is the essence of this chapter. Each species here today represents a long chain of evolution and fills a unique ecological role (called its niche) in the Earth's communities and ecosystems. These species, communities, and ecosystems are also essential for future evolution as populations of species continue to adapt to changes in environmental conditions.

FIGURE 5-1 Natural capital: the Earth, a blue and white planet in the black void of space. Currently, it has the right physical and chemical conditions to allow the development of life as we know it.

There is grandeur to this view of life ... that, whilst this planet has gone cycling on ... endless forms most beautiful and most wonderful have been, and are being, evolved.

CHARLES DARWIN

CHAPTER PURPOSE AND QUESTIONS

Chapter 5 discusses how biodiversity evolved on this planet. The chapter addresses the following questions:

5-1 How do scientists account for the emergence of life on the Earth?

5-2 What is evolution, and how has it led to the current diversity of organisms on the Earth?

5-3 What is an ecological niche, and how does it help a population adapt to changing environmental conditions?

5-4 How are speciation, extinction, and diversity related?

5-5 What is the future of evolution and what should be our role in this future?

5-1 ORIGINS OF LIFE

How Did Life Emerge on the Primitive Earth? Chemistry First, Then Biology

Evidence indicates that the Earth's life is the result of about 1 billion years of chemical evolution to form the first cells, followed by about 3.7 billion years of biological evolution to form the species we find on the Earth today.

How did life on the Earth evolve to its present incredible diversity of species? We do not know the full answers to these questions. But considerable evidence suggests that life on the Earth developed in two phases over the past 4.6–4.7 billion years (Figure 5-2).

The first phase was **chemical evolution** of the organic molecules, biopolymers, and systems of chemical reactions needed to form the first cells. This took about 1 billion years.

This was followed by *biological evolution* from single-celled prokaryotic bacteria (Figure 4-3b, p. 62), to single-celled eukaryotic creatures (Figure 4-3a, p. 62), and then to multicellular organisms. This second phase has been going on for about 3.7 billion years (Appendix 4).

How Do We Know What Organisms Lived in the Past? Scientific Detective Work

Most of our knowledge about past life comes from fossils, chemical analysis, cores drilled out of buried ice, and DNA analysis.

Most of what we know of the Earth's life history comes from **fossils:** mineralized or petrified replicas of skeletons, bones, teeth, shells, leaves, and seeds, or impressions of such items. Fossils give us physical evidence of organisms that lived long ago and reveal what their internal structures looked like.

Despite its importance, the fossil record is uneven and incomplete. Some forms of life left no fossils, some fossils have decomposed, and others are yet to be found. The fossils we have found so far are believed to represent only about 1% of all the species that have ever lived.

Evidence about the Earth's early history also comes from chemical analysis and measurements of the half-lives of radioactive elements in primitive rocks and fossils. Information also comes from analysis of material in cores drilled out of buried ice and from comparisons of DNA of past and current organisms.

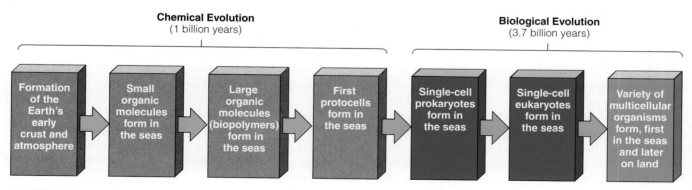

FIGURE 5-2 Summary of the hypothesized chemical and biological evolution of the Earth. This drawing is not to scale. Note that the time span for biological evolution is almost four times longer than that for chemical evolution.

What Is Evolution? Changing Genes

Evolution is the change in a population's genetic makeup over time.

According to scientific evidence, the major driving force of adaptation to changes in environmental conditions is **biological evolution, or evolution.** It is the change in a population's genetic makeup through successive generations. Note that *populations, not individuals, evolve by becoming genetically different.*

According to the **theory of evolution** first described in detail by Charles Darwin, all species descended from earlier, ancestral species. In other words, life comes from life. This widely accepted scientific theory explains how life has changed over the past 3.7 billion years and why life is so diverse today. Religious and other groups offer other explanations, but this is the accepted scientific explanation.

Biologists use the term **microevolution** to describe the small genetic changes that occur in a population. They use the term **macroevolution** to describe long-term, large-scale evolutionary changes through which new species form from ancestral species and other species are lost through extinction. Macroevolution also involves changes that occur at higher levels than species, such as the evolution of new genera, families, or classes of species (see Appendix 4).

How Does Microevolution Work? Changes in the Gene Pool

A population's gene pool changes over time when beneficial changes or mutations in its DNA molecules are passed on to offspring.

The first step in evolution is the development of *genetic variability* in a population. Every population of a species has a **gene pool:** its collection of genes or genetic resources potentially available to members' offspring in the next generation. *Microevolution* is a change in a population's gene pool over time.

Members of a population generally have the same number and kinds of genes. But a particular gene may have two or more different molecular forms, called **alleles.** Sexual reproduction leads to a random shuffling or recombination of alleles. As a result, each individual in a population (except identical twins) has a different combination of alleles.

Genetic variability in a population originates through **mutations:** random changes in the structure or number of DNA molecules in a cell that can be inherited by offspring. Mutations can occur in two ways. One is by exposure of DNA to external agents such as radioactivity, X-rays, and natural and human-made chemicals (called *mutagens*). The other is the result of random mistakes that sometimes occur in coded genetic instructions when DNA molecules are copied each time a cell divides and whenever an organism reproduces.

Mutations can occur in any cells, but only those in reproductive cells are passed on to offspring. Some mutations are harmless but most are lethal. *Every so often, a mutation is beneficial.* The result is new genetic traits that give the bearer and its offspring better chances for survival and reproduction under existing environmental conditions or when conditions change.

Mutations are random and unpredictable, are the only source of totally new genetic raw material (alleles), and are rare. Life is a genetic shuffle. Once created by mutation, new alleles can be shuffled together or recombined *randomly* to create new combinations of genes in populations of sexually reproducing species. In addition to mutations, another source of evolutionary change is the trading of genes between bacteria.

What Role Does Natural Selection Play in Microevolution? Backing Reproductive Winners

Some members of a population may have genetic traits that enhance their ability to survive and produce offspring with these traits.

Natural selection occurs when some individuals of a population have genetically based traits that increase their chances of survival and their ability to produce offspring with the same traits. Three conditions are necessary for evolution of a population by natural selection.

There must be *genetic variability* for a trait in a population. The trait must be *heritable,* meaning it can be passed from one generation to another. And the trait must somehow lead to **differential reproduction.** This means it must enable individuals with the trait to reproduce more offspring than other members of the population.

An **adaptation,** or **adaptive trait,** is any heritable trait that enables organisms to better survive and reproduce under prevailing environmental conditions. Natural selection causes any allele or set of alleles that result in an adaptive trait to become more common in succeeding generations, and alleles without the trait to become less common.

When faced with a critical change in environmental conditions, a population of a species has three possibilities: adapt to the new conditions through natural selection, migrate (if possible) to an area with more favourable conditions, or become extinct.

The process of microevolution can be summarized simply: *genes mutate, individuals are selected, and populations evolve.*

Biologists recognize three types of natural selection:

- *Directional natural selection* (Figure 5-3, left), in which changing conditions cause allele frequencies to shift so that individuals at one end of the spectrum become more common. An example of this is when insect populations develop genetic resistance to being sprayed with pesticides. This type of natural selection is most common during periods of environmental change or when members of a population migrate to a different habitat.

- *Stabilizing natural selection* (Figure 5-3, centre), which tends to eliminate individuals on both ends of the genetic spectrum. This form of natural selection occurs when an environment changes little and most members of the population are well adapted to that environment.

- *Diversifying natural selection* (Figure 5-3, right), which occurs when conditions favour individuals at both ends of the genetic spectrum, at the expense of individuals with intermediate traits. This type of natural selection may cause a population to be split into

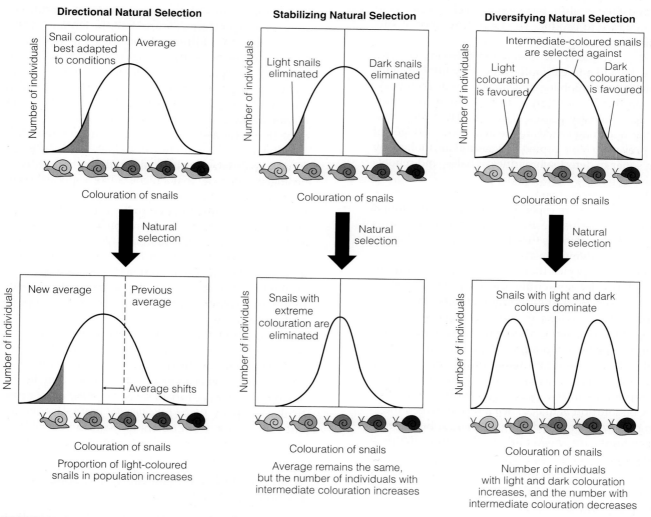

FIGURE 5-3 Three ways in which natural selection can occur, using the trait of colouration in a population of snails. In *directional natural selection*, changing environmental conditions select organisms with alleles that deviate from the norm so their offspring (lighter-coloured snails) make up a larger proportion of the population. In *stabilizing selection*, environmental factors eliminate fringe individuals (light- and dark-coloured snails) and increase the number of individuals with average genetic makeup (intermediate-coloured snails). In *diversifying natural selection*, environmental factors favour individuals with uncommon traits (light- and dark-coloured snails) and greatly reduce those with average traits (intermediate-coloured snails).

two groups, possibly providing a pressure toward the formation of new species.

What Is Coevolution? An Arms Race between Interacting Species

Interacting species can engage in a back-and-forth genetic contest in which each gains a temporary genetic advantage over the other.

Some biologists have proposed that *interactions between species* can also result in microevolution in each of their populations. According to this hypothesis, when populations of two different species interact over a long time, changes in the gene pool of one species can lead to changes in the gene pool of the other. This process is called **coevolution.** In this give-and-take evolutionary game, each species is in a genetic race to produce the largest number of surviving offspring.

One example is the interaction between bats and moths. Bats like to eat moths, and they hunt at night and use echolocation to navigate and locate their prey. They do this by emitting extremely high-frequency and high-intensity pulses of sound. Then they analyze the returning echoes to create a sonic "image" of their prey. (We have copied this natural technology by using sonar to detect submarines, whales, and schools of fish.)

As a countermeasure, some moth species have evolved ears that are especially sensitive to the sound frequencies bats use to find them. When the moths hear the bat frequencies they try to escape by falling to the ground or flying evasively.

Some bat species then evolved ways to counter this defence by switching the frequency of their sound pulses. Some moths then evolved their own high-frequency clicks to jam the bats' echolocation system (we have also learned to jam radar). Some bat species then adapted by turning off their echolocation system and using the moth's clicks to locate their prey. Each species continues refining its adaptations in this ongoing coevolutionary contest. Coevolution is like an arms race between interacting populations of different species. Sometimes the predators are ahead and at other times the prey get the upper hand.

> ### DID YOU KNOW
> Much of the research described in this section was conducted by Canadian professor Brock Fenton and his students. Fenton has been a professor of biology at York University and Western University in Ontario. He is an internationally recognized expert on the behaviour, ecology, and evolution of bats.

5-3 ECOLOGICAL NICHES AND ADAPTATION

What Is an Ecological Niche? How Species Coexist

Each species in an ecosystem has a specific role or way of life.

If asked what role a certain species such as a bat or a fish plays in an ecosystem, an ecologist would describe its **ecological niche,** or simply **niche** (pronounced "nitch"). It is a species' way of life or functional role in a community or ecosystem and involves everything that affects its survival and reproduction.

A species' ecological niche includes the *adaptations* or *adaptive traits* its members have acquired through evolution. It also includes that species' range of tolerance for various physical and chemical conditions, such as temperature (Figure 4-13, p. 68) and water availability. In addition, it includes the types and amounts of resources the species uses (such as food or nutrients and space), how it interacts with other living and nonliving components of the ecosystems in which it is found, and the role it plays in the energy flow and matter cycling in an ecosystem. Finding out about these things for just one species takes a lot of research.

The ecological niche of a species is different from its **habitat,** the physical location where it lives. Ecologists often say that a niche is like a species' occupation, whereas habitat is like its address.

A species' **fundamental niche** is the full potential range of physical, chemical, and biological conditions and resources it could theoretically use if there were no direct competition from other species. However, in a particular ecosystem, different species often compete with one another for one or more of the same resources. In other words, the niches of competing species overlap.

To survive and avoid competition for the same resources, a species usually occupies only part of its fundamental niche in a particular community or ecosystem—what ecologists call its **realized niche.** By analogy, you may be capable of being president of a particular company (your *fundamental professional niche*), but competition from others may mean you become only a vice president (your *realized professional niche*).

What Are Generalist and Specialist Species? Broad and Narrow Niches

Some species have broad ecological roles and others have narrower or more specialized roles.

Scientists use the niches of species to broadly classify them as *generalists* or *specialists*. **Generalist species** have broad niches (Figure 5-4, right curve). They can live in many different places, eat a variety of foods,

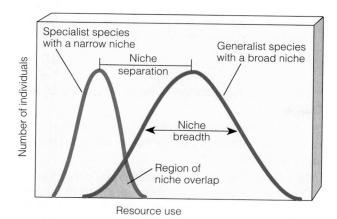

FIGURE 5-4 Overlap of the niches of two different species: a specialist and a generalist. In the overlap area the two species compete for one or more of the same resources. As a result, each species can occupy only a part of its fundamental niche; the part it occupies is its realized niche. Generalist species have a broad niche (right), and specialist species have a narrow niche (left).

and tolerate a wide range of environmental conditions. Flies, cockroaches, mice, rats, white-tailed deer, raccoons, coyotes, copperheads, channel catfish, and humans are generalist species.

Specialist species have narrow niches (Figure 5-4, left curve). They may be able to live in only one type of habitat, use only one or a few types of food, or tolerate only a narrow range of climatic and other environmental conditions. This makes them more prone to extinction when environmental conditions change.

For example, *tiger salamanders* are specialists because they can breed only in fishless ponds where their larvae will not be eaten. Threatened *red-cockaded woodpeckers* carve nest holes almost exclusively in

longleaf pines that are at least 75 years old. China's highly endangered *giant pandas* feed almost exclusively on various types of bamboo. Figure 5-5 shows shorebirds that feed in specialized niches on crustaceans, insects, and other organisms on sandy beaches and their adjoining coastal wetlands.

Is it better to be a generalist than a specialist? It depends. When environmental conditions are fairly constant, as in a tropical rain forest, specialists have an advantage because they have fewer competitors. But under rapidly changing environmental conditions, the generalist usually is better off than the specialist.

Natural selection can lead to an increase in specialized species when the niches of species compete intensely for scarce resources. Over time one species may evolve into a variety of species with different adaptations that reduce competition and allow them to share limited resources.

This **divergent evolution** of a single species into a variety of similar species with specialized niches can be illustrated by various species of honeycreepers on the island of Hawaii. Starting with a single ancestor, a variety of honeycreeper species evolved with different types of beaks specialized to feed on different types of food sources such as specific insects, nectar from different types of flowers, and certain types of seeds and fruit (Figure 5-6, p. 100).

Continued research has shown that the progenitors of the Hawaiian honeycreepers were likely Eurasian rosefinches that arrived from Asia about 5.7 million years ago. The adaptive radiation and speciation that followed can be related to the opportunities, constraints, and timing of events afforded by the sequential formation of the Hawaiian Islands (Lerner et al., 2011).

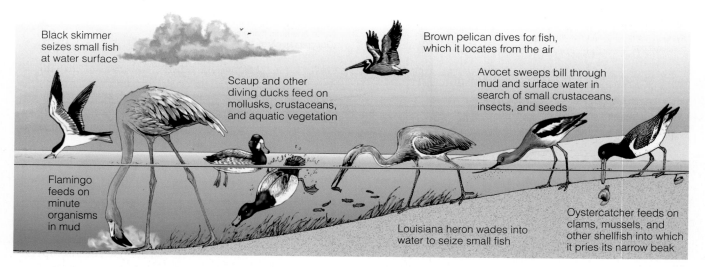

FIGURE 5-5 Specialized feeding niches of various bird species in a coastal wetland. Such resource partitioning reduces competition and allows sharing of limited resources.

Fruit and seed eaters

Greater Koa-finch

Kona Grosbeak

Akiapolaau

Maui Parrotbill

Insect and nectar eaters

Kuai Akialaoa

Amakihi

Crested Honeycreeper

Apapane

Unknown finch ancestor

FIGURE 5-6 Evolutionary divergence of honeycreepers into a variety of specialized ecological niches. Each of these related species has a beak specialized to take advantage of certain types of food resources.

In contrast, **convergent evolution** occurs when two distantly related groups of organisms develop similarities because they are adapting to similar environmental constraints or opportunities. For example, Australian sugar gliders and North American flying squirrels have evolved a similar appearance and a common ability to glide from tree to tree, yet the two species are from lineages (marsupials and placental mammals) that separated about 180 million years ago (Figure 5-7).

What Limits Adaptation? Life Is a Genetic Dice Game

A population's ability to adapt to new environmental conditions is limited by its gene pool and how fast it can reproduce.

Will adaptations to new environmental conditions in the not-too-distant future allow our skin to become more resistant to the harmful effects of ultraviolet radiation, our lungs to cope with air pollutants, and our liver to better detoxify pollutants?

The answer is *no* because of two limits to adaptations in nature. *First*, a change in environmental conditions can lead to adaptation only for genetic traits already present in the gene pool of a population. You must have dice to play the genetic dice game.

Second, even if a beneficial heritable trait is present in a population, the population's ability to adapt may be limited by its reproductive capacity. Populations of genetically diverse species that reproduce quickly—such as weeds, mosquitoes, rats, bacteria, or cockroaches—often adapt to a change in environmental conditions in a short time. In contrast, species that cannot produce large numbers of offspring rapidly, such as elephants, tigers, sharks, and humans, take a long time (typically thousands or even millions of years) to adapt through natural selection. You have to be able to throw the genetic dice fast.

Here is some *bad news* for most members of a population. Even when a favourable genetic trait is present in a population, most of the population would have

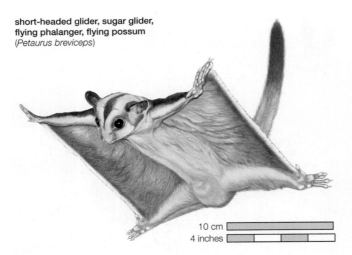

short-headed glider, sugar glider, flying phalanger, flying possum
(*Petaurus breviceps*)

10 cm
4 inches

southern flying squirrel, North American flying squirrel
(*Glaucomys volans*)

10 cm
4 inches

FIGURE 5-7 Convergent evolution as exemplified by Australian sugar gliders and North American flying squirrels, which show amazing similarities even though they are from lineages that separated millions of years ago. (© Universal Images Group Limited/Alamy)

to die or become sterile so that individuals with the trait could predominate and pass the trait on. Thus, most players get kicked out of the genetic dice game before they have a chance to win. This means that most members of the human population would have to die prematurely for hundreds of thousands of generations for a new genetic trait to predominate. This is hardly a desirable solution to the environmental problems we face.

What Are Two Commonly Misunderstood Aspects of Evolution?

Evolution is about leaving the most descendants, not about acquiring specific traits or being the strongest.

There are two common misconceptions about evolution. One is that organisms evolve in response to the use and disuse of different structures. For example, Jean-Baptiste de Lamarck (1744–1829) speculated that giraffes developed long necks as a result of stretching them to feed on the highest branches of trees; he thought that these *acquired* characteristics were then passed on to their young. According to Charles Darwin (1809–82), giraffes that possessed the longest necks would best be able to compete for food in times of shortage and would therefore leave *more young*, bearing the successful traits of their parents, through a process of *natural selection*. Since Darwin, various alternatives to these ideas have been proposed. For example, some researchers have pointed out that the long legs and necks of giraffes also afford them great protection from predators, and that male giraffes with the longest necks gain preferential access to females by outcompeting other males in physical contests called "necking" in which the males batter each other with their heads and necks (Simmons and Scheepers, 1996; Mitchell and Skinner, 2003). Note that the three latter

ideas all involve natural selection and are centred on factors that would promote differential production of young, not on characteristics acquired during an organism's lifetime.

The other misconception is that "survival of the fittest" means "survival of the strongest." To biologists, *fitness* is a measure of reproductive success, not strength. Thus the fittest individuals are those that leave the most descendants.

5-4 SPECIATION, EXTINCTION, AND BIODIVERSITY

How Do New Species Evolve? Moving Out and Moving On

A new species arises when members of a population are isolated from other members so long that changes in their genetic makeup prevent them from producing fertile offspring if they get together again.

Under certain circumstances, natural selection can lead to an entirely new species. In this process, called **speciation,** two species arise from one. For sexually reproducing species, a new species is formed when some members of a population can no longer breed with other members to produce fertile offspring.

The most common mechanism of speciation (especially among animals) is called *allopatric speciation*. It takes place in two phases: geographic isolation and reproductive isolation. **Geographic isolation** occurs when different groups of the same population become physically isolated from one another for long periods.

For example, part of a population may migrate in search of food and then begin living in another area with different environmental conditions (Figure 5-8). Populations also may become separated by a physical

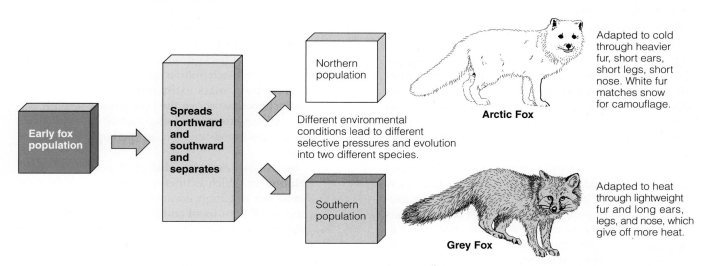

FIGURE 5-8 How geographic isolation can lead to reproductive isolation, divergence, and speciation.

barrier (such as a mountain range, stream, lake, or road), by a change such as a volcanic eruption or earthquake, or when a few individuals are carried to a new area by wind or water. Other causes are the advance of glaciers during ice ages, changes in sea level that can create islands, shifts in ocean currents, a warmer or cooler climate that shifts vegetation northward or southward or up or down slopes, and a drier climate that divides a large lake into several small lakes.

The second phase of allopatric speciation is **reproductive isolation.** It occurs when mutation and natural selection operate independently in the gene pools of two geographically isolated populations. If this *divergence* process continues long enough, members of isolated populations of a sexually reproducing species may become so different in genetic makeup that when they get together again, they cannot produce live, fertile offspring. Then one species has become two, and speciation has occurred through *divergent evolution.*

For some rapidly reproducing organisms, this type of speciation may occur within hundreds of years. For most species it takes from tens of thousands to millions of years, which makes it difficult to observe and document the appearance of a new species.

A less common form of speciation is called *sympatric speciation.* It is the creation of new species when groups in a population living close together are unable to interbreed because of a mutation or subtle behavioural changes. Some insects are candidates for this type of speciation when, for example, two populations that are feeding on different types of plants experience different mutations.

What Is Extinction? Going, Going, Gone

A species becomes extinct when its populations cannot adapt to changing environmental conditions.

After speciation, the second process affecting the number and types of species on the Earth is **extinction,** in which an entire species ceases to exist. Fossil records indicate that species tend to exist for 1–10 million years before becoming extinct, although catastrophic events accelerate the extinction process.

For most of the Earth's geological history, species have faced incredible challenges to their existence. Continents have broken apart and moved over millions of years (Figure 5-9). The Earth's land area has repeatedly shrunk as continents have been flooded, and expanded when the world's oceans have shrunk. At other times, much of the planet's land has been covered with ice.

The Earth's life has also had to cope with volcanic eruptions, meteorites and asteroids crashing onto the planet, and releases of large amounts of methane trapped beneath the ocean floor. Some of these events created dust clouds that shut down or sharply reduced photosynthesis long enough to eliminate huge numbers of producers and, soon thereafter, the consumers that fed on them.

Populations of species in some places have also been reduced or eliminated by newly arrived migrant species or species that are accidentally or deliberately introduced into new areas. More recently, the human species arrived and began using or degrading more and more of the Earth's resources and habitats. Today's biodiversity represents the species that have survived and thrived despite environmental upheavals.

What Is the Difference between Background Extinction, Mass Extinction, and Mass Depletion? Wiping Out Large Groups

All species eventually become extinct, but sometimes drastic changes in environmental conditions eliminate large groups of species.

Extinction is the ultimate fate of all species, just as death is for all individual organisms. Biologists estimate that more than 99% of all the species that ever existed are now extinct.

As local environmental conditions change, a certain number of species disappear at a low rate, called **background extinction.** Based on the fossil record and analysis of ice cores, biologists estimate that the average annual background extinction rate is one to five species for each million species on the Earth.

In contrast, **mass extinction** is a significant rise in extinction rates above the background level. It is a catastrophic, widespread (often global) event in which large groups of existing species (perhaps 25–70%) are wiped out.

Scientists have also identified periods of **mass depletion** in which extinction rates are higher than normal but not high enough to classify as a mass extinction. Recent fossil and geological evidence casts doubt on the hypothesis that there have been five mass extinctions over the past 500 million years as is reported in many biology and environmental science textbooks. The new evidence suggests that there have

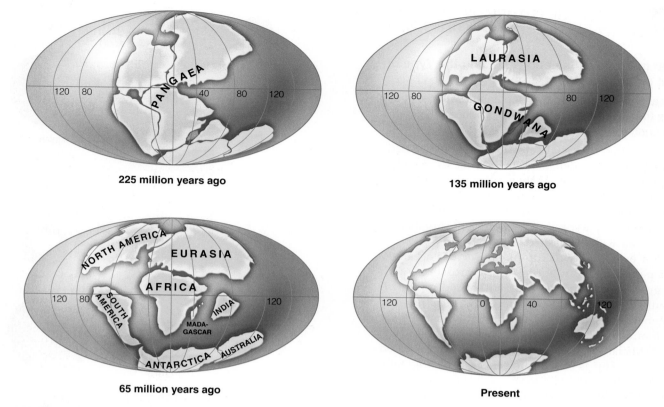

225 million years ago

135 million years ago

65 million years ago

Present

FIGURE 5-9 *Continental drift,* the extremely slow movement of continents over millions of years on several gigantic plates. This process plays a role in the extinction of species and the rise of new species. Populations are geographically and eventually reproductively isolated as land masses float apart and new coastal regions are created. Rock and fossil evidence indicates that about 200–250 million years ago, all of the Earth's present-day continents were locked together in a supercontinent called Pangaea (top left). About 180 million years ago, Pangaea began splitting apart as the Earth's huge plates separated and eventually resulted in today's locations of the continents (bottom right).

been two mass extinctions and three mass depletions during this period.

How Are Human Activities Affecting the Earth's Biodiversity? The Earth Giveth and We Taketh

The scientific consensus is that human activities are decreasing the Earth's biodiversity.

Speciation minus extinction equals *biodiversity,* the planet's genetic raw material for future evolution in response to changing environmental conditions. Extinction is a natural process. But much evidence indicates that humans have recently become a major force in the premature extinction of species. According to biologists Stuart Pimm and Edward O. Wilson, three independent measures estimate that during the 20th century, extinction rates increased by 100–1 000 times the natural background extinction rate of about one to five species per million species per year. In other words, the annual estimated human-caused extinction rate is 100 to 1 000 species per million species.

Wilson and Pimm warn that projected increases in the human population and resource consumption may cause the premature extinction of at least one-fifth of the Earth's current species by 2030 and half by the end of the century. This could constitute a new *mass depletion* and possibly a new *mass extinction.* According to Wilson, if we make an "all-out effort to save the biologically richest parts of the world, the amount of loss can be cut at least by half."

On our short time scale, such major losses cannot be recouped by formation of new species; it took millions of years after each of the Earth's past mass extinctions and depletions for life to recover to the previous level of biodiversity. If the recovery period lasts at least 5 million years, this would be 20 times longer than we have been around as a species.

We are also destroying or degrading ecosystems such as tropical forests, coral reefs, and wetlands that are centres for future speciation. Genetic engineering cannot stop this loss of biodiversity because genetic engineers rely on natural biodiversity for their genetic raw material.

5-5 WHAT IS THE FUTURE OF EVOLUTION?

What Is Artificial Selection? Getting the Type of Fruit or Dog You Want

Humans pick members of a population with genetic traits they like and breed them to produce offspring with such traits.

We have used **artificial selection** to change genetic characteristics of populations. In this process, we select one or more desirable genetic traits in the population of a plant or animal, such as a type of wheat, fruit, or dog. Then we use *selective breeding* to end up with populations of the species containing large numbers of individuals with the desired traits.

For example, two crop plants such as a variety of a pear and of an apple can be crossbred with the goal of producing a pear with a more reddish colour (Figure 5-10). This is repeated for a number of generations until the desired trait in the pear predominates.

Artificial selection results in many domesticated breeds or hybrids of the same species, all originally developed from one wild species. For example, despite their widely different genetic traits, the hundreds of different breeds of dogs are members of the same species because they can interbreed and produce fertile offspring.

Artificial selection has yielded food crops with higher yields, cows that give more milk, trees that grow faster, and a variety of types of dogs and cats.

But traditional crossbreeding is a slow process. And it can combine traits only from species that are close to one another genetically.

What Is Genetic Engineering? Transferring Genes between Species

Genetic engineers create genetically modified organisms by transplanting genes from one species to the DNA of another species.

Recently scientists have learned how to use genetic engineering to speed up our ability to manipulate genes. **Genetic engineering,** or **gene splicing,** is a set of techniques for isolating, modifying, multiplying, and recombining genes from different organisms. It enables scientists to transfer genes between different species that would never interbreed in nature. For example, genes from a fish species can be put into a tomato or strawberry.

The resulting organisms are called **genetically modified organisms (GMOs)** or **transgenic organisms.** Figure 5-11 outlines the steps involved in developing a genetically modified or transgenic plant. Study this figure carefully.

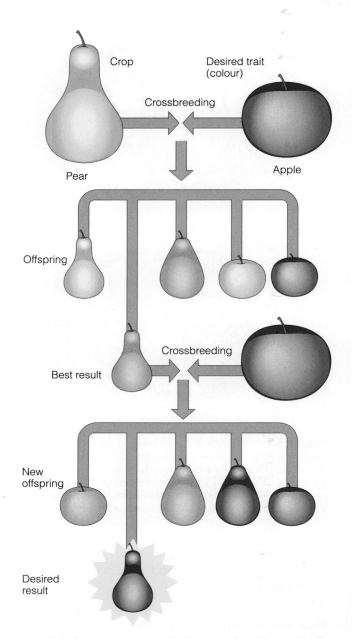

FIGURE 5-10 *Traditional crossbreeding* of species that are fairly close to one another genetically.

Gene splicing takes about half as much time to develop a new crop or animal variety and costs less than traditional crossbreeding. Although traditional crossbreeding involves mixing the genes of similar types of organisms through breeding, genetic engineering allows us to transfer traits between different types of organisms.

Scientists have used gene splicing to develop modified crop plants, genetically engineered drugs, and pest-resistant plants. They have also created genetically engineered bacteria to help clean up spills of oil and other toxic pollutants.

Genetic engineers have also learned how to produce a *clone* or genetically identical version of an

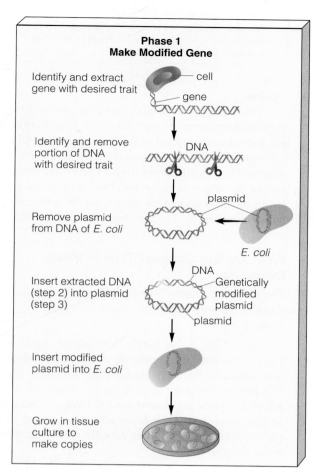

Phase 1
Make Modified Gene

Identify and extract gene with desired trait — cell, gene

Identify and remove portion of DNA with desired trait — DNA

Remove plasmid from DNA of *E. coli* — plasmid, *E. coli*

Insert extracted DNA (step 2) into plasmid (step 3) — DNA, Genetically modified plasmid, plasmid

Insert modified plasmid into *E. coli*

Grow in tissue culture to make copies

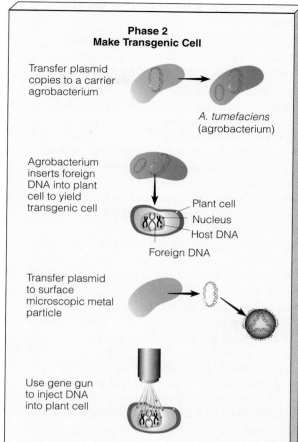

Phase 2
Make Transgenic Cell

Transfer plasmid copies to a carrier agrobacterium — *A. tumefaciens* (agrobacterium)

Agrobacterium inserts foreign DNA into plant cell to yield transgenic cell — Plant cell, Nucleus, Host DNA, Foreign DNA

Transfer plasmid to surface microscopic metal particle

Use gene gun to inject DNA into plant cell

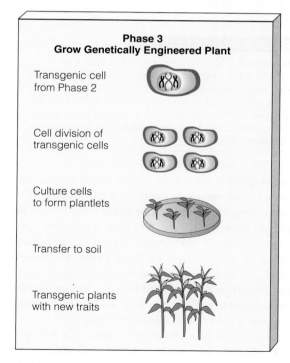

Phase 3
Grow Genetically Engineered Plant

Transgenic cell from Phase 2

Cell division of transgenic cells

Culture cells to form plantlets

Transfer to soil

Transgenic plants with new traits

individual in a population. Scientists have made clones of domestic animals, such as sheep and cows, and may someday be able to clone humans—a possibility that excites some people and horrifies others.

Bioengineers have developed chickens that lay low-cholesterol eggs, tomatoes with genes that can help prevent some types of cancer, and bananas and potatoes that contain oral vaccines to treat various viral diseases in developing countries where needles and refrigeration are not available.

Researchers envision using genetically engineered animals to act as biofactories for producing drugs, vaccines, antibodies, hormones, industrial chemicals such as plastics and detergents, and human body organs. This new field is called **biopharming.** For example, cows may be able to produce insulin for treating diabetes, perhaps more cheaply than making the insulin in laboratories. Have you considered this field as a career choice?

FIGURE 5-11 *Genetic engineering.* Steps in genetically modifying a plant.

What Are Some Concerns about the Genetic Revolution? Genetic Wonderland or Genetic Wasteland

Genetic engineering has great promise, but it is an unpredictable process and raises a number of privacy, ethical, legal, and environmental issues.

The hype about genetic engineering can lead us to believe that its results are controllable and predictable. In reality, most current forms of genetic engineering are messy and unpredictable. Genetic engineers can insert a gene into the nucleus of a cell but with current technology they do not know whether the cell will incorporate the new gene into its DNA. They also do not know where the new gene will be located in the DNA molecule's structure and what effects this will have on the organism.

Thus, *genetic engineering is a trial-and-error process* with many failures and unexpected results. Indeed, the average success rate of current genetic engineering experiments is only about 1%.

Some people have genes that make them more likely to develop certain genetic diseases or disorders. We now have the power to detect these genetic deficiencies, even before birth. This raises some important issues. If gene therapy is developed for correcting these deficiencies, who will get it? Will it be mostly for the rich? Will this mean more abortions of genetically defective fetuses? Will health insurers refuse to insure people with certain genetic defects that could lead to health problems? Will employers refuse to hire them?

CONSIDER, DISCUSS, OR DEBATE

Should genetic screening be required as part of an application for a job, health insurance, or life insurance? What are the implications? DNA testing is becoming more common and affordable. For about $400, you can have your DNA genotyped from a sample of your saliva (https://www.23andme.com/howitworks). What do you think about this?

Some people dream of a day when our genetic prowess could eliminate death and aging altogether. As one's cells, organs, or other parts wear out or are damaged, they would be replaced with new ones. These replacement parts might be grown in genetic engineering laboratories or biopharms. Or people might choose to have a clone available for spare parts. Several countries have banned human cloning, but the research is taking place anyway and human clones may appear in the not-too-distant future.

This raises a number of questions: Is it moral to do this? Who decides? Who regulates it? Will genetically designed humans and clones have the same legal rights as other people?

CONSIDER, DISCUSS, OR DEBATE

Should we legalize the production of human clones if a reasonably safe technology for doing so becomes available?

What might be the environmental impacts of such genetic developments on resource use, pollution, and environmental degradation? If everyone could live with good health as long as they wanted for a price, sellers of body makeovers would encourage customers to line up. Each of these wealthy, long-lived people could have an enormous ecological footprint for perhaps centuries.

What Are Our Options? Time to Make Decisions

There are arguments over how much we should regulate genetic engineering research and development.

In the 1990s, a backlash developed against the increasing use of genetically modified food plants and animals. Some protesters are strongly against this new technology for a variety of reasons. Others advocate slowing down and taking a closer look at the short- and long-term advantages and disadvantages of this and other rapidly emerging genetic technologies.

Or at the very least, they say, we should require that all genetically modified crops and animal products and foods containing such components be clearly labelled as such. This would give consumers a more informed choice, as do the food labels that now require listing ingredients and nutritional information. Makers of genetically modified products strongly oppose such labelling (as food manufacturers opposed the other types of food labelling now in use) because they fear it would hurt sales.

Supporters of genetic engineering wonder why there is so much concern. After all, we have been genetically modifying plants and animals for centuries. Now we have a faster, better, and perhaps cheaper way to do it, so why not use it?

But proponents of more careful control of genetic engineering point out that most new technologies have had unintended harmful consequences (Figure 3-4, p. 40). The ecological lesson is that whenever we intervene in nature we must pause and ask, "What happens next?" This is why many analysts are cautious about rushing into genetic engineering and other forms of biotechnology without more careful evaluation of possible unintended consequences. See Section 14-6 for further discussion of genetic engineering in food production.

CONSIDER, DISCUSS, OR DEBATE

Should there be stricter government control over the development and use of genetic engineering technology?

How Did We Become Such a Powerful Species So Quickly? Brain and Thumb Power

We have thrived as a species mostly because of our complex brains and strong opposable thumbs.

Like other species, we have survived and thrived so far because we have certain adaptive traits. What are they?

First, look at the traits we do not have. We lack exceptional strength, speed, and agility. We do not have weapons such as claws or fangs, and we lack a protective shell or body armour.

Our senses are unremarkable. We see only visible light—a tiny fraction of the spectrum of electromagnetic radiation that bathes the Earth. We cannot see infrared radiation, as a rattlesnake can, or the ultraviolet light that guides some insects to their favourite flowers.

We cannot see as well or as far as an eagle or see well in the night like some owls and other nocturnal creatures. We cannot hear the high-pitched sounds that help bats manoeuvre in the dark. Our ears cannot pick up low-pitched sounds that are the songs of whales as they glide through the world's oceans. We cannot smell as keenly as a dog or a wolf. By such measures, our physical and sensory powers are pitiful.

Yet we have survived and flourished within less than a twitch of the Earth's 3.7-billion-year evolutionary history. Analysts attribute our success to two evolutionary adaptations: a *complex brain* and *strong opposable thumbs* that allow us to grip and use tools better than the few other animals that have thumbs. This has enabled us to develop technologies that extend our limited senses, weapons, and protective devices.

As a newly evolved infant species, we have quickly developed many powerful technologies to take over much of the Earth's life-support systems to meet our basic needs and rapidly growing wants. We named ourselves *Homo sapiens sapiens*—the doubly wise species. If we keep degrading the life-support system for us and other species, some say we should be called *Homo ignoramus*—the unwise species. During this century, we will probably learn which of these names is appropriate.

The *good news* is that we can change our ways. We can learn more about how to work with nature by understanding and copying the ways it has sustained itself for several billion years despite major changes in environmental conditions.

In the Earth's ballet of life that has been playing on the global stage for about 3.7 billion years, life and death are interconnected. Some species appear and some disappear, but the show goes on. We only recently became members of this evolutionary ballet. Will we temporarily interrupt the show, take out some of the dancers, and get kicked off the stage? Or will we learn the rules of the ballet and have a long run? We live in interesting and challenging times.

All we have yet discovered is but a trifle in comparison with what lies hid in the great treasury of nature.

ANTONIE VAN LEEUWENHOEK

CHAPTER REVIEW

1. Review the Key Questions for this chapter on p. 95. Explain how the planet Earth appears to be "just right" for life as we know it. What would have happened if the Earth had been different in its characteristics (larger, farther from the sun, or with a different spin)?

2. What is *biological evolution*? What is *natural selection*? What is a *fossil* and why are fossils important in understanding biological evolution? What is a *mutation* and what role do mutations play in evolution by natural selection? What is an *adaptation (adaptive trait)*? What is *differential reproduction*? How did we become such a powerful species?

3. Summarize the *theory of evolution* in a few sentences. What is *microevolution* as compared to *macroevolution*? Describe three types of natural selection.

4. What are two limits to evolution by natural selection? What are two myths about evolution through natural selection? What is *coevolution*? Distinguish between *divergent evolution* and *convergent evolution*.

5. What is an *ecological niche*? Distinguish between *specialist species* and *generalist species* and give an example of each.

6. What is *speciation*? Distinguish between *geographic isolation* and *reproductive isolation* and explain how they can lead to the formation of a new species.

7. Describe how geologic processes and climate change have affected natural selection in the past. How might these factors combine to affect organisms in the future?

8. What is *extinction*? What is an *endemic species* and why might it be vulnerable to extinction? Distinguish between *background extinction* and *mass extinction*.

9. Distinguish between *artificial selection* and *genetic engineering (gene splicing)* and describe some examples.

What are some possible social, ethical, and environmental problems that might be associated with the widespread use of genetic engineering? What are a *gene pool* and an *allele*? How might these terms be involved in an explanation of *allopatric speciation*?

10. What is the relationship between biodiversity and the characteristics of our planet? Why is biodiversity so strongly linked with the other three *principles of sustainability* described in Chapter 1?

CRITICAL THINKING

1. **(a)** How would you respond to someone who tells you that he or she does not believe in biological evolution because it is "just a theory"? **(b)** How would you respond to a statement that we should not worry about air pollution because through natural selection the human species will develop lungs that can detoxify pollutants?

2. How would you respond to someone who says that because extinction is a natural process we should not worry about the loss of biodiversity?

3. Explain why you are for or against each of the following: **(a)** requiring labels indicating the use of genetically engineered components in any food item, **(b)** using genetic engineering to develop "superior" human beings, and **(c)** using genetic engineering to eliminate aging and death.

4. Congratulations! You are in charge of the future evolution on the Earth. What are the three most important things you would do?

PROJECTS

1. An important adaptation of humans is a strong opposable thumb, which allows us to grip and manipulate things with our hands. As a demonstration of the importance of this trait, fold each of your thumbs into the palm of its hand and then tape them securely in that position for an entire day. After the demonstration, make a list of the things you could not do without the use of your thumbs.

2. Use the library or the Internet to find out what controls now exist on genetically engineered organisms and how well such controls are enforced.

3. Use the library or the Internet to find bibliographic information about at least two of the following people mentioned in the chapter: *Charles Darwin, Brock Fenton, Jean-Baptiste de Lamarck, Antonie van Leeuwenhoek, Stuart Pimm, Edward O. Wilson, Tuzo Wilson.*

Climate and Terrestrial Biodiversity

Blowing in the Wind: A Story of Connections

Wind, **a vital** part of the planet's circulatory system, connects most life on the Earth. Without wind, the tropics would be unbearably hot and most of the rest of the planet would freeze.

Winds also transport nutrients from one place to another. Dust rich in phosphates and iron blows across the Atlantic from the Sahara Desert in Africa (Figure 6-1). This helps build up agricultural soils in the Bahamas and supplies nutrients for plants in the upper canopy of rain forests in Brazil. Iron-rich dust blowing from China's Gobi Desert falls into the Pacific Ocean between Hawaii and Alaska. This input of iron stimulates the growth of phytoplankton, the minute producers that support ocean food webs. This is the *good news*.

The *bad news* is that wind also transports harmful viruses, bacteria, fungi, and particles of long-lived pesticides and toxic metals. Particles of reddish-brown soil and pesticides banned in North America are blown from Africa's deserts and eroding farmlands into the sky, and drift back to North America.

More *bad news.* Some types of fungi in this dust may play a role in degrading or killing coral reefs in the Florida Keys and the Caribbean. Scientists are currently studying possible links between contaminated African dust and a sharp rise in rates of asthma in the Caribbean since 1973.

Particles of iron-rich dust from Africa that enhance the productivity of algae have also been linked to outbreaks of toxic algal blooms—referred to as *red tides*—off the East Coast of North America. People who eat shellfish contaminated by a toxin produced in red tides can become paralyzed or even die. Europe and the Middle East also receive contaminated African dust.

Pollution and dust from rapidly industrializing China and Central Asia blow across the Pacific Ocean and degrade air quality over western North America. In 2001, climate scientists reported that a huge dust storm of soil particles blown from northern China had blanketed areas from Canada to Arizona with a layer of dust. Studies show that Asian pollution contributes as much as 10% to West Coast smog, a threat expected to increase as China industrializes.

(continued)

FIGURE 6-1 Some of the dust shown here, blowing from Africa's Sahara Desert, can end up as a mix of soil nutrients and toxic pollutants showering down on South, Central, and North America.

NASA

There is also *mixed news.* Particles from volcanic eruptions ride the winds, circle the globe, and change the Earth's temperature for a while. Emissions from the 1991 eruption of Mount Pinatubo in the Philippines cooled the Earth slightly for three years, temporarily masking signs of global warming. And volcanic ash, like the blowing desert dust, adds valuable trace minerals to the soil where it settles.

The lesson, once again, is that there is no away because *everything is connected.* Wind acts as part of the planet's circulatory system for heat, moisture, plant nutrients, and long-lived pollutants we put into the air. Movement of soil particles from one place to another by wind and water is a natural phenomenon. But when we disturb the soil and leave it unprotected, we hasten and intensify this process.

Wind is also an important factor in climate through its influence on global air circulation patterns. Climate, in turn, is crucial for determining what kinds of plant and animal life are found in the major biomes of the biosphere, as discussed in this chapter.

To do science is to search for repeated patterns, not simply to accumulate facts, and to do the science of geographical ecology is to search for patterns of plant and animal life that can be put on a map.

ROBERT H. MACARTHUR

CHAPTER PURPOSE AND QUESTIONS

Chapter 6 describes the main features of climate that determine where characteristic assemblages of flora and fauna will thrive on this planet. The chapter addresses the following questions:

6-1   What key factors determine the Earth's weather?

6-2   What key factors determine the Earth's climate?

6-3   How does climate determine where the Earth's major biomes are found?

6-4   What are the major types of desert biomes, and how do human activities affect them?

6-5   What are the major types of grassland biomes, and how do human activities affect them?

6-6   What are the major types of forest biomes, and how do human activities affect them?

6-7   Why are mountain biomes important, and how do human activities affect them?

6-1   WEATHER: A BRIEF INTRODUCTION

What Is Weather? When Air Masses Meet

Weather is the result of the atmospheric conditions in a particular area over short time periods and is produced mostly by interacting air masses.

Weather is an area's short-term atmospheric conditions—typically over hours or days. Examples of atmospheric conditions are temperature, pressure, moisture content, precipitation, sunshine, cloud cover, and wind direction and speed.

Meteorologists use equipment on weather balloons, aircraft, ships, and satellites, as well as radar and stationary sensors, to obtain data on weather variables. They feed the data into computer models to draw weather maps. Other computer models project the weather for the next several days by calculating the probabilities that air masses, winds, and other factors will move and change in certain ways.

Much of the weather you experience is the result of interactions between the leading edges or fronts of moving masses of warm and cold air. Weather changes as one air mass replaces or meets another. The most dramatic changes in weather occur along a **front,** the boundary between two air masses with different temperatures and densities.

A **warm front** is the boundary between an advancing warm air mass and the cooler one it is replacing (Figure 6-2, top). Because warm air is less dense (weighs less per unit of volume) than cool air, an advancing warm front rises up over a mass of cool air. As the warm front rises, its moisture begins condensing into droplets to form layers of clouds at different altitudes. Gradually the clouds thicken, descend to a lower altitude, and often release their moisture as rainfall. A moist warm front can bring days of cloudy skies and drizzle.

A **cold front** (Figure 6-2, bottom) is the leading edge of an advancing mass of cold air. Because cold air is denser than warm air, an advancing cold front stays close to the ground and wedges underneath less dense warmer air. An approaching cold front produces rapidly moving, towering clouds called *thunderheads.*

As a cold front passes through, we often experience high surface winds and thunderstorms. After the front passes through, we usually have cooler temperatures and a clear sky.

Near the top of the troposphere, 7–16 kilometres (4–10 miles) above sea level, are powerful winds called **jet streams** (Figure 6-3). These rivers of high-speed air are several hundred kilometres across, 2–3 kilometres (1–2 miles) deep, and travelling at speeds as high as 400 kilometres (250 miles) per hour. Jet streams generally move from west to east and can affect weather patterns by steering high- or low-pressure systems, and

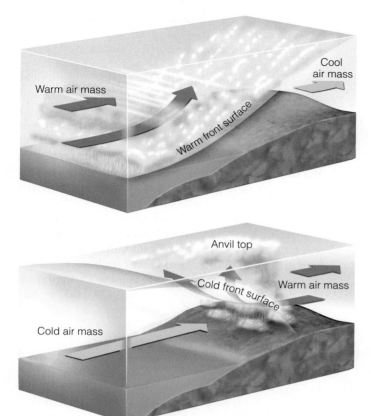

FIGURE 6-2 A *warm front* (top) occurs when an advancing mass of warm air meets and rises up over a retreating mass of denser cool air. A *cold front* (bottom) is the boundary formed when a mass of cold air wedges beneath a retreating mass of less dense warm air.

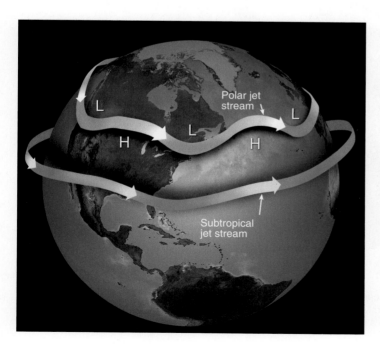

by blocking the movement of upper-level moisture and air. For example, changes in the position of the jet stream could prevent moist air from blowing over a region, causing a drought, or the jet stream might funnel moisture and energy to another area, producing violent storms and flooding.

SELF CHECK

The jet stream and other meteorological factors
You can monitor the position of the jet stream and other meteorological factors such as highs and lows by going to the website of the Environment Canada Weather Office at http://www.weatheroffice.gc.ca/jet_stream/index_e.html. Do this regularly and form your own conclusions about the impact of the jet stream on your weather.

What Are Highs and Lows? Pressure Changes

Weather is affected by up and down movements of masses of air with high and low atmospheric pressure.

Weather is also affected by changes in atmospheric pressure. *Air pressure* results from zillions of tiny molecules of gases (mostly nitrogen and oxygen) in the atmosphere zipping around at incredible speeds and hitting and bouncing off anything they encounter.

Atmospheric pressure is greater near the Earth's surface because the molecules in the atmosphere are squeezed together under the weight of the air above. An air mass with high pressure, called a **high,** contains cool, dense air that descends toward the Earth's surface and becomes warmer. Fair weather follows as long as the high-pressure air mass remains over an area.

In contrast, a low-pressure air mass, called a **low,** produces cloudy and sometimes stormy weather. Because of its low pressure and low density, the centre of a low rises, and its warm air expands and cools. When the temperature drops below a certain level where condensation takes place, called the *dew point,* moisture in the air condenses and forms clouds. If the droplets in the clouds coalesce into large and heavy drops, precipitation occurs. Recall that the condensation of water vapour into water drops usually requires that the air contain suspended tiny particles of material such as dust, smoke, sea salts, or volcanic ash. These so-called condensation nuclei provide surfaces on which the droplets of water can form and coalesce. Now you know how rain forms.

FIGURE 6-3 A jet stream is a rapidly flowing air current that moves west to east in a wavy pattern. This figure shows a polar jet stream and a subtropical jet stream in winter. In reality, jet streams are discontinuous and their positions vary from day to day. (From AHRENS. *Meteorology Today*, 1E. © 2012 Nelson Education Ltd. Reproduced by permission. www.cengage.com/permissions)

What Are Tornadoes and Tropical Cyclones? Weather Godzillas

Tornadoes and tropical storms are weather extremes that can cause lots of damage but can sometimes have beneficial ecological effects.

Sometimes we experience *weather extremes*. Two examples are violent storms called *tornadoes* (which form over land) and *tropical cyclones* (which form over warm ocean waters and sometimes pass over coastal land).

Tornadoes or *twisters* are swirling funnel-shaped clouds that form over land. They can destroy houses and cause other serious damage in areas when they touch down on the Earth's surface. The United States is the world's most tornado-prone country, followed by Canada.

Tornadoes are usually formed in the American Midwest, when a large, dry cool air front moving southward from Canada runs into a large mass of humid air moving northward from the Gulf of Mexico. Most tornadoes occur in the spring and summer when fronts of cool air from the north penetrate deeply into the midwestern plains.

As the large warm-air mass moves rapidly over the more dense mass of cool air it rises rapidly and forms strong vertical convection currents that suck air upward, as shown in Figure 6-4. Trace the flows in this figure. Scientists hypothesize that the rising vortex of air starts spinning because the air near the ground in the funnel is moving slower than the air above. This rolls or spins the air ahead of the advancing front in a vertically rising air mass or vortex.

Once considered to be rare events in Canada, tornadoes are happening more frequently. In an average year, Canada experiences 80 tornadoes resulting in two deaths, 20 injuries, and tens of millions of dollars in damage. Although they can occur anywhere from

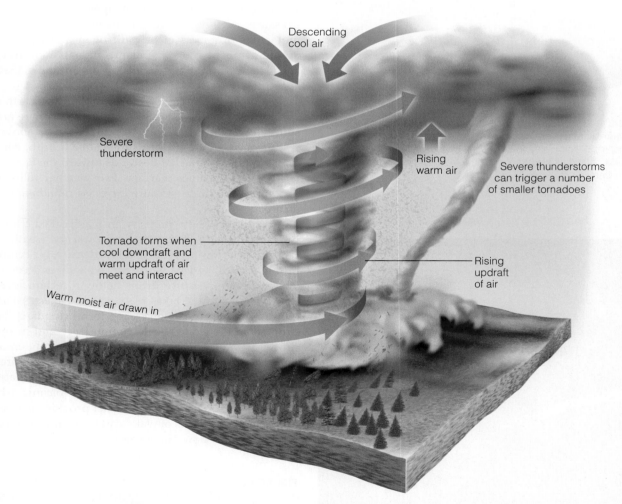

Descending cool air

Severe thunderstorm

Rising warm air

Severe thunderstorms can trigger a number of smaller tornadoes

Tornado forms when cool downdraft and warm updraft of air meet and interact

Rising updraft of air

Warm moist air drawn in

FIGURE 6-4 Formation of a *tornado* or *twister*. Although twisters can form any time of the year, the most active tornado season in North America is usually in spring and summer. Meteorologists cannot tell us with great accuracy when and where most tornadoes will form.

coast to coast and as far north as Edmonton, tornadoes are most common in southern Ontario, Alberta, and southeastern Quebec. Canada's most severe tornadoes on record are the Regina tornado of 1912 and the Edmonton tornado of 1987, which claimed 28 and 27 lives, respectively, and injured hundreds.

You can learn more about tornadoes by visiting the websites of Public Safety Canada (http://www.publicsafety.gc.ca/res/em/nh/to/index-eng.aspx) and Natural Resources Canada (http://atlas.nrcan.gc.ca/site/english/maps/environment/naturalhazards/naturalhazards1999/majortornadoes/1).

The United States experiences about 1 300 tornadoes annually, averaging 60 deaths and $500 million in damages per year. According to Edwards (2012), the deadliest U.S. tornado was the Tri-State tornado of 1925, which killed 695 people. The costliest U.S. tornado was the May 2011 Joplin Missouri tornado, which caused $28 billion worth of damage.

Large and dangerous storms called *tropical cyclones* are spawned by the formation of low-pressure cells of air over warm tropical seas. Figure 6-5 shows how a tropical cyclone is formed. *Hurricanes* are tropical cyclones in the Atlantic Ocean; those forming in the Pacific Ocean are called *typhoons*. Tropical cyclones are large (400–1 600 kilometres/250–994 miles across) and gather their strength slowly. Scientists are able to use an array of methods, including weather satellites, reconnaissance flights, and Doppler radar, to monitor the formation and movement of cyclones.

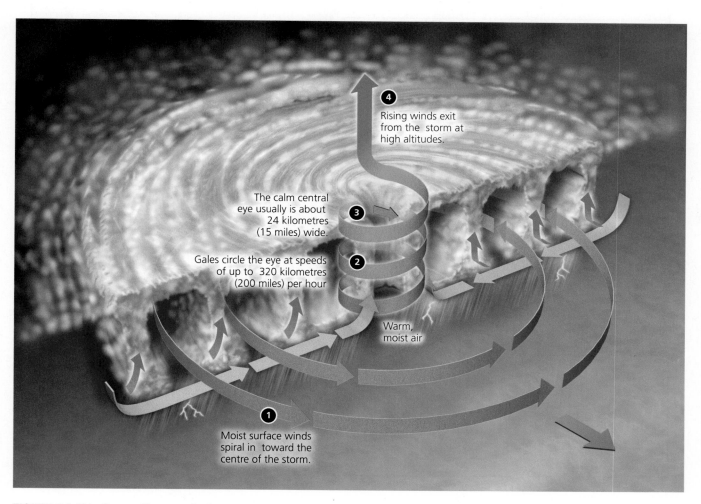

FIGURE 6-5 This diagram illustrates the formation of a *tropical cyclone*. Those forming in the Atlantic Ocean are called *hurricanes*; those forming in the Pacific Ocean are called *typhoons*.

For a tropical cyclone to occur, the temperature of the ocean has to be at least 27°C (81°F) to a depth of 46 metres (150 feet). A tropical cyclone forms when areas of low pressure over the warm ocean draw in air from the surrounding high-pressure areas. The Earth's rotation makes those winds spiral counterclockwise in the northern hemisphere and clockwise in the southern hemisphere (see Figure 6-10, p. 117). Moist air, warmed by the heat of the ocean, rises in a vortex in the centre of the storm until it becomes a tropical cyclone (Environment Canada, 2012; National Hurricane Center, 2012).

Figure 6-6 shows the paths of the 19 storms of the 2011 Atlantic hurricane season as they moved heat and moisture away from the tropics toward temperate latitudes. The storms were classified as tropical depressions or tropical storms if their maximum sustained winds were below 62 kilometres per hour (38 miles per hour) or from 63–117 kilometres (39–72 miles per hour) per hour, respectively. They were reclassified as hurricanes or major hurricanes if their maximum sustained winds rose above 118 kilometres per hour (73 miles per hour) and 178 kilometres per hour (111 miles per hour), respectively. Tropical storms that pass close to Canada can result in strong winds, rain, flooding, damage to trees, power outages, and other serious consequences; Environment Canada (http://www.ec.gc.ca) keeps records of the effects of tropical storms.

The United Nations Intergovernmental Panel on Climate Change (2007) found that the destructiveness of hurricanes, the length of storm duration, and the degree of storm intensity have all increased since the 1970s, and that these trends are strongly correlated with rises in tropical sea temperature. The report stated that these trends will likely continue to grow through the 21st century, with increases in sea level temperature and rising sea levels.

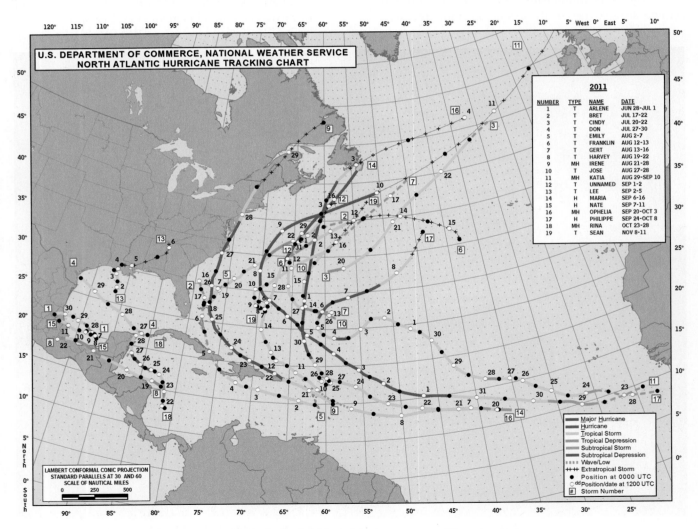

FIGURE 6-6 The 2011 Atlantic hurricane season had a total of 19 tropical storms; seven of these became hurricanes, including three major hurricanes. (From National Oceanographic and Atmospheric Administration, http://www.nhc.noaa.gov)

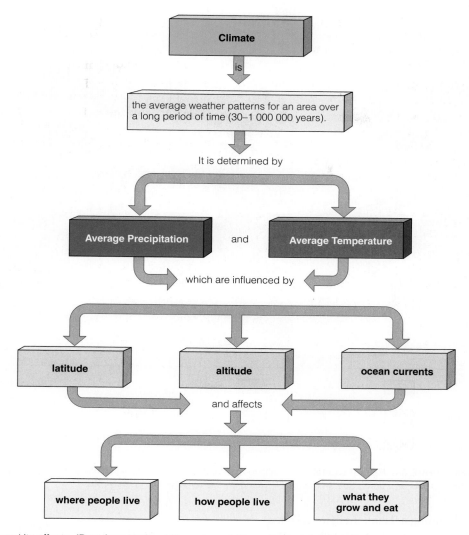

FIGURE 6-7 Climate and its effects. (Data from National Oceanic and Atmospheric Administration)

> SELF CHECK
>
> **Witness Cyclones from Space** You can safely experience cyclones if you visit the National Oceanographic and Atmospheric Administration website at http://www.nnvl.noaa.gov/MediaDetail.php?MediaID=897&MediaTypeID=2. The site has a 4.5-minute simulation of the 2011 hurricane season, based on data from the *GOES* satellite, that allows you to watch tropical cyclones forming and moving in the Caribbean Sea and Atlantic Ocean.

6-2 CLIMATE: A BRIEF INTRODUCTION

What Is Climate? Long-Term Weather and Global Air Circulation

Climate is the average temperature and average precipitation of an area over long periods of time, which in turn are affected by global air circulation.

Climate is a region's long-term atmospheric conditions—typically over decades. *Average temperature* and *average precipitation* are the two main factors determining a region's climate and its effects on people, as shown in Figure 6-7.

Figure 6-8 (p. 116) is a generalized map of the Earth's major climate zones. In what type of climate zone do you live?

The temperature and precipitation patterns that lead to different climates are caused primarily by the amount of incoming solar energy per unit area of land, air circulation over the Earth's surface, and water circulation. Solar energy heats the atmosphere, evaporates water, helps create seasons, and causes air to circulate.

Four major factors determine global air circulation patterns. One is the *uneven heating of the Earth's surface.* Air is heated much more at the equator, where the sun's rays strike directly throughout the year, than at the poles, where sunlight strikes at an angle and thus is spread out over a much greater area. You can

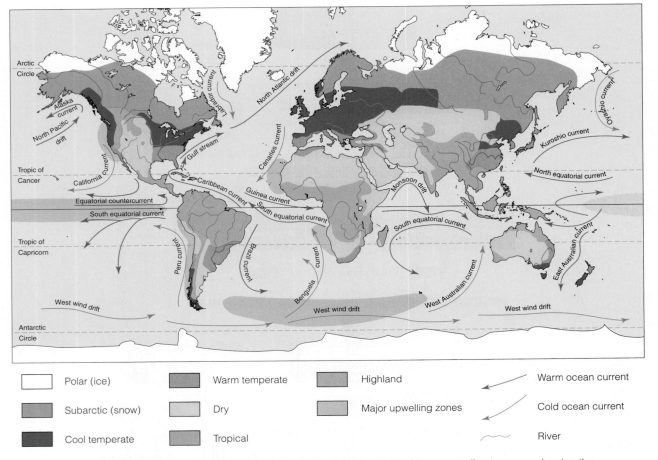

☐ Polar (ice)	▨ Warm temperate
▨ Subarctic (snow)	☐ Dry
▨ Cool temperate	▨ Tropical

▨ Highland	↙ Warm ocean current
▨ Major upwelling zones	⁄ Cold ocean current
	∿ River

CENGAGENOW **ACTIVE FIGURE 6-8 Natural capital:** generalized map of the Earth's current climate zones, showing the major contributing ocean currents and drifts. *See an animation based on this figure at* CengageNOW.

observe this effect by shining a flashlight in a darkened room on the middle of a spherical object such as a basketball. These differences in the amount of incoming solar energy help explain why tropical regions near the equator are hot, polar regions are cold, and temperate regions in between generally have intermediate average temperatures.

A second factor is *seasonal changes in temperature and precipitation.* The Earth's axis—an imaginary line connecting the north and south poles—is tilted. As a result, various regions are tipped toward or away from the sun as the Earth makes its yearlong revolution around the sun (Figure 6-9). This creates opposite seasons in the northern and southern hemispheres.

A third factor is *rotation of the Earth on its axis.* As the Earth rotates, its surface turns faster beneath air masses at the equator and slower beneath those at the poles. This deflects air masses moving north and south to the west or east over different parts of the Earth's surface (Figure 6-10, p. 117). The direction of air movement in these different areas sets up belts of *prevailing winds*—major surface winds that blow almost continually and distribute air and moisture over the Earth's surface.

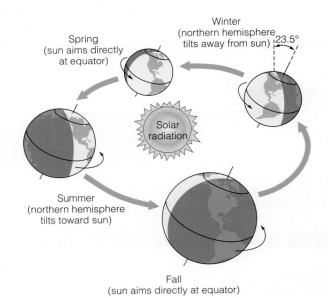

FIGURE 6-9 Seasons in the northern and southern hemispheres are caused by the tilt of the Earth's axis. As the planet makes its annual revolution around the sun on an axis tilted about 23.5°, various regions are tipped toward or away from the sun. The resulting variations in the amount of solar energy reaching the Earth create the seasons.

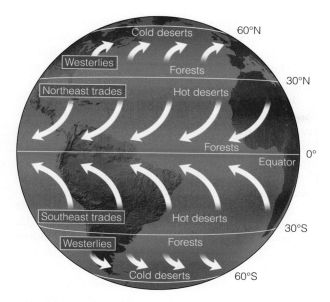

FIGURE 6-10 The Earth's rotation deflects the movement of the air over different parts of the Earth and creates global patterns of prevailing winds.

Fourth, *properties of air, water, and land* affect global air circulation. Heat from the sun evaporates ocean water and transfers heat from the oceans to the atmosphere, especially near the hot equator.

This evaporation of water creates cyclical convection cells that circulate air, heat, and moisture both vertically and from place to place in the troposphere, as shown in Figure 6-11. Trace the flows in this diagram. To understand this cycle, remember two things. *First,* hot air tends to rise, cool, and release moisture as precipitation. *Second,* cool air tends to sink, get warmer, and lose its moisture by evaporation (not precipitation).

The Earth's air and water circulation patterns and its mixture of continents and oceans lead to an irregular distribution of climates and patterns of vegetation, as shown in Figure 6-12.

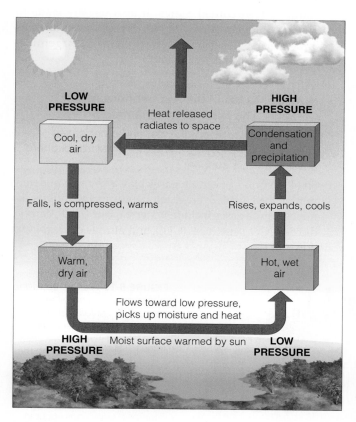

FIGURE 6-11 Transfer of energy by convection in the atmosphere. *Convection* occurs when matter warms, becomes less dense, and rises within its surroundings. This efficient means of heat transfer occurs in the planet's interior, oceans, and atmosphere (as shown here). Distribution of heat and water occurs in the atmosphere because vertical convection currents stir up air in the troposphere and transport heat and water from one area to another in circular convection cells called *Hadley cells.*

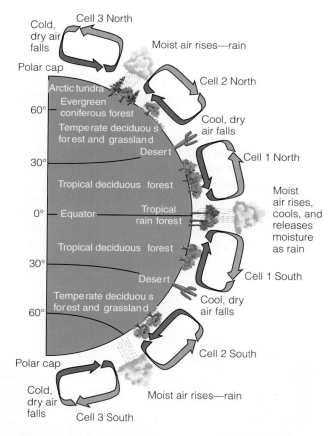

FIGURE 6-12 Natural capital: global air circulation and biomes. Heat and moisture are distributed over the Earth's surface by vertical currents that form six large convection cells (Hadley cells) at different latitudes. The direction of airflow and the ascent and descent of air masses in these convection cells determine the Earth's general climatic zones. The resulting uneven distribution of heat and moisture over the planet's surface leads to the forests, grasslands, and deserts that make up the Earth's biomes.

How Do Ocean Currents and Winds Affect Regional Climates? Moving Heat and Air Around

Ocean currents and winds influence climate by redistributing heat received from the sun from one place to another.

The oceans absorb heat from the air circulation patterns just described, with the bulk of this heat absorbed near the warm tropical areas. This heat plus differences in water density create warm and cold ocean currents (Figure 6-8). These currents, driven by winds and the Earth's rotation, redistribute heat received from the sun from one place to another and thus influence climate and vegetation, especially near coastal areas. They also help mix ocean waters and distribute nutrients and dissolved oxygen needed by aquatic organisms.

Winds can also affect regional climates and distribution of some forms of aquatic life. For example, wind blowing along steep western coasts of some continents pushes surface water away from the land. This outgoing surface water is replaced by an **upwelling** of cold, nutrient-rich bottom water, as shown in Figure 6-13.

Upwellings, whether far from shore or near shore, bring plant nutrients from the deeper parts of the ocean to the surface. In turn, these nutrients support large populations of phytoplankton, zooplankton, fish, and fish-eating seabirds.

What Are El Niño and La Niña? Changing Winds, Altered Upwellings, and Freaky Weather

El Niño occurs when a change in the direction of tropical winds warms coastal surface water, suppresses upwellings, and alters much of the Earth's weather. La Niña is the reverse of this effect.

Every few years in the Pacific Ocean, normal shore upwellings (Figure 6-14, left) are affected by changes in climate patterns called the *El Niño–Southern Oscillation,* or *ENSO* (Figure 6-14, right). Trace the flows and components of the diagram in Figure 6-14.

In an ENSO, often called *El Niño,* prevailing tropical trade winds blowing westward weaken or reverse direction. This warms up surface water along the South and North American coasts, which suppresses the normal upwellings of cold, nutrient-rich water. The decrease in nutrients reduces primary productivity and causes a sharp decline in the populations of some fish species.

A strong ENSO can trigger extreme weather changes over at least two-thirds of the globe (Figure 6-15, p. 119)—especially in lands along the Pacific and Indian Oceans—and distorts the fast-moving jet stream that flows high above North America.

La Niña, the reverse of El Niño, cools some coastal surface waters, and brings back upwellings. Typically La Niña means more Atlantic Ocean hurricanes, colder winters in Canada and the northeastern United States, and warmer and drier winters in the southeastern and southwestern United States. It also usually leads to wetter winters in the Pacific Northwest, torrential rains in Southeast Asia, lower wheat yields in Argentina, and more wildfires in Florida.

How Do Gases in the Atmosphere Affect Climate? The Natural Greenhouse Effect

Water vapour, carbon dioxide, and other gases influence climate by warming the lower troposphere and the Earth's surface.

Small amounts of certain gases play a key role in determining the Earth's average temperatures and thus its climates. These gases include water vapour (H_2O), carbon dioxide (CO_2), methane (CH_4), and nitrous oxide (N_2O).

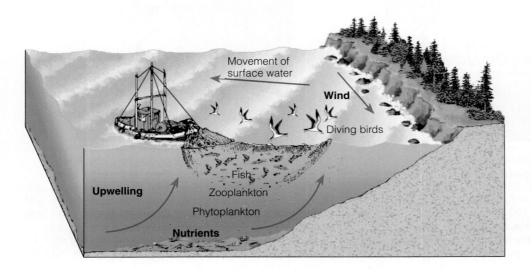

FIGURE 6-13 A *shore upwelling* (shown here) occurs when deep, cool, nutrient-rich waters are drawn up to replace surface water moved away from a steep coast by wind flowing along the coast toward the equator. Such areas support large populations of phytoplankton, zooplankton, fish, and fish-eating birds. *Equatorial upwellings* occur in the open sea near the equator (Figure 6-8) when northward and southward currents interact to push deep waters and their nutrients to the surface, thus greatly increasing primary productivity in such areas.

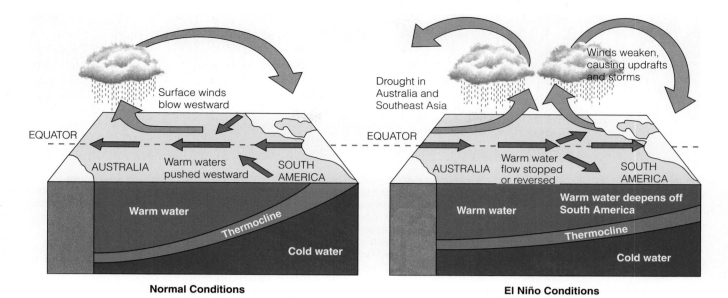

Normal Conditions

El Niño Conditions

FIGURE 6-14 Normal trade winds blowing westward cause shore upwellings of cold, nutrient-rich bottom water in the tropical Pacific Ocean near the coast of Peru (left). A zone of gradual temperature change called the *thermocline* separates the warm and cold water. Every few years a climate shift known as the *El Niño–Southern Oscillation (ENSO)* disrupts this pattern. Westward-blowing trade winds weaken or reverse direction, which depresses the coastal upwellings and warms the surface waters off South America (right). When an ENSO lasts 12 months or longer, it severely disrupts populations of plankton, fish, and seabirds in upwelling areas and can trigger extreme weather changes over much of the globe (see Figure 6-15).

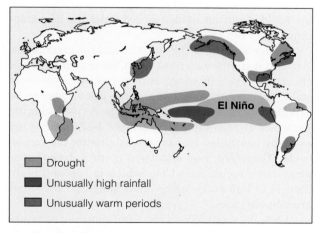

FIGURE 6-15 Typical global climatic effects of an El Niño–Southern Oscillation. During the 1996–8 ENSO, huge waves battered the California coast, and torrential rains caused widespread flooding and mudslides. In Peru, floods and mudslides killed hundreds of people, left about 250 000 people homeless, and ruined harvests. Drought in Brazil, Indonesia, and Australia led to massive wildfires in tinder-dry forests. India and parts of Africa also experienced severe drought. A catastrophic ice storm hit Canada and the northeastern United States, but the southeastern United States had fewer hurricanes. (Data from National Oceanic and Atmospheric Administration)

Together these gases, known as **greenhouse gases,** allow mostly visible light and some infrared radiation and ultraviolet (UV) radiation from the sun to pass through the troposphere. The Earth's surface absorbs much of this solar energy. This transforms it to longer-wavelength infrared radiation, which rises into the troposphere.

Some of this infrared radiation escapes into space and some is absorbed by molecules of greenhouse gases and emitted into the troposphere in all directions as even longer-wavelength infrared radiation. Some of this released energy is radiated into space and some warms the troposphere and the Earth's surface. This natural warming effect of the troposphere is called the **greenhouse effect,** diagrammed in Figure 6-16.

It is not the natural greenhouse effect, and the greenhouse gases of natural origin, that are of concern; it is the *anthropogenic* (human-generated) contribution of greenhouse gases that threatens to artificially enhance the greenhouse effect to problematic levels (see Chapter 21).

Carbon dioxide (CO_2) is the greenhouse gas of primary concern. It is released from many natural sources such as respiration of plants and animals, decay of organic material, fires, and volcanoes (Figure 4-28, p. 82). However, human activities such as burning fossil fuels, cutting down forests, and farming have released large quantities of CO_2 from terrestrial reservoirs to the atmosphere. Since the industrial revolution of the late 1700s, levels of atmospheric CO_2 have risen from 280 ppm to 390 ppm.

Another greenhouse gas, **methane** (CH_4), is released through natural processes such as

(a) Rays of sunlight penetrate the lower atmosphere and warm the Earth's surface.

(b) The Earth's surface absorbs much of the incoming solar radiation and degrades it to longer-wavelength infrared (IR) radiation, which rises into the lower atmosphere. Some of this IR radiation escapes into space as heat and some is absorbed by molecules of greenhouse gases and emitted as even longer-wavelength IR radiation, which warms the lower atmosphere.

(c) As concentrations of greenhouse gases rise, their molecules absorb and emit more infrared radiation, which adds more heat to the lower atmosphere.

FIGURE 6-16 Natural capital: the *natural greenhouse effect*. Without the atmospheric warming provided by this natural effect, the Earth would be a cold and mostly lifeless planet. According to the widely accepted greenhouse theory, when concentrations of greenhouse gases in the atmosphere rise, the average temperature of the troposphere rises. (From STARR. *Biology: Concepts and Applications* w/CD-ROM + InfoTrac, 4E. © 2000 Cengage Learning. Reproduced by permission. www.cengage.com/permissions)

decomposition of organic matter, but it is also released as a metabolic waste product of the livestock we raise and as a result of humans tapping into fossil-fuel deposits. Since the late 1700s, atmospheric concentrations of methane have risen by 250%. Although there is much less methane in the atmosphere than carbon dioxide, each molecule of CH_4 has 23 times the heat-trapping ability of each molecule of CO_2. In other words, CH_4 has a *global warming potential* of 23 relative to CO_2 (which is taken as a standard and assigned a value of 1).

Ozone (O_3) is best known for filtering UV light as part of the stratospheric ozone layer and as a component of photochemical smog in the lower troposphere. It is also a greenhouse gas with a global warming potential of 17. Concentrations of ozone in the troposphere have risen 36% since the late 1700s.

Halocarbons, including **chlorofluorocarbons (CFCs)** and hydrofluorocarbons (HFCs), are best known for depleting the ozone layer (Chapter 21), but they also function as very potent greenhouse gases. For example, HFC-23 has a global warming potential of 12 000. Fortunately, since the Montreal and Copenhagen protocols (p. 636) placed controls on the production of these chemicals, their abundance is declining.

Nitrous oxide (N_2O) has also been increased by human activities such as raising cattle, manufacturing chemicals, farming using synthetic nitrogen fertilizers, and burning gasoline in our cars. These levels have risen 18% since the late 1700s. Although nitrous oxide is much less abundant than carbon dioxide, each molecule of nitrous oxide has 298 times the heat-trapping ability of CO_2.

Water vapour is the most abundant greenhouse gas, and it contributes most to the natural greenhouse effect. However, its concentration has been relatively stable for centuries and so it does not appear to be driving industrial-age climate change. As well, altering the water cycle of our planet (Figure 4-27, p. 80) is not as easily controlled by humans as altering the carbon cycle. Therefore, our efforts to control greenhouse gases have focused on CO_2, which is less abundant than H_2O but much more abundant than the other greenhouse gases.

Overall, about 55% of the anthropogenic enhancement of the greenhouse effect is thought to be due to the effect of increased CO_2 concentrations. The estimated contributions of the other greenhouse gases are CH_4 (17%), O_3 (12%), halocarbons (11%), and N_2O (5%) (Blasing, 2012).

How Does Topography of the Earth's Surface Affect Local Climate? Creating Deserts and Warming Cities

Mountains and cities affect local and regional climates.

Various topographic features of the Earth's surface can create local and regional climatic conditions that differ from the general climate of a region. For

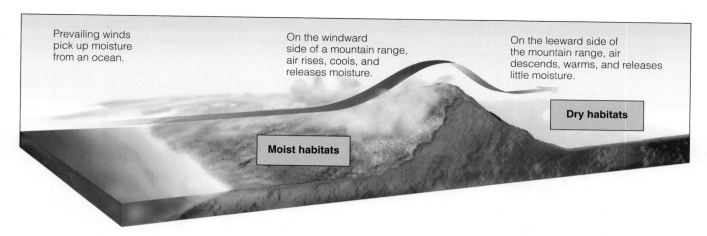

Prevailing winds pick up moisture from an ocean.

On the windward side of a mountain range, air rises, cools, and releases moisture.

On the leeward side of the mountain range, air descends, warms, and releases little moisture.

Dry habitats

Moist habitats

FIGURE 6-17 The *rain shadow effect* is a reduction of rainfall on the side of high mountains facing away from prevailing surface winds. It occurs when warm, moist air in prevailing onshore winds loses most of its moisture as rain and snow on the windward (wind-facing) slopes of a mountain range. This accounts for the dryness of the North American Great Plains, which are in the rain shadow of the Rocky Mountains. An extreme product of this effect is the Mojave Desert, which is downwind from the Sierra Nevada Mountains in California.

example, mountains interrupt the flow of prevailing surface winds and the movement of storms. When moist air blowing inland from an ocean reaches a mountain range, it cools as it is forced to rise and expand. This causes the air to lose most of its moisture as rain and snow on the windward (wind-facing) slopes.

As the drier air mass flows down the leeward (away from the wind) slopes, it draws moisture out of the plants and soil over which it passes. The lower precipitation and the resulting semiarid or **arid** conditions on the leeward side of high mountains are called the **rain shadow effect** (Figure 6-17). This is one way some deserts form.

Cities also create distinct **microclimates.** Bricks, concrete, asphalt, and other building materials absorb and hold heat, and buildings block wind flow. Motor vehicles and the climate control systems of buildings release large quantities of heat and pollutants. As a result, cities tend to have more haze and smog, higher temperatures, and lower wind speeds than the surrounding countryside.

Now that you have the basics of climate we can examine how it applies to ecology.

SELF CHECK

Greenhouse and Urban effects Consider your past experiences with actual greenhouses, or with a closed car heating up in the sun. Were these situations effective illustrations of the greenhouse effect? Have you ever observed a cloud of pollution hanging over a city, or noticed that snow had melted within a city but not outside the city? Think of ingenious ways to use simple instruments and digital cameras to document greenhouse and urban effects in the environment around you, and show your results to others!

6-3 BIOMES: CLIMATE AND LIFE ON LAND

Why Do Different Organisms Live in Different Places? Think Climate

Different climates lead to different communities of organisms, especially vegetation.

Why is one area of the Earth's land surface a desert, another a grassland, and another a forest? Why do different types of deserts, grasslands, and forests exist? The general answer to these questions is differences in *climate* (Figure 6-8), caused mostly by differences in average temperature and precipitation due to global air and water circulation (Figure 6-12).

Figure 6-18 shows how scientists have divided the world into 12 major biomes. They are **terrestrial** regions with characteristic types of natural ecological communities adapted to the climate of each region. Study Figure 6-18 (p. 122) carefully and identify the type of biome you live in.

By comparing Figure 6-18 with Figure 6-8, you can see how the world's major biomes vary with climate. Make this comparison for the area where you live. Canada's major biomes are shown in Figure 6-19 (p. 123).

Average annual precipitation and temperature (as well as soil type, Figure 4-26, p. 79) are the most important factors in producing tropical, temperate, or polar deserts, grasslands, and forests.

On maps, such as the one in Figure 6-18, biomes are presented as having boundaries and being covered with the same general type of vegetation. In reality, *biomes are not uniform.* They consist of a *mosaic*

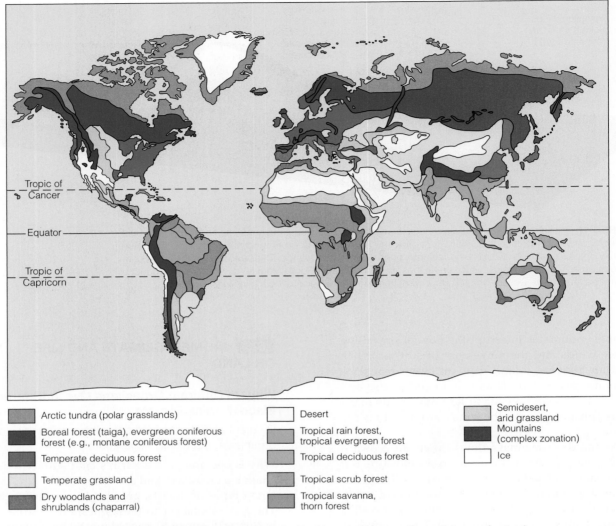

■ Arctic tundra (polar grasslands)	☐ Desert	▨ Semidesert, arid grassland
■ Boreal forest (taiga), evergreen coniferous forest (e.g., montane coniferous forest)	▨ Tropical rain forest, tropical evergreen forest	■ Mountains (complex zonation)
▨ Temperate deciduous forest	▨ Tropical deciduous forest	☐ Ice
☐ Temperate grassland	▨ Tropical scrub forest	
▨ Dry woodlands and shrublands (chaparral)	▨ Tropical savanna, thorn forest	

CENGAGENOW™ **ACTIVE FIGURE 6-18 Natural capital:** the Earth's major *biomes*—the main types of natural vegetation in different undisturbed land areas—result primarily from differences in climate. Each biome contains many ecosystems whose communities have adapted to differences in climate, soil, and other environmental factors. In reality, people have removed or altered much of this natural vegetation in some areas for farming, livestock grazing, lumber and fuelwood, mining, and construction. *See an animation based on this figure at* CengageNOW.

of patches, with somewhat different biological communities but with similarities unique to the biome. These patches occur mostly because the resources plants and animals need are not uniformly distributed. Go to a natural area in or near where you live and see if you can find patches with different vegetation.

Figure 6-20 (p. 123) shows how climate and vegetation vary with **latitude** (distance from the equator) and **altitude** (elevation above sea level). If you climb a tall mountain from its base to its summit, you can observe changes in plant life similar to those you would encounter in travelling from the equator to the Earth's poles.

6-4 DESERT BIOMES

What Are the Major Types of Deserts? Hot, Medium, and Cold

Deserts have little precipitation and little vegetation and are found in tropical, temperate, and polar regions.

A **desert** is an area where evaporation exceeds precipitation. Annual precipitation is low and often scattered unevenly throughout the year. Deserts have sparse, widely spaced, mostly low vegetation.

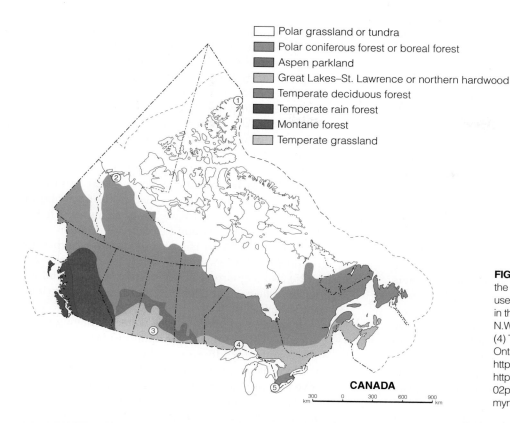

Polar grassland or tundra
Polar coniferous forest or boreal forest
Aspen parkland
Great Lakes–St. Lawrence or northern hardwood
Temperate deciduous forest
Temperate rain forest
Montane forest
Temperate grassland

CANADA

300 0 300 600 900
km   km

FIGURE 6-19 Canada's major biomes: the numbers indicate locations that were used for Canadian climate data discussed in this chapter: (1) Alert, Nunavut; (2) Inuvik, N.W.T.; (3) Regina, Saskatchewan; (4) Thunder Bay, Ontario; (5) Point Pelee, Ontario. (From http://globalforestwatch.org; http://www.weatheroffice.ec.gc.ca; http://www.mobot.org/education/02programsresources/mappingenvironment/mynaturalcommunity/biomes.htm)

Altitude
Mountain ice and snow
Tundra (herbs, lichens, mosses)
Coniferous Forest
Deciduous Forest
Tropical Forest

Latitude

Tropical Forest   Deciduous Forest   Coniferous Forest   Tundra (herbs, lichens, mosses)   Polar ice and snow

FIGURE 6-20 Generalized effects of altitude (left) and latitude (right) on climate and biomes. Parallel changes in vegetation type occur when we travel from the equator to the poles or from lowlands to mountaintops. This generalized diagram shows only one of many possible sequences.

Deserts cover about 30% of the Earth's land surface and are found mostly in tropical and subtropical regions (Figure 6-18). The largest deserts are found in the interiors of continents, far from moist sea air and moisture-bearing winds. Other, more local deserts form on the downwind sides of mountain ranges because of the rain shadow effect (Figure 6-17).

In hot deserts, during the day the baking sun warms the ground in the desert. At night, however, most of the heat stored in the ground radiates quickly into the atmosphere. This occurs because desert soils have little vegetation and moisture to help store the heat, and the skies are usually clear. This explains why in a desert you may roast during the day but shiver at night.

A combination of low rainfall and different average temperatures creates tropical, temperate, and cold deserts (Figures 6-18 and 6-20). Take a close look at the graphs in Figure 6-21.

Tropical deserts (Figure 6-21, left) are hot and dry most of the year. They have few plants and a hard, windblown surface strewn with rocks and some sand. They are the deserts we often see in movies.

In *temperate deserts,* daytime temperatures are high in summer and low in winter and there is more precipitation than in tropical deserts (Figure 6-21, centre). The sparse vegetation consists mostly of widely dispersed, drought-resistant shrubs and cacti or other succulents adapted to the lack of water and temperature variations, as shown in Figure 6-22 (p. 125). Trace how nutrients and energy flow through the ecosystem in this diagram.

In cold deserts, winters are very cold, summers are warmer, and precipitation is low. The *polar deserts* of Canada and other northern nations are characterized by receiving less than 250 millimetres (10 inches) of precipitation per year, and the mean temperature of the warmest month is less than 10°C (50°F) (Figure 6-21, right). The ground is mostly hard rock and gravel, with less than 5% plant cover. Snow can be present all year.

In the semiarid zones between deserts and grasslands, we find *semidesert.* This biome is dominated by thorn trees and shrubs adapted to long dry spells followed by brief, sometimes heavy rains.

How Do Desert Plants and Animals Survive? Get Water Any Way You Can

Desert plants and animals have a number of strategies for getting enough water to survive in very dry climates.

Adaptations for survival in hot deserts have two themes. One is *beat the heat* and the other is *every drop of water counts.* Desert plants exposed to the sunlight must conserve enough water for survival and lose enough heat so they do not overheat and die.

Plants in hot deserts have evolved a number of strategies for doing this. During long hot and dry spells plants such as mesquite and creosote drop their leaves to survive in a dormant state. **Succulent** (fleshy) **plants,** such as the saguaro ("sah-WAH-ro") cactus, have three adaptations. They have no leaves, which can lose water by evapotranspiration. They store water and synthesize food in their expandable, fleshy tissue. And they reduce water loss by opening their pores (stomata) to take up carbon dioxide (CO_2) only at night. What a great evolutionary solution to a difficult problem.

Some desert plants use deep roots to tap into groundwater. Others such as prickly pear (Figure 6-22, p. 125) and saguaro cacti use widely spread, shallow roots to collect water after brief showers and store it in their spongy tissue.

Evergreen plants conserve water by having wax-coated leaves that minimize evapotranspiration. Others, such as annual wildflowers and grasses, store much of their biomass in seeds that remain inactive, sometimes for years, until they receive enough water to germinate. Shortly after a rain these seeds germinate, grow, carpet some deserts with a dazzling array of colourful flowers, produce new seed, and die, all in only a few weeks.

Most animals of hot deserts are small. Some beat the heat by hiding in cool burrows or rocky crevices by day and coming out at night or in the early morning. Others become dormant during periods of extreme heat or drought.

Some desert animals have physical adaptations for conserving water. Insects and reptiles have thick outer coverings to minimize water loss through evaporation, and their wastes are dry feces and a dried concentrate of urine. Many spiders and insects get their water from

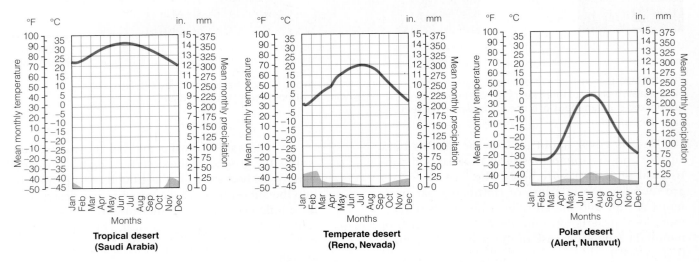

FIGURE 6-21 Climate graphs showing typical variations in annual temperature (the graphed line) and precipitation (the shaded area on the graph) in tropical, temperate, and polar (cold) deserts.

Red-tailed hawk

Gambel's quail

Yucca

Jack rabbit

Collared lizard

Agave

Prickly pear cactus

Roadrunner

Darkling beetle

Bacteria

Diamondback rattlesnake

Fungi

Kangaroo rat

| ➡ Producer to primary consumer | ➡ Primary to secondary consumer | ➡ Secondary to higher-level consumer | ➡ All producers and consumers to decomposers |

FIGURE 6-22 Natural capital: some components and interactions in a *temperate desert ecosystem*. When these organisms die, decomposers break down their organic matter into minerals that plants use. Coloured arrows indicate transfers of matter and energy between producers; primary consumers (herbivores); secondary, or higher-level, consumers (carnivores); and decomposers. Organisms are not drawn to scale.

dew or from the food they eat. Arabian oryxes survive by licking the dew that accumulates at night on rocks and on one another's hair.

Adaptations for survival in a polar desert revolve around combating the effects of cold and dryness. Plants are extremely low to take advantage of warmth at the surface of the ground, and to avoid the drying effect of wind in summer and the abrading effect of wind-blown snow in winter. Lichens, hardy mosses, and waxy cushion-form plants can survive in these dry and exposed locations. Plants tend to propagate by vegetative means because the summer is too short for reliable seed production and pollinating insects may not always be present in the High Arctic. Animal life is limited by the low plant productivity. Most birds migrate to avoid winter. Small creatures like lemmings live under the snow for much of the year. Larger Arctic animals have warm coats and are mobile enough to find areas with more shelter and food than the open polar desert.

Deserts take a long time to recover from disturbances because of their slow plant growth, low species diversity, slow nutrient cycling (because of little bacterial activity in their soils), and lack of water.

6-5 GRASSLAND, TUNDRA, AND CHAPARRAL BIOMES

What Are the Major Types of Grasslands? Hot, Mild, and Cold

Grasslands have enough precipitation to support grasses but not enough to support large stands of trees and are found in tropical, temperate, and polar regions.

Grasslands, or **prairies,** are regions with enough average annual precipitation to support grasses (and in some areas, a few trees). Most grasslands are found in the interiors of continents (Figure 6-18).

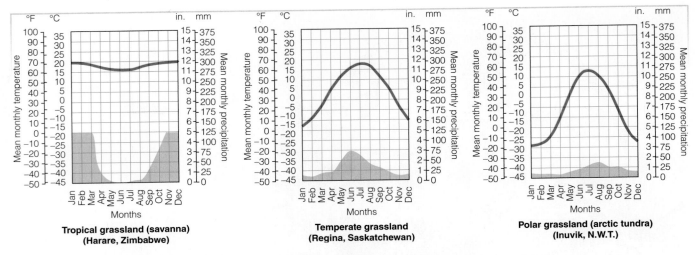

FIGURE 6-23 Climate graphs showing typical variations in annual temperature (the graphed line) and precipitation (the shaded area on the graph) in tropical, temperate, and polar (arctic tundra) grasslands.

Grasslands persist because of a combination of seasonal drought, grazing by large herbivores, and occasional fires—all of which keep large numbers of shrubs and trees from growing. The three main types of grasslands—tropical, temperate, and polar (tundra)—result from combinations of low average precipitation and various average temperatures (Figures 6-18 and 6-19). Take a close look at the graphs in Figure 6-23.

What Are Tropical Grasslands and Savannas? Hot with On-and-Off Rain

Savannas are hot places that have rain, except during dry seasons, and enormous herds of hoofed animals occupying different ecological niches.

One type of tropical grassland, called a *savanna*, usually has warm temperatures year-round, two prolonged dry seasons, and abundant rain the rest of the year (Figure 6-23, left). African tropical savannas contain enormous herds of *grazing* (grass- and herb-eating) and *browsing* (twig- and leaf-nibbling) hoofed animals that feed on a wide variety of savanna plants, as shown in Figure 6-24 (p. 127). In this diagram, note the number of different niches that allow these animals to coexist.

As part of their niches, these and other large herbivores have evolved specialized eating habits that minimize competition between species for vegetation. For example, giraffes eat leaves and shoots from the tops of trees, elephants eat leaves and branches farther down, Thompson's gazelles and wildebeests prefer short grass, and zebras graze on longer grass and stems.

Many large savanna animal species are killed for their economically valuable coats and parts (tigers), tusks (rhinoceroses), and ivory tusks (elephants).

Humans have attempted to raise cattle in some savanna areas. Often these herds have helped convert savannas to deserts. One reason is that cattle require a lot more water than native herbivores (Figure 6-24) that are better adapted to the savanna climate. To get enough water the cattle must move back and forth between water holes. This frequent movement reduces their meat yield, tramples vegetation, and compacts large areas of soil.

Another problem is that cattle have moist droppings. As the droppings dry, they heat up in the sun, kill the grass underneath, and form patches of a nearly impenetrable soil covering (sometimes called *fecal pavement*). In contrast, native herbivores, such as antelope, produce dry fecal pellets that are readily decomposed with the nutrients returned to the soil. This illustrates a basic ecological rule: *Do not try to raise a plant or animal in an environment to which it is not adapted.*

What Are Temperate Grasslands? Good Weather and Soils for Crops and Livestock

Temperate grasslands with cold winters and hot and dry summers have deep and fertile soils that make them widely used for growing crops and grazing cattle.

Temperate grasslands cover vast expanses of plains and gently rolling hills in the interiors of North and South America, Europe, and Asia (Figure 6-18). In these grasslands, winters are bitterly cold, summers are hot and dry, and annual precipitation is fairly sparse and falls unevenly through the year (Figure 6-23, centre).

FIGURE 6-24 Natural capital: some of the grazing animals found in different parts of the African savanna. These species share vegetation resources by occupying different feeding niches.

Because the aboveground parts of most of the grasses die and decompose each year, organic matter accumulates to produce a deep, fertile soil (Figure 4-26, top middle, p. 79). This soil is held in place by a thick network of intertwined roots of drought-tolerant grasses unless the topsoil is plowed up and allowed to blow away by prolonged exposure to high winds found in these biomes. The natural grasses are also adapted to fires ignited by lightning or set deliberately. The fires burn the plant above the ground but do not harm the roots, from which new life can spring.

Types of temperate grasslands in North America are the *tall-grass prairies* (Figure 6-25, p. 128) and *short-grass prairies* of midwestern Canada and the United States. Trace the nutrient and energy flows and transfers in Figure 6-25. Here winds blow almost continuously and evaporation is rapid, often leading to fires in the summer and fall.

Many of the world's natural temperate grasslands have disappeared because they are great places to grow crops (Figure 6-26, p. 128, and Chapter 14) and graze cattle. They are often flat, easy to plow, and have fertile, deep soils. However, plowing breaks up the soil and leaves it vulnerable to erosion by wind and water, and overgrazing can transform grasslands to semidesert or desert.

With the near elimination of the bison (p. 21) and with plows that could break the dense turf, North America's long-grass prairies have become breadbaskets that produce huge quantities of grain. Only tiny protected remnants of the original prairies remain.

On the western short-grass prairie, cattle and sheep have replaced antelope and bison. Much of the sagebrush desert of the American West is the result of overgrazing of short-grass prairie.

What Are Polar Grasslands? Bitterly Cold Plains

Polar grasslands are covered with ice and snow except during a brief summer.

Polar grasslands, or *arctic tundra,* occur just south of the arctic polar ice cap (Figure 6-18). During most of the year these treeless plains are bitterly cold (Figure 6-23, right), swept by frigid winds, and covered with ice and snow. Winters are long and dark, and the scant precipitation falls mostly as snow, making this a "freezing desert."

This biome is carpeted with a thick, spongy mat of low-growing plants, primarily grasses, mosses, and dwarf woody shrubs, as shown in Figure 6-27. Trace the energy flows and nutrient transfers in this diagram. Trees or tall plants cannot survive in the cold and windy tundra because they would lose too much of their heat. Most of the annual growth of the tundra's plants occurs during the six- to eight-week summer, when sunlight shines almost around the clock.

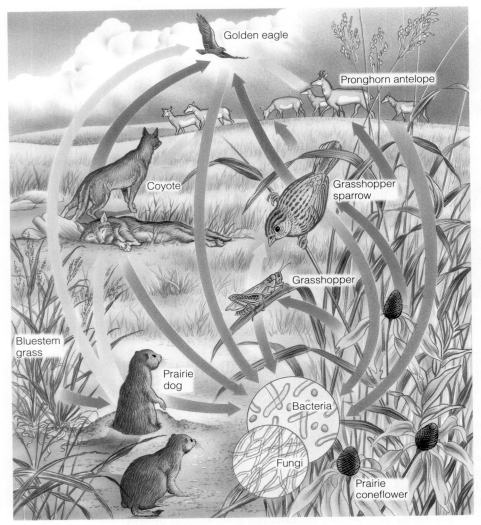

Golden eagle

Pronghorn antelope

Coyote

Grasshopper
sparrow

Grasshopper

Bluestem
grass

Prairie
dog

Bacteria

Fungi

Prairie
coneflower

 Producer
to primary
consumer

 Primary
to secondary
consumer

 Secondary to
higher-level
consumer

 All producers and
consumers to
decomposers

CENGAGENOW™ **ACTIVE**
FIGURE 6-25 Natural capital:
some components and interactions
in *a temperate prairie ecosystem* in
North America. When these organisms die, decomposers break down
their organic matter into minerals that
plants use. Coloured arrows indicate transfers of matter and energy
between producers; primary consumers (herbivores); secondary, or
higher-level, consumers (carnivores);
and decomposers. Organisms
are not drawn to scale. *See an
animation based on this figure at
CengageNOW.*

© Terrance Klassen/Alamy

FIGURE 6-26 Natural capital degradation: replacement of
much of the natural grassland of the prairies with monoculture
crops. This has an impact on natural biodiversity and increases
rates of soil erosion.

One effect of the extreme cold is **permafrost,** a
perennially frozen layer of the soil that forms not
far below the surface when the water there freezes.
During the brief summer the permafrost layer keeps
melted snow and ice from soaking into the ground (see
Figure 4-26, p. 79). Then the waterlogged tundra forms
a large number of shallow lakes, marshes, bogs, ponds,
and other seasonal wetlands. Hordes of mosquitoes,
blackflies, and other insects thrive in these shallow
surface pools. They feed large colonies of migratory
birds (especially waterfowl) that return from the south
to nest and breed in the bogs and ponds.

The arctic tundra's permanent animal residents
are mostly small herbivores such as lemmings, hares,
voles, and ground squirrels that can burrow underground or take shelter in snow to avoid the cold.
Predators such as weasels, snowy owls, and arctic foxes

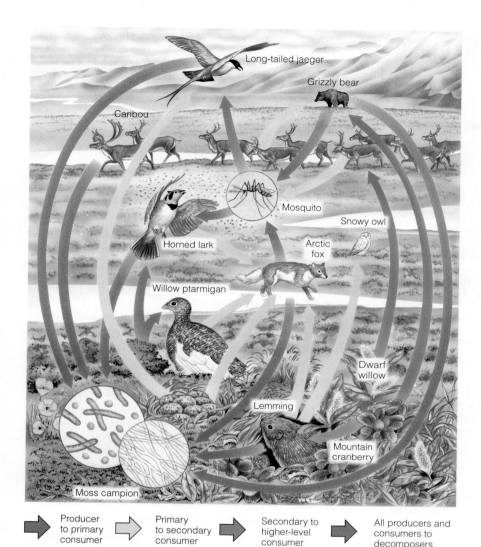

Long-tailed jaeger

Grizzly bear

Caribou

Mosquito

Snowy owl

Horned lark

Arctic fox

Willow ptarmigan

Dwarf willow

Lemming

Mountain cranberry

Moss campion

| Producer to primary consumer | Primary to secondary consumer | Secondary to higher-level consumer | All producers and consumers to decomposers |

FIGURE 6-27 Natural capital: some components and interactions in an *arctic tundra (polar grassland) ecosystem.* When these organisms die, decomposers break down their organic matter into minerals that plants use. Coloured arrows indicate transfers of matter and energy between producers; primary consumers (herbivores); secondary, or higher-level, consumers (carnivores); and decomposers. Organisms are not drawn to scale.

eat them. Animals in this biome survive the intense winter cold through adaptations such as thick coats of fur (arctic wolf, arctic fox, and musk oxen), feathers (snowy owl), and living underground or under snow (arctic lemming).

Because of the cold, decomposition is slow. With low decomposer populations, the soil is poor in organic matter and in nitrates, phosphates, and other minerals. Human activities—mostly oil drilling sites, pipelines, mines, and military bases—leave scars that persist for centuries.

Another type of tundra, called *alpine tundra,* occurs above the limit of tree growth but below the permanent snow line on high mountains. The vegetation is similar to that found in arctic tundra, but it gets more sunlight than arctic vegetation and has no permafrost layer.

Figure 6-28 (p. 130) lists major human impacts on grasslands. What are the direct and indirect effects of your lifestyle on grassland biomes?

What Is Chaparral? Great Place to Live, but Beware of Fires and Mudslides

This temperate shrubland has a wonderful climate but is subject to fires in the fall followed by flooding and mudslides.

In many coastal regions that border on deserts, such as southern California and the Mediterranean, we find a biome known as *temperate shrubland* or *chaparral.* Closeness to the sea provides a slightly longer winter rainy season than nearby temperate deserts have, and fogs during the spring and fall reduce evaporation.

Chaparral consists mostly of dense growths of low-growing evergreen shrubs and occasional small trees with leathery leaves that reduce evaporation. During the long hot and dry summers, chaparral vegetation becomes very dry and highly flammable. In the fall, fires started by lightning or human activities spread with incredible swiftness.

FIGURE 6-28 Natural capital degradation: major human impacts on the world's grasslands.

Research reveals that chaparral is adapted to and maintained by periodic fires. Many of the shrubs store food reserves in their fire-resistant roots and have seeds that sprout only after a hot fire. With the first rain, annual grasses and wildflowers spring up and use nutrients released by the fire. New shrubs grow quickly and crowd out the grasses.

People like living in this biome because of its favourable climate. But those living in chaparral assume the high risk of losing their homes and possibly their lives to frequent fires and mudslides.

Some people in southern California learned this lesson in the fall of 2003 when fires raging through chaparral areas destroyed several thousand homes and killed 20 people. After fires often comes the hazard of flooding and mudslides; when heavy rains come, great torrents of water pour off the unprotected burned hillsides to flood lowland areas. *Bottom line*: Chaparral has a great climate but is a risky place to live.

6-6 FOREST BIOMES

What Are the Major Types of Forests? Hot, Mild, and Cold

Forests have enough precipitation to support stands of trees and are found in tropical, temperate, and polar regions.

Undisturbed areas with moderate to high average annual precipitation tend to be covered with **forest,** which contains various species of trees and smaller forms of vegetation. The three main types of forest—tropical, temperate, and *boreal* (polar)—result from combinations of this precipitation level and various average temperatures (Figures 6-18 and 6-19, pp. 122 and 123, respectively). Take a close look at the graphs in Figure 6-29.

What Are Tropical Rain Forests? Centres of Biodiversity

These forests have heavy rainfall on most days and have a diversity of life forms occupying a variety of specialized niches in distinct layers.

Tropical rain forests are found near the equator, where hot, moisture-laden air rises and dumps its moisture (Figure 6-12). Trace the nutrient flows and energy

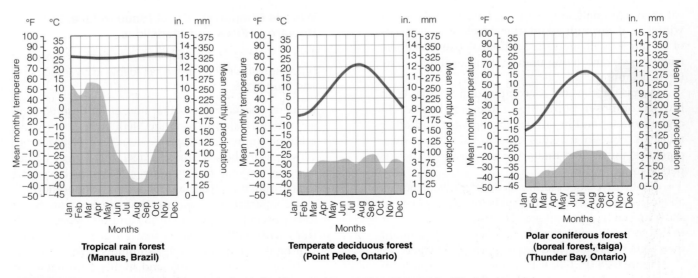

Tropical rain forest (Manaus, Brazil)

Temperate deciduous forest (Point Pelee, Ontario)

Polar coniferous forest (boreal forest, taiga) (Thunder Bay, Ontario)

FIGURE 6-29 Climate graphs showing typical variations in annual temperature (the graphed line) and precipitation (the shaded area on the graph) in tropical, temperate, and polar forests.

Blue and gold macaw

Harpy eagle

Ocelot

Squirrel monkeys

Climbing monstera palm

Slaty-tailed trogon

Katydid

Green tree snake

Tree frog

Ants

Bacteria

Bromeliad

Fungi

| ➡ Producer to primary consumer | ➡ Primary to secondary consumer | ➡ Secondary to higher-level consumer | ➡ All producers and consumers to decomposers |

CENGAGENOW™ **ACTIVE FIGURE 6-30 Natural capital:** some components and interactions in a *tropical rain forest ecosystem*. When these organisms die, decomposers break down their organic matter into minerals that plants use. Coloured arrows indicate transfers of matter and energy between producers; primary consumers (herbivores); secondary, or higher-level, consumers (carnivores); and decomposers. Organisms are not drawn to scale. *See an animation based on this figure at* CengageNOW.

transfers in Figure 6-30. These forests have a warm annual mean temperature (which varies little either daily or seasonally), high humidity, and heavy rainfall almost daily (Figure 6-29, left).

Tropical rain forests are dominated by **broadleaf evergreen plants,** which keep most of their broad leaves year-round. Typically, this biome's huge trees have shallow roots and wide bases that support their massive weight. The tops of the trees form a dense canopy that blocks most light from reaching the forest floor. Many of the plants that live at the ground level have enormous leaves to capture what little sunlight filters through to the dimly lit forest floor.

Individual trees may be draped with vines that reach to their tops to gain access to sunlight. Their trunks and branches may contain large numbers of *epiphytes* (or air plants), such as some types of orchids and other plants. These plants grow without soil, get water from the humid air and rain, and receive nutrients falling from the trees' upper leaves and limbs.

Tropical rain forests are teeming with life and have incredible biological diversity. These diverse life forms occupy a variety of specialized niches in distinct layers, based in the plants' case mostly on their need for sunlight, as shown in Figure 6-31 (p. 132). Much of the animal life, particularly insects, bats, and birds, lives in the sunny *canopy* layer, with its abundant shelter and supplies of leaves, flowers, and fruits. To study life in the canopy, ecologists climb trees, use tall construction cranes, and build platforms and boardwalks in the upper canopy.

Stratification of specialized plant and animal niches in the layers of a tropical rain forest enables coexistence of a great variety of species. Although these forests cover only about 2% of the Earth's land surface, they are habitats for at least half of the Earth's terrestrial species.

Dropped leaves, fallen trees, and dead animals decompose quickly because of the warm, moist conditions and hordes of bacteria, fungi, insects, and other

FIGURE 6-31 Natural capital: stratification of specialized plant and animal niches in various layers of a *tropical rain forest*. The presence of these specialized niches enables species to avoid or minimize competition for resources and results in the coexistence of a great variety of species.

detritivores. This rapid recycling of scarce soil nutrients is why little litter is found on the ground. Instead of being stored in the soil, most nutrients released by decomposition are taken up quickly and stored by trees, vines, and other plants. This explains why tropical rain forest soils have so few plant nutrients (Figure 4-26, bottom left, p. 79). Because of their poor soils, these are not good places to clear and grow crops or graze cattle.

What Are Temperate Deciduous Forests? Seasonal Changes and Beautiful Colours

Most of the trees in these forests survive winter by dropping their leaves, which decay and produce a nutrient-rich soil.

Temperate deciduous forests grow in areas with moderate average temperatures that change significantly with the season. Trace the nutrient transfers and energy flows in Figure 6-32 (p. 133). These areas have long, warm summers, cold but not too severe winters, and abundant precipitation, often spread fairly evenly throughout the year (Figure 6-29, centre).

This biome is dominated by a few species of **broadleaf deciduous plants** such as oak, hickory, maple, poplar, and beech trees. They survive cold winters by dropping their leaves in the fall and becoming dormant. Each spring they grow new leaves that change in the fall into an array of reds and golds before dropping.

Temperate deciduous forests have fewer tree species than tropical rain forests. But the penetration of more sunlight supports a richer diversity of plant life at ground level. Because of the fairly low rate of decomposition, these forests accumulate a thick layer of slowly decaying leaf litter that is a storehouse of nutrients (Figure 4-26, bottom middle, p. 79).

The temperate deciduous forests of eastern North America were once home for such large predators as bears, wolves, foxes, wildcats, and mountain lions (pumas). Today most of the predators have been killed or displaced, and the dominant mammal species often is the white-tailed deer, along with smaller mammals such as squirrels, rabbits, opossums, raccoons, and mice. Some of these diverse forests have been cleared

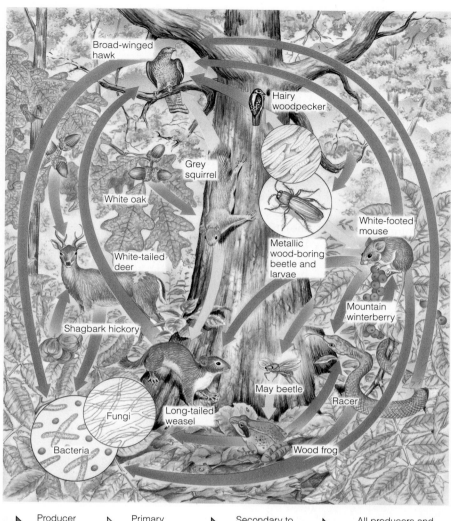

Broad-winged hawk

Hairy woodpecker

Grey squirrel

White oak

White-tailed deer

White-footed mouse

Metallic wood-boring beetle and larvae

Mountain winterberry

Shagbark hickory

Fungi

Bacteria

Long-tailed weasel

May beetle

Racer

Wood frog

→ Producer to primary consumer

→ Primary to secondary consumer

→ Secondary to higher-level consumer

→ All producers and consumers to decomposers

FIGURE 6-32 Natural capital: some components and interactions in a *temperate deciduous forest ecosystem*. When these organisms die, decomposers break down their organic matter into minerals that plants use. Coloured arrows indicate transfers of matter and energy between producers; primary consumers (herbivores); secondary, or higher-level, consumers (carnivores); and decomposers. Organisms are not drawn to scale.

and replaced with *tree plantations* consisting of only one tree species.

Warblers, robins, and other bird species migrate to these forests during the summer to feed and breed. Many of these species are declining in numbers because of loss or fragmentation of their summer and winter habitats.

What Are Evergreen Coniferous Forests? Green and Cold

These forests in cold climates consist mostly of cone-bearing evergreen trees that keep their needles year-round to help the trees survive long and cold winters.

Evergreen coniferous forests, also called *boreal forests* and *taigas* ("TIE-guhs"), are found just south of the arctic tundra in northern regions across North America,

Asia, and Europe (Figure 6-18). In this subarctic climate, winters are long, dry, and extremely cold, with sunlight available only 6–8 hours a day in the northernmost taiga. Summers are short, with mild to warm temperatures (Figure 6-29, right), and the sun typically shines 19 hours a day.

Most boreal forests are dominated by a few species of *coniferous* (cone-bearing) *evergreen plants* such as spruce, fir, cedar, hemlock, and pine trees that keep some of their narrow-pointed leaves (needles) all year long. This adaptation also allows the trees to take advantage of the brief summers without having to take time to grow new needles; their spire-like shape and the relatively flexible branches allow these trees to shed snow efficiently. Plant diversity is low because few species can survive the winters when soil moisture is frozen.

Beneath the stands of trees is a deep layer of partially decomposed conifer needles and leaf litter.

Decomposition is slow because of the low temperatures, waxy coating of conifer needles, and high soil acidity. As the conifer needles decompose, they make the thin, nutrient-poor soil acidic and prevent most other plants (except certain shrubs) from growing on the forest floor (Figure 4-26, bottom right, p. 79).

These biomes contain a variety of wildlife, as depicted in Figure 6-33. Trace the flow of energy and nutrients in this diagram. During the brief summer the soil becomes waterlogged, forming acidic bogs, or *muskegs,* in low-lying areas of these forests. Warblers and other insect-eating birds feed on hordes of flies, mosquitoes, and caterpillars.

To the south, the boreal forest grades through a transition zone known as *aspen parkland* (Figure 6-19) before it meets the temperate grassland. Foresters consider this zone to be part of the boreal forest; people who live in the prairies regard it as part of the grassland biome. With its grassy openings and scattered stands of trees, the aspen parkland is an intermediate zone, combining features of grassland and forest.

What Are Temperate Rain Forests? Dripping Green Giants and Mosses

Coastal areas support huge cone-bearing evergreen trees such as redwoods and Douglas fir in a cool and moist environment.

Coastal coniferous forests or *temperate rain forests* are found along temperate coasts with ample rainfall or moisture from dense ocean fogs. Dense stands of large conifers such as Sitka spruce, Douglas fir, and redwoods are common in undisturbed areas of these biomes along the coast of North America, from Canada to California.

Producer to primary consumer

Primary to secondary consumer

Secondary to higher-level consumer

All producers and consumers to decomposers

FIGURE 6-33 Natural capital: some components and interactions in an *evergreen coniferous (boreal or taiga) forest ecosystem.* When these organisms die, decomposers break down their organic matter into minerals that plants use. Coloured arrows indicate transfers of matter and energy between producers; primary consumers (herbivores); secondary, or higher-level, consumers (carnivores); and decomposers. Organisms are not drawn to scale.

FIGURE 6-34 The Great Lakes–St. Lawrence Forest contains both deciduous and coniferous trees, along with an abundant flora and fauna.

Most of the trees are evergreen because the abundance of water means that they have no need to shed their leaves. Tree trunks and the ground are frequently covered with mosses and ferns in this cool and moist environment. As in tropical rain forests, little light reaches the forest floor.

The ocean moderates the temperature so winters are mild and summers are cool. The trees in these moist forests depend on frequent rains and moisture from summer fog that rolls in off the Pacific.

Figure 6-35 (p. 136). lists major human impacts on the world's forests. What direct and indirect impacts does your lifestyle have on forest biomes?

6-7 MOUNTAIN BIOMES

Why Are Mountains Ecologically Important? High-Altitude Biodiversity Sanctuaries

Mountains are high-elevation forested islands of biodiversity and often have snow-covered peaks that reflect solar radiation and gradually release water to lower-elevation streams and ecosystems.

Some of the world's most spectacular and important environments are mountains, which make up almost a fourth of the world's land surface. Mountains are places where dramatic changes in altitude, climate,

---

SPOTLIGHT

The Great Lakes–St. Lawrence Forest

The Great Lakes–St. Lawrence Forest, or Northern Hardwood Forest, is a distinctive and important region in Ontario (Figure 6-34). It has a mix of deciduous trees such as maples, yellow birch, and red oak and coniferous trees such as red pine, white pine, and eastern hemlock.

Some people regard the Great Lakes–St. Lawrence Forest as simply the overlap of two great biomes: boreal forest and temperate deciduous forest. Others consider this region to be a biome in its own right. In any case, it is a distinctive-looking forest of wind-twisted white pines and flaming fall colours—made famous by the art of Canada's Group of Seven and by the beauty of Algonquin Provincial Park.

The Great Lakes–St. Lawrence Forest is populated by game and fur-bearers, including moose, deer, black bears, wolves, and many others. The region is managed for wood, wildlife, and recreational opportunities.

Climate and Terrestrial Biodiversity

Natural Capital Degradation

Forests

- Clearing and degradation of tropical forests for agriculture, livestock grazing, and timber harvesting

- Clearing of temperate deciduous forests in North America, Europe, and Asia for timber, agriculture, and urban development

- Clearing of evergreen coniferous forests in North America, Finland, Sweden, and Russia

- Conversion of diverse forests to less biodiverse tree plantations

- Damage to soils from off-road vehicles

FIGURE 6-35 **Natural capital degradation:** major human impacts on the world's forests.

Natural Capital Degradation

Mountains

- Landless poor migrating uphill to survive

- Timber extraction

- Mineral resource extraction

- Hydroelectric dams and reservoirs

- Increasing tourism (such as hiking and skiing)

- Air pollution from industrial and urban centres

- Increased ultraviolet radiation from ozone depletion

- Soil damage from off-road vehicles

FIGURE 6-36 **Natural capital degradation:** major human impacts on the world's mountains.

soil, and vegetation take place over a very short distance (Figure 6-20, left).

Because of the steep slopes, mountain soils are especially prone to erosion when the vegetation holding them in place is removed by natural disturbances (such as landslides and avalanches) or human activities (such as timber cutting and agriculture). Many mountains are *islands of biodiversity* surrounded by a sea of lower-elevation landscapes transformed by human activities.

Mountains play important ecological roles. They contain the majority of the world's forests, which when combined with the topographic variations of mountains provide diverse habitats for much of the world's terrestrial biodiversity. They often are habitats for endemic species found nowhere else on Earth, and they serve as sanctuaries for animal species driven from lowland areas.

They also help regulate the Earth's climate when their snow- and ice-covered tops reflect solar radiation back into space. Mountains affect sea levels as a result of decreases or increases in glacial ice—most of which is locked up in Antarctica (the most mountainous of all continents). Finally, mountains play a critical role in the hydrologic cycle by gradually releasing melting ice, snow, and water stored in the soils and vegetation of mountainsides to small streams.

Despite their ecological, economic, and cultural importance, the fate of mountain ecosystems

has not been a high priority of many governments throughout the world. Mountain ecosystems are coming under increasing pressure from human activities (Figure 6-36). Fortunately, Canada has a set of large and near-contiguous parks in the Rocky Mountains (Chapter 11). Conservationists and politicians in both Canada and the United States are developing a Yellowstone to Yukon (Y2Y) Conservation Initiative to protect the unique natural heritage of this biologically and economically important region.

In this chapter, we examined the connections among weather, climate, and the distribution of the Earth's terrestrial biomes. Three general ecological lessons emerge from this study. *First,* different climates occur as a result of currents of air and water flowing over an unevenly heated planet spinning on a tilted axis. *Second,* different climates result in different communities of organisms, or biomes. *Third,* everything is connected.

When we try to pick out anything by itself, we find it hitched to everything else in the universe.
JOHN MUIR

CHAPTER REVIEW

1. Review the Key Questions for this chapter on p. 110. Describe the environmentally beneficial and harmful effects of the Earth's winds.

2. Distinguish between *weather* and *climate*. Describe three major factors that determine how air circulates in the lower atmosphere. Describe how the properties of air, water, and land affect global air circulation. How is heat distributed to different parts of the ocean? Explain how global air circulation and ocean currents lead to the forests, grasslands, and deserts that make up the Earth's terrestrial biomes.

3. Define and give four examples of a *greenhouse gas*. What is the *greenhouse effect* and why is it important to the Earth's life and climate? What is the *rain shadow effect* and how can it lead to the formation of inland deserts? Why do cities tend to have more haze and smog, higher temperatures, and lower wind speeds than the surrounding countryside?

4. What is a *biome*? Explain why there are three major types of each of the major biomes (*deserts, grasslands,* and *forests*). Describe how climate and vegetation vary with latitude and elevation. Rank Canada's biomes by size, from largest to smallest.

5. Describe how plants and animals survive in the three major types of deserts. Give examples of the specific adaptations of the organisms that live in these places.

6. Describe the three major types of grasslands in terms of their climate, soil, and vegetation. What is a savanna? Why have many of the world's temperate grasslands disappeared? What is *permafrost*? What is *tundra*?

7. What is a *forest system* and what are the three major types of forests? Describe how these three types differ in their climate and vegetation. Why do most soils in tropical rain forests have few plant nutrients? Why is biodiversity so high in tropical rain forests? Describe what happens in temperate deciduous forests in the winter and fall. What are coastal coniferous or temperate rain forests? What important ecological roles do mountains play?

8. Study the climate graphs (Figures 6-21, 6-23, and 6-29). What exactly are the differences in temperature and moisture among (a) the three deserts, (b) the three grasslands, and (c) the three forests? What exactly are the differences in temperature and moisture among the three examples of biomes in (a) tropical areas, (b) temperate areas, and (c) polar areas?

9. Describe human activities that have affected the world's (a) deserts, (b) grasslands, (c) forests, and (d) mountains. Which of these places have been most, and least, impacted?

10. Describe the connections between the Earth's winds, climates, and biomes, and the four *principles of sustainability* (Chapter 1).

CRITICAL THINKING

1. List a limiting factor for each of the following ecosystems: (a) a desert, (b) arctic tundra, (c) alpine tundra, (d) the floor of a tropical rain forest, and (e) a temperate deciduous forest.

2. Why do deserts and arctic tundra support a much smaller biomass of animals than do tropical forests?

3. Why do most animals in a tropical rain forest live in its trees?

4. What biomes are best suited for (a) raising crops and (b) grazing livestock? How can crops and livestock be produced with less impact on the area?

5. Congratulations! You are in charge of the world. What are the three most important features of your plan to help sustain the Earth's terrestrial biodiversity?

PROJECTS

1. How has the climate changed in the area where you live during the past 50 years? Investigate the beneficial and harmful effects of these changes. How have these changes benefited or harmed you personally?

2. Use the library or the Internet to learn more about the characteristics of deserts. Then use the Internet to learn more about the arid ecosystem found at Osoyoos, British Columbia. In your opinion, does this area qualify as Canada's only desert? Should steps be taken to preserve its flora and fauna? If so, what steps?

3. Use the library or the Internet to learn more about the flora and fauna of the Great Lakes–St. Lawrence Forest. Should this area be considered a subdivision of the boreal biome, a subdivision of the temperate deciduous biome, or a biome in its own right?

4. Visit the websites of Environment Canada (http://www.weatheroffice.gc.ca) and Natural Resources Canada (http://www.nrcan.gc.ca) to learn more about Canada's most devastating tornadoes. What precautions would you take in the event of a major tornado outbreak in your area?

Aquatic Biodiversity

Why Should We Care about Coral Reefs?

CASE STUDY

In the shallow coastal zones of warm, tropical, and subtropical oceans we often find **coral reefs** (Figure 7-1, left). These stunningly beautiful natural wonders are among the world's oldest, most diverse, and most productive ecosystems.

Coral reefs are formed by massive colonies of tiny animals called *polyps*. They slowly build reefs by secreting a protective crust of limestone (calcium carbonate) around their soft bodies.

When the polyps die, their empty crusts remain as a platform for more reef growth. The result is an elaborate network of crevices, ledges, and holes that serve as calcium carbonate "condominiums" for a variety of marine animals.

Coral reefs involve a mutually beneficial relationship between the polyps and tiny single-celled algae called *zooxanthellae* ("zoh-ZAN-thel-ee") that live in the tissues of the polyps. The algae provide the polyps with colour, food, and oxygen through photosynthesis and help produce calcium carbonate, which forms the coral skeleton. The polyps in turn provide the algae with a well-protected home and some of their nutrients. This is a win-win deal for both species.

Coral reefs provide a number of important ecological and economic services. When coral polyps form their limestone shells they remove carbon dioxide from the atmosphere as part of the carbon cycle. Coral reefs act as natural barriers that help protect about 15% of the world's coastlines from erosion by battering waves and storms. They also support at least one-fourth of all identified marine species and about two-thirds of marine fish species and produce about a tenth of the global fish catch.

The reefs provide jobs and building materials (which can help destroy the reefs) for some of the world's poorest countries and support fishing and tourism industries worth billions of dollars each year.

Finally, these biological treasures give us an underwater world to study and enjoy. Coral reefs provide these free ecological and economic services while occupying less than 0.1% of the world's ocean area—amounting to an area about twice the size of the Maritime provinces. They are true wonders of biodiversity!

Bad news. About one-fourth of the world's coral reefs have been lost to coastal development, pollution, overfishing, warmer ocean temperatures, and other stresses. And these threats are increasing.

One problem is *coral bleaching* (Figure 7-1, right). It occurs when a coral becomes stressed and expels most of its colourful algae, leaving an underlying ghostly white skeleton of calcium carbonate. Two causes are increased water temperature and runoff of silt that covers the coral and prevents photosynthesis. Unable to grow or repair themselves, the corals eventually die unless the stress is removed and algae recolonize them.

Aquatic scientists view coral reefs as "aquatic biodiversity savings banks" and sensitive biological indicators

(*continued*)

FIGURE 7-1 A healthy coral reef covered by colourful algae (left) and a bleached coral reef that has lost most of its algae (right) because of changes in the environment (such as cloudy water or too warm temperatures). With the algae gone, the white limestone of the coral skeleton becomes visible. If the environmental stress is not removed and no other alga species fill the abandoned niche, the corals die. These diverse and productive ecosystems are being damaged and destroyed at an alarming rate.

Tischenko Irina/Shutterstock

Ville Frisk/Shutterstock

of environmental conditions in their aquatic environment. The decline and degradation of these colourful oceanic sentinels should serve as a warning about the health of their habitats and the oceans that provide us with crucial ecological and economic services.

If there is magic on this planet, it is contained in water.
LOREN EISLEY

CHAPTER PURPOSE AND QUESTIONS

Chapter 7 describes aquatic ecosystems and the impacts of human activities on our planet's aquatic biodiversity. The chapter addresses the following questions:

7-1 What are the basic types of aquatic life zones, and what factors influence the kinds of life they contain?

7-2 What are the major types of saltwater life zones, and how do human activities affect them?

7-3 What are the major types of freshwater life zones, and how do human activities affect them?

7-1 AQUATIC ENVIRONMENTS

What Are the Two Major Types of Aquatic Life Zones? Salty and Fresh

Saltwater and freshwater aquatic life zones cover almost three-fourths of the Earth's surface.

The **aquatic** equivalents of biomes are called *aquatic life zones*. The major types of organisms found in aquatic environments are determined by the water's *salinity*—the amounts of various salts such as sodium chloride (NaCl) dissolved in a given volume of water. As a result, aquatic life zones are divided into two major types: *saltwater* or *marine* (such as estuaries, coastlines, coral reefs, coastal marshes, mangrove swamps, and oceans) and *freshwater* (such as lakes, ponds, streams, rivers, and inland wetlands). Figure 7-2 shows the distribution of the world's major oceans, lakes, rivers, coral reefs, and mangroves.

The world's saltwater and freshwater aquatic systems cover about 71% of the Earth's surface. We can think of the world's rivers, streams, lakes, and oceans as a giant circulatory system transporting water from one place to another as part of the Earth's water cycle (Figure 4-27, p. 80). These aquatic systems also play vital roles in the Earth's

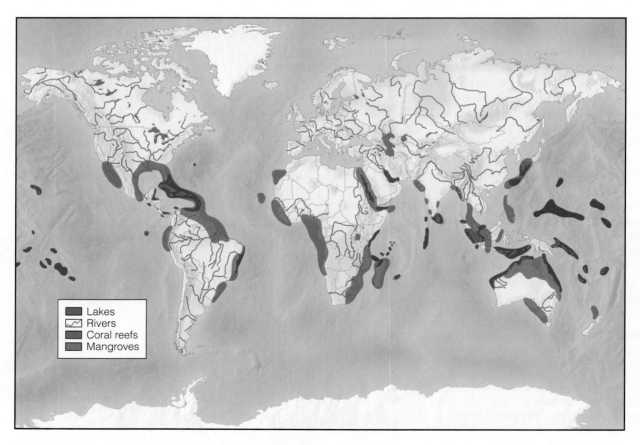

Lakes
Rivers
Coral reefs
Mangroves

FIGURE 7-2 Natural capital: distribution of the world's major saltwater oceans, coral reefs, mangroves, and freshwater lakes and rivers.

biological productivity, climate, biogeochemical cycles, and biodiversity.

What Kinds of Organisms Live in Aquatic Life Zones? Floaters, Swimmers, Crawlers, and Decomposers

Aquatic systems contain floating, drifting, swimming, bottom-dwelling, and decomposer organisms.

Saltwater and freshwater life zones contain four major types of organisms. One group consists of weakly swimming, free-floating **plankton** carried by currents. There are three major types of plankton. One is **phytoplankton** ("FIE-toe-plank-ton," Greek for "drifting plants"), or *plant plankton*. They and many types of algae are the producers that support most aquatic food chains and food webs. Another type is **zooplankton** ("ZOE-oh-plank-ton," Greek for "drifting animals"), or *animal plankton*. They consist of primary consumers (herbivores) that feed on phytoplankton and secondary consumers that feed on other zooplankton. They range from single-celled protozoa to large **invertebrates** such as jellyfish.

Improved technologies for filtering and analyzing water have revealed huge populations of much smaller plankton called **ultraplankton**—photosynthetic bacteria no more than 2 micrometres (40 millionths of an inch) wide. Scientists estimate that these extremely small plankton may be responsible for 70% of the primary productivity near the ocean surface.

A *second group* of organisms consists of **nekton**, strongly swimming consumers such as fish, turtles, and whales. A *third group*, called **benthos**, dwells on the bottom. Examples are barnacles and oysters that anchor themselves to one spot, worms that burrow into the sand or mud, and lobsters and crabs that walk about on the bottom. A fourth group consists of **decomposers** (mostly bacteria) that break down the organic compounds in the dead bodies and wastes of aquatic organisms into simple nutrient compounds for use by producers.

How Do Aquatic Systems Differ from Terrestrial Systems? Living without Boundaries and Large Temperature Fluctuations

Living in water has its benefits and drawbacks.

Living in an aquatic environment has advantages and disadvantages (Figure 7-3). Several differences between aquatic and terrestrial systems also hinder the ability of researchers to understand aquatic systems. One is that aquatic systems have less pronounced and fixed physical boundaries than terrestrial ecosystems. This makes it difficult to count and manage populations of aquatic organisms.

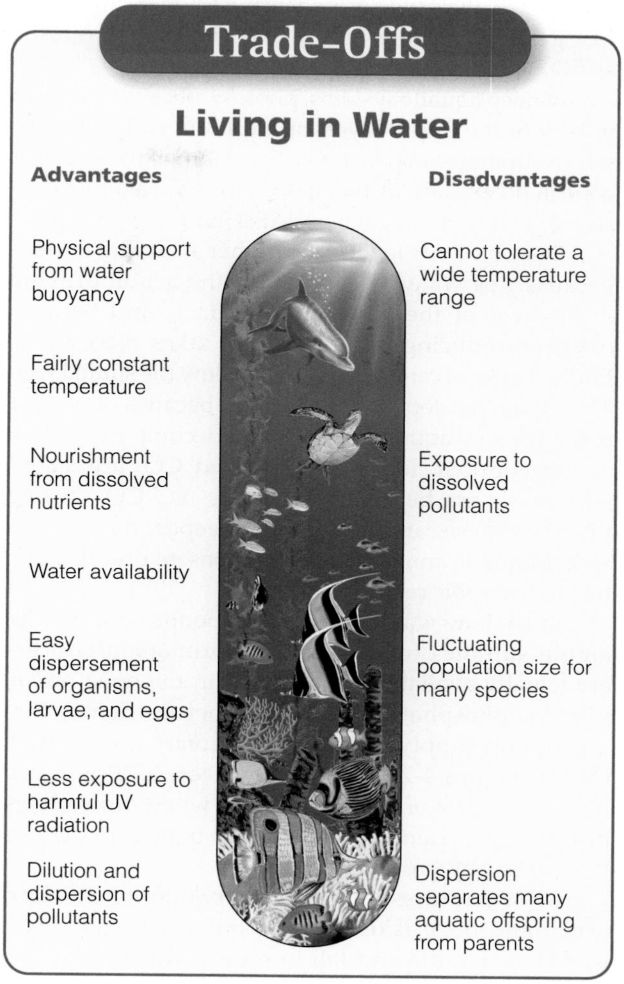

Trade-Offs

Living in Water

Advantages	Disadvantages
Physical support from water buoyancy	Cannot tolerate a wide temperature range
Fairly constant temperature	
Nourishment from dissolved nutrients	Exposure to dissolved pollutants
Water availability	
Easy dispersement of organisms, larvae, and eggs	Fluctuating population size for many species
Less exposure to harmful UV radiation	
Dilution and dispersion of pollutants	Dispersion separates many aquatic offspring from parents

FIGURE 7-3 Trade-offs: advantages and disadvantages of living in water.

Also, food chains and webs in aquatic systems are usually more complex and longer than those in terrestrial biomes. One reason is that the fluid medium of water systems and the variety of bottom habitats open up ways of getting food that are not available on land. Another difference is that aquatic systems (especially marine systems) are more difficult to monitor and study than terrestrial systems because of their size and because they are largely hidden from view.

What Factors Limit Life at Different Depths in Aquatic Life Zones? Living in Layered Zones

Life in aquatic systems is found in surface, middle, and bottom layers.

Most aquatic life zones can be divided into three layers: *surface, middle,* and *bottom*. A number of environmental factors determine the types and numbers of organisms found in these layers. Examples are *temperature, access to sunlight for photosynthesis, dissolved oxygen content,* and *availability of nutrients* such as carbon (as dissolved CO_2 gas), nitrogen (as NO_3^-), and phosphorus (mostly as PO_4^{3-}) for producers.

In deep aquatic systems, photosynthesis is confined mostly to the upper layer, or **euphotic zone,** through which sunlight can penetrate. The depth of the euphotic zone in oceans and deep lakes can be reduced by excessive algal growth (algal blooms) clouding the water.

Dissolved O_2 levels are higher near the surface because this water is exposed to the action of wind and waves at the air–water interface, and because oxygen-producing photosynthesis takes place there. Photosynthesis cannot take place below the sunlit layer. Thus at lower depths O_2 levels fall because of aerobic respiration by aquatic animals and decomposers.

In contrast, levels of dissolved CO_2 are *low* in surface layers because producers use CO_2 during photosynthesis and are *high* in deeper, dark layers where aquatic animals and decomposers produce CO_2 through aerobic respiration.

In shallow waters in streams, ponds, and oceans, ample supplies of nutrients for primary producers are usually available. By contrast, in the open ocean, nitrates, phosphates, iron, and other nutrients often are in short supply and limit net primary productivity (NPP) (Figure 4-23, p. 75). However, NPP is much higher in parts of the open ocean where upwellings bring such nutrients from the ocean bottom to the surface for use by producers.

Most creatures living on the bottom of the deep ocean and deep lakes depend on animal and plant plankton that die and fall into deep waters. Because this food is limited, deep-dwelling fish species tend to reproduce slowly. This makes them especially vulnerable to depletion from overfishing.

7-2 SALTWATER LIFE ZONES

Why Should We Care about the Oceans? Givers of Life

Although oceans occupy most of the Earth's surface and provide many ecological and economic services, we know less about them than we do about the moon.

A more accurate name for Earth would be *Ocean* because saltwater oceans cover about 71% of the planet's surface (Figure 7-4). They contain about 250 000 known species of marine plants and animals and provide many important ecological and economic services, shown in Figure 7-5. Take a good look at this figure that describes part of your life-support system.

As landlubbers we have a distorted and limited view of our watery home. We know more about the surface of the moon than about the oceans that cover most of the Earth. According to aquatic scientists, the

Ocean hemisphere   Land–ocean hemisphere

FIGURE 7-4 Natural capital: the ocean planet. The salty oceans cover about 71% of the Earth's surface. About 97% of the Earth's water is in the interconnected oceans, which cover 90% of the planet's mostly ocean hemisphere (left) and 50% of its land–ocean hemisphere (right). Freshwater systems cover less than 1% of the Earth's surface.

scientific investigation of poorly understood marine and freshwater aquatic systems is a *research frontier* whose study could result in immense ecological and economic benefits.

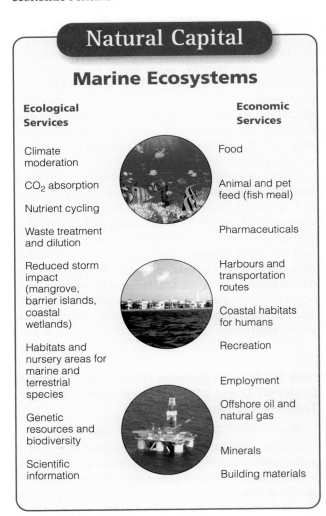

Natural Capital

Marine Ecosystems

Ecological Services	Economic Services
Climate moderation	Food
CO_2 absorption	Animal and pet feed (fish meal)
Nutrient cycling	
Waste treatment and dilution	Pharmaceuticals
Reduced storm impact (mangrove, barrier islands, coastal wetlands)	Harbours and transportation routes
	Coastal habitats for humans
Habitats and nursery areas for marine and terrestrial species	Recreation
	Employment
Genetic resources and biodiversity	Offshore oil and natural gas
	Minerals
Scientific information	Building materials

FIGURE 7-5 Natural capital: major ecological and economic services provided by marine systems.

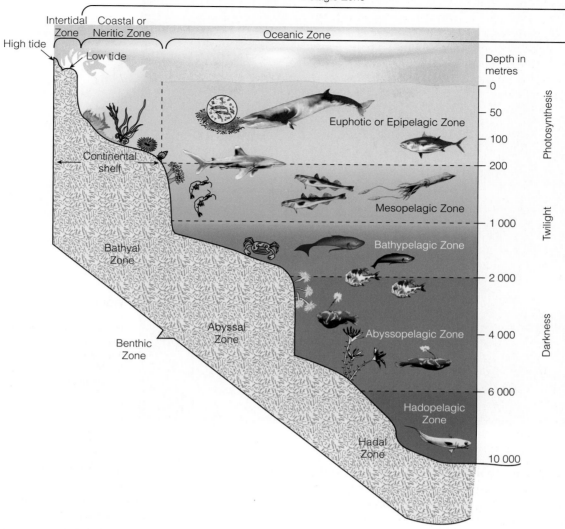

FIGURE 7-6 Natural capital: major life zones in an ocean (not drawn to scale). There are benthic zones (on the ocean floor) and pelagic zones (in the water column). Most solar energy is absorbed in the euphotic or epipelagic zone, and light diminishes with increasing depth. A different assemblage of organisms inhabits each of the zones.

What Is the Coastal Zone? Abundant Life Near the Shore

The coastal zone makes up less than 10% of the world's ocean area but contains 90% of all marine species.

Oceans have two major life zones: the *coastal zone* and the *open sea* (Figure 7-6). The **coastal zone** is the warm, nutrient-rich, shallow water that extends from the high-tide mark on land to the gently sloping, shallow edge of the *continental shelf* (the submerged part of the continents). This zone has numerous interactions with the land and thus human activities easily affect it.

Although it makes up less than a tenth of the world's ocean area, the coastal zone contains 90% of all marine species and is the site of most large commercial marine fisheries. Most ecosystems found in the coastal zone have a high net primary productivity per unit of area. This occurs because of the zone's ample supplies of sunlight and plant nutrients flowing from land and distributed by wind and ocean currents.

What Are Estuaries, Coastal Wetlands, and Mangrove Swamps? Stressed Centres of Biological Productivity

Several highly productive coastal ecosystems are under increasing stress from human activities.

One highly productive area in the coastal zone is an **estuary,** a partially enclosed area of coastal water where sea water mixes with fresh water and nutrients from rivers, streams, and runoff from land (Figure 7-7, p. 144).

FIGURE 7-7 View of an *estuary* taken from space. The photo shows the sediment plume at the mouth of Madagascar's Betsiboka River as it flows through the estuary and into the Mozambique Channel. Because of its topography, heavy rainfall, and the clearing of forests for agriculture, Madagascar is the world's most eroded country.

Estuaries and their associated **coastal wetlands** (land areas covered with water all or part of the year) include river mouths, inlets, bays, sounds, mangrove forest swamps in sheltered regions along tropical coasts, and salt marshes (Figure 7-8, p. 145) in temperate zones.

Temperature and salinity levels vary widely in estuaries and coastal wetlands because of the daily rhythms of the tides and seasonal variations in the flow of fresh water into the estuary. They are also affected by unpredictable flows of fresh water from coastal land and rivers after heavy rains and of salt water from the ocean as a result of storms, hurricanes, and typhoons. You have to be tough to survive in this harsh and variable environment.

The dominant organisms in **mangrove forest swamps** are trees that can grow in salt water. These trees have extensive roots that extend above the water, where they can obtain oxygen and provide support for the plant. These nutrient-rich forests are found in sheltered regions along tropical coasts (Figure 7-2). Because ocean waves do not reach these saltwater ecosystems, they collect mud and anaerobic sediment.

The constant water movement in estuaries and their associated coastal wetlands stirs up the nutrient-rich silt, making it available to producers. These systems filter toxic pollutants, excess plant nutrients, sediments, and other pollutants. They reduce storm damage by absorbing waves and storing excess water produced by storms. And they provide food, habitats, and nursery sites for a wide variety of aquatic species.

Bad news. We are degrading or destroying some of the ecological services that these important ecosystems provide at no cost. Researchers estimate that more than a third of the world's mangrove forests have been destroyed—mostly for developing aquaculture shrimp farms, growing crops, and coastal development projects.

What Niches Do Rocky and Sandy Shores Provide? Hold On, Dig In, or Hang Out in a Shell

Organisms in coastal areas experiencing daily low and high tides have evolved a number of ways to survive under harsh and changing conditions.

The area of shoreline between low and high tides is called the **intertidal zone.** This is not an easy place to live. Its organisms must be able to avoid being swept away or crushed by waves, and avoid or cope with

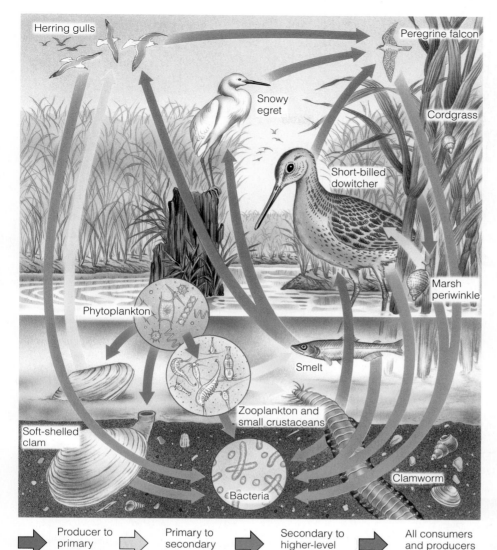

Herring gulls

Peregrine falcon

Snowy egret

Short-billed dowitcher

Cordgrass

Marsh periwinkle

Phytoplankton

Smelt

Zooplankton and small crustaceans

Soft-shelled clam

Bacteria

Clamworm

Producer to primary consumer

Primary to secondary consumer

Secondary to higher-level consumer

All consumers and producers to decomposers

FIGURE 7-8 Natural capital: some components and interactions in a *salt marsh ecosystem* in a temperate area. When these organisms die, decomposers break down their organic matter into minerals used by plants. Coloured arrows indicate transfers of matter and energy between consumers (herbivores), secondary (or higher-level) consumers (carnivores), and decomposers. Organisms are not drawn to scale.

being immersed during high tides and left high and dry (and much hotter) at low tides. They must also survive changing levels of salinity when heavy rains dilute salt water. To deal with such stresses, most intertidal organisms hold on to something, dig in, or hide in protective shells.

Some coasts have steep *rocky shores* pounded by waves. The numerous pools and other niches in the intertidal zone of rocky shores contain a great variety of species with different niches as shown in the top part of Figure 7-9 (p. 146).

Other coasts have gently sloping *barrier beaches,* or *sandy shores,* with niches for different marine organisms as shown in the bottom portion of Figure 7-9. Most of them are hidden from view and survive by burrowing, digging, and tunnelling in the sand. These sandy beaches and their adjoining coastal wetlands are also home to a variety of shorebirds that feed in

specialized niches on crustaceans, insects, and other organisms (Figure 5-5, p. 99).

What Are Coral Reefs? Aquatic Oases of Biodiversity

Coral reefs are biologically diverse and productive ecosystems that are increasingly stressed by human activities.

Coral reefs (Figure 7-1 and photo on p. ix) form in clear, warm coastal waters of the tropics and subtropics (Figure 7-2). Coral reefs are ecologically complex in terms of the many interactions among the diverse organisms that live there, as shown in Figure 7-10 (p. 147).

These reefs are vulnerable to damage because they grow slowly and are disrupted easily. They also thrive only in clear, warm, and fairly shallow water of

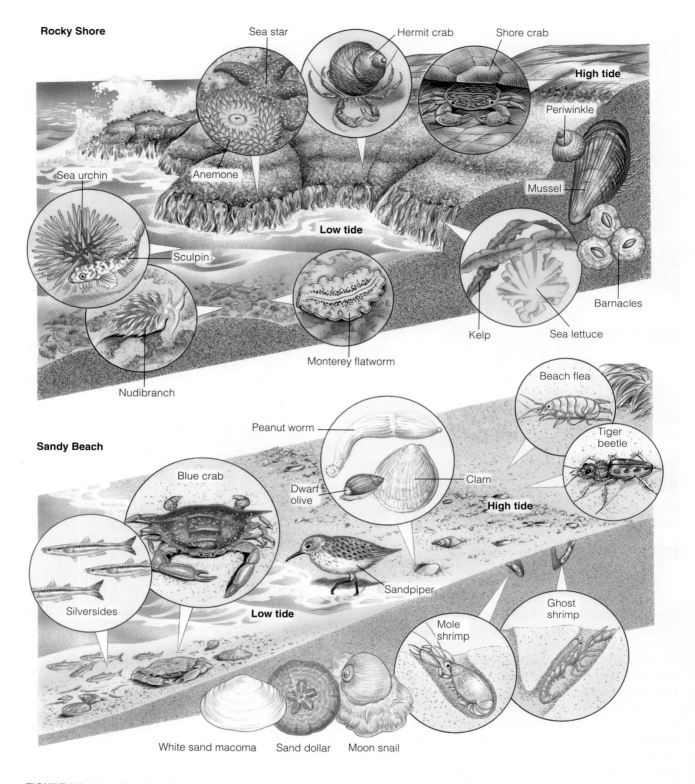

FIGURE 7-9 Living between the tides. Some organisms with specialized niches found in various zones on rocky shores (top) and sandy beaches (bottom). Organisms are not drawn to scale.

constant high salinity. Corals can live only in water with a temperature of 18–30°C (64–86°F). Coral bleaching (Figure 7-1, right) can be triggered by an increase of just 1°C (1.8°F) above this maximum temperature.

The biodiversity of coral reefs can be reduced by natural disturbances such as severe storms, fresh-water floods, and invasions of predatory fish. But throughout their long geologic history, coral reefs

Producer to primary consumer	Primary to secondary consumer	Secondary to higher-level consumer	All consumers and producers to decomposers

FIGURE 7-10 Natural capital: some components and interactions in a *coral reef ecosystem*. When these organisms die, decomposers break down their organic matter into minerals used by plants. Coloured arrows indicate transfers of matter and energy between producers, primary consumers (herbivores), secondary (or higher-level) consumers (carnivores), and decomposers. Organisms are not drawn to scale.

have been able to adapt to such natural environmental changes.

Today the biggest threats to the survival and biodiversity of many of the world's coral reefs come from sediment runoff and other human activities (Figure 7-11, p. 148). Scientists are concerned that these threats are occurring so rapidly (over decades) and over such a wide area that many of the world's coral reef systems may not have enough time to adapt.

Good news. There is growing evidence that coral reefs can recover when given a chance. When localities or nations have imposed restrictions on reef fishing or reduced inputs of nutrients and other pollutants, reefs have rebounded. About 27% of the world's coral reefs are located within marine protected areas (MPAs) where they may receive some level of protection (Mumby and Harborne, 2010).

Bad News. Only 6% of the world's coral reefs are located within *effectively managed* MPAs (http://www.wri.org/project/reefs-at-risk). Furthermore, large-scale changes are occurring that could affect coral reefs everywhere. The ocean is gradually becoming more acidic as it absorbs excess CO_2 from the atmosphere. The CO_2 reacts with seawater, forming a weak acid that can dissolve the calcium carbonate that makes up corals. See page 519 for further details of ocean acidification.

Natural Capital Degradation

Coral Reefs

Ocean warming

Soil erosion

Algae growth from fertilizer runoff

Mangrove destruction

Coral reef bleaching

Rising sea levels

Increased UV exposure from ozone depletion

Using cyanide and dynamite to harvest coral reef fish

Coral removal for building material, aquariums, and jewellery

Increasing ocean acidification

FIGURE 7-11 **Natural capital degradation:** major threats to coral reefs.

What Biological Zones Are Found in the Open Sea? Where Is the Light?

The open ocean consists of a brightly lit surface layer, a dimly lit middle layer, and a dark bottom zone.

The sharp increase in water depth at the edge of the continental shelf separates the coastal zone from the vast volume of the ocean called the **open sea.** Primarily on the basis of the penetration of sunlight, it is divided into vertical zones as shown in Figure 7-6.

The *euphotic zone* is the lighted upper zone where floating drifting phytoplankton carry out photosynthesis. Nutrient levels are low (except around upwellings), and levels of dissolved oxygen are high. Large, fast-swimming predatory fish such as swordfish, sharks, and bluefin tuna populate this zone.

The *bathyal zone* is the dimly lit middle zone that does not contain photosynthesizing producers because of a lack of sunlight. Various types of zooplankton and smaller fish, many of which migrate to the surface at night to feed, populate this zone.

The lowest zones, called the *abyssal* and *hadal zones*, are dark, very cold, and under immense pressure. Relatively few species live here. Some examples are sea cucumbers, tube worms, and deep-sea anglerfish.

Most organisms of the deep waters and ocean floor get their food from showers of dead and decaying organisms (detritus) drifting down from upper lighted levels of the ocean. Some of these organisms, including many types of worms, are *deposit feeders*, which take mud into their guts and extract nutrients from it. Others such as oysters, clams, and sponges are *filter feeders*, which pass water through or over their bodies and extract nutrients from it. On parts of the dark, deep ocean floor near hydrothermal vents, scientists have found communities of organisms where specialized bacteria use chemosynthesis to produce their own food and food for other organisms feeding on them.

Average primary productivity and NPP per unit of area (Figure 4-23) are quite low in the open sea except at an occasional equatorial upwelling, where currents bring up nutrients from the ocean bottom. However, because the open sea covers so much of the Earth's surface, it makes the largest contribution to the Earth's overall NPP.

Currently, about 45% of the world's population lives along coasts or within 100 kilometres (62 miles) of a coast. Some 13 of the world's 19 megacities with populations of 10 million or more people are in coastal zones. By 2030, at least 6.3 billion people—equal to the world's entire population in 2003—are expected to live in or near coastal zones. Figure 7-12 lists major human impacts on marine systems.

CONSIDER, DISCUSS, OR DEBATE

What actions could be taken by society to solve the problems shown in Figures 7-11 and 7-12? What strategic moves could *you* make if you decided to confront a few of these problems and focus your efforts on making a difference?

Natural Capital Degradation

Marine Ecosystems

Half of coastal wetlands lost to agriculture and urban development

Over one-third of mangrove forests lost since 1980 to agriculture, development, and aquaculture shrimp farms

About 10% of world's beaches eroding because of coastal development and rising sea level

Ocean bottom habitats degraded by dredging and trawler fishing boats

About 75% of the world's coral reefs threatened

FIGURE 7-12 **Natural capital degradation:** major human impacts on the world's marine systems.

7-3 FRESHWATER LIFE ZONES

What Are Freshwater Life Zones? Lakes, Wetlands, Rivers

Freshwater ecosystems provide important ecological and economic services even though they cover less than 1% of the Earth's surface.

> **DID YOU KNOW**
>
> Canada's coastline is the longest of any country in the world. If you walked the full 243 000 kilometres at an average rate of 20 kilometres per day, it would take you 33 years and you would trek past three oceans!

Freshwater life zones occur where water with a dissolved salt concentration of less than 1% by volume accumulates on or flows through the surfaces of terrestrial biomes. Examples are *standing* (lentic) bodies of fresh water such as lakes, ponds, and inland wetlands and *flowing* (lotic) systems such as streams and rivers. Although freshwater systems cover less than 1% of the Earth's surface, they provide a number of important ecological and economic services (Figure 7-13). The volume of fresh water that we use provides us with free services worth about $3 trillion a year—equal to about 7% of the value of all goods and services provided annually by the entire global economy.

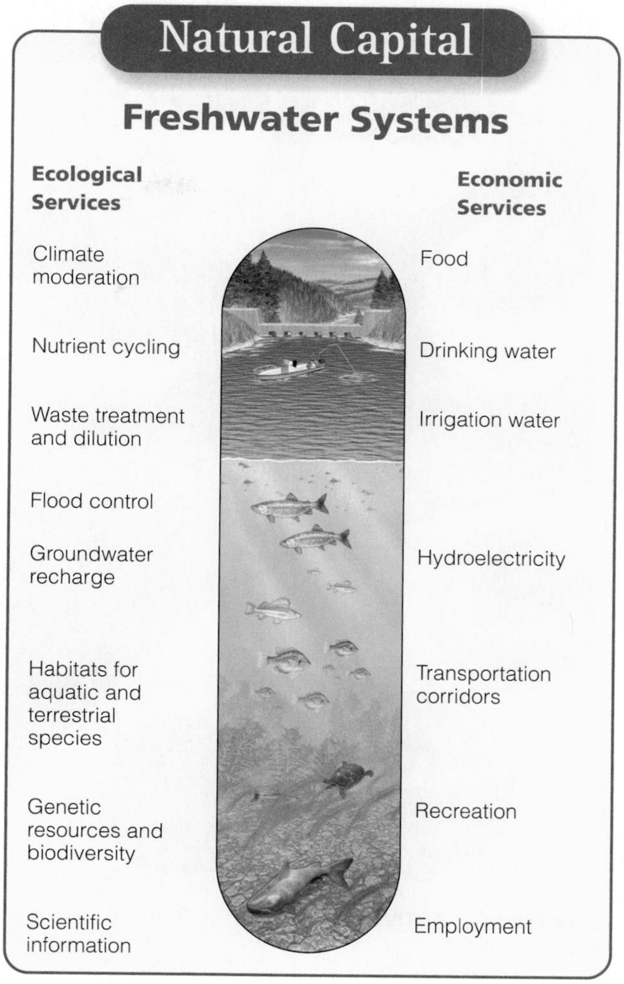
Natural Capital
Freshwater Systems
Ecological Services
Economic Services
Climate moderation
Nutrient cycling
Waste treatment and dilution
Flood control
Groundwater recharge
Habitats for aquatic and terrestrial species
Genetic resources and biodiversity
Scientific information
Food
Drinking water
Irrigation water
Hydroelectricity
Transportation corridors
Recreation
Employment

FIGURE 7-13 Natural capital: major ecological and economic services provided by freshwater systems.

> **DID YOU KNOW**
>
> Canada has about 20% of the world's freshwater supply. It covers about 9% of our land surface. Some of Canada's water is over 100 000 years old and is found at the base of our Arctic ice caps.

What Life Zones Are Found in Freshwater Lakes? Life in Layers

Lakes consist of sunlit surface layers near and away from the shore, and at deeper levels a dark layer and a bottom zone.

Lakes are large natural bodies of standing fresh water formed when precipitation, runoff, or groundwater seepage fill depressions in the Earth's surface. Causes of such depressions include *glaciation* (the Great Lakes of North America), *crustal displacement* (Lake Nyasa in East Africa), and volcanic activity (Crater Lake in Oregon). Lakes are supplied with water from rainfall, melting snow, and streams that drain the surrounding watershed.

Lakes normally consist of four distinct zones that are defined by their depth and distance from shore as shown in Figure 7-14 (p. 150). The top layer is the *littoral zone* ("LIT-tore-el"). It consists of the shallow sunlit waters near the shore to the depth at which rooted plants stop growing, and it has a high biological diversity. It has adequate nutrients from bottom sediments. Bulrushes and cattails are plentiful near the shore, and water lilies and entirely submerged plants flourish at the deepest depths of the littoral zone.

Next is the *limnetic zone* ("lim-NET-ic"): the open, sunlit water surface layer away from the shore that extends to the depth penetrated by sunlight. As the main photosynthetic body of the lake, its producers supply the food and oxygen that support most of the lake's consumers.

Next is the *profundal zone* ("pro-FUN-dahl"): the deep, open water where it is too dark for photosynthesis. Without sunlight and plants, oxygen levels are low. Fish adapted to its cooler and darker water are found in this zone.

Finally, at the bottom of the lake we find the *benthic zone* ("BEN-thic"). Mostly decomposers and detritus feeders and fish that swim from one zone to the other inhabit it. It is nourished mainly by detritus that falls from the littoral and limnetic zones and by sediment washing into the lake.

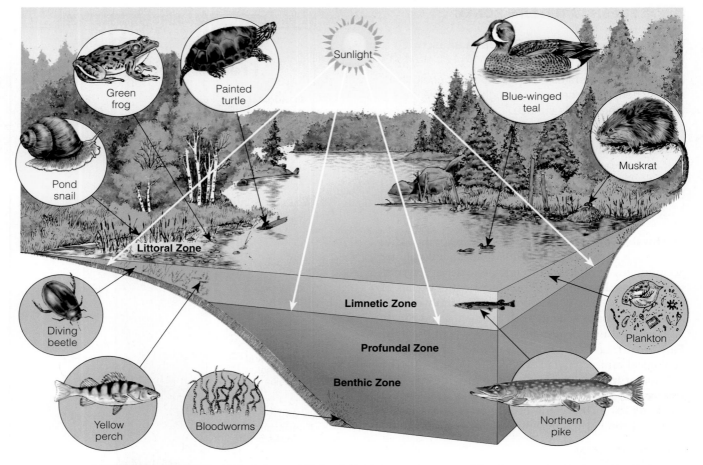

CENGAGENOW ACTIVE FIGURE 7-14 The distinct zones of life in a fairly deep temperate zone lake. *See an animation based in this figure at* CengageNow.

What Temperature Zones Are Found in Freshwater Lakes? Three Summer Temperature Zones

Most Canadian lakes exhibit temperature layers in the summer.

In summer, most Canadian lakes are affected by thermal stratification. Water near the surface, which is heated by the sun and mixed by the action of wind and waves, becomes a distinct layer of warm well-oxygenated water called the **epilimnion.** Beneath the epilimnion, the temperature changes rapidly over a short distance; this is the **thermocline.** The abrupt change in temperature and relative lack of mixing serve as a barrier to the transport of nutrients, oxygen, and organisms like fish that cannot tolerate sudden temperature change. The cold water below the thermacline is termed the **hypolimnion.** This layer of water often has a lower concentration of oxygen because it is isolated from the surface by the thermal stratification of the lake (Figure 7-15, p. 151).

In fall, thermal stratification breaks down. The surface water, cooled by exposure to cold air, sinks to the bottom of the lake and sets up a convection that brings nutrients up from the bottom and mixes oxygen down from the surface. This period is termed **fall turnover.**

In winter, the temperature throughout the water column is relatively uniform except the upper portion that cools to 0°C (32°F) and becomes ice. Cold water dissolves oxygen well, so levels of oxygen may be relatively high throughout the water column, supporting the survival of fish.

In spring as ice melts and the surface water warms from 0°C to 4°C (32–39°F), it actually becomes more dense (cold water reaches its maximum density at 4°C); it sinks and sets up a convection mixing nutrients from the bottom and oxygen from the surface—this is **spring turnover.**

As the surface water becomes warmer than 4°C, it becomes less dense than cooler water. It remains near the surface and thermal stratification begins to build toward another summer season.

> **CONSIDER, DISCUSS, OR DEBATE**
>
> How might pollutants that consume oxygen affect a lake at different points during the lake's annual temperature cycle? Consider the effects of declining oxygen levels on organisms living in different portions of the water column.

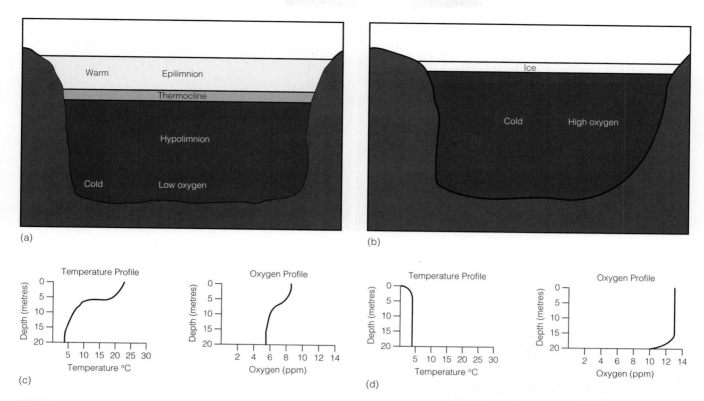

FIGURE 7-15 Temperature and dissolved oxygen vary seasonally, and with depth, in lakes. (a) shows a summer lake stratified into temperature layers: epilimnion, thermocline, and hypolimnion. (b) shows the lack of temperature layers in a winter lake. (c) shows temperature and oxygen profiles of a summer lake that could be measured by lowering a temperature probe and an oxygen probe down through the water column. (d) shows temperature and oxygen profiles of a winter lake. (Based on MILLER, *Living in the Environment*, 9e. © 1996 Brooks/Cole, a part of Cengage Learning, Inc.)

How Do Plant Nutrients Affect Lakes? Too Much of a Good Thing Is Not Good

A lake's supply of plant nutrients from its environment affects its physical and chemical conditions and the types and numbers of organisms it can support.

Ecologists classify lakes according to their nutrient content and primary productivity. A newly formed lake generally has a small supply of plant nutrients and is called an **oligotrophic** (poorly nourished) **lake** (Figure 7-16, left, p. 152). This type of lake is often deep, with steep banks. Glacier melt and mountain streams carrying little sediment supply water to such lakes. Because there is little sediment or microscopic life to cloud the water, such a lake usually has crystal-clear blue or green water and has small populations of phytoplankton and fish (such as smallmouth bass and trout). Because of their low levels of nutrients, these lakes have a low net primary productivity.

Over time, sediment, organic material, and inorganic nutrients wash into an oligotrophic lake, and plants grow and decompose to form bottom sediments. A lake with a large or excessive supply of nutrients (mostly nitrates and phosphates) needed by producers is called a **eutrophic** (well-nourished) **lake** (Figure 7-16, right). Such lakes typically are shallow and have murky brown or green water with poor visibility. Because of their high levels of nutrients, these lakes have a high net primary productivity.

In warm months the bottom layer of a eutrophic lake often is depleted of dissolved oxygen. Human inputs of nutrients from the atmosphere and from nearby urban and agricultural areas can accelerate the eutrophication of lakes, a process called *cultural eutrophication*. Many lakes fall somewhere between the two extremes of nutrient enrichment and are called **mesotrophic lakes.**

> **DID YOU KNOW**
>
> The Great Lakes are the largest concentration of liquid fresh water on the planet. The system includes the world's largest lake (Lake Superior); four other Great Lakes; and numerous rivers, streams, and wetlands. If you were to walk the 10 000-kilometre shoreline of the Great Lakes at an average rate of 20 kilometres per day, it would take you 500 days to complete the journey!

What Are the Major Characteristics of Freshwater Streams and Rivers? A Downhill Ride

Water flowing from mountains to the sea creates different aquatic conditions and habitats.

Precipitation that does not sink into the ground or evaporate is **surface water.** It becomes **runoff** when it

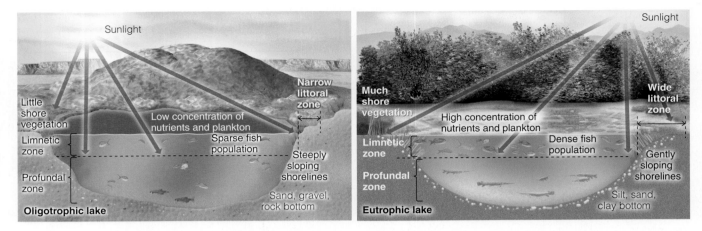

FIGURE 7-16 An *oligotrophic*, or nutrient-poor, lake (left) and a *eutrophic*, or nutrient-rich, lake (right). Mesotrophic lakes fall between these two extremes of nutrient enrichment. Nutrient inputs from human activities can accelerate eutrophication and lead to algae blooms and fish die-offs. This can reduce the fish populations shown for a eutrophic lake.

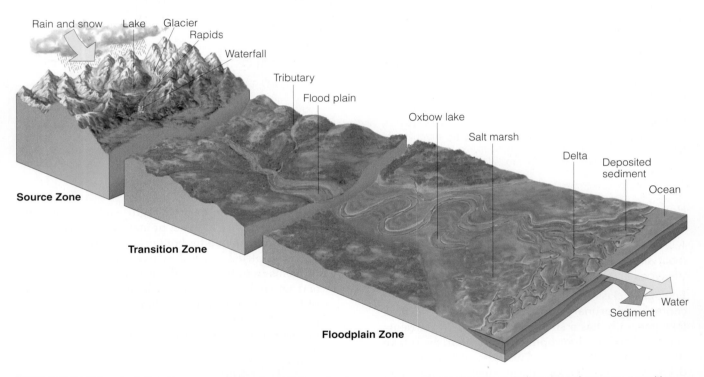

FIGURE 7-17 Natural capital: three zones in the downhill flow of water: *source zone* containing mountain (headwater) streams, *transition zone* containing wider, lower-elevation streams, and *floodplain zone* containing rivers, which empty into the ocean.

flows into streams. The land area that delivers runoff, sediment, and dissolved substances to a stream is called a **watershed,** or **drainage basin.** Small streams join to form rivers, and rivers flow downhill to the ocean as shown in Figure 7-17.

In many areas, streams begin in mountainous or hilly areas that collect and release water falling to the Earth's surface as rain or snow that melts during warm seasons. The downward flow of surface water and groundwater from mountain highlands to the sea takes place in three different aquatic life zones with different environmental

conditions: the *source zone,* the *transition zone,* and the *floodplain zone* (Figure 7-17). Rivers in different areas can differ somewhat from this generalized model.

In the first, narrow *source zone* (Figure 7-17, top), headwaters, or mountain highland streams of cold, clear water, rush over waterfalls and rapids. As this turbulent water flows and tumbles downward, it dissolves large amounts of oxygen from the air. Since the water moves rapidly, floating plankton are less important. Instead, most plants such as algae and mosses are attached to rocks.

Since the water is shallow, light can usually penetrate to the bottom. But most of these streams are not very productive because of a lack of nutrients. Most nutrients come from organic matter (mostly leaves, branches, and the bodies of living and dead insects) that falls into the stream from nearby land.

This zone is populated by cold-water fish (such as trout in some areas), which need lots of dissolved oxygen. Many fish and other animals in fast-flowing headwater streams have compact and flattened bodies that allow them to live under stones.

In the *transition zone* (Figure 7-17, middle), the headwater streams merge to form wider, deeper streams that flow down gentler slopes with fewer obstacles. The warmer water and other conditions in this zone support more producers (phytoplankton) and a variety of cool-water and warm-water fish species (such as bass) with slightly lower oxygen requirements.

In the *floodplain zone* (Figure 7-17, bottom), streams join into wider and deeper rivers that meander across broad, flat valleys. Water in this zone usually has higher temperatures and less dissolved oxygen than water in the first two zones. These slow-moving rivers sometimes support fairly large populations of producers such as algae and **cyanobacteria** and rooted aquatic plants along the shores. Because of increased erosion and runoff over a larger area, water in this zone often is muddy and contains high concentrations of suspended particulate matter (silt). The main channels of these slow-moving, wide, and murky rivers support distinctive varieties of fish (carp and catfish), whereas their backwaters support species similar to those present in lakes. They are nice places to fish. At its mouth, a river may divide into many channels as it flows through coastal wetlands and estuaries, where the river water mixes with ocean water (Figure 7-7).

As streams flow downhill, they become powerful shapers of land. Over millions of years, the friction of sediment moved by water levels mountains and cuts deep canyons, and the rock and soil the water removes are deposited as sediment in low-lying areas.

Streams are fairly open ecosystems that receive many of their nutrients from bordering land ecosystems. We have established farmlands and constructed dams, power plants that need cooling water, sewage treatment plants, cities, recreation areas, and shipping terminals in the watersheds along the shores of rivers and streams, especially in their transition and floodplain zones. This greatly increases the flow of plant nutrients, sediment, and pollutants into these ecosystems. To protect a stream or river system from excessive inputs of nutrients and pollutants, we must protect the land around it.

What Are Freshwater Inland Wetlands? Natural Sponges

Inland wetlands absorb and store excess water from storms and provide a variety of wildlife habitats.

Inland wetlands are lands covered with fresh water all or part of the time (excluding lakes, reservoirs, and streams) and located away from coastal areas. Four main categories of inland wetlands are found in Canada:

- *Marshes* (Figure 7-18a) are the most common wetland type. They are dominated by cattails and other reeds, bulrushes, and pond lilies. There is typically open water, although some marshes are only seasonally flooded. Marshes are nutrient rich and are one of the most productive ecosystems on the planet. Characteristic inhabitants include muskrats, mink, red-winged black birds, frogs, and turtles. Marshes are neutral to alkaline with a pH of 7–8.

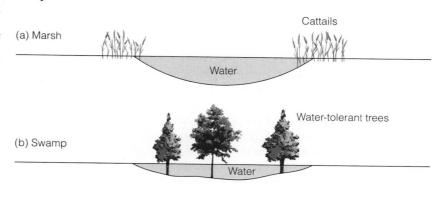

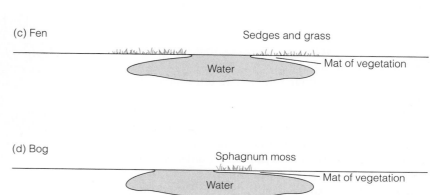

FIGURE 7-18 Main categories of inland wetlands. (a) *Marshes* are nutrient-rich ecosystems dominated by cattails, reeds, bulrushes, and pond lilies. (b) *Swamps* are productive ecosystems characterized by water-tolerant trees and a wide range of wild species. (c) *Fens* are a type of peatland dominated by sedges and typically found in Canada's arctic and subarctic regions. (d) *Bogs* are a highly acidic type of peatland dominated by sphagnum moss.

- *Swamps* (Figure 7-18b) are dominated by water-tolerant trees such as black spruce, black ash, cedars, silver maples, and red maples. There may or may not be free-standing water all year. These generally nutrient-rich and productive ecosystems provide habitat for a wide range of wild species. Swamps are neutral with a pH of 7.

- *Fens* (Figure 7-18c) are a type of peatland. Some mosses are present, but the predominant plants are sedges, notable for their three-sided stems ("sedges have edges") and grasses. The vegetation of fens can encroach on open water, gradually covering small bodies of water. Typically found in the arctic and subarctic regions of Canada, fens have more nutrients and more plant diversity than bogs. They are acidic with a pH of 5–8.

- *Bogs* (Figure 7-18d) are a type of peatland dominated by sphagnum moss. Bogs have wet spongy ground, and there can be a floating mat of vegetation that encroaches on open water. Among the different wetland types, bogs are the most acidic, with a pH of 3–5. As a result of the acidic environment, decomposition and productivity are extremely low, which accounts for the discovery of *bog men*—perfectly preserved individuals who fell through floating bog mats thousands of years ago.

The famous *prairie potholes* are marshes that formed 10 000 years ago as melting glaciers retreated northward in Central Canada. They are highly productive because of the rich soil and hot summer temperatures of the grassland biome. Prairie potholes team with aquatic plants and invertebrates, and serve as habitat to more than 50% of the wild ducks hatched in North America.

Some wetlands are covered with water year-round. Others, called *seasonal wetlands,* usually are underwater or soggy for only a short time each year. They include prairie potholes, floodplain wetlands, and bottomland hardwood swamps. Some stay dry for years before being covered with water again. In such cases, scientists must use the composition of the soil or the presence of certain plants (such as cattails, bulrushes, or red maples) to determine that a particular area is really a wetland.

In addition to their role as habitat, inland wetlands perform a number of important services. They absorb pollutants, improve water quality, slow soil erosion, provide flood control, and store greenhouse gases. They also yield recreational benefits, economic spinoffs (such as wild rice, fish, fur, cranberries, and peat), and educational opportunities (http://www.aquatic.uoguelph.ca/wetlands/wetlandFrames.htm).

DID YOU KNOW

About 18% of Canada is covered in wetlands. This represents 25% of the world's wetlands—the largest wetland area in the world!

What Are the Impacts of Human Activities on Freshwater Systems? Using and Abusing Rivers and Wetlands

We have built dams, levees, and dikes that reduce the flow of water and alter wildlife habitats in rivers; established nearby cities and farmlands that pollute streams and rivers; and filled in inland wetlands to grow food and build cities.

Human activities have four major impacts on freshwater systems. *First,* dams, diversions, or canals fragment almost 60% of the world's 237 large rivers. This alters and destroys wildlife habitats along rivers and in coastal deltas and estuaries by reducing water flow.

Second, flood control levees and dikes built along rivers alter and destroy aquatic habitats. *Third,* cities and farmlands add pollutants and excess plant nutrients to nearby streams and rivers.

Fourth, many inland wetlands have been drained or filled to grow crops or have been covered with concrete, asphalt, and buildings. In southern Ontario, about 70% of the original wetlands have been converted from their natural state to support alternative uses such as agriculture and housing. In the "prairie pothole" region of southern Manitoba, about 75% of the original wetlands have been lost (largely to agriculture). Throughout Canada wetlands are under the greatest stress near urban areas. In fact, 90–95% of the original wetlands have disappeared in well-urbanized and intensely farmed regions northwest of Lake Ontario and north of Lake Erie. Other high-risk zones include the Prairie provinces, southern Quebec, and parts of the Maritimes (Figure 7-19). Other regions of

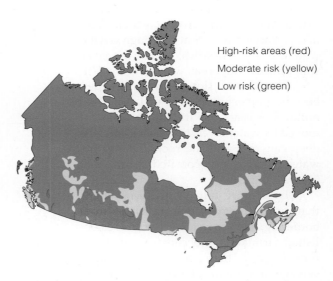

High-risk areas (red)

Moderate risk (yellow)

Low risk (green)

FIGURE 7-19 Natural Capital degradation: across Canada, wetlands near urban and agricultural areas are under the greatest pressure. (Source: Natural Resources Canada, *The Atlas of Canada*, http://atlas.nrcan.gc.ca/site/english/learningresources/theme_modules/wetlands/index.html/#facts. Reproduced with the permission of Natural Resources Canada, 2012.)

the world show similar trends. Germany and France have lost 80% of their wetlands. California has lost more than 90%.

In this chapter, we have seen that human activities are severely stressing and overloading many of the world's aquatic systems. *Good news.* Research shows when such activities are reduced most of these systems can recover fairly quickly as long as aquatic life zones are not overfished or overloaded with pollutants and excessive nutrients.

According to scientists, we urgently need more research on how the world's aquatic systems work. With such information we will have a clearer picture of the impacts of our activities on the Earth's aquatic biodiversity and how we can reduce these impacts.

All at last returns to the sea—to Oceanus, the ocean river, like the ever-flowing stream of time, the beginning and the end.

RACHEL CARSON

CHAPTER REVIEW

1. Review the Key Questions for this chapter on p. 140. What is a *coral reef*? What are the benefits of coral reefs? What is coral bleaching? What other factors can negatively impact coral reefs?

2. What percentage of the Earth's surface is covered with water? What is an *aquatic life zone*? Distinguish between a *saltwater (marine) life zone* and a *freshwater life zone*. What major types of organisms live in the top, middle, and bottom layers of aquatic life zones? Define *plankton* and describe three types of plankton. Distinguish among *nekton, benthos,* and *decomposers* and give an example of each. What four factors determine the types and numbers of organisms found in the three layers of aquatic life zones?

3. What major ecological and economic services are provided by marine systems? What are the three major life zones in an ocean? Distinguish between the *coastal zone* and the *open sea*. Distinguish between an *estuary* and a *coastal wetland* and explain why they have high net primary productivities. What is a *mangrove forest swamp* and what is its ecological and economic importance? What is the *intertidal zone*? Distinguish between rocky and sandy shores. Why does the open sea have a low net primary productivity?

4. What specific human activities pose major threats to marine systems, to mangrove forest swamps, and to coral reefs?

5. Distinguish between lotic and lentic systems. What are the properties of each? Describe thermal stratification of a summer lake. What is the significance of thermal stratification to the life forms within a lake?

6. What major ecological and economic services do freshwater systems provide? What four life zones are found in most lakes? Distinguish among *oligotrophic, eutrophic,* and *mesotrophic lakes*. What is *cultural eutrophication*?

7. Define *surface water, runoff,* and *watershed (drainage basin)*. Name and describe the three zones that a stream passes through as it flows from mountains to the sea. Which zones are the most impacted by humans?

8. Give four examples of *inland wetlands* and explain the ecological importance of such wetlands. What are some economic benefits of wetlands?

9. What are four ways in which human activities are disrupting and degrading freshwater systems? Where in Canada are inland wetlands in the most jeopardy? What percentage of inland wetlands has already been lost in some areas of Canada?

10. What steps would you take to ensure the sustainability of coral reefs if you were: **(a)** a conservation-minded politician living on a reef-protected tropical island, or **(b)** a world official in charge of a global reef recovery plan?

CRITICAL THINKING

1. List a limiting factor for each of the following: **(a)** the surface layer of a tropical lake, **(b)** the surface layer of the open sea, **(c)** an alpine stream, **(d)** a large, muddy river, **(e)** the bottom of a deep lake.

2. Why do terrestrial organisms evolve tolerances to broader temperature ranges than aquatic organisms do?

3. Why do aquatic plants such as phytoplankton tend to be very small, whereas most terrestrial plants such as trees tend to be larger and have more specialized structures such as stems and leaves for growth? Why are some aquatic animals, especially marine mammals such as whales, extremely large compared with terrestrial animals?

4. How would you respond to someone who proposes that we use the deep portions of the world's oceans to deposit our radioactive and other hazardous wastes because the deep oceans are vast and are located far away from human habitats? Give reasons for your response.

5. Someone tries to sell you several brightly coloured pieces of dry coral. Explain in biological terms why this transaction is probably fraudulent.

6. Developers want to drain a large area of inland wetlands in your community and build a large housing development. List **(a)** the main arguments the developers would use to support this project and **(b)** the main

arguments ecologists would use in opposing this project. If you were an elected city official, would you vote for or against this project? Can you come up with a compromise plan?

7. You are a lawyer arguing in court for sparing an undeveloped old-growth tropical rain forest and a coral reef from severe degradation or destruction by development. Write your closing statement for the defence of each of these ecosystems. If the judge decides you can save only one of the ecosystems, which one would you choose, and why?

8. Congratulations! You are in charge of the world. What are the three most important features of your plan to help sustain the Earth's aquatic biodiversity?

PROJECTS

1. Search for information about mangrove trees, using the Internet and library. Are the different species of mangrove trees closely related? What characteristics do they have in common? What characteristics do they have that make them a good place for fish to breed?

2. If possible, visit a nearby lake or reservoir. Would you classify it as oligotrophic, mesotrophic, or eutrophic? What are the primary factors contributing to its nutrient enrichment? Which of these factors are related to human activities?

3. Examine a topographic map for the area around a stream or lake near where you live to define the watershed for the stream. What human activities occur in the watershed? What influence, if any, do you expect these activities to have on the ecology of the stream or lake?

4. Read the *Reefs at Risk Revisited* executive summary located at http://pdf.wri.org/reefs_at_risk_revisited_executive_summary.pdf. Create a two-page plan of action for protecting the world's coral reefs from all the factors that are currently threatening them.

5. Use the library or the Internet to find bibliographic information about *Loren Eisley* and *Rachel Carson*, whose quotes appear at the beginning and end of this chapter.

Flying Foxes: Keystone Species in Tropical Forests

The durian (Figure 8-1, top) is a prized fruit growing in Southeast Asian tropical forests. The odour of this football-sized fruit is so strong that it is illegal to have them on trains and in many hotel rooms in Southeast Asia. But its custardlike flesh has been described as "exquisite," "sensual," "intoxicating," and "the world's finest fruit."

Durian fruits come from a wild tree that grows in the tropical rain forest. Various species of nectar-, pollen-, and fruit-eating bats called *flying foxes* (Figure 8-1, bottom right) pollinate the flowers that hang high in durian trees (Figure 8-1, left). This pollination by flying foxes is an example of *mutualism*: an interaction between two species in which both species benefit.

Many species of flying foxes are listed as endangered, and most populations are much smaller than historical numbers. One reason is deforestation. Another is hunting these bat species for their meat, which is sold in China and other parts of Asia. The bats also are killed to keep them from eating commercially grown fruits. Flying foxes are easy to hunt because they tend to congregate in large numbers when they feed or sleep.

Some ecologists classify flying foxes as *keystone species* because of the important roles they play in sustaining tropical forest communities. In addition to pollinating many plant species, the plant seeds they disperse in their droppings help maintain forest biodiversity and regenerate deforested areas.

Thus, many other species depend on flying fox species. This explains why ecologists are concerned that the decline of flying fox populations could lead to a cascade of linked extinctions.

The story of flying foxes and durians illustrates the unique role (niche) of interacting species in a community. When populations of different species in a community interact with one another, they influence one another's ability to survive and reproduce. In this chapter, we will look at these and other interactions and processes that occur in biological communities.

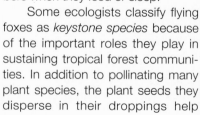

FIGURE 8-1 Flying foxes (bottom right) are bats that play key ecological roles in tropical rain forests in Southeast Asia by pollinating (left) and spreading the seeds of durian trees. Durians (top) are a highly prized tropical fruit.

Animal and vegetable life is too complicated a problem for human intelligence to solve, and we can never know how wide a circle of disturbance we produce in the harmonies of nature when we throw the smallest pebble into the ocean of organic life.

GEORGE PERKINS MARSH

CHAPTER PURPOSE AND QUESTIONS

Chapter 8 describes how species in a community respond to each other and to changes to their environment. The chapter addresses the following questions:

8-1   What is community structure?

8-2   What roles do various species play within a community?

8-3   How do predators and prey interact within a community?

8-4   What other types of interactions occur within a community?

8-5   How do communities change as environmental conditions change?

8-6   How are ecological complexity and ecological stability related?

8-1 COMMUNITY STRUCTURE AND SPECIES DIVERSITY

What Is Community Structure? Appearance, Diversity, and Niches

Biological communities differ in their physical appearance, the types and numbers of species they contain, and the ecological roles their species play.

Ecologists use three characteristics to describe a biological community. One is *physical appearance*: the relative sizes, stratification, and distribution of its populations and species, as shown in Figure 8-2 for various terrestrial communities. There are also differences in the physical structures and zones of communities in aquatic life zones such as oceans, rocky shores and sandy beaches, lakes, river systems, and inland wetlands.

The physical structure within a particular type of community or ecosystem can also vary. Most large terrestrial communities and ecosystems consist of a mosaic of vegetation patches of differing size. Life is patchy.

Community structure also varies around its *edges* where one type of community makes a transition to a different type of community. For example, the edge area between a forest and an open field may be

FIGURE 8-2 Natural capital: generalized types, relative sizes, and stratification of plant species in various terrestrial communities.

sunnier, warmer, and drier than the forest interior and have a different combination of species than the forest and field interiors.

However, increased edge area from **habitat fragmentation** makes many species more vulnerable to stresses such as predators and fire. It also creates barriers that can prevent some species from colonizing new areas and finding food and mates.

A second characteristic of a community is its **species diversity:** a combination of its number of different species (**species richness**) and the abundance of individuals within each of its species (**species evenness**). For example, suppose we have two communities each with a total of 20 different species and 200 individuals and thus the same species diversity. But these communities could differ in their species richness and species evenness. For example, suppose community A has 10 individuals in each of its 20 species, and community B has 10 species with 2 individuals each and 10 other species, each with 18 individuals. Which community has the highest species evenness?

A third characteristic is a community's *niche structure:* the number of ecological niches, how they resemble or differ from each other, and how species interact with one another. Studies indicate that the most species-rich environments are tropical rain forests, coral reefs, the deep sea, and large tropical lakes. Communities such as a tropical rain forest or a coral reef with a large number of different species (high species richness) generally have only a few members of each species (low species evenness).

Several factors affect the species diversity in communities. One is *latitude* (distance from the equator) in terrestrial communities (Figure 8-3). For most plants and animals, species diversity is highest in the tropics and declines from the equator to the poles. Another factor is *pollution* in aquatic systems (Figure 8-4). Other factors are habitat diversity, NPP, habitat disturbance, and time.

What Determines the Number of Species on Islands? Island Size and Isolation

The number of species on an island is determined by how fast new species arrive and old species become extinct, the island's size, and how far it is from the mainland.

In the 1960s, Robert MacArthur and Edward O. Wilson began studying communities on islands to discover why large islands tend to have more species of a certain category such as insects, birds, or ferns than do small islands. To explain these differences in species richness with respect to island size, MacArthur and Wilson proposed the **species equilibrium model,** or

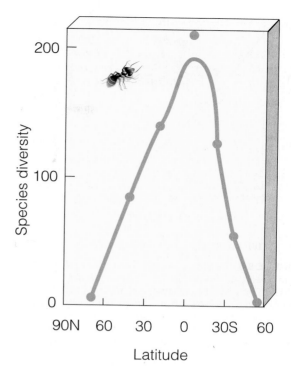

FIGURE 8-3 Changes in species diversity at different latitudes (distances from the equator) in terrestrial communities for ants and of North and Central America. As a general rule, species diversity steadily declines as we go away from the equator toward either pole. (From STARR. *Biology: Concepts and Applications* w/CD-ROM + InfoTrac, 4E. © 2000 Cengage Learning. Reproduced by permission. www.cengage.com/permissions)

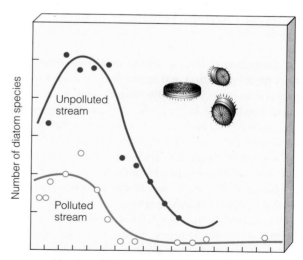

FIGURE 8-4 Changes in the species diversity and species abundance of diatom species in an unpolluted stream and a polluted stream. Both species diversity and species abundance decrease with pollution.

the **theory of island biogeography.** According to this widely accepted model, a balance between two factors determines the number of different species found

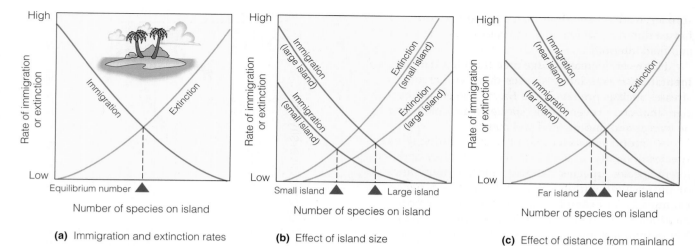

(a) Immigration and extinction rates   **(b)** Effect of island size   **(c)** Effect of distance from mainland

FIGURE 8-5 The *species equilibrium model* or *theory of island biogeography,* developed by Robert MacArthur and Edward O. Wilson. (a) The equilibrium number of species (blue triangle) on an island is determined by a balance between the immigration rate of new species and the extinction rate of species already on the island. (b) With time, large islands have a larger equilibrium number of species than smaller islands because of higher immigration rates and lower extinction rates on large islands. (c) Assuming equal extinction rates, an island near a mainland will have a larger equilibrium number of species than a more distant island because the immigration rate is greater for a near island than for a more distant one.

on an island: the rate at which new species immigrate to the island and the rate at which existing species become extinct on the island.

The model projects that at some point the rates of immigration and extinction should reach an equilibrium point (Figure 8-5a) that determines the island's average number of different species. This is a fairly complex idea, so study Figure 8-5 carefully.

According to the model, two features of an island affect its immigration and extinction rates and thus its species diversity. One is the island's *size,* with a small island tending to have fewer different species than a large one (Figure 8-5b). One reason is that a small island generally has a lower immigration rate because it is a smaller target for potential colonizers. In addition, a small island should have a higher extinction rate because it usually has fewer resources and less diverse habitats for its species.

A second factor is an island's *distance from the nearest mainland* (Figure 8-5c). According to the model, if we have two islands about equal in size and other factors, the island closer to a mainland source of **immigrant species** should have the higher immigration rate and thus a higher species richness—assuming that extinction rates on both islands are about the same.

In recent years, conservation biologists have used the model to help protect wildlife in *habitat islands* such as national parks surrounded by a sea of developed and fragmented land.

What Roles Do Various Species Play in Communities? A Biological Play with Many Parts

Communities can contain native, non-native, indicator, keystone, and foundation species that play different ecological roles.

Ecologists often use labels—such as *native, non-native, indicator, keystone,* or *foundation*—to describe the major ecological roles or niches various species play in communities. Any given species may play more than one of these five roles in a particular community.

Native species are those that normally live and thrive in a particular community. Others that evolve somewhere else and then migrate into or are deliberately or accidentally introduced into a community are called **non-native (or exotic) species, invasive species, or alien species.**

Throughout the Earth's long history of life, species in one part of the world have migrated from one community to another. But moving into a new community is not easy. Most organisms arriving in a new community do not survive because they are not able to find a suitable niche under their new environmental conditions.

But sometimes a non-native species can thrive and crowd out native species—an example of unintended and unexpected consequences. In 1957, for example, Brazil imported wild African bees to help increase honey production. Instead, the bees displaced domestic honeybees and reduced the honey supply.

Since then, these non-native bee species, popularly known as "killer bees," have moved northward into Central America and parts of the southwestern United States, such as Texas, Arizona, New Mexico, and California. They are still heading north but should be stopped eventually by cold winters in the central United States unless they can adapt genetically to cold weather.

They are not the killer bees portrayed in some horror movies, but they are aggressive and unpredictable. Since arriving in the United States in 1990, Africanized honeybees have caused the deaths of 14 humans. Most of the people killed by these honeybees died because they were allergic to their stings or they fell down or became trapped and could not flee.

We will revisit the subject of non-native species in Chapters 12 and 13.

What Are Indicator Species? Living Clues to Environmental Conditions

Certain species have exacting requirements or specific sensitivities that make them useful indicators in terms of the presence or absence of those conditions.

Some species provide excellent clues to key environmental conditions. For instance, birds such as boreal chickadees, spruce grouse, grey jays, crossbills, and grosbeaks are so strongly associated with boreal forest conditions that when these birds are seen in combination, they are considered to be **indicator species** of boreal forests.

Other species may be particularly sensitive to conditions that reflect aspects of habitat quality. The presence or absence of trout species in water within their range of tolerance (Figure 4-13, p. 68) is an indicator of water quality because trout need clean water with high levels of dissolved oxygen. Certain species of stoneflies, mayflies, caddisflies, seed shrimps, snails, and other aquatic invertebrates are used as indicators of water quality in streams and rivers (Fiset, 1995).

Birds and butterflies are excellent biological indicators because they are widely distributed and affected quickly by environmental changes such as loss or fragmentation of their habitats and introduction of chemical pesticides. Many species of birds and butterflies are declining in response to these conditions.

Using a living organism to monitor environmental quality is not new. Coal mining is a dangerous occupation, partly because of the underground presence of poisonous and explosive gases, many of which have no detectable odour. In the 1800s and early 1900s, coal miners took caged canaries into mines to act as early-warning sentinels. These birds sing loudly and often. If they quit singing for a long period and they appeared to be distressed, miners took this as an indicator for the presence of poisonous or explosive gases and got out of the mine.

CONSIDER, DISCUSS, OR DEBATE

If you were assessing the water quality downstream from a factory, why might it be important to look for the presence or absence of indicator species rather than just testing a few samples of water for the presence of pollutants?

Case Study: Why Are Amphibians Vanishing? Warnings from Frogs

The disappearance of many of the world's amphibian species may indicate a decline in environmental quality in many parts of the world.

Amphibians (frogs, toads, and salamanders) live part of their lives in water and part on land and are classified as indicator species. Frogs, for example, are good indicator species of environmental quality and pollution because they are especially vulnerable to disruption at various points in their life cycle, shown in Figure 8-6 (p. 162). As tadpoles they live in water and eat plants, and as adults they live mostly on land and eat insects that can expose them to pesticides. Their eggs have no protective shells to block ultraviolet (UV) radiation or pollution. As adults, they take in water and air through their thin, permeable skins that can readily absorb pollutants from water, air, or soil.

Since 1980, hundreds of the world's estimated 6 300 amphibian species have been vanishing or declining in almost every part of the world, even in protected wildlife reserves and parks.

No single cause has been identified to explain the amphibian declines. However, scientists have identified a number of factors that can affect frogs and other amphibians at various points in their life cycle.

One factor is *habitat loss and fragmentation,* especially because of the draining and filling of inland wetlands, deforestation, and development. Another is *prolonged drought,* which dries up breeding pools so that few tadpoles survive. Dehydration from lack of water can also weaken amphibians and make them more susceptible to fatal viruses, bacteria, fungi, and parasites.

Pollution can also play a role. Frog eggs, tadpoles, and adults are very sensitive to many pollutants, including insecticides, herbicides, fertilizers, and endocrine disruptors (Chapter 19). Exposure to such pollutants can also make them more vulnerable to bacterial, viral, and fungal diseases. Endocrine disrupters can cause an array of sexual abnormalities (p. 459).

One particular fungus that has been identified at the scene of some amphibian declines is the

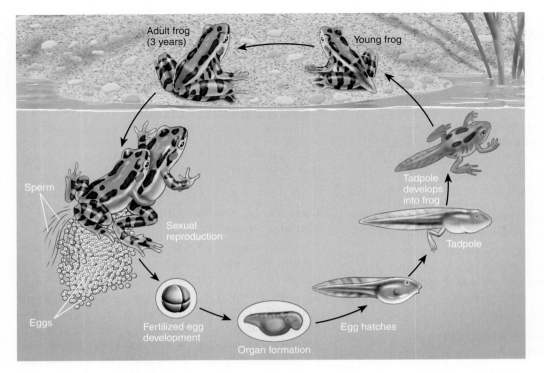

FIGURE 8-6 Typical life cycle of a frog. Populations of various frog species can decline because of the effects of various harmful factors at different points in their life cycle. Such factors include habitat loss, drought, pollution, increased ultraviolet radiation, parasitism, disease, overhunting for food (frog legs), and non-native predators and competitors.

Chytrid fungus. A particular species of this fungus— *Batrachochytrium dendrobatidis*—is known to infect the skin of amphibians, often causing respiratory problems and death. The fungus is highly contagious and can spread rapidly among amphibians. *Chytridiomycosis* is the term used to refer to this disease.

Increases in UV radiation caused by reductions in stratospheric ozone—caused when certain chemicals we make drift up into the stratosphere—can harm young embryos of amphibians found in shallow ponds. *Increased incidence of parasitism* by a flatworm (trematode) may account for deformities found in some frog species but not the worldwide decline of amphibians.

Overhunting can be a factor, especially in Asia and France, where frog legs are a delicacy. Populations of some amphibians can also be reduced by *immigration or introduction of non-native predators and competitors* (such as fish). A combination of the factors listed above probably is responsible for the decline or disappearance of most amphibian species.

So why should we care if various amphibian species become extinct? Scientists give three reasons. *First,* it suggests that environmental quality is deteriorating in parts of the world because amphibians are sensitive biological indicators of changes in environmental conditions such as habitat loss and degradation, pollution, UV exposure, and climate change.

Second, adult amphibians play important ecological roles in biological communities. For example, amphibians eat more insects (including mosquitoes) than do birds. In some habitats, extinction of certain amphibian species could lead to extinction of other species, such as reptiles, birds, aquatic insects, fish, mammals, and other amphibians that feed on them or their larvae.

Third, from a human perspective, amphibians represent a genetic storehouse of pharmaceutical products waiting to be discovered. Compounds in hundreds of secretions from amphibian skin have been isolated and some are used as painkillers and antibiotics and in treating burns and heart disease.

The plight of some amphibian indicator species is a warning signal. They do not need us, but we and other species need them.

What Are Keystone Species? Major Players Who Help Keep Ecosystems Running Smoothly

Keystone species help determine the types and numbers of various other species in a community.

A keystone is the wedge-shaped stone placed at the top of a stone archway. Remove this stone and the arch collapses. In some communities, certain species called **keystone species** apparently play a similar role. They have a much larger effect on the types and abundances of many other species in a community than their numbers would suggest.

According to this hypothesis, keystone species play critical ecological roles. Originally, ecologists focused on *top predator* keystone species that feed on and help regulate populations of other species. Examples are wolves, polar bears, leopards, lions, alligators, and

Why Should We Care about Beavers?

Beavers (*Castor canadensis*) are the largest rodents in North America (Figure 8-7). An average adult weighs 16 kilograms (35 pounds), but beavers as large as 40 kilograms (90 pounds) have been documented. Over 10 000 years ago, a giant species of beaver (*Castoroides ohioensis*)—the size of a small bear weighing about 200 kilograms (450 pounds)—coexisted with early humans. Modern beavers are widely distributed in forested habitat across North America.

The beaver's main claim to fame is its ability to alter its habitat to suit its own purposes. Beavers build dams of wood and mud, converting forest streams to ponds. The pond then functions as a moat, protecting the beaver lodge. The rising pond floods nearby forest, allowing beavers easy access to trees that they fell for repairing the dam and for bark that they use as food. During the summer, beavers store food in the form of tree branches sunk to the bottom of the pond. In winter, the beavers swim out under the ice to collect this food.

In damming forest streams, beavers cause major changes to the surrounding area. The productive wetlands resulting from the beavers' actions become home to many other species that could not otherwise exist. Over time, beaver ponds fill with silt, and beavers exhaust the supply of trees that they can easily reach from their ponds. They then abandon their ponds, which

drain and become beaver meadows—home to a new set of species.

Beavers are called *allogenic engineers* because they mechanically modify material from one form to another while cutting trees and building dams. They are also known as *ecological shapers* because of the impact they have on the habitat and species around them. The ability of beavers to create rich habitats for other animals led Aboriginal people to regard them as the *sacred centre of the land*. Ecologists say that beavers are performing *niche construction* as they alter the environment to benefit themselves and their offspring for perhaps generations to come. Beavers can certainly be called *keystone species* since they have major impacts on a host of other species that depend on their activities. Some ecologists would further distinguish beavers as *foundation species* since the important function that they serve is one of providing the habitat required by numerous species.

Beavers have other claims to fame. Pursuit of beaver pelts was

the basis of the historical fur trade and provided much incentive for exploration, interaction with Aboriginal people, and commerce that extended all the way back to Europe. Beavers were such an integral part of the emerging economy that a coin was created that had the value of one beaver pelt. Eventually, beavers were overtrapped until a change of European fashion from fur hats to silk hats allowed populations to recover.

Today beavers are in great abundance. They are sometimes regarded as pests when their dams flood roadways. Specially designed underwater pipes called *beaver bafflers* are used to manage water levels in beaver ponds without stimulating the beavers' instinct to block this drainage.

Officially designated as a national animal of Canada, beavers appeared on Canada's first stamps and continue to grace the back of the Canadian nickel.

FIGURE 8-7 The beaver—a bioengineer capable of changing the environment to improve its own habitat—creates conditions favourable for many other species.

great white sharks. Eventually, ecologists realized that other roles could have a crucial impact. One such role is *pollination* of flowering plants by bees, hummingbirds, bats, and other species.

Yet another example of a keystone species is the whitebark pine (*Pinus albicauilis*) that grows in the mountains of southern British Columbia, Alberta, and the northern U.S. states. These trees produce seeds in the size of peas that are rich in protein and fat. The seeds are an important food source that can help animals such as bears, squirrels, and seed-eating birds like Clark's nutcrackers to survive winter. As well, the trees stabilize steeply sloped mountain soils, moderate the rate of snow-melt, and provide cover for alpine species. However, fire suppression, insect infestations, and white pine blister rust threaten this keystone species. To learn more, visit http://www.whitebarkpine.ca and see Pigott (2010).

Have you thanked a *dung beetle* today? Maybe you should, because these keystone species rapidly remove, bury, and recycle animal wastes or dung. Without them we would be up to our eyeballs in such waste, and many plants would be starved for nutrients. These beetles also churn and aerate the soil, making it more suitable for plant life.

Ecologist Robert Paine conducted a controlled experiment along the rocky Pacific coast of the state of Washington that demonstrated the role of the sea star *Piaster orchaceus* as a keystone species in an intertidal zone community (Figure 7-9, top, p. 146). He removed sea stars from one community but not from an adjacent community, which served as a control group. In both communities, he monitored the populations of 18 other species. In the community from which he removed the sea stars, all of the 18 species disappeared except mussels. In the community where the sea stars remained, they ate the mussels and kept them from multiplying and crowding out other species.

The loss of a keystone species can lead to population crashes and extinctions of other species in a community that depend on it for certain services. According to biologist Edward O. Wilson, "The loss of a keystone species is like a drill accidentally striking a power line. It causes lights to go out all over."

What Are Foundation Species? Players Who Create New Habitats and Niches

Foundation species can create and enhance habitats that can benefit other species in a community.

Some ecologists use the term *foundation species* to refer to those keystone species that play a major role in shaping communities by creating and enhancing habitat that benefits other species. For example, elephants push over, break, or uproot trees, creating forest openings in the savanna grasslands and woodlands of Africa. This promotes the growth of grasses and other forage plants that benefit smaller grazing species such as antelope. It also accelerates nutrient cycling rates. Some bat and bird foundation species can regenerate deforested areas and spread fruit plants by depositing plant seeds in their droppings. Alligators dig deep depressions, or gator holes, that hold water during dry spells and serve as refuges for aquatic life.

8-3 SPECIES INTERACTIONS: COMPETITION AND PREDATION

How Do Species Interact? Ways to Get an Edge

Competition, predation, parasitism, mutualism, and commensalism are ways in which species can interact and increase their ability to survive.

When different species in a community have activities or resource needs in common, they may interact with one another. Members of these species may be harmed, helped, or unaffected by the interaction. Ecologists identify five basic types of interactions between species: *interspecific competition, predation, parasitism, mutualism,* and *commensalism.*

The most common interaction between species is **competition** for shared or scarce resources such as space and food. Ecologists call such competition between *species* **interspecific competition.**

When this occurs, parts of the fundamental niches of the competing species overlap (Figure 5-4, p. 99). With significant overlap, one of the competing species must migrate, if possible, to another area, shift its feeding habits or behaviour through natural selection and evolution, suffer a sharp population decline, or become extinct in that area.

Humans are in competition with many other species for space, food, and other resources. As we convert more and more of the Earth's land and aquatic resources and net primary productivity to our uses we deprive many other species of resources they need to survive.

How Have Some Species Reduced or Avoided Competition? Share the Wealth by Becoming More Specialized

Some species evolve adaptations that allow them to reduce or avoid competition for resources with other species.

Over a time scale long enough for evolution to occur, some species competing for the same resources evolve adaptations that reduce or avoid competition. One way this happens is through **resource partitioning.**

It occurs when species competing for similar scarce resources evolve more specialized traits that allow them to use shared resources at different times, in different ways, or in different places.

Through evolution, the fairly broad niches of two competing species (Figure 8-8, top) can become more specialized (Figure 8-8, bottom) so that the species can share limited resources. When lions and leopards live in the same area, lions take mostly larger animals as prey, and leopards take smaller ones. Hawks and owls feed on similar prey, but hawks hunt during the day and owls hunt at night.

Ecologist Robert H. MacArthur studied the feeding habits of five species of North American warblers (small insect-eating birds) that hunt for insects and nest in the same type of spruce tree. He found that the bird species minimized the overlap of their niches and reduced competition among the species through resource partitioning. They did this by concentrating much of their hunting for insects in different parts of the spruce trees (Figure 8-9), employing different hunting tactics, and nesting at slightly different times. Other examples are shown in Figure 5-5 (p. 99).

FIGURE 8-9 Sharing the wealth: *resource partitioning* of five species of common insect-eating warblers in the spruce forests of eastern North America. Each species minimizes competition with the others for food by spending at least half its feeding time in a distinct portion (shaded areas) of the spruce trees, and consuming somewhat different insect species. (After R. H. MacArthur, "Population Ecology of Some Warblers in Northeastern Coniferous Forests," *Ecology* 36 (1958): 533–536)

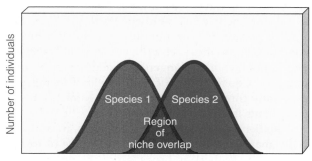

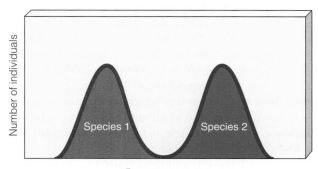

FIGURE 8-8 Natural capital: *resource partitioning* and *niche specialization* as a result of competition between two species. The top diagram shows the overlapping niches of two competing species. The bottom diagram shows that through evolution the niches of the two species become separated and more specialized (narrower in their range of resource use) so that they avoid competing for the same resources.

How Do Predator and Prey Species Interact? Eating and Being Eaten

Predator species feed on all or parts of other species called prey.

In **predation,** members of one species (the **predator**) feed directly on all or part of a living organism of another species (the **prey**). In this interaction, the predators benefit and the prey are harmed. The two kinds of organisms are said to have a **predator–prey relationship.** Such relationships are depicted in Figures 4-11 (p. 67), 4-12 (p. 67), 4-18 (p. 72), and 4-19 (p. 73).

Most of the world's predation is not the kind we see in many nature documentaries such as lions killing zebras or bears plucking salmon from streams. Instead, most predation occurs unseen at the microscopic level in soils and in the sediments of aquatic systems.

At the individual level, members of the prey species are clearly harmed. But at the population level, predation plays a role in evolution by natural selection. Predation can benefit the prey species because predators often kill the sick, weak, aged, and least fit members of a population (Case Study, below). This gives remaining prey better access to food supplies and prevents excessive population growth. Predation also helps successful genetic traits to become more dominant in the prey population through natural selection. This can enhance the reproductive success and long-term survival of the prey species.

Some people tend to view predators with contempt. When a hawk tries to capture and feed on a rabbit, some root for the rabbit. Yet the hawk, like all predators, is merely trying to get enough food to feed itself and its young; in the process, it is playing an important ecological role in controlling rabbit populations.

Case Study: Why Are Sharks Important Species? Culling the Oceans and Helping Improve Human Health

Some shark species eat and remove sick and injured ocean animals and some can help us learn how to fight cancer and immune system disorders.

The world's 370 shark species vary widely in size. The smallest is the dwarf dog shark, about the size of a large goldfish. The largest is the whale shark, the world's largest fish. It can grow to 15 metres (50 feet) long and weigh as much as two full-grown African elephants!

Various shark species, feeding at the top of food webs, cull injured and sick animals from the ocean and thus play an important ecological role. Without such shark species, the oceans would be overcrowded with dead and dying fish.

Many people—influenced by movies (such as *Jaws*), popular novels, and widespread media coverage

of a fairly small number of shark attacks per year—think of sharks as people-eating monsters. However, the three largest species—the whale shark, basking shark, and megamouth shark—are gentle giants. They swim through the water with their mouths open, filtering out and swallowing huge quantities of *plankton*.

Every year, members of a few species of shark—mostly great white, bull, tiger, grey reef, lemon, hammerhead, shortfin mako, and blue—typically injure 60–100 people worldwide. Since 1990, sharks have killed an average of 7 people per year. Most attacks are by great white sharks, which feed on sea lions and other marine mammals and sometimes mistake divers and surfers for their usual prey (Figure 8-10; p. 167).

Media coverage of such attacks greatly distorts the danger from sharks. You are 30 times more likely to be killed by lightning than by a shark, and your chance of being killed by lightning is extremely small.

For every shark that kills or injures a person, we kill at least 1 million sharks, a total of about 100 million sharks each year. Sharks are caught mostly for their fins and then thrown back into the water to die.

Shark fins are widely used in Asia as a soup ingredient and as a pharmaceutical cure-all. They are worth as much as $563 per kilogram ($256 per pound). In high-end Hong Kong restaurants, a single bowl of shark fin soup can cost as much as $100!

According to a 2001 study by Wild Aid, shark fins sold in restaurants throughout Asia and in Chinese communities in cities such as New York, San Francisco, and London contain dangerously high levels of toxic mercury. Consumption of high levels of mercury is especially threatening for pregnant women, fetuses, and infants feeding on breast milk.

Sharks are also killed for their livers, meat (especially mako and thresher), hides (a source of exotic, high-quality leather), and jaws (especially great whites, whose jaws can sell for up to $10 000). They are also killed because we fear them. Some sharks (especially blue, mako, and oceanic whitetip) die when they are trapped in nets or lines deployed to catch swordfish, tuna, shrimp, and other commercially important species.

In addition to their important ecological roles, sharks can save human lives. They are helping us learn how to fight cancer, which sharks almost never get. Scientists are also studying their highly effective immune system because it allows wounds to heal without becoming infected.

Sharks have three natural traits that make them prone to population declines from overfishing. They take a long time to reach sexual maturity (10–24 years), have only a few off spring (between 2 and 10) once every year or two, and have long gestation (pregnancy) periods (up to 24 months for some species).

Sharks are among the most vulnerable and least protected animals on the Earth. Eight of the world's

FIGURE 8-10 Great white sharks are streamlined predators at or near the top of ocean food chains.

© Jeffrey L. Rotman/CORBIS

shark species are in danger of extinction. In 2003, experts estimated that populations of a number of commercially valuable shark species have decreased by 90% since 1992.

With more than 400 million years of evolution behind them, sharks have had a long time to get things right. Preserving their evolutionary genetic development begins with the knowledge that sharks do not need us, but we and other species need them.

> **CONSIDER, DISCUSS, OR DEBATE**
>
> What would the oceans be like without sharks? Should we make an effort to save shark species? Consider the ethical, ecological, evolutionary, economic, and safety issues.

How Do Predators Increase Their Chances of Getting a Meal? Pursue, Ambush, and Immobilize

Some predators are fast enough to catch their prey, some hide and lie in wait, and some inject chemicals to paralyze their prey.

Predators have a variety of methods that help them capture prey. **Herbivores** can simply walk, swim, or fly up to the plants they feed on.

Carnivores feeding on mobile prey have three main options: *ambushing, stalking,* or *pursuing.* Ambushing involves lying in wait for prey to come within range. Examples include crocodiles waiting for wildebeest to come to the water's edge for a drink, and praying mantises waiting on flowers for butterflies. The success rate per unit time is low, but energy expenditures for the predators are also low. Some form of camouflage is often involved so that the predator will not be noticed by the prey. Stalking involves a slow methodical means of gaining close proximity to the prey, followed by a quick rush. Examples include house cats sneaking up before pouncing on small birds, and great blue herons slowly wading close to fish before suddenly striking with their bills. The predator spends some time and energy while searching and approaching, but the attack phase is brief and has low energy costs. In pursuit hunting, the predators may invest a great deal of energy in pursuing and subduing their prey. An example would be wolves chasing down a moose. Note that in this example, a pack of wolves functions as a team to be able to gain a large energy payoff at the end of a successful hunt.

Some predators use chemical warfare to attack their prey. For example, some spiders and snakes use venom to paralyze their prey and to deter their predators.

How Do Prey Defend Themselves Against or Avoid Predators? Escape, Repel, Deceive, and Poison

Some prey escape their predators or have protective shells or thorns, some camouflage themselves, and some use chemicals to repel or poison predators.

Prey species have evolved many ways to avoid predators, including the ability to run, swim, or fly fast, and a highly developed sense of sight or smell that alerts them to the presence of predators. Other avoidance adaptations are protective shells (as on armadillos, which roll themselves up into an armour-plated ball, and turtles), thick bark (giant sequoia), spines (porcupines), and thorns (cacti and rosebushes). Many lizards have brightly coloured tails that break off when they are attacked, often giving them enough time to escape.

Other prey species use the camouflage of certain shapes or colours or the ability to change colour (chameleons and cuttlefish). Some insect species have evolved shapes that look like twigs (Figure 8-11a), bark, thorns, or even bird droppings on leaves. A leaf insect may be almost invisible against its background (Figure 8-11b), and an arctic hare in its white winter fur blends into the snow. A spotted cheetah blends into the grass as it watches for grazing animals to chase down and kill.

Chemical warfare is another common strategy. Some prey species discourage predators with chemicals that are *poisonous* (oleander plants), *irritating* (stinging nettles and bombardier beetles, Figure 8-11c), *foul smelling* (skunks, skunk cabbages, and stinkbugs), or *bad tasting* (buttercups and monarch butterflies, Figure 8-11d). When attacked, some species of squid and octopus emit clouds of black ink to confuse the predator and allow them to escape.

Scientists have identified more than 10 000 defensive chemicals made by plants. Some are herbivore poisons such as cocaine, caffeine, cyanide, opium,

(a) Span worm

(b) Wandering leaf insect

(c) Bombardier beetle

(d) Foul-tasting monarch butterfly

(e) Poison dart frog

(f) Viceroy butterfly mimics monarch butterfly

(g) Hind wings of Io moth resemble eyes of a much larger animal

(h) When touched, snake caterpillar changes shape to look like head of snake

FIGURE 8-11 Some ways in which prey species avoid their predators by (a, b) *camouflage*, (c–e) *chemical warfare*, (d, e) *warning colouration*, (f) *mimicry*, (g) *deceptive looks*, and (h) *deceptive behaviour*.

strychnine, peyote, nicotine, and rotenone, some of which we use as an insecticide. Others are herbivore repellents such as pepper, mustard, nutmeg, oregano, cinnamon, and mint, all of which we use to flavour or spice up our food. Major pharmaceutical companies view the plant world as a vast drugstore to study as a source for new medicines to treat a variety of human diseases and as a source of natural pesticides. Scientists going into nature to find promising natural chemicals are called *bioprospectors.* You might consider a career doing this fascinating work.

Many bad-tasting, bad-smelling, toxic, or stinging prey species have evolved *warning colouration,* brightly coloured advertising that enables experienced predators to recognize and avoid them. They flash a warning, "Eating me is risky." Examples are brilliantly coloured poisonous frogs (Figure 8-11e), red-, yellow-, and black-striped coral snakes, and foul-tasting monarch butterflies (Figure 8-11d) and grasshoppers.

Based on colouration, biologist Edward O. Wilson gives us two rules for evaluating possible danger from an unknown animal species we encounter in nature. *First,* if it is small and strikingly beautiful, it is probably poisonous. *Second,* if it is strikingly beautiful and easy to catch, it is probably deadly.

Edible butterfly species, such as the nonpoisonous viceroy (Figure 8-11f), gain some protection by looking and acting like the foul-tasting monarch butterfly, a protective device known as *Batesian mimicry.* Predators learn even faster to avoid two or more species of foul-tasting organisms that resemble each other, a phenomenon called *Mullerian mimicry.*

Some prey species use *behavioural strategies* to avoid predation. Some attempt to scare off predators by puffing up (blowfish), spreading their wings (peacocks), or mimicking a predator (Figure 8-11h). Some moths have wings that look like the eyes of much larger animals (Figure 8-11g). Other prey species gain some protection by living in large groups (schools of fish, herds of antelope, flocks of birds).

Disease-carrying bacteria and fungi also attack species. Animals such as ants that live in complex social societies containing millions to trillions of individuals survive onslaughts by harmful infectious bacteria and fungi by evolving glands that secrete antibiotics and antifungals. Indeed, because of these secretions, the outer surface of an ant is almost free of bacteria and fungi and is much cleaner than most human skin. The ecological lessons from ants are simple and powerful. In a world ruled by bacteria, never bet against the bacteria and always rely on a variety of weapons!

Some biologists have begun exploring the use of antibiotics produced by ants to treat human infectious diseases. So far two antibiotic patents have been filed based on studying ants, and there are more to come. You might consider a career in this research frontier.

What Are Parasites, and Why Are They Important? Living on or in Another Species

Although parasites can harm their host organisms, they can promote community biodiversity.

Parasitism occurs when one species (the *parasite*) feeds on part of another organism (the *host*), usually by living on or in the host. In this relationship, the parasite benefits and the host is harmed.

Parasitism can be viewed as a special form of predation. But unlike a conventional predator, a parasite usually is much smaller than its host (prey) and rarely kills its host. Also, most parasites remain closely associated with, draw nourishment from, and may gradually weaken their hosts over time.

Tapeworms, disease-causing microorganisms, and other **endoparasites** live *inside* their hosts. **Ectoparasites** attach themselves to the *outside* of their hosts. Examples are ticks, fleas, mosquitoes, mistletoe plants, and fungi that cause diseases such as athlete's foot. Some parasites move from one host to another, as fleas and ticks do; others, such as tapeworms, spend their adult lives with a single host.

Some parasites have little contact with their host. For example, in North America cowbirds are **brood parasites** that lay their eggs in the nests of other birds and then let the host birds raise their young.

From the host's point of view, parasites are harmful, but parasites play important ecological roles. Collectively, the matrix of parasitic relationships in a community acts somewhat like glue that helps hold the various species in a community together. Parasites also promote biodiversity by helping keep some species from becoming so plentiful that they eliminate other species.

How Do Species Interact so That Both Species Benefit? Win-Win Relationships

Pollination, fungi that help plant roots take up nutrients, and bacteria in your gut that help digest your food are examples of species interactions that benefit both species.

In **mutualism,** two species interact in a way that benefits both. The *pollination mutualism* between flowering plants and animals such as insects, birds, and bats is one of the most common forms of mutualism.

Some species benefit from *nutritional mutualism.* *Lichens,* hardy species that can grow on trees or barren rocks, consist of colourful photosynthetic algae and chlorophyll-lacking fungi living together. The fungi provide a home for the algae, and their bodies collect and hold moisture and mineral nutrients used by both species. The algae, through photosynthesis, provide sugars as food for themselves and the fungi.

A mutualistic relationship that combines nutrition and protection is *birds* that ride on the backs of large animals like African buffalo, elephants, and rhinoceroses (Figure 8-12a). The birds remove and eat parasites from the animal's body and often make noises warning the animal when predators approach.

Another example is *clownfish species,* which live within sea anemones, whose tentacles sting and paralyze most fish that touch them (Figure 8-12b). The clownfish, which are not harmed by the tentacles, gain protection from predators and feed on the detritus left from the meals of the anemones. The sea anemones benefit because the clownfish protect them from some of their predators.

Another example of nutritional mutualism is the highly specialized fungi that combine with plant roots to form mycorrhizae (from the Greek words for fungus and roots). The fungi get nutrition from the plant's roots. In turn the fungi benefit the plant by using their myriad networks of hairlike extensions to improve the plant's ability to extract nutrients and water from the soil (Figure 8-12c).

This relationship between plants' roots and fungi is particularly important in northern pine forests, where trees often are rooted in extremely poor soil. An interesting twist to this story illustrates the idea of organisms functioning as a community: the fungus spores that aid root function are spread by many species of small mammals as they eat the fungi, tunnel in the soil, and defecate—unwittingly enhancing the pine forest upon which the entire community depends (Maser et al., 1978).

In *gut inhabitant mutualism,* vast armies of organisms such as bacteria live in an animal's digestive tract. The bacteria receive a sheltered habitat and food from their host. In turn, they help break down (digest) their

(a) Oxpeckers and black rhinoceros

(b) Clownfish and sea anemone

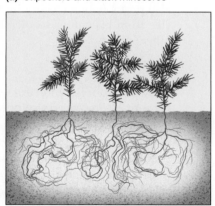

(c) Mycorrhizal fungi on juniper seedlings in normal soil

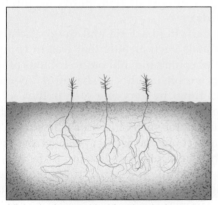

(d) Lack of mycorrhizal fungi on juniper seedlings in sterilized soil

FIGURE 8-12 Examples of *mutualism.* (a) Oxpeckers (or tickbirds) feed on and remove parasitic ticks that infest large thick-skinned animals such as a black rhinoceros. (b) A clownfish gains protection and food by living among deadly stinging sea anemones and helps protect the anemones from some of their predators. (c) Beneficial effects of mycorrhizal fungi attached to roots of juniper seedlings on plant growth compared with (d) growth of such seedlings in sterilized soil without mycorrhizal fungi.

host's food. Examples are the bacteria inside a termite's gut that digest wood or cellulose and provide the termite with food. Similarly, bacteria in your gut help digest the food you eat. Thank these little critters for helping keep you alive.

It is tempting to think of mutualism as an example of cooperation between species, but actually it involves each species benefiting by exploiting the other.

How Do Species Interact so That One Benefits but the Other Is Not Harmed? Do No Harm

Some species interact in a way that helps one species but has little if any effect on the other.

Commensalism is a species interaction that benefits one species but has little, if any, effect on the other species. One example is a *redwood sorrel*, a small herb. It benefits from growing in the shade of tall redwood trees, with no known negative effects on the redwood trees.

Another example is plants called **epiphytes** (such as some types of orchids and bromeliads) that attach themselves to the trunks or branches of large trees in tropical and subtropical forests. These so-called *air plants* benefit by having a solid base on which to grow. They also live in an elevated spot that gives them better access to sunlight, water from the humid air and rain, and nutrients falling from the tree's upper leaves and limbs. This apparently does not harm the tree.

> **CONSIDER, DISCUSS, OR DEBATE**
>
> What are some Canadian examples of chemical warfare, warning colouration, parasitism, mutualism, and commensalism? Consider how widely each of these terms could be applied through a vast range of organisms.

8-5 ECOLOGICAL SUCCESSION: COMMUNITIES IN TRANSITION

How Do Ecosystems Respond to Change? Shifting Community Composition

Over time new environmental conditions can cause changes in community structure that lead to one group of species being replaced by other groups.

All communities change their structure and composition over time in response to changing environmental conditions. The gradual change in species composition of a given area is called **ecological succession.** During succession some species colonize an area and their populations become more numerous, whereas populations of other species decline and may even disappear.

Ecologists recognize two types of ecological succession, depending on the conditions present at the beginning of the process. One is **primary succession,** which involves the gradual establishment of biotic communities on nearly lifeless ground. With the other, more common type, called **secondary succession,** biotic communities are established in an area where some type of biotic community is already present.

What Is Primary Succession? Establishing Life on Lifeless Ground

Over long periods, a series of communities with different species can develop in lifeless areas where there is no soil or bottom sediment.

Primary succession begins with an essentially lifeless area where there is no soil in a terrestrial ecosystem (Figure 8-13, p. 171) or no bottom sediment in an aquatic ecosystem. Examples include bare rock exposed by a retreating glacier or severe soil erosion, newly cooled lava, an abandoned highway or parking lot, or a newly created shallow pond.

Primary succession usually takes an extremely long time. One reason is that before a community can become established on land, there must be soil. Depending mostly on the climate, it takes natural processes several hundred to several thousand years to produce fertile soil.

Soil formation begins when hardy **pioneer species** attach themselves to inhospitable patches of bare rock. Examples are wind-dispersed lichens and mosses, which can withstand the lack of moisture and soil nutrients and hot and cold temperature extremes found in such habitats.

These tough species start the soil formation process on patches of bare rock by trapping wind-blown soil particles and tiny pieces of detritus, producing tiny bits of organic matter, and secreting mild acids that slowly fragment and break down the rock. This chemical breakdown (weathering) is hastened by physical weathering such as the fragmentation of rock that occurs when water freezes in cracks and expands. This is a slow process. It may take a lichen 100 years to grow as large as a dinner plate.

As patches of soil build up and spread, a new plant community replaces the community of lichens and mosses. Most of these plants are tiny **annuals** that live for only a year. However, they produce flowers and seeds that fall to the ground and can germinate for the following growing season. These taller plants eliminate the lichens by depriving them of sunlight.

A community of *small* **perennial** *grasses* (plants that live for more than two years without having to reseed) and *herbs* or *ferns* normally replaces the annual

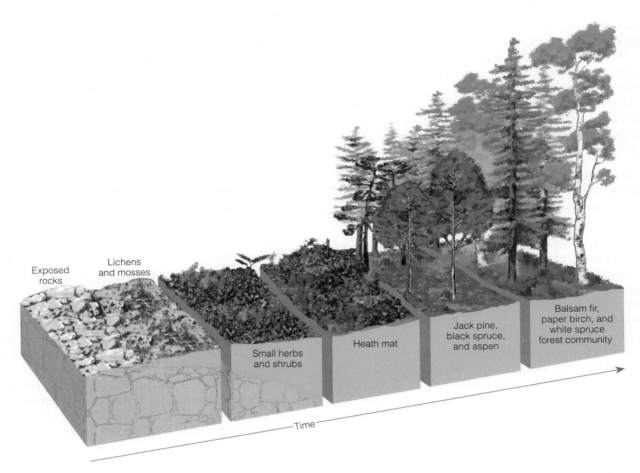

Exposed rocks

Lichens and mosses

Small herbs and shrubs

Heath mat

Jack pine, black spruce, and aspen

Balsam fir, paper birch, and white spruce forest community

Time

FIGURE 8-13 Natural capital: starting from ground zero. *Primary ecological succession* on bare rock exposed by a retreating glacier in the boreal forest biome.

plant community. The seeds of these plants germinate after arriving on the wind and in the rain, in the droppings of birds, or on the coats of mammals.

These **early successional plant species** grow close to the ground, can establish large populations quickly under harsh conditions, and have short lives. Some of their roots penetrate the rock and help break it up into more soil particles. The decay of their wastes and dead bodies also adds more nutrients to the soil.

After hundreds to a thousand or more years, the soil may be deep and fertile enough to store enough moisture and nutrients to support the growth of less hardy **midsuccessional plant species** of herbs, grasses, and low shrubs. Trees that need lots of sunlight and are adapted to the area's climate and soil usually replace these species.

As these tree species grow and create shade, they are replaced by **late successional plant species** (mostly trees) that can tolerate shade. Unless fire, flooding, severe erosion, tree cutting, climate change, or other natural or human processes disturb the area, what was once bare rock becomes a complex forest community.

Primary succession can also take place in newly created small ponds as a result of an influx of sediments and nutrients in runoff from the surrounding land. This sediment can support seeds or spores of plants reaching the pond by winds, birds, or other animals. Over time this process can transform the pond first into a marsh and eventually to dry land.

What Is Secondary Succession? Life Building on Life

A series of communities with different species can develop in places containing some soil or bottom sediment.

Secondary succession begins in an area where the natural community of organisms has been disturbed, removed, or destroyed but some soil or bottom sediment remains. Compared to primary succession this is life in the fast lane. Candidates for secondary succession include abandoned farmlands, burned or cut forests, heavily polluted streams, and land that has been dammed or flooded. Because some soil or sediment is present, new vegetation can usually begin to germinate within a few weeks. Seeds can be present in soils, or they can be carried from nearby plants by wind or by birds and other animals.

European settlers cleared the mature forests and planted the land with crops. Later they abandoned some of this farmland because of erosion, loss of soil nutrients, or changes in economic conditions. Figure 8-14 shows one way that such abandoned farmland has undergone secondary succession over 150–200 years.

Descriptions of ecological succession usually focus on changes in vegetation. But these changes in turn affect food and shelter for various types of animals. Thus as succession proceeds, the numbers and types of animals and decomposers also change.

As we have seen, primary and secondary succession involve changes in community structure. Thus the various stages of succession have different patterns of species diversity, trophic structure, niches, nutrient cycling, and energy flow and efficiency (Table 8-1, p. 174).

How Do Species Replace One Another in Ecological Succession? Creating Beneficial and Hostile Conditions

Some species create conditions that favour the species that replace them; some create conditions that hinder their replacements; and some get along with the next group of species.

Ecologists have identified three factors that affect how and at what rate succession occurs. One is *facilitation,* in which one set of species makes an area suitable for species with different niche requirements. For example, as lichens and mosses gradually build up soil on a rock in primary succession, herbs and grasses can colonize the site. Similarly, plants such as legumes add nitrogen to the soil, making it more suitable for other plants found at later stages of succession.

A second factor is *inhibition,* in which early species hinder the establishment and growth of other species. Inhibition often occurs when plants release toxic chemicals that reduce competition from other plants.

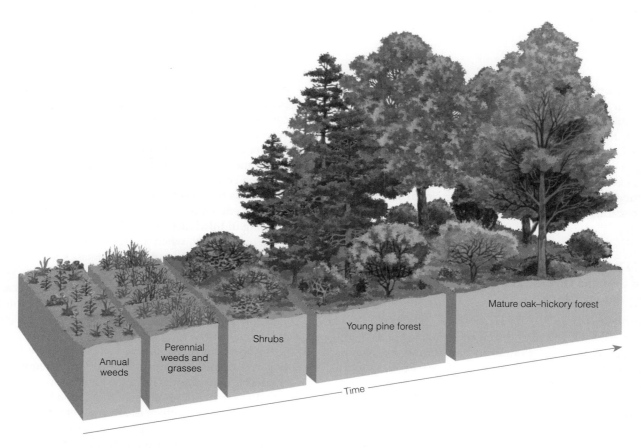

FIGURE 8-14 Natural capital: natural restoration of disturbed land. *Secondary ecological succession* of plant communities on an abandoned farm field in the temperate deciduous forest biome. It would take about 150–200 years after the farmland was abandoned for the area to be covered with a mature oak and hickory forest. A new disturbance such as deforestation or fire would create conditions favouring pioneer species. Then, in the absence of new disturbances, secondary succession would recur over time, although not necessarily in the same sequence shown here.

Community Ecology **173**

Table 8-1 Ecosystem Characteristics at Immature and Mature Stages of Ecological Succession

Characteristic	Immature Ecosystem (Early Successional Stage)	Mature Ecosystem (Late Successional Stage)
Ecosystem Structure		
Plant size	Small	Large
Species diversity	Low	High
Trophic structure	Mostly producers, few decomposers	Mixture of producers, consumers, and decomposers
Ecological niches	Few, mostly generalized	Many, mostly specialized
Community organization (number of interconnecting links)	Low	High
Ecosystem Function		
Biomass	Low	High
Net primary productivity	High	Low
Food chains and webs	Simple, mostly plant → herbivore with few decomposers	Complex, dominated by decomposers
Efficiency of nutrient recycling	Low	High
Efficiency of energy use	Low	High

Succession then can proceed only when a fire, bulldozer, or other human or natural disturbance removes most of the inhibiting species.

A third factor is *tolerance,* in which late successional plants are largely unaffected by plants at earlier stages of succession. Tolerance may explain why late successional plants can thrive in **mature communities** without eliminating some early successional and mid-successional plants.

How Do Disturbances Affect Succession and Species Diversity? Setting Back the Community Clock

Changes in environmental conditions that disrupt a community can set back succession.

A **disturbance** is a change in environmental conditions that disrupts a community or ecosystem. Examples are fire, drought, flooding, mining, clear-cutting a forest, plowing a grassland, applying pesticides, climate change, and invasion by non-native species. Environmental disturbances can range from catastrophic to mild and can be caused by natural changes or human activities. At any time during primary or secondary succession, such disturbances can convert a particular stage of succession to an earlier stage.

Many people think of all environmental disturbances as harmful. Large catastrophic disturbances can devastate communities and ecosystems. But many ecologists contend that in the long run some types of disturbances, even catastrophic ones such as fires and hurricanes, can be beneficial for the species diversity of some communities. Such disturbances create new conditions that can discourage or eliminate some species but encourage others by releasing nutrients and creating unfilled niches.

For example, when a large tree falls in a tropical forest, this local disturbance increases sunlight and nutrients for growth of plants in the understory. When a log hits a rock in an intertidal zone, it dislodges or kills many of the organisms that are growing on the rock and provides space for colonization by new intertidal organisms.

According to the *intermediate disturbance hypothesis,* communities that experience fairly frequent but moderate disturbances have the greatest species diversity. Researchers hypothesize that in such communities, moderate disturbances are large enough to create openings for colonizing species in disturbed areas but mild and infrequent enough to allow the survival of some mature species in undisturbed areas. Some field experiments support this hypothesis, but the scientific jury is still out on whether it applies to all types of communities.

Does Succession Proceed Along an Expected Path, and Is Nature in Balance? Things Are Always Changing

Scientists cannot project the course of a given succession or view it as preordained progress toward a stable climax community that is in balance with its environment.

We may be tempted to conclude that ecological succession is an orderly sequence in which each stage leads automatically to the next, more stable stage. According to this classic view, succession proceeds along an expected path until a certain stable type of **climax community** occupies an area. Such a community is dominated by a few long-lived plant species and is in balance with its environment. This equilibrium model of succession is what ecologists meant years ago when they talked about the *balance of nature.*

Over the last several decades, many ecologists have changed their views about balance and equilibrium in nature. When these ecologists look at a community or ecosystem, such as a young forest, they see continuous change and instability instead of equilibrium and stability.

Under the old *balance-of-nature* view, a large terrestrial community undergoing succession eventually became covered with an expected type of climax vegetation. But a close look at almost any community reveals that it consists of an ever-changing mosaic of vegetation patches at various stages of succession. These patches result from a variety of mostly unexpected small and medium-sized disturbances.

Such research indicates that *we cannot project the course of a given succession or view it as preordained progress toward an ideally adapted climax community.* Rather, succession reflects the ongoing struggle by different species for enough light, nutrients, food, and space. This allows each to survive and gain reproductive advantages over other species by occupying as much of its fundamental niche as possible.

This change in the way we view what is happening in nature explains why a growing number of ecologists prefer terms such as *biotic change* instead of *succession*—which implies an ordered and expected sequence of changes. Many ecologists have also replaced the term *climax community* with terms such as *mature community* or a mosaic of *vegetation patches* at various stages of succession.

8-6 ECOLOGICAL STABILITY, COMPLEXITY, AND SUSTAINABILITY

What Is Stability? Long-Term Sustainability through Continuous Change

Living systems maintain some degree of stability or sustainability through constant change in response to changing environmental conditions.

All systems from a cell to the biosphere are constantly changing in response to changing environmental conditions. Continents move, the climate changes, and disturbances and succession change the composition of communities. Even without human actions, ecological communities have always faced change.

So how do living organisms, communities, ecosystems, and the biosphere face changes and survive? All living systems, from single-celled organisms to the biosphere, contain complex networks of negative and positive feedback loops that interact to provide some degree of **stability** or sustainability over each system's expected life span.

This stability is maintained only by constant change in response to changing environmental conditions. For example, in a mature tropical rain forest, some trees die and others take their places. However, unless the forest is cut, burned, or otherwise destroyed, you would still recognize it as a tropical rain forest 50 or 100 years from now.

It is useful to distinguish among three aspects of stability or sustainability in living systems. One is **inertia,** or **persistence:** the ability of a living system to resist being disturbed or altered. A second is **constancy:** the ability of a living system such as a population to keep its numbers within the limits imposed by available resources. A third factor is **resilience:** the amount of disturbance that a living system can successfully absorb without being fundamentally changed (for example, from a forest to a grassland).

Does Ecological Complexity Increase Ecological Stability? Mixed Results

Having many different species can provide some ecological stability or sustainability for communities, but we do not know whether this applies to all communities nor the minimum number of species needed for such stability.

In ecological terms, **complexity** refers to the number of species in a community (species richness) at each trophic level and the number of trophic levels in a community. It is one measure of a community's biodiversity.

In the 1960s, most ecologists believed the greater the species diversity and the accompanying web of feeding and biotic interactions in an ecosystem, the greater its stability. According to this hypothesis, a complex and biodiverse community with a diversity of species and feeding paths has more ways to respond to most environmental stresses because it does not have "all its eggs in one basket." This is a useful hypothesis, but recent research has found exceptions to this intuitively appealing idea.

Because no community can function without some producers and decomposers, there is a minimum threshold of species diversity below which communities and ecosystems cannot function. Beyond this, it is difficult to know whether simple communities are less stable than complex and biodiverse ones or to identify the threshold of species diversity needed to maintain community stability. Recent research by ecologist David Tilman and others suggests that communities with more species tend to have a higher net primary productivity and can be more resilient than simpler ones.

Many studies support the idea that some level of biodiversity provides insurance against catastrophe. But how much biodiversity is needed in various communities remains uncertain. For example, some recent research suggests that the average annual net primary productivity of an ecosystem reaches a peak with 10–40 producer species. Many ecosystems contain more producer species than this, but it is difficult to distinguish among those that are essential and those that are not. We need much more of this type of research.

Part of the problem is that ecologists disagree on how to define *stability*. Does an ecosystem need

> **DID YOU KNOW**
>
> Many of our ideas about resilience come from Canadian forest entomologist C. S. Holling (b. 1930), who gained worldwide recognition for his promotion of adaptive management policies. Holling founded the Resilience Alliance (an international research group that investigates adaptive systems) and edited the 1978 book *Adaptive Environmental Assessment and Management*. To learn more about the now-retired ecologist, visit http://nersp.nerdc.ufl.edu/~arm/people/holling.html.

both high inertia and high resilience to be considered stable? Evidence suggests that some ecosystems have one of these properties but not the other. For example, tropical rain forests have high species diversity and high inertia; that is, they are resistant to significant alteration or destruction.

However, once a large tract of tropical forest is severely degraded, the community's resilience sometimes is so low that the forest may not be restored. Nutrients (which are stored primarily in the vegetation, not in the soil) and other factors needed for recovery may no longer be present. Such a large-scale loss of forest cover may also change the local or regional climate so that forests can no longer be supported.

By contrast, grasslands are much less diverse than most forests and have low inertia because they burn easily. However, because most of their plant matter is stored in underground roots, these ecosystems have high resilience and recover quickly. Grassland can be destroyed only if its roots are plowed up and something else is planted in its place, or if it is severely overgrazed by livestock or other herbivores. *Bad news.*

We have been doing both of these things in some grassland areas for many decades.

Another difficulty is that populations, communities, and ecosystems are rarely, if ever, at equilibrium. Instead, nature is in a continuing state of disturbance, fluctuation, and change.

> **DID YOU KNOW**
>
> James Kay (1954–2004), an associate professor of Environment and Resource Studies at the University of Waterloo, demonstrated in his writings that disorder, uncertainty, and lack of equilibrium are predictable consequences of the second law of thermodynamics. In a nutshell, all highly ordered systems—including life, societies, and economies—maintain their basic structure and grow at the expense of increasing disorder in the world around them. Kay, a physicist by training, focused his research efforts on developing an ecosystems approach to sustainable development. He was co-editor of *The Ecosystem Approach: Complexity, Uncertainty, and Managing for Sustainability*. To learn more about Kay's achievements, visit his website at http://www.jameskay.ca/about/ecosys.html.

Why Should We Bother to Protect Natural Systems? The Precautionary Principle

Sometimes we should take precautionary measures to prevent serious harm even if some of the cause-and-effect relationships have not been established.

Some developers argue that if biodiversity does not necessarily lead to increased ecological stability, there is no point in trying to preserve and manage old-growth forests and other ecosystems. They conclude that we should cut down diverse old-growth forests, use the timber resources, and replace the forests with tree plantations of single tree species. Furthermore, they say, we should convert most of the world's grasslands to crop fields, drain and develop inland wetlands, dump our toxic and radioactive wastes into the deep ocean, and not worry about the premature extinction of species.

Ecologists point out that just because a system is not in equilibrium or balance does not mean that it cannot suffer from environmental degradation. They point to overwhelming evidence that human disturbances are disrupting some of the **ecosystem services** that support and sustain all life and all economies. They contend that our ignorance about the effects of our actions means we need to use great caution in making potentially harmful changes to communities and ecosystems on the fairly short-term time frame that concerns us.

As an analogy, we know that eating too much of certain types of foods and not getting enough exercise can greatly increase our chances of a heart attack, diabetes, and other disorders. But the exact connections between these health problems, chemicals in various foods, exercise, and genetics are still under study. We could use this uncertainty and unpredictability as an excuse to continue overeating and not exercising. But if you go ahead and ruin your health, you are in a poor position to benefit from any knowledge you might acquire in the future. The wise course is to take immediate action based on whatever knowledge is available to you in the present.

This approach is based on the **precautionary principle:** when there is evidence that a human activity can harm our health or bring about changes in environmental conditions that can affect our economies or quality of life, we should take measures to prevent harm even if some of the cause-and-effect relationships have not been fully established scientifically. This principle is based on the commonsense idea behind many adages such as "Better safe than sorry," "Look before you leap," "First, do no harm," and "Slow down for speed bumps."

We see the precautionary principle at work in the 1982 World Charter for Nature, in the 1987 Montreal Protocol, in all oceans-related international agreements since the 1992 Rio Declaration on Environment and Development, and in all European Union policy since 2000. The precautionary principle also guides resource management decisions made by Fisheries and Oceans Canada, and is reflected in a host of terrestrial applications ranging from regulating chemicals to protecting wildlife.

In this chapter, we have seen how interactions among organisms in a community determine their abundances and distributions. Such interactions also serve as agents of natural selection on one another through *coevolution*. They also have significant effects on the structure and function of the ecosystems in which these organisms live. Everything is connected.

No part of the world is what it was before there were humans.

Lawrence B. Slobodkin

CHAPTER REVIEW

1. Review the Key Questions for this chapter on p. 158. Explain how flying foxes act as *keystone species* in tropical forests. Explain why we should care about protecting this species from extinction.

2. Name three characteristics used to describe a biological community. Differentiate between *species richness* and *species evenness*. What is meant by the *niche structure* of a community? Describe and give an example of *resource partitioning* and explain how it can increase species diversity.

3. Define *interspecific competition, predation, parasitism, mutualism,* and *commensalism* and give an example of each. Explain how each of these types of interaction can affect the population sizes of species in ecosystems. What is a *predator–prey relationship*? Describe three ways that prey species can avoid predators and three ways that predators can capture prey.

4. The term *indicator species* can have different meanings. What different sorts of information can be "indicated" by the presence or absence of a given species? Give some examples of organisms that are viewed as indicator species. What does each example "indicate"?

5. What is the ecological importance of beavers? Explain why each of the following terms has been used to

describe beavers: *allogenic engineers, ecological shapers, keystone species,* and *fundamental species.*

6. What factors are thought to be responsible for amphibian decline? For each factor, devise a plan of action to help remedy the problem.

7. What is *ecological succession*? Distinguish between *primary ecological succession* and *secondary ecological succession* and give an example of each. Explain why succession does not follow a predictable path. In terms of stability, distinguish among *inertia (persistence), constancy,* and *resilience*. Explain how living systems achieve some degree of stability or sustainability by undergoing constant change in response to changing environmental conditions.

8. Differentiate among *facilitation, inhibition,* and *tolerance* in terms of succession.

9. What is the *precautionary principle*? What are some pros and cons of observing this principle? Name some applications of this principle.

10. How would a community of organisms likely respond to: **(a)** the passing of time, **(b)** disturbance on a large scale, **(c)** the steady disappearance of species from the community, and **(d)** the increasing invasion of exotic new species into the community?

CRITICAL THINKING

1. How would you respond to someone who claims it is not important to protect areas of temperate and polar biomes because most of the world's biodiversity is in the tropics?

2. Why is the species diversity of a large island usually higher than that on a smaller island?

3. Why are predators generally less abundant than their prey?

4. How would you determine whether a particular species found in a given area is a keystone species?

5. Describe how evolution can affect predator–prey relationships.

6. How would you reply to someone who argues that **(a)** we should not worry about our effects on natural systems because succession will heal the wounds of human activities and restore the balance of nature, **(b)** efforts to preserve natural systems are not worthwhile because nature is largely unpredictable, and **(c)** because there is no balance in nature we should cut down diverse old-growth forests and replace them with tree plantations?

7. Suppose a storm blows down most of the trees in a park. Timber company officials offer to salvage the fallen trees to reduce the chances of fire and to improve the area's appearance. Others argue that the damaged forest should be left alone because storms and other natural events are part of nature, and the dead trees will serve as a source of nutrients for natural recovery through ecological succession. What do you think should be done, and why?

8. Congratulations! You are in charge of the world. What are the three most important features of your plan to help sustain the Earth's biological communities?

PROJECTS

1. Make field studies, consult research papers, and interview people to identify and evaluate **(a)** the effects of the deliberate introduction of a beneficial non-native species into the area where you live and **(b)** the effects of the deliberate or accidental introduction of a harmful non-native species into the area where you live.

2. Use the library or Internet to find and describe two species not discussed in this textbook that are engaged in **(a)** a commensalistic interaction, **(b)** a mutualistic interaction, and **(c)** a parasite–host relationship.

3. Visit a nearby natural area and identify examples of **(a)** mutualism and **(b)** resource partitioning.

4. Use the library or Internet to identify the parasites most likely to be found in and on your body.

5. Visit a nearby land area such as a partially cleared or burned forest or grassland or an abandoned crop field and record signs of secondary ecological succession. Study the area carefully to see whether you can find patches that are at different stages of succession because of various disturbances. If possible, back up your observations by consulting local experts who know the history of this property.

6. Use the library or the Internet to learn more about at least two of the following people mentioned in the chapter: *C. S. Holling, James Kay, Robert MacArthur, George Perkins Marsh, Robert Paine, Lawrence Slobodkin, David Tilman, Edward O. Wilson.*

Population Ecology

Whooping Cranes: Back from the Brink of Extinction

The ongoing saga of the whooping crane is a conservation success story that involved a coordinated effort on the part of Canada and U.S. wildlife organizations. At one time, the whooping crane (*Grus americana*) was a widely distributed species in North America. However, a variety of factors—including hunting, egg collection, and conversion of wetlands for farming—took their toll. By 1941, the crane population had declined to 22: the species was on the brink of extinction.

Conservation efforts were hampered by the fact that relatively little was known about whooping cranes. How could they be protected if their breeding grounds were unknown? Fortunately, on June 30, 1954, two men flying a helicopter over Wood Buffalo National Park (WBNP) in Canada's Northwest Territories observed three large white cranes. Dr. Bill Fuller, a biologist with the Canadian Wildlife Service (and subsequently a professor at the University of Alberta), identified the birds and located their nesting grounds.

This population of wild birds, now known as the Aransas/Wood Buffalo Whooping Crane Flock, winter in the Aransas National Wildlife Refuge in Texas and then migrate 4 000 kilometres to their breeding range in WBNP (Figure 9-1). Their numbers have grown from 16 cranes to the 278 cranes counted in February of 2011. Between 1968 and 1996, eggs from this population were used to create captive-breeding programs and to establish other wild populations.

As part of an effort to reintroduce cranes to their former range in central Florida, the Florida Non-migratory Whooping Crane Flock was created in 1993. Today, there are an estimated 20 birds in this population.

A second migrating population of cranes—the Wisconsin/Florida Migratory Whooping Crane Flock—was established in 2000. Here, handlers wear crane costumes to prevent the cranes from imprinting on people, and scientists lead migrating flocks to their destinations using

(continued)

(a) A pair of whooping cranes

(b) Current and former whooping crane locations

(c) Costumed worker uses an ultra-light aircraft to guide migration

FIGURE 9-1 Contrasts in whooping crane conservation: whereas the Aransas/Wood Buffalo National Park whooping crane flock is a natural population that guides its own migration, the Wisconsin/Florida migratory flock was introduced and requires ongoing human intervention.

ultralight aircraft. Unorthodox as these methods seem, they work: there are now 115 birds in this population. In 2010–11, 24 whooping cranes were released at the White Lake Conservation Area in southern Louisiana in order to establish another non-migratory flock.

Today, there are an estimated 599 whooping cranes: 437 in wild populations and 162 in captive populations. As an *endangered species* in Canada and the United States, these cranes are protected by half a dozen pieces of legislation, and both countries cooperate through the International Recovery Plan for the Whooping Crane.

What does the future hold? Scientists aim to increase the whooping crane population to 1 000 cranes by 2032. However, genetic problems (probably stemming from the small population sizes of the past) appear to be affecting the chicks. As well, human activities are expanding along the migration routes and near the wintering grounds. Scientists will have to find ways to cope with these new challenges.

In looking at nature … never forget that every single organic being around us may be said to be striving to increase its numbers.

CHARLES DARWIN, 1859

CHAPTER PURPOSE AND QUESTIONS

Chapter 9 discusses population dynamics and some of their implications for the environment. The chapter addresses the following questions:

9-1 How do populations change in size, density, makeup, and distribution in response to environmental stress?

9-2 How do species differ in their reproductive patterns?

9-3 How is genetics linked to the size and survival of a population?

9-4 What are the major impacts of human activities on populations, communities, and ecosystems?

9-1 POPULATION DYNAMICS AND CARRYING CAPACITY

What Are the Major Characteristics of a Population? Changing and Clumping

Populations change in size, density, and age distribution, and most members of populations live together in clumps or groups.

Population dynamics is a study of how populations change in *size* (total number of individuals), *density*

(number of individuals in a certain space), and *age distribution* (the proportion of individuals of each age in a population) in response to changes in environmental conditions.

Populations can also change in how they are distributed in their habitat. Three general patterns of **population distribution** or **dispersion** in a habitat are *clumping, uniform dispersion,* and *random dispersion* (Figure 9-2).

The populations of most species live in clumps or groups (Figure 9-2a). Examples are patches of vegetation, cottonwood trees clustered along streams, wolf packs, flocks of geese, and schools of fish. Viewed from above, most of the world's landscapes are patchy with clumps of various plant and animal species found here and there. The same thing is found when we view the underwater world and the soil beneath our feet.

Why clumping? Four reasons. *First,* the resources a species needs vary greatly in availability from place to place. *Second,* living in herds, flocks, and schools can provide better protection from predators. *Third,* living in packs gives some predator species such as wolves a better chance of getting a meal. *Fourth,* some animal species form temporary groups for mating and caring for their young.

Some species maintain a fairly constant distance between individuals. By having this pattern, creosote bushes in a desert (Figure 9-2b) have better access to scarce water resources. Organisms with a random distribution (Figure 9-2c) are fairly rare. The world is mostly clumpy.

CONSIDER, DISCUSS, OR DEBATE

Which plants and animals in Canada have a uniform dispersion? Why would they have this pattern? Which plants and animals in Canada might have a random dispersion, and why would they exhibit this pattern?

What Factors Govern Changes in Population Size? Entrances and Exits on the Global Stage

Populations increase through births and immigration and decrease through deaths and emigration.

Four variables—*births, deaths, immigration,* and *emigration*—govern changes in **population size**. A population increases by birth and immigration and decreases by death and emigration:

$$\text{Population change} = (\text{Births} + \text{Immigration}) - (\text{Deaths} + \text{Emigration})$$

These variables depend on changes in resource availability and other environmental changes (Figure 9-3).

A population's *age structure* can have a strong effect on how rapidly its size increases or decreases. Age structures are usually described

(a) Clumped (elephants)

(b) Uniform (creosote bush)

(c) Random (dandelions)

FIGURE 9-2 Generalized *dispersion patterns* for individuals in a population throughout their habitat. The most common pattern is *clumps* of members of a population throughout their habitat, mostly because resources are usually found in patches.

in terms of organisms that are not mature enough to reproduce (the *prereproductive stage*), those that are capable of reproduction (the *reproductive stage*), and those that are too old to reproduce (the *postreproductive stage*).

The size of a population that includes a large proportion of young organisms in their reproductive stage or that will soon enter this stage is likely to increase.

In contrast, the size of a population dominated by individuals past their reproductive stage is likely to decrease. The size of a population with a fairly even distribution among these three stages will likely remain stable because the reproduction by younger individuals will be roughly balanced by the deaths of older individuals. These ideas will be revisited in Chapter 10.

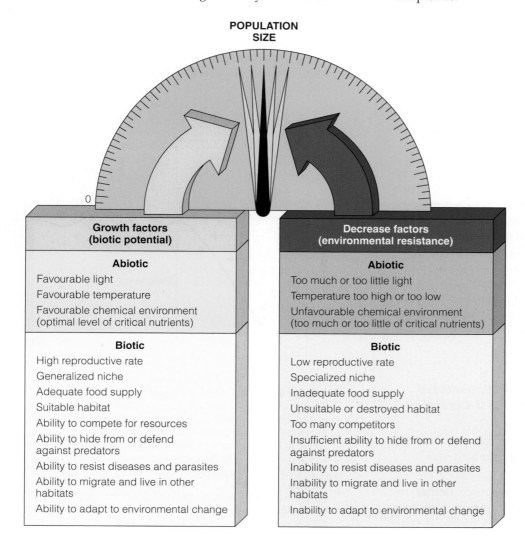

POPULATION SIZE

0

Growth factors (biotic potential)

Abiotic
Favourable light
Favourable temperature
Favourable chemical environment (optimal level of critical nutrients)

Biotic
High reproductive rate
Generalized niche
Adequate food supply
Suitable habitat
Ability to compete for resources
Ability to hide from or defend against predators
Ability to resist diseases and parasites
Ability to migrate and live in other habitats
Ability to adapt to environmental change

Decrease factors (environmental resistance)

Abiotic
Too much or too little light
Temperature too high or too low
Unfavourable chemical environment (too much or too little of critical nutrients)

Biotic
Low reproductive rate
Specialized niche
Inadequate food supply
Unsuitable or destroyed habitat
Too many competitors
Insufficient ability to hide from or defend against predators
Inability to resist diseases and parasites
Inability to migrate and live in other habitats
Inability to adapt to environmental change

FIGURE 9-3 Ecological trade-offs: factors that tend to increase or decrease the size of a population. Whether the size of a population grows, remains stable, or decreases depends on interactions between its growth factors (*biotic potential*) and its decrease factors (*environmental resistance*).

What Limits Population Growth? Resources and Competitors

No population can grow indefinitely because resources such as light, water, and nutrients are limited and because of the presence of competitors or predators.

Populations vary in their capacity for growth, also known as the **biotic potential** of a population. The **intrinsic rate of increase (r)** is the rate at which a population would grow if it had unlimited resources. Most populations grow at a rate slower than this maximum.

Individuals in populations with a high rate of growth typically *reproduce early in life, have short generation times* (the time between successive generations), *can reproduce many times* (have a long reproductive life), and *have many offspring each time they reproduce.*

Some species have an astounding biotic potential. Without any controls on population growth, the descendants of a single female housefly could total about 5.6 trillion houseflies within about 13 months. If this exponential growth kept up, within a few years there would be enough houseflies to cover the Earth's entire surface!

Fortunately, this is not realistic because *no population can grow indefinitely*. In the real world, a rapidly growing population reaches some size limit imposed by a shortage of one or more limiting factors, such as light, water, space, or nutrients, or by too many competitors or predators. *In nature there are always limits to population growth*. This important lesson from nature is the main message of this chapter.

Environmental resistance consists of all factors that act to limit the growth of a population. The size of the population of a particular species in a given place and time is determined by the interplay between its biotic potential and environmental resistance (Figure 9-3).

Together, biotic potential and environmental resistance determine the **carrying capacity (K).** This is the maximum number of individuals of a given species that can be sustained indefinitely in a given space (area or volume). The growth rate of a population decreases as its size nears the carrying capacity of its environment because resources such as food and water begin to dwindle.

What Is the Difference between Exponential and Logistic Population Growth? J-Curves and S-Curves

With ample resources a population can grow rapidly, but as resources become limited its growth rate slows and levels off.

A population with few if any resource limitations grows exponentially. In *exponential growth*, a population grows at a fixed rate such as 1% or 2%. It starts slowly and grows faster as the population increases because the base size of the population is growing. Plotting the number of individuals against time yields a **J-shaped** growth curve (Figure 9-4, lower part of curve). Whether an exponential growth curve looks steep or "fast" depends on the time period of observation, how fast the population is growing, and the scale at which the curve is drawn. Exponential growth is characteristic of invasive species, and the human population since the industrial revolution. Whooping crane populations have been experiencing slow but exponential growth in response to the conservation efforts discussed in the Case Study (p. 179).

Logistic growth involves rapid exponential population growth followed by a steady decrease in population growth with time until the population size levels off. This occurs as the population encounters environmental resistance and its rate of growth decreases as it approaches the carrying capacity of its environment (Figure 9-4, top half of curve). After levelling off, such a population typically fluctuates slightly above and below the carrying capacity.

A plot of the number of individuals against time yields a sigmoid, or **S-shaped,** logistic growth curve (the whole curve in Figure 9-4). Figure 9-5 shows such a case involving sheep on the island of Tasmania, south of Australia, in the early 19th century.

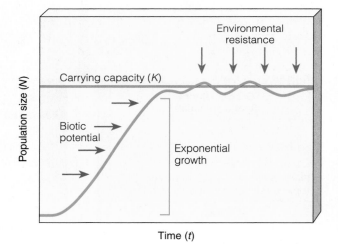

FIGURE 9-4 No population can grow forever. *Exponential growth* (lower part of the curve) occurs when resources are not limiting and a population can grow at near its *intrinsic rate of increase (r)* or biotic potential. Such exponential growth is converted to *logistic growth*, in which the growth rate decreases as the population gets larger and faces environmental resistance. With time, the population size stabilizes at or near the *carrying capacity (K)* of its environment and results in the sigmoid (S-shaped) population growth curve shown in this figure. Depending on resource availability, the size of a population often fluctuates around its carrying capacity.

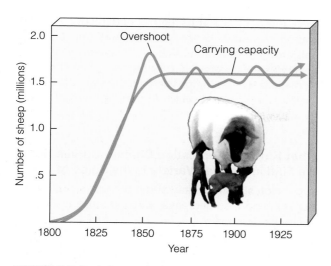

FIGURE 9-5 *Logistic growth* of a sheep population on the island of Tasmania between 1800 and 1925. After sheep were introduced in 1800, their population grew exponentially because of ample food. By 1855, they overshot the land's carrying capacity. Their numbers then stabilized and fluctuated around a carrying capacity of about 1.6 million sheep.

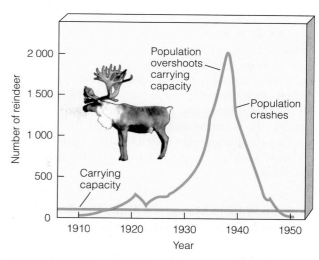

FIGURE 9-6 Exponential growth, overshoot, and population crash of reindeer introduced to a small island off the southwest coast of Alaska. When 26 reindeer (24 of them female) were introduced in 1910, lichens, mosses, and other food sources were plentiful. By 1935, the herd's population had soared to 2 000, overshooting the island's carrying capacity. This led to a population crash, with the herd plummeting to only 8 reindeer by 1950.

What Happens If the Population Size Exceeds the Carrying Capacity? Diebacks

When a population exceeds its resource supplies, many of its members die unless they can switch to new resources or move to an area with more resources.

The populations of some species do not make a smooth transition from exponential growth to logistic growth. Instead they use up their resource supplies and temporarily *overshoot,* or exceed, the carrying capacity of their environment. This occurs because of a *reproductive time lag:* the period needed for the birth rate to fall and the death rate to rise in response to resource overconsumption. Sometimes it takes a while for the message to get out.

In such cases the population suffers a **dieback,** or *crash,* unless the excess individuals can switch to new resources or move to an area with more resources. Such a crash occurred when reindeer were introduced onto a small island off the southwest coast of Alaska (Figure 9-6).

Humans are not exempt from factors that can limit or reduce populations, as shown by the tragedy on Easter Island (p. 34). Ireland also experienced a population crash after a fungus destroyed the potato crop in 1845. About 1 million people died, and 3 million others migrated to other countries.

Technological, social, and other cultural changes have extended the Earth's carrying capacity for humans. We have increased food production and used large amounts of energy and matter resources to make normally uninhabitable areas habitable. A critical question is how long we will be able to keep doing this on a planet with a finite size and finite resources, and with a human population whose size and per capita resource use are growing exponentially.

> **CONSIDER, DISCUSS, OR DEBATE**
>
> Which population growth curve will most likely apply to human beings in the future? Explain your answer. What assumptions are you making?

How Does Population Density Affect Population Growth? Some Effects of Clumping

A population's density may or may not affect how rapidly it can grow.

Population density is the number of individuals in a population found in a particular space. *Density-independent population controls* affect a population's size regardless of its density. Such controls include floods, hurricanes, unseasonable weather, fire, habitat destruction (such as clearing a forest of its trees or filling in a wetland), pesticide spraying, and pollution. For example, a severe freeze in late spring may kill many individuals in a plant population, regardless of density.

Some factors that limit population growth have a greater effect as a population's density increases. Examples of such *density-dependent population controls* include competition for resources, predation, parasitism, and infectious disease.

Infectious disease is a classic type of density-dependent population control. An example is the *bubonic plague*, which swept through densely populated European cities during the 14th century. The bacterium causing this disease normally lives in rodents. It was transferred to humans by fleas that fed on infected rodents and then bit humans. The disease spread like wildfire through crowded cities, where sanitary conditions were poor and rats were abundant. At least 25 million people in European cities died from the disease.

How Do Wildlife Managers Apply the Concepts of Growth Curves and Carrying Capacity?

Wildlife managers use their knowledge of population growth to fulfill their management objectives.

Wildlife managers are called upon to use their knowledge of ecology, biology, and in particular population growth to achieve desired outcomes. For instance, a wildlife manager might be asked to ensure that a bison herd does not outgrow the *carrying capacity* of the national park in which it lives, or to produce a large sustainable fish harvest, or to provide a profitable annual moose hunt to support the economy of a region.

On the basis of Figure 9-4, a wildlife manager realizes that when a population first arrives in an area, or is at low numbers, it has a large *biotic potential* for population growth. Food and space are relatively plentiful; the population will initially grow at exponential rates.

If this is an invasive species with no local predators, competitors, parasites, or diseases, it may continue to grow exponentially for an extended period. However, endemic species in diverse ecosystems have well-established predators, competitors, parasites, and diseases that provide *environmental resistance* to their population growth. This resistance increases at high population densities as organisms come into closer contact, and as food and cover become more limited. Population growth slows and numbers stabilize at or near carrying capacity, as shown in Figure 9-4.

A wildlife manager might wish to increase carrying capacity by improving habitat or adding food. Another strategy would be to decrease environmental resistance—perhaps through predator control—although there is a risk that the population will overshoot its carrying capacity and crash to low numbers (Figure 9-6).

Yet another strategy would be to harvest about 50% of the animals, pushing population numbers about halfway down the curve (Figure 9-4) where the biotic potential again favours rapid population growth. The idea of **maximum sustained yield** is to harvest as many animals as possible (often about 50%) while hopefully leaving enough animals to sustain the population.

Since this approach runs the risk of depleting the population beyond its capacity to rebound quickly, many wildlife managers prefer to use *optimum sustained yield.* This typically involves harvesting 30% or fewer of the animals, and allowing predators to fulfill a role by providing some natural selection and culling unhealthy animals.

What Kinds of Population Change Curves Do We Find in Nature? Variety Is the Spice of Life

Population sizes may stay about the same, suddenly increase and then decrease, vary in regular cycles, or change erratically.

In nature we find four general types of population fluctuations: *stable, irruptive, cyclic,* and *irregular* (Figure 9-7). A species whose population size fluctuates slightly above and below its carrying capacity is said to have a fairly stable population size (Figures 9-5 and 9-7a). Such stability is characteristic of many species found in undisturbed tropical rain forests, where average temperature and rainfall vary little from year to year.

Some species, such as the raccoon and feral house mouse, normally have a fairly *stable* population. However, their population growth may occasionally explode, or *irrupt,* to a high peak and then crash to a more stable lower level or, in some cases, to a very low level (Figures 9-6 and 9-7b). Many short-lived, rapidly reproducing species such as algae and many insects have irruptive population cycles that are linked to

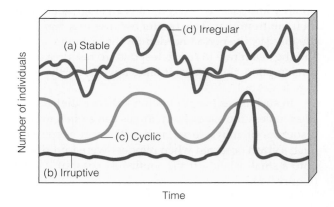

FIGURE 9-7 General types of simplified population change curves found in nature. (a) The population size of a species with a fairly *stable* population fluctuates slightly above and below its carrying capacity. (b) The populations of some species may occasionally explode, or *irrupt,* to a high peak and then crash to a more stable lower level. (c) Other species undergo sharp increases in their numbers, followed by crashes over fairly regular time intervals. Predators sometimes are blamed, but the actual causes of such boom-and-bust cycles are poorly understood. (d) The population sizes of some species change irregularly for mostly unknown reasons.

seasonal changes in weather or nutrient availability. For example, in temperate climates, insect populations grow rapidly during the spring and summer and then crash during the hard frosts of winter.

The third type consists of *cyclic fluctuations* of population size over a regular time period (Figure 9-7c). Examples are lemmings, whose populations rise and fall every 3–4 years, and lynx and snowshoe hare, whose populations generally rise and fall in a 10-year cycle.

Finally, some populations appear to have *irregular behaviour* in their changes in population size, with no recurring pattern (Figure 9-7d). Some scientists attribute this behaviour to chaos in such systems. Other scientists contend that it may be orderly behaviour whose details and interactions are still poorly understood.

Do Predators Control Population Size? The Lynx–Hare Cycle

The population sizes of some predators and their prey change in cycles that appear to be caused by interaction between the two species, but other factors may be involved.

Some species that interact as predator and prey undergo cyclic changes in their numbers: sharp increases are followed by crashes (Figure 9-8).

For decades, predation has been the explanation for the 10-year population cycles of the snowshoe hare and its predator, the Canadian lynx. According to this *top-down control* hypothesis, lynx preying on hares periodically reduce the hare population. The shortage of hares then reduces the lynx population, which allows the hare population to build up again. At some point the lynx population increases to take advantage of the increased supply of hares, starting the cycle again. Controlled laboratory experiments involving branconid wasp predators and bean weevil

prey produce a similar pattern of out-of-phase fluctuations in the predator and prey populations.

Some research has cast doubt on this appealing hypothesis. Researchers have found that some snowshoe hare populations have similar 10-year boom-and-bust cycles on islands where lynx are absent. These scientists hypothesize that the periodic crashes in the hare population can also be influenced by their food supply. Large numbers of hares can die following a period when they consume food plants faster than the plants can be replenished, especially during winter.

Once the hare population crashes, the plants recover and the hare population begins rising again in a hare–plant cycle. If this *bottom-up control* hypothesis is correct, the lynx do not control hare populations. Instead, the changing hare population size may cause fluctuations in the lynx population.

The two hypotheses are not mutually exclusive. One problem is that the simple model of the predator–prey relationship assumes that the lynx are the only predators of hares and that the lynx prey only on hares. Neither is true in many of the real-life communities where these species are found. According to extensive research by UBC professor Charles J. Krebs, the 10-year population cycle of snowshoe hares in boreal forests is caused by an interaction between predation (by lynx, coyotes, and other predators) and food supplies (especially in winter).

CONSIDER, DISCUSS, OR DEBATE

Krebs also studied lemming cycles in the Far North. Visit Kreb's website at UBC and compare lemming cycles (http://www.zoology.ubc.ca/~krebs/papers/254.pdf) with snowshoe hare cycles (http://www.zoology.ubc.ca/~krebs/papers/180.pdf). Note that these are only two of the many papers that have been written about lemming and snowshoe hare cycles.

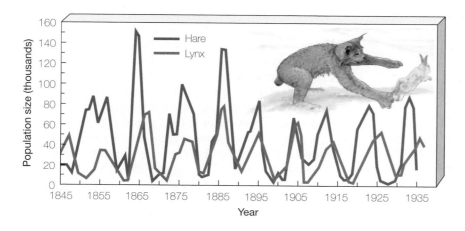

FIGURE 9-8 Population cycles for the snowshoe hare and Canadian lynx. At one time scientists believed these curves provided circumstantial evidence that these predator and prey populations regulated one another. More recent research suggests that the periodic swings in the hare population are caused by a combination of predation by lynx and other predators (*top-down population control*) and changes in the availability of the food supply for hares. The rise and fall of the hare population apparently helps determine the lynx population (*bottom-up population control*). (Data from D. A. MacLulich)

9-2 REPRODUCTIVE PATTERNS AND SURVIVAL

How Do Species Reproduce? Sexual Partners Are Not Always Needed

Some species reproduce without having sex and others reproduce by having sex.

Reproductive individuals in populations of species have an inherent evolutionary drive to ensure that as many members of the next generation as possible will carry their genes. This increases the chance that their population will undergo evolution through natural selection.

Two types of **reproduction** can pass genes on to offspring. One is **asexual reproduction,** in which all off-spring are exact genetic copies (clones) of a single parent. This is common in species such as bacteria that have only one cell. Each cell can divide to produce two identical cells that are genetic clones, or replicas of the original.

The second type is **sexual reproduction,** in which organisms produce offspring by combining sex cells or gametes (such as sperm and ovum) from both parents. This produces offspring with combinations of genetic traits from each parent.

Sexual reproduction has three disadvantages. *First,* males do not give birth. This means that females have to produce twice as many offspring to maintain the same number of young in the next generation as an asexually reproducing organism. *Second,* there is an increased chance of genetic errors and defects during the splitting and recombination of chromosomes. *Third,* courtship and mating rituals consume time and energy, can transmit disease, and can inflict injury on males of some species as they compete for sexual partners.

So if sexual reproduction has some serious disadvantages, why do 97% of the Earth's species use it? According to biologists, this happens because of two important advantages of sexual reproduction. One is that it provides a greater genetic diversity in offspring. A population with many different genetic possibilities has a greater chance of reproducing when environmental conditions change than does a brood of genetically identical clones. In addition, males of some species can gather food for the female and the young, as well as protect and help train the young.

What Types of Reproductive Patterns Do Species Have? Opportunists and Competitors

Some species have a large number of small offspring and give them little parental care, whereas other species have a few larger offspring and take care of them until they can reproduce.

In 1967, Robert H. MacArthur and Edward O. Wilson suggested that species could be classified into two

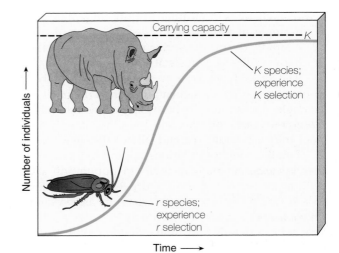

FIGURE 9-9 Positions of r-*selected* and K-*selected* species on the sigmoid (S-shaped) population growth curve.

fundamental reproductive patterns: r-*selected* and K-*selected species.* This classification depends on their position on the sigmoid (S-shaped) population growth curve (Figure 9-9) and the characteristics of their reproductive patterns (Figure 9-10).

Species with a capacity for a high rate of population increase (*r*) are called ***r*-selected species** (Figure 9-9 and Figure 9-10, left). Such species reproduce early and put most of their energy into reproduction. Examples are algae, bacteria, rodents, annual plants (such as dandelions), and most insects.

These species have many, usually small offspring and give them little or no parental care or protection. They overcome the massive loss of offspring by producing so many that a few will survive to reproduce many more offspring to begin the cycle again.

Such species tend to be *opportunists.* They reproduce and disperse rapidly when conditions are favourable or when a disturbance opens up a new habitat or niche for invasion, as in the early stages of ecological succession.

Environmental changes caused by disturbances can allow opportunist species to gain a foothold. However, once established, their populations may crash because of unfavourable changes in environmental conditions or invasion by more competitive species. This helps explain why most *r*-selected or opportunist species go through irregular and unstable boom-and-bust cycles in their population size.

At the other extreme are *competitor* or **K-selected species** (Figure 9-9 and Figure 9-10, right). These species tend to reproduce late in life and have a small number of offspring with fairly long life spans.

Typically the offspring of such species develop inside their mothers (where they are safe), are born

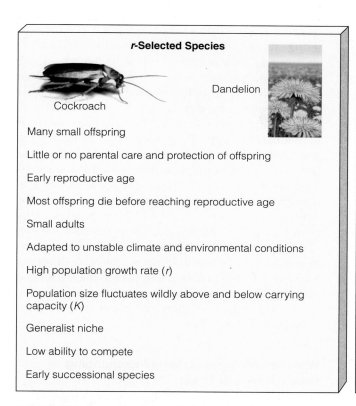

r-Selected Species

Cockroach

Dandelion

Many small offspring

Little or no parental care and protection of offspring

Early reproductive age

Most offspring die before reaching reproductive age

Small adults

Adapted to unstable climate and environmental conditions

High population growth rate (r)

Population size fluctuates wildly above and below carrying capacity (K)

Generalist niche

Low ability to compete

Early successional species

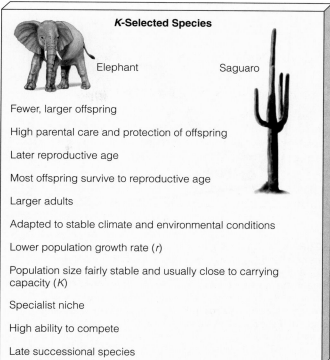

K-Selected Species

Elephant

Saguaro

Fewer, larger offspring

High parental care and protection of offspring

Later reproductive age

Most offspring survive to reproductive age

Larger adults

Adapted to stable climate and environmental conditions

Lower population growth rate (r)

Population size fairly stable and usually close to carrying capacity (K)

Specialist niche

High ability to compete

Late successional species

FIGURE 9-10 Generalized characteristics of r-*selected*, or opportunist, species and K-*selected*, or competitor, species. Many species have characteristics between these two extremes.

fairly large, mature slowly, and are cared for and protected by one or both parents until they reach reproductive age. This reproductive pattern results in a few big and strong individuals that can compete for resources and reproduce a few young to begin the cycle again.

They are called *K*-selected species because they tend to do well in competitive conditions when their population size is near the carrying capacity (*K*) of their environment. Their populations typically follow a logistic growth curve.

Most large mammals (such as elephants, whales, and humans), birds of prey, and large and long-lived plants (such as the saguaro cactus, oak trees, and most tropical rain forest trees) are *K*-selected species. Many *K*-selected species—especially those with long generation times and low reproductive rates such as elephants, rhinoceroses, and sharks—are prone to extinction.

Most organisms have reproductive patterns between the extremes of *r*-selected species and *K*-selected species, or they change from one extreme to the other under certain environmental conditions. In agriculture we raise both *r*-selected species (crops) and *K*-selected species (livestock).

The reproductive pattern of a species may give it a temporary advantage. But *the availability of suitable habitat for individuals of a population in a particular area is what determines its ultimate population size.* Regardless of how fast a species can reproduce, there can be no more dandelions than there is dandelion habitat and no more zebras than there is zebra habitat in a particular area.

CONSIDER, DISCUSS, OR DEBATE

Which species of plants and animals in Canada are *K*-selected? Which are *r*-selected? Which of these specific organisms have the potential to become either pests or species at risk? Justify your answers with reference to reproductive traits and other important attributes of these organisms.

What Are Survivorship Curves? At What Age Is Death Most Likely?

The populations of different species vary in how long individual members typically live.

Individuals of species with different reproductive strategies tend to have different *life expectancies*. One way to represent the age structure of a population is with a **survivorship curve,** which shows the percentages of the members of a population surviving at different ages. There are three generalized types of survivorship curves: *late loss, early loss,* and *constant loss* (Figure 9-11). Which type of curve applies to the human species?

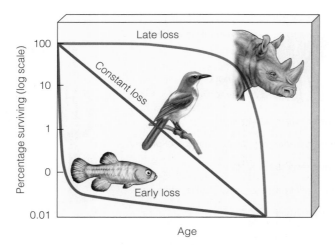

FIGURE 9-11 Three general survivorship curves for populations of different species, obtained by showing the percentages of the members of a population surviving at different ages. A *late loss* population (such as elephants, rhinoceroses, and humans) typically has high survivorship to a certain age, then high mortality. A *constant loss* population (such as many songbirds) shows a fairly constant death rate at all ages. For an *early loss* population (such as annual plants and many bony fish species), survivorship is low early in life. These generalized survivorship curves only approximate the behaviour of species.

A *life table* shows the numbers of individuals at each age on a survivorship curve. It shows the projected life expectancy and probability of death for individuals at each age.

Insurance companies use life tables of human populations to determine policy costs for customers. Life tables show that women in Canada survive an average of six years longer than men. This explains why a 65-year-old Canadian man normally pays more for life insurance than a 65-year-old Canadian woman.

9-3 EFFECTS OF GENETIC VARIATIONS ON POPULATION SIZE

What Role Does Genetics Play in the Size of Populations? The Vulnerability of Small, Isolated Populations

Variations in genetic diversity can affect the survival of small, isolated populations.

In most large populations, genetic diversity is fairly constant. The loss or addition of individuals has little effect on the total gene pool.

However, genetic factors can affect the survival and genetic diversity of small, isolated populations. Several factors can play a role in the loss of genetic diversity and the survival of such populations. One is the *founder effect* when a few individuals in a population colonize a new habitat that is geographically isolated

from other members of the population (Figure 5-8, p. 101). In such cases, limited genetic diversity or variability may threaten the survival of the colonizing population. Another problem is a *demographic bottleneck.* It occurs when only a few individuals in a population survive a catastrophe such as a fire or hurricane. Lack of genetic diversity may limit the ability of these individuals to rebuild the population. A third factor is **genetic drift.** It involves random changes in the gene frequencies in a population that can lead to unequal reproductive success. For example, some individuals may breed more than others and their genes may eventually dominate the gene pool of the population. This change in gene frequency could help or hinder the survival of the population. The founder effect is one cause of genetic drift. A fourth factor is *inbreeding.* It occurs when individuals in a small population mate with one another. This can increase the frequency of defective genes within a population and affect its long-term survival (Futuyma, 2009).

What Are Metapopulations? Exchanging Genes Now and Then

Variations in genetic diversity are linked to the survival of small, isolated populations.

As a landscape becomes fragmented, populations become smaller and more spatially separated. Small disjunct populations can be subject to **inbreeding depression** and are more apt to be driven extinct by catastrophic events such as severe storms or extreme temperatures. However, members of some populations may still be able to exchange genes with other populations through the dispersal of individuals (animals) or seeds (plants). Such collections of interacting local populations of a species are called *metapopulations*.

Conservation biologists can map out the locations of metapopulations and use this information to provide **corridors** and migration routes to enhance the overall population size, genetic diversity, and survival of related local populations (Primack, 2010).

9-4 HUMAN IMPACTS ON NATURAL SYSTEMS: TAKING STOCK

How Have Humans Modified Natural Ecosystems? Our Big Footprints

We have used technology to alter much of the rest of nature in ways that threaten the survival of many other species and could reduce the quality of life for our own species.

In this and the six preceding chapters, we have looked at key concepts of science and ecology. It is time to review what lessons we can learn from this study of how nature operates and sustains itself. But first let us look at our environmental impact on the Earth.

To survive and provide resources for growing numbers of people, we have modified, cultivated, built on, or degraded a large and increasing area of the Earth's natural systems. Excluding Antarctica, our activities have directly affected to some degree about 83% of the Earth's land surface (Figure 9-12). Figure 9-13 (p. 190) compares some of the characteristics of natural and human-dominated systems.

We have used technology to alter much of the rest of nature to meet our growing needs and wants in nine major ways:

1) *Reducing biodiversity by destroying, fragmenting, and degrading wildlife habitats.* This happens when we clear forests, dig up grasslands, and fill in wetlands to grow food or to construct buildings, highways, and parking lots.

2) *Reducing biodiversity by simplifying and homogenizing natural ecosystems.* Communities and ecosystems dominated by humans tend to have fewer species and fewer community interactions than do undisturbed ecosystems. When we plow grasslands and clear forests, we often replace thousands of interrelated plant and animal species with one crop or one kind of tree—called a **monoculture.** Then we

spend a lot of time, energy, and money trying to protect such monocultures against threats such as invasions by *opportunist species* of plants (weeds) and *pests*—mostly insects, to which a monoculture crop is like an all-you-can-eat restaurant. Another threat is invasions by *pathogens*—fungi, viruses, or bacteria—that harm the plants and animals we want to raise.

3) *Using, wasting, or destroying an increasing percentage of the Earth's net primary productivity that supports all consumer species (including humans).* This factor is the main reason we are crowding out or eliminating the habitats and food supplies of a growing number of other species.

4) *Unintentionally strengthening some populations of pest species and disease-causing bacteria.* This has occurred through overuse of pesticides and antibiotics that has speeded up natural selection and caused genetic resistance to these chemicals.

5) *Eliminating some predators.* Some ranchers want to eliminate wolves, coyotes, eagles, and other predators that occasionally kill sheep. They also want to eradicate bison or prairie dogs that compete with their sheep or cattle for grass. A few big-game hunters push for elimination of predators that prey on game species.

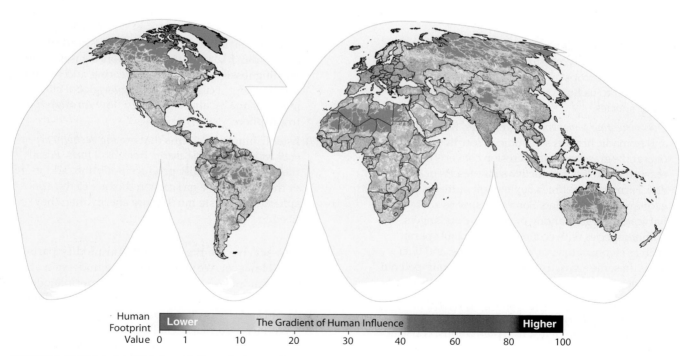

FIGURE 9-12 **Natural capital degradation:** the human footprint on the Earth's land surface—in effect the sum of all ecological footprints (Figure 1-7, p. 8) of the human population. Colours represent the percentage of each area influenced by human activities. Excluding Antarctica and Greenland, human activities have directly affected to some degree about 83% of the Earth's land surface and 98% of the area where it is possible to grow rice, wheat, or maize. (Data from Wildlife Conservation Society and the Center for International Earth Science Information Network at Columbia University [CIESIN]. Reprinted by permission.)

Property	Natural Systems	Human-Dominated Systems
Complexity	Biologically diverse	Biologically simplified
Energy source	Renewable solar energy	Mostly nonrenewable fossil fuel energy
Waste production	Little, if any	High
Nutrients	Recycled	Often lost or wasted
Net primary productivity	Shared among many species	Used, destroyed, or degraded to support human activities

FIGURE 9-13 Learning from nature: some typical characteristics of natural and human-dominated systems. Note that many properties of the two different systems are diametrically opposed.

6) *Deliberately or accidentally introducing new or non-native species into ecosystems.* Most of these species, such as food crops and domesticated livestock, are beneficial to us but a few are harmful to us and other species.

7) *Overharvesting some renewable resources.* Ranchers and nomadic herders sometimes allow livestock to overgraze grasslands until erosion converts these ecosystems to less productive semi-deserts or deserts. Farmers sometimes deplete soil nutrients by excessive crop growing. Some fish species are overharvested. Illegal hunting or poaching endangers wildlife species with economically valuable parts such as elephant tusks, rhinoceros horns, and tiger skins. In some areas, fresh water is being pumped out of underground aquifers faster than it is replenished.

8) *Interfering with the normal chemical cycling and energy flows in ecosystems.* Soil nutrients can erode from monoculture crop fields, tree plantations, construction sites, and other simplified ecosystems and overload and disrupt other ecosystems such as lakes and coastal ecosystems. Chemicals such as chlorofluorocarbons (CFCs) released into the atmosphere can increase the amount of harmful ultraviolet energy reaching the Earth by reducing ozone levels in the stratosphere. Emissions of carbon dioxide and other greenhouse gases—from burning fossil fuels and from clearing and burning forests and grasslands—can trigger global climate change by altering energy flow through the troposphere.

9) Establishing ecosystems that are *increasingly dependent on nonrenewable energy from fossil fuels*. Fossil fuel systems typically produce pollution, add more of the greenhouse gas carbon dioxide to the atmosphere, and waste much more energy than they need to.

To survive we must exploit and modify parts of nature. However, we are beginning to understand that any human intrusion into nature has multiple effects, most of them unintended and unpredictable (Figure 3-4, p. 40 and Connections, p. 192).

We face two major challenges. *First,* we need to maintain a balance between simplified, human-altered ecosystems and the more complex natural ecosystems on which we and other species depend. *Second,* we need to slow down the rates at which we are altering nature for our purposes. If we simplify, homogenize, and degrade too much of the planet to meet our needs and wants, what is at risk is the quality of life for members of our species and other species we drive to premature extinction.

SELF CHECK

What is your contribution? How many of the nine problems listed above do you *directly* contribute to through your own conscious actions? How many of these problems do you *indirectly* influence through your lifestyle choices? Are there ways that you could alter your direct actions or lifestyle choices to begin contributing to the *solution* of these problems?

How Can We Live More Sustainably? Learn from Nature

We can develop more sustainable economies and societies by mimicking the four major ways that nature has adapted and sustained itself for several billion years.

Recall that we finished Chapter 1 on the following theme: *If we can find out how nature has sustained itself for billions of years, and design our human systems this way, then (a) we will be working in harmony with nature, and (b) our human systems will be designed to be sustainable.*

Let us reflect on the four principles of sustainability that underlie nature (summarized in Figure 1-14 p. 16). In brief: (1) natural systems are based on various forms of solar energy, (2) matter is continuously recycled, (3) biodiversity responds to the opportunities provided by abundant resources and healthy environments, and (4) natural populations are regulated to fit the carrying capacity of the environment that supports them.

How can these principles be applied to human systems? Figure 9-14 shows how nature works on the left side of the diagram, and how we should work on the right side of the diagram. If we derived our power mostly from solar energy, then we would have a virtually inexhaustible supply of energy with few environmental consequences. If we cycled our matter efficiently, then we would greatly decrease our problems of resource supply while remarkably reducing our waste and pollution. If we protected and wisely managed ecosystems that housed abundant biodiversity, then we would have intact and functioning ecosystems providing us with their natural services. If we kept our human populations within the carrying capacity of the regions supporting these populations, then it would be much easier to supply everyone with their needs without destroying the environment that supports us.

Do these answers seem too simple? Look back over the nine problems caused by humans (p. 189) and notice how many of these problems could be solved through the application of the four principles of sustainability.

Solutions

Principles of Sustainability

How Nature Works		Lessons for Us
Runs on renewable solar energy.		Rely mostly on renewable solar energy.
Recycles nutrients and wastes. There is little waste in nature.		Prevent and reduce pollution and recycle and reuse resources.
Uses biodiversity to maintain itself and adapt to new environmental conditions.		Preserve biodiversity by protecting ecosystem services and preventing premature extinction of species.
Regulates a species' population size and resource use by interactions with its environment and other species.		Reduce births and wasteful resource use to prevent environmental overload and depletion and degradation of resources.

FIGURE 9-14 Solutions: the four principles of sustainability (left) derived from observing nature have implications for the long-term sustainability of human societies (right). We should learn to understand and work with nature.

How Are We Doing at Solving Our Sustainability Issues? Monitoring the Millennium Development Goals

Recall that the United Nations established eight Millennium Development Goals, each one with targets and deadlines to meet.

Many of our environmental problems are in fact global problems because we share the air, water, climate, fisheries, pollution, and future with so many other people. As mentioned in Chapter 1, the United Nations is coordinating a global response to these problems by means of its eight Millennium Development Goals. Note that while the UN is taking the lead in this initiative, this global agency is doing so with the support of governments, NGOs, and industries all over the world. Visit the Millennium Development Goals website (http://www.undp.org/mdg/) and see for yourself the descriptions of the eight goals.

The Millennium Development Goal most appropriate to this chapter is Goal 7, Target A (Figure 9-15).

CONNECTIONS

Ecological Surprises

Malaria once infected 9 out of 10 people in North Borneo, now known as Sabah. In 1955, the World Health Organization (WHO) began spraying the island with dieldrin (a DDT relative) to kill malaria-carrying mosquitoes. The program was so successful that the dreaded disease was nearly eliminated.

But unexpected things began to happen. The dieldrin also killed other insects, including flies and cockroaches living in houses. The islanders applauded. But then small insect-eating lizards that also lived in the houses died after gorging themselves on dieldrin-contaminated insects.

Next, cats began dying after feeding on the lizards. Then, in the absence of cats, rats flourished and overran the villages. When the people became threatened by sylvatic plague carried by rat fleas, the WHO parachuted healthy cats onto the island to help control the rats. Operation Cat Drop worked.

But then the villagers' roofs began to fall in. The dieldrin had killed wasps and other insects that fed on a type of caterpillar that either avoided or was not affected by the insecticide. With most of its predators eliminated, the caterpillar population exploded, munching its way through its favourite food: the leaves used in thatched roofs.

Ultimately, this episode ended happily: both malaria and the unexpected effects of the spraying program were brought under control. Nevertheless, this chain of unintended and unforeseen events emphasizes the unpredictability of interfering with an ecosystem. It reminds us that when we intervene in nature, we need to ask, "Now what will happen?"

Critical Thinking

Do you believe the beneficial effects of spraying pesticides on Sabah outweighed the resulting unexpected and harmful effects? Explain.

Millennium Development Goal 7:

ENSURE ENVIRONMENTAL SUSTAINABILITY

Ensure Environmental Sustainability

Target 7A: Integrate the principles of sustainable development into country policies and programs, and reverse the loss of environmental resources. http://www.undp.org/mdg/

FIGURE 9-15 Plan of action: Millennium Development Goal 7 takes aim at environmental sustainability through specific targets. Only part of Target 7A, concerning *principles of sustainable development*, is considered here. Other goals and targets appear in subsequent chapters in close conjunction with the material they address. (http://www.undp.org/mdg/)

Here the UN is seeking to ensure environmental sustainability by (a) *integrating the principles of sustainable development* into the policies and practices of each country, and (b) *reducing the loss of environmental resources*—such as natural resources, biodiversity, and environmental services. This is a direct application of the ideas described in this textbook!

What progress is being made as governments, NGOs, and industries all over the world strive to meet

Goal 7, Target A? A number of key reports have been released, including *The Millennium Development Goals Report 2011, Unlocking Progress: MDG Acceleration on the Road to 2015,* and *What Will It Take to Achieve the MDGs? An International Assessment.* These reports say that positive steps are being made in the world, such as examples of increased **reforestation** and sustainable ecotourism, but they also emphasize that the pace of environmental reforms must be greatly accelerated if we are to achieve the goal of environmental sustainability by 2015.

Students will be excited to realize they can track the successes and failures of initiatives throughout the world by means of websites established for this purpose by the United Nations. There is an MDG Monitor Page (http://www.mdgmonitor.org/) and other sites such as the UNDP Eight Goals for 2015 page (http://www.undp.org/content/undp/en/home/mdgoverview/) for following the progress of active groups. Here is an indication of the types of activities that are being reported:

- A UNDP-sponsored project has led to reforestation along the shared border of Haiti and the Dominican Republic.

- A group in Colombia has protected their forests by creating markets for non-timber forest products such as nuts and fruits.

- A group in Cambodia has protected biodiversity in local ecosystems by developing an ecotourism industry.

- Thirteen countries have cooperated to restore the ecosystems of the Danube River Basin, which had been damaged by 75 years of pollution.

The jury is still out regarding whether enough will be accomplished on time, but the world—as represented by the UN Millennium Development Goals program—appears to be headed in the right direction.

We cannot command nature except by obeying her.

Sir Francis Bacon

CHAPTER REVIEW

1. Review the Key Questions for this chapter on p. 180. Explain how whooping cranes were brought back from the edge of extinction. Describe a wildlife habitat program and another program that uses ultralight aircraft. Which approach is associated with the greatest number of whooping cranes? Are these birds safe from extinction now? What hazards and hurdles remain for these birds?

2. What is *population dynamics*? Why do most populations live in clumps? Name and describe four types of population fluctuations.

3. Describe four variables that govern changes in population size and write an equation showing how they interact. What is a population's *age structure* and what are three major age group categories? Distinguish among the *biotic potential, intrinsic rate of increase, exponential growth, environmental resistance, carrying capacity,* and *logistic growth* of a population, and use these concepts to explain why there are always limits to population growth in nature. Define and give an example of a *population crash*.

4. Name and describe three types of *survivorship curve*. Identify a plant or animal in Canada that is a good example of each of these survivorship curves.

5. Describe what is meant by the following terms: *founder effect, demographic bottleneck, genetic drift,* and *inbreeding depression.*

6. What is a *fragmented landscape* and what effect can it have on populations? Distinguish between a *population* and a *metapopulation.*

7. Distinguish between r-*selected species* and K-*selected species* and give an example of each type. Define *population density* and explain how it can affect the size and growth rates of populations.

8. One example in the text described a population of reindeer on an island without predators. What happened next, and why?

9. Another example described a population of lynx and snowshoe hares. What was happening in that example, and why? Weigh the evidence and explain whether this appeared to be a case of *top-down control* or *bottom-up control*.

10. Describe nine ways that humans have impacted the planet and created environmental problems. Use the *four principles of sustainability* (Chapter 1) to suggest solutions for each problem. Why are we not already doing all of the things you suggest?

CRITICAL THINKING

1. Why do biotic factors that regulate population growth tend to depend on population density?

2. Why are pest species likely to be extreme r-selected species? Why are many endangered species likely to be extreme K-selected species?

3. Why is an animal that devotes most of its energy to reproduction likely to be small and weak?

4. Given current environmental conditions, if you had a choice would you rather be an r-strategist or a K-strategist? Explain your answer.

5. List the type of survivorship curve you would expect given descriptions of the following organisms:

   a. This organism is an annual plant. It lives only one year. During that time, it sprouts, reaches maturity, produces many wind-dispersed seeds, and dies.

   b. This organism is a mammal. It reaches maturity after 10 years. It bears one young every two years. The parents and the rest of the herd protect the young.

6. Explain why a simplified ecosystem such as a cornfield usually is much more vulnerable to harm from insects and plant diseases than a more complex, natural ecosystem such as a grassland. Does this mean that we should never convert a grassland to a cornfield? Explain. What restrictions, if any, would you put on such conversions?

7. How has the human population generally been able to avoid environmental resistance factors that affect other populations? Is this likely to continue? Explain.

8. Reread the Case Study on page 179.

   a. What lessons did we learn from the experience of bringing whooping cranes back from the brink of extinction?

   b. Are whooping cranes safe today? What population levels would be considered safe?

   c. What lengths—and expense—should we go to for whooping cranes? Is there too much intervention in whooping crane management? Can we afford such conservation measures for all species?

Slowing Population Growth in Thailand: A Success Story

Can a country sharply reduce its population growth in only 15 years? Thailand did.

In 1971, Thailand adopted a policy to reduce its population growth. When the program began, the country's population was growing at a very rapid rate of 3.2% per year, and the average Thai family had 6.4 children.

Fifteen years later in 1986, the country's population growth rate had been cut in half to 1.6%. By 2011, the rate had fallen to 0.6%, and the average number of children per family was 1.7.

There are a number of reasons for this impressive achievement. They include the creativity of the government-supported family planning program, a high literacy rate among women (98%), an increased economic role for women and advances in women's rights, and better health care for mothers and children. Other factors are the openness of the Thai people to new ideas and support of family planning by the country's religious leaders (95% of Thais are Buddhist). A key factor was the willingness of the government to encourage and financially support family planning and to work with the private, nonprofit Population and Community Development Association (PCDA).

Mechai Viravidaiya (Figure 10-1) led the way in reducing the country's population growth rate. This public relations genius and former government economist launched the PCDA in 1974 to help make family planning a national goal. PCDA workers handed out condoms at festivals, movie theatres, and even traffic jams, and they developed ads and witty songs about contraceptive use (Figure 10-2). Between 1971 and 2011, the percentage of married women using modern birth control rose from 15% to 80%—higher than the 62% usage in developed countries and the 55% usage in developing countries (PRB, 241; UNFPA, 2011).

Viravidaiya helped establish a German-financed revolving loan plan to enable people participating in family planning programs to install toilets and drinking water systems. Low-rate loans were offered to farmers practising family planning. The government also offers loans to individuals from a fund that increases as their village's level of contraceptive use rises. Education and economic rewards work.

(continued)

FIGURE 10-1 **Individuals matter:** *Mechai Viravidaiya,* a charismatic leader, played a major role in Thailand's successful efforts to reduce its population growth. In 1974, he established the private, nonprofit Population and Community Development Association (PCDA) to help implement family planning as a national goal.

FIGURE 10-2 A PCDA worker hands out condoms to publicize family planning.

All is not completely rosy. Although Thailand has done well in slowing population growth and raising per capita income, it has been less successful in reducing pollution and improving public health. Its capital, Bangkok, is plagued with notoriously high levels of traffic congestion and air pollution.

The problems we face are vast and complex, but come down to this: we are 6.8 billion people living together on one planet. The process of fulfilling our wants and needs is stripping the Earth of its biotic capacity to produce life; a climactic burst of consumption by a single species is overwhelming the skies, earth, waters, and fauna.

PAUL HAWKEN (2010)

CHAPTER PURPOSE AND QUESTIONS

Chapter 10 discusses world population growth and some of the challenges associated with it. The chapter addresses the following questions:

10-1   How is population size affected by birth, death, fertility, and migration rates?

10-2   How is population size affected by age structure?

10-3   How can we influence population size?

10-4   What success have India and China had in slowing population growth?

10-5   How can global population growth be reduced?

10-1   FACTORS AFFECTING HUMAN POPULATION SIZE

What Is Demography and Why Is It Important? How Population Change Affects Life, Death, and Economies

Changes in the size, composition, and distribution of human populations have important health, social, economic, and environmental effects.

How long are you likely to live and what will probably kill you? How many people are there in the country or area where you live and how many people are likely to live there in the future? How many children are you likely to have? How likely are you to get married or divorced? What kind of job will you probably have and how many times are you likely to change jobs? What are your chances of promotion? When are you likely to retire? About how many times will you move?

Demography is devoted to finding answers to these and other population-related questions. **Demography** is the study of the size, composition, and distribution of human populations and the causes and consequences of changes in these characteristics. Specialists in this field are called *demographers*.

How Is Population Size Affected by Birth Rates and Death Rates? Entrances and Exits

Population increases because of births and immigration, and decreases through deaths and emigration.

Human populations grow or decline through the interplay of three factors: *births, deaths,* and *migration*. **Population change** is calculated by subtracting the number of people leaving a population (through death and **emigration**) from the number entering it (through birth and **immigration**) during a specified period of time (usually a year):

Population change = (Births + Immigration) − (Deaths + Emigration)

When births plus immigration exceed deaths plus emigration, population increases; when the reverse is true, population declines.

Instead of using the total numbers of births and deaths per year, demographers use the **birth rate,** or **crude birth rate** (the number of live births per 1 000 people in a population in a given year), and the **death rate,** or **crude death rate** (the number of deaths per 1 000 people in a population in a given year). Figure 10-3 shows the crude birth and death rates for various groupings of countries in 2008.

How Fast Is the World's Population Growing? Good and Bad News

The rate at which the world's population increases has slowed, but the population is still growing fairly rapidly.

Birth rates and death rates are coming down worldwide, but death rates have fallen more sharply than birth rates. As a result, more births are occurring than deaths; every second, there is a net gain of 2.6 more people being added to the world's population. At this rate, we share the Earth and its resources with about 227 000 more people each day—98% of them in developing countries.

The rate of the world's annual population change is usually expressed as a percentage:

$$\text{Annual rate of natural population change (\%)} = \frac{\text{Birth rate} - \text{Death rate}}{1\ 000 \text{ persons}} \times 100$$
$$= \frac{\text{Birth rate} - \text{Death rate}}{10}$$

Exponential population growth has not disappeared but is occurring at a slower rate. The rate of the world's annual population growth (natural increase) dropped by almost half between 1963 and 2011, from 2.2% to 1.2%. This is *good news* but during the same period the population base more than doubled, from

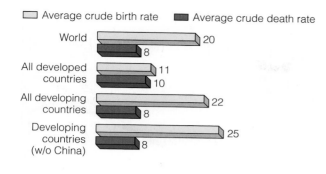

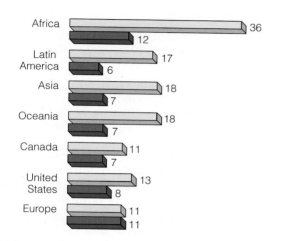

FIGURE 10-3 Average crude birth and death rates for various groupings of countries in 2011. (Data from Population Reference Bureau)

3.2 billion to 7 billion. This drop in the rate of population increase is somewhat like learning that a truck heading straight at you has slowed from 100 kilometres per hour (kph) to 55 kph while its weight has doubled.

An exponential growth rate of 1.2% may seem small. But in 2011 it added about 83 million people to the world's population, compared to 69 million added in 1963, when the world's population growth rate reached its peak. An increase of 83 million people per year is roughly equal to adding another 2.5 Canadas every year!

Also, there is a big difference between exponential population growth rates in developed and developing countries. In 2011, the population of developed countries was growing at a rate of 0.2%. That of the developing countries was 1.4%—7 times faster.

As a result of these trends, the population of the developed countries, currently at 1.2 billion, is expected to change little in the next 50 years. In contrast, the population of the developing countries is projected to rise steadily from 5.7 billion in 2011 to 8.3 billion in 2050.

What five countries have the largest numbers of people? Number 1 is China with 1.3 billion people—about one of every five people in the world. Number 2 is India with 1.2 billion people—about one of every

six people. Together China and India—with roughly the same geographic areas—have 36% of the world's population. Number 3 is the United States, with 312 million people or 4.5% of the world's population. With 34.5 million people, Canada weighs in at number 36 of 230 countries.

How Long Does It Take to Double the Number of People on the Planet? The Rule of 70

Doubling time is how long it takes for a population growing at a specified rate to double its size.

One measure of population growth is **doubling time:** the time (usually in years) it takes for a population growing at a specified rate to double its size. A quick way to calculate doubling time is to use the **rule of 70:** 70/percentage growth rate = doubling time in years (a formula derived from the basic mathematics of exponential growth). For example, in 2011 the world's population grew by 1.2%. If that rate continued, the Earth's population would double in about 58 years (70/1.2 = 58 years).

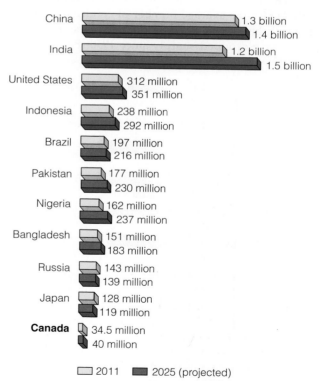

FIGURE 10-4 The world's 10 most populous countries in 2011 contrasted with Canada. In 2011, more people lived in China than in all of Europe, Russia, North America, Japan, and Australia combined. Projected populations for the year 2025 are also given. (Data from World Bank and Population Reference Bureau)

The population of the African country of Nigeria is increasing by 2.8% a year. How long will it take for its population to double?

How Have Global Fertility Rates Changed? Having Fewer Babies per Woman

The average number of children that a woman bears has dropped sharply since 1950, but the number is not low enough to stabilize the world's population in the near future.

Fertility is the number of births that occur to an individual woman or in a population. Two types of fertility rates affect a country's population size and growth rate. The first type, **replacement-level fertility**, is the number of children a couple must bear to replace themselves. It is slightly higher than two children per couple (2.1 in developed countries and as high as 2.5 in some developing countries), mostly because some female children die before reaching their reproductive years.

Does reaching replacement-level fertility mean an immediate halt in population growth? No, because so many future parents are alive. If each of today's couples had an average of 2.1 children and their children also had 2.1 children, the world's population would still grow for 50 years or more (assuming death rates do not rise).

The second type of fertility rate is the **total fertility rate (TFR):** the average number of children a woman typically has during her reproductive years. *Good news.* TFRs have dropped sharply since 1950 (Figure 10-5).

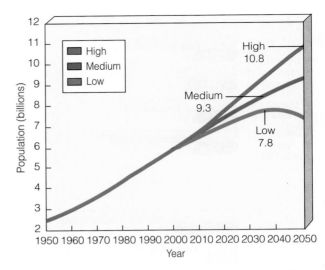

FIGURE 10-6 UN world population projections, assuming that by 2050 the world's total fertility rate is 2.5 (high), 2.0 (medium), or 1.5 (low) children per woman. The most likely projection is the medium one—9.3 billion by 2050. (Data from United Nations)

In 2011, the average global TFR was 2.5 children per woman. It was 1.7 in developed countries (down from 2.5 in 1950) and 2.6 in developing countries (down from 6.5 in 1950). The highest TFRs are in Africa, with some countries like Somalia and Niger having TFRs as high as 6.4 and 7.0, respectively, in 2011.

So how many of us are likely to be here in 2050? Answer: From 7.8 to 10.8 billion, depending on the world's projected average TFR (Figure 10-6). The medium projection is 9.3 billion people. About 98% of the growth in all three of these estimates is projected to take place in developing countries, where extreme poverty (living on less than $1.25 per day) is a way of life for about 1.4 billion people.

How do the population dynamics of Canada compare to those of its North American neighbours the United States and Mexico? Find out by looking at Figure 10-7 (p. 199).

What Factors Affect Birth Rates and Fertility Rates? Reducing Births

The number of children women have is affected by the cost of raising and educating children, educational and employment opportunities for women, infant deaths, marriage age, and availability of contraceptives and abortions.

Many factors affect a country's average birth rate and TFR. One is the *importance of children as a part of the labour force.* Proportions of children working tend to be higher in developing countries—especially in rural areas, where children begin working to help raise crops at an early age.

Another economic factor is the *cost of raising and educating children.* Birth and fertility rates tend to be lower in developed countries, where raising children

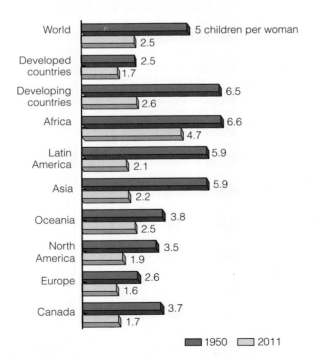

FIGURE 10-5 Good news: decline in total fertility rates for various groupings of countries, 1950–2011. (Data from United Nations and Population Reference Bureau)

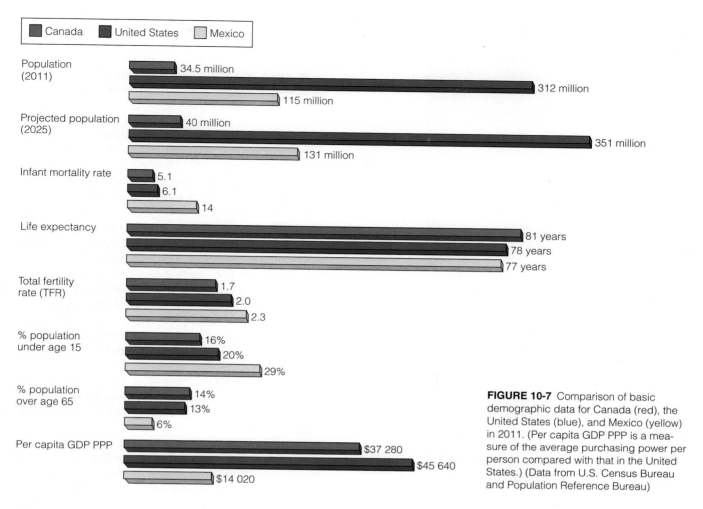

Population (2011)
Canada: 34.5 million
United States: 312 million
Mexico: 115 million

Projected population (2025)
Canada: 40 million
United States: 351 million
Mexico: 131 million

Infant mortality rate
Canada: 5.1
United States: 6.1
Mexico: 14

Life expectancy
Canada: 81 years
United States: 78 years
Mexico: 77 years

Total fertility rate (TFR)
Canada: 1.7
United States: 2.0
Mexico: 2.3

% population under age 15
Canada: 16%
United States: 20%
Mexico: 29%

% population over age 65
Canada: 14%
United States: 13%
Mexico: 6%

Per capita GDP PPP
Canada: $37 280
United States: $45 640
Mexico: $14 020

FIGURE 10-7 Comparison of basic demographic data for Canada (red), the United States (blue), and Mexico (yellow) in 2011. (Per capita GDP PPP is a measure of the average purchasing power per person compared with that in the United States.) (Data from U.S. Census Bureau and Population Reference Bureau)

is much more costly because they do not enter the labour force until they are in their late teens or 20s.

The *availability of private and public pension systems* affects how many children couples have. Pensions eliminate parents' need to have many children to help support them in old age.

Urbanization plays a role. Why? Because people living in urban areas usually have better access to family planning services and tend to have fewer children than those living in rural areas where children are needed to perform essential tasks.

Another important factor is *the educational and employment opportunities available for women*. TFRs tend to be low when women have access to education and paid employment outside the home. In developing countries, women with no education generally have two more children than women with a secondary school education.

Another factor is the *infant mortality rate*. In areas with low infant mortality rates, people tend to have a smaller number of children because fewer children die at an early age.

Average age at marriage (or, more precisely, the average age at which women have their first child) also plays a role. Women normally have fewer children when their average age at marriage is 25 or older.

Birth rates and TFRs are also affected by the *availability of legal abortions*. Each year about 190 million women become pregnant. The United Nations and the World Bank estimate that about 46 million of these women get abortions: 26 million of them legal and 20 million illegal (and often unsafe).

The *availability of reliable birth control methods* (Figure 10-8, p. 200) allows women to control the number and spacing of the children they have. *Religious beliefs, traditions, and cultural norms* also play a role. In some countries, these factors favour large families and strongly oppose abortion and some forms of birth control.

What Factors Affect Death Rates? Reducing Deaths

Death rates have declined because of increased food supplies, better nutrition, advances in medicine, improved sanitation, and safer water supplies.

The rapid growth of the world's population over the past 100 years was not caused by a rise in the crude birth rate. Instead, it was caused largely by a decline in crude death rates, especially in developing countries.

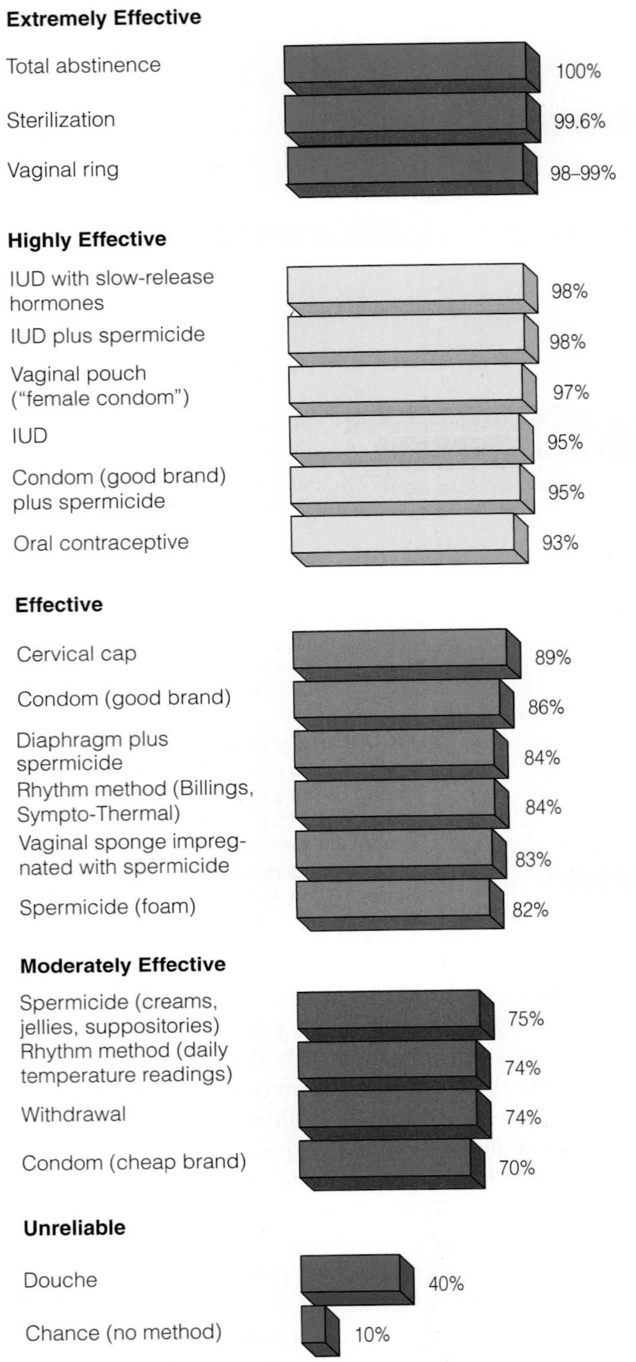

Extremely Effective

Total abstinence — 100%

Sterilization — 99.6%

Vaginal ring — 98–99%

Highly Effective

IUD with slow-release hormones — 98%

IUD plus spermicide — 98%

Vaginal pouch ("female condom") — 97%

IUD — 95%

Condom (good brand) plus spermicide — 95%

Oral contraceptive — 93%

Effective

Cervical cap — 89%

Condom (good brand) — 86%

Diaphragm plus spermicide — 84%

Rhythm method (Billings, Sympto-Thermal) — 84%

Vaginal sponge impregnated with spermicide — 83%

Spermicide (foam) — 82%

Moderately Effective

Spermicide (creams, jellies, suppositories) — 75%

Rhythm method (daily temperature readings) — 74%

Withdrawal — 74%

Condom (cheap brand) — 70%

Unreliable

Douche — 40%

Chance (no method) — 10%

FIGURE 10-8 Typical effectiveness rates of birth control methods. Percentages are based on the number of undesired pregnancies per 100 couples using a specific method as their sole form of birth control for a year. For example, an effectiveness rating of 93% for oral contraceptives means that for every 100 women using the pill regularly for a year, 7 will get pregnant. Effectiveness rates tend to be lower in developing countries, primarily because of lack of education. Globally about 39% of the world's people using contraception rely on sterilization (32% of females and 7% of males), followed by IUDs (22%), the pill (14%), and male condoms (7%). Preferences in North America are female sterilization (26%), the pill (25%), male condoms (19%), and male sterilization (10%). (Data from Alan Guttmacher Institute, Henry J. Kaiser Family Foundation, and the United Nations Population Division)

More people started living longer and fewer infants died because of increased food supplies and distribution, better nutrition, medical advances such as vaccines and antibiotics, improved sanitation, and safer water supplies (which curtailed the spread of many infectious diseases).

Two useful indicators of overall health of people in a country or region are **life expectancy** (the average number of years a newborn infant can expect to live) and the **infant mortality rate** (the number of babies out of every 1 000 born who die before their first birthday).

Great news. The global life expectancy at birth increased from 48 years to 70 years (78 years in developed countries and 68 years in developing countries) between 1955 and 2011. It is projected to reach 74 in developing countries by 2050. Between 1900 and 2011, life expectancy in Canada increased from less than 50 to 81 years and is projected to reach 83 years by 2050.

Bad news. In the world's poorest and least developed countries, mainly in Africa, life expectancy is 59 years or less. In many African countries, life expectancy is expected to fall further because of more deaths from AIDS.

Infant mortality is viewed as the best single measure of a society's quality of life because it reflects a country's general level of nutrition and health care. A high infant mortality rate usually indicates insufficient food (**undernutrition**), poor nutrition (malnutrition), and a high incidence of infectious disease (usually from contaminated drinking water and weakened disease resistance from undernutrition and malnutrition).

Good news. Between 1965 and 2011, the world's infant mortality rate dropped from 20 per 1 000 live births to 5 in developed countries and from 118 to 48 in developing countries. *Bad news.* At least 4 million infants (most in developing countries) die of preventable causes during their first year of life—an average of 11 000 mostly unnecessary infant deaths per day. This is equivalent to 55 jumbo jets, each loaded with 200 infants under age 1, crashing each day with no survivors!

The Canadian infant mortality rate declined from about 140 in 1900 to 5.1 in 2011. This sharp decline was a major factor in the marked increase in Canadian average life expectancy during this period.

In the United States, infant mortality was 6.1 in 2011, higher than the rate in 47 other countries. Three factors keep the U.S. infant mortality rate higher than it could be: *inadequate health care for poor women during pregnancy and for their babies after birth, drug addiction among pregnant women,* and *a high teenage birth rate.*

Is Population Growth in Canada Slowing or Increasing? Some Projections

Population growth in Canada will likely stabilize sometime between 2030 and the end of the century.

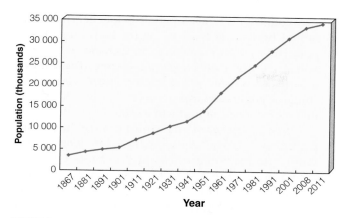

FIGURE 10-9 Population growth in Canada. (Statistics Canada, Population urban and rural, by province and territory, http://www40.statcan.ca/l01/cst01/demo62a-eng.htm)

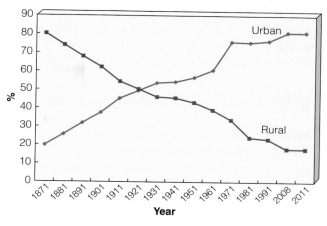

FIGURE 10-10 The Canadian population shifted from rural to urban over time. (Statistics Canada, Population urban and rural, by province and territory, http://www40.statcan.ca/l01/cst01/demo62a-eng.htm)

Before the arrival of the Europeans, Canada was home to some 300 000 Aboriginal people. In the wake of contact with the Europeans, diseases and violent conflicts reduced their numbers to about 60 000. In the period of colonization that followed, large numbers of Europeans (mostly from Britain and France) arrived in the New World. About 6 million immigrants arrived in North America between 1500 and 1700. Between 1820 and 1900, roughly 50 million Europeans immigrated to North America.

In 1867, the year of Confederation, there were about 3.3 million people in Canada. The population grew steadily at a rate of about 2% per year and gradually slowed (Figure 10-9). For example, in 1921 the rate of natural growth was 19 per 1 000 population (with a birth rate of 29 per 1 000 and a death rate of 10 per 1 000); by 2011, the rate of natural growth was 4 per 1 000 population (with a birth rate of 11 per 1 000 and a death rate of 7 per 1 000).

Over time, there were changes in the proportions of Canadians inhabiting different regions. In general, the Maritime provinces and Quebec declined in relative proportions while British Columbia and the Prairie provinces increased. As well, Canadians became increasingly urban to the point that today 81% of us live in cities (Figure 10-10).

There have been ongoing changes in fertility trends. Today about 50% of Canadian mothers are over 30, and the total fertility rate (1.7 children per woman in 2011) has dropped below the figure of 2.1 children needed for replacement.

Immigration remains a crucial factor, supplying about two-thirds of Canada's population growth (7 per 1 000 population in 2008). The largest contributors are China (16%), India (12%), Philippines (6%), Pakistan (5%), and the United States (2%). Most immigrants are drawn to large cities such as Toronto, Vancouver, and Montreal;

by 2017, about half of the people in Toronto and Vancouver will be visible minorities.

The population is aging rapidly as the bulge of baby boomers moves into the senior years. According to Statistics Canada, the median age of Canadians today is 40; by 2031, one-quarter of the Canadian population will be 65 or older.

If current fertility and immigration trends persist, the Canadian population will stabilize at about 50 million people before the end of the century (Figure 10-11). Two other projections based on reduced levels of fertility

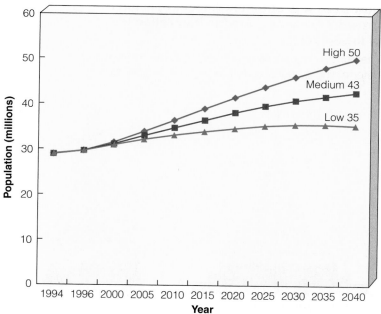

FIGURE 10-11 Three Canadian population projections based on different assumptions. The highest projection (stabilizing at 50 million) is based on current trends, whereas the other two projections (stabilizing at 43 million and 35 million) represent scenarios involving reductions in fertility and immigration. (Statistics Canada, Population urban and rural, by province and territory, http://www40.statcan.ca/l01/cst01/demo62a-eng.htm)

and immigration show populations levelling off at 35 million (by 2030) and 43 million (by 2040) (Figure 10-11, page 201). The Aboriginal population now exceeds 1 million and is growing twice as fast as the rest of the population.

10-2 ## POPULATION AGE STRUCTURE

What Are Age Structure Diagrams? Sorting People by Age Groups

The number of people in young, middle, and older age groups determines how fast populations grow or decline.

As mentioned earlier, even if the replacement-level fertility rate of 2.1 were magically achieved globally tomorrow, the world's population would keep growing for at least another 50 years (assuming no large increase in death rates). The reason is a population's **age structure**: the distribution of males and females in each age group.

Demographers construct a population age structure diagram by plotting the percentages or numbers of males and females in the total population in each of three age categories: *prereproductive* (ages 0–14), *reproductive* (ages 15–44), and *postreproductive* (ages 45 and up). Figure 10-12 presents generalized age structure diagrams for countries with rapid, slow, zero, and negative population growth rates. Which of these figures best represents the country where you live?

How Does Age Structure Affect Population Growth? Teenagers Are the Population Wave of the Future

The number of people under age 15 is the major factor determining a country's future population growth.

Any country with many people below age 15 (represented by a wide base in Figure 10-12, left) has a powerful built-in momentum to increase its population size unless death rates rise sharply. The number of births will rise even if women have only one or two children, because a large number of girls will soon be moving into their reproductive years.

What is perhaps the world's most important population statistic? Answer: *27% of the people on the planet were under 15 years old in 2011.* These 1.9 billion young people are poised to move into their prime reproductive years. In developing countries the number is even higher: 29%, compared with 16% in developed countries.

We live in a *demographically divided world*. To see why, look at Figure 10-13 (p. 203).

How Do the Canadian and U.S. Populations Compare? Similar but Not the Same

Although the populations of Canada and the United States are similar in many respects, there are important differences that have environmental implications.

Canada and the United States are affluent nations with strong economic and cultural links. The two countries are practically identical in terms of degree of urbanization, access to birth control, availability of safe drinking water, and use of energy (Table 10-1, p. 203). Americans are marginally younger and more fertile. Canadians live slightly longer and have a lower infant mortality rate (Figure 10-7, p. 199).

The two populations have been growing at similar rates (Canada at 1.0% versus the United States at 0.8%). Both populations responded to the end of World War II with a burst of fertility known as the *baby boom*

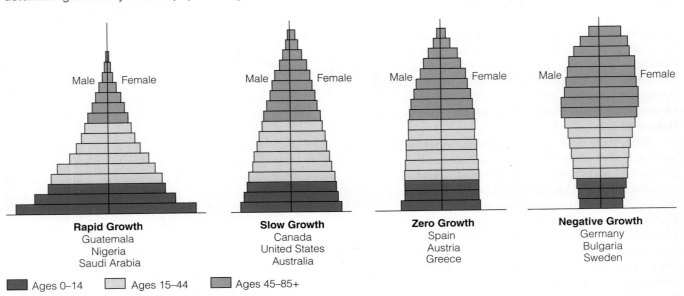

Rapid Growth	**Slow Growth**	**Zero Growth**	**Negative Growth**
Guatemala	Canada	Spain	Germany
Nigeria	United States	Austria	Bulgaria
Saudi Arabia	Australia	Greece	Sweden

■ Ages 0–14   ☐ Ages 15–44   ■ Ages 45–85+

FIGURE 10-12 Generalized population age structure diagrams for countries with rapid (1.5–3%), slow (0.3–1.4%), zero (0–0.2%), and negative population growth rates (a declining population). (Data from Population Reference Bureau)

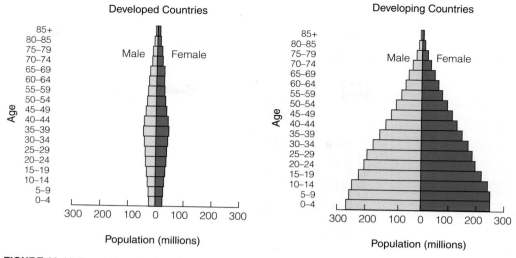

FIGURE 10-13 Population structure by age and sex in developing countries and developed countries, 2006. (Data from United Nations Population Division and Population Reference Bureau)

Table 10-1 Comparison of Canadian and U.S. Populations		
	Canada	**United States**
% Urban	80	79
% Married women using contraception	74	79
% Access to improved water	100	99
Area (sq. km)	9 984 670	9 826 675
Population (mid-2011)	34.5 million	312 million
Density (per sq. km)	3	32

Source: Population Reference Bureau and CIA *World Factbook*.

(Figure 10-14, p. 204). Canada's slightly higher net migration rate (7 immigrants per 1 000 population compared with the U.S. rate of 3 immigrants per 1 000) helps to compensate for our modestly lower total fertility rate.

A key difference between the two countries is population size. The U.S. population (the 3rd largest in the world) is 10 times larger than the Canadian population, which ranks 36th largest in the world. Since both countries are approximately the same size, this would seem to indicate that Canadians live at one-tenth the density (Table 10-1). However, this is too simple an analysis in that density varies by region— being highest in the Maritimes, Ontario, and Quebec, and lowest in the North. Furthermore, about 90% of Canadians live within 160 kilometres (100 miles) of the Canada–U.S. border (Figure 10-15, p. 205), and 81% of Canadians live in cities. Thus, although it is possible to live in very remote circumstances in Canada, most Canadians live at densities comparable to those found in the United States.

The use of space by the Canadian population has important environmental consequences. The parts of Canada where most Canadians live (namely, cities clustered near the Canada–U.S. border) are exposed to relatively high amounts of air and water pollution (Chapters 20 and 22). On the other hand, Canada has more low-density regions—and thus more wilderness and undisturbed ecosystems—than the United States and many other countries.

How Can Age Structure Diagrams Be Used to Make Population and Economic Projections? Looking into a Crystal Ball

Changes in the distribution of a country's age groups have long-lasting economic and social impacts.

As mentioned above, between 1946 and 1964 Canada and the United States had a *baby boom*—a burst of fertility following World War II. Over time this group looks like a bulge moving up through the country's age structure (Figure 10-14).

Baby boomers now make up nearly half of all adult North Americans. As a result, they dominate the population's demand for goods and services. They also play an increasingly important role in deciding who gets elected and what laws are passed. Baby boomers who created the youth market in their teens and 20s are now creating the 50-something market and will soon move on to create a 60-something market. In 2011 the first baby boomers turned 65, and the number of North Americans over age 65 will grow sharply through 2029. According to some analysts, the retirement of baby boomers is likely to create a shortage of workers in North America unless immigrant workers replace some of these retirees.

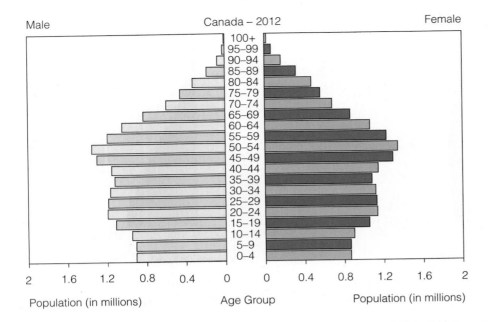

Male   Canada – 2012   Female

Population (in millions)   Age Group   Population (in millions)

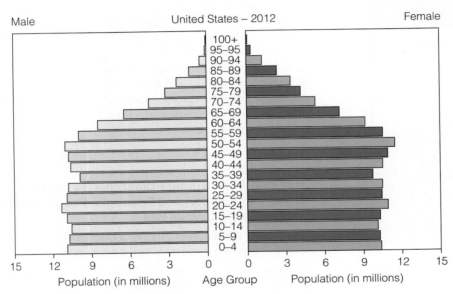

Male   United States – 2012   Female

Population (in millions)   Age Group   Population (in millions)

FIGURE 10-14 The age structure diagrams of Canada and the United States in 2012. Both show postwar "baby booms" that are moving up the age classes over time. The main difference between the two pyramids is that the Canadian population is about 10 times smaller than the U.S. population. (U.S. Census Bureau International Database)

Much of the economic burden of helping support a large number of retired baby boomers will fall on the *baby-bust generation*. It consists of people born between 1965 and 1976.

Retired baby boomers are likely to use their political clout to force the smaller number of people in the baby-bust generation to pay higher income, health-care, and Canada Pension Plan taxes.

In other respects, the baby-bust generation should have an easier time than the baby-boom generation. Fewer people will be competing for educational opportunities, jobs, and services. Also, labour shortages may drive up their wages, at least for jobs requiring education or technical training beyond high school. However, this may not happen, if many large companies operating at the global level (multinational companies) continue to export jobs to other countries.

Members of the baby-bust group may find it difficult to get job promotions as they reach middle age because members of the much larger baby-boom group will occupy most upper-level positions. Many baby boomers may delay retirement because of improved health, the need to accumulate adequate retirement funds, or extension of the retirement age needed to begin collecting government pensions.

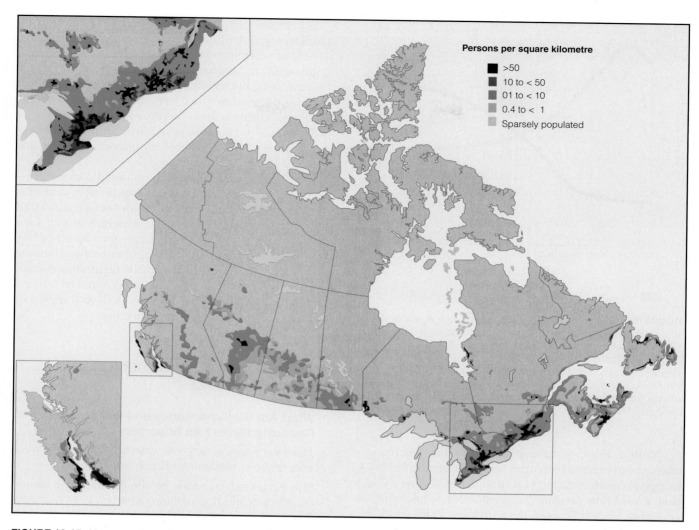

FIGURE 10-15 About 90% of Canadians live within 160 kilometres (100 miles) of the Canada–U.S.A. border. (CIA, *The World Factbook*, 2010; Statistics Canada, *Canadian Demographics at a Glance*, 2008)

The baby-bust generation is being followed by the *echo-boom generation* consisting of people born since 1977.

From these few projections, we can see that any booms or busts in the age structure of a population create social and economic changes that ripple through a society for decades.

What Are Some Effects of Population Decline from Reduced Fertility? Sliding Down a Hill Too Fast Can Hurt

Rapid population decline as a result of more older people and fewer young people can lead to long-lasting economic and social problems.

The populations of most of the world's countries are projected to grow throughout most of this century. By 2008, however, 40 countries had populations that were either stable (annual growth rates at or below 0.3%) or declining. All are in Europe, except Japan. This means that about 14% of humanity (about 900 million people) lives in countries with stable or declining populations.

As the age structure of the world's population changes and the percentage of people age 60 or older increases (Figure 10-16, p. 206), more countries will begin experiencing population declines. If population decline is gradual, its harmful effects usually can be managed.

But rapid population decline, like rapid population growth, can lead to serious economic and social problems. A country undergoing rapid population decline because of a "baby bust" or "birth dearth" has a sharp rise in the proportion of older people. They consume an increasingly larger share of medical care, government pension funds, and other costly public services funded by a decreasing number of working taxpayers. Such countries can also face labour shortages unless they rely more on greatly increased automation or immigration of foreign workers.

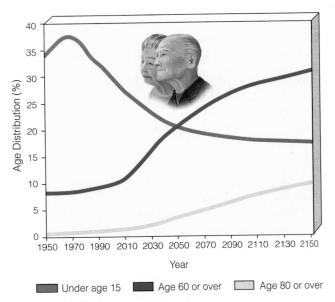

FIGURE 10-16 *Global aging.* Projected percentage of world population under age 15, age 60 or over, and age 80 or over, 1950–2150, assuming the medium fertility projection shown in Figure 10-6. Between 1998 and 2050, the number of people over age 80 is projected to increase from 66 million to 370 million. The cost of supporting a much larger elderly population will place enormous strains on the world's economy. (Data from the United Nations)

Without babies to replenish the labour force and pay taxes, governments of countries such as Japan and some European countries facing rapid population decline will have a hard time funding the pensions of people who are living longer. To keep their finances in the black they will probably need to take unpopular steps, such as raising the retirement age, cutting retirement benefits, raising taxes, and increasing legal immigration.

What Are Some Effects of Population Decline from a Rise in Death Rates? The AIDS Tragedy

Large numbers of deaths from AIDS disrupt a country's social and economic structure by removing many young adults from its age structure.

Globally between 2000 and 2050, AIDS is projected to cause the premature deaths of 278 million people in 53 countries—38 of them in Africa. These premature deaths are roughly equal to nine times the population of Canada. Read this paragraph again and think about the enormity of this tragedy.

Hunger and malnutrition kill mostly infants and children, but AIDS kills many young adults. This change in the age structure of a country has a number of harmful effects. One is a sharp drop in average life expectancy. In 16 African countries where up to a third of the adult population is infected with HIV, life expectancy could drop to 35–40 years of age.

Another effect is a loss of a country's most productive young adult workers and trained personnel such as scientists, farmers, engineers, teachers, and government, business, and health-care workers. This causes a significant increase in the number of orphans whose parents have died from AIDS—about 40 million African children have become orphans because of AIDS. It also causes a sharp drop in the number of productive adults available to support the young and elderly and to grow food.

Analysts call for the international community—especially developed countries—to develop and fund a massive program to help countries ravaged by AIDS in Africa and elsewhere. The program would have two major goals. One is to reduce the spread of HIV through a combination of improved education and health care. The other is to provide financial assistance for education and health care and volunteer teachers and health-care and social workers to help compensate for the missing young adult generation.

10-3 SOLUTIONS: INFLUENCING POPULATION SIZE

What Are the Advantages and Disadvantages of Reducing Births? An Important Controversy

There is disagreement over whether the world should encourage or discourage population growth.

The projected increase of the human population from 7 to 9.3 billion or more between 2011 and 2050 (Figure 10-6) raises an important question: *Can the world provide an adequate standard of living for 2.3 billion more people without causing widespread environmental damage?*

Controversy surrounds this and two related questions: whether the Earth is overpopulated, and what measures, if any, should be taken to slow population growth. To some the planet is already overpopulated. To others we should encourage population growth to help stimulate economic growth by having more consumers.

Some analysts believe that asking how many people the world can support is the wrong question. They liken it to asking how many cigarettes one can smoke before getting lung cancer. Instead, they say, we should be asking what the *optimum sustainable population* of the Earth might be, based on the planet's *cultural carrying capacity*. The idea here is that instead of aiming to populate the Earth with the maximum number of people who can be maintained at a very basic level of existence (essentially the carrying capacity discussed in Chapter 9), we should be thinking about how many people can live *sustainably* while still keeping important cultural luxuries such as education and parks. Obviously, fewer people can be maintained at a cultural carrying capacity than at a very basic level. This implies that decisions would have to be made about population size, and purposeful family planning would have to be pursued to arrive at that optimal number.

What is the optimum population size for the world? Estimates range from as high as 20 billion to as low as 2 billion. Some analysts think optimum population size is a meaningless concept.

Those who do not believe the Earth is overpopulated point out that the average life span of the world's 7 billion people is longer today than at any time in the past and is projected to get longer. They say that the world can support billions more people. They also see more people as the most valuable resource for solving the problems we face and stimulating economic growth by becoming consumers.

Some believe that all people should be free to have as many children as they want. And some view any form of population regulation as a violation of their religious beliefs. Others see it as an intrusion into their privacy and personal freedom. Some developing countries and some members of minorities in developed countries regard population control as a form of genocide to keep their numbers and power from rising.

Proponents of slowing and eventually stopping population growth have a different view. They point out that we fail to provide the basic necessities for one out of six people on the Earth today. If we cannot or will not do this now, they ask, how will we be able to do this for the projected 2.3 billion more people by 2050?

Proponents of slowing population growth warn of two serious consequences if we do not sharply lower birth rates. One possibility is a higher death rate because of declining health and environmental conditions in some areas—something that is already happening in parts of Africa. Another is increased resource use and environmental harm as more consumers increase their already large ecological footprint in developed countries and in developing countries such as China and India that are undergoing rapid economic growth.

Population increase and the consumption that goes with it can increase environmental stresses such as *infectious disease, biodiversity losses, loss of tropical forests, fisheries depletion, increasing water scarcity, pollution of the seas,* and *climate change.*

Proponents of this view recognize that population growth is not the only cause of these problems. But they argue that adding several hundred million more people in developed countries and several billion more in developing countries can only intensify existing environmental and social problems.

These analysts believe people should have the freedom to produce as many children as they want, but only if it does not reduce the quality of other people's lives now and in the future, either by impairing the Earth's ability to sustain life or by causing social disruption. They point out that limiting the freedom

of individuals to do anything they want, in order to protect the freedom of other individuals, is the basis of most laws in modern societies.

CONSIDER, DISCUSS, OR DEBATE

Do you think that the Earth as a whole is overpopulated? What are some solutions to the problem of overpopulation?

How Can Economic Development Help Reduce Birth Rates? Economics Worked Once, but Will It Work Again?

History indicates that as countries become economically developed, their birth and death rates decline.

Demographers have examined the birth and death rates of western European countries that industrialized during the 19th century. From these data they developed a hypothesis of population change known as the **demographic transition**: as countries become industrialized, first their death rates and then their birth rates decline.

According to this hypothesis, the transition takes place in four stages (Figure 10-17):

First is the *preindustrial stage,* when there is little population growth because harsh living conditions lead to both a high birth rate (to compensate for high infant mortality) and a high death rate.

Next is the *transitional stage,* when industrialization begins, food production rises, and health care improves. Death rates drop and birth rates remain high, so the population grows rapidly (typically 2.5–3% a year).

During the third phase, called the *industrial stage,* the birth rate drops and eventually approaches the death rate as industrialization, medical advances, and modernization become widespread. Population growth continues, but at a slower and perhaps fluctuating rate, depending on economic conditions. Most developed countries and a few developing countries are in this third stage.

The last phase is the *postindustrial stage,* when the birth rate declines further, equalling the death rate and reaching **zero population growth.** Then the birth rate falls below the death rate and population size decreases slowly. Forty countries containing about 14% of the world's population have entered this stage and more of the world's developed countries are expected to enter this phase by 2050.

In most developing countries today, death rates have fallen much more than birth rates. In other words, these developing countries are still in the transitional stage, halfway up the economic development ladder, with high population growth rates.

Some economists believe that developing countries will make the demographic transition over the next few decades. But some population analysts fear

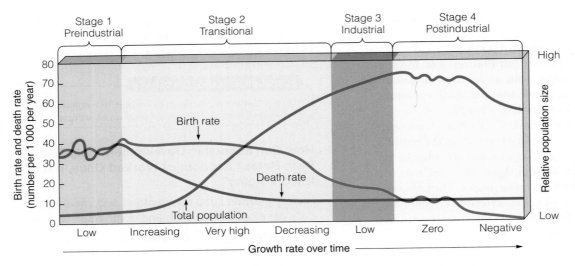

CENGAGENOW
ACTIVE FIGURE
10-17 Generalized model of the demographic transition. *See an animation based on this figure at CengageNow.*

that the still-rapid population growth in many developing countries will outstrip economic growth and overwhelm local life-support systems. This could cause many of these countries to be caught in a *demographic trap* at stage 2, the transition stage. This is now happening in a number of developing countries, especially in Africa. Indeed, some of the countries in Africa being ravaged by the HIV/AIDS epidemic are falling back to stage 1 as their death rates rise.

Analysts also point out that some of the conditions that allowed developed countries to develop are not available to many of today's developing countries. One problem is a shortage of skilled workers to produce the high-tech products necessary to compete in today's global economy. Another is a lack of the financial capital and other resources that allow rapid economic development.

Two other problems hinder economic development in many developing countries. One is a sharp rise in their debt to developed countries. Much of the income of such countries must be used to pay the interest on their debts. This leaves too little money for improving social, health, and environmental conditions.

Another problem is that since 1980 developing countries have been receiving less economic assistance from developed countries. Indeed, since the mid-1980s, developing countries have paid developed countries $40–50 billion a year (mostly in debt interest) more than they have received from these countries.

How Can Family Planning Help Reduce Birth and Abortion Rates and Save Lives? Planning for Babies Works

Family planning has been a major factor in reducing the number of births and abortions throughout most of the world.

Family planning provides educational and clinical services that help couples choose how many children to have and when to have them. Such programs vary from culture to culture, but most provide information on birth spacing, birth control, and health care for pregnant women and infants.

Family planning has helped raise the use of modern forms of contraception by married women in their reproductive years in developing countries from 10% in the 1960s to 54% in 2011.

Studies also show that family planning has been responsible for at least 55% of the drop in TFRs in developing countries, from 6 in 1960 to 2.6 in 2011. Two examples of countries that have sharply reduced their population growth are Thailand (p. 195) and Iran (Case Study, p. 209). Family planning has also reduced the number of legal and illegal abortions per year and the risk of maternal and fetus death from pregnancy.

Despite such successes, there is also some *bad news. First,* according to the United Nations Population Fund, 42% of all pregnancies in the developing countries are unplanned and 26% end with abortion. *Second,* an estimated 200 million women in developing countries want to limit the number and determine the spacing of their children, but they lack access to contraceptive services. According to the United Nations, extending family planning services to these women and to those who will soon be entering their reproductive years could prevent an estimated 52 million unwanted pregnancies a year and more than 22 million induced abortions a year!

Some analysts call for expanding family planning programs to include teenagers and sexually active unmarried women, who are excluded in many existing programs. For teenagers, many advocate much greater emphasis on abstinence.

Another suggestion is to develop programs that educate men about the importance of having fewer children and taking more responsibility for raising them. Proponents also call for greatly increased research on developing new, more effective, and more acceptable birth control methods for men.

Finally, a number of analysts urge pro-choice and pro-life groups to join forces in greatly reducing unplanned births and abortions, especially among teenagers.

Case Study: Family Planning in Iran— A Success Story

Since 1989 Iran has used family planning and public education to cut its rate of population growth in half and reduce the average number of children per woman from 7 to 2.

When Ayatollah Khomeini assumed power in Iran in 1979, he did away with the family planning programs the Shah of Iran had put into place in 1967. He saw large families as a way to increase the size of his army.

Iranians responded and the country's population growth reached 4.4%—one of the world's highest rates. But this rapid growth in numbers began to overburden the country's economy and environment.

In 1989, the government reversed its policy and restored its family planning program. Government agencies were mobilized to raise public awareness of population issues, encourage smaller families, and provide free modern contraception. Religious leaders helped by mounting a crusade for smaller families. TV stations were used to provide family planning information throughout the country.

Iran became the first country to require couples to take a class on contraception before they could receive a marriage licence. Between 1970 and 2011, the country also increased female literacy from 25% to 96% and female school enrollment from 60% to 100% at the public school level (81% at the high school level).

These efforts paid off. Between 1989 and 2011, the country cut its population growth rate from 2.5% to 1.2% and its average family size from 7 children to 2—a remarkable change.

How Can Empowering Women Help Reduce Birth Rates? Ensuring Education, Jobs, and Rights

Women tend to have fewer children if they are educated, have a paying job outside the home, and do not have their human rights suppressed.

What key factors lead women to have fewer and healthier children? Three things: education, paying jobs outside the home, and living in societies where their rights are not suppressed. ·

Roughly half of the world's people are female. Women do almost all of the world's domestic work and child care, with little or no pay. Women also provide more unpaid health care than all the world's organized health services combined.

They also do 60–80% of the work associated with growing food, gathering fuelwood, and hauling water in rural areas of Africa, Latin America, and Asia (Figure 10-18). As one Brazilian woman put it, "For poor women the only holiday is when you are asleep."

Globally women account for two-thirds of all hours worked but receive only 10% of the world's income, and they own less than 2% of the world's land. In most developing countries, women do not have the legal right to own land or to borrow money. Women also make up 70% of the world's poor and 64% of the 800 million illiterate adults worldwide who can neither read nor write.

According to United Nations Population Agency's executive director Thorya Obaid, "Many women in the developing world are trapped in poverty by illiteracy, poor health, and unwanted high fertility. All of these contribute to environmental degradation and tighten the grip of poverty. If we are serious about sustainable development, we must break this vicious cycle."

| 4:45 a.m. Wake, wash, and eat | 5:00 a.m.– 5:30 a.m. Walk to fields | 5:30 a.m.– 3:00 p.m. Work in fields | 3:00 p.m.– 4:00 p.m. Collect firewood | 4:00 p.m.– 5:30 p.m. Pound and grind corn | 5:30 p.m.– 6:30 p.m. Collect water | 6:30 p.m.– 8:30 p.m. Cook for family and eat | 8:30 p.m.– 9:30 p.m. Wash dishes and children | 9:30 p.m. Go to bed |

FIGURE 10-18 Typical workday for a woman in rural Africa. In addition to their domestic work, rural African women perform about 75% of all agricultural work. (Data from the United Nations)

Breaking out of this trap means giving women everywhere full legal rights and the opportunity to become educated and earn income outside the home. Achieving this would slow population growth, promote human rights and freedom, reduce poverty, and slow environmental degradation—a win-win result.

Empowering women by seeking gender equality will take some major social changes. This will be difficult to achieve in male-dominated societies but it can be done.

Good news. An increasing number of women in developing countries are taking charge of their lives and reproductive behaviour. They are not waiting around for the slow processes of education and cultural change. As it expands, such bottom-up change by individual women will play an important role in stabilizing population and providing women with equal rights.

> **CONSIDER, DISCUSS, OR DEBATE**
> Have women achieved total equality in Canadian society, or do glass ceilings and other barriers to gender equality remain?

10-4 CASE STUDIES: INDIA AND CHINA

What Success Has India Had in Controlling Its Population Growth? Some Progress but Not Enough

For over five decades India has tried to control its population growth with only modest success.

The world's first national family planning program began in India in 1952, when its population was nearly 400 million. In 2011, after 59 years of population control efforts, India was the world's second most populous country, with a population of 1.2 billion.

In 1952, India added 5 million people to its population. In 2011 it added 17 million. By 2050, the population of India is projected to surpass the population of China. Figure 10-19 (p. 211) compares demographic data for India and China.

India faces a number of already serious poverty, malnutrition, and environmental problems that could worsen as its population continues to grow rapidly. By global standards, India's people are poor. Nearly half of India's labour force is unemployed or can find only occasional work.

India currently is self-sufficient in food grain production. Still, about 20% of its population and 42% of its children suffer from malnutrition, mostly because of poverty.

Furthermore, India faces serious resource and environmental problems. With 17% of the world's people, it has just 2.3% of the world's land resources and 2% of the world's forests. About half of the country's cropland is degraded as a result of soil erosion, waterlogging, salinization, overgrazing, and deforestation. In addition, over two-thirds of India's water is seriously polluted and sanitation services often are inadequate.

Without its longstanding family planning program, India's population and environmental problems would be growing even faster. Still, to its supporters the results of the program have been disappointing for several reasons: poor planning, bureaucratic inefficiency, the low status of women (despite constitutional guarantees of equality), extreme poverty, and lack of administrative and financial support.

The government has provided information about the advantages of small families for years. Yet Indian women still have an average of 2.6 children. One reason is that most poor couples believe they need many children to do work and care for them in old age. Another is the strong cultural preference for male children, which means some couples keep having children until they produce one or more boys. These factors in part explain why even though 90% of Indian couples know of at least one modern birth control method, only 47% actually use one.

What Success Has China Had in Controlling Its Population Growth? Good Progress, Enforced with an Iron Hand

Since 1970, China has used a government-enforced program to cut its birth rate in half and sharply reduce its total fertility rate.

Since 1970, China has made impressive efforts to feed its people and bring its population growth under control. Between 1972 and 2011, China cut its crude birth rate in half and cut its total fertility rate from 5.7 to 1.5 children per woman (Figure 10-19).

To achieve its sharp drop in fertility, China has established the world's most extensive, intrusive, and strict population control program. Couples are strongly urged to postpone marriage and to have no more than one child. Married couples who pledge to have no more than one child receive extra food, larger pensions, better housing, free medical care, salary bonuses, free school tuition for their one child, and preferential treatment in employment when their child enters the job market. Couples who break their pledge lose such benefits.

The government also provides married couples with ready access to free sterilization, contraceptives, and abortion. This helps explain why about 90% of married women in China use modern contraception.

Government officials realized in the 1960s that the only alternative to strict population control was mass starvation. China has a strong centralized communist government. Thus, unlike India, it has been able to impose a population policy throughout its society.

China has 19% of the world's population. But it has only 7% of the world's fresh water and cropland,

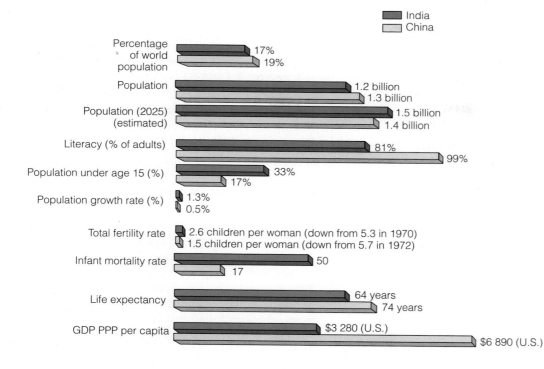

India
China

Percentage of world population	17% (India)	
	19% (China)	
Population	1.2 billion (India)	
	1.3 billion (China)	
Population (2025) (estimated)	1.5 billion (India)	
	1.4 billion (China)	
Literacy (% of adults)	81% (India)	99% (China)
Population under age 15 (%)	33% (India)	17% (China)
Population growth rate (%)	1.3% (India)	0.5% (China)
Total fertility rate	2.6 children per woman (down from 5.3 in 1970) (India)	1.5 children per woman (down from 5.7 in 1972) (China)
Infant mortality rate	50 (India)	17 (China)
Life expectancy	64 years (India)	74 years (China)
GDP PPP per capita	$3 280 (U.S.) (India)	$6 890 (U.S.) (China)

FIGURE 10-19 Comparison of basic demographic data for India (green) and China (yellow) in 2011. (Data from United Nations and Population Reference Bureau)

4% of its forests, and 2% of its oil. Soil erosion in China is serious and apparently getting worse. In the 1970s, the Chinese government had a system of health clinics that provided basic health care for its huge rural farm population. This system collapsed in the 1980s as China embraced capitalist economic reforms. According to government estimates, more than 800 million people—9 of every 10 rural Chinese—now have no health insurance or social safety net.

Population experts expect China's population to peak around 2040 and then begin a slow decline. This has led some members of China's parliament to call for amending the country's one-child policy so that some urban couples can have a second child. The goal would be to provide more workers to help support China's aging population.

What lesson can other countries learn from China? One possibility is to try to curb population growth before they must choose between mass starvation and coercive measures that severely restrict human freedom.

10-5 CUTTING GLOBAL POPULATION GROWTH

What Can We Do to Slow Population Growth? New Visions

Experience indicates that the best way to slow population growth is a combination of investing in family planning, reducing poverty, and elevating the status of women.

In 1994, the United Nations held its third International Conference on Population and Development (ICPD) in Cairo, Egypt. At this landmark meeting, the governments of 179 countries committed to taking action on the following major goals by 2015:

- Provide universal access to family planning services and reproductive health care

- Improve health care for infants, children, and pregnant women

- Develop and implement national population policies

- Improve the status of women and expand education and job opportunities for young women

- Provide more education, especially for girls and women

- Increase the involvement of men in child-rearing responsibilities and family planning

- Sharply reduce poverty

- Greatly reduce unsustainable patterns of production and consumption

The momentum of this program was carried forward and magnified by the Millennium Summit, involving more than 150 world leaders who met in New York City in September 2000 to discuss the role of the UN going into the new century. This group drew up and signed the UN Millennium Declaration. Arising from this, eight Millennium Development Goals (MDGs) were established, encompassing 21 specific targets

2

Millennium Development Goal 2:

Achieve Universal Primary Education

Target 2A: Ensure that, by 2015, children everywhere, boys and girls alike, will be able to complete a full course of primary schooling.

3

Millennium Development Goal 3:

Promote Gender Equality and Empower Women

Target 3A: Eliminate gender disparity in primary and secondary education, preferably by 2005, and in all levels of education no later than 2015.

4

Millennium Development Goal 4:

Reduce Child Mortality

Target 4A: Reduce by two-thirds, between 1990 and 2015, the under-five mortality rate.

5

Millennium Development Goal 5:

Improve Maternal Health

Target 5A: Reduce by three-quarters, between 1990 and 2015, the maternal mortality ratio.
Target 5B: Achieve, by 2015, universal access to reproductive health.

Courtesy of the UNDP

FIGURE 10-20 *UN Millennium Development Goals in Action:* Four Millennium Development Goals focus on the issues of this chapter. Clearly, the UN views issues of education, gender equality, health, and population regulation as central to sustainable development. (http://www.undp.org/mdg/)

What Progress Has Been Made Regarding Millennium Development Goals 2 to 5? Some Progress, but We Need to Provide More Aid

In order to deal with global environmental problems, we will have to help developing nations solve their issues related to population growth and development.

Goal 2, universal primary education, is an expensive proposition for developing countries. The net enrollment ratio reached 89% in developing countries in 2009; however, progress was slowed by the 2008–9 global economic downturn. Greater funding and focus will be required to achieve the goal of primary schooling for all children by 2015.

Goal 3, promoting gender equality and empowering women, has shown mixed progress. In developing countries overall, 96 girls are enrolled in primary and secondary schools for every 100 boys. Gender parity has been achieved in some regions, such as the Caribbean, Latin America, and parts of Asia. The percentage of women in nonagricultural employment has increased from 35% in 1990 to about 40% in 2009. In 2011, women held 19.3% of parliamentary seats worldwide, compared to 11.6% in 1995.

Goal 4, a two-thirds reduction in the under-five mortality rate by 2015, appears to still be possible. Some regions, such as North Africa and Eastern Asia, have already achieved a 68% reduction in under-five deaths. Most regions had reductions of at least 50% by 2009. This target could be attainable if special efforts are made to address undernutrition, postnatal care, and three leading causes of childhood death in developing countries: pneumonia, diarrhea, and malaria.

Goal 5 has two targets: to reduce maternal mortality by three-quarters and to provide universal access to reproductive health by 2015. For developing countries overall, the maternal mortality ratio dropped 34% between 1990 and 2008. At least 90 countries have shown reductions of 40% or greater; however, the goal of 75% reduction in maternal mortality by 2015 remains a huge challenge. Some key improvements would be increased access to trained health-care workers during delivery and increased access to education and birth control for women. The second target, universal access to reproductive health, remains far off. On a positive note, the proportion of pregnant women attended at least once during a pregnancy increased from 64% in 1990 to 81% in 2009. However, the proportion of pregnant women receiving the recommended number of

associated with 60 indicators by which progress could be monitored. These goals united and refocused many of the commitments made by UN conferences of the 1990s, aimed at a 2015 deadline. The MDGs were presented in a concise and understandable format, facilitating the global exchange of information via the Internet and other media.

Four of the eight MDGs (Figure 10-20) apply to the population-related issues of this chapter. This emphasizes that the UN regards human population growth as a key factor underlying many environmental problems. It also reflects the idea that if people, particularly women, are educated and empowered, and if health is assured, then many of the factors that drive unregulated population growth will be removed.

Take a close look at each of the goals and targets in Figure 10-20. Now look back at some of the problems that we described earlier in this chapter. Recall that education and family planning have been shown to help people in Iran and other developing nations to gain control over their reproduction (pp. 209–210). Recall that woman have been relatively powerless to control their lives and reproduction (pp. 208–210) and that various measures of mortality have been high in developing nations (Figures 10-3 and 10-7; pp. 197 and 199) necessitating large families as insurance against high death rates. No wonder the UN has focused on these priorities in attempting to curb rapid population growth.

four visits is only about 50%. Furthermore, the number of reproductive-age women is increasing and funding is not keeping pace (UN, 2011).

The above Millennium Development Goals are causing governments to move in the right directions, but to be successful all of these goals will require more money. The UN position on funding is that it will have to be provided by developed nations and by strategies such as forgiving the debts of developing nations. These funding and governance aspects of the MDGs will be addressed in Chapters 26 (Economics, Environment, and Sustainability) and 27 (Politics, Environment, and Sustainability).

Our concluding message in this chapter is that issues of environmental sustainability are heavily impacted by human population growth. In order to be able to solve these issues, it is important for us to help developing nations deal with their development and population-regulation hurdles in a timely fashion, before the expense of this assistance grows beyond our financial means.

Our numbers expand but Earth's natural systems do not.

LESTER R. BROWN

CHAPTER REVIEW

1. Review the Key Questions for this chapter on p. 196. Compare the population-regulation schemes pursued by Thailand, China, India, and Iran. What are the pros and cons of each? Explain.

2. List three factors that account for the rapid growth of the world's human population over the past 200 years. How many of us are likely to be here in 2050? What will the world be like?

3. What is the *cultural carrying capacity* of a population? How should we apply this concept in considering the question of whether the Earth is overpopulated?

4. List four variables that affect the *population change* of an area and write an equation showing how they are related. Distinguish between *crude birth rate* and *crude death rate*. What five countries had the largest numbers of people in 2011?

5. What is *fertility rate?* Distinguish between *replacement-level fertility rate* and *total fertility rate (TFR)*. Explain why reaching the replacement-level fertility rate will not stop global population growth until about 50 years have passed (assuming that death rates do not rise).

6. Describe population growth in Canada, the United States, India, and China. Which of these countries do you consider overpopulated? Why?

7. List ten factors that can affect the birth rate and death rate of a country. Distinguish between *life expectancy* and *infant mortality rate* and explain how they affect the population size of a country. Why does the United States have a lower life expectancy and higher infant mortality rate than Canada? What is *migration* and how does it relate to population growth in Canada?

8. What is the *age structure* of a population? Explain how it affects population growth and economic growth. What is a *baby boom*? What are some problems related to an aging population?

9. What is the *demographic transition* and what are its four stages? What factors could hinder some developing countries from making this transition? Why do some analysts think that demographic transition will not function as well for developing nations as it did for developed nations? What is *family planning?* Describe the roles of family planning, reducing poverty, and elevating the status of women in slowing population growth.

10. How well do you think the four *Millennium Development Goals* outlined at the end of the chapter will work? How could they be improved? Go online and find out more about how well the MDGs are working.

CRITICAL THINKING

1. Why is it rational for a poor couple in a developing country such as India to have four or five children? What changes might lead such a couple to consider their behaviour irrational?

2. Choose what you consider to be a major local, national, or global environmental problem, and describe the role of population growth in this problem. Compare your answer with those of your classmates.

3. Do you believe that Canada's population is too high? What about the population of the province where you live? As part of your answer, refer to Canada's *carrying capacity* and its *cultural carrying capacity*, and explain the differences between the two.

4. Should everyone have the right to have as many children as they want? Explain.

5. Some people have proposed that the Earth could solve its population problem by shipping people off to space colonies, each containing about 10 000 people. Assuming we could build such large-scale, self-sustaining space stations, how many people would have to be shipped off each day to provide living spaces for the 83 million people added to the Earth's population this year? Current space shuttles can handle about 6–8 passengers. If this capacity could be increased to 100 passengers per shuttle, how many shuttles would have to be launched per day to offset the 83 million people added this year? According to your calculations, determine whether this proposal is a logical solution to the Earth's population problem.

6. Some people believe the most important goal is to sharply reduce the rate of population growth in developing countries, where 98% of the world's population growth is expected to take place. Some people in developing countries agree that population growth in these countries can cause local environmental problems. But they contend that the most serious environmental problem the world faces is disruption of the global life-support system for the human species by high levels of resource consumption per person in developed countries, which use 80% of the world's resources. What is your view on this issue? Explain.

7. Suppose the cloning of human beings becomes possible without any serious health effects for cloned individuals. What effect might this have on the world's population size and growth rate? Explain.

8. Congratulations! You are in charge of the world. List the three most important features of your population policy.

PROJECTS

1. Do some research aimed at the objective of halving the world's population growth rate within the next 20 years. Develop a detailed plan that would achieve this goal, including any differences between policies in developing countries and those in developed countries. Justify each part of your plan. Try to anticipate what problems you might face in implementing the plan, and devise strategies for dealing with these problems.

2. Prepare an age structure diagram for your community. Use the diagram to project future population growth and economic and social problems.

3. Use the library or the Internet to learn more about the eight Millennium Development Goals and the progress that has been achieved so far.

4. Visit the website of the Population Reference Bureau (http://www.prb.org) and other websites mentioned in this chapter to learn more about populations and demography.

ECOLOGICAL FOOTPRINT ANALYSIS

The chart below shows selected population data for two different countries, A and B.

	Country A	Country B
Population (millions)	144	82
Crude birth rate	43	8
Crude death rate	18	10
Infant mortality rate	100	3.8
Total fertility rate	5.9	1.3
Percentage of population under 15 years old	45	14
Percentage of population older than 65 years	3	19
Average life expectancy at birth	47	79
Percentage urban	44	75

1. Calculate the rates of natural increase for the populations of Country A and Country B. From the rates of natural increase and the data in the table, suggest whether A and B are developed or developing countries, and explain the reasons for your answers.

2. Describe where each of the two countries may be in terms of their stage in the demographic transition (Figure 10-17, p. 208). Discuss factors that could hinder Country A from progressing to later stages in the demographic transition.

3. Explain how the percentage of people under 15 years of age in Country A and in Country B could affect the per capita and total ecological footprints of each country.

Sustaining Terrestrial Biodiversity: Managing and Protecting Ecosystems

Clayoquot Sound, B.C.

Clayoquot ("klak-wot") Sound is a grouping of inlets on the west coast of Vancouver Island, British Columbia (Figure 11-1), with a largely forested watershed of about 265 000 hectares (655 000 acres) (http://focs.ca/about/clayoquot-sound/). The area is rich in forest values, most notably old-growth forest that is an outstanding example of the coastal temperate rain forest biome. This forest type covers less than 0.2% of the world's land surface, yet 18–25% of this forest is in British Columbia, with Clayoquot Sound encompassing some of the best of it. Other forest values include its importance as a First Nations heritage site, spectacular scenery, commercial fishery, and timber industry.

Long-standing disputes have taken place over this land. In 1993, the situation intensified as thousands of concerned people, including First Nations, local citizens, and environmentalists from all over the world, assembled in Clayoquot Sound to protest a decision by the B.C. government to allow more than two-thirds of the area to be logged. After a dramatic standoff that resulted in the arrest of more than 850 protestors, the government established the Clayoquot Sound Scientific Panel to study the situation and make recommendations.

In 1995, the panel released a report that included 120 recommendations about how the Clayoquot Sound area should be managed. The report recommended, for example, that ecological assessments should be done before any logging takes place in watersheds that are currently untouched; harvest levels should be based on careful watershed planning; key elements of the forest such as snags, cavity trees, and woody debris should be left in place; and some areas of old-growth trees should be set aside from logging (Clayoquot Sound Scientific Panel, 1995).

In 1996, a major timber company set up a joint venture called Iisaak Forest Resources with the local First Nations people. The company proposed to do some logging in the area but strictly in the sustainable ways recommended by the scientific panel.

In 2000, an area of 350 000 hectares (865 000 acres) that included both terrestrial and marine components was established as a United Nations Educational, Scientific and Cultural Organization (UNESCO) biosphere reserve (p. 242). While this designation does not offer any additional regulation or protection, it acknowledges the importance of the place and is a recognition of the community's sustainable development goals. The story seemed to have reached a happy ending. However, in 2006 Clayoquot Sound was in the news again. A joint government–First Nations board had agreed to allow eight new watershed management plans involving road building and logging, alarming the public and prompting renewed scrutiny of management in the area.

The story at Clayoquot Sound continues to unfold. The area now attracts 1 million visitors every year who come to

(continued)

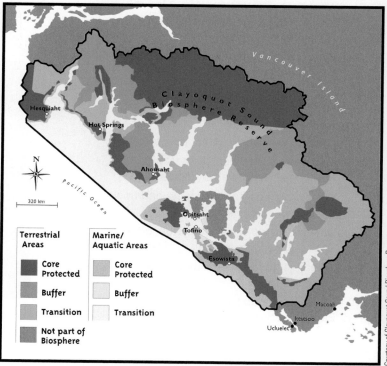

FIGURE 11-1 The map shows the core, buffer, and transition zones of Clayoquot Sound Biosphere Reserve in British Columbia. (From Clayoquot Biosphere Trust, http://clayoquotbiosphere.org/web/)

Courtesy of Clayoquot Sound Biosphere Reserve.

enjoy the sound for its beauty and whale-watching and kayaking opportunities. Ecotourism, fishing, and aquaculture are now driving the local economy more than logging. However, tensions remain because logging continues, and some members of the public are monitoring those operations aggressively. Developments and controversies can be tracked by checking the website of the Friends of Clayoquot Sound for recent news (http://focs.ca/news/).

SELF CHECK

See Clayoquot Sound with your own eyes! If you enter words such as "Clayoquot AND tour AND video" into a search engine, you will find many short, entertaining videos that illustrate some of the exciting and beautiful features of Clayoquot Sound. You can also find many photo sites featuring Clayoquot Sound and the biosphere reserve, such as the one at http://www.oceanlight.com/lightbox.php.

Canada's very rich natural hertage can only be saved for posterity if the people of Canada alive today really want it to be saved.

HRH Prince Philip, Duke of Edinburgh, former president of WWF-International

CHAPTER PURPOSE AND QUESTIONS

Chapter 11 discusses some of the pressures on the Earth's biodiversity, as well as strategies for protecting and sustaining it. The chapter addresses the following questions:

11-1   How have human activities affected the Earth's biodiversity?

11-2   What is conservation biology? What role does bioinformatics play in helping sustain biodiversity?

11-3   What are the major types of public lands in Canada, and how are they used?

11-4   Why are forest resources important, and how are they used, managed, and sustained?

11-5   What is the status of Canada's forests?

11-6   How serious is tropical deforestation, and how can we help sustain tropical forests?

11-7   What problems do parks face, and how should we manage them?

11-8   How should we establish, design, protect, and manage terrestrial nature reserves?

11-9   What is ecological restoration, and why is it important?

11-10 What can we do to help sustain the Earth's biodiversity?

11-1   HUMAN IMPACTS ON TERRESTRIAL BIODIVERSITY

How Have Human Activities Affected Global Biodiversity? Increasing Our Ecological Footprint

We have depleted and degraded some of the Earth's biodiversity, and these threats are expected to increase.

Figure 11-2 lists factors that tend to increase or decrease biodiversity. Many of our activities decrease biodiversity (Figure 11-3). According to biodiversity expert Edward O. Wilson, "The natural world is everywhere disappearing before our eyes—cut to pieces, mowed down, plowed under, gobbled up, replaced by human artifacts."

Consider a few examples of how human activities have decreased and degraded the Earth's terrestrial biodiversity. According to the results of a 2008 study on the impact of the human ecological footprint on the Earth's land (Figure 9-12, p. 189), we have disturbed to some extent at least half and probably about 83% of the Earth's land surface (excluding Antarctica and Greenland).

About 82% of temperate deciduous forests have been cleared, fragmented, and dominated because their soils and climate are very favourable for growing food and urban development. Chaparral and thorn scrub, temperate grasslands, temperate rain forests, and tropical dry forests have also been greatly disturbed by human activities. Tundra, tropical deserts,

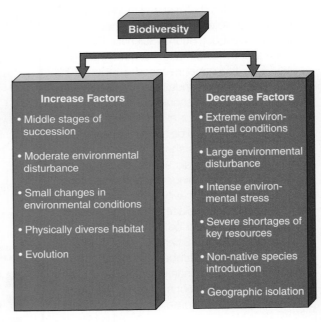

FIGURE 11-2 Factors that tend to increase or decrease the Earth's biodiversity.

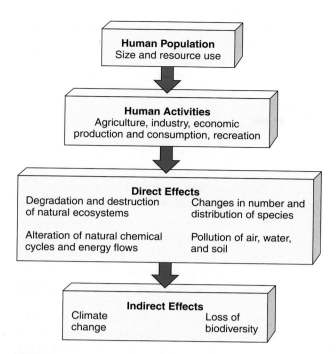

FIGURE 11-3 Natural capital degradation: major connections between human activities and the Earth's biodiversity.

and land covered with ice are the least disturbed biomes because their harsh climates and poor soils make them unappealing to most human activities.

In Canada, many of the wetlands across the country were lost to agriculture and drainage before wetland conservation programs began (p. 296). Certain critical habitats had all but disappeared before efforts were made to save the remainder; for instance, only about 1% of the tallgrass prairie ecoregion currently remains. The Carolinian forest of southern Ontario has been reduced to a few remnants in places like Pelee National Park. As well, invasive species (such as emerald ash borers and gypsy moths) are damaging forests and causing other sorts of ecosystem disruptions.

By some estimates, humans use, waste, or destroy about 10–55% of the net primary productivity of the planet's terrestrial ecosystems. And biologists estimate that the current global extinction rate of species is at least 100 times and probably 1 000 to 10 000 times what it was before humans existed.

These threats to the world's biodiversity are projected to increase sharply by 2018 (Figure 11-4). Study this figure carefully.

Figure 11-5 (p. 218) outlines the goals, strategies, and tactics for preserving and restoring the Earth's terrestrial ecosystems (as discussed in this chapter) and preventing the premature extinction of species (as discussed in Chapter 12). Sustaining aquatic diversity is discussed in Chapter 13.

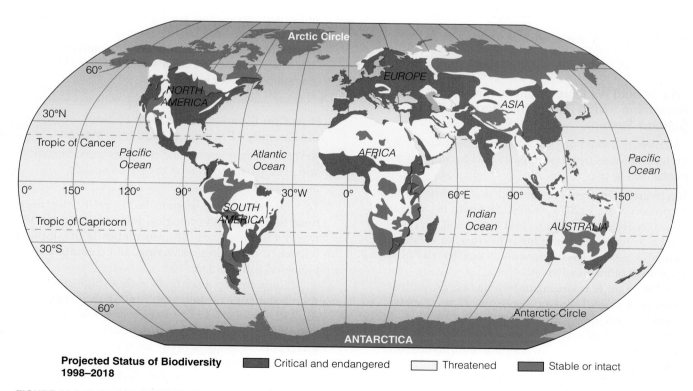

Projected Status of Biodiversity 1998–2018 ■ Critical and endangered □ Threatened ■ Stable or intact

FIGURE 11-4 Natural capital degradation: projected status of the Earth's biodiversity between 1998 and 2018. (Data from World Resources Institute, World Conservation Monitoring Center, and Conservation International)

Sustaining Terrestrial Biodiversity: Managing and Protecting Ecosystems

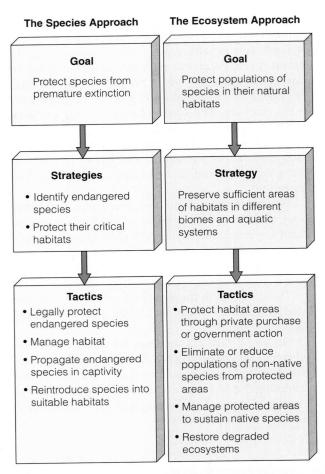

The Species Approach

Goal
Protect species from premature extinction

↓

Strategies
- Identify endangered species
- Protect their critical habitats

↓

Tactics
- Legally protect endangered species
- Manage habitat
- Propagate endangered species in captivity
- Reintroduce species into suitable habitats

The Ecosystem Approach

Goal
Protect populations of species in their natural habitats

↓

Strategy
Preserve sufficient areas of habitats in different biomes and aquatic systems

↓

Tactics
- Protect habitat areas through private purchase or government action
- Eliminate or reduce populations of non-native species from protected areas
- Manage protected areas to sustain native species
- Restore degraded ecosystems

FIGURE 11-5 Solutions: goals, strategies, and tactics for protecting biodiversity.

Why Should We Care about Biodiversity? Sustaining a Vital Part of the World's Life Support System

Biodiversity should be protected from degradation by human activities because it exists and because of its usefulness to us.

Biodiversity researchers contend that we should act to preserve the Earth's overall diversity because its genes, species, ecosystems, and ecological processes have two types of value. One is **intrinsic** or **existence value** because these components of biodiversity exist, regardless of their use to us.

The other is **instrumental value** because of their usefulness to us. There are two major types of instrumental values. One consists of *use values* that benefit us in the form of economic goods and services, ecological services, recreation, scientific information, and preserving options for such uses in the future.

Another type consists of *nonuse values*. One is the *existence value* in knowing that a redwood forest, wilderness, or endangered species exists, even if we will never see it or get direct use from it. *Aesthetic value* is another nonuse value because many people appreciate a tree, forest, wild species, or vista because of its beauty. *Bequest value* is a third type of nonuse value. It is based on a willingness of some people to pay to protect some forms of natural capital for use by future generations.

11-2 CONSERVATION BIOLOGY

What Is Conservation Biology? Emergency Action to Sustain Biodiversity

Conservation biology uses rapid response strategies to stem the loss and degradation of the world's biodiversity.

Conservation biology is a multidisciplinary science that originated in the 1970s. Its goal is to use emergency responses to slow down the rate at which we are destroying and degrading the Earth's biodiversity. Conservation biologists identify the most endangered and species-rich ecosystems, called *hot spots*. They then send in Rapid Assessment Teams of biologists to evaluate the situations, make recommendations, and take emergency action to stem the loss of biodiversity in such areas.

Conservation biology is based on Aldo Leopold's ethical principle that something is right when it tends to maintain the Earth's life-support systems for us and other species and wrong when it does not. The Society of Conservation Biology is now one of the fastest growing of all scientific societies and there are a dozen new scientific journals in this field. Have you considered a career in this field?

How Can Bioinformatics Help Protect Biodiversity? Providing Good Information

Bioinformatics analyzes and provides basic biological and ecological information to help us sustain biodiversity.

To understand and sustain biodiversity, we need basic biological and ecological information about the world's wild species. **Bioinformatics** is the applied science of managing, analyzing, and communicating biological information.

Bioinformatics uses tools such as high-resolution digitized images to photograph and analyze specimens of all known species and any new ones that are identified. It also builds computer databases to hold these images, DNA sequences for identifying bacteria and other microorganisms, and other biological information about the world's species and ecosystems. Such information is readily available through the Internet to anyone who wants it (see http://www.scq.ubc.ca/what-is-bioinformatics/).

11-3 PUBLIC LANDS IN CANADA

What Are the Major Types of Public Lands? Land for Current and Future Generations

More than 90% of the land in Canada consists of publicly owned national forests, resource lands, parks, wildlife refuges, and protected wilderness areas.

With 93% of its land under public ownership, Canada as a whole truly belongs to its citizens. A large percentage of the publicly owned land in Canada is used for resource extraction, recreation, education, research, and wildlife conservation. Many of these public lands are forested and, as such, contain much of the country's biodiversity.

The federal government manages 16% of Canada's forested land. Federal lands consist of national parks, national marine conservation areas, wildlife refuges, bird sanctuaries, and other protected areas.

Provincial and territorial governments manage 77% of Canada's public lands. These holdings include Crown lands used to grow forests and to extract other resources. There are also hundreds of provincial parks and a wide assortment of wildlife refuges.

The biomes that make up Canada are remarkably diverse, ranging from arctic tundra, to deciduous forest, to prairie grassland (Chapter 6). More precisely, Canada's biomes can be divided into ecozones with more homogeneous characteristics (Figure 11-6). On an even finer scale, Parks Canada has identified

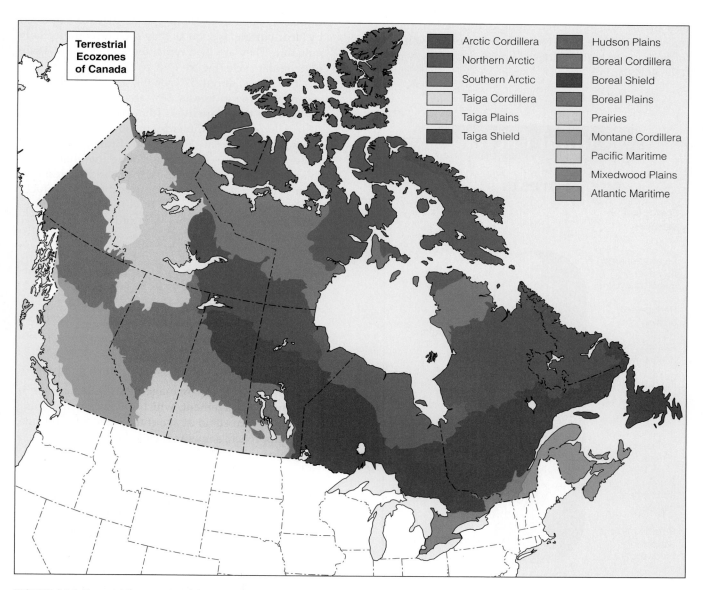

Terrestrial Ecozones of Canada

Arctic Cordillera	Hudson Plains
Northern Arctic	Boreal Cordillera
Southern Arctic	Boreal Shield
Taiga Cordillera	Boreal Plains
Taiga Plains	Prairies
Taiga Shield	Montane Cordillera
	Pacific Maritime
	Mixedwood Plains
	Atlantic Maritime

FIGURE 11-6 Terrestrial ecozones of Canada. (Based on Environment Canada, Terrestrial Ecozones of Canada, http://www.ec.gc.ca/soer-ree/English/vignettes/Terrestrial/terr.cfm)

39 natural regions in Canada that should be represented in the country's national parks system (p. 235).

11-4 MANAGING AND SUSTAINING FORESTS

What Are the Major Types of Forests? Old-Growth, Second-Growth, and Tree Plantations

Some forests have not been disturbed by human activities for several hundred years, others have grown back after being cut, and some consist of planted stands of a particular tree species.

Forests with at least 10% tree cover occupy about 30% of the Earth's land surface (excluding Greenland and Antarctica). Figure 6-18 (p. 122) shows the distribution of the world's boreal, temperate, and tropical forests. These forests provide many important values, in the form of both ecological and economic services (Figure 11-7).

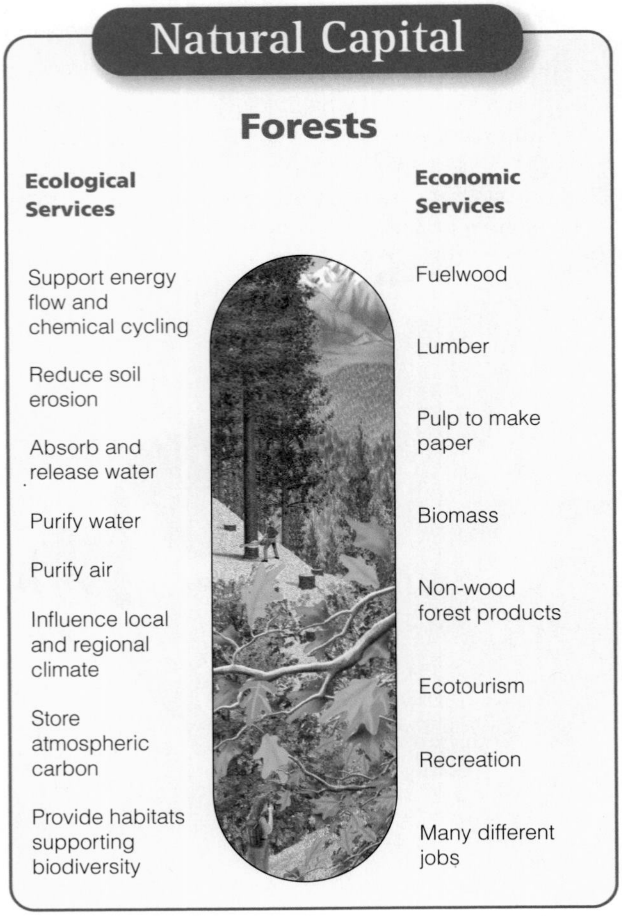

Natural Capital

Forests

Ecological Services	Economic Services
Support energy flow and chemical cycling	Fuelwood
Reduce soil erosion	Lumber
Absorb and release water	Pulp to make paper
Purify water	Biomass
Purify air	
Influence local and regional climate	Non-wood forest products
Store atmospheric carbon	Ecotourism
	Recreation
Provide habitats supporting biodiversity	Many different jobs

FIGURE 11-7 Natural capital: Forests provide many values, including ecological and economic services.

Forest managers and ecologists classify forests into three major types based on age and structure. One type is an **old-growth forest:** an uncut forest or regenerated forest that has not been seriously disturbed by human activities or natural disasters for at least several hundred years. Old-growth forests are storehouses of biodiversity because they provide ecological niches for a multitude of wildlife species (Figure 6-31, p. 132).

A second type is a **second-growth forest:** a stand of trees resulting from secondary ecological succession (Figure 8-14, p. 173). Forests like this develop after the trees in an area have been removed by *human activities* (such as clear-cutting for timber or conversion to cropland) or by *natural forces* (such as fire, hurricanes, or volcanic eruption).

A **tree plantation,** also called a **tree farm,** is a third type (see photo on p. viii). It is a managed tract with uniformly aged trees of one species that are harvested by clear-cutting as soon as they become commercially valuable. They are then replanted and clear-cut again in a regular cycle (Figure 11-8, p. 221).

Currently, about 57% of the world's forests are secondary-growth forests, 36% are old-growth forests, and 7% are tree plantations (that produce about one-fifth of the world's commercial wood). Five countries—Canada, the Russian Federation, Brazil, the United States, and China—account for more than half of the total forest area. About 30% of the world's forests are used to produce wood and non-wood forest products. The remaining forest areas have purposes such as multiple-use (24%), conservation and protection (20%), social services (4%), and other uses (23%) (FAO, 2010).

What Are the Major Types of Forest Management? Simple Tree Plantations and Diverse Forests

Some forests consist of one or two species of commercially important tree species that are cut down and replanted, and others contain diverse tree species harvested individually or in small groups.

There are two forest management systems. One is **even-aged management,** which involves maintaining trees in a given stand at about the same age and size. In this approach, sometimes called *industrial forestry,* a simplified *tree plantation* replaces a biologically diverse old-growth or second-growth forest. The plantation consists of one or two fast-growing and economically desirable species that can be harvested every 6–10 years, depending on the species (Figure 11-8).

A second type is **uneven-aged management,** which involves maintaining a variety of tree species in a stand at many ages and sizes to foster natural regeneration. Here the goals are biological diversity; long-term sustainable production of high-quality timber; selective cutting of individual mature or intermediate-aged

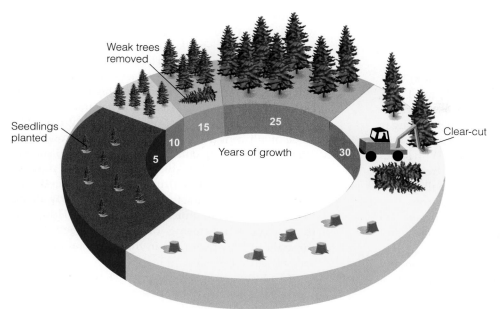

Weak trees removed

Seedlings planted

Clear-cut

Years of growth

FIGURE 11-8 Short (25- to 30-year) rotation cycle of cutting and regrowth of a monoculture tree plantation in modern industrial forestry. In tropical countries, where trees can grow more rapidly year-round, the rotation cycle can be 6–10 years.

trees; and **multiple uses** of the forest for timber, wildlife, watershed protection, and recreation.

The fate of the world's remaining forests will be decided mostly by governments, which own about 80% of the remaining forests in developing countries. Governments in both developing and developed countries are under conflicting pressures from those wanting to log forests and convert them to agricultural land and urban development and conservationists who want to protect them—especially the world's remaining old-growth forests.

According to a study by the World Wildlife Fund, intensive but sustainable management of as little as one-fifth of the world's forests—an area twice the size of India—could meet the world's current and future demand for commercial wood and fibre. This intensive use of the world's tree plantations and some of its secondary forests would leave the world's remaining old-growth forest untouched.

How Are Trees Harvested and Regenerated? Using a Variety of Silvicultural Methods

Silvicultural methods of harvesting and regenerating trees should be chosen to suit the forest.

Once plans have been formulated and approved, the first concrete step in forest management is to build roads for access and timber removal. Even carefully designed logging roads have a number of harmful effects (Figure 11-9). They include increased erosion and sediment runoff into waterways, habitat fragmentation, and biodiversity loss. Logging roads also expose forests to invasion by non-native pests, diseases, and wildlife species. They also open once-inaccessible forests to farmers, miners, ranchers, hunters, and off-road vehicle users. After an area has been made accessible by a network of logging roads, it can no longer be considered a wilderness.

Foresters then harvest and regenerate the forest using a variety of **silvicultural** (from the Latin words

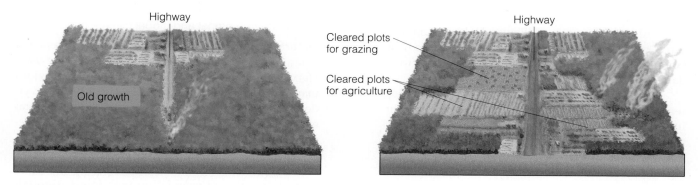

Highway

Old growth

Highway

Cleared plots for grazing

Cleared plots for agriculture

FIGURE 11-9 Natural capital degradation: building roads into previously inaccessible forests facilitates timber extraction but also paves the way to their fragmentation, destruction, and degradation.

silvi, "forest," and *culture*, "to grow") methods. Since a given method of harvesting is closely associated with the type of regeneration that will follow, foresters plan their operations in terms of the *silvicultural systems* (harvesting plus regeneration methods) that they will use in different types of forest (Figure 11-10, p. 223). **Selection cutting** is an appropriate silvicultural system for light-intolerant trees, such as sugar maples and yellow birches, which regenerate best under the shelter of an established canopy. With selection cutting, intermediate-aged or mature trees in an uneven-aged forest are cut singly or in small groups (Figure 11-10a). Selection cutting reduces crowding, encourages growth of younger trees, maintains an uneven-aged stand of trees of different species, and allows natural regeneration from surrounding trees. It can also help protect the site from soil erosion and wind damage, remove diseased trees, and allow a forest to be used for multiple purposes.

Some loggers use an extreme form of selective cutting called *high grading* to selectively cut trees in tropical forests. It involves cutting and removing only the largest and best specimens of the most desirable species. Studies show that for every large tree cut down, 16 or 17 other trees are damaged or pulled down because a network of vines usually connects the trees in tropical forest canopies. This reduction of the forest canopy causes the forest floor to become warmer, drier, and more flammable and increases erosion of the forest's thin and usually nutrient-poor soil.

Some trees, such as red oaks and white pines, grow best in moderate sunlight. A silvicultural system appropriate for these trees is **shelterwood cutting**, which removes trees in a series of cuts that are spaced over time. For example, the first cut might remove one-third of the trees, meanwhile thinning the canopy and stimulating the growth of seedlings and young trees. A second cut, 10 years later, might remove another third of the trees, again creating opportunities for seedlings and young trees to grow. After another 10 years, the final one-third of the original trees might be harvested, but by then the forest would consist of younger trees that had been given opportunities to grow 10 and 20 years ago (Figure 11-10b). Note that forest cover was in place continuously, wildlife habitats remained, and the soil was never laid bare to be damaged by erosion.

Some trees, such as black spruce and red pines, regenerate best in conditions allowing brighter light. In this type of forest, a form of **clear-cutting** would typically be chosen. Clear-cutting removes all the trees from an area in a single cutting (Figure 11-10d). Figure 11-11 lists some of the advantages and disadvantages commonly associated with clear-cuts. However, there are variables to be considered when assessing the pros and cons of a clear-cut. You can imagine that a huge open clear-cut on a mountainside would pose a much higher risk of soil erosion than would a series of smaller meadow-like clear-cuts on level ground. Another variable to consider is the shape of the clear-cut. When foresters harvest trees in a series of long, thin clear-cuts, this is called **strip cutting** (Figure 11-10e). This choice has the advantage of regenerating seedlings relatively easily from the seeds of adjacent trees, and the forest that grows back after a series of strip cuts can resemble natural succession (compare Figure 11-10e with Figure 8-14, p. 173).

Yet another silvicultural system is **seed-tree cutting**. In this case, the foresters remove nearly all the trees in one cutting, much like a clear-cut. However, they leave a scattering of mature "seed trees" throughout the area to aid in the regeneration of the forest (Figure 11-10c).

In addition to *natural regeneration*, whereby a forest perpetuates itself without assistance, there is *human-assisted natural regeneration*. This can be accomplished in various ways such as by making appropriate silvicultural choices that favour the regeneration of a given type of forest. As well, *enrichment planting* uses human effort to increase the density of a regenerating forest by planting seedlings. For more information about silviculture, see Bowes (2010) and Ministry of Natural Resources (2011).

SELF CHECK

Test yourself. If you were obliged to harvest timber from light-loving pine forests along a steep mountainside, which silvicultural method would you choose?

Arguments could be made for (i) strip cutting at right angles to the slope, or (ii) selection cutting single trees or small groups of trees. It would depend on many factors such as size and density of trees, light levels, slope, and so on.

What Are the Harmful Environmental Effects of Deforestation? Biodiversity Loss and Climate Change

Cutting down large forest areas reduces biodiversity and the ecological services forests provide and can contribute to regional and global climate change.

Deforestation is the temporary or permanent removal of large expanses of forest for agriculture or other uses. Harvesting timber and fuelwood from forests provides many economic benefits (Figure 11-7, right). However, deforestation can have many harmful environmental effects (Figure 11-12) that can reduce the ecological services provided by forests (Figure 11-7, left).

If left alone long enough, forests that have been logged or converted to cropland can revert to second-growth and even old-growth forests through secondary ecological succession. But this is not always the case. If deforestation occurs over a large enough

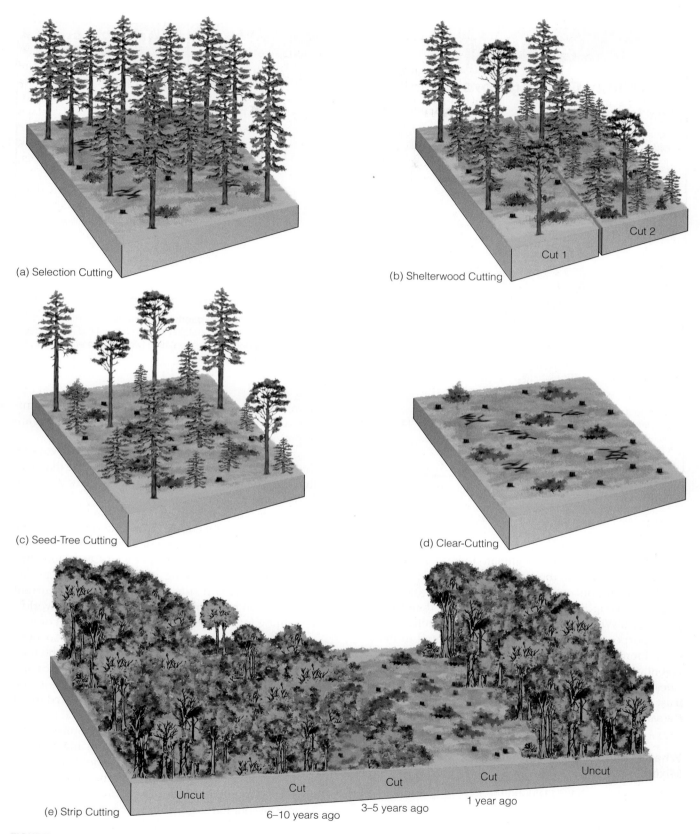

(a) Selection Cutting

(b) Shelterwood Cutting

Cut 1

Cut 2

(c) Seed-Tree Cutting

(d) Clear-Cutting

(e) Strip Cutting

Uncut

Cut

Cut

Cut

Uncut

6–10 years ago

3–5 years ago

1 year ago

FIGURE 11-10 Silvicultural systems.

Trade-Offs

Clear-Cutting Forests

Advantages	Disadvantages
Higher timber yields	Reduces biodiversity
Maximum economic return in shortest time	Disrupts ecosystem processes
Can reforest with genetically improved fast-growing trees	Destroys and fragments some wildlife habitats
Short time to establish new stand of trees	Leaves moderate to large openings
Needs less skill and planning	Increases soil erosion
Best way to harvest tree plantations	Increases sediment water pollution and flooding when done on steep slopes
Good for tree species needing full or moderate sunlight for growth	Eliminates most recreational value for several decades

FIGURE 11-11 Trade-offs: advantages and disadvantages of clear-cutting forests. Pick the single advantage and disadvantage that you think are the most important.

Natural Capital Degradation

Deforestation

- Decreased soil fertility from erosion
- Runoff of eroded soil into aquatic systems
- Premature extinction of species with specialized niches
- Loss of habitat for migratory species such as birds and butterflies
- Regional climate change from extensive clearing
- Release of CO_2 into atmosphere from burning and tree decay
- Accelerated flooding

FIGURE 11-12 Natural capital degradation: harmful environmental effects of deforestation that can reduce the ecological services provided by forests. Which two of these effects do you think are the most serious?

area, it can cause a region's climate to become hotter and drier and prevent the return of a forest.

Deforestation can also contribute to projected global warming if trees are removed faster than they grow back. When forests are cleared for agriculture or other purposes and burned, the carbon stored in the trees' biomass is released into the atmosphere as the greenhouse gas carbon dioxide (CO_2). Research indicates that when an old-growth forest is cut, it takes at least 200 years for a replacement forest to accumulate the same amount of carbon stored in the original forest.

What Is Happening to the World's Forests? Mixed News

Human activities have reduced the Earth's forest cover by about 50%, and deforestation is continuing at a fairly rapid rate, except in most temperate forests in North America and Europe.

Global estimates of forest cover change are difficult to make because of lack of satellite and radar data, unmonitored land-use change, and different definitions of what constitutes a forest. But forest surveys are improving because of better satellite data.

Here are two pieces of *bad news. First,* surveys by the World Resources Institute (WRI) indicate that over the past 8 000 years human activities have reduced the Earth's original forest cover by about 50%.

Second, surveys by the UN Food and Agricultural Organization (FAO) and the World Resources Institute indicate that the global rate of forest cover loss from 2000 to 2016 averaged 0.13% per year. Over four-fifths of these losses are taking place in the tropics. The World Resources Institute estimates that if current deforestation rates continue, about 40% of the world's remaining intact forests will have been logged or converted to other uses within 10–20 years, if not sooner.

Here are two pieces of *good news. First,* the total area of many temperate forests in North America and Europe has increased slightly because of reforestation from secondary ecological succession on cleared forest areas and abandoned croplands.

Second, some of the cut areas of tropical forest have increased tree cover from regrowth and planting of tree plantations. But ecologists do not believe that tree plantations with their much lower biodiversity should be counted as forest any more than croplands should be counted as grassland. According to ecologist Michael L. Rosenzweig, "Forest plantations are just cornfields whose stalks have gotten very tall and turned to wood. They display nothing of the majesty of natural forests."

Should there be a global effort to reduce the cutting of old-growth forests? Give reasons for your answer. How would this global effort be accomplished in Canada? In tropical countries?

How Much Are the World's Ecological Services Worth? Putting a Price Tag on Mother Nature's Services

The huge economic value of the ecological services provided by the world's forests and other ecosystems is rarely counted in making decisions about how to use these ecosystems.

Currently forests are valued mostly for their economic services (Figure 11-7, right). But suppose we estimate and take into account the ecological services provided by forests (Figure 11-7, left). Then researchers say that the economic value of their long-term ecological services would be much greater than their short-term economic services.

In 1997, a team of ecologists, economists, and geographers attempted to estimate the monetary worth of the Earth's natural ecological services. According to this crude appraisal led by ecological economist Robert Costanza of the University of Vermont, the economic value of income from the Earth's ecological services is at least $36 trillion (U.S.) per year! This is fairly close to the $42 trillion value of all of the goods and services produced throughout the world in 2004. To provide an annual natural income of $36 trillion per year, the world's natural capital would have a value of at least $500 trillion—an average of about $73 000 for each person on Earth!

Based on these estimates, *biodiversity is the world's biggest financial asset.* But unless this natural asset is given a financial value that is included in evaluating how we use forests and other ecological resources, it will be used unsustainably and destroyed or degraded for short-term profit.

To estimate the monetary values of the ecological services provided by the world's natural capital, the researchers divided the Earth's surface into 16 biomes (Figure 6-18, p. 122) and aquatic life zones. They omitted deserts and tundra because of a lack of data. Then they agreed on a list of 17 goods and services provided by nature and sifted through more than 100 studies that attempted to put a dollar value on such services in the 16 different types of ecosystems.

According to this appraisal, the world's forests provide us with ecological services worth about $4.7 trillion (U.S.) per year—equal in value to about one-tenth of all of the goods and services produced in the world annually.

The researchers say their estimates could easily be too low by a factor of 10 to 1 million or more. For example, their calculations included only estimates of the ecosystem services themselves, not the natural capital that generates them. They also omitted the value of nonrenewable minerals and fuels.

They hope such estimates will call people's attention to three important facts. The Earth's ecosystem services are essential for all humans and their economies, their economic value is huge, and they are an ongoing source of ecological income as long as they are used sustainably.

Why have we not changed our accounting system to reflect these losses? One reason is that economic savings provided by conserving nature benefit everyone now and in the future, whereas profits made by exploiting nature are immediate and benefit a relatively small group of individuals. A second reason is that many current government subsidies and tax incentives support destruction and degradation of forests and other ecosystems for short-term economic gain. We get more of what we reward.

How Can We Manage Forests More Sustainably? Making Sustaining Forests Profitable

We can use forests more sustainably by including the economic value of their ecological services, harvesting trees no faster than they are replenished, and protecting old-growth and vulnerable areas.

Biodiversity researchers and a growing number of foresters call for more sustainable forest management. Figure 11-13 lists ways to do this. Which two of these solutions do you believe are most important?

Solutions

Sustainable Forestry

- Grow more timber on long rotations
- Rely more on selection cutting and strip cutting
- No clear-cutting, seed-tree, or shelterwood cutting on steeply sloped land
- No fragmentation of remaining large blocks of forest
- Sharply reduce road building into uncut forest areas
- Leave most standing dead trees and fallen timber for wildlife habitat and nutrient recycling
- Certify timber grown by sustainable methods
- Include ecological services of trees and forests in estimating economic value

FIGURE 11-13 Solutions: ways to manage forests more sustainably.

Some conservation biologists suggest four ways to estimate how much of the world's remaining forests to protect. *First,* include estimates of the economic value of their ecological services in all decisions. *Second,* protect enough forest so that the rate of forest loss and degradation by human and natural factors in a particular area is balanced by the rate of forest renewal. *Third,* identify and protect forest areas that are centres of biodiversity and that are threatened by economic development. *Fourth,* establish and use methods to evaluate timber that has been grown sustainably, as discussed below.

Solutions: How Can We Certify Sustainably Grown Timber? Set Standards and Bring in Outside Evaluators

Organizations have developed standards for certifying that timber has been harvested sustainably and that wood products have been produced from sustainably harvested timber.

Certifying forests is a way of assuring the public that forest products such as wood and wood pulp have been grown and harvested using sound and environmentally approved processes that protect biodiversity and other forest values. As of 2011, Canada's forest industry had certified 151 million hectares (373 million acres) of forested land across the country using at least one of the four recognized certification programs that exist (Table 11-1). Many forest companies describe their progress with certification on their websites.

Canada's first certified sustainable forest, meeting the standards of the Forest Stewardship Council in 1998, was the Haliburton Forest and Wild Life Reserve Ltd. (http://www.haliburtonforest.com). In addition to producing wood products in a sustainable manner, this privately owned forest in Central Ontario's Haliburton Highlands offers visitors a wide variety of activities, ranging from hiking and canoeing to snowmobiling and howling with wolves. Certification has provided obvious benefits for the public and for the biodiversity in this forest; at the same time, it has increased rather than reduced economic opportunities for Haliburton's owners.

In 2001, the World Wildlife Fund (WWF) called on the world's five largest companies that harvest and process timber and buy wood products to adopt the Forest Stewardship Council's sustainable management principles. According to the WWF, by doing this these five companies could essentially halt logging of old-growth forests and still meet the world's industrial wood and wood fibre needs using one-fifth of the world's forests.

Good news. In 2002, Mitsubishi, one of the world's largest forestry companies, announced that it would have third parties certify its forestry operations using standards developed by the Forest Stewardship Council.

Table 11-1 Certified Forests in Canada

Standard Used	Area Certified (in hectares)
CSA **Canadian Standards Association** (Canada's National Sustainable Forest Management Standards) Based on national and international criteria for sustainable forestry management; it addresses environmental, social, and economic issues and requires public participation.	57.1 million
SFI **Sustainable Forestry Initiative Program** (Developed by the American Forestry and Paper Association) Includes environmental objectives and performance measures; integrates forestry with conservation goals.	55.1 million
FSC **Forest Stewardship Council** Aimed at sustainable management of the world's forests using environmental, social, and economic criteria; stresses the need for national and regional standards.	16.3 million
Total certified forest with double-counting removed	150.6 million

Sources: Canadian Sustainable Forestry Certification Coalition, http://www.certificationcanada.org; and The National Forestry Database (2012).

And Home Depot, Lowe's, Andersen, and other major sellers of wood products in North America have agreed to sell only wood certified as being sustainably grown by independent groups such as the Forest Stewardship Council (to the degree that certified wood is available).

11-5 FOREST RESOURCES AND MANAGEMENT IN CANADA

What Is the Status of the Canadian Forest? Many Uses

The Canadian forest provides a wide variety of economic and environmental benefits.

Forests have a major impact on many parts of the Canadian landscape. Forests moderate climate, purify water, stabilize soil, store carbon, and serve as habitat for much of Canada's terrestrial biodiversity. Forests provide employment and a range of valuable products

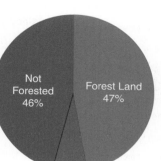

Canada's Lands

Not Forested 46%

Forest Land 47%

Other Treed Land 7%

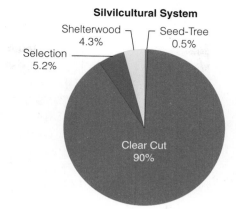

Silvilcultural System

Shelterwood 4.3%

Seed-Tree 0.5%

Selection 5.2%

Clear Cut 90%

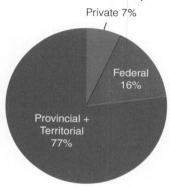

Forest Land Ownership

Private 7%

Federal 16%

Provincial + Territorial 77%

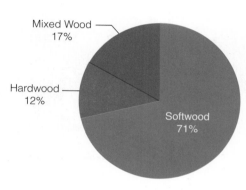

Forest Types

Mixed Wood 17%

Hardwood 12%

Softwood 71%

FIGURE 11-14 Some Canadian forest facts at a glance. (The State of Canada's Forests, Annual Report 2011, Canadian Forest Service, Natural Resources Canada)

such as wood, pulp, and maple syrup. As well, forests provide opportunities for recreation, tourism, education, and aesthetic appreciation.

About 54% of Canada's land surface is forested. Approximately 47% is considered to be *forest land* or *productive forest* capable of generating forest products. The remaining 7% is other treed land around farms, parks, buildings, and wetlands that is used primarily for purposes other than forestry.

The productive forest consists primarily of *softwood* (**coniferous trees**) (Figure 11-14). Canada has 10% of the world's forest and 30% of the world's boreal forest. About 40% of Canada's forest is managed through integrated land-use planning and forest certification programs. Less than 1% of Canada's forests are harvested each year to provide an *annual allowable cut* of approximately 240 million cubic metres of wood. About 90% of the trees are harvested by clear-cutting (CFS, 2011).

Canada's forest regions are illustrated in Figure 11-15 and described in Table 11-2 (p. 228). The largest of these regions is the *boreal forest*—a dense coniferous forest that stretches across much of Canada. The trees grade

north toward tundra, becoming smaller and more scattered, through a transition region called the *taiga*. The trees grade south from boreal forest toward open prairie through a transition region called the *aspen parkland*.

The forest industry contributed $24 billion to Canada's gross domestic product in 2011 and directly employed about 200 000 Canadians (Natural Resources Canada, 2012). Forest products include not only wood, pulp, paper, and cardboard, but also a wide variety of commodities and services such as maple syrup, furs, craft supplies, recreation, and tourism. According to the Canadian Forest Service, at least 66% of Canada's biodiversity can be found in our forested ecosystems.

The cutting edge of innovation in forestry can be found in Canada's Model Forests. Arising from initiatives planned at the 1992 Earth Summit held in Rio de Janeiro, Brazil, there is now a network of 14 nonprofit member organizations representing the Model Forest of Canada (Figure 11-15). These forests are living laboratories where techniques of sustainable forest management are researched, applied, and monitored. Each Model Forest has its own partners and projects

Sustaining Terrestrial Biodiversity: Managing and Protecting Ecosystems

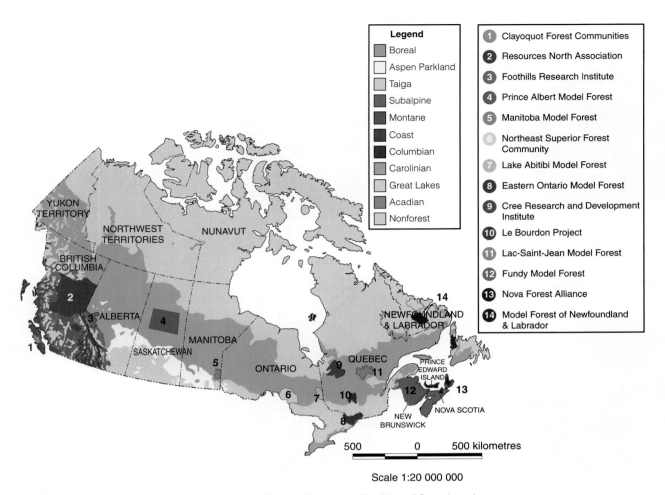

FIGURE 11-15 Canada's forest regions and model forests. (Based on *The Atlas of Canada* and The Canadian Model Forest Network)

Legend
- Boreal
- Aspen Parkland
- Taiga
- Subalpine
- Montane
- Coast
- Columbian
- Carolinian
- Great Lakes
- Acadian
- Nonforest

1. Clayoquot Forest Communities
2. Resources North Association
3. Foothills Research Institute
4. Prince Albert Model Forest
5. Manitoba Model Forest
6. Northeast Superior Forest Community
7. Lake Abitibi Model Forest
8. Eastern Ontario Model Forest
9. Cree Research and Development Institute
10. Le Bourdon Project
11. Lac-Saint-Jean Model Forest
12. Fundy Model Forest
13. Nova Forest Alliance
14. Model Forest of Newfoundland & Labrador

Scale 1:20 000 000

Table 11-2 Forest Regions of Canada	
Forest Region	**Description**
Boreal Forest	A widespread coniferous forest. Largely black spruce, white spruce, and tamarack. Jack pine and balsam fir are common in the East; lodgepole pine and subalpine fir are common in the West. Some poplars and white birch.
Aspen Parkland	A transition forest between the boreal forest and open grasslands. Trembling aspens and willows are typical trees.
Taiga	A transition forest between boreal forest and open tundra. White spruce, black spruce, and tamarack become smaller and more scattered toward the North.
Subalpine Forest	In the mountain uplands of Alberta and British Columbia. Typical trees are Englemann spruce, subalpine fir, and lodgepole pine.
Montane Forest	In central British Columbia and in hills and valleys of southwestern Alberta. Typical trees are Douglas fir, lodgepole pine, Englemann spruce, and trembling aspen.
Coast Forest	Large, fast-growing trees near the Pacific coast. Red cedar, western hemlock, Sitka spruce, and coastal Douglas fir are typical trees.
Columbia Forest	Moist parts of interior British Columbia. Western red cedar, western hemlock, western white pine, Douglas fir, and grand fir.
Carolinian Forest	The remnants of the northern extreme of deciduous forests; this area has been largely altered through agriculture and urbanization. Major species include sugar maple, beech, white elm, butternut, and basswood.
Great Lakes–St. Lawrence Forest	The area around the Great Lakes, the St. Lawrence Valley, and the Ottawa Valley. Typical trees are sugar maple, eastern white pine, red pine, eastern hemlock, and yellow birch.
Acadian Forest	Found in the Maritime provinces. Red spruce, balsam fir, yellow birch, and sugar maple are typical trees.

Sources: Rowe (1972) and The State of Canada's Environment 2004–2005, Natural Resources Canada.

but the knowledge gained is pooled throughout the network and beyond Canada to Model Forests in other countries (http://www.modelforest.net).

What Threatens Certain Tree Species across Canada? Insects

Both native and non-native insect species can cause significant damage to the Canadian forest.

Native species of pests such as forest tent caterpillars (*Malacosoma disstria*) and spruce budworms (*Choristoneura* spp) occur widely and can affect large areas of forest throughout much of Canada. Mountain pine beetles (*Dendroctonus ponderosae*) have been causing unprecedented levels of damage in British Columbia and have spread to forests in Alberta. In 2010, mountain pine beetles accounted for half of all the forest area defoliated by major insect pests in Canada (http://cfs.nrcan.gc.ca/?lang=en). This and other pest-related topics will be dealt with in greater detail in Chapter 23.

Invasive or non-native insect species can be particularly troublesome since they lack the predators and competitors that kept them in check in their native lands. Gypsy moths (*Lymantria dispar*) have had an impact on Eastern Canadian forests, but the problem comes and goes as populations of gypsy moths fluctuate. The emerald ash borer (*Agrilus planipennis*) is a new threat in southern Ontario (Figure 11-16). It was first noticed in 2002 when ash trees were attacked in

FIGURE 11-16 The emerald ash borer is an invasive insect that attacks ash trees in southern Ontario and the United States.

the city of Windsor and in Essex County, Ontario. This insect is a native of Asia that was probably transported to North America in wooden packing material of shipping containers. All native ashes are in danger of being attacked and defoliated. Canadian and U.S. authorities are working on strategies to control this insect.

Tree damage from insects can be reduced through inspection of imported timber, removal of infected trees, and the use of chemicals and natural predators to help control insect pests.

How Do Fires Affect Forests? Surface, Crown, and Ground Fires

Forest fires can burn away flammable underbrush and small trees, burn large trees and leap from treetop to treetop, or burn flammable materials found under the ground.

Three types of fires can affect forest ecosystems. Some, called **surface fires** (Figure 11-17, left), usually burn only undergrowth and leaf litter on the forest floor. These fires can kill seedlings and small trees but spare most mature trees and allow most wild animals to escape.

FIGURE 11-17 Surface fires (left) usually burn undergrowth and leaf litter on a forest floor and can help prevent more destructive crown fires (right) by removing flammable ground material. Sometimes carefully controlled surface fires are deliberately set to prevent buildup of flammable ground material in forests.

Occasional surface fires have a number of ecological benefits. They burn away flammable ground material and help prevent more destructive fires. They also release valuable mineral nutrients (tied up in slowly decomposing litter and undergrowth), stimulate the germination of certain tree seeds (such as those of the lodgepole pine and jack pine), and help control pathogens and insects. In addition, some wildlife species such as deer, moose, elk, muskrat, woodcock, and quail depend on occasional surface fires to maintain their habitats and provide food in the form of vegetation that sprouts after fires.

Some extremely hot fires, called **crown fires** (Figure 11-17, right), may start on the ground but eventually burn whole trees and leap from treetop to treetop. They usually occur in forests that have had no surface fires for several decades. This allows dead wood, leaves, and other flammable ground litter to build up. These rapidly burning fires can destroy most vegetation, kill wildlife, increase soil erosion, and burn or damage human structures in their paths.

Sometimes surface fires go underground and burn partially decayed leaves or peat. Such **ground fires** are most common in northern peat bogs. They may smoulder for days or weeks and are difficult to detect and extinguish.

Fires bring both destruction and renewal to the Canadian forest. About 3 million hectares of forest burn each year. One-third of the fires are caused by lightning and the remaining two-thirds are the result of human activity. Most fires are fought except in remote areas and in some national parks. Trees are burned in fires, but many will not be destroyed and some, like jack pine, require fires to open their cones. After a fire, there will be a great surge of renewal as a flush of nutrients and increased sunlight reach the forest floor. Fire helps to maintain biodiversity by creating gaps in the forest canopy. Many organisms are dependent on the changes in forest succession brought about by fires.

How Can We Reduce the Need to Harvest Trees for Timber and Papermaking? Stop Waste and Make Paper from Tree-Free Fibres

Almost two-thirds of the wood consumed in North America is wasted, and much of the paper we use could be made from agricultural wastes, recycled paper, and fast-growing crops such as kenaf and hemp.

One way to reduce the pressure to harvest trees is to improve the efficiency of wood use. According to the Worldwatch Institute and forestry analysts, *up to 60% of the wood consumed in North America is wasted unnecessarily.* This occurs because of inefficient use of construction materials, excess packaging, overuse of junk mail, inadequate paper recycling, and failure to reuse wooden shipping containers.

One way to reduce the pressure to harvest trees for paper production is to make paper by using fibre that does not come from trees. *Tree-free fibres* for making paper come from two sources: *agricultural residues* left over from crops (such as wheat and other grains) and *fast-growing crops* (such as kenaf and industrial hemp).

China uses tree-free pulp from rice straw and other agricultural wastes left after harvest to make almost two-thirds of its paper. Most of the small amount of tree-free paper produced in the United States is made from the fibres of a rapidly growing woody annual plant called *kenaf* (pronounced "kuh-NAHF").

Compared to pulpwood, kenaf needs less herbicide because it grows faster than most weeds and reduces insecticide use because its outer fibrous covering is nearly insect proof. Growing kenaf does not deplete soil nitrogen because it is a nitrogen fixer. And breaking down kenaf fibres takes less energy and fewer chemicals and thus produces less toxic waste water than using conventional trees.

In Canada, considerable progress has been made in terms of recycling paper and sawmill fibres. According to the Canadian Forestry Service, Canadian mills recycle about 5 million tonnes of paper per year into new products. Roughly 80% of the fibre for new Canadian paper comes from recovered paper (24%) and sawmill residues (56%). This is the highest amount of paper and residues ever used in making Canadian paper.

11-6 TROPICAL DEFORESTATION

How Fast Are Tropical Forests Being Cleared and Degraded, and Why Should We Care? Protecting the Priceless

Large areas of ecologically and economically important tropical forests are being cleared and degraded at a fast rate.

Tropical forests cover about 6% of the Earth's land area. Climatic and biological data suggest that mature tropical forests once covered at least twice as much area as they do today, with most of the destruction occurring since 1950. Satellite scans and ground-level surveys used to estimate forest destruction indicate that large areas of tropical forests are being cut rapidly in parts of South America (especially Brazil), Africa, and Asia.

Studies indicate that more than half of the world's species of terrestrial plants and animals live in tropical rain forests. Brazil has about 30% of the world's remaining tropical rain forest in the vast Amazon basin, which is about two-thirds the size of Canada. In 1970, deforestation affected only 1% of the area of the Amazon basin. By 2003, almost 20% had been deforested or degraded.

The Canadian Boreal Forest Agreement

The boreal forest is a vast green coniferous forest that stretches across northern Canada from Newfoundland to British Columbia (pp. 123, 133, 228). It is home to Aboriginal people and to many species of plants and animals, including species at risk such as woodland caribou (*Rangifer tarandus*, p. 267). It is also an area containing many different resources such as wood, minerals, diamonds, and fossil fuels, which companies have been trying to develop. The boreal forest has been negatively impacted by logging, development, fragmentation, disturbance, invasive species, and climate change. According the David Suzuki Foundation (http://www .davidsuzuki.org), boreal forests and peatlands are being degraded faster than the Amazon rain forests.

However, in May 2010, the **Canadian Boreal Forest agreement**—the largest commercial forest conservation plan in history—came into effect. The agreement involves 21 timber companies, all members of the Forest Products Association of Canada (FPAC), which manages two-thirds of all the certified forests in Canada. It also involves nine leading environmental organizations such as the David Suzuki Foundation and Greenpeace. These groups have decided to work together to support

a plan that will conserve large areas of Canada's boreal forest, protect threatened woodland caribou, and provide a competitive edge for the timber companies involved, on the 72 million hectares (178 million acres) of boreal forest that are licensed to the FPAC members.

The foresters have agreed to suspend new logging operations on 29 million hectares (72 million acres) of boreal forest until plans for protected areas can be finalized. They will put in place sustainable forestry practices and will conduct their operations in accordance with conservation plans aimed at aiding threatened caribou. The conservation groups will commit to supporting the efforts made by FPAC members. They will use

their resources to promote global recognition of the sustainable forestry being practised, and they will stop boycotting products of these companies.

The success of this agreement also depends on the support and involvement of First Nations people since much of the boreal forest is in traditional First Nations territory. The boreal forest has been home to some of Canada's Aboriginal people for thousands of years, and they have developed much traditional knowledge of how to sustainably use the resources of the boreal forest (Karst, 2010). You can learn more about the Canadian Boreal Forest Agreement at http://www .canadianborealforestagreement.com.

Courtesy of Lisa Cancade Hackett

According to a study by researcher James Alcock, without immediate and aggressive action to reduce current forest destruction and degradation practices, Brazil's original Amazon rain forests may largely disappear within 40–50 years.

You probably have not heard about the loss of most of Brazil's Atlantic coastal rain forest. This less famous forest once covered about 12% of Brazil's land area. Now 93% of it has been cleared and most of what is left is recovering from previous cutting episodes. This represents a major loss of biodiversity because an area in this forest a little larger than two typical suburban house lots in Canada has 450 tree species! The entire country of Canada has only 180 native tree species.

There are disagreements about how rapidly tropical forests are being deforested and degraded because of three factors. *First,* it is difficult to interpret satellite images. *Second,* some countries hide or exaggerate deforestation rates for political and economic reasons. *Third,* governments and international agencies define forest, deforestation, and forest degradation in different ways.

For these reasons, estimates of global tropical forest loss vary from 50 000 square kilometres (19 300 square miles) to 170 000 square kilometres (65 600 square miles) per year. This is high enough to lose or degrade half of the world's remaining tropical forests in 35–117 years.

Most biologists believe that cutting and degrading most remaining old-growth tropical forests is a serious

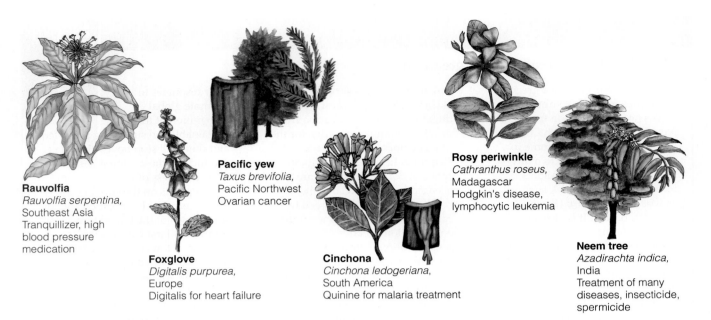

Rauvolfia
Rauvolfia serpentina,
Southeast Asia
Tranquillizer, high
blood pressure
medication

Pacific yew
Taxus brevifolia,
Pacific Northwest
Ovarian cancer

Foxglove
Digitalis purpurea,
Europe
Digitalis for heart failure

Cinchona
Cinchona ledogeriana,
South America
Quinine for malaria treatment

Rosy periwinkle
Cathranthus roseus,
Madagascar
Hodgkin's disease,
lymphocytic leukemia

Neem tree
Azadirachta indica,
India
Treatment of many
diseases, insecticide,
spermicide

FIGURE 11-18 Natural capital: *nature's pharmacy.* Parts of these and a number of other plants and animals (many of them found in tropical forests) are used to treat a variety of human ailments and diseases. Nine of the ten leading prescription drugs originally came from wild organisms. About 2 100 of the 3 000 plants identified by the National Cancer Institute as sources of cancer-fighting chemicals come from tropical forests. Despite their economic and health potential, fewer than 1% of the estimated 125 000 flowering plant species in tropical forests (and a mere 1 100 of the world's 260 000 known plant species) have been examined for their medicinal properties. Once the active ingredients in the plants have been identified, they can usually be produced synthetically. Many potentially useful tropical plant species are likely to become extinct before we can study them.

global environmental problem because of the important ecological and economic services they provide (Figure 11-7). For example, tropical forest plants provide chemicals used as blueprints for making most of the world's prescription drugs (Figure 11-18). And cutting these forests faster than they can grow back contributes to projected global warming because these forests are a storehouse for huge quantities of carbon, safely stored as organic compounds in plant biomass.

What Causes Tropical Deforestation and Degradation? The Big Five

The primary causes of tropical deforestation and degradation are population growth, poverty, environmentally harmful government subsidies, debts owed to developed countries, and failure to value ecological services.

Tropical deforestation results from a number of interconnected primary and secondary causes (Figure 11-19, p. 233). Population growth and poverty combine to drive subsistence farmers and the landless poor to tropical forests, where they try to grow enough food to survive. Government subsidies can accelerate deforestation by making timber or other tropical forest resources cheap, relative to the economic value of the ecological services they provide. Governments in Indonesia, Mexico, and Brazil also encourage the poor

to colonize tropical forests by giving them title to land they clear. This can help reduce poverty but can lead to environmental degradation unless the new settlers are taught how to use such forests more sustainably. In addition, international lending agencies encourage developing countries to borrow huge sums of money from developed countries to finance projects such as roads, mines, logging operations, oil drilling, and dams in tropical forests. Another cause is failure to value ecological services of forests (Figure 11-7, left).

The depletion and degradation of a tropical forest begins when a road is cut deep into the forest interior for logging and settlement and hunters are hired to kill wild animals to provide loggers and other work crews with meat.

Loggers typically use selection cutting to remove the best timber (high grading). This topples many other trees because of their shallow roots and the network of vines connecting trees in the forest's canopy. Timber exports to developed countries contribute significantly to tropical forest depletion and degradation. But domestic use accounts for more than 80% of the trees cut in developing countries.

After the best timber has been removed, timber companies often sell the land to ranchers. Within a few years they typically overgraze it and sell it to settlers who have migrated to the forest hoping to grow enough

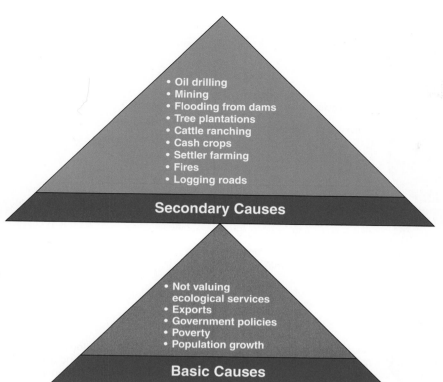

• Oil drilling
• Mining
• Flooding from dams
• Tree plantations
• Cattle ranching
• Cash crops
• Settler farming
• Fires
• Logging roads

Secondary Causes

• Not valuing ecological services
• Exports
• Government policies
• Poverty
• Population growth

Basic Causes

FIGURE 11-19 Natural capital degradation: major interconnected primary and secondary causes of the destruction and degradation of tropical forests. The importance of specific secondary causes varies in different parts of the world.

food to survive. Then they move their land-degrading ranching operations to another forest area. According to a 2004 report by the Center for International Forestry Research, the rapid spread in cattle ranching is the biggest threat to the Amazon's tropical forests.

The settlers cut most of the remaining trees, burn the debris after it has dried for about a year, and plant crops using slash-and-burn agriculture (Figure 2-2, p. 23). They can also endanger some wild species by hunting them for what is called bushmeat. After a few years of crop growing and rain erosion, the nutrient-poor tropical soil is depleted of nutrients. Then the settlers move on to newly cleared land.

In some areas—especially Africa and Latin America—large sections of tropical forest are cleared for raising cash crops such as sugarcane, bananas, pineapples, strawberries, and coffee—mostly for export to developed countries. Tropical forests are also cleared for mining and oil drilling and to build dams on rivers that flood large areas of the forest.

Healthy rain forests do not burn. But increased logging, settlements, grazing, and farming along roads built in these forests results in fragments of forest (Figure 11-9, p. 221) that dry out. This makes such areas easier to ignite by lightning and for farmers and ranchers to burn. In addition to destroying and degrading biodiversity, this releases large amounts of carbon dioxide into the atmosphere.

Solutions: How Can We Reduce Deforestation and Degradation of Tropical Forests? Prevention Is Best

There are a number of ways to slow and reduce the deforestation and degradation of tropical forests.

Analysts have suggested various ways to protect tropical forests and use them more sustainably (Figure 11-20). One method is to help new settlers in tropical forests learn how to practise small-scale sustainable agriculture and forestry. The Lacandon Maya Indians of Chiapas, Mexico, for example, use a multi-layered system of agroforestry to cultivate as many as 75 crop species on 1-hectare (2.5-acre) plots for up to seven years. After that, they plant a new plot to allow regeneration of the soil in the original plot.

In the lush rain forests of Peru's Palcazú Valley, Yaneshé Indians use strip cutting (Figure 11-10e) to harvest tropical trees for lumber. Tribe members also act as consultants to help other forest dwellers set up similar systems.

Another approach is to sustainably harvest some of the renewable resources such as fruits and nuts in rain forests. For example, about 6 000 families in the Petén region of Guatemala make a comfortable living by sustainably extracting various rain forest products.

Another approach is to use **debt-for-nature swaps** to make it financially profitable for countries to

Sustaining Tropical Forests

Prevention

Protect most diverse and endangered areas

Educate settlers about sustainable agriculture and forestry

Phase out subsidies that encourage unsustainable forest use

Add subsidies that encourage sustainable forest use

Protect forests with *debt-for-nature* swaps and *conservation easements*

Certify sustainably grown timber

Reduce illegal cutting

Reduce poverty

Slow population growth

Restoration

Actively plant appropriate trees

Rehabilitate degraded areas

Encourage regrowth through secondary succession

Concentrate farming and ranching on already cleared areas

FIGURE 11-20 Solutions: ways to protect tropical forests and use them more sustainably. Which two of these solutions do you believe are the most important?

protect tropical forests. In such a swap, participating countries act as custodians of protected forest reserves in return for foreign aid or debt relief. Since the first debt-for-nature swap in 1987, governments and private groups have carried out more than 20 such swaps in 10 countries.

Another important tool is using an international system for evaluating and certifying tropical timber produced by sustainable methods. Loggers can also use gentler methods for harvesting trees. For example, cutting canopy vines (lianas) before felling a tree can reduce damage to neighbouring trees by 20–40%, and using the least obstructed paths to remove the logs can halve the damage to other trees. In addition, governments and individuals can mount efforts to reforest and rehabilitate degraded tropical forests and watersheds. Another suggestion is to clamp down on illegal logging.

Solutions: The Incredible Neem Tree

The neem tree could eventually benefit almost everyone on the Earth.

Suppose a single plant existed that could quickly reforest degraded land, supply fuelwood and lumber in dry areas, provide natural alternatives to toxic pesticides, be used to treat numerous diseases, and help control human population growth? There is one: the *neem tree*, a broadleaf evergreen member of the mahogany family.

This remarkable tropical species, native to India and Burma, is ideal for reforestation because it can grow to maturity in only 5–7 years. It grows well in poor soil in semiarid lands such as those in Africa, providing abundant fuelwood, lumber, and lamp oil.

It also contains various natural pesticides. Chemicals from its leaves and seeds can repel or kill more than 200 insect species, including termites, gypsy moths, locusts, boll weevils, and cockroaches.

Extracts from neem seeds and leaves (Figure 11-18) can fight bacterial, viral, and fungal infections. Villagers call the tree a "village pharmacy" because its chemicals can relieve so many different health problems. People also use the tree's twigs as an antiseptic toothbrush and the oil from its seeds to make toothpaste and soap.

That is not all. Neem-seed oil evidently acts as a strong spermicide and may help in the development of a much-needed male birth control pill. According to a study by the U.S. National Academy of Sciences, the neem tree "may eventually benefit every person on the planet."

Despite its numerous advantages, ecologists caution against widespread planting of neem trees outside its native range. As a non-native species, it could take over and displace native species because of its rapid growth and resistance to pests. But proponents say the benefits of neem trees far outweigh such risks. What do you think?

11-7 NATIONAL PARKS

What Are National Parks, and How Are They Threatened? Under Assault

Countries have established over 1 100 national parks, but most are threatened by human activities.

Today more than 1 100 national parks larger than 10 square kilometres (4 square miles) are located in more than 120 countries.

According to a 1999 study by the World Bank and the World Wildlife Fund, only 1% of the parks in developing countries receive protection. Local people invade most of the unprotected parks in search of wood, cropland, game animals, and other natural products for their daily survival. Loggers, miners, and wildlife poachers (who kill animals to obtain and sell items such as rhino horns, elephant tusks, and furs) also invade many of these parks. Park services in developing countries typically have too little money and too few personnel to fight these invasions, either by force or by education.

Another problem is that most national parks are too small to sustain many large animal species. Also, many parks suffer from invasions by non-native species that can reduce the populations of some native species and cause ecological disruption.

Case Study: National Parks and Marine Conservation Areas in Canada

National parks and marine conservation areas in Canada help to protect biodiversity.

The federal government has set aside 36 national parks and 6 national park reserves as outstanding examples of Canada's natural heritage for the long-term enjoyment and benefit of present and future generations of Canadians (Figure 11-21, p. 236). National park reserves are intended to become national parks as soon as Aboriginal claims or other issues are settled. These areas are managed according to a preservationist ethic that emphasizes maintaining the land and its ecosystems in the same condition for future generations (p. 28). Commercial resource extraction is not allowed. A top priority is to protect the integrity and health of park ecosystems from any type of abuse or overuse. (In contrast, many U.S. national parks are suffering from crowding, overuse, erosion, pollution, and invasion by exotic species.)

Canada's first national park, Banff, was established in 1885 as a means of encouraging people to use the newly created CP railway (Chapter 2). A further 35 national parks have followed with the most recent, Torngat Mountains in Labrador, being added in 2005. The long-term goal is to have 55 national parks in the system, representing sites of outstanding beauty and natural significance that have been identified within Canada's 39 natural regions (Parks Canada, 2008).

National parks occupy only 3% of Canada's land mass, but they play an important role in protecting the country's biodiversity. More than 70% of Canada's plant species and 80% of its vertebrate animal species are represented within national parks. Several of Canada's national parks have played pivotal roles in saving endangered species. Wood Buffalo National Park has provided safe haven for whooping cranes throughout their struggle to increase in numbers from the brink of extinction (p. 179). Elk Island National Park, Wood Buffalo National Park, and Riding Mountain National Park have provided habitats for herds of plains bison and wood bison.

National parks are administered by Parks Canada, an agency of the federal government. The Canada National Parks Act (2001) outlines how these areas will be managed for the long-term benefits of Canadians, stressing the importance of ecological health and integrity.

Parks Canada has also identified 29 marine regions that will be protected in future initiatives. Currently, there are three existing national marine conservation areas (NMCAs). Fathom Five National Marine Park on Georgian Bay, Ontario, was Canada's first NMCA; the site of 22 shipwrecks, it has clear fresh water and impressive underwater topography (Figure 11-21). Saguenay St. Lawrence National Marine Park is an area of exceptional biodiversity where the waters of the St. Lawrence Estuary mix with those of the Saguenay Fjord (Figure 11-22, p. 237). Lake Superior National Marine Conservation Area was established in October 2007. The area has many species of fish and birds that inhabit the waters and nearby islands, as well as 50 shipwrecks—including one that Jacques Cousteau described as the most beautiful shipwreck in the world. A fourth site—Gwaii Haanas in the Queen Charlotte Islands of British Columbia—is an NMCA reserve; it is an underwater extension of the existing

FIGURE 11-21 National parks and national marine parks of Canada. (1) Fathom Five National Marine Park, (2) Saguenay St. Lawrence National Marine Park, and (3) Lake Superior National Marine Conservation Area. (Based on national parks and national marine conservation areas, National Parks Directorate Operational Services)

Gwaii Haanas National Park Reserve and offers a unique opportunity to protect the rich biodiversity of this area from mountain top to ocean depths.

> **DID YOU KNOW**
>
> Canada has the world's longest coastline. It extends over 243 000 kilometres along three oceans (Atlantic, Arctic, and Pacific) and 9 500 kilometres along the shores of the Great Lakes.

Figure 11-23 lists a number of suggestions for sustaining and expanding national park systems in Canada and other countries.

11-8 NATURE RESERVES

How Much of the Earth's Land Should We Protect from Human Exploitation? The Answer Is More

Ecologists believe that we should protect more land to help sustain the Earth's biodiversity.

Most ecologists and conservation biologists believe the best way to preserve biodiversity is through a worldwide network of protected areas. Currently about 12% of the Earth's land area has been protected strictly or partially in nature reserves, parks, wildlife refuges,

FIGURE 11-22 Wildlife of Saguenay St. Lawrence National Marine Park.

And this 12% figure is misleading because no more than 5% of these areas are actually protected. Thus, we have allowed 95% of the Earth's terrestrial areas to remain vulnerable to potentially harmful human activities.

Conservation biologists call for protecting at least 20% of the Earth's land area in a global system of biodiversity reserves that includes multiple examples of all the Earth's biomes. Setting aside and helping sustain such a system will take action and funding by national governments (Case Study, p. 239), private groups (Solutions, p. 241), and cooperative ventures involving governments, businesses, and private conservation groups. Protection does not mean just drawing dotted lines around an area; it refers to ecologically sound management of areas.

Some progress is being made. In 2001, the Brazilian government launched a program to establish 80 parks in the Amazon River basin on government-owned lands and asked the World Wildlife Fund to help plan the system. Brazil now has a complex of tropical parks that helps to protect their biodiversity while attracting tourist dollars (UNEP, 2011).

On the other hand, many developers and resource extractors oppose protecting even the current 12% of the Earth's remaining undisturbed ecosystems. They contend that most of these areas contain valuable resources that would add to economic growth.

Ecologists and conservation biologists disagree. They view protected areas as islands of biodiversity that help sustain all life and economies and that serve as centres of future evolution.

Solutions

National Parks

- Integrate plans for managing parks and nearby federal lands

- Add new parkland near threatened parks

- Buy private land inside parks

- Locate visitor parking outside parks and use shuttle buses for entering and touring heavily used parks

- Increase funds for park maintenance and repairs

- Survey wildlife in parks

- Raise entry fees for visitors and use funds for park management and maintenance

- Limit number of visitors to crowded park areas

- Increase number and pay of park rangers

- Encourage volunteers to give visitor lectures and tours

- Seek private donations for park maintenance and repairs

FIGURE 11-23 Solutions: suggestions for sustaining and expanding a national park system in Canada, the United States, and other countries. Which two of these solutions do you believe are the most important? (Wilderness Society and National Parks and Conservation Association)

CONSIDER, DISCUSS, OR DEBATE

List the short- and long-term pros and cons of protecting 12–20% of the Earth from human exploitation.

Case Study: Other Lands That Protect Canadian Biodiversity

In addition to a system of national parks, Canada has many other areas that protect biodiversity.

Canada has 37 Ramsar sites that protect wetlands of international importance, many bird sanctuaries established in support of the North American Waterfowl Management Plan (Figure 11-24, page 238), and 15 World Heritage Sites that protect areas of scientific or aesthetic value in addition to habitats of endangered species (Figure 11-25, p. 239). As well, there are 16 biosphere reserves where a central core area protects biodiversity while compatible human activities, such as education and research, take place in surrounding buffer zones (Figure 11-25 and p. 239).

wilderness, and other areas. In other words, we have reserved 88% of the Earth's land for us, and most of the remaining 12% we have protected is ice, tundra, or desert where we do not want to live because it is too cold or too hot.

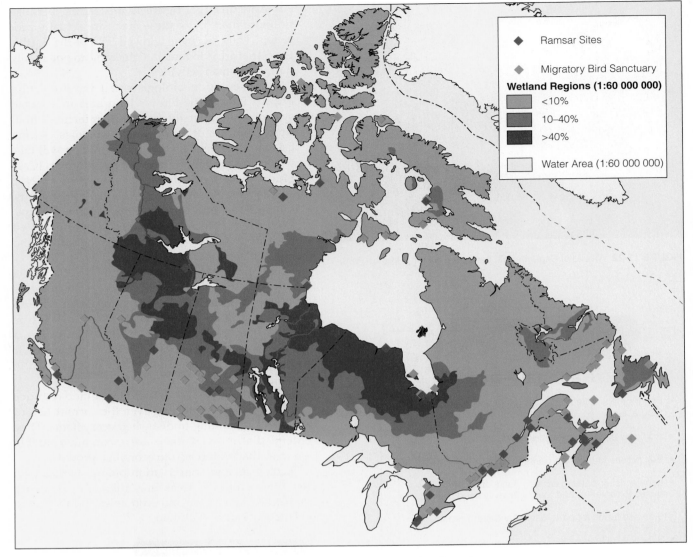

FIGURE 11-24 Locations of Canada's Ramsar wetlands and migratory bird sanctuaries. (Based on Ramsar Wetlands, http://www.ramsar.org)

There are also many small ecological reserves scattered throughout the country to protect biodiversity and to permit research and education. As well, there are local parks, wetlands, woods, and other unofficial "hot spots" where naturalists gather simply because biodiversity is there. These are the sorts of places that local nature lovers and grassroots groups frequent at all biologically meaningful hours of the day and night, and defend with passion.

Provincial parks typically operate according to a conservationist ethic; in other words, the emphasis is on wise use of resources. Extraction of resources may be permitted; for instance, Algonquin Provincial Park in Ontario is the province's largest supplier of yellow birch logs. Provincial parks have a range of different purposes (from recreational parks to wilderness parks); however, they all supply habitat for wildlife and many provincial parks have active programs that facilitate wildlife and educate the public about wildlife.

Brian Naylor, a biologist with the Ministry of Natural Resources (MNR) in North Bay, Ontario, suggests that all these parks and refuges do not prevent habitat fragmentation between these areas from occurring and eventually creating problems for wildlife. For this reason, forest managers on Crown land and private landowners need to be aware of how their particular parcels of land fit into the big picture of maintaining corridors between wildlife areas. Naylor makes it part of his job to keep landowners and foresters informed about the key roles they play as stewards of biologically important habitats.

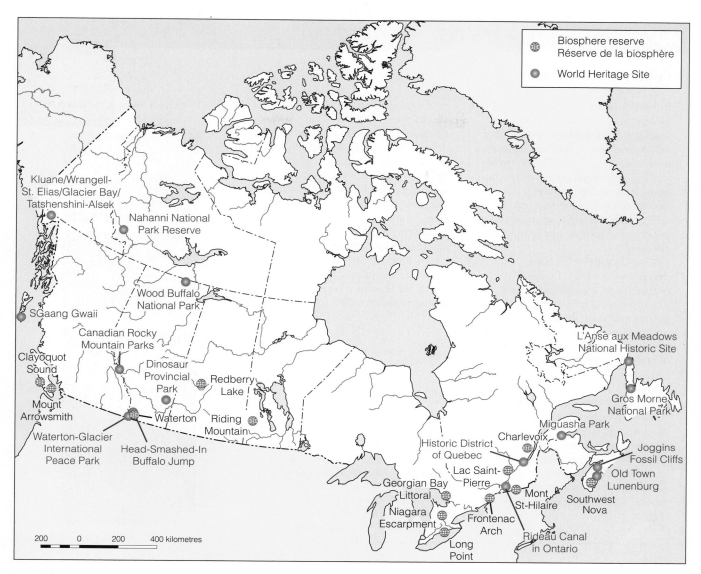

FIGURE 11-25 Canadian biosphere reserves (globe shapes) and World Heritage Sites (red circles). (Canadian Biosphere Reserves Association, Natural Resources Canada)

About 90% of Ontario is Crown land. Forest management on this land must adhere to wildlife requirements spelled out by a series of MNR management guides. One such requirement is that important features of the habitat—such as raptor nests, vernal ponds, standing dead trees, and downed woody debris—not be impacted by forestry operations. Some of the requirements take a *coarse filter* approach and provide for whole communities of organisms; others take a *fine filter* approach to ensure that species with specialized needs are not overlooked. Animals that receive special consideration during forest operations include ospreys, martens, piliated woodpeckers, deer, forest raptors, fur-bearers, cavity-nesting birds, and herons.

DID YOU KNOW

Canada has set aside more area of Ramsar wetlands (about 130 000 square kilometres) than any other nation.

Case Study: What Has Costa Rica Done to Protect Some of Its Land from Degradation? A Global Conservation Leader

Costa Rica has devoted a larger proportion of land than any other country to conserving its significant biodiversity.

Tropical forests once completely covered Central America's Costa Rica, which is smaller in area than Nova Scotia and about one-tenth the size of Manitoba.

Sustaining Terrestrial Biodiversity: Managing and Protecting Ecosystems

Endangered Spaces

In 1989, an important book edited by Monte Hummel was published. Unlike many books that preceded it, *Endangered Spaces* does not focus on individual endangered *species* to be studied and saved on a one-by-one basis. Instead, the authors point out that there are endangered *spaces*—critical habitats—that are disappearing and require our immediate attention.

One chapter in the book describes how the Canadian prairies were transformed from a wilderness of blowing grass into an endless cultivated garden within the space of one human lifetime. What would be the result of farming every bit of ground right to the edge of the road? Where would the prairie dog colonies be? Without them, how would the burrowing owls and black-footed ferrets (both of which need prairie dog colonies) live, and so on? An astonishing web of endangered prairie animals and plants were shown to hinge around one crucial factor—habitat (Figure 11-26).

Endangered Spaces was a wake-up call for Canadians. There was no need to wait for DNA-cloning specialists to save the day. Ordinary people could put things right in the places they cared about by securing critical habitat. Canadians expressed their support, and key lands were purchased and protected through the World Wildlife Fund and the Nature Conservancy.

Endangered Spaces is essential reading for students of the environment; the lessons it contains are still just as relevant today.

FIGURE 11-26 Three prairie species united by their need for habitat. Black-tailed prairie dogs (*threatened*) need space in grasslands to dig their prairie dog towns. Black-footed ferrets (*extirpated*) need to eat prairie dogs. And burrowing owls (*endangered*) need to live in empty prairie dog holes.

Between 1963 and 1983, politically powerful ranching families cleared much of the country's forests to graze cattle. They exported most of the beef produced to the United States and western Europe.

Despite such widespread forest loss, tiny Costa Rica is a superpower of biodiversity, with an estimated 500 000 plant and animal species. A single park in Costa Rica is home to more bird species than all of North America.

In the mid-1970s, Costa Rica established a system of reserves and national parks that by 2003 included about a quarter of its land—6% of it in reserves for indigenous peoples. Costa Rica now devotes a larger proportion of its land to biodiversity conservation than any other country!

The country's parks and reserves are consolidated into eight *megareserves* designed to sustain about 80% of Costa Rica's biodiversity (Figure 11-27). Each reserve contains a protected inner core surrounded

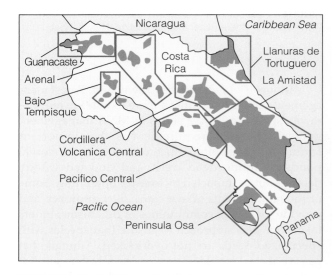

FIGURE 11-27 Solutions: Costa Rica has consolidated its parks and reserves into eight *megareserves* designed to sustain about 80% of the country's rich biodiversity.

by buffer zones that local and indigenous people use for sustainable logging, food growing, cattle grazing, hunting, fishing, and ecotourism.

Costa Rica's biodiversity conservation strategy has paid off. Today the $1 billion a year tourism business—almost two-thirds of it from ecotourists—is the country's largest source of income.

To reduce deforestation the government has eliminated subsidies for converting forests to cattle grazing land. And it pays landowners to maintain or restore tree coverage. This helps stabilize the climate by absorbing carbon dioxide, controlling flooding, and purifying water. The goal is to make sustaining forests profitable. As a result Costa Rica has gone from having one of the world's highest deforestation rates to one of the lowest.

A concern is that without careful government control, the 1 million tourists visiting Costa Rica each year could degrade some of the protected areas. Increased tourism could also stimulate the building of too many hotels, resorts, and other potentially harmful forms of development.

Solutions: The Nature Conservancy: Land Conservation through Private Action

The Nature Conservancy has used private and corporate donations to create the world's largest system of private natural areas and wildlife sanctuaries.

Since its founding by a group of professional ecologists in 1951, the *Nature Conservancy*—with more than 1 million members worldwide—has created the world's largest system of private natural areas and wildlife sanctuaries in 30 countries.

The organization uses private and corporate donations to maintain a fund for buying ecologically important pieces of land or wetlands threatened by development or other human activities. If it cannot buy land for habitat protection, the conservancy helps landowners obtain tax benefits in exchange for accepting legal restrictions or conservation easements preventing development. Landowners also receive sizable tax deductions by donating their land to the Nature Conservancy in exchange for lifetime occupancy rights.

According to John C. Sawhill, former president of the Nature Conservancy, "In the end, our society will be defined not only by what we create, but by what we refuse to destroy."

Should Reserves Be as Large as Possible? Generally, but Not Always

Large reserves usually are the best way to protect biodiversity, but in some places several well-placed, medium-sized, and isolated reserves can do the job.

Large reserves sustain more species and provide greater habitat diversity than do small reserves. They also minimize the area of outside edges exposed to natural disturbances (such as fires and hurricanes), invading species, and human disturbances from nearby developed areas.

However, research indicates that in some locales, several well-placed, medium-sized, and isolated reserves may better protect a wider variety of habitats and preserve more biodiversity than a single large reserve of the same area. A mixture of large and small reserves (Figure 11-27) may be the best way to protect a variety of species and communities against a number of different threats.

Establishing **connectivity** with protected *habitat corridors* between reserves can help support more species and allow migration of vertebrates that need large ranges. They also permit migration of individuals and populations when environmental conditions in a reserve deteriorate and help preserve animals that must make seasonal migrations to obtain food. Corridors permit **gene flow** so that residents of a particular patch of habitat will not become inbred through the lack of opportunity to mate with nonrelatives. Corridors may also enable some species to shift their ranges if global climate change makes their current ranges uninhabitable.

The Yellowstone-to-Yukon (Y2Y) Conservation Initiative (http://www.y2y.net/) is a joint Canada–U.S. charitable organization that seeks to protect wild ecosystems along the mountainous regions stretching between Yellowstone National Park, Montana, through Alberta and British Columbia, to the Yukon. Established in 1997, this group aims at preserving wildlife corridors throughout the region as well as protecting the core habitat of large animals such as grizzly bears.

In Ontario, a number of wildlife corridors centred on Algonquin Provincial Park are in various stages of planning or **lobbying**. The Algonquin-to-Adirondack (A2A) Conservation Initiative (http://www.georgewright.org/52stephe.pdf/) would provide an important corridor for wolves and other mobile animals between Algonquin Provincial Park in Ontario and Adirondack Park in New York. The Temagami–Algonquin Wildlife Corridor (http://www.ancientforest.org/flb22.pdf/) would allow for wildlife dispersal between Algonquin Provincial Park and Lady Evelyn–Smoothwater Provincial Park in the Temagami District to the north. The Superior–Temagami Corridor (http://www.ancientforest.org/flb10.html/) between the Temagami region and Lake Superior would protect examples of pristine landscapes and would help to counter the effects of forest fragmentation associated with lumbering, mining, and other forms of development. Ecologist Peter

Quinby and others have been champions of the need to establish these corridors while the opportunities still remain.

On a smaller scale, but no less important, is the Oak Ridges Moraine Wildlife Corridor (http://www.toronto.ca/moraine/) north of Toronto. The Oak Ridges Moraine is a major geological landform that stretches 160 kilometres from the Niagara Escarpment to Rice Lake near Peterborough. The area is the headwaters of 65 river systems, acts as a refuge to many forest birds, and is one of the last continuous wildlife corridors in southern Ontario.

What Are Biosphere Reserves? A Great Idea

Biosphere reserves have an inner protected core surrounded by two buffer zones that can be used by local people for sustainable extraction of resources for food and fuel.

In 1971, the UN Educational, Scientific, and Cultural Organization (UNESCO) created the Man and the Biosphere (MAB) Programme. A major goal of the program is to establish at least one (and ideally five or more) *biosphere reserves* in each of the Earth's 193 biogeographical zones. Today there are 580 biosphere reserves in 114 countries.

Each reserve must be large enough to contain three zones (Figure 11-28). The *core area* contains an important ecosystem that the government legally protects from all human activities except nondestructive research and monitoring.

A *buffer zone* surrounds and protects the core area. In this zone, emphasis is on nondestructive research, education, and recreation. Local people can also carry out sustainable logging, agriculture, livestock grazing, hunting, and fishing in this buffer zone, as long as such activities do not harm the core.

Finally, a second *buffer,* or *transition zone,* surrounds the inner buffer. In this zone, local people can engage in more intensive but sustainable forestry, grazing, hunting, fishing, agriculture, and recreation than in the inner buffer zone. This allows local people to be enlisted as partners in protecting a reserve from unsustainable uses.

So far, most biosphere reserves fall short of the ideal and receive too little funding for their protection and management. An international fund to help countries protect and manage biosphere reserves would cost about $100 million (U.S.) per year—about what the world's nations spend on weapons every 90 minutes.

What Is Adaptive Ecosystem Management? Cooperation and Flexibility

People with competing interests can work together to develop adaptable plans for managing and sustaining nature reserves.

Managing and sustaining a nature reserve is difficult. One problem is that reserves are constantly changing in response to environmental changes. Another is that they are affected by a variety of biological, cultural, economic, and political factors. In addition, their size, shape, and biological makeup often are determined by political, legal, and economic factors that depend on land ownership and conflicting public demands rather than by ecological principles and considerations.

One way to deal with these uncertainties and conflicts is through *adaptive ecosystem management*. It is based on using four principles. *First,* integrate ecological, economic, and social principles to help maintain and restore the sustainability and biological diversity of reserves while supporting sustainable economies and communities. *Second,* seek ways to get government agencies, private conservation organizations, scientists, business interests, and private landowners to reach a consensus on how to achieve common conservation objectives.

Third, view all decisions and strategies as scientific and social experiments and use failures as opportunities for learning and improvement. *Fourth,* emphasize continual information gathering, monitoring, reassessment, flexibility, adaptation, and innovation in the face of uncertainty and usually unpredictable change. Figure 11-29 summarizes the adaptive ecosystem management process.

Biosphere Reserve

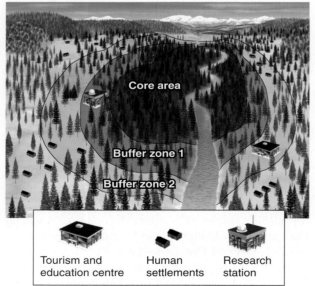

FIGURE 11-28 Solutions: a model *biosphere reserve*. In traditional parks and wildlife reserves, well-defined boundaries keep people out and wildlife in. By contrast, biosphere reserves recognize people's needs for access to sustainable use of various resources in parts of the reserve.

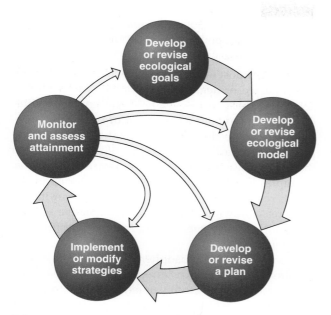

FIGURE 11-29 Solutions: the adaptive ecosystem management process.

What Areas Should Receive Top Priority for Establishing Reserves? Hot Spots

We can prevent or slow down losses of biodiversity by concentrating efforts on protecting hot spots where significant biodiversity is under immediate threat.

In reality, few countries are physically, politically, or financially able to set aside and protect large biodiversity reserves. To protect as much of the Earth's remaining biodiversity as possible, it would make sense to concentrate on saving areas of rich diversity that are under immediate threat.

In 1988, Norman Myers identified 10 **hot spots** of plant *endemism* (i.e., many of the species occurring in each hot spot were found nowhere else on Earth) that were being affected by high rates of habitat destruction. He reasoned that these hot spots should be a top priority for conservation efforts since so many unique plant species, and presumably other components of the ecosystem, were in jeopardy there.

In order to qualify as a hot spot, a region had to contain at least 1 500 species of vascular plants that were endemic and had to have lost at least 70% of its original habitat.

Myers and his colleagues at Conservation International (http://www.conservation.org/) continued with this work, and many other scientists began to focus on hot spots.

Now 34 hotspots have been identified (Figure 11-30) that contain 75% of the world's most threatened birds, mammals, and amphibians within only 2.3% of the Earth's terrestrial surface area (Mittermeier et al., 2005). These global hot spots of biodiversity truly must be defended.

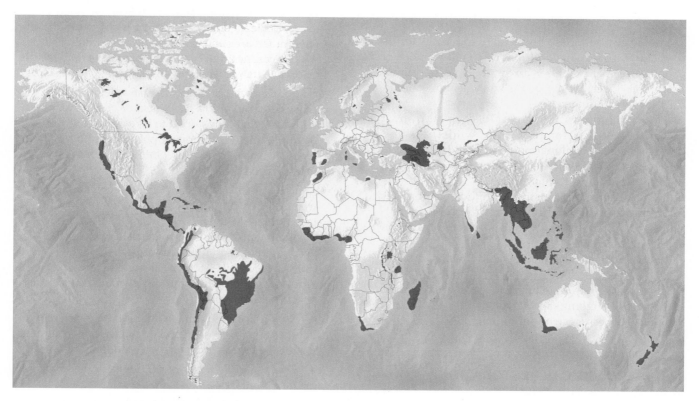

CENGAGENOW **ACTIVE FIGURE 11-30 Endangered natural capital:** *25 hot spots* identified by ecologists as important but endangered centres of biodiversity that contain a large number of endemic plant and animal species found nowhere else. Research is adding new hot spots to this list. (Data from the Center for Applied Biodiversity Science at Conservation International) *See an animation based on this figure at* CengageNOW.

What Is Wilderness, and Why Is It Important? Land Protected from Us

Wilderness is land legally set aside in a large enough area to prevent or minimize harm from human activities.

Wilderness supporters cite several reasons for preserving wild places. One is that they are areas where people can experience the beauty of nature and observe natural biological diversity. Such areas can also enhance the mental and physical health of visitors by allowing them to get away from noise, stress, development, and large numbers of people. Wilderness preservationist John Muir advised us,

Climb the mountains and get their good tidings. Nature's peace will flow into you as the sunshine into the trees. The winds will blow their freshness into you, and the storms their energy, while cares will drop off like autumn leaves.

Even those who never use wilderness areas may want to know they are there, a feeling expressed by novelist Wallace Stegner:

Save a piece of country ... and it does not matter in the slightest that only a few people every year will go into it. This is precisely its value. ... We simply need that wild country available to us, even if we never do more than drive to its edge and look in. For it can be a means of reassuring ourselves of our sanity as creatures, a part of the geography of hope.

Some critics oppose protecting wilderness for its scenic and recreational value for a small number of people. They believe this is an outmoded concept that keeps some areas of the planet from being economically useful to humans.

Most biologists disagree. To them the most important reasons for protecting wilderness and other areas from exploitation and degradation are to *preserve their biodiversity* as a vital part of the Earth's natural capital and to *protect them as centres for evolution* in response to mostly unpredictable changes in environmental conditions. In other words, wilderness is a biodiversity savings account and an eco-insurance policy.

Some analysts also believe wilderness should be preserved because the wild species it contains have a right to exist (or struggle to exist) and play their roles in the Earth's ongoing saga of biological evolution and ecological processes, without human interference.

11-9 ECOLOGICAL RESTORATION

How Can We Rehabilitate and Restore Damaged Ecosystems? Making Amends for Our Actions

Scientists have developed a number of techniques for rehabilitating and restoring degraded ecosystems and creating artificial ecosystems.

Bad news. Almost every natural place on the Earth has been affected or degraded to some degree by human activities. *Good news.* Much of the environmental damage we have inflicted on nature is at least partially reversible through **ecological restoration:** the process of repairing damage caused by humans to the biodiversity and dynamics of natural ecosystems. Examples include replanting forests, restoring grasslands, restoring wetlands, reclaiming urban industrial areas (brownfields), reintroducing native species, removing invasive species, and freeing river flows by removing dams.

Farmer and philosopher Wendell Berry says we should try to answer three questions in deciding whether and how to modify or rehabilitate natural ecosystems. *First,* what is here? *Second,* what will nature permit us to do here? *Third,* what will nature help us do here?

By studying how natural ecosystems recover, scientists are learning how to speed up repair operations using a variety of approaches. They include the following:

- *Restoration:* trying to return a particular degraded habitat or ecosystem to a condition as similar as possible to its natural state. However, we often lack knowledge about the previous composition of a degraded area and changes in climate, soil, and species composition can make it impossible to restore an area to its earlier state.

- *Rehabilitation:* attempts to turn a degraded ecosystem back into a functional or useful ecosystem without trying to restore it to its original condition. Examples include removing pollutants and replanting areas such as mining sites, landfills, and clear-cut forests to reduce soil erosion.

- *Remediation:* cleaning up chemical contaminants from a site by physical or chemical methods to protect human health and as a first step toward redevelopment of a site for human use. For example, an abandoned and polluted industrial plant—called a *brownfield*—may be cleaned up and then redeveloped into office buildings, apartments, a sports field, or a park.

- *Replacement:* replacing a degraded ecosystem with another type of ecosystem. For example, a productive pasture or tree farm may replace a degraded forest.

- *Creating artificial ecosystems:* for example, creating artificial wetlands.

Researchers have suggested five basic science-based principles for carrying out ecological restoration:

- Mimic nature and natural processes and ideally let nature do most of the work, usually through secondary ecological succession.

- Re-create important ecological niches that have been lost.

- Rely on pioneer species, keystone species, foundation species, and natural ecological succession to facilitate the restoration process.

- Control or remove harmful non-native species.

- If necessary, reconnect small patches to form larger ones and create corridors where existing patches are isolated.

Some analysts worry that environmental restoration could encourage continuing environmental destruction and degradation by suggesting any ecological harm we do can be undone. Some go further and say that we do not understand the incredible complexity of ecosystems well enough to restore or manage damaged natural ecosystems.

And ecologists point out that preventing ecosystem damage in the first place is cheaper and more effective than any form of ecological restoration. According to ecological restoration expert John Berger, "The purpose of ecological restoration is to repair previous damage, not legitimize further destruction."

Restorationists agree that restoration should not be used as an excuse for environmental destruction. But they point out that so far we have been able to protect or preserve no more than about 5% of nature from the effects of human activities. So ecological restoration is badly needed for much of the world's ecosystems that we have damaged.

They also point out that if a restored ecosystem differs from the original system this is better than nothing. And natural ecosystems are always changing anyway. They also contend that increased experience will improve the effectiveness of ecological restoration.

> **CONSIDER, DISCUSS, OR DEBATE**
>
> Should we mount a massive effort to restore ecosystems we have degraded even though this will be quite costly? Who should pay? What happens if the responsible parties cannot be found, or if the prospect of paying restoration fees causes companies to relocate in countries with lower environmental standards?

Case Study: Ecological Restoration of a Tropical Dry Forest in Costa Rica

A degraded tropical dry forest in Costa Rica is being restored in a cooperative venture between tropical ecologists and local people.

Costa Rica is the site of one of the world's largest *ecological restoration* projects. In the lowlands of the country's Guanacaste National Park (Figure 11-27),

a small tropical dry deciduous forest has been burned, degraded, and fragmented by large-scale conversion to cattle ranches and farms.

Now it is being restored and relinked to the rain forest on adjacent mountain slopes. The goal is to eliminate damaging non-native grass and cattle and re-establish a tropical dry forest ecosystem over the next 100–300 years.

Daniel Janzen, professor of biology at the University of Pennsylvania and a leader in the field of **restoration ecology,** has helped galvanize international support and has raised more than $10 million (U.S.) for this restoration project. He recognizes that ecological restoration and protection of the park will fail unless the people in the surrounding area believe they will benefit from such efforts. Janzen's vision is to make the nearly 40 000 people who live near the park an essential part of the restoration of the degraded forest, a concept he calls *biocultural restoration.*

By actively participating in the project, local residents reap educational, economic, and environmental benefits. Local farmers make money by sowing large areas with tree seeds and planting seedlings started in Janzen's lab. Local grade school, high school, and university students and citizens' groups study the ecology of the park and go on field trips to the park. The park's location near the Pan American Highway makes it an ideal area for ecotourism, which stimulates the local economy.

The project also serves as a training ground in tropical forest restoration for scientists from all over the world. Research scientists working on the project give guest classroom lectures and lead some of the field trips.

Janzen recognizes that in a few decades today's children will be running the park and the local political system. If they understand the ecological importance of their local environment, they are more likely to protect and sustain its biological resources. He believes that education, awareness, and involvement—not guards and fences—are the best ways to restore degraded ecosystems and protect largely intact ecosystems from unsustainable use.

11-10 WHAT CAN WE DO?

What Should Be Our Priorities? An Eight-Step Program

Biodiversity expert Edward O. Wilson has proposed eight priorities for protecting most of the world's remaining ecosystems and species.

In 2002, Edward O. Wilson, considered to be one of the world's foremost experts on biodiversity, published a book called *The Future of Life.* In this book, he proposed the following priorities for protecting most of the world's remaining ecosystems and species:

- *Take immediate action to preserve the world's biological hot spots* (Figure 11-30).

- *Keep intact the world's remaining old-growth forests and cease all logging of such forests.*

- *Complete the mapping of the world's terrestrial and aquatic biodiversity so we know what we have and can make conservation efforts more precise and cost-effective.*

- *Determine the world's marine hot spots and assign them the same priority for immediate action as for those on land*—more on this in Chapter 13.

- *Concentrate on protecting and restoring everywhere the world's lakes and river systems, which are the most threatened ecosystems of all*—more on this in Chapter 13.

- *Ensure that the full range of the Earth's terrestrial and aquatic ecosystems are included in a global conservation strategy.*

- *Make conservation profitable.* This involves finding ways to raise the income of people who live in or near nature reserves so they can become partners in their protection and sustainable use. It also requires providing financial help from private and government sources to governments that protect their forests and other nature reserves.

- *Initiate ecological restoration projects worldwide* to heal some of the damage we have done and increase the share of the Earth's land and water allotted to the rest of nature.

According to Wilson, such a conservation strategy would cost about $30 billion (U.S.) per year—an amount that could be provided by a tax of one cent per cup of coffee. According to biologist David Suzuki, "We must try our best in everything we do not to disrupt the natural systems around us because, ultimately, we are completely dependent on them. That is what sustainability is all about."

What Can You Do?

Sustaining Terrestrial Biodiversity

- Plant trees and take care of them.

- Recycle paper and buy recycled paper products.

- Buy wood and wood products made from trees that have been grown sustainably.

- Help rehabilitate or restore a degraded area of forest or grassland near your home.

- When building a home, save all the trees and as much natural vegetation and soil as possible.

- Landscape your yard with a diversity of plants natural to the area instead of having a monoculture lawn.

FIGURE 11-31 What can you do? Ways to help sustain terrestrial biodiversity.

This strategy for protecting the Earth's precious biodiversity will not be implemented without bottom-up political pressure on elected officials from individual citizens and groups. It will also require cooperation among key people in government, the private sector, science, and engineering using adaptive management (Figure 11-29). Figure 11-31 lists some ways you can help sustain the Earth's terrestrial biodiversity.

We abuse land because we regard it as a commodity belonging to us. When we see land as a community to which we belong, we may begin to use it with love and respect.

ALDO LEOPOLD

CHAPTER REVIEW

1. Review the Key Questions for this chapter on p. 216. What can be gained, and lost, by conserving the terrestrial and marine ecosystems of Clayoquot Sound? What advantages are associated with having the area recognized as a United Nations biosphere reserve? Read about biosphere reserves on p. 242. What types of activities should be allowed and disallowed in the core, buffer, and transition areas (Figure 11-1, p. 215) at Clayoquot Sound?

2. What is *conservation biology*? What is *bioinformatics*? Distinguish between *instrumental values* and *intrinsic values*.

3. Distinguish among an *old-growth forest*, a *second-growth forest*, and a *tree plantation (tree farm or commercial forest)*. What major ecological and economic benefits do forests provide? Describe the efforts of scientists and economists to put a price tag on the major ecological services provided by forests and other ecosystems.

4. What harm is caused by building roads into previously inaccessible forests? Distinguish among *selection cutting, clear-cutting, strip cutting, seed-tree cutting*, and *shelterwood cutting* in the harvesting of trees. What are the major advantages and disadvantages of each method of cutting trees?

5. What are two types of forest fires? What are some eco-logical benefits of occasional surface fires? What are four ways to reduce the harmful impacts of diseases and insects on forests? What effects might projected global warming have on forests?

6. What parts of the world are experiencing the greatest forest losses? Define *deforestation* and list some of its major harmful environmental effects. What are the major basic and secondary causes of tropical deforestation?

7. Describe four ways to manage forests more sustain-ably. What is certified timber? What are four ways to reduce the harm to forests and to people from forest fires? What are three ways to reduce the need to har-vest trees? What is the fuelwood crisis and what are three ways to reduce its severity?

8. What major environmental threats affect national parks? How could national parks in Canada and other countries be managed more sustainably? What percentage of the world's land has been set asideand protected as nature reserves, and what percentage do conservation biologists believe should be protected?

9. How should nature reserves be designed and con-nected? Describe what Costa Rica has done to estab-lish nature reserves. What is *wilderness* and why is it important? Describe the controversy over pro-tecting wilderness. What is a *biological hot spot* and why is it important to protect such areas? Why is it also important to protect areas where deteriorating ecosystem services threaten people and other forms of life?

10. What is *ecological restoration?* What are the four parts of a strategy for carrying out ecological restoration and rehabilitation? Describe the ecological restoration of a tropical dry forest in Costa Rica. Define and give three examples of *reconciliation (applied) ecology.*

CRITICAL THINKING

1. Use the Parks Canada website (http://www.pc.gc.ca) to learn about Canada's national parks. Choose one national park and make a table that summarizes the park's date of creation, area, and special features.

2. Use the Internet to learn about a wilderness issue or controversy directly affecting Canada. Outline both sides of the issue.

3. Explain why you agree or disagree with each of the proposals for providing more sustainable use of forests throughout the world, listed in Figure 11-13, p. 225.

4. Should there be a ban on the use of off-road motorized vehicles and snowmobiles in national or provincial parks? What about other public lands? Explain.

5. Visit Ontario's Forests website (http://ontariosforests .mnr.gov.on.ca) and analyze one of its forest manage-ment guides. Evaluate the guide in terms of its effec-tiveness in protecting the wildlife habitat in question.

6. In the early 1990s, Miguel Sanchez, a subsistence farmer in Costa Rica, was offered $600 000 by a hotel developer for a piece of land that he and his family had been using sustain-ably for many years. The land contained an old-growth rain forest and a black sand beach in an area under rapid development. Sanchez refused the offer. What would you have done if you were a poor subsistence farmer in Miguel Sanchez's position? Explain your decision.

7. Should developed countries provide most of the money to preserve remaining tropical forests in developing countries? Explain.

8. If ecosystems are undergoing constant change, why should we **(a)** establish and protect nature reserves and **(b)** carry out ecological restoration?

9. Congratulations! You are in charge of protecting and sustaining the world's terrestrial biodiversity. List the three most important features of your policies for using and managing **(a)** forests and **(b)** parks.

PROJECTS

1. Obtain a topographic map of the region where you live and use it to identify local, provincial, and federally owned lands in the form of parks, rangeland, forests, and wilderness areas. Identify the government agency or agencies responsible for managing each of these areas, and try to evaluate how well these agencies are preserving the natural resources on this public land on your behalf.

2. What has happened during the past 50 years to the biome in which you live? How much, if any, of it remains in its original state? How much of it should be protected from further degradation? How much of it could be restored? Find out from books, maps, the Internet, and conversations with old-timers.

3. If possible, try to visit **(a)** a diverse old-growth forest, **(b)** an area that has been recently clear-cut, and **(c)** an area that was clear-cut 5–10 years ago. Compare the biodiversity, soil erosion, and signs of rapid water runoff in each of the three areas.

4. For many decades, New Zealand has had a policy of meeting all its demand for wood and wood prod-ucts by growing timber on intensively managed tree plantations. Use the library or Internet to evaluate the

effectiveness of this approach and its major advantages and disadvantages.

5. Use the library and Internet to find one example of a successful ecological restoration project not discussed in this chapter and one that failed. For your example, describe the strategy used, the ecological principles involved, and why the project succeeded or failed.

ECOLOGICAL FOOTPRINT ANALYSIS

Study the data below on deforestation in five countries, and answer the questions that follow.

Country	Area of Tropical Rain Forest (square kilometres)	Area of Deforestation per Year (square kilometres)	Annual Rate of Tropical Forest Loss
A	1 800 000	50 000	
B	55 000	3 000	
C	22 000	6 000	
D	530 000	12 000	
E	80 000	700	

1. What is the annual rate of tropical rain forest loss, as a percentage of total forest area, in each of the five countries? Answer by filling in the blank column in the table.

2. What is the annual rate of tropical deforestation collectively in all of the countries represented in the table?

3. According to the table, and assuming the rates of deforestation remain constant, which country's tropical rain forest will be completely destroyed first?

4. Assuming the rate of deforestation in country C remains constant, how many years will it take for all of its tropical rain forests to be destroyed?

5. Assuming that a hectare (1.0 hectare = 0.01 square kilometre) of tropical rain forest absorbs 0.85 metric tons of carbon dioxide per year, what would be the total annual growth in the carbon footprint (carbon emitted but not absorbed by vegetation because of deforestation) in metric tons of carbon dioxide per year from deforestation for each of the five countries in the table?

Sustaining Biodiversity: The Species Approach

The Passenger Pigeon: Gone Forever

In 1813, bird expert John James Audubon saw a single flock of passenger pigeons that he estimated was 16 kilometres (10 miles) wide and hundreds of kilometres long, and contained perhaps a billion birds. The flock took three days to fly past him and was so dense that it darkened the skies.

By 1914, the passenger pigeon (Figure 12-1) had disappeared forever. How could a species that was once the most common bird in North America and probably the world become extinct in only a few decades? The answer is, humans wiped them out. The main reasons for the extinction of this species were uncontrolled commercial hunting and loss of the bird's habitat and food supply as forests were cleared to make room for farms and cities.

Passenger pigeons were good to eat, their feathers made good pillows, and their bones were widely used for fertilizer. They were easy to kill because they flew in gigantic flocks and nested in long, narrow colonies.

Commercial hunters would capture one pigeon alive, sew its eyes shut, and tie it to a perch called a stool. Soon a curious flock would land beside this "stool pigeon"— a term we now use to describe someone who turns in another person for breaking the law. Then the birds would be shot or ensnared by nets that might trap more than 1 000 birds at once.

Beginning in 1858, passenger pigeon hunting became a big business. Shotguns, traps, artillery, and even dynamite were used. People burned grass or sulphur below their roosts to suffocate the birds. Shooting galleries used live birds as targets. In 1878, one professional pigeon trapper made $60 000 by killing 3 million birds at their nesting grounds near Petoskey, Michigan!

By the early 1880s, only a few thousand birds remained. At that point, recovery of the species was doomed because the females laid only one egg per nest each year. On March 24, 1900, a young boy in Ohio shot the last known wild passenger pigeon. The last passenger pigeon on Earth, a hen named Martha after

Martha Washington, died in the Cincinnati Zoo in 1914. Her stuffed body is now on view at the National Museum of Natural History in Washington, D.C.

Eventually all species become extinct or evolve into new species. But biologists estimate that human activities have increased the **natural rate of extinction** by a factor of 1 000 to 10 000—perhaps more. Studies indicate that this rate of loss of biodiversity is expected to increase as the human population grows, consumes more resources, disturbs more of the Earth's land and aquatic systems, and uses more of the Earth's net plant productivity that supports all species.

© jack thomas/Alamy

FIGURE 12-1 Lost natural capital: passenger pigeons have been extinct in the wild since 1900. The last known passenger pigeon died in the Cincinnati Zoo in 1914.

The last word in ignorance is the person who says of an animal or plant: "What good is it?" …. If the land mechanism as a whole is good, then every part of it is good, whether we understand it or not…. Harmony with land is like harmony with a friend; you cannot cherish his right hand and chop off his left.

ALDO LEOPOLD

CHAPTER PURPOSE AND QUESTIONS

Chapter 12 discusses factors that threaten terrestrial biodiversity by increasing species extinction rates. The chapter addresses the following questions:

12-1   What are the three types of species extinction?

12-2   Why should we preserve wild species?

12-3   What is the role of habitat loss and degradation?

12-4   What is the role of deliberately introduced species?

12-5   How serious is the illegal taking or killing of wild species?

12-6   What is the effect of predator control?

12-7   How can international treaties help to protect endangered species?

12-8   What is an extirpated species?

12-9   What is the role of wildlife refuges and sanctuaries?

12-10 What is reconciliation ecology?

12-1   SPECIES EXTINCTION

What Are Three Types of Species Extinction? Local, Ecological, and Biological

Species can become extinct locally, ecologically, or globally.

Biologists distinguish among three levels of species extinction. One is *local extinction*. It occurs when a species is no longer found in an area it once inhabited but is still found elsewhere in the world. Most local extinctions involve losses of one or more populations of a species.

The second type is *ecological extinction*. It occurs when so few members of a species are left that it can no longer play its ecological roles in the biological communities where it is found.

The third type is *biological extinction*, when a species is no longer found anywhere on the Earth (Figures 12-1 and 12-2). Biological extinction is forever.

Canada has lost 15 species to extinction (Table 12-1, p. 263). Five are briefly described below:

- **Great auk (*Pinguinis impennis*).** Great auks were penguin-like birds that stood 1 metre tall (Figure 12-2). They were excellent swimmers, but slow and clumsy on land. Great auks lived on small islands in the Far North. Sailors and fishermen slaughtered them for meat and fat. The last 50 great auks that remained were collected for museum specimens. They were extinct by 1844.

- **Labrador duck (*Camptorhyncus labradorium*).** These ducks nested along the coast of Labrador. Native people and fishermen hunted them for meat and eggs. Before they became extinct by 1875, labrador ducks were killed in greater numbers as part of a commercial trade in feathers.

- **Passenger pigeon (*Ectopistes migratorius*).** At one time, the passenger pigeon may have been the

| Passenger pigeon | Great auk | Labrador duck | Sea mink | Dawson caribou |

FIGURE 12-2 Lost natural capital: these are five of Canada's extinct (sub) species.

most common bird in the world (Case Study, p. 249). Their numbers were depressed quickly by commercial hunters who used nets and dynamite, and by a habitat that became less hospitable as large forests were transformed into farmland. Despite the warnings of naturalists, no effective conservation measures were taken. The last wild passenger pigeon was shot in 1900. The last of the small group of passenger pigeons that resided in the Cincinnati Zoo died in 1914.

■ **Sea mink (*Mustela macrodon*).** Sea mink inhabited the islands and coastlines of the Maritime provinces. Twice as large as ordinary mink, they were prized for their reddish pelts and were hunted to extinction by 1900.

■ **Dawson caribou or Queen Charlotte Island caribou (*Rangifer tarandus dawsoni*).** This diminutive subspecies of caribou inhabited the Queen Charlotte Islands. As a result of overhunting by fishermen who frequented the islands, they were extinct by 1935.

The most recent additions to this group were the Lake Ontario population of Atlantic salmon (*Salmo salar*), listed as extinct in 2010, and the Ungava Peninsula population of grizzly bears (*Ursus arctos*), listed as extinct in 2012. Visit http://www.cosewic.gc.ca/ to learn more about extinct Canadian species.

What Are Endangered and Threatened Species? Ecological Smoke Alarms

An endangered species could soon become extinct, and a threatened species is likely to become extinct.

Biologists classify species heading toward biological extinction as either *endangered* or *threatened*. An **endangered species** has so few individual survivors that the species could soon become extinct over all or most of its natural range. A **threatened species** is still abundant in its natural range but, because of declining numbers, is likely to become endangered in the near future.

Some species have characteristics that make them more vulnerable than others to ecological and biological extinction (Figure 12-3). As biodiversity expert Edward O. Wilson puts it, "the first animal species to go are the big, the slow, the tasty, and those with valuable parts such as tusks and skins."

Studies by the World Conservation Union, Conservation International, and the World Wide Fund for Nature illustrate that different groups of organisms are threatened to various degrees by human activities. Figure 12-4 shows that plants, fishes, and amphibians tend to be in the most danger of premature extinction.

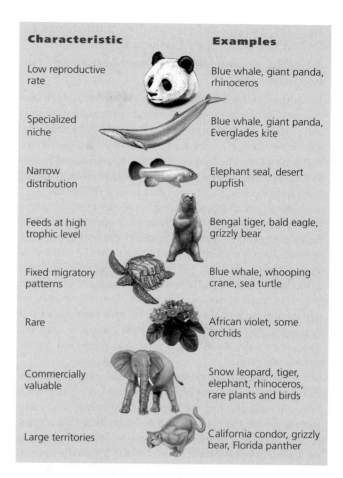

Characteristic	Examples
Low reproductive rate	Blue whale, giant panda, rhinoceros
Specialized niche	Blue whale, giant panda, Everglades kite
Narrow distribution	Elephant seal, desert pupfish
Feeds at high trophic level	Bengal tiger, bald eagle, grizzly bear
Fixed migratory patterns	Blue whale, whooping crane, sea turtle
Rare	African violet, some orchids
Commercially valuable	Snow leopard, tiger, elephant, rhinoceros, rare plants and birds
Large territories	California condor, grizzly bear, Florida panther

FIGURE 12-3 Characteristics of species that are prone to ecological and biological extinction.

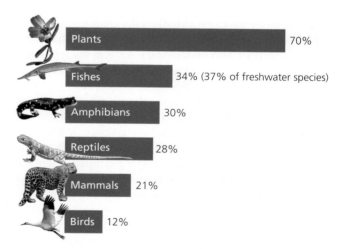

Plants	70%
Fishes	34% (37% of freshwater species)
Amphibians	30%
Reptiles	28%
Mammals	21%
Birds	12%

FIGURE 12-4 Endangered natural capital: percentage of various types of species threatened with premature extinction because of human activities. (Data from World Conservation Union, Conservation International, and World Wide Fund for Nature)

How Do Biologists Estimate Extinction Rates? Peering into a Cloudy Looking Glass

Scientists use measurements and models to estimate extinction rates.

Evolutionary biologists estimate that 99.9% of all species that ever existed are now extinct because of a combination of background extinction, mass extinctions, and mass depletions taking place over thousands to millions of years. Biologists also talk of an *extinction spasm*, in which large numbers of species are lost over a period of a few centuries or at most 1 000 years.

Biologists trying to catalogue extinctions have three problems. *First*, the extinction of a species typically takes such a long time that it is not easy to document. *Second*, we have identified only about 1.4–1.8 million of the world's estimated 5–100 million species. *Third*, we know little about most of the species we have identified.

The truth is we do not know how many species are becoming extinct each year mostly because of our activities. But scientists do the best they can with the tools they have to estimate past and projected future extinction rates.

One approach is to study past records documenting the rate at which mammals and birds have become extinct since we came on the scene, and compare this with the fossil records of such extinctions prior to our arrival. For example, there is a detailed study on extinction of Pacific island birds by early human colonists. Since the 1960s the International Union for the Conservation of Nature and Natural Resources (IUCN)—also known as the World Conservation Union—has kept *Red Lists* that have become the world standard for listing all threatened species throughout the world. These lists provide baseline information on how some of the Earth's biodiversity changes over time. Biologists use these lists to identify species that have become extinct, and to determine shifts in the types and numbers of species endangered by human activities.

Another way that biologists project future extinction rates is to observe how the number of species present increases with the size of an area. This *species–area relationship* suggests that on average, a 90% loss of habitat causes the extinction of about 50% of the species living in that habitat. For example, scientists estimate that about 50% of the world's existing terrestrial species live in tropical forests and that about one-third of the remaining tropical forests will be cut or burned during the next few decades. If these assumptions are valid, the species–area relationship suggests about 1 million species in these tropical forests will become extinct during this period.

The methods just described give similar estimates of past and future extinction rates. They also provide strong evidence that human actions have caused recent extinctions and that the situation will get worse.

Scientists also use models to estimate the risk that a particular population of a species will become endangered or extinct within a certain time.

Estimates of future extinction rates vary because of differing assumptions about the Earth's total number of species, the proportion of these species found in tropical forests, the rate at which tropical forests are being cleared, and the reliability of the methods used to make these estimates.

How Are Human Activities Affecting Extinction Rates? Taking Out More Species

Biologists estimate that the current rate of extinction is at least 1 000 to 10 000 times the rate before we arrived.

In due time all species become extinct, but there is considerable evidence that we are hastening the final exit for a growing number of species. Before we came on the scene the estimated extinction rate was roughly one species per million annually. This amounted to an annual extinction rate of about 0.0001% per year.

Using the methods just described, biologists conservatively estimate that the current rate of extinction is at least 1 000 to 10 000 times the rate before we arrived. This amounts to an annual extinction rate of 0.1% to 1% per year.

So how many species are we probably losing prematurely each year? This depends on how many species are on the Earth. Assuming that the extinction rate is 0.1%, each year we are losing 5 000 species per year if there are 5 million species, 14 000 if there are 14 million species (biologists' current best guess), and 100 000 if there are 100 million species.

Most biologists would consider the premature loss of 1 million species over 100–200 years an extinction crisis or spasm that, if kept up, would lead to a mass depletion or even a mass extinction. At an extinction rate of 0.1% a year, the time it would take to lose 1 million species would be 200 years if there were a total of 5 million species, 71 years with a total of 14 million species, and 10 years with 100 million species. How many years would it take to lose 1 million species for each of these three species estimates if the extinction rate is 1% a year?

According to researchers Edward O. Wilson and Stuart Primm, at a 1% extinction rate at least 20% of the world's current animal and plant species could be gone by 2030 and 50% could vanish by the end of this century. In the words of biodiversity expert Norman Myers, "Within just a few human generations, we shall—in the absence of greatly expanded conservation efforts—impoverish the biosphere to an extent that will persist for at least 200 000 human generations or twenty times longer than the period since humans emerged as a species."

Most biologists consider extinction rates of 0.1–1% to be conservative estimates for several reasons. *First,* both the rate of species loss and the extent of biodiversity loss are likely to increase during the next 50–100 years because of the projected exponential growth of the world's human population and per capita resource use. In other words, the size of our already large ecological footprint (Figure 1-7, p. 8 and Figure 9-12, p. 189) is likely to increase.

Second, current and projected extinction rates are much higher than the global average in parts of the world that are endangered centres of biodiversity. Conservation biologists estimate that such biologically rich areas could lose one-fourth to one-half of their estimated species within a few decades. They urge us to focus our efforts on slowing the much higher rates of extinction in such *hot spots* (Figure 11-30, p. 243) as the best and quickest way to protect much of the Earth's biodiversity from being lost prematurely.

Third, we are eliminating, degrading, and simplifying many biologically diverse environments—such as tropical forests, tropical coral reefs, wetlands, and estuaries—that serve as potential colonization sites for the emergence of new species. Thus, in addition to increasing the rate of extinction, we may also be limiting long-term recovery of biodiversity by reducing the rate of speciation for some types of species. In other words, we are also creating a *speciation crisis.*

Philip Levin, Donald Levin, and other biologists also argue that the increasing fragmentation and disturbance of habitats throughout the world may increase the speciation rate for rapidly reproducing opportunist species such as weeds, rodents, and cockroaches and other insects. Thus the real threat to biodiversity from current human activities may not be a permanent decline in the number of species but a long-term erosion in the Earth's variety of species and habitats.

Some people, most of them not biologists, say the current estimated extinction rates are too high and are based on inadequate data and models. Researchers agree that their estimates of extinction rates are based on inadequate data and sampling. They continually strive to get better data and improve the models they use to estimate extinction rates.

However, they point to clear evidence that human activities have increased the rate of species extinction and that this rate is likely to rise. According to these biologists, arguing over the numbers and waiting to get better data and models should not be used as excuses for inaction. They call for us to implement a *precautionary strategy* now to help prevent a significant decrease in the Earth's genetic, species, ecological, and functional diversity.

To these biologists, we are not heeding the warning of Aldo Leopold about preserving biodiversity as we tinker with the Earth: "To keep every cog and wheel is the first precaution of intelligent tinkering."

12-2 IMPORTANCE OF WILD SPECIES

Why Should We Preserve Wild Species? They Have Value

We should not cause the premature extinction of species because of the economic and ecological services they provide.

So what is all the fuss about? If all species eventually become extinct, why should we worry about losing a few more because of our activities? Does it matter that the passenger pigeon, the 80–100 remaining Florida panthers, or some unknown plant or insect in a tropical forest becomes prematurely extinct because of our activities?

We know that new species eventually evolve to take the place of ones lost through extinction spasms, mass depletions, or mass extinctions. So why should we care if we speed up the extinction rate over the next 50–100 years? The answer is that *it will take at least 5 million years for speciation to rebuild the biodiversity we are likely to destroy during this century!*

Conservation biologists and ecologists say we should act now to prevent the premature extinction of species because of their **instrumental value** based on their usefulness to us in the form of economic and ecological services. For example, species provide economic value in the form of food crops, fuelwood and lumber, paper, and medicine (Figure 11-18, p. 232).

Another instrumental value is the *genetic information* in species. Genetic engineers use this information to produce new types of crops (Figure 5-11, p. 105) and foods, and edible vaccines for viral diseases such as hepatitis B. Carelessly eliminating many of the species making up the world's vast genetic library is like burning books before we read them. Wild species also provide a way for us to learn how nature works and sustains itself.

The Earth's wild plants and animals also provide us with *recreational pleasure.* Each year North Americans spend over three times as many hours watching wildlife—doing nature photography and bird watching, for example—as they spend on watching movies or professional sporting events.

Wildlife tourism, or *ecotourism,* generates at least $500 billion per year worldwide, and perhaps twice that much. Conservation biologist Michael Soulé estimates that one male lion living to age 7 generates $515 000 in tourist dollars in Kenya, but only $1 000 if killed for its skin. Similarly, over a lifetime of 60 years a Kenyan elephant is worth about $1 million in ecotourist revenue—many times more than its tusks are worth when sold illegally for their ivory.

Ideally, ecotourism should not cause ecological damage. In addition, it should provide income for local people to motivate them to preserve wildlife and funds for the purchase and maintenance of wildlife preserves and conservation programs. Much ecotourism does not meet these standards, and excessive and unregulated ecotourism can destroy or degrade fragile areas and promote premature species extinction.

Case Study: Why Should We Care About Bats? Ecological Allies

Because of the important ecological and economic roles bats play, we should view them as valuable allies, not as enemies to kill.

Worldwide there are more than 1 100 known species of bats—the only mammals that can fly. However, bats have two traits that make them vulnerable to extinction. *First,* they reproduce slowly. *Second,* many bat species live in huge colonies in caves and abandoned mines, which people sometimes block. This prevents them from leaving to get food and can disturb their hibernation.

Bats play important ecological roles. About 70% of all bat species feed on crop-damaging nocturnal insects and other insect pest species such as mosquitoes. This makes them the major nighttime SWAT team for such insects.

In some tropical forests and on many tropical islands, *pollen-eating bats* pollinate flowers, and *fruit-eating bats* distribute plants throughout tropical forests by excreting undigested seeds.

As keystone species, such bats are vital for maintaining plant biodiversity and for regenerating large areas of tropical forest cleared by human activities. If you enjoy bananas, cashews, dates, figs, avocados, or mangos, you can thank bats.

Many people mistakenly view bats as fearsome, filthy, aggressive, rabies-carrying bloodsuckers. But most bat species are harmless to people, livestock, and crops. In North America, only 10 people have died of bat-transmitted disease in four decades of record keeping; more North Americans die each year from falling coconuts.

SPOTLIGHT

White Nose Syndrome Is Killing Bats

White nose syndrome (WNS) is a disease affecting bats that was first reported in New York State in winter 2006, yet it has already killed 5–7 million bats. It is called *white nose syndrome* because a newly discovered fungus, *Geomyces destructans,* grows on the muzzles of the diseased bats, giving their noses a whitish appearance. It affects bats that hibernate communally in caves. Bats that have the disease are unusually active, even flying outside the cave in winter. Of course, there are no flying insects for the bats to eat in winter and so they quickly exhaust their energy stores.

WNS has now been reported in four Canadian provinces (New Brunswick, Nova Scotia, Quebec, and Ontario) and throughout much of the eastern United States. Canadian and American wildlife agencies are cooperating to study and try to control WNS; however, the disease is expected to spread quickly and to have a devastating effect on hibernating bat populations. The little brown bat (*Myotis lucifugus*) is normally one of our most common bats, but it was placed on the endangered species list in 2012 in anticipation of massive declines over the next decade (COSEWIC, 2012b; Forbes, 2012).

Marvin Moriarty/USFWS

Because of unwarranted fears of bats and lack of knowledge about their vital ecological roles, several bat species have been driven to extinction. Currently, about one-fourth of the world's bat species, including the ghost bat, are listed as endangered or threatened. Conservation biologists urge us to view bats as valuable allies, not as enemies.

What Is the Intrinsic Value of Species? Existence Rights

Some people believe that each wild species has an inherent right to exist.

Some people believe that each wild species also has *intrinsic* or *existence* value based on its inherent right to exist and play its ecological roles, regardless of its usefulness to us. Biologist Edward O. Wilson believes most people feel obligated to protect other species and the Earth's biodiversity because most humans seem to have a natural affinity for nature that he calls *biophilia* (see Connections, p. 256). As novelist Fyodor Dostoevsky said in his 1889 novel *The Brothers Karamazov*, "Love the animals, love the plants, love everything. If you love everything, you will perceive the divine mystery in things. Once you perceive it, you will begin to comprehend it better every day. And you will come at last to love the whole world with an all-embracing love."

Some people distinguish between the survival rights of plants and those of animals, mostly for practical reasons. Poet Alan Watts once said he was a vegetarian "because cows scream louder than carrots."

Other people distinguish among various types of species. For example, they might think little about getting rid of the world's mosquitoes, cockroaches, rats, or disease-causing bacteria.

Some proponents of existence rights, such as Nobel Prize winner Albert Schweitzer, go further and assert that each individual organism has a right to survive without human interference. Others apply this to individuals of some species but not to those of other species. Unless they are strict vegetarians, for example, some people see no harm in having others kill domesticated animals in slaughterhouses to provide them with meat, leather, and other products. But these same people might deplore the killing of wild animals such as deer, squirrels, or rabbits. Or they might put out a feeder for birds but then try to kill or discourage other species, such as squirrels, that are drawn to this food source.

Some conservation biologists also caution us not to think only of protecting relatively big organisms—the plants and animals we can see and are familiar with. They remind us that the true foundation of the Earth's ecosystems and ecological processes are the small organisms: the invisible bacteria and the algae,

fungi, and other *microorganisms* that decompose the bodies of larger organisms and recycle the nutrients needed by all life (Case Study, p. 59).

CONSIDER, DISCUSS, OR DEBATE

How do you think other species should be treated? Are your opinions on this subject consistent with your actions (for example, do you hunt, fish, eat meat, wear leather or fur, keep pets, or swat mosquitoes)? Do you distinguish between various types of species? Is there a rational basis for the distinctions you make, or are they arbitrary and/or based on emotion?

12-3 EXTINCTION THREATS FROM HABITAT LOSS AND DEGRADATION

What Is the Role of Habitat Loss and Degradation? Creating Homeless Species

The greatest threat to a species is the loss and degradation of the place where it lives.

Figure 12-5 (p. 256) shows the basic and secondary causes of the endangerment and premature extinction of wild species. Conservation biologists sometimes summarize the main secondary factors leading to premature extinction using the acronym **HIPPO** for **h**abitat destruction and fragmentation, **i**nvasive (alien) species, **p**opulation growth (too many people consuming too many resources), **p**ollution, and **o**verharvesting.

According to biodiversity researchers, the greatest threat to wild species is habitat loss, degradation, and fragmentation. In other words, many species have a hard time surviving after we take over their ecological "house" and food supplies and make them homeless.

Deforestation of tropical forests is the greatest eliminator of terrestrial species, followed by the destruction of wetlands and plowing of grasslands. Globally, temperate biomes have been affected more by habitat loss and degradation than have tropical biomes because of widespread development in temperate countries over the past 200 years. Emphasis is now shifting to many tropical biomes.

According to the Nature Conservancy, the major types of habitat disturbance threatening endangered species in North America are, in order of diminishing importance: agriculture, commercial development, water development, outdoor recreation (including off-road vehicles), livestock grazing, and pollution.

Island species, many of them **endemic species** found nowhere else on Earth, are especially vulnerable to extinction when their habitats are destroyed, degraded, or fragmented.

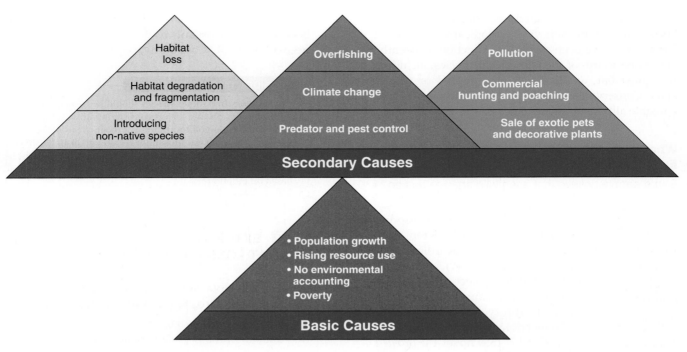

FIGURE 12-5 Basic and secondary causes of depletion and premature extinction of wild species. The biggest direct causes of wildlife depletion and premature extinction are loss, fragmentation, and degradation of habitat, and deliberate or accidental introduction of non-native species into ecosystems.

What Is the Role of Habitat Fragmentation? Isolating and Weakening Populations of Species

Species are more vulnerable to extinction when their habitats are divided into smaller, more isolated patches.

Habitat fragmentation occurs when a large, continuous area of habitat is reduced in area and divided into smaller, more scattered, and isolated patches or "habitat islands." This divides populations of a species into smaller and more isolated groups that are more vulnerable to predators, invasion by more competitive species, disease, and catastrophic events such as a storm or fire. Also, it creates barriers that can hinder some species from dispersing and colonizing new areas, getting enough to eat, and finding mates.

Certain types of species are especially vulnerable to local and regional extinction because of habitat fragmentation. They include species that are rare, that need to roam unhindered over large areas, and that cannot rebuild their population because of a low reproductive capacity. Also included are species with specialized niches and species that are sought by people for furs, food, medicines, or other uses.

The theory of island biogeography (p. 159) has been used to understand the effects of fragmentation on species extinction and to develop ways to help prevent such extinction.

Case Study: How Do Human Activities Affect Bird Species? A Disturbing Message from the Birds

Our activities are causing serious declines in the populations of many bird species.

Approximately 70% of the world's 9 800 known bird species are declining in numbers, and about one of every eight bird species is threatened with extinction, mostly because of habitat loss and fragmentation. A 2002 National Audubon Society study found that a quarter of all North American bird species are declining in numbers or are at risk of disappearing.

Non-native species are the second-greatest threat to birds. They include bird-eating cats, rats, brown-tree snakes, and mongooses.

Birds can also be loved to death. A third of the world's 330 parrot species are threatened from a combination of habitat loss and capture for the pet trade (often illegal), especially in Europe and North America.

At least 23 species of seabirds face extinction because they are being drowned after becoming hooked on kilometres of baited lines put out by fishing boats. Millions of migrating birds are killed each year when they collide with power lines, communications towers, and skyscrapers that we have erected in the middle of their migration routes. Each year North American hunters kill about 125 million birds, but approximately 1 billion birds are killed in North America each year by flying into glass windows (Figure 12-6).

Other threats to birds are oil spills, exposure to pesticides, herbicides that destroy their habitats, and swallowing toxic lead shotgun pellets left in wetlands and lead sinkers left by anglers. Poorly regulated illegal hunting and capture also take a heavy toll.

Conservation biologists view this decline of bird species as an early warning of the greater loss of biodiversity to come. The reason is that birds are excellent *environmental indicators* because they live in every climate and biome, respond quickly to environmental changes in their habitats, and are easy to track and count.

Besides serving as indicator species, birds play important ecological roles. These include helping control populations of rodents and insects (which decimate many tree species), pollinating a variety of flowering plants, spreading plants throughout their habitats by consuming and excreting plant seeds, and scavenging dead animals. Conservation biologists urge us to listen more carefully to what birds are telling us about the state of the environment.

FIGURE 12-6 Every year, more than a billion birds die in collisions with human-built structures in North America. Tall buildings with glass windows and bright lights are particularly hazardous to birds.

The Canadian Press/Aaron Harris

12-4 EXTINCTION THREATS FROM NON-NATIVE SPECIES

What Is the Role of Deliberately Introduced Species? Good and Bad News

Many non-native species provide us with food, medicine, and other benefits, but a few can wipe out some native species, disrupt ecosystems, and cause large economic losses.

We depend heavily on non-native organisms for ecosystem services, food, shelter, medicine, and aesthetic enjoyment.

According to a 2000 study by ecologist David Pimentel, introduced species such as corn, wheat, rice, other food crops, cattle, poultry, and other livestock provide more than 98% of the food supply in most developed nations. Similarly, non-native tree species are grown in about 85% of the world's tree plantations. Some deliberately introduced species have also helped control pests.

The problem is that some introduced species have no natural predators, competitors, parasites, or pathogens to help control their numbers in their new habitats. Such species can reduce or wipe out populations of many native species and trigger ecological disruptions. Invasive species such as purple loosestrife, gypsy moths, zebra mussels, round gobies, emerald ash borers, and Asian carp are discussed in Chapters 11, 13, and 23.

After habitat loss and degradation, the deliberate or accidental introduction of non-native species into ecosystems is the biggest cause of animal and plant extinctions. Non-native species put added pressure on endangered and threatened species by changing ecosystems and by competing with native species that may be already struggling to survive. They are also blamed for about two-thirds of fish extinctions in North America between 1900 and 2000. One example of a deliberately introduced plant species is the *kudzu* ("CUD-zoo") *vine*, which grows rampant in the southeastern United States (see Case Study).

Deliberately introduced animal species have also caused ecological and economic damage. An example is the estimated 1 million European *wild (feral) boars*, or *hogs*, found in parts of British Columbia and the Prairie provinces as well as Florida, Texas, and other states. They breed like rabbits, have razor-sharp tusks, compete for food with endangered animals, root up farm fields, and cause traffic accidents. Game and wildlife officials have had little success in controlling their numbers. Another example is the more than 30 million *feral cats* and 40 million *outdoor pet cats* in North America; they kill about 570 million birds per year!

Case Study: A Plant Introduction with Unintended Consequences

The rapidly growing kudzu vine has spread throughout much of the southern United States and is almost impossible to control.

In the 1930s, the *kudzu vine* was imported from Japan and planted in the southeastern United States to help control soil erosion. It does control erosion. But it is so prolific and difficult to kill that it engulfs hillsides, gardens, trees, abandoned houses and cars, stream banks, patches of forest, and anything else in its path (Figure 12-7).

This vine, sometimes called "the vine that ate the South," has spread throughout much of the southern United States. It could spread as far north as the Great Lakes by 2040 if projected global warming occurs.

Kudzu is considered a menace in the United States, but Asians use a powdered kudzu starch in beverages, gourmet confections, and herbal remedies for a range of diseases. A Japanese firm has built a large kudzu farm and processing plant in Alabama and ships the extracted starch to Japan.

Although kudzu can engulf and kill trees, it could eventually help save trees from loggers. Research indicates that kudzu may be used as a source of tree-free paper.

Solutions: How Can We Reduce Threats from Non-Native Species? Prevention Pays

Prevention is the best way to reduce the threats from non-native species because once they have arrived it is difficult and expensive to slow their spread.

Once a non-native species gets established in an ecosystem, its wholesale removal is almost impossible—

FIGURE 12-7 Kudzu taking over an abandoned house. This vine can grow 5 centimetres (2 inches) per hour and is now found from east Texas to Florida and as far north as southeastern Pennsylvania and Illinois. Kudzu was deliberately introduced into the United States for erosion control, but it cannot be stopped by being dug up or burned. Grazing by goats and repeated doses of herbicides can destroy it, but goats and herbicides also destroy other plants, and herbicides can contaminate water supplies.

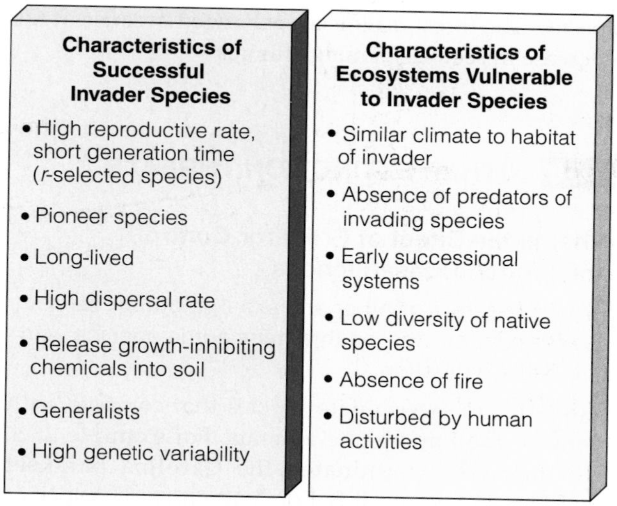

Characteristics of Successful Invader Species	Characteristics of Ecosystems Vulnerable to Invader Species
• High reproductive rate, short generation time (*r*-selected species) • Pioneer species • Long-lived • High dispersal rate • Release growth-inhibiting chemicals into soil • Generalists • High genetic variability	• Similar climate to habitat of invader • Absence of predators of invading species • Early successional systems • Low diversity of native species • Absence of fire • Disturbed by human activities

FIGURE 12-8 Threats to natural capital: some general characteristics of successful invader species and ecosystems vulnerable to invading species.

somewhat like trying to get smoke back into a chimney or trying to unscramble an egg. Thus the best way to limit the harmful impacts of non-native species is to prevent them from being introduced and becoming established.

There are several ways to do this. One is to identify major characteristics that allow species to become successful invaders and the types of ecosystems that are vulnerable to invaders (Figure 12-8). Such information can be used to screen out potentially harmful invaders. In 2003, marine ecologist Kevin Lafferty and his colleagues reported that many invading animal species gained a competitive advantage in their new homes because they leave behind about half of their native parasites and diseases.

We can also inspect imported goods that are likely to contain invader species. A third strategy is to identify major harmful invader species and pass international laws banning their transfer from one country to another, as is now done for endangered species.

Prevention and control can help. But many of these invaders are tiny, hard to detect, and able to breed rapidly. We also need to remind ourselves that the globalization of our economies and lifestyles is what helps bring these new and unwanted biological immigrants into countries throughout the world.

12-5 EXTINCTION THREATS FROM POACHING AND HUNTING

How Serious Is the Illegal Taking or Killing of Wild Species? Making Big Money

Some protected species are killed for their valuable parts or are sold live to collectors.

Organized crime has moved into illegal wildlife smuggling because of the huge profits involved. Smuggling wildlife—including many endangered species—is the third-largest and most lucrative illegal cross-border smuggling activity after arms and drugs. At least two-thirds of all live animals illegally smuggled around the world die in transit.

Poverty is one reason behind the illegal smuggling of wild species. Some poor people struggling to survive in areas with rich stores of wildlife kill or trap such species to make enough money to survive and feed their families. What would you do in the same situation? Others are professional poachers.

To poachers, a *live mountain gorilla* is worth about $150 000, a *panda pelt* $100 000 (only about 1 500 pandas are left in the wild), a *chimpanzee* $50 000, and an *Imperial Amazon macaw* $30 000. A *rhinoceros horn* is worth as much as $28 600 per kilogram ($13 000 per pound) because of its use in dagger handles in the Middle East and as a fever reducer and alleged aphrodisiac in China—the world's largest consumer of wildlife—and other parts of Asia.

In 1950, an estimated 100 000 tigers existed in the world. Despite international protection, today approximately 3 500 tigers remain in the wild (about 1 400 in India), mostly because of habitat loss and poaching for fur and bones. Bengal tigers are at risk because a tiger fur sells for about $100 000 in Tokyo. With the body parts of a single tiger worth $5 000–$20 000, it is not surprising that illegal hunting has skyrocketed, especially in India. Without emergency action, few or no tigers may be left in the wild within 20 years.

As commercially valuable species become endangered, their black market demand soars. This increases their chances of premature extinction from poaching. Most poachers are not caught. And the money they can make far outweighs the small risk of being caught, fined, or imprisoned.

Case Study: The Rising Demand for Bushmeat in Africa: Hungry People Trying to Survive

Rapid population growth in parts of Africa has increased the number of people hunting wild animals for food or for sale of their meat to restaurants.

Indigenous people in much of West and Central Africa have sustainably hunted wildlife for *bushmeat* as a source of food for centuries. But in the last two decades the level of hunting for bushmeat in some areas has skyrocketed.

In forests throughout West and Central Africa virtually every type of wild animal is being hunted by local people, frequently illegally, for food or to supply restaurants (Figure 12-9, page 260). The bushmeat trade is also increasing in Southeast Asia, the Caribbean, and Central and South America.

FIGURE 12-9 *Bushmeat,* such as this gorilla head, is consumed as a source of protein by local people in parts of West Africa and sold in the national and international marketplace. You can find bushmeat on the menu in Cameroon and the Congo in West Africa as well as in Paris, France, and Brussels, Belgium—often supplied by illegal poaching.

Killing wild animals for bushmeat has become more widespread for four reasons. *First,* an eightfold increase in Africa's population during the last century has led to more people hunting and trapping wild animals. *Second,* logging roads have allowed miners, ranchers, and settlers to move into once inaccessible forests. *Third,* restaurants in many parts of the world have begun serving bushmeat dishes. *Fourth,* many people living in poverty find that selling wild animals or their valuable parts to collectors, meat suppliers, and poachers is a way to make enough money to survive.

So what is the big deal? After all, people have to eat. And for most of the time our species has been around we survived by hunting and gathering wild species.

The problem is that the current depletion of bushmeat species in some areas has ecological impacts. It has caused the local extinction of many animals in West Africa and has driven one species—Miss Waldron's red colobus monkey—to complete extinction. It is also a factor in greatly reducing gorilla, orangutan, and chimpanzee populations. For example, wealthy patrons of some restaurants regard gorilla meat as a source of status and power.

It also threatens forest carnivores such as crowned eagles and leopards by depleting their main prey

species. The forest itself is also changed because of the decrease in seed-dispersing animals.

12-6 OTHER EXTINCTION THREATS

What Is the Effect of Predator Control? Unintended Consequences

Killing predators or other animals that bother us or cause economic losses threatens some species with premature extinction.

People try to exterminate species that compete with them for food and game animals. For example, U.S. fruit farmers exterminated the Carolina parakeet around 1914 because it fed on fruit crops. The species was easy prey because when one member of a flock was shot, the rest of the birds hovered over its body, making themselves easy targets.

Each year, farmers and ranchers in North America shoot, poison, or trap thousands of coyotes, wolves, bobcats, and other species that prey on livestock, on species prized by game hunters, and on crops or fish raised in aquaculture ponds. Since the early 1900s, farmers and ranchers have poisoned, trapped, or shot many of North America's prairie dogs because horses and cattle sometimes step into the burrows and break their legs. At the same time, much of the native prairie grasslands that these animals needed for habitat disappeared. These combined events nearly wiped out the black-footed ferret, which preyed on the prairie dog. This is another example of unintended consequences because of not understanding the connections between species.

What Is the Role of the Market for Exotic Pets and Decorative Plants? Are We Really Pet and Plant Lovers?

Legal and illegal trade in wildlife species used as pets or for decorative purposes threatens some species with extinction.

The global legal and illegal trade in wild species for use as pets is a huge and very profitable business. However, for every live animal captured and sold in the pet market, an estimated 50 others are killed.

More than 25 million North American households have exotic birds as pets, 85% of them imported. More than 60 bird species, mostly parrots, are endangered or threatened because of this wild bird trade. According to the U.S. Fish and Wildlife Service, collectors of exotic birds may pay $10 000 (U.S.) for a threatened hyacinth macaw smuggled out of Brazil; however, during its lifetime a single macaw left in the wild might yield as much as $165 000 (U.S.) in tourist income.

Other wild species whose populations are depleted because of the pet trade include amphibians, reptiles, mammals, and tropical fish (taken mostly from the coral reefs of Indonesia and the Philippines). Divers commonly catch tropical fish by using plastic squeeze bottles of cyanide to stun them. For each fish caught alive, many more die. In addition, the cyanide solution kills the coral animals that create the reef, which is a centre for marine biodiversity.

Things do not have to be this way. Pilai Poonswad decided to do something about poachers taking hornbills—large, beautiful, and rare birds—from a rain forest in Thailand. She visited the poachers in their villages and showed them why the birds are worth more alive than dead. Now she has a number of ex-poachers earning much more money than they did before by taking ecotourists into the forest to see these magnificent birds. Because of their vested financial interest in preserving the hornbills, they also help protect them from poachers.

Some exotic plants, especially orchids and cacti, are endangered because they are gathered (often illegally) and sold to collectors to decorate houses, offices, and landscapes. North America imports about 75% of all orchids and 99% of all live cacti sold each year. A collector may pay $5 000 for a single rare orchid, and a single rare mature crested saguaro cactus can earn cactus rustlers as much as $15 000.

In other words, collecting exotic pets and plants kills large numbers of them and endangers many of these species and others that depend on them.

CONSIDER, DISCUSS, OR DEBATE

Are the collectors of exotic pets and plants acting as lovers or haters of the species they collect? Should we leave most exotic species in the wild? What exceptions should be made, if any? How can exotic species be enjoyed while still living in their natural habitats?

What Are the Roles of Climate Change and Pollution? Speeding Up the Treadmill and Poisoning Species

Projected climate change and exposure to pollutants will push more species toward premature extinction.

Most natural climate changes in the past have taken place over very long periods of time. This gave species time to adapt to the changes or to move to more suitable locations. But considerable evidence indicates that human activities, such as generating large quantities of greenhouse gases and deforesting large tracts of land, will likely bring about rapid climate changes during this century (Chapter 21). This will alter the habitats of many species and will probably accelerate the extinction of species.

Scientists project that global warming will alter 33–80% of the world's habitats by 2100, with the most extreme changes happening at high latitudes (Malcolm et al., 2002). Habitats are projected to change 10 times faster than during the recent post-glacial period; this would be problematic to many species of plants and animals. Some species would have difficulty moving to suitable locations, particularly as the landscape becomes more fragmented. Some would be unlikely to adapt to the changing conditions. A landmark paper by Thomas et al. (2004) projected that changes in climate and habitat by 2050 could commit 15–37% of species to extinction. While some authors suggest that this may be an overestimate (Botkin et al., 2007), others predict that extinction rates will be higher because of additional pressures that displaced populations will face in dealing with dispersal, competition, and parasitism (Urban et al., 2012).

Canada would be particularly susceptible to climate change–induced habitat alteration because of its northern location. Even subtle differences in temperature could cause significant changes in factors such as depth of snow, duration of ice cover, properties of frozen ground, dryness of habitats, and frequency of fires. According to the WWF and the David Suzuki Foundation, more than 45% of Canada's habitats (65% in the boreal and Arctic regions) could be altered by the end of the century, resulting in a 20% loss of species.

Parks Canada has studied the possible effects of climate-induced habitat changes on the national parks of Canada. Park officials project that most parks will be warmer, drier, and subject to more frequent and intense forest fires. They suggest that 65% of the habitat in national parks could be fundamentally altered, causing difficulties for many organisms. The boreal forest itself is a cold-weather ecosystem that would need to "migrate" 100–700 kilometres (62–435 miles) further north within 100 years in order to match the projected changes in climate.

Some changes are already apparent in Canada. Polar bears in some subpopulations have declining body conditions and are being forced to change their hunting patterns and denning locations to accommodate changes in sea ice and snow cover. Caribou populations are facing increasing difficulties with warmer weather conditions such as being exposed to freezing rain instead of snow. According to the Audubon Society (2009), North American birds have moved their ranges 56 kilometres (35 miles) further north on average over the past 40 years, and many of these species are in decline. While it is too early to draw definite conclusions, the precautionary principle (p. 176) would suggest that we study the matter and pay close attention to any emerging trends.

Pollution is another stressor that can threaten populations and species in a number of ways. A major extinction threat is from the unintended effects of pesticides (Chapter 25). Every year, pesticide use in North America kills more than 67 million birds and 6–14 million fish. Pesticides have been implicated as one of the factors affecting declining amphibian populations, and they likely threaten other species that are already struggling to survive. As we will see in future chapters, organisms are exposed to chemicals that are toxic, carcinogenic, or gender-changing (Chapter 19). Depending on where and how they live, wild species may have to deal with varying degrees of air pollution (Chapter 20), water pollution (Chapter 22), and exposure to UV radiation from the sun (Chapter 21). Organisms may be bio-accumulating harmful fat-soluble substances throughout their lives, simply by living in environments close to sources of pollution.

All of these factors contribute to the pressures exerted on wild species by human activities.

12-7 PROTECTING WILD SPECIES: THE RESEARCH AND LEGAL APPROACH

How Can International Treaties Help Protect Endangered Species? Some Success

International treaties have helped reduce the international trade of endangered and threatened species, but enforcement is difficult.

Several international treaties and conventions help protect endangered or threatened wild species. One of the most far-reaching is the 1975 *Convention on International Trade in Endangered Species (CITES)*. This treaty, now signed by 175 countries, lists more than 950 species that cannot be commercially traded as live specimens or wildlife products because they are in danger of extinction. The treaty also restricts international trade of about 5 000 species of animals and 28 000 species of plants that are at risk of becoming threatened.

CITES has helped reduce international trade in many threatened animals, including elephants, crocodiles, and chimpanzees. However, the effects of this treaty are limited because enforcement is difficult and varies from country to country, and convicted violators often pay only small fines. Also, member countries can exempt themselves from protecting any listed species. And much of the highly profitable illegal trade in wildlife and wildlife products goes on in countries that have not signed the treaty.

The *Convention on Biological Diversity (CBD)*, ratified by 191 countries, legally binds signatory governments to reversing the global decline of biological diversity. The treaty requires each signatory nation to inventory its biodiversity and develop a *national conservation strategy*—a detailed plan for managing and preserving its biodiversity.

Implementing this treaty has been slow because some key countries, such as the United States, have not ratified it. Also, it has no severe penalties or other enforcement mechanisms.

What Is COSEWIC, and How Does It Contribute to Wildlife Species Protection in Canada? Risk Assessment

The Committee on the Status of Endangered Wildlife in Canada is an organization that provides expert assessments of species at risk in Canada.

The Committee on the Status of Endangered Wildlife in Canada (COSEWIC) was established in 1977 following a conference of government wildlife directors in Fredericton. At that conference, the need for a unified national approach to wildlife species at risk was a major issue. COSEWIC's original mandate was to consider mammals, birds, reptiles, amphibians, fish, and plants; over time, the organization widened its responsibilities to include mollusks, arthropods, lichens, and mosses.

COSEWIC's membership includes academics, government wildlife experts, independent specialists, and Aboriginal people, as well as representatives from the provincial or territorial wildlife agencies, the Canadian Wildlife Service, the Department of Fisheries and Oceans, Parks Canada Agency, and the Federal Biodiversity Information Partnership. Much of the organization's work is done by subcommittees of experts who deal with specific groups of organisms such as birds, arthropods, plants and lichens, and marine mammals.

COSEWIC is best known for the lists it produces of Canadian species that are in jeopardy, organized according to risk category. By 1978, COSEWIC had developed the following five risk categories:

- *Extinct (X)*. A wildlife species that no longer exists.

- *Extirpated (XT)*. A wildlife species no longer existing in the wild in Canada, but occurring elsewhere.

- *Endangered (E)*. A wildlife species facing imminent extirpation or extinction.

- *Threatened (T)*. A wildlife species likely to become endangered if limiting factors are not reversed.

- *Special Concern (SC)*. A wildlife species that may become threatened or endangered because of a combination of biological characteristics and identified threats (http://www.cosewic.gc.ca).

Whereas COSEWIC's 1978 list identified only 17 species considered to be at risk, the 2012 list names

Table 12-1 Summary of COSEWIC Assessment Results as of May 2012*: Risk Status According to Taxonomic Group

Taxon	Extinct	Extirpated	Endangered	Threatened	Special Concern	Totals
Mammals	3	2	23	17	29	74
Birds	3	2	29	27	20	81
Reptiles	0	4	18	11	9	42
Amphibians	0	2	10	5	6	23
Fishes	7	3	50	40	49	149
Arthropods	0	4	31	5	6	46
Molluscs	1	2	19	3	7	32
Vascular Plants	0	3	94	47	43	187
Mosses	1	1	8	3	4	17
Lichens	0	0	5	3	6	14
Totals	**15**	**23**	**287**	**161**	**179**	**665**

*Species in at-risk categories include those designated as extirpated, endangered, threatened, or special concern.

Source: Please refer to www.cosewic.gc.ca for the most current list, as numbers change after each assessment meeting to reflect the new assessments. Canadian Wildlife Species at Risk. Committee on the Status of Endangered Wildlife in Canada, http://www.cosewic.gc.ca/eng/sct0/rpt/rpt_csar_e.cfm. COSEWIC, 2012. Reproduced with permission of the Minister of Public Works and Government Services, 2012.

650 at-risk species as well as 15 species that are already extinct (Table 12-1).

COSEWIC's other responsibilities include developing prioritized lists of species requiring assessments and providing the government and the public with reports on species that have been assessed. The work of this committee is objective, transparent, and research-based; it does not take into account cost considerations, legal issues, or political priorities.

How Can Federal Legislation Help Protect Endangered Species? A Wide-Ranging Act in Canada

One of Canada's most important wildlife protection laws is the Species at Risk Act (SARA).

The Species at Risk Act (SARA), which became law in 2003, is a federal act that provides legal protection for wildlife species. The act has three main objectives: (1) to prevent Canadian species from becoming extirpated or extinct, (2) to assist the recovery of endangered and threatened species, and (3) to encourage conservation and management practices that will prevent other Canadian species from becoming at risk.

SARA designates COSEWIC as the independent body of experts responsible for identifying and assessing species at risk. The act protects listed endangered and threatened species and their critical habitats. It recognizes that compensation may be required when landowners are prevented from developing land that

is identified as critical habitat. It creates a *public registry* where documents related to the act can be inspected by the public. SARA also aligns efforts to save species at risk with other existing legislation such as Aboriginal and treaty rights.

Under the terms of SARA, the government receives advice about species at risk from COSEWIC. However, the government makes its own list, referred to as the *List of Wildlife Species at Risk* (or *Schedule 1* of the original act), which contains the names of the species that the government is prepared to offer legal protection. Once species are on that list, they receive immediate legal protection if they reside on federal lands, or are an aquatic species or migratory bird. Species that do not so qualify still receive protection, but through a more gradual process since provincial or territorial governments need to become involved.

For species that are added to the List of Wildlife Species at Risk, a *recovery strategy* must be prepared within one year for endangered species, or within two years for threatened species. A *management plan* must be prepared within three years for a species of special concern.

As an example of this point, Ontario released its new Endangered Species Act in 2007. Environmental groups were initially full of praise, saying that Ontario had the best endangered species legislation in the world, incorporating a good balance of science and flexibility. However, two years later a coalition of leading environmental groups issued a report card that gave the Ontario government low marks for not moving swiftly enough in implementing the act. Specifically, the provincial government received failing marks for not making use of available science and for not listening to the recommendations of recovery teams that were working with the endangered species. They also received failing marks for 3 of 10 endangered species because important habitat was not being protected in a timely manner (Save Ontario's Species, 2009). The environmental groups still praised the legislation but lamented the government's unwillingness to quickly and fully apply the legislation.

Recovery plans identify critical habitats that need to be set aside. The public registry allows for a 60-day period in which people can view and comment on these plans before further actions are taken. Five years after initiating a recovery strategy or a management plan, the government must issue a progress report.

SARA has teeth! For serious offences, individuals can face fines as high as $250 000 and up to five years in jail; a corporation can be fined a maximum of $1 million per offence. Under SARA, it is an offence to

- kill, harm, harass, capture, or take an individual of a listed endangered, threatened, or extirpated species;

- possess, collect, buy, sell, or trade an individual of a listed endangered, threatened, or extirpated species, or its parts or derivatives; or

- damage or destroy the residence of one or more individuals of a listed endangered or threatened species, or a listed extirpated species if a recovery strategy has recommended its reintroduction into the wild in Canada.

Any Canadian resident who is 18 or older can apply to the government if she or he believes that a SARA offence may have been committed. For more information, visit the SARA Public Registry at http://www.sararegistry.gc.ca.

How Have Canadians Responded to SARA? Mixed Feelings

Canadians support SARA in principle, but are unhappy about flaws in its implementation.

SARA has its critics. In April 2004, Environmental Defence Canada published a "report card" that gave the Canadian government a C for creating SARA but an F for implementing it (Figure 12-10). One of the group's main complaints was that only 66% of the species at risk designated by COSEWIC appeared in SARA's List of Wildlife Species at Risk.

David Suzuki expressed concern in 2008 when, at the five-year anniversary of SARA coming into force, only 445 of COSEWIC's 551 species at risk (81%) were eligible for protection under the act (http://www.davidsuzuki.org/issues/wildlife-habitat/science/

GRADES FOR NATIONAL ACCORD IMPLEMENTATION	
Nova Scotia	B
Canada	C
Manitoba	C–
Newfoundland and Labrador	C–
Prince Edward Island	C–
New Brunswick	C–
Ontario	D+
Quebec	D
Nunavut	D–
Saskatchewan	D–
British Columbia	F
Alberta	F
Yukon	F
Northwest Territories	F

GRADE FOR SARA IMPLEMENTATION	
Canada	F

FIGURE 12-10 A March 2004 "report card" published by Environmental Defence Canada gave the federal government a C for designing the *Species at Risk Act* but an F for implementing it. Most provinces were rated poorly for their protection of species at risk. (Reprinted by permission of Environmental Defence)

endangered-species-legislation/canadas-species-at-risk-act/). He felt that social and economic factors were being given priority over urgent conservation goals. As of 2012, only 496 of COSEWIC's 650 species at risk (76%) were protected under SARA, leaving 24% of these species exposed.

Another very serious concern is that SARA applies only to areas of federal jurisdiction—about 5% of the land area of Canada. SARA has a *safety net* provision whereby the federal government can intervene if provincial or territorial measures fail to adequately protect a species. However, in 2006, the Harper government declined to intervene when the B.C. government made its controversial decision to continue logging spotted owl habitat despite the fact that these birds are classified as endangered by COSEWIC, with a population estimated to be as low as 17.

By 2009, there were 16 or fewer spotted owls remaining in B.C.—down from approximately 100 pairs in 1990. Seven owls had been taken into a captive breeding program in 2008, leaving nine or fewer birds in the wild. Note that the Spotted Owl Population Enhancement Team that recommended the captive breeding program in 2007 stressed that there would be no point in setting up this program without also protecting critical habitat so that owls could be returned to the wild. However, provincially sanctioned foresters continued to cut down spotted owl old-growth habitat, and the federal government did not intervene (David Suzuki Foundation, 2012; Delaney, 2011). The spotted owls of B.C. appear to have revealed a serious crack in how SARA is being implemented.

Not surprisingly, the 2009 report card from Ecojustice (formerly the Sierra Legal Defence Fund), David Suzuki Foundation, Nature Canada, and Environmental Defence (http://www.naturecanada.ca/pdf/SpeciesAtRisk_reportApril2009.pdf/) gave the federal government low marks for its ineffectiveness at applying SARA. Specifically, the federal government received a D for its inadequate listing of species at risk, a D– for shortcomings in its recovery strategies for species, an "incomplete" for the missing action plans for achieving recovery of species, and two Fs for failing to provide habitat protection and for failing to use the safety net clause (see above), for an overall grade of F. The report makes the point that SARA has many commendable features but they have to be used properly to be effective.

SARA may simply be experiencing growing pains. There is a general consensus that while the legislation is a necessary first step, it needs to be applied more widely and more seriously. This will require cooperation between the federal, provincial, and territorial governments, and a willingness on the part of more provinces to update their wildlife legislation with SARA-like policies.

CONSIDER, DISCUSS, OR DEBATE

What do you consider the strengths and weaknesses of SARA? If you were a federal minister in charge of implementing SARA, how would you proceed? If you were a provincial minister in charge of developing legislation to protect species at risk, what would you include in your legislation? What steps would you take to ensure that your policies were being implemented in an effective manner?

12-8 COSEWIC'S FIVE RISK CATEGORIES: SOME CANADIAN EXAMPLES

What Is an Extirpated Species? Gone but Reintroduction Still Possible

The greater prairie chicken and the black-footed ferret are two extirpated species in Canada that at present lack the conditions that would make them good candidates for reintroduction.

COSEWIC's summary of species at risk (Table 12-1) classifies 23 Canadian species as *extirpated*. An extirpated species is one that no longer exists in Canada but is found—at least for now—in other parts of the world.

One example of a species extirpated from Canada is the greater prairie chicken (*Tympanuchus cupido*), a chicken-like grouse with bared plumage, a round tail, and feathered toes (Figure 12-11). Males have a pair

FIGURE 12-11 Greater prairie chickens once performed their colourful mating displays in the Canadian prairies but are now extirpated.

of obvious orange sacs on their necks that they inflate during mating displays. In the 1870s and 1880s, in response to the increased height of native grasses that occurred following the disappearance of plains bison, greater prairie chickens moved into the Canadian prairies from the United States. By 1900, more than 1 million greater prairie chickens were living and breeding in the prairie grasslands. Over time, natural grasslands were consumed by agriculture, which gradually occupied the space between farms. The numbers of greater prairie chickens in Canada gradually diminished, and by 1977 they were gone. These birds are still found in scattered habitat fragments in the United States. In 1993, a greater-prairie-chicken recovery team was formed to consider re-establishing the birds; the team concluded that there was insufficient ungrazed native grassland to ensure success and that the venture would be too costly.

Another notable victim of extirpation from Canada is the black-footed ferret (*Mustela nigripes*), a slender member of the weasel family (*mustelid*) with a black mask, black feet, and black-tipped tail (Figure 12-12). Historically, black-footed ferrets were found in Alberta, Saskatchewan, and Manitoba as well as in the American plains. They lived in large prairie dog towns and relied on prairie dogs for food and shelter, hunting them at night when they were sleeping and then taking over their burrows. Gradually, agriculture replaced the native grasslands that prairie dogs needed for habitat; as well, prairie dogs were hunted, trapped, and poisoned by farmers. As prairie dog populations declined, so did black-footed ferrets. The last ferrets were seen in Canada around 1974. They were believed to be extinct until a small colony was found in Wyoming; these animals were captured and

FIGURE 12-12 Black-footed ferrets live in prairie dog towns and hunt prairie dogs at night when they are sleeping. Black-footed ferrets have been extirpated from Canada but exist in three U.S. locations.

FIGURE 12-13 Wild Vancouver Island marmots live at high elevations on Vancouver Island; a captive-breeding program is aimed at increasing the size of the wild population.

a captive-breeding program involving the Toronto Metro Zoo and seven U.S. breeding facilities increased their numbers to 750. Ferrets have been released in three U.S. locations, but reintroductions are proving to be difficult since captive-born ferrets are easy prey for wild predators. A Canadian black-footed-ferret recovery team studying prairie dog populations in southwestern Saskatchewan has thus far concluded that there are not yet enough prairie dogs to support the reintroduction of these animals.

What Is an Endangered Species? At Risk for Extirpation or Extinction

The Vancouver Island marmot and Fowler's toads are among the 287 endangered species in Canada.

COSEWIC classifies 287 Canadian species as *endangered* (Table 12-1). An endangered species is one that is in serious jeopardy and facing imminent extirpation or extinction. Extirpation still leaves a slim chance that the lost species can be reintroduced through a successful recovery strategy; losing a species through extinction means losing it forever. Two endangered species in Canada are described below.

The Vancouver Island marmot (*Marmota vancouverensis*) is a dark-coloured alpine marmot (Figure 12-13) that is found only on Vancouver Island. It is unique in terms of its genetics, behaviour, and ecology. The population has been studied closely since the 1980s; through intensive conservation efforts, the population has been raised from 30 wild marmots in 2003 to 320–370 wild marmots living on 28 mountains by fall 2011. Part of the problem is that the hunting success of

wolves, cougars, and golden eagles has increased as the marmots have been concentrated by the effects of logging. A recovery strategy for Vancouver Island marmots, in effect since 1994, includes a captive-breeding program that aims to raise the wild population to self-sustaining levels of about 600 animals. Other elements of the recovery strategy include the use of fences, nets, human guards, and a hunting dog to deter predators.

SELF CHECK

Populations are dynamic. Visit http://www.marmots .org to see how the recovery efforts are going. How many pups have they counted in the wild this year? How many marmots have been taken by predators?

Fowler's toads (*Bufo fowleri*) are small toads (Figure 12-14) whose Canadian presence is restricted to three small remnant populations along Lake Erie (Figure 12-15). More common in the United States, these

FIGURE 12-14 Fowler's toads are small toads that are extremely sensitive to pesticides.

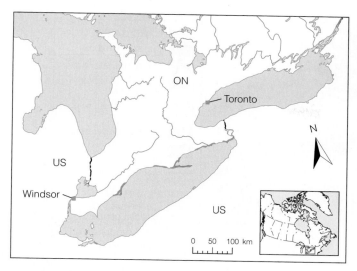

FIGURE 12-15 In Canada, Fowler's toads are found only in a few small populations along the shore of Lake Erie. (Data from http://www.sararegistry.gc.ca/)

FIGURE 12-16 Swift foxes are the smallest of the North American wild dogs. Once *extirpated* from Canada, reintroductions and conservation measures have improved the status of swift foxes to *threatened*.

toads are highly sensitive to pesticides at all stages of their life cycle. Their habitat is becoming fragmented. As with many amphibians, their population numbers fluctuate but at the low end of a fluctuation, their population numbers are very small. Experts suggest that Fowler's toads have a 20% chance of becoming extirpated within the next 100 years. Classified at present as endangered, they are protected by SARA.

What Is a Threatened Species? At Risk of Becoming Endangered

Swift foxes and woodland caribou are among the Canadian species considered threatened because of disturbances to their habitats.

COSEWIC classifies 161 Canadian species as *threatened* (Table 12-1). A threatened species is one that is likely to become endangered if present trends continue. A few examples of species in this category are described next.

The swift fox (*Vulpes velox*) is a small fox (Figure 12-16) that was formerly widely distributed on the Great Plains, both in Canada and the United States. When COSEWIC published its first list of species at risk in 1978, the swift fox was categorized as *extirpated*. It had been trapped for its fur, and poisoned by baits that were put out to kill coyotes and ground squirrels; the last Canadian swift fox had been shot in Saskatchewan in 1928. Beginning in 1983, about 1 000 swift foxes that were live-trapped in the United States or born in captivity were released in the Canadian prairies. Swift foxes were then categorized as *endangered* until the population was judged to be stable and self-sustaining in 2009. Since then, swift foxes have been recategorized as *threatened*.

Members of the deer family, woodland caribou (*Rangifer tarandus caribou*) are well adapted to snow and cold (Figure 12-17). Woodland caribou (Boreal population) have a wide distribution across the North (Figure 12-18). However, their habitat is becoming fragmented by forestry practices, mining, and the spread of agriculture. Woodland caribou are sensitive to disturbances, such as road and pipeline construction, and are facing the additional challenge of climate change. For these reasons, the Boreal population of caribou is considered to be threatened and is protected by SARA.

The Boreal population is not the only caribou population in Canada. There is a tiny, isolated population of woodland caribou, known as the Atlantic-Gaspesie population, which lives south of the St. Lawrence River in Quebec and is considered endangered; a Southern Mountain population of woodland caribou in British Columbia that is considered threatened; a Northern Mountain population that is of special concern; Peary

FIGURE 12-17 Woodland caribou exist in several populations that face various degrees of endangerment.

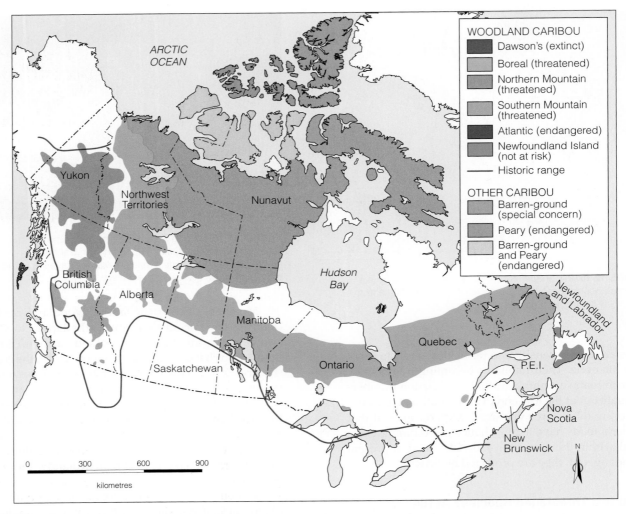

FIGURE 12-18 The Boreal population of woodland caribou has the widest distribution of any group of caribou. (Based on http://www.gov.mb.ca/conservation/wildlife/sar/fs/wlcaribou.html; http://www.gis.unbc.ca/courses/geog413/projects/2010/willame/index.htm; http://en.wikipedia.org/wiki/File:Rangifer_tarandus_Map_NA.svg)

caribou (*Rangifer tarandus pearyi* [endangered]) on the High Arctic islands; and barren-ground caribou (*Rangifer tarandus groenlandicus* [special concern]) on the Arctic mainland. For more information on this topic, visit the Species at Risk Public Registry (http://www.sararegistry.gc.ca/default_e.cfm).

What Is a Species of Special Concern? In Danger of Becoming Threatened

Polar bears and mountain beavers are among the 179 Canadian species that are "of special concern" as they cope with serious challenges facing their populations.

COSEWIC classifies 179 Canadian organisms as *species of special concern* (Table 12-1). A species of special concern has biological characteristics that, when combined with factors affecting their populations, could cause them to become threatened.

For example, the polar bear (*Ursus maritimus*) is the largest terrestrial carnivore in the world (Figure 12-19). Polar bears are distributed throughout the circumpolar Arctic and are well adapted to living in these conditions. However, they are threatened by hunters since females can breed once every 3.6 years on average and typically have only two cubs per litter. The ability of polar bears to hunt seals on pack ice is being undermined by climate change (Chapter 21). They are also susceptible to bioaccumulation of fat-soluble contaminants such as DDT and PCBs. Polar bears are not listed on Schedule 1 of SARA and so are not protected. If threats to polar bear populations continue unabated, polar bears could be added to Schedule 1 of the Species at Risk Act through a *regulatory amendment*, following a public consultation and government agreement.

The mountain beaver (*Aplodontia rufa*) is the world's most primitive rodent (Figure 12-20, p. 269),

FIGURE 12-19 Polar bears are top predators in the Arctic, but they face a number of serious threats, such as climate change.

FIGURE 12-20 Mountain beavers are primitive rodents that have a limited distribution and require deep, moist soils for tunnelling.

named for its habit of chewing bark and gnawing off branches. Mountain beavers live in forested areas of southern British Columbia. They are energetic burrowers and require deep soil in order to create an extensive system of tunnels. These tunnels are most suitable if they are moist-to-wet except for a dry portion where the nest site is located. Threats to mountain beavers include clear-cutting and other forestry practices that erode or dry the soil. Some of their habit has been lost to urbanization and agriculture, and mountain beavers appear to have difficulty dispersing to new locations. Their situation will worsen if they continue to lose habitat to development or if climate change warm and dries their habitat. Mountain beavers are protected under Schedule 1 of SARA as well as the B.C. Wildlife Act.

12-9 PROTECTING WILD SPECIES: THE SANCTUARY APPROACH

What Is the Role of Wildlife Refuges and Sanctuaries? Protect Resident Wildlife and Aid Migrating Birds

In Canada and the United States, various types of wildlife refuges are concentrated along major bird migration routes.

Wildlife refuges and sanctuaries are intended to protect habitat and the resident wildlife. Many of them are strategically located to facilitate the protection of migrating birds, particularly waterfowl. As they migrate to and from their breeding grounds, birds tend to travel along major migration corridors or *flyways* (Figure 12-21, p. 270). Ducks Unlimited Canada and the North American Waterfowl Management Plan help to ensure that many wetlands are protected in the various types of reserves situated along major migration routes, especially in the prairies where several flyways exist. More than three-quarters of refuges in the United States are concentrated along flyways.

Bad news. In a 2006 paper entitled "Protected Areas and Prospects for Endangered Species Conservation in Canada," Isabelle Deguise and Jeremy Kerr of the University of Ottawa studied the effectiveness of the current network of parks and other wildlife refuge areas in protecting species at risk in Canada. They compared the number of terrestrial species at risk that were being sheltered in these reserves with the numbers of those species in randomly generated "park networks" of the same total area and number of reserves.

Because they were created specifically for that purpose, you might expect that existing parks systems would shelter most of the species at risk and most of the biodiversity. However, the authors found that the established systems of parks and other reserves rarely performed better than the randomly generated reserves.

Deguise and Kerr made several other observations in their paper:

- Some of the most threatened parts of Canada have few or no protected areas.

- Even where protected areas are found, species at risk are no more likely to be found in existing reserves than outside the reserves.

- Endangered species are concentrated in areas that are characterized by extensive human use, and it is hard to establish reserves in these areas.

- National parks and many other protected lands were established not for protecting species at risk or biodiversity, but for other purposes such as education, recreation, and preserving natural features of the landscape.

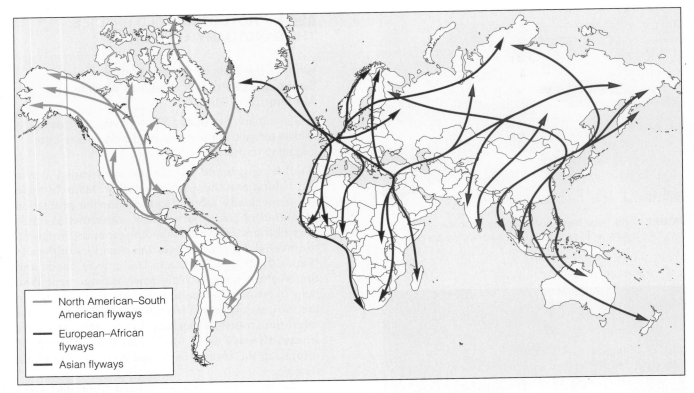

FIGURE 12-21 Natural capital: major *flyways* used by migratory birds, mostly waterfowl. Each route has a number of subroutes. Some countries along such flyways have entered into agreements and treaties to protect crucial habitats, especially wetlands, needed by such species, both along their migration routes and at each end of their journeys.

- Many of the reserves are small and therefore unlikely to be effective by themselves at protecting species.

For Deguise and Kerr, protecting species at risk must involve the integration of conservation practices in the landscapes between existing reserves. This recalls MNR biologist Brian Naylor's argument that the management taking place on Crown and private lands between parks is key to species conservation (p. 238).

CONSIDER, DISCUSS, OR DEBATE

What changes would make reserves effective in aiding species at risk? What sort of conservation practices should occur on the lands between reserves? To what extent should the public be involved?

Can Gene Banks, Botanical Gardens, and Farms Help Save Most Endangered Plant Species? Important but Limited Solutions

Establishing gene banks and botanical gardens and using farms to raise endangered species can help protect species from extinction, but these options lack funding and storage space.

Gene or *seed banks* preserve genetic information and endangered plant species by storing their seeds in refrigerated, low-humidity environments. The world's more than 100 seed banks have focused on storing seeds of the approximately 100 plant species that provide us with food—with just 14 plants providing about 90% of the **calories** in our food. Some banks are beginning to store seeds for a wider range of species that may be threatened with extinction or a loss of genetic diversity. Scientists urge the establishment of many more such banks, especially in developing countries.

But seed banks are expensive to operate and can be destroyed by accidents. Also, because stored seeds do not evolve, they may not survive when used in the future.

The world's 2 500 *botanical gardens* and *arboretums* contain living plants, representing almost one-third of the world's known plant species. However, they contain only about 3% of the world's rare and threatened plant species.

Botanical gardens also help educate an estimated 150 million visitors a year about the need for plant conservation. But these sanctuaries have too little storage capacity and too little funding to preserve most of the world's rare and threatened plants.

We can take pressure off some endangered or threatened species by raising them on *farms* for commercial sale. One example is the use of farms in Florida to raise alligators for meat and hides. Another example is *butterfly farms* in Papua New Guinea, where many butterfly species are threatened by habitat destruction and fragmentation, commercial overexploitation, and environmental degradation.

Can Zoos and Aquariums Help Protect Most Endangered Animal Species? Important but Expensive and Limited

Zoos and aquariums can help protect endangered animal species, but lack funding and storage space.

Zoos, aquariums, game parks, and animal research centres are being used to preserve some individuals of critically endangered animal species, with the long-term goal of reintroducing the species into protected wild habitats. Two techniques for preserving endangered terrestrial species are egg pulling and captive breeding. *Egg pulling* involves collecting wild eggs laid by critically endangered bird species and then hatching them in zoos or research centres. In *captive breeding*, some or all of the wild individuals of a critically endangered species are captured for breeding in captivity, with the aim of reintroducing the offspring into the wild.

Other techniques for increasing the populations of captive species include artificial insemination, surgical implantation of eggs of one species into a surrogate mother of another species (embryo transfer), use of incubators, and cross-fostering (in which the young of a **rare species** are raised by parents of a similar species). Scientists also use computer databases of the family lineages of species in zoos and DNA analysis to match individuals for mating—a computer dating service for zoo animals—and to prevent genetic erosion through inbreeding.

Proponents urge zoos and wildlife managers to collect and freeze cells of endangered species for possible cloning. They believe that such miniature *frozen zoos* could play a role in bringing back depleted species in the future.

The ultimate goal of captive breeding programs is to build up populations to a level where they can be reintroduced into the wild. However, before conservation biologists attempt a reintroduction they study the factors that originally caused the species to become endangered, whether these factors still exist, and whether there is enough suitable habitat available.

After more than two decades of captive breeding efforts, only a handful of endangered species have been returned to the wild. Examples include the black-footed ferret, California condor, Arabian oryx, and golden lion tamarin. Most reintroductions fail because of lack of suitable habitat, inability of individuals bred in captivity to survive in the wild, or renewed over-hunting or capture of some returned species.

Lack of space and money limits efforts to maintain populations of endangered animal species in zoos and research centres. The captive population of each species must number 100–500 individuals to avoid extinction through accident, disease, or loss of genetic diversity through inbreeding. Recent genetic research indicates that 10 000 or more individuals are needed for an endangered species to maintain its capacity for biological evolution.

According to one estimate, using all the space in accredited North American zoos for captive breeding could sustain only about 100 large animal species on a long-term basis. Thus the major conservation role of zoos will be to help educate the public about the ecological importance of the species they display and the need to protect habitat.

Public aquariums that exhibit unusual and attractive fish and some marine animals, such as seals and dolphins, also help educate the public about the need to protect such species. In North America, more than 35 million people visit aquariums each year. However, public aquariums have not served as effective gene banks for endangered marine species, especially marine mammals that need large volumes of water.

Instead of seeing zoos and aquariums as sanctuaries, some critics see most of them as prisons for once-wild animals. They also contend that zoos and aquariums foster the false notion that we do not need to preserve large numbers of wild species in their natural habitats.

Some people criticize zoos and aquariums for putting on shows with animals wearing clothes, riding bicycles, or performing tricks. They see this as fostering the idea that the animals are there primarily to entertain us by doing things people do and in the process raising money for their keepers.

Conservation biologists point out that zoos, aquariums, and botanical gardens, regardless of their benefits and drawbacks, are not biologically or economically feasible solutions for most of the world's current endangered species and the much larger number expected over the next few decades.

12-10 RECONCILIATION ECOLOGY

What Is Reconciliation Ecology? Rethinking Conservation Strategy

Reconciliation ecology involves finding ways to share the places we dominate with other species.

In 2003, ecologist Michael L. Rosenzweig wrote the book *Win-Win Ecology: How Earth's Species Can Survive in the Midst of Human Enterprise.* He strongly supports the eight-point program of Edward O. Wilson to help save the Earth's natural habitats by establishing and protecting nature reserves (p. 245). He also supports the species protection strategies discussed in this chapter.

But he contends that in the long run these approaches will fail for two reasons. One is that current reserves are devoted to saving only about 5% of nature. To Rosenzweig the real challenge is to help sustain wild species in the human-dominated portion of nature that makes up 95% of the planetary ecological "cake."

The other problem is that setting aside funds and refuges and passing laws to protect endangered and threatened species are essentially desperate attempts to save species that are in deep trouble. This can help a few species, but the real challenge is learning how to keep species from getting to such a point in the first place.

Rosenzweig suggests that we develop a new form of conservation biology called **reconciliation ecology.** It is the science of inventing, establishing, and maintaining new habitats to conserve species diversity in places where people live, work, or play. In other words, we need to learn how to share the spaces we dominate with other species. For instance, we can construct nest boxes to encourage birds and other creatures to live nearby (see the Case Study below).

How Can We Implement Reconciliation Ecology? Observe, Be Creative, and Cooperate with Your Neighbours

Some people are finding creative ways to practise reconciliation ecology in their neighbourhoods and cities.

Practising reconciliation ecology begins by looking at the habitats we prefer. Given a choice, most people prefer a grassy and fairly open habitat with a few scattered trees. We also like water and prefer to live near a stream, lake, river, or ocean. We also love flowers.

The problem is that most species do not like what we like or cannot survive in the habitats we prefer. No wonder so few of them live with us.

So what do we do? Reconciliation ecology goes beyond efforts to attract birds to backyards. For example, providing a self-sustaining habitat for a butterfly species may require 20 or so neighbours to band together. Doing this for an insect-eating bat species could help keep down mosquitoes and other pesky insects in a neighbourhood.

CASE STUDY

Using Reconciliation Ecology to Protect Bluebirds

Consider the case of bluebird conservation. *Bad news.* Populations of bluebirds in much of eastern North America are declining.

There are two reasons. One is that these birds nest in tree holes of a certain size. Dead and dying trees once provided plenty of these holes. But today timber companies often cut down all of the trees, and homeowners manicure their property by removing dead and dying trees.

A second reason is that two aggressive, abundant, and non-native bird species—starlings and house sparrows—also like to nest in tree holes and take them away from bluebirds. To make matters worse, starlings eat the blueberries the bluebirds need to survive during the winter.

Good news. People have come up with a creative way to help save the bluebird. They have designed nest boxes with holes large enough to accommodate bluebirds but too small for starlings. They also found that house sparrows like shallow boxes, so they made the bluebird boxes deep enough to make them unattractive nesting sites for the sparrows.

In 1979, the North American Bluebird Society was founded to spread the word and encourage people to use bluebird boxes on their property and to keep house cats away from nesting bluebirds. Now bluebird numbers are increasing where they have been assisted.

Properly designed nest boxes have been used to encourage other types of birds such as purple martens. Providing roosting boxes for bats will allow them to live near people and control populations of insect pests.

Restoration ecology works! Perhaps you might want to consider a career in this exciting new field.

Critical Thinking

See if you can come up with a reconciliation project to help protect a threatened bird or other species in your neighbourhood or on the grounds of your school.

iStockphoto/Thinkstock

Another form of restoration ecology involves replacing some monoculture yards in neighbourhoods with diverse yards using plant species adapted to local climates that are selected to attract certain species. This would make neighbourhoods more biologically diverse and interesting, keep down insect pests, and require less use of noisy and polluting lawnmowers.

Communities could have contests and awards for people designing the most biodiverse and species-friendly yards and gardens. Signs could describe the type of ecosystem being mimicked and the species being protected as a way to educate and encourage experiments by other people.

In Berlin, Germany, people have planted gardens on many large rooftops. These can be designed to support a variety of species by varying the depth and type of soil and their exposure to sun. Such roofs also save energy by providing insulation, help cool cities, and conserve water by reducing evapotranspiration. Reconciliation ecology proponents call for a global campaign to use the roofs of the world to help sustain biodiversity.

San Francisco's Golden Gate Park is a 410-hectare (1 012-acre) oasis of gardens and trees in the midst of a large city. It is a good example of reconciliation ecology because it was designed and planted by humans who transformed it from a system of sand dunes.

Canadian and U.S. military forces control areas of land that are largely maintained in a wild state. Rosenzweig and other reconciliation ecologists believe that some of this land could serve as laboratories for developing and testing reconciliation ecology ideas.

Some college campuses and schools might also serve as reconciliation ecology laboratories. How about your campus or school?

In this chapter, we have seen that protecting the terrestrial species that make up part of the Earth's biodiversity from premature extinction is a difficult, controversial, and challenging responsibility. Figure 12-22 lists some things you can do to help prevent the premature extinction of species.

What Can Canadians Do to Protect Species? Get Involved

In Canada, there are a variety of conservation initiatives whose success depends on citizen participation.

Performed today by many thousands of participants (Figure 12-23), the annual *Christmas Bird Count* (*CBC*) can yield useful scientific results. Before

What Can You Do?

Protecting Species

- Do not buy furs, ivory products, and other materials made from endangered or threatened animal species.

- Do not buy wood and paper products produced by cutting remaining old-growth forests in the tropics.

- Do not buy birds, snakes, turtles, tropical fish, and other animals that are taken from the wild.

- Do not buy orchids, cacti, and other plants that are taken from the wild.

FIGURE 12-22 What can you do? Ways to help avoid premature extinction of species.

1900, there was a tradition in which people went out on Christmas Day and shot birds and small mammals to see how many they could collect! On Christmas Day 1900, an American ornithologist organized birders in locations ranging from Toronto, Ontario, to Pacific Grove, California, and instructed them to go out and count birds instead. So began the tradition of Christmas Bird Counts throughout North America and Latin

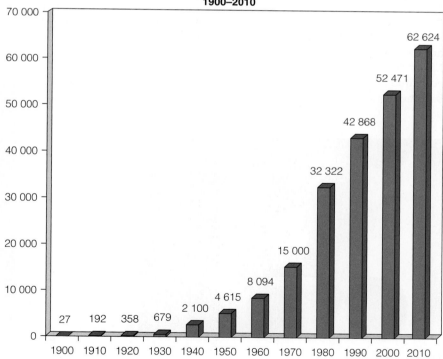

FIGURE 12-23 The number of participants in the annual Christmas Bird Count has increased dramatically since the survey in 1900. (Data from http://www.audubon.org)

America. The North American CBC database, which is available at http://www.audubon.org/bird/cbc, provides valuable information on avian trends. You can use the database to determine the numbers of a particular endangered species, to map bird distributions, or to track changes over time. Bird Studies Canada coordinates the Canadian part of the annual CBC survey, and posts national, provincial, and regional summaries on its website at http://www.bsc-eoc.org/birdmon/default/datasets.jsp?code=CBC.

Organized by Bird Studies Canada and the Cornell Laboratory of Ornithology, among other partners, *Project FeederWatch* (formerly the *Ontario Feeder Watch Survey*) collects long-term data on populations of winter birds that visit feeders throughout North America. The project, which actively involves and educates the public, is an excellent vehicle for surveying birds that summer in remote areas farther north and are readily accessible to people only in winter. The close scrutiny of birds at winter feeders allows for the detection of unusual traits such as deformed bills (Figure 12-24). More information on Project FeederWatch is available at http://watch.birds.cornell.edu/PFW/.

The Canadian Lakes Loon Survey was initiated in 1981 to monitor changes in populations of common loons (*Gavia immer*) thought to be attributable to acid rain, shoreline development, and human activities on lakes (Figure 12-25). The program recruits volunteers to survey the lake of their choice at least three times a year: in June to count pairs of loons occupying the lake, in July to count the newly hatched chicks, and in August to record the number of chicks that survived summer. Data are made available to the public and are used in guiding loon conservation. The Canadian Lakes Loon Survey has increased the profile of loons, educated the public, and inspired lake residents to become fiercely protective of their loons.

FIGURE 12-25 The sights, sounds, and behaviours of common loons have made them symbols of the North and endeared them to the public.

Nocturnal Owl Surveys have been taking place in Canada since 1995. One night in April—before the spring sounds of frogs and other nocturnal forest creatures can interfere—volunteers broadcast tape-recorded calls of different species of owls into the forest. Owls that hear these sounds react territorially by hooting or approaching (Figure 12-26). Volunteers are trained to recognize the sounds of various owl species and to take into account factors such as wind or distant highway traffic that might interfere with sound transmission. In a similar vein, the *Amphibian Road Call Count* and the *Backyard Frog Survey* gather information on the distribution and seasonal cycles of frogs and toads by using volunteers to monitor their calls.

FIGURE 12-24 Birds can be seen close up during the winter feeder surveys organized by Project FeederWatch. Unusual species, colourations, and traits—such as the deformed bill of this chickadee—can be observed and enumerated.

FIGURE 12-26 Owls may hoot or even approach when participants in the Nocturnal Owl Survey broadcast owl calls into the forest at night. This great grey owl is curious and territorial.

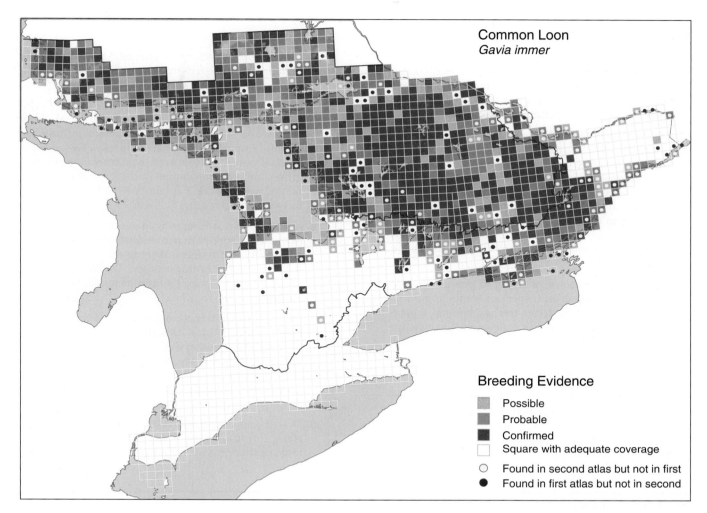

FIGURE 12-27 Cadman, M.D., D.A. Sutherland, G.G. Beck, D. Lepage, and A.R. Couturier (eds.). 2007. *Atlas of the Breeding Birds of Ontario, 2001–2005*. Bird Studies Canada, Environment Canada, Ontario Field Ornithologists, Ontario Ministry of Natural Resources, and Ontario Nature, Toronto xxii + 706 pp. Map provided by Andrew Couturier, Bird Studies Canada, and used with permission from the *Atlas of the Breeding Birds of Ontario, 2001–2005* (Cadman et al., 2007).

Between 1981 and 2005, public participation was instrumental in the compilation of a set of wildlife atlases, including the *Ontario Breeding Bird Atlas*, the *Ontario Herpetofaunal Atlas*, and the *Atlas of the Mammals of Ontario*. The province of Ontario was subdivided into 10 × 10 kilometre squares that were assigned to individual volunteers. Volunteers visited their assigned grid squares and recorded all instances of the species under observation. Data were coded to indicate the species, the type of evidence (photograph, collected sample, sighting, sound, etc.), and the location. Locations were recorded using the Universal Transverse Mercator Grid (UTM) system, which could pinpoint a given observation to a 100 × 100 metre site. If unusual records were collected, experts could visit the site for verification. The maps that resulted are extremely useful. Although the volunteers were lay people, they had some training, and each observation was ranked in terms of its certainty (for example, a clear photograph of an animal ranked higher than a less direct sign such as finding the animal's burrow). The atlas maps show locations in Ontario where species were located, along with a ranking of certainty (Figure 12-27).

We know what to do. Perhaps we will act in time.
EDWARD O. WILSON

CHAPTER REVIEW

1. Review the Key Questions for this chapter on p. 250. What factors led to the premature extinction of the passenger pigeon? Why did the population not recover? What do we know now that we didn't know then about helping species avoid extinction?

2. Distinguish between *background extinction* and *mass extinction*. What is the *extinction rate* of a species? Describe how scientists estimate extinction rates. Give four reasons why many extinction experts believe that human activities are now causing a mass extinction. Distinguish between the following categories of risk and give an example for each: *extirpated, endangered, threatened,* and *special concern.* List some characteristics that make some species especially vulnerable to extinction.

3. What are two reasons for trying to prevent the premature extinction of wild species? Name five extinct Canadian animals. What is the *instrumental value* of a species? List four types of instrumental values provided by wild species. What is the *intrinsic (existence) value* of a species?

4. What is biophilia? Why should we care about bats?

5. What is *HIPPO*? In order, what are the six largest causes of premature extinction of species resulting from human activities? Why are island species especially vulnerable to extinction? What is habitat fragmentation, and how does it threaten many species?

6. Describe the threats to bird species in the world and in Canada. List three reasons why we should be alarmed by the decline of bird species.

7. Give two examples of the harmful effects of non-native species that have been introduced (a) deliberately and (b) accidentally. List ways to limit the harmful impacts of non-native species. Describe the roles of population growth, overconsumption, pollution, and climate change in the premature extinction of wild species. Explain how global warming is threatening polar bears.

8. Describe the poaching of wild species and give three examples of species that are threatened by this illegal activity. Why are tigers likely to disappear from the wild by the end of this century? Describe the threat to some forms of wildlife from increased hunting for bushmeat.

9. Describe two international treaties that are used to help protect species. Describe Canada's Species at Risk Act, how successful it has been, and any controversies over this act. What is COSEWIC and what is its function? Describe the roles of wildlife refuges, gene banks, botanical gardens, wildlife farms, zoos, and aquariums in protecting some species.

10. Describe how protecting wild species from premature extinction (**Core Case Study**) is in keeping with the four *scientific principles of sustainability* (p.16).

CRITICAL THINKING

1. How do (a) population growth, (b) poverty, and (c) climate change affect biodiversity?

2. Discuss your gut-level reaction to the following statement: "Eventually all species become extinct. Thus it does not really matter that the passenger pigeon is extinct and that the whooping crane, the Vancouver Island marmot, and the world's remaining rhinoceros and tiger species are endangered mostly because of human activities." Be honest about your reaction, and give arguments for your position.

3. (a) Do you accept the ethical position that each species has the inherent right to survive without human interference, regardless of whether it serves any useful purpose for humans? Explain. Would you extend this right to *Anopheles* mosquito species, which transmit malaria, and to infectious bacteria? (b) Do you believe each individual of an animal species has an inherent right to survive? Explain. Would you extend such rights to individual plants and microorganisms and to tigers that have killed people? Explain.

4. Explain why you agree or disagree with (a) using animals for research, (b) keeping animals captive in a zoo or aquarium, and (c) killing surplus animals produced by a captive-breeding program in a zoo when no suitable habitat is available for their release.

5. What would you do if (a) your yard and house were invaded by ants, (b) you found bats flying around your yard at night, and (c) deer invaded your yard and ate your shrubs and vegetables?

6. Which of the following statements best describes your feelings toward wildlife? (a) As long as it stays in its space, wildlife is OK. (b) As long as I do not need its space, wildlife is OK. (c) I have the right to use wildlife habitat to meet my own needs. (d) When you have seen one redwood tree, fox, elephant, or some other form of wildlife, you have seen them all, so lock up a few of each species in a zoo or wildlife park and do not worry about protecting the rest. (e) Wildlife should be protected.

7. List your three favourite wild species. Examine why they are your favourites. Are they cute and cuddly looking, like the giant panda and the koala? Do they have humanlike qualities, like apes or penguins that walk upright? Are they large, like elephants or blue whales? Are they beautiful, like tigers and monarch butterflies? Are any of them plants? Are any of them species such as bats, sharks, snakes, or spiders, which

most people are afraid of? Are any of them microorganisms that help keep you alive? Reflect on what your choice of favourite species tells you about your attitudes toward most wildlife. Reflect on the choices of your classmates.

8. Environmental groups in a heavily forested province want to restrict logging in some areas to save the habitat of an endangered squirrel. Timber company officials argue that the well-being of one type of squirrel is not as important as the well-being of the many families affected if the restriction causes them to lay off hundreds of workers. If you had the power to decide this issue, what would you do and why? Can you come up with a compromise?

9. Explain why some developers and extractors of resources on public land oppose the development of databases of wild species.

10. Congratulations! You are in charge of preventing the premature extinction of the world's existing species from human activities. What would be the three major components of your program to accomplish this goal?

PROJECTS

1. Make a log of your own consumption of all products for a single day. Relate your level and types of consumption to the **(a)** decline of wildlife species and **(b)** increased destruction, degradation, and fragmentation of wildlife habitats in Canada and in tropical forests.

2. Identify examples of habitat destruction or degradation in your community that have had harmful effects on the populations of various wild plant and animal species. Develop a management plan for rehabilitating these habitats and species.

3. Choose a particular animal or plant species that interests you and use the library or the Internet to find out **(a)** its numbers and distribution, **(b)** whether it is threatened with extinction, **(c)** the major future threats to its survival, **(d)** actions that are being taken to help sustain this species, and **(e)** a type of reconciliation ecology that might be useful in sustaining this species.

4. Work with your classmates to develop an experiment in reconciliation ecology for your campus.

5. Use the Internet to learn about different species at risk, why they are at risk, and what degree of protection they are receiving in Canada.

13 Sustaining Aquatic Biodiversity

CASE STUDY

A Biological Roller Coaster Ride in Lake Victoria

Lake Victoria, shared by Kenya, Tanzania, and Uganda in East Africa, is the world's second largest freshwater lake (Figure 13-1, right). It has been in ecological trouble for more than two decades.

Until the early 1980s, Lake Victoria had more than 500 species of fish found nowhere else. About 80% of them were from a group of diverse colourful fishes known as cichlids (pronounced "SIK-lids"), each species having its own unique ecological niche.

Since 1980 some 200 of the cichlid species have become extinct, and some of those that remain are in trouble.

Four factors caused this dramatic loss of aquatic biodiversity. *First*, there was a large increase in the population of the Nile perch (Figure 13-1, left). This fish was deliberately introduced into the lake during the 1950s and 1960s to stimulate local economies and the fishing industry, which exports large amounts of the fish to several European countries. The population of this large, prolific, and ravenous fish exploded by displacing the cichlids, and by 1985 the Nile perch had wiped out many of them.

Also, the Native people who depended on the cichlids for protein cannot afford the perch, and the mechanized fishing industry has put most small-scale fishers and fish vendors out of business. This has increased poverty and protein malnutrition.

Second, in the 1980s the lake began experiencing frequent algal blooms because of nutrient runoff from surrounding farms, deforested land, untreated sewage, and declines in the populations of the algae-eating cichlids. This greatly decreased oxygen levels in the lower depths of the lake and drove remaining native cichlids and other fish species to shallower waters, where they are more vulnerable to fishing nets. The turbid water caused by eutrophication also made it hard for female cichlids to select mates by colour, leading to the extinction of some species.

Third, since 1987 the nutrient-rich lake has been invaded by the water hyacinth. This rapidly growing plant carpeted large areas of the lake, blocked sunlight, deprived fish and plankton of oxygen, and reduced the diversity of important aquatic plant species. *Good news.* The population of water hyacinths has been reduced sharply by introducing two weevils for biological control and mechanical removal at strategic locations.

Fourth, the Nile perch now shows signs of being overfished. This may allow a gradual return of some of the remaining cichlids.

(continued)

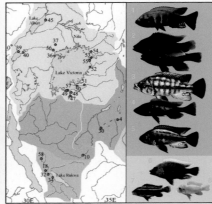

FIGURE 13-1 What is being won and lost at Lake Victoria? The Nile perch (left) is a large introduced species useful for food and sports-fishing. However, the native cichlids (right) have undergone an explosion of evolution and diversity over the past 12 000 years. Cichlids can be used for food, are highly desired for zoos and public aquariums, and are fascinating to geneticists and evolutionary biologists. The map image above shows Lake Victoria, the surrounding watersheds (coloured), and some of the cichlids that remain. (Yohey Terai et al., "The effect of selection on a long wavelength-sensitive (LWS) opsin gene of Lake Victoria cichlid fishes" PNAS 99(24):15501–15506. Copyright 2002 National Academy of Sciences, U.S.A.)

John Warburton-Lee Photography / Alamy

This ecological story shows the dynamics of large aquatic systems and illustrates that we can never do just one thing when we intrude into an ecosystem of connected species. There are always unintended consequences.

The coastal zone may be the single most important portion of our planet. The loss of its biodiversity may have repercussions far beyond our worst fears.

G. CARLETON RAY

13-1   AN OVERVIEW OF AQUATIC BIODIVERSITY

What Do We Know about the Earth's Aquatic Biodiversity? Some but Not Nearly Enough

We know fairly little about the biodiversity of the world's marine and freshwater systems.

The world's interconnected oceans cover 71% of the planet's surface. The oceans support a variety of species at different depths (Figure 7-6, p. 143, and Figure 13-2, p. 280).

About 63% of the roughly 30 000 known fish species exist in marine systems—50% in coastal waters, 12% in the deep sea, and 1% in open ocean. The remaining 37% live in freshwater systems.

Freshwater aquatic systems also contain a variety of visible plant and animal species (Figure 13-3, p. 280) and microscopic species. Many lakes contain an assortment of species found in different layers (Figure 7-14,

p. 150). As they flow from their mountain (headwater) streams to the ocean, river systems have a variety of ecological habitats that support different aquatic species (Figure 7-17, p. 152).

We have explored only about 5% of the Earth's global ocean and know fairly little about its biodiversity and how it works. We also know fairly little about freshwater biodiversity. Scientific investigation of poorly understood marine and freshwater aquatic systems is a *research frontier* whose study could result in immense ecological and economic benefits.

Recent studies have shown that the coastal waters around North America are in deep trouble. Four proposed strategies are being considered by the Canadian and U.S. governments. *First,* pass comprehensive legislation to protect, sustain, and restore the living oceans. *Second,* dramatically increase federal funding of ocean research. *Third,* shift the focus of fisheries management from setting catch limits for individual species to preserving aquatic ecosystems and habitats. *Fourth,* establish a network of marine reserves, linked by protected corridors, to protect fish breeding and nursery grounds.

What Are Some General Patterns of Marine Biodiversity? Abundant Life Near the Water's Edge and in the Deep

Coral reefs, coastal areas, and the ocean bottom are centres of marine biodiversity.

Despite the lack of knowledge about overall marine biodiversity, scientists have established several general patterns. *First,* the greatest marine biodiversity occurs in *coral reefs* (Figure 7-10, p. 147), *estuaries,* and the *deep-ocean floor. Second,* biodiversity is higher near coasts than in the open sea because of the greater variety of producers, habitats, and nursery areas in coastal areas.

Third, biodiversity is higher in the bottom (benthic) region of the ocean than in the surface (pelagic) region because of the greater variety of habitats and food sources on the ocean bottom. *Fourth,* the lowest marine biodiversity probably is found in the middle depths of the open ocean. Can you explain why?

Why Should We Care about Aquatic Biodiversity? Keeping Us Alive and Supporting Our Economies

The world's marine and freshwater systems provide important ecological and economic services.

Marine systems provide a variety of important ecological and economic services (Figure 7-5, p. 142). Globally, we get about 6% of our total protein and almost a fifth of our animal protein from marine fish and shellfish.

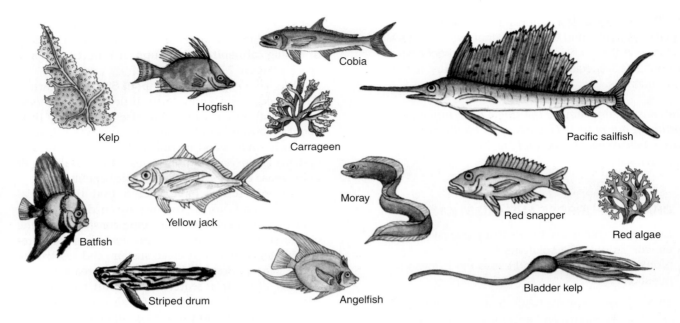

FIGURE 13-2 Natural capital: marine biodiversity. Some ocean inhabitants.

Labels: Kelp, Hogfish, Cobia, Carrageen, Pacific sailfish, Batfish, Yellow jack, Moray, Red snapper, Red algae, Striped drum, Angelfish, Bladder kelp

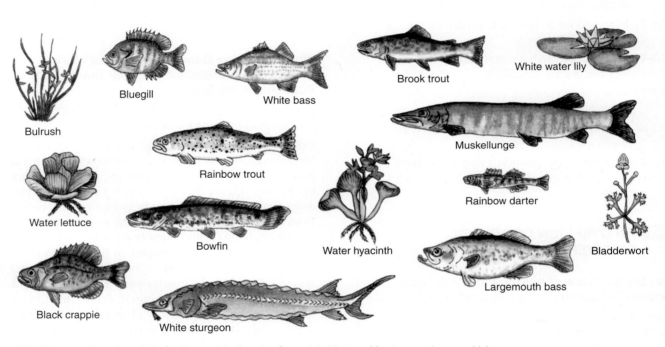

FIGURE 13-3 Natural capital: freshwater biodiversity. Some inhabitants of freshwater rivers and lakes.

Labels: Bulrush, Bluegill, White bass, Brook trout, White water lily, Rainbow trout, Muskellunge, Water lettuce, Bowfin, Water hyacinth, Rainbow darter, Bladderwort, Black crappie, White sturgeon, Largemouth bass

Seaweed and other organisms provide chemicals used in cosmetics and pharmaceuticals worth $400 million (U.S.) per year. Chemicals from several types of algae, sea anemones (Figure 8-12b, p. 170), sponges, and mollusks have antibiotic and anticancer properties. Anticancer chemicals have also been extracted from porcupine fish, puffer fish, and shark liver. We use chemicals from seaweeds and octopuses to treat hypertension and coral material to reconstruct our bones. These are only a few of many examples.

Freshwater systems also provide important ecological and economic services (page 149). Although lakes, rivers, and wetlands occupy only 1% of the Earth's surface, they provide ecological and economic services worth trillions of dollars per year.

13-2 HUMAN IMPACTS ON AQUATIC BIODIVERSITY

How Has Habitat Loss and Degradation Affected Marine Biodiversity? Our Large Aquatic Footprints

Human activities have destroyed or degraded a large proportion of the world's coastal wetlands, coral reefs, mangroves, and ocean bottom.

The greatest threat to the biodiversity of the world's oceans is loss and degradation of habitats. Here are four examples. *First,* during the last century we lost about half of the world's coastal wetlands. This can decrease fish catches in coastal waters because coastal wetlands and marshes provide essential spawning, feeding, and nursery areas for major commercial fish species.

Second, more than one-fourth of the world's diverse coral reefs have been severely damaged, mostly by human activities (Figure 7-11, p. 148). By 2050, another 70% of the world's coral reefs may be severely damaged or eliminated.

Third, more than a half of the world's original mangrove forest swamps have disappeared, mostly because of clearing for coastal development, growing crops, and aquaculture shrimp farms. Such activities threaten many of the world's remaining mangrove systems.

Fourth, many bottom habitats are being degraded and destroyed by dredging operations and trawler boats, which, like giant submerged bulldozers, drag huge nets weighted down with heavy chains and steel plates over ocean bottoms to harvest bottom fish and shellfish. Each year thousands of trawlers scrape and disturb an area of ocean bottom equal to the combined size of Brazil and India and about 150 times larger than the area of forests clear-cut each year. Recovery in heavily trawled areas rarely is possible because of repeated scraping. Slow-growing, long-lived corals, sponges, and fish are particularly vulnerable to trawling. In 2004, some 1 134 scientists signed a statement urging the United Nations to declare a moratorium on bottom trawling on the high seas.

How Have Human Activities Affected Marine Fish Populations and Species? Gone Fishing, Fish Gone

Most of the world's commercially valuable marine fish species are overfished or fished near their limits.

Studies indicate that about 85% of the world's 200 commercially valuable marine fish species (many of these found in North American waters) are either overfished or fished to their estimated sustainable yield (Figure 13.4). Overfishing is the greatest threat

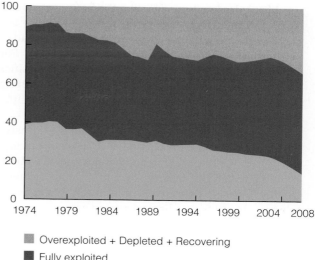

FIGURE 13-4 **Natural capital degradation:** the proportion of underexploited or moderately exploited fish populations has declined from 40% in the mid-1970s to about 15% in 2008. In other words, the other 85% of the fish stocks are already fully exploited or are already depleted by overexploitation. (Data from United Nations. *The Millennium Development Goals Report 2011*, p. 52. Courtesy of the UNDP.)

to populations of fish that live in surface waters. Populations of bottom-dwelling fish are affected by a combination of overfishing and disruption of habitat by trawler fishing.

In most cases, overfishing leads to **commercial extinction**. This is usually only a temporary depletion of fish stocks, as long as depleted areas and fisheries are allowed to recover. But this is changing. Today fish are hunted throughout the world's oceans by a global fleet of millions of fishing boats—some of them longer than a football field. These fleets, most supported by government subsidies, use sonar, satellite global positioning systems, and aircraft to find fish. Then they catch them by deploying gigantic nets or lines containing many thousands of hooks that can stretch as far as 80 kilometres (50 miles). Modern industrial fishing can cause 80% depletion of a target fish species in only 10–15 years.

One result of the increasingly efficient global hunt for fish is that *big fish in many populations of commercially valuable species are becoming scarce.* In 2003, Dalhousie University fishery scientists Ransom Myers and Boris Worm looked at fishing data for 13 commercial fisheries since 1952. Their data indicate that during the last 45 years the abundance of large open-ocean fish such as swordfish, marlins, tunas, and sharks and bottom-dwelling groundfish such as cod plummeted by 90%! A 2004 study by Jeffrey Hutchings and John Reynolds found that 230 populations of marine fish have suffered an 83% drop in breeding population size from known historic levels.

Many depleted species, like the bottom-dwelling North Atlantic cod, may never recover because too much of their habitat has been destroyed or degraded or there are too few survivors to find mates. For example, after stocks had dropped by 97–99% since the early 1960s, Canada closed its cod fishery, putting thousands out of work. After a decade there is little sign of recovery.

The smaller fish are next. As the fishing industry has depleted its most valuable and larger species, it has begun working its way down marine food webs to exploit smaller and faster-growing varieties at lower trophic levels. If this process continues, it will begin to unravel food webs, disrupt marine ecosystems, and hinder the recovery of fish feeding at higher trophic levels because the species they eat have also been overfished.

If this happens, the most abundant remaining species will be jellyfish, barnacles, and plankton. If we keep vacuuming the seas, McDonald's may begin serving barnacle burgers instead of fish sandwiches.

Most fishing boats are after one or a small number of commercially valuable species. However, their gigantic nets and incredibly long lines of hooks also catch nontarget species, called *bycatch*. Almost one-third of the world's annual fish catch consists of such species that are thrown overboard dead or dying. In addition to wasting potential sources of food, this can deplete the populations of bycatch species that play important ecological roles in oceanic food webs.

To sum it up: *Many species are overfished, big fish are becoming scarce, smaller fish are next, and we throw away 30% of the fish we catch.*

How Have Human Activities Affected the Survival of Aquatic Species? Many Extinctions on the Horizon

Marine and aquatic fish are threatened with premature extinction by human activities more than any other group of species.

Human activities such as overfishing, habitat destruction and degradation, invasions by non-native species, and pollution are endangering a number of aquatic species. According to marine biologists, at least 1 200 marine species have become extinct in the past few hundred years, and many thousands of additional marine species could disappear during this century. Indeed, *fish are threatened with extinction by human activities more than any other group of animals* (Figure 12-4, p. 251).

Also, according to the UN Food and Agriculture Organization and the World Wildlife Fund, at least a fifth of the world's 10 000 known freshwater fish species are threatened with extinction or have already become extinct. Indeed, freshwater animals are disappearing five times faster than land animals.

The tiny seahorse is vulnerable to global extinction chiefly because in dried form it is used in traditional Chinese medicine to treat heart disease, asthma, impotence, and a host of other ills.

How Have Non-Native Species Affected Fish Populations and Species? Invasive Species Are Changing Aquatic Ecosystems

Non-native species are an increasing threat to marine and freshwater biodiversity.

Another problem is the deliberate or accidental introduction of hundreds of non-native species into coastal waters, wetlands, and lakes throughout the world. These bioinvaders can displace or cause the extinction of native species and disrupt ecosystem functions, as happened to Lake Victoria (p. 278). Bioinvaders are blamed for about two-thirds of fish extinctions in North America between 1900 and 2000.

Many aquatic invaders arrive in the ballast water of ships when it is discharged in the waters of ports. One way to reduce this threat is to require ships to discharge their ballast water and replace it with salt water at sea before entering ports. Other ways are to require ships to sterilize their ballast water or pump nitrogen into it (see Individuals Matter, p. 284).

Let us take a look at several aquatic invaders that are causing problems in Canada. The *Eurasian ruffe* (*Gymnocephalus cernuus*) is a small fish (approximately 10 centimetres, or 4 inches, in length) that was introduced to North America in the mid-1980s, probably in ballast water from ships originating in Europe (Figure 13-5); with populations spreading rapidly in Lake Superior and Lake Huron, this exotic fish competes with native fish for food and habitat. The *round goby* (*Neogobius melanostomus*) is another exotic fish that apparently arrived in ballast water of foreign ships around 1990 (Figure 13-6, p. 283). An aggressive bottom-dweller, it tolerates degraded waters, feeds voraciously, and reproduces prolifically.

Rusty crayfish (*Orconectes rusticus*) are native to the Ohio River basin but have spread to Ontario, where

FIGURE 13-5 The Eurasian ruffe has a glassy eye and rows of dark spots between the spines of its dorsal fin.

FIGURE 13-6 The round goby has raised, froglike eyes, thick lips, and a single scallop-shaped pelvic (bottom) fin that can be used as a suction cup for anchoring the fish to rocks in fast currents.

they outdo local species in their consumption of fish eggs. *Spiny water fleas* (*Bythotrephes longimanus*) and *fishhook fleas* (*Cercopagis pengoi*) are tiny crustaceans that devour much of the plankton in lakes and travel from lake to lake on the fishing lines of anglers (Figure 13-7). Aquatic plants such as *Eurasian watermilfoil* (*Myriophyllum spicatum*) and *fanwort* (*Cabomba caroliniana*) cause problems by growing prolifically and clogging waterways; they spread when people unknowingly transfer bits of plant material from lake to lake on their boats or empty aquariums into natural waters.

Purple loosestrife (*Lythrum salicaria*) is a perennial plant that grows in wetlands in parts of Europe (Figure 13-8). In the early 1880s, it was imported to North America as an ornamental plant. It was also released accidentally into waterways in ballast water contaminated with its seeds.

A single plant can produce more than 2.5 million seeds a year. The seeds are spread by water; in mud;

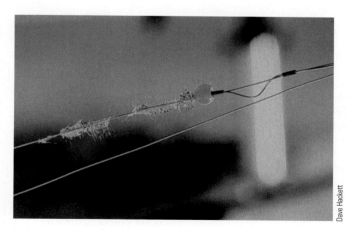

FIGURE 13-7 Spiny water fleas are visible to the naked eye as they cling to fishing lines.

FIGURE 13-8 The purple loosestrife has a tightly clustered pink-purple spike of flowers and a ridged square stem. This plant can be spread by means of its numerous tiny seeds, or vegetatively from small fragments of stems or roots.

and by becoming attached to wildlife, livestock, people, and tire treads.

> **DID YOU KNOW**
>
> You can help to control invasive species by becoming informed and avoiding actions that contribute to their spread. Research control programs in your area and invasive species hotlines that allow you to report these species when you see them.

Few native plants can compete with this prolific and highly productive plant. This explains why it has spread to temperate and boreal wetlands in at least six provinces and in nearly every U.S. state.

As it spreads, it reduces wetland biodiversity by displacing native vegetation and reducing habitat for some forms of wetland wildlife. Some conservationists call this plant the "purple plague."

Good news. Biologists in Canada and the United States have introduced two beetles that are natural predators of purple loosestrife in Europe: *Galerucella pusilla* and *Galerucella calmariensis*. The introduced predators are feeding on purple loosestrife and greatly decreasing its vigour, thus allowing native plants to compete with it (OFAH, 2012). As well, Dr. Nosko of Nipissing University has found that herbivory from native insects increases over time as local insects become accustomed to the new food source presented by purple loosestrife.

13-3 PROTECTING AND SUSTAINING MARINE BIODIVERSITY

Why Is It Difficult to Protect Marine Biodiversity? Out of Sight, Out of Mind

Coastal development, the invisibility and vastness of the world's oceans, and lack of legal jurisdiction hinder protection of marine biodiversity.

There are several reasons why protecting marine biodiversity is difficult. One is rapidly growing coastal development and the accompanying massive inputs of sediment and other wastes from land into coastal waters. This harms shore-hugging species and threatens biologically diverse and highly productive coastal ecosystems such as coral reefs, marshes, and mangrove forest swamps.

Another factor is that much of the damage to the oceans and other bodies of water is not visible to most people. And many people incorrectly view the seas as an inexhaustible resource that can absorb an almost infinite amount of waste and pollution.

In addition, most of the world's ocean area lies outside the legal jurisdiction of any country. Thus it is an open-access resource, subject to overexploitation because of the tragedy of the commons.

How Can We Protect Endangered and Threatened Marine Species? Legal Agreements and Awareness

We can use laws, international treaties, and education to help reduce the premature extinction of marine species.

One widely used method for protecting biodiversity is identifying and protecting endangered, threatened, and rare species, as has been done to help save a number of endangered terrestrial species (Chapter 12).

This strategy has also been used to protect a number of endangered and threatened marine reptiles (turtles) and mammals (especially whales, seals, and sea lions; Figure 13-9, p. 285). Each year plastic items dumped from ships and left as litter on beaches threaten the lives of millions of marine mammals, turtles, and seabirds that ingest, become entangled in, choke on, or are poisoned by such debris.

Three of eight major sea turtle species (Figure 13-10, p. 285) are endangered (Kemp's ridley, leatherbacks, and hawksbills), and the rest are threatened, mostly because of four factors. *First* is loss or degradation of beach habitat where they come ashore to lay eggs. *Second* is the legal and illegal taking of eggs. *Third* is the increased use of turtles as sources of food, medicinal ingredients, tortoiseshell (for jewellery), and leather from their flippers. *Fourth*, many turtles are unintentionally captured and drowned by commercial fishing boats—especially shrimp trawlers and those using long lines of hooks. Conservationists estimate that each year the global longline fishing industry unintentionally hooks and kills as many as 40 000 sea turtles as bycatch. In 2004, the United States banned long-line swordfish fishing off the Pacific coast to save dwindling sea turtle populations.

INDIVIDUALS MATTER

Killing Invader Species and Saving Shipping Companies Money

A large cargo ship typically has a dozen or more ballast tanks below deck. Each tank is the size of a high-school gymnasium and holds millions of litres of water.

When a ship takes on cargo and leaves port it pumps water into the ballast tanks to keep it low in the water, submerge its rudder, and help maintain stability. This water also contains large numbers of fish, crabs, clams, and other species (many of

them microscopic) found in the port's local waters.

When the ship's cargo is removed at its destination its ballast water is released until the ship is loaded again. This dumps millions of foreign organisms into rivers and bays. Thus cargo ships moving about 80% of the goods traded internationally play the primary role in the release of nonnative aquatic organisms into various parts of the world.

In 2002, researchers Mario Tamburri and Kerstin Wasson found that pumping nitrogen gas into ballast tanks while a ship is at sea virtually eliminates dissolved oxygen in the ballast water. This saves the shipping industry money by reducing corrosion of a ship's steel compartments. In addition, within three days it kills most fish, crabs, clams, and other potential invader species lurking in the ballast tanks.

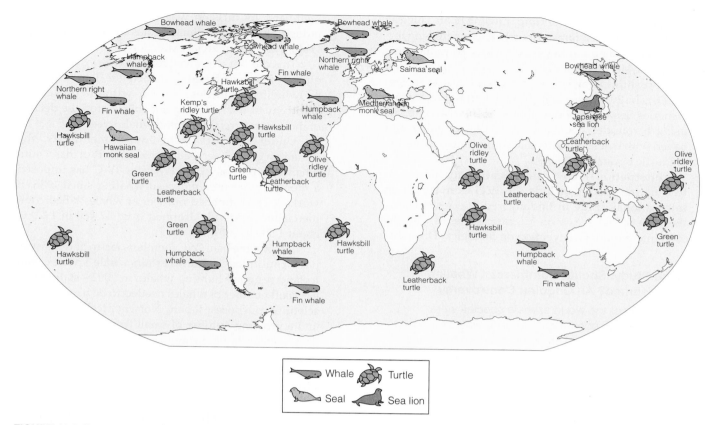

FIGURE 13-9 Natural capital degradation: endangered and threatened marine mammals (whales, seals, and sea lions) and reptiles (turtles). Many marine fish, seabirds, and invertebrate species are also threatened.

FIGURE 13-10 Natural capital degradation: major species of sea turtles that have roamed the seas for 150 million years, showing their relative adult sizes. Three of these species (Kemp's ridleys, leatherbacks, and hawksbills) are endangered, and the rest are threatened as a result of human activities.

Until recently, U.S. shrimp trawling boats killed as many as 55 000 sea turtles (mostly endangered loggerheads and Kemp's ridleys) each year. To reduce this slaughter, since 1989 the U.S. government has required offshore shrimp trawlers to use turtle exclusion devices (TEDs). In 2004, researchers at the National Marine Fisheries Service reported that longline fishing boats using a rounder hook with a smaller opening and baited with mackerel instead of squid could reduce the sea turtle bycatch by 65–90%.

International laws and treaties to help protect marine species include the 1975 Convention on International Trade in Endangered Species (CITES), the 1979 Global Treaty on Migratory Species, and the 1995 International Convention on Biological Diversity.

Case Study: Should Commercial Whaling Be Resumed? An Ongoing Controversy

After many of the world's whale species were overharvested, commercial whaling was banned in 1970, but there are efforts to overturn this ban.

Cetaceans are an order of mostly marine mammals ranging in size from the 0.9-metre (3-foot) porpoise to the giant 15- to 30-metre (50- to 100-foot) blue whale. These are more than 80 species that can be divided into two major groups: toothed whales and baleen whales.

Toothed whales, such as the porpoise, sperm whale, and killer whale (orca), bite and chew their food and feed mostly on squid, octopus, and other marine animals. Baleen whales, such as the blue, grey, humpback, and finback, are filter feeders. Instead of teeth they have several hundred horny plates made of baleen, or whalebone, that hang down from the upper jaw. These plates filter plankton from the seawater, especially tiny shrimplike krill (Figure 4-19, p. 73). Baleen whales are the more abundant of the two cetacean groups.

Whales are fairly easy to kill because of their large size and their need to come to the surface to breathe. Mass slaughter has become efficient with the use of radar and airplanes to locate them, fast ships, harpoon guns, and inflation lances that pump dead whales full of air and make them float.

Whale harvesting, mostly in international waters, has followed the classic pattern of a tragedy of the commons, with whalers killing an estimated 1.5 million whales between 1925 and 1975. This overharvesting reduced the populations of 8 of the 11 major species to the point at which it no longer paid to hunt and kill them (commercial extinction). It also drove some commercially prized species such as the giant blue whale to the brink of biological extinction (see Case Study, p. 287).

In 1946, the International Convention for the Regulation of Whaling established the International Whaling Commission (IWC), which now has 89 nation members. Its mission was to regulate the whaling industry by setting annual quotas to prevent overharvesting and commercial extinction.

This did not work well for two reasons. First, IWC quotas often were based on inadequate data or ignored by whaling countries. Second, without powers of enforcement the IWC was not able to stop the decline of most commercially hunted whale species.

Under pressure from environmentalists, the Canadian government, and governments of many nonwhaling countries in the IWC, the IWC has imposed a moratorium on commercial whaling since 1986. It worked. The estimated number of whales killed commercially worldwide dropped from 42 480 in 1970 to about 1 500 in 2009.

Despite the ban, IWC members Japan and Norway have continued to hunt certain whale species, and Iceland resumed hunting whales in 2002—stating that a certain number of whales needed to be harvested for scientific purposes. Japan, Norway, Iceland, Russia, and a growing number of small tropical island countries—which Japan brought into the IWC to support its position—continue working to overthrow the IWC ban on commercial whaling and reverse the international ban on buying and selling whale products.

They argue that commercial whaling should be allowed because it has long been a traditional part of the economies and cultures of countries such as Japan, Iceland, and Norway. They also contend that the ban is based on emotion, not updated scientific estimates of whale populations.

The moratorium on commercial whaling has led to a sharp rebound in the estimated populations of sperm, pilot, and minke whales. Proponents of resuming whaling see no scientific reason for not resuming controlled and sustainable hunting of these species and other whale species with populations of at least 1 million.

Conservationists disagree. Some argue that whales are peaceful, intelligent, sensitive, and highly social mammals that pose no threat to humans and should be protected for ethical reasons. Others question IWC estimates of the allegedly recovered whale species, noting the inaccuracy of past IWC estimates of whale populations. Also, many conservationists fear that opening the door to any commercial whaling may eventually lead to widespread harvests of most whale species by weakening current international disapproval and legal sanctions against commercial whaling.

Proponents of resuming whaling say that people in other countries that admire whales have no right to tell Japanese, Norwegians, and other whaling culture countries that they must not eat the giant mammals. This would be like people in India who consider cows sacred telling Americans and Europeans that they should not be allowed to eat beef.

Case Study: Near Extinction of the Blue Whale—Big Species Are Easy to Kill

Commercial whaling almost drove the blue whale to extinction, and it may never recover.

The biologically endangered blue whale (Figure 13-11) is the world's largest animal. Fully grown, it is longer than three train boxcars and weighs more than 25 elephants. The adult has a heart the size of a Volkswagen Beetle car, and some of its arteries are so big that a child could swim through them.

Blue whales spend about eight months a year in Antarctic waters. There they find an abundant supply of krill (Figure 4-19, p. 73), which they filter by the trillions daily from seawater. During the winter they migrate to warmer waters where their young are born.

Before commercial whaling began, an estimated 200 000 blue whales roamed the Antarctic Ocean. Today the species has been hunted to near biological extinction for its oil, meat, and bone. There are probably fewer than 5 000 of these whales left.

A combination of prolonged overharvesting and certain natural characteristics of blue whales caused its decline. Their huge size made them easy to spot. They were caught in large numbers because they grouped together in their Antarctic feeding grounds. They also take 25 years to mature sexually and have only one offspring every 2–5 years. This low reproductive rate makes it difficult for the species to recover once its population falls beneath a certain threshold.

Blue whales have not been hunted commercially since 1964 and have been classified as an endangered species since 1975. Despite this protection, some marine biologists fear that too few blue whales remain for the species to recover and avoid extinction. Others believe that with continued protection they will make a slow comeback.

FIGURE 13-11 The great blue whale is the largest animal that ever existed on Earth, yet this gentle giant has been pushed to the brink of extinction by past whaling practices.

© David Fleetham/Alamy

CONSIDER, DISCUSS, OR DEBATE

What are the best arguments for and against whaling? Where do you stand on this issue?

What Is the Role of International Agreements and Protected Marine Sanctuaries? Hopeful but Limited Progress

Nations have established various types of marine sanctuaries, but most receive only partial protection and fully protected areas make up less than 0.01% of the world's ocean area.

Under the United Nations Law of the Sea, all coastal nations have sovereignty over the waters and seabed up to 19 kilometres (12 miles) offshore. They also have almost total jurisdiction over their Exclusive Economic Zone (EEZ), which extends 320 kilometres (200 miles) offshore. Taken together, the nations of the world have jurisdiction over 36% of the ocean surface and 90% of the world's fish stocks. However, instead of using this law to protect their fishing grounds, many governments promoted overfishing, subsidized new fishing fleets, and failed to establish and enforce stricter regulation of fish catches.

Since 1986, the World Conservation Union (IUCN) has helped establish a global system of *marine protected areas* (MPAs), mostly at the national level. An MPA is an area of ocean protected from some or all human activities. The more than 5 880 existing MPAs provide partial protection for about 1.5% of the Earth's total ocean area.

In addition, the United Nations Environment Programme has spearheaded efforts to develop 12 regional agreements to protect large marine areas shared by several countries.

At least 100 of the world's more than 580 biosphere reserves (p. 242) include coastal or marine habitats. *Marine reserves*—also known as fully protected areas or no-take MPAs—are areas where no extraction and alteration of any living or nonliving resources is allowed. More than 20 coastal nations, including Canada and the United States, have established marine reserves that vary widely in size. An example of a no-take marine reserve is the Chagos Marine Reserve, about 500 kilometres (310 miles) south of the Maldives in the Indian Ocean. It is 540 000 square kilometres (208 000 square miles) in size, is home to more than 1 000 species of reef fish, and shelters half of the recorded species of coral in the Indian Ocean. It also contains the world's largest living coral structure—the Great Chagos Bank—which is 12 640 square kilometres (4 880 square miles) of mostly submerged coral reefs.

Scientific studies show that within fully protected marine reserves, fish populations double, fish size grows by almost a third, fish reproduction triples, and species diversity increases by almost one-fourth. Furthermore, this improvement happens within 2–4 years after strict protection begins and lasts for decades. However, less than 1% of the world's ocean area consists of fully protected marine reserves. In other words, *we have failed to strictly protect 99% of the world's ocean area from human exploitation.*

In 1997, a group of international marine scientists called for governments to increase fully protected marine reserves to at least 20% of the ocean's surface by 2020. The 2003 Pew Fisheries Commission study recommended establishing many more protected marine reserves in coastal waters and connecting them with protected corridors so fish can move back and forth. In 2004, marine biologist Elliott Norse proposed establishment of *movable marine reserves* that move with the animals as they migrate through the oceans.

What Is the Role of Integrated Coastal Management? Cooperation Can Work

Some communities have worked together to develop integrated plans for managing their coastal areas.

Integrated coastal management is a community-based effort to develop and use coastal resources more sustainably. The overall aim is for groups competing for the use of coastal resources to identify shared problems and goals. Then they attempt to develop workable, cost-effective, and adaptable solutions that preserve biodiversity and environmental quality while meeting economic and social needs. In other words, they develop and implement integrated plans using the principles of *adaptive ecosystem management* (Figure 11-29, p. 243).

Ideally, the overall goal is to zone the land and sea portions of an entire coastal area. Such zoning would include some fully protected marine reserves where no exploitive human activities are allowed and other zones where different kinds and levels of human activities are permitted. Australia's huge Great Barrier Reef Marine Park is managed this way. Currently, more than 100 integrated coastal management programs are being developed throughout the world.

SELF CHECK

How important are marine protected areas (MPAs), in your opinion? Why did the Living Oceans Society give Canada an F for MPAs whereas Australia received an A and the United States received a B/C?

Go to http://www.livingoceans.org/sites/default/files/reports/ MPAReportCard_09.pdf **and find out!**

How Can We Manage Fisheries to Sustain Stocks and Protect Biodiversity? Many Ideas

There are a number of ways to manage marine fisheries more sustainably and protect marine biodiversity.

Overfishing is a serious threat to biodiversity in coastal waters and to some marine species in open-ocean waters. Figure 13-12 lists measures that analysts have suggested for managing global fisheries more sustainably and protecting marine biodiversity. Most of these approaches rely on some sort of government regulation.

But in nature there are almost always surprises because we still have little understanding of how ecosystems work. For example, researchers have found that reducing fishing to protect fish stocks can harm populations of some seabirds.

In the North Sea, the bycatch tossed back into the sea is eaten by a seabird species called the great skua. Because of such an abundance of food the size of the great skua population rose sharply. But reducing fish quotas has meant fewer discards for these seabirds. To make up for the loss these birds have been preying on other seabirds such as kittiwakes and puffins—another example of unintended consequences from our actions.

One way to reduce overfishing is to develop better measurements and models for projecting fish populations. Until recently, management of commercial fisheries has been based primarily on the *maximum sustained yield (MSY)*. It involves using a mathematical model to project the maximum number of fish that can be harvested annually from a fish stock without causing a population drop.

But experience has shown that the MSY concept has helped hasten the collapse of most commercially valuable stocks for several reasons. *First*, populations and growth rates of fish stocks are difficult to measure. *Second*, population sizes of fish stocks usually are based on unreliable and sometimes underreported catch figures by fishers. *Third*, harvesting a particular species at its estimated maximum sustainable level can affect the populations of other target and nontarget fish species and other marine organisms—those pesky connections again. *Fourth*, fishing quotas are difficult to enforce and many groups managing fisheries have ignored projected MSYs for short-term political or economic reasons.

In recent years, fishery biologists and managers have begun placing more emphasis on the *optimum sustained yield (OSY)* concept. This approach attempts to take into account interactions with other species and

Solutions

Managing Fisheries

Fishery Regulations

Set catch limits well below the maximum sustainable yield

Improve monitoring and enforcement of regulations

Economic Approaches

Sharply reduce or eliminate fishing subsidies

Charge fees for harvesting fish and shellfish from publicly owned offshore waters

Certify sustainable fisheries

Protected Areas

Establish no-fishing areas

Establish more marine protected areas

Rely more on integrated coastal management

Consumer Information

Label sustainably harvested fish

Publicize overfished and threatened species

Bycatch

Use wide-meshed nets to allow escape of smaller fish

Use net escape devices for seabirds and sea turtles

Ban throwing edible and marketable fish back into the sea

Aquaculture

Restrict coastal locations for fish farms

Control pollution more strictly

Depend more on herbivorous fish species

Non-Native Invasions

Kill organisms in ship ballast water

Filter organisms from ship ballast water

Dump ballast water far at sea and replace with sea water

FIGURE 13-12 Solutions: ways to manage fisheries more sustainably and protect marine biodiversity.

to provide more room for error. But it still depends on the poorly understood biology of fish and changing ocean conditions. Also, many bodies governing fisheries ignore OSY estimates for short-term political and economic reasons.

Another approach is *multispecies management* of a number of interacting species, which takes into account their competitive and predator–prey interactions. Such models are still in the development and testing stage.

A more ambitious approach is to develop complex computer models for managing multispecies fisheries in *large marine systems*. However, it is a political challenge to get groups of nations to cooperate in planning and managing them.

Despite the scientific and political difficulties, some limited management of several large marine systems is under way. Examples include the Mediterranean Sea by 17 of the 18 nations involved and the Great Barrier Reef under the exclusive control of Australia.

A basic problem is the uncertainties built into using any of these approaches. As a result, many fishery scientists and environmentalists are increasingly interested in using the *precautionary principle* (p. 177) for managing fisheries and large marine systems. This means sharply reducing fish harvests and closing some overfished areas until they recover and we have more information about what levels of fishing can be sustained.

Case Study: Management Gone Wrong—Cod on the Grand Banks

The once-bountiful stock of cod on the Grand Banks collapsed when warnings were ignored and the resource was overharvested.

In 1497, Giovanni Caboto (called "John Cabot" by the British) reported dense populations of cod on the Grand Banks that rise from the continental shelf east of Newfoundland. For 400 years thereafter, fishermen from North America and Europe harvested the East Coast fishery. They used hooks and lines and small nets, and they preserved their catch by salting or drying it.

By the 20th century, fishing vessels were larger and driven by steam engines that allowed more precise handling and the ability to operate in almost any weather. Ships began to haul nets behind them. By the 1940s, *pair-trawling* was practised in which two ships cooperated to pull a much larger net through the sea. In the 1950s and 1960s, an increasing number of *factory ships* arrived in the Grand Banks area; these ships could haul giant nets, pull them aboard using specially designed rear ramps, freeze the catch, and remain in the area to continue fishing. In the late 1960s and 1970s, the fishing fleets gained technology that allowed them to find fish using sonar and to haul nets at precisely controlled depths.

As early as the 1930s, fishing nations began to realize that some fishing stocks were being overharvested. In 1949, Canada and 10 other fishing nations created the International Convention for the Northwest Atlantic Fisheries (ICNAF) to help manage the resource. Initially the ICNAF could only

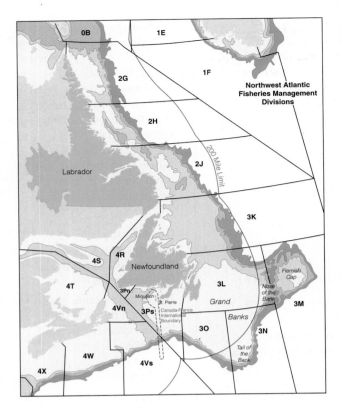

FIGURE 13-13 Canada has been performing regular monitoring, control, and surveillance patrols beyond its 320-kilometre (200-mile) EEZ to the "nose" and "tail" of the Grand Banks, plus the Flemish Cap. These are three important fish-spawning areas that must be protected from illegal fishing if the fish stocks are to recover. (Department of Geography, Memorial University of Newfoundland)

recommend, but by 1970 there was enough evidence of declining fish stocks that the ICNAF was granted the authority to set Total Allowable Catch (TAC) limits for some stocks. Unfortunately, the TAC limits were high and there were loopholes that allowed overharvesting to continue.

In 1977, Canada declared a 320-kilometre (200-mile) *exclusive economic zone (EEZ)* in an effort to protect the declining Grand Banks fishery from foreign fleets (Figure 13-13). This still left the "tail" and "nose" of the Grand Banks—important fish-spawning areas—vulnerable.

In 1979, the ICNAF was replaced by the Northwest Atlantic Fisheries Organization (NAFO). NAFO set limits, but some fishing fleets from NAFO countries registered their vessels to non-NAFO countries and returned to fish just outside Canada's 320-kilometre (200-mile) EEZ while ignoring NAFO quotas.

Tensions increased as the Canadian fleet grew and the fish stock continued to decline. By 1980, Canadian scientists warned that cod fishing should be banned on the Grand Banks, but the government was concerned about jobs being lost and ignored the warnings for

12 years. Then, in 1992, the Canadian government set major quota reductions in place for several species of fish including a moratorium on fishing for cod (except for a few small inshore operations). Since the mid-1980s, fishing fleets had been targeting other species such as *turbot* (or *Greenland halibut*), and there were fears that these stocks too were in serious decline.

In 1994, Minister of Fisheries and Oceans Brian Tobin introduced the Canadian Fisheries Protection Act to allow the Department of Fisheries and Oceans to arrest foreign ships that violated conservation measures. In 1995, Canadian vessels boarded the Spanish trawler *Estai*, arrested the crew, and seized the cargo; they found that 79% of the catch consisted of undersized turbot caught with illegal nets, and that 25 tonnes of American plaice (an endangered species prohibited by NAFO) were hidden in secret compartments aboard the ship. Many Canadians applauded; some nations thought that Canada had committed an act of piracy. At any rate, this dramatic sequence of events brought to world attention the desperate state of the East Coast fishery.

From 1990 to 2002, the cod harvest of Newfoundland and Labrador fell from 246 000 tonnes to 21 000 tonnes (Figure 13-14). Many millions of dollars and thousands of jobs were lost. There are some harsh lessons to be learned here about the cost of not prioritizing conservation measures to protect the biological resource upon which so much depends.

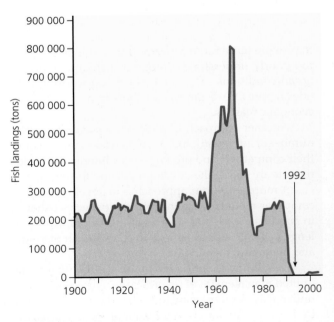

FIGURE 13-14 Natural capital degradation: the Atlantic cod fishery near Newfoundland was overexploited for years by fishing fleets from many countries. The cod population collapsed by 1992 and has not recovered to a harvestable level despite a moratorium on fishing for cod. (Data from Millennium Ecosystem Assessment, 2005)

Diversifying Demands on the Fishery

In response to the cod moratorium of 1992, the fishing industry of Newfoundland and Labrador moved away from its focus on cod and diversified its demands on the environment by pursuing a wider range of food possibilities. The fishing fleets increasingly made use of other species of fish such as turbot, redfish, yellowtail flounder, hake, herring, and mackerel.

The shellfish industry developed greatly, basing its success on diverse populations of marine crustaceans and molluscs such as snow crabs, shrimps, lobsters, clams, whelks, and scallops. By 2002, the value of the total seafood harvest (fish and shellfish) was twice what it had been in 1990 when cod was still the focus.

The aquaculture industry also began to grow, producing increasing numbers of food items such as Atlantic salmon, steelhead trout, and blue molluscs in fish farms. In an ironic twist, recent attention has been paid to learning how to raise cod in fish farms. There are pros and cons to fish farming, as will be discussed in Chapter 14, but this could be one way to return cod to the dinner table while taking the pressure off wild populations of cod.

To help fish stocks recover, Canada is continuing with rigorous conservation measures extending surveillance to key fish-spawning areas just beyond its 320-kilometre (200-mile) limit (Figure 13-13). The cod population now appears to be slowly growing, but it is still only 10% of what it was before the decline.

Case Study: Managing West Coast Salmon— A Complicated Issue

Even though the West Coast wild salmon fishery was clearly in decline, insufficient conservation actions were taken until the stocks hit a shocking low point.

In 1990, the Canadian West Coast wild-salmon-fishing industry brought in a catch of 96 000 tonnes valued at $263 million. By 2002, the catch had shrunk to 33 000 tonnes (a 66% reduction) valued at $52 million. In 2008, the Canadian catch had fallen to 5 400 tonnes (a 94% reduction relative to 1990) valued at $20 million.

A number of factors were thought to contribute to the decline. *First*, the salmon were overharvested as the fishing fleet became more efficient. In 1972, for instance, Canadian fishing crews in seine boats toiled for 51 days to bring in their quotas; 20 years later, crews in large modern boats were able to reach their quotas after four days of fishing; as well, the size of allowable catch was raised during the 20-year period.

Second, salmon fishing has an international dimension. Canada, the United States, and other countries pursue these fish. Canada and the United States are the main stakeholders and share the majority of the harvest as well as the responsibility for management. The 1985 Pacific Salmon Treaty, signed by Prime Minister Brian Mulroney and U.S. President Ronald Reagan, was intended to end the long-standing "salmon wars" between these two countries, but it did not. Canada and the United States continued to disagree about relative allotments and other details. Meanwhile, the fishery continued to decline.

Third, the management of salmon is complicated by their life cycles. Salmon breed in streams that can clearly be differentiated by nationality; however, they spend much of their lives swimming freely in the ocean. When they move toward their natal streams to breed, they are intercepted by fishing fleets before it is clear where they are going. "Canadian salmon" are being caught by U.S. fleets and vice versa.

Fourth, salmon numbers fluctuate from year to year in response to a wide variety of influences, including changes in ocean temperatures. Scientists suggest that climate change, which will warm the ocean and rivers, will make it harder for salmon to survive since they require cold, well-oxygenated water. Human interference with the valuable services of rivers (Figure 13-15)

Natural Capital

Ecological Services of Rivers

- Deliver nutrients to sea to help sustain coastal fisheries
- Deposit silt that maintains deltas
- Purify water
- Renew and renourish wetlands
- Provide habitats for wildlife

FIGURE 13-15 Natural capital: important ecological services provided by rivers.

impacts the salmon, which require unobstructed high-quality rivers for part of their complex life cycle (Figure 13-16). But rivers are blocked by dams (p. 346), heated by human enterprises, disturbed by forestry and farming operations, and polluted by chemicals and sediments. The First Nations People, supported by a supreme court decision, are demanding their rights to catch salmon for food and ceremonial purposes. And there is a recreational harvest to consider.

Fifth, while the wild salmon harvest was declining, the farming of salmon in open-net cages in the sea was increasing. By 2009, about 80% of B.C.'s salmon harvest came from salmon farms and only about 20% came from wild populations (Figure 13-17). While this might seem to be a good situation in terms of taking pressure off the wild populations, there seemed to be some evidence that fish farming was having a negative impact on wild salmon. For example, parasitic sea lice (see Section 14-8) can build up to high concentrations in and near the open-net cages used for salmon farming; although sea lice do less damage to adult salmon, they can kill juvenile salmon and this may be a factor as wild juvenile salmon swim past fish farms on their way out to sea.

The variety and uncertainty of all these factors prevented a speedy implementation of conservation

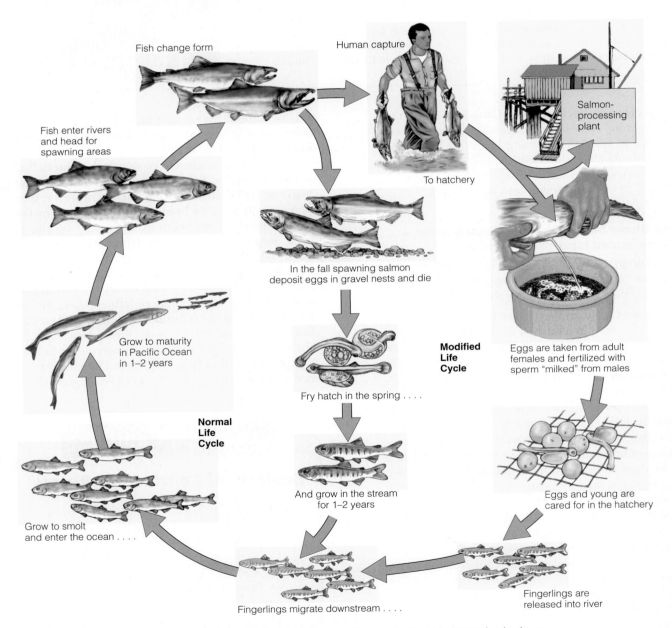

FIGURE 13-16 Normal life cycle of wild salmon (left) and human-modified life cycle of hatchery-raised salmon (right). Salmon spend part of their lives in fresh water and part in salt water.

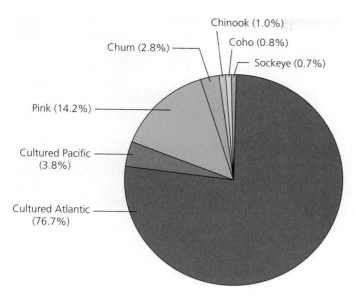

Chinook (1.0%)
Coho (0.8%)
Chum (2.8%)
Sockeye (0.7%)
Pink (14.2%)
Cultured Pacific (3.8%)
Cultured Atlantic (76.7%)

FIGURE 13-17 The B.C. salmon harvest was about 80% farmed salmon in 2009, shown here as cultured Atlantic and cultured Pacific salmon. Pink salmon was the most commonly captured species of wild salmon. (Data from the B.C. Ministry of Agriculture)

measures such as those listed in Figure 13-18. Fortunately, the attention generated by the shockingly low wild-salmon harvest galvanized many into action. In November 2009, the Commission of Inquiry into the Decline of Sockeye Salmon in the Fraser River was initiated; this involved new studies being launched and much participation by a broad range of interested parties. Commissioner Bruce Cohen heard 900 submissions about the topic and numerous changes are expected to follow in the wake of his 2012 report. Many

Solutions

Rebuilding Salmon Populations

Allowing sufficient salmon to escape harvest

Protecting the spawning beds

Releasing juvenile salmon from hatcheries to underpopulated streams

Releasing extra water from dams when needed

Building fish ladders so adult salmon can bypass dams during upstream migration

Reducing sediment, pollution, and heat in salmon rivers

Banning dams from some stream areas

FIGURE 13-18 Solutions: some strategies used to rebuild salmon populations in rivers.

other fish- or conservation-related groups initiated their own studies and published their own reports. In February 2010, Canada's first *salmon stronghold* was established at Harrison River, about 100 kilometres (62 miles) from Vancouver; this means that the watershed has been recognized as a core area of salmon abundance and diversity, warranting comprehensive habitat protection. As well, various groups have been vocal about the need to change salmon farming from a system that uses open-net cages to one that ensures containment of the farmed fish and their associated wastes and parasites within impermeable barriers (Living Oceans Society, 2012). See Section 14-8 for further discussion of the pros and cons of aquaculture.

CONSIDER, DISCUSS, OR DEBATE

How could the lessons learned from mismanaging the East Coast cod fishery be applied to saving the West Coast salmon fishery?

Should We Use the Marketplace to Control Access to Fisheries? Good and Bad News about an Interesting Idea

Some countries try to prevent overfishing by giving each fishing vessel quotas that can be bought or sold in the marketplace.

Some countries are using a market-based system called *individual transfer quotas (ITQs)* to help control access to fisheries. The government gives each fishing vessel owner a specified percentage of the total allowable catch (TAC) for a fishery in a given year.

Owners are permitted to buy, sell, or lease their quotas like private property. Currently about 50 of the world's fisheries are managed by the ITQ system. It was introduced in New Zealand in 1986 and in Iceland in 1990. In these countries, there has been some reduction in overfishing and the overall fishing fleet and an end to government fishing subsidies that encourage overfishing.

But enforcement has been difficult, some fishers illegally exceed their quotas, and the wasteful bycatch has not been reduced.

Environmentalists have identified four problems with the ITQ approach and have made suggestions for its improvement. *First,* in effect it transfers ownership of publicly owned fisheries to private commercial fishers but still makes the public responsible for the costs of enforcing and managing the system. *Remedy:* Collect fees (not to exceed 5% of the value of the catch) from quota holders to pay for the costs of government enforcement and management of the ITQ system.

Second, it can squeeze out small fishing vessels and companies because they do not have the capital to buy ITQs from others. For example, five years after the ITQ system was implemented in New Zealand, three companies controlled half the ITQs. *Remedy:* Do not allow any fisher or fishing company to accumulate more than a fifth of the total quota of a fishery.

Third, the ITQ system can increase poaching and sales of illegally caught fish on the black market, as has happened to some extent in New Zealand. Some of this comes from small-scale fishers who receive no quota or too small a quota to make a living. Some also comes from larger-scale fishers who deliberately exceed their quotas. *Remedy:* Require strict record keeping and have well-trained observers on all fishing vessels with quotas.

Fourth, the fishing quotas (TACS) are often set too high to prevent overfishing. *Remedy:* Leave 10–50% of the estimated MSY of an ITQ fishery as a buffer to protect the fishery from unexpected decline.

13-5 PROTECTING, SUSTAINING, AND RESTORING LAKES AND RIVERS

Case Study: Can the Great Lakes Survive Repeated Invasions by Invasive Species? They Keep Coming

Invasions by non-native species have upset the ecological functioning of the Great Lakes for decades, and more invaders keep arriving.

Invasions by non-native species are a major threat to the biodiversity and ecological functioning of lakes, as illustrated by what has happened to the Great Lakes.

Collectively, the Great Lakes are the world's largest body of fresh water. Since the 1920s, they have been invaded by at least 180 non-native species and the number keeps rising. Many of the exotic invaders arrive on the hulls or in bilge water discharges of oceangoing ships that have been entering the Great Lakes through the St. Lawrence seaway for over 40 years.

One of the biggest threats, *sea lampreys (Petromyzon marinus)*, reached the western lakes through the Welland Canal as early as 1920. This parasite attaches itself to almost any kind of fish and kills the victim by sucking out its blood (Figure 13-19). Over the years it has depleted populations of many important sport fish species such as lake trout.

Canada and the United States keep the lamprey population down by applying a chemical that kills their larvae in their spawning streams—at a cost of about $15 million a year.

Around 1986, larvae of the *zebra mussel (Dreissena polymorpha)* arrived in ballast water discharged from a European ship (Figure 13-20). This thumbnail-sized non-native species reproduces rapidly and has no

FIGURE 13-19 The invasion of sea lampreys devastated the Great Lakes fishery. Scientists now control lamprey numbers using chemical larvicides.

FIGURE 13-20 Zebra mussels are thumbnail-sized mussels with striped shells. Often found in dense clusters attached to solid substrates, they are rapidly invading freshwater ecosystems.

known natural enemies in the Great Lakes. As a result, it has displaced other mussel species and depleted the food supply for some other Great Lakes species. The mussels have also clogged irrigation pipes, shut down water intake systems for power plants and city water supplies, fouled beaches, and grown in huge masses on boat hulls, piers, pipes, rocks, and almost any exposed aquatic surface. This mussel has also spread to freshwater communities in parts of southern Canada and 30 states in the United States.

Possible *good news.* In 2001, scientists reported on the use of an oscillating dipole apparatus to produce what is popularly known as a "zebra mussel death ray." It emits extremely low frequency electromagnetic waves that can kill zebra mussels, apparently without harming the environment or other species. This approach is being evaluated. New methods for treating ballast water have also been developed (see Individuals Matter, p. 284).

Zebra mussels may not be good for us and some fish species but they can benefit a number of aquatic plants. By consuming algae and other microorganisms, the mussels increase water clarity, which permits deeper penetration of sunlight and more photosynthesis. This allows some native plants to thrive and return the plant composition of Lake Erie (and presumably other lakes) closer to what it was 100 years ago. Because the plants provide food and increase dissolved oxygen, their comeback may benefit certain aquatic animals.

More *bad news.* Around 1991, a larger and potentially more destructive species, the *quagga mussel* (*Dreissena bugensis*), invaded the Great Lakes, probably discharged in the ballast water of a Russian freighter. It can survive at greater depths and tolerate more extreme temperatures than the zebra mussel. There is concern that it may spread widely and interfere with the productivity of aquatic ecosystems.

Four different species of *Asian carp*—bighead, silver, grass, and black carp—have been imported to the United States to control excess vegetation during catfish aquaculture. All four species have escaped. At least two of the species are working their way up the Mississippi River toward Lake Michigan. American authorities are trying to stop the fish with electric barriers, sonic bubble curtains, underwater speakers that broadcast annoying noises, and chemicals meant to repel fish. Why all the fuss? Some scientists suggest that if these carp gain access to the Great Lakes, they will consume vast amounts of food, grow to 45 kilograms (100 pounds), and become the dominant species of the Great Lakes system. Currently, the fish have been sighted in the Chicago Sanitary and Ship Canal that joins the Mississippi River to Lake Michigan, just 60 kilometres (37 miles) from the lake. Stay tuned.

How Can Freshwater Fisheries Be Managed and Sustained?

Freshwater fisheries can be sustained by building and protecting populations of desirable species, preventing overfishing, and maintaining habitat quality.

Sustainable management of freshwater fish involves encouraging populations of commercial and sport fish species and preventing such species from being overfished. Ways to do this include regulating the time and length of fishing seasons and the number and size of fish that can be taken, ensuring enforcement of regulations, and educating the public and politicians about the importance of effective management.

Maintaining habitat quality is also fundamental. This can involve preserving water quality by taking steps to prevent pollutants, sediments from soil erosion, and excess heat from degrading water bodies on which fish depend. Other measures might include protecting spawning beds, creating vegetation buffer zones to provide shade and prevent soil erosion, controlling human activities that negatively impact fish, making sure that there are no barriers to fish migration and that there is sufficient water supply, and ensuring the availability of important habitat features such as boulders and coarse woody debris. Groups or individuals have on occasion stepped in to champion the cause of a particular body of water and its entire ecosystem.

Case Study: Managing a Freshwater Fishery

The management of Lake Nipissing, a renowned freshwater fishery, illustrates many of the problems and techniques involved in fisheries management.

Lake Nipissing is a mesotrophic (p. 151) freshwater lake, with a surface area of 873 square kilometres (337 square miles) and an average depth of 4.5 metres (15 feet), in central Ontario. The lake has more than 40 species of fish; however, it is known as a famous walleye-fishing lake and fisheries managers are mindful of the intense pressure on walleye populations as they plan and implement their harvesting and conservation strategies for the lake (Figure 13-21).

Lake Nipissing is fished for 124 000 to 868 000 angling hours in summer, and 169 000 to 644 000 angling hours in winter. Sports-fishers extract 15 000 to 127 000 kilograms of walleye from Lake Nipissing each year. There is also a commercial gill-netting

FIGURE 13-21 Biologist Richard Rowe and technician Jamie Geauvreau of the Ontario Ministry of Natural Resources lift an index gill net on Lake Nipissing during the annual walleye population assessment.

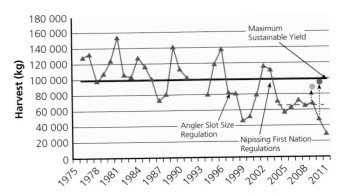

FIGURE 13-22 Trends in Lake Nipissing total walleye harvest (angler harvest plus First Nations commercial harvest) showing recent management efforts compared with a maximum sustainable yield biological reference point. The fisheries management objective since 2004 was to maintain harvest at two-thirds the maximum sustainable yield (dotted red line) to ensure sustainability of the walleye stock. Recent management efforts appear to be showing promise, but only when both major sources of harvest are regulated effectively. Anecdotal information and observational reports suggest that actual harvests in 2009 and 2010 (grey dots) were well above reported harvests, with consequences for the fishery. Further diagrams and analysis will be presented on the book's website at www.nelson.com/livingintheenvironment3e.com. (Courtesy of Richard Rowe, Lake Nipissing Fisheries Manager)

fishery operated by Nipissing First Nation, and this industry harvests 36 000 to 70 000 kilograms of walleye each year.

Despite the best efforts of fisheries biologists, the walleye harvest has often exceeded the maximum sustainable yield (Chapter 9) that biologists felt the population could sustain. After collecting data on the walleye population, the fisheries biologists identified their management challenges and used a variety of strategies and techniques to bring the situation under control (Figure 13-22). The management science behind the Lake Nipissing walleye fishery will be explained in detail in a special section of this book's website at www.nelson.com/livingintheenvironment3e.com.

13-6 PROTECTING, SUSTAINING, AND RESTORING WETLANDS

How Are Wetlands Regarded in Canada? Some Progress

Wetlands are now recognized as valuable and worthy of protection.

Once dismissed as uninhabitable lands to be drained for farming or sold inexpensively to real-estate developers, wetlands are now seen as highly productive ecosystems and centres of biodiversity (pages 153–154; Figure 11-24, p.238). In addition to providing habitat, they filter pollutants from water, prevents floods, slow soil erosion,

and store greenhouse gases. They present recreational, educational, and economic opportunities. Lake and coastal wetlands are vital nurseries for fish stocks.

Wetlands in Canada are diminishing. For example, 75% of the wetlands of the Prairie pothole region—crucial for nesting waterfowl—are gone. About 70% of the wetlands of southern Ontario have been converted into farms and subdivisions.

There are continuing attempts to preserve wetlands. The *North American Waterfowl Management Plan* protects thousands of hectares of wetlands in order to provide habitat for ducks. In response to the 1981 *Convention on Wetlands of International Importance* (also known as the *Ramsar Convention*), Canada set aside 37 Ramsar sites totalling 13 million hectares of wetlands (Figure 11-24). Provinces have evaluation systems that allow them to categorize wetlands according to their biological, social, and hydrological values, as well as additional special features. Provincially significant wetlands can be protected from development and may offer tax advantages to their private-sector owners.

Organizations ranging from tiny grassroots groups to Ducks Unlimited are staunch defenders of wetlands. Figure 13-23 lists ways to help sustain wetlands in Canada and elsewhere. In some cases, wetlands that were degraded are being restored to once again provide their many valuable services (see Case Study below).

Case Study: The Sackville Waterfowl Park

The Sackville Waterfowl Park is a restored wetland success story.

The town of Sackville, New Brunswick, has a unique feature: located just a five-minute stroll from the heart of downtown is an award-winning waterfowl park. At one time a vast natural salt marsh, this area was

---

Solutions

Protecting Wetlands

Protect existing wetlands

Develop incentives and appreciation for wetlands

Steer development away from existing wetlands

Require creation and evaluation of a new high-quality wetland before destroying an existing wetland

Restore degraded wetlands

Control invasions by non-native species

FIGURE 13-23 Solutions: ways to help sustain wetlands.

FIGURE 13-24 Sackville's Waterfowl Park: the entrance to a world of water and wildlife.

Millennium Development Goal 7:

Ensure Environmental Sustainability

Target 7A: Integrate the principles of sustainable development into country policies and programmes and reverse the loss of environmental resources.

Target 7B: Reduce biodiversity loss, achieving, by 2010, a significant reduction in the rate of loss.

7.1 Proportion of land area covered by forest

7.4 Proportion of fish stocks within safe biological limits

7.6 Proportion of terrestrial and marine areas protected

7.7 Proportion of species threatened with extinction

FIGURE 13-25 Sustaining biodiversity: Millennium Development Goal 7 takes aim at environmental sustainability through specific targets and indicators. Target 7A is particularly relevant to forestry topics we covered in Chapter 11 and to fishery topics we covered in Chapter 13. Target 7B addresses the biodiversity issues of Chapters 11, 12, and 13. Indicators 7.1, 7.4, 7.6, and 7.7 are used to assess progress toward those targets. (http://www.undp.org/mdg/)

ditched and drained for farming by Acadian settlers who arrived in the late 1600s. Today, through the efforts and funding of the Town of Sackville, Ducks Unlimited Canada, and other partners and helpers, the area has been transformed into a 22-hectare (55-acre) freshwater mecca for birds, tourists, and townsfolk (Figure 13-24).

The park features 3–5 kilometres of boardwalk and winding trails, as well as many viewing platforms and scenic locations from which visitors can engage in bird watching. In this wetland and partly forested habitat, more than 160 species of birds and roughly 200 species of plants have been observed. At least 30 species of birds breed in the Sackville Waterfowl Park, and the park's location on the Atlantic flyway make it a convenient stopover for migrants from distant places during the spring or fall. In addition to boosting tourism in the area, the park has created educational opportunities, and served as a backdrop for festivals celebrating waterfowl, art, and theatre.

13-7 CHECKING OUR PROGRESS AT SUSTAINING BIODIVERSITY

How Well Are We Proceeding with Millennium Goal 7? Mixed Progress

Our progress at sustaining aquatic and terrestrial biodiversity has been a mixture of successes and failures.

The eight Millennium Development Goals were introduced and described in Chapters 1, 9, and 10. Goal 7—aimed at ensuring environmental sustainability—has a Target A that addresses *principles of sustainability* that we covered in Chapter 9. Here we will focus on aspects of Targets 7A and 7B that relate to the three biodiversity chapters (Chapters 11, 12, and 13) we

have just covered. There are four specific indicators used to monitor progress toward achieving these targets (Figure 13-25):

- Indicator 7.1, the proportion of land covered by forest, continues to decline. However, the decline is slowing through decreasing rates of deforestation, through increasing tree-planting, and through natural succession. For example, the net rate of loss of forest area was 8.9 million hectares per year in the 1990s compared to 5.2 million hectares per year recently. Deforestation is still occurring at alarming rates in South America and in Africa. In North America, gains and losses of forests have essentially come into balance. Asia and Europe now have a positive net balance, but it is not enough to compensate for the continuing losses in many tropical countries.

- Indicator 7.4, the proportion of fish stocks within safe biological limits, continues to decrease. Now only 15% of fish stocks are considered to be underexploited or **moderately exploited,** compared to 40% in the mid-1970s. As mentioned on pages 281–282, larger fish are becoming scarce, meaning that the breeding-age fish are being removed from the population. We need to take fast action by changing our management techniques, setting aside more marine protected areas, and taking other steps outlined in Chapter 13.

- Indicator 7.6, the proportion of terrestrial and marine areas protected, is increasing. There are now over 150 000 protected areas covering 13% of the world's land area. However, only 1.5% of the Earth's ocean ecosystems receive at least partial respite within marine protected areas (p. 287). More marine ecosystems need to be protected, particularly in view of declining fish stocks (above) and of the increasing importance of fish protein for human food (Chapter 14).

- Indicator 7.7, the proportion of species threatened with extinction, continues to rise. There are now about 17 000 species of plants and animals at risk of extinction, and the number is increasing rapidly. Even in Canada, where we have large tracts of space, high affluence, and agencies dedicated to protecting wild species, our list of species at risk grows larger every year.

Target 7B, concerning biodiversity loss, was aimed at 2010 rather than at 2015 because of the urgency of the situation. Clearly, a significant reduction in the rate of loss was not achieved by 2010, and it seems unlikely that it will be achieved by 2015; however, a dedicated effort to preserve habitat in the biodiversity hot spots of our planet could do much to reduce biodiversity loss. The UN and other agencies are developing new initiatives to accelerate progress toward meeting Goal 7B by 2015 and to guide biodiversity efforts in the period beyond 2015.

You are invited to keep track of progress toward the Millennium Development Goals at websites designed for that purpose (http://www.mdgmonitor.org/), and to look back through Chapters 11 to 13 for ideas about actions to take in support of biodiversity.

To promote conservation, fishers and officials need to view fish as a part of a larger ecological system, rather than simply as a commodity to extract.

ANNE PLATT MCGINN

CHAPTER REVIEW

1. Review the Key Questions for this chapter on p. 279. Describe how human activities have upset ecological processes in East Africa's Lake Victoria (**Core Case Study**). How would you go about helping this lake to recover?

2. What are three general patterns of marine biodiversity? Why is marine biodiversity higher **(a)** near coasts than in the open sea and **(b)** on the ocean's bottom than at its surface? Describe the threat to marine biodiversity from bottom trawling.

3. Describe the collapse of the cod fishery in the northwest Atlantic and some of its side effects. Compare the West Coast salmon fishery with the East Coast cod fishery in terms of management mistakes that were made. Describe the effects of trawler fishing, purse-seine fishing, longlining, and drift-net fishing.

4. How have laws and treaties been used to help sustain aquatic species? Describe international efforts to protect whales from overfishing and premature extinction. Describe threats to sea turtles and efforts to protect them.

5. Describe the use of marine protected areas and marine reserves to help sustain aquatic biodiversity and ecosystem services. What percentage of the world's oceans is fully protected from harmful human activities in marine reserves? Describe the roles of fishing communities and individual consumers in regulating fishing and coastal development. What is integrated coastal management?

6. How can the precautionary principle help in managing fisheries and large marine systems? How can government subsidies encourage overfishing? Describe the advantages and disadvantages of using individual transfer rights to help manage fisheries.

7. Describe how consumers can help to sustain fisheries, aquatic biodiversity, and ecosystem services by making careful choices in purchasing seafood.

8. Describe each of the following terms: bycatch, maximum sustained yield, optimum sustained yield, exclusive economic zone, and Ramsar Convention.

9. Describe the major threats to the world's rivers and other freshwater systems. What major ecological services do rivers provide? Describe invasions of the Great Lakes by non-native species. Describe ways to help sustain rivers.

10. What are six priorities for protecting terrestrial and aquatic biodiversity? Relate the ecological problems of Lake Victoria (**Core Case Study**) to the four *scientific principles of sustainability*.

CRITICAL THINKING

1. What three actions would you take to deal with the ecological and economic problems of Africa's Lake Victoria?

2. Give two examples of threats to aquatic systems from invasive species. How does climate change threaten aquatic biodiversity?

3. Why is it more difficult to identify and protect endangered marine species than to protect such species on land?

4. List three methods for using the precautionary principle as a way to manage marine fisheries and help protect marine biodiversity.

5. Should fishers harvesting fish from a country's publicly owned waters be required to pay the government (taxpayers) fees for the fish they catch? Explain. If your livelihood depended on commercial fishing, would you be for or against such fees?

6. Are you for or against using Individual Transfer Quotas (p. 293) as the major method for managing fisheries? Explain. What are the alternatives?

7. Congratulations! You are in charge of protecting the world's aquatic biodiversity. List the three most important points of your policy to accomplish this goal.

PROJECTS

1. Survey the condition of a nearby wetland, coastal area, river, or stream. Has its condition improved or deteriorated during the last 10 years? What local, provincial, or national efforts are being used to protect this aquatic system? Develop a plan for protecting it.

2. Work with your classmates to develop an experiment in aquatic reconciliation ecology for your campus or local community.

3. Use the library or the Internet to learn more about different species of whales, their history of use, the current status of their populations, and any specific controversies about harvesting or protecting each species.

4. Use the library or the Internet to learn more about invasive species. Prepare a chart that summarizes the main biological features of several species and the strategies that might be used to control their spread.

5. Go online and learn about the UN Millennium Development Goals. Choose a goal, a target, and its indicators. Do some online research and determine from the latest information whether or not the target will be achieved on time.

ECOLOGICAL FOOTPRINT ANALYSIS

A *fishprint* provides a measure of a country's fish harvest in terms of area. The unit of area used in fishprint analysis is the global hectare (gha), a unit weighted to reflect the relative ecological productivity of the area fished. When compared with the fishing area's sustainable *biocapacity*, its ability to provide a stable supply of fish year after year in terms of area, its fishprint indicates whether the country's fishing intensity is sustainable. The fishprint and biocapacity are calculated using the following formulae:

Fishprint (in gha) = metric tons of fish harvested per year/productivity in metric tons per hectare × weighting factor

Biocapacity (in gha) = sustained yield of fish in metric tons per year/productivity in metric tons per hectare × weighting factor

The following graph shows the Earth's total fishprint and biocapacity. Study it and answer the following questions.

1. Based on the graph:

   a. What is the current status of the global fisheries with respect to sustainability?

   b. In what year did the global fishprint begin exceeding the biological capacity of the world's oceans?

   c. By how much did the global fishprint exceed the biological capacity of the world's oceans in 2000?

2. Assume a country harvests 18 million metric tons of fish annually from an ocean area with an average productivity of 1.3 metric tons per hectare and a weighting factor of 2.68. What is the annual fishprint of that country?

3. If biologists determine that this country's sustained yield of fish is 17 million metric tons per year:

   a. What is the country's sustainable biological capacity?

   b. Is the county's fishing intensity sustainable?

   c. To what extent, as a percentage, is the country under- or overshooting its biological capacity?

CASE STUDY — Organic Farming: A Growing Trend

Organic farming is a sustainable system of food production aimed at producing high-quality nutritious food with little or no reliance on synthetic pesticides and chemical fertilizers. Globally, the industry is worth more than $59 billion per year and is growing rapidly throughout the world (Figure 14-1A). For many people, organic farming is more than a business: it is a social movement and an integral part of the *green lifestyle* promoted by environmentalists.

Does organic farming produce superior food? This is a hotly debated issue in agricultural circles, and the scientific answer is not yet clear. Moreover, there are institutions and interest groups that stand to lose or gain with the success of organic farming—so the topic can be politically charged. What is clear is that the consumers of organic produce are willing to pay higher prices for it.

In order to obtain organic certification, farmers have to follow strict guidelines set forth by the National Standard of Canada for Organic Agriculture. The Standards Council of Canada uses International Organization for Standardization (ISO) guidelines to accredit organic certification organizations in Canada. In June 2009, the Canadian Food Inspection Agency authorized a Canada Organic Label (below, centre) that can be displayed only on approved products with 95% or greater organic content.

Currently, organic farming makes up only about 1.8% of the agriculture in Canada, but it is growing rapidly. In 2011, there were 4 120 farms producing certified or transitioning-to-certified organic products throughout Canada (Figure 14-1B). The principal organic crops of the Prairie provinces and Ontario are grains such as wild rice, buckwheat, rye, and caraway. Organic fruits, vegetables, and greenhouse crops (Figure 14-1C)

(*continued*)

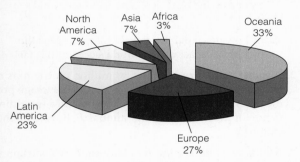

North America 7%
Asia 7%
Africa 3%
Oceania 33%
Latin America 23%
Europe 27%

FIGURE 14-1A Global area under organic management. (FiBL-Survey, 2012)

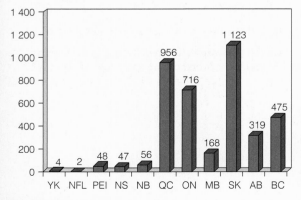

FIGURE 14-1B Number of certified organic producers in Canada. (Data from the Canadian Organic Growers, 2010)

AP Photo-Richard Drew/The Canadian Press

FIGURE 14-1C Organic produce from a certified farm.

are the most common products of organic farms in British Columbia and the Maritimes. Roughly 50% of Quebec's organic market is devoted to the production of maple syrup.

Canada's relatively clean environment, cool climate (reducing pest and disease problems), and proximity to the huge U.S. market all bode well for the future of organic farming in this country. Spurred by a public that is becoming more health-conscious and more aware of food choices, even conventional farmers are seeking to offer their customers at least some organic produce.

In 2012, the Government of Canada invested $13 million in the creation of a new research centre called the Platform for Innovation in Organic Agriculture. This centre is intended to accelerate research, development, and knowledge transfer in various aspects of organic crop production.

There are two spiritual dangers in not owning a farm. One is the danger of supposing that breakfast comes from the grocery, and the other that heat comes from the furnace.

ALDO LEOPOLD

CHAPTER PURPOSE AND QUESTIONS

Chapter 14 discusses the world's crop, meat, and fish production systems and how they can be made more sustainable. The chapter addresses the following questions:

14-1 How is the world's food produced?

14-2 How are the green revolution and traditional methods used to raise crops?

14-3 How are soils being degraded and eroded?

14-4 How can farming methods enhance soil conservation?

14-5 How much has food production increased, and how does this relate to solving hunger without degrading the environment?

14-6 How can we increase the production of crops, meat, and fish and shellfish?

14-7 What are some of the issues of meat production?

14-8 What are some of the issues of catching and raising more fish and shellfish?

14-9 How can we shift to more sustainable agricultural systems?

14-10 How are we progressing at eradicating hunger?

What Systems Provide Us with Food? The Challenges Ahead

Croplands, rangelands, and ocean fisheries supply most of our food, and, since 1950, production from all three systems has increased dramatically.

Historically, humans have depended on three systems for their food supply. *Croplands* mostly produce grains, and provide about 77% of the world's food. *Rangelands* produce meat, mostly from grazing livestock, and supply about 16% of the world's food. *Ocean fisheries* supply about 7% of the world's food.

Since 1950, there has been a significant increase in global food production from all three systems. This occurred because of technological advances such as increased use of tractors and farm machinery as well as high-tech fishing boats and gear; inorganic chemical fertilizers; irrigation; pesticides; high-yield varieties of wheat, rice, and corn; densely populated feedlots and enclosed pens for raising cattle, pigs, and chickens; and aquaculture ponds and ocean cages for raising some types of fish and shellfish.

We face important challenges in increasing food production without causing serious environmental harm. To feed the world's 8.9 billion people projected to exist in 2050, we must produce and equitably distribute more food than has been produced since agriculture began about 10 000 years ago, and do it in an environmentally sustainable manner.

Can we do this? Some analysts say we can, mostly by using genetic engineering (Figure 5-11, p. 105). Others have doubts. They are concerned that environmental degradation, pollution, lack of water for irrigation, overgrazing by livestock, overfishing, and loss of vital ecological services may limit future food production. A key problem is that human activities continue to take over or degrade more of the planet's *net primary productivity*, which supports all life.

We also face the challenge of sharply reducing poverty because about one out of five people do not have enough land to grow their own food or enough money to buy sufficient food—regardless of how much is available. The great irony of food production is that while more than 1 billion people (mostly in developing countries) do not have enough food to maintain good health, more than 1 billion people (mostly in developed countries) face health problems associated with an overabundance of food.

How Do Our Food Production Systems Compare with Natural Ecosystems? Simpler and Less Sustainable

Human-designed food systems often ignore the ecological principles that shape natural ecosystems.

Our food production systems—**agroecosystems**—are remarkably different from natural ecosystems. Most of our ideas about growing crops and raising animals were learned by trial and error over centuries, and gradually changed as new equipment, techniques, and information became available. Our knowledge of the ecological principles underlying natural ecosystems is relatively recent, and is often poorly applied to our agroecosystems. Some of the differences between agroecosystems and natural ecosystems include the following:

- Natural ecosystems tend to stabilize the soil under plant cover. Soil moisture is protected from the drying effect of sunlight and air, and roots hold the soil in place preventing erosion by wind or water. Decomposing dead plants enrich the soil with nutrients and organic matter. In contrast, our agroecosystems that involve plowing expose the soil to erosion and lose soil moisture that would normally be protected by plant cover. Major nutrients can be replaced artificially using chemical fertilizers, but trace nutrients and organic matter are depleted by these methods. More sustainable practices would include methods of farming that avoid breaking the soil or that put back organic matter into the soil (pp. 311–314).

- Natural ecosystems tend to evolve over time, with adaptations promoting the survival and reproduction of the many organisms involved. This results in resilient ecosystems attuned to current and changing conditions. In contrast, agroecosystems are designed to promote human choices such as crops of a particular colour or shape or flavour. These choices are typically focused on developing traits other than survival and reproduction, leaving these systems vulnerable to disruptions and reliant on humans for protection and propagation. In the past, crops were modified to achieve desired traits through careful cross-breeding from existing varieties of crops; now many crops are modified by means of genetic engineering (pp. 319–320).

- Natural systems are driven by solar energy. Agroecosystems are often driven by large investments of fossil fuels, mechanization, and human intervention; such systems may be feasible only when fossil fuels and other agricultural supplies are available and cost-efficient. Solutions can involve low-input agriculture and low-tech sustainable agriculture (pp. 307–308).

- Natural ecosystems are typically undergoing a process of **succession** as pioneer organisms capitalize on an opportunity to colonize a freshly disturbed area and are gradually replaced by species typical of a mature ecosystem (pp. 171–175). In contrast, many methods of food production devote much time and energy to holding succession at a desired stage.

For example, many crops are annual plants sown into bare soil in order to be exposed to bright sunlight; this simulates an early stage of succession, year after year, and guarantees that the crops will have to compete with other pioneer plants (which we call "weeds" when they grow among our crops). Solutions can include polyculture (p. 308) and conservation tillage (pp. 311–312).

- Natural ecosystems involve a great deal of structural diversity (p. 71). Differences in physical spaces among plants, and among canopies of leaves, allow for a great variety of microhabitats that can be colonized by organisms that feed on potential pests. In contrast, agroecosystems tend to have uniform spacing among plants, leaving relatively few options for pest-predators requiring shelter. Solutions can include agroforestry and polyculture (p. 308).

- Natural ecosystems typically contain a great deal of biological diversity, including rich communities of genetically diverse organisms, and complex food webs with many predators and competitors that tend to keep potential prey species in check. In contrast, most agroecosystems tend to be simple monocultures of a single species of crop-plant, or perhaps even one specific genetically similar variety of a crop-plant. Such ecosystems are vulnerable to diseases and pests that can overwhelm the defences of the crop, particularly in the absence of the natural pest control exerted by diverse ecosystems. Solutions can include polyculture (p. 308), ecological cultivation practices (p. 577), biological pest control (p. 578), and integrated pest management (p. 580).

What Plants and Animals Feed the World? Our Three Most Important Crops

Wheat, rice, and corn provide more than half of the calories in the food consumed by the world's people.

The Earth has perhaps 30 000 plant species with parts that people can eat. Since the beginning of agriculture about 10 000 of the species have been used as a source of food for people and livestock. Today only 14 plant and 8 terrestrial animal species supply an estimated 90% of our global intake of calories. Just three grain crops—*wheat*, *rice*, and *corn*—provide more than half the calories people consume. These three grains, and most other food crops, are ***annuals***, whose seeds must be replanted each year. This dependence on just a few plant species for food represents a dramatic reduction in agricultural biodiversity.

Two-thirds of the world's people survive primarily on traditional grains (mainly rice, wheat, and corn), mostly because they cannot afford meat. As incomes rise, most people consume more meat and other products of domesticated livestock, which in turn means more grain consumption by those animals.

Fish and shellfish are an important source of food for about 1 billion people, mostly in Asia and in coastal areas of developing countries. But on a global scale fish and shellfish supply only 7% of the world's food and about 6% of the protein in the human diet.

What Are the Major Types of Food Production? High-Input and Low-Input Agriculture

About 80% of the world's food supply is produced by industrialized agriculture and 20% by subsistence agriculture.

There are two major types of agricultural systems: *industrialized* and *traditional*. **Industrialized agriculture,** or **high-input agriculture,** uses large amounts of fossil fuel energy, water, commercial fertilizers, and pesticides to produce single crops (monocultures) or livestock animals for sale. Practised on about a fourth of all croplands, mostly in developed countries (Figure 14-2), high-input industrialized agriculture has spread since the mid-1960s to some developing countries.

Plantation agriculture is a form of industrialized agriculture used primarily in tropical developing countries. It involves growing *cash crops* (such as bananas, coffee, soybeans, sugarcane, cocoa, and vegetables) on large monoculture plantations, mostly for sale in developed countries.

An increasing amount of livestock production in developed countries is industrialized. Large numbers of cattle are brought to densely populated *feedlots,* where they are fattened up for about four months before slaughter. Most pigs and chickens in developed countries spend their lives in densely populated pens and cages and eat mostly grain grown on croplands.

Traditional agriculture consists of two main types, which together are practised by about 2.7 billion people (42% of the world's people) in developing

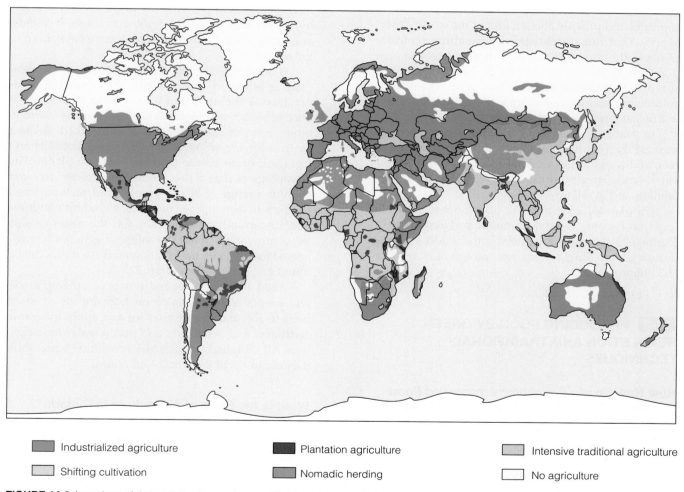

Industrialized agriculture

Shifting cultivation

Plantation agriculture

Nomadic herding

Intensive traditional agriculture

No agriculture

FIGURE 14-2 Locations of the world's principal types of food production. Excluding Antarctica and Greenland, agricultural systems cover almost one-third of the Earth's land surface.

Natural Capital

Croplands

Ecological Services	**Economic Services**
• Help maintain water flow and soil infiltration	• Food crops
• Provide partial erosion protection	• Fibre crops
• Can build soil organic matter	• Crop genetic resources
• Store atmospheric carbon	
• Provide wildlife habitat for some species	• Jobs

FIGURE 14-3 Natural capital: ecological and economic services provided by croplands.

countries and provide about a fifth of the world's food supply. **Traditional subsistence agriculture** typically uses mostly human labour and draft animals to produce only enough crops or livestock for a farm family's survival. Examples of this very low-input type of agriculture include numerous forms of shifting cultivation in tropical forests and nomadic livestock herding.

In **traditional intensive agriculture,** farmers increase their inputs of human and draft labour, **fertilizer,** and water to get a higher yield per area of cultivated land. They produce enough food to feed their families and to sell for income.

Croplands, like natural ecosystems, provide important ecological and economic services listed in Figure 14-3. Indeed, agriculture is the world's largest industry, providing a living for one out of every five (1.3 billion) people.

14-2 PRODUCING FOOD BY GREEN REVOLUTION AND TRADITIONAL TECHNIQUES

How Have Green Revolutions Increased Food Production? High-Input Monocultures in Action

Since 1950, most of the increase in global food production has come from using high-input agriculture to produce more crops on each unit of land.

Farmers can produce more food by farming more land or getting higher yields per unit of area from existing cropland. Since 1950, most of the increase in global food production has come from increased yields per unit of area of cropland in a process called the **green revolution.**

The green revolution involves three steps. *First,* develop and plant monocultures (Figure 6-26, p. 128) of selectively bred or genetically engineered high-yield varieties of key crops such as rice, wheat, and corn. *Second,* produce high yields by using large inputs of fertilizer, pesticides, and water. *Third,* increase the number of crops grown per year on a plot of land through *multiple cropping.*

This high-input approach dramatically increased crop yields in most developed countries between 1950 and 1970 in what is called the *first green revolution* (Figure 14-4, blue areas, p. 305).

A *second green revolution* has been taking place since 1967. It involves introducing fast-growing dwarf varieties of rice (Figure 14-5, p. 305) and wheat (developed by Norman Bourlag, who later received a Nobel Peace Prize for his work) into several developing countries in tropical and subtropical climates (Figure 14-4, green areas, p. 305). Producing more food on less land is also an important way to protect biodiversity by saving large areas of forests, grasslands, wetlands, and easily eroded mountain terrain from being used to grow food.

Golden rice (Figure 14-6, p. 305) is a new genetically engineered form of rice that contains beta-carotene, a chemical that is converted to Vitamin A once digested, and more dietary iron than is found in other forms of rice. Scientists accomplished this feat by transferring snippets of DNA from daffodils and from soil bacteria into conventional rice plants. The advantage is that a diet containing golden rice can counter a range of health problems of malnourished children in developing countries, including blindness and susceptibility to diseases. On the negative side are controversies about the safety of genetically engineered foods. More information on these topics can be found on pp. 104–106 and pp. 319–320.

Yield increases depend not only on fertile soil and ample water but also on high inputs of fossil fuels to run machinery, produce and apply **inorganic fertilizers** and pesticides, and pump water for irrigation. All told, high-input green revolution agriculture uses about 8% of the world's oil output.

What Is the State of Agriculture in Canada? Good News and Bad News

Agriculture continues to be an important part of Canada's economy, but the industry is grappling with environmental costs and emerging threats.

Agriculture is a $95 billion industry in Canada, accounting for 8.8% of its gross national product.

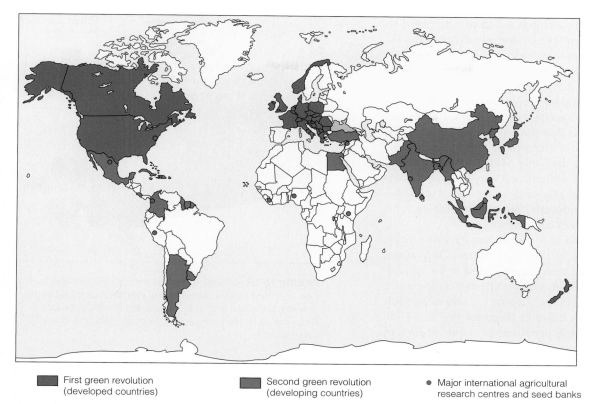

First green revolution (developed countries)

Second green revolution (developing countries)

● Major international agricultural research centres and seed banks

FIGURE 14-4 Countries whose crop yields per unit of land area increased during the two green revolutions. The first (blue) took place in developed countries between 1950 and 1970; the second (green) has occurred since 1967 in developing countries with enough rainfall or irrigation capacity. Several agricultural research centres and gene or seed banks (red dots) play a key role in developing high-yield crop varieties.

FIGURE 14-5 Solutions: in the second *green revolution*, a high-yield semi-dwarf variety of rice called IR-8 (left) was developed by cross-breeding PETA rice from Indonesia (centre) and DGWG rice from China (right). The new strain had shorter stalks that could support larger heads of grain without toppling, which worked well in rice fields with heavier applications of fertilizer.

FIGURE 14-6 Solutions: as part of the *gene revolution* happening now, golden rice is a genetically engineered strain of rice with enhanced nutritional qualities that can compensate for vitamin A deficiency, which is often a problem for malnourished children in developing countries. The colour of golden rice is due to the presence of beta carotene.

About 1.8% of the workforce is directly involved in agriculture, but when spin-off industries such as food manufacturing are considered, 15% of the Canadian workforce is involved. The number of farms has been declining in recent decades, but the average size of farms has been increasing due to mechanization, economic pressures, and social changes, among other factors. The net result is that the amount of land farmed in Canada (68 million hectares or 160 million acres) has remained about the same over the past 50 years. Canada produces an agricultural surplus and exports $30 billion worth of raw and value-added goods—including grains, oilseeds, fruits, vegetables, and meats—to 200 different countries.

Much of Canada is too cool, too dry, too rocky, or lacking adequate soil for agriculture. Only about 7% of our terrestrial area is considered to be agricultural land. Precipitation, soil quality, and temperature are among the factors that determine where agriculture is practised in Canada (Figures 14-7A, 14-7B, and 14-7C. The Prairie provinces account for 83% of the farmland, whereas Ontario and Quebec have a combined total of 13%. Dry conditions and extreme temperatures make the Prairies an ideal environment for producing most of Canada's wheat, barley, oats, soybeans, canola, hay, and cattle. Ontario and Quebec produce most of the country's poultry, pigs, dairy, and maple syrup. British Columbia is famous for its fruit, wine, and salmon. The Maritimes are best known for their potatoes and seafood.

There are environmental costs to agriculture, including soil erosion, water pollution, pesticide use, and disruption of habitat. Canadian agriculture is grappling with new threats beyond the conventional

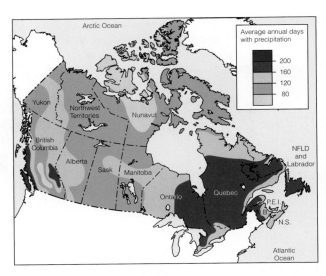

FIGURE 14-7B Number of days of precipitation in Canada. The East and West receive more days of precipitation than Central Canada. (Modified from *Canada and the World—An Atlas Resource*, G. J. Matthews and R. Morrow, 1995, Prentice Hall Canada Inc.)

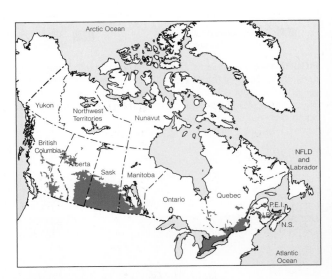

FIGURE 14-7C Distribution of agricultural land in Canada. (Modified from *Canada and the World—An Atlas Resource*, G. J. Matthews and R. Morrow, 1995, Prentice Hall Canada Inc.)

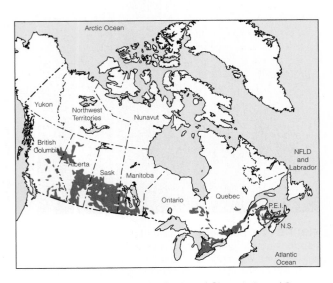

FIGURE 14-7A Canadian distribution of Class 1, 2, and 3 soils: Suitable for sustained production of crops. (Modified from *Canada and the World—An Atlas Resource*, G. J. Matthews and R. Morrow, 1995, Prentice Hall Canada Inc.)

struggles with the weather, the economy, and competition with other producers. In 2003, **bovine spongiform encephalopathy (BSE),** or **mad cow disease,** was detected in a single cow in Alberta; steps were immediately taken to eradicate the problem, but not before Canada's beef industry was subjected to trade restrictions and a consumer backlash. Since then, the Canadian Food Inspection Agency (http://www.inspection.gc.ca) has detected and safely dealt with 19 cases of BSE in cattle. **Avian influenza** has decimated poultry flocks in Europe and Asia, and incidents of avian influenza have been detected and eradicated on poultry farms in Canada (Chapter 19). **Biotechnology** is intended to benefit humans, but **genetically modified crops** are an innovation that has proven to be highly controversial for agriculture (p. 319).

Case Study: The United States: Agribusiness Giant

America's industrialized agricultural system is huge and efficient but also has a larger environmental impact than any other U.S. industry.

In the United States, industrialized farming has become *agribusiness* as big companies and larger family-owned farms have taken control of almost three-fourths of U.S. food production. According to environmental educator David Orr, "The U.S. food system is increasingly dominated by 'superfarms,' which are roughly to farming what Wal-Mart is to retailing."

In total annual sales, agriculture is bigger than the automotive, steel, and housing industries combined. It generates about 18% of the country's gross national income and almost a fifth of all jobs in the private sector, employing more people than any other industry. With only 0.3% of the world's farm labour force, U.S. farms produce about 17% of the world's grain and nearly half of the world's corn and soybean exports.

The industrialization of agriculture has been made possible by the availability of cheap energy, most of it from oil. Putting food on the table consumes about 17% of all commercial energy used in the United States each year. Considering the energy used to grow, store, process, package, transport, refrigerate, and cook all plant and animal food, *about 10 units of nonrenewable fossil fuel energy are needed to put 1 unit of food energy on the table.* By comparison, every unit of energy from human labour in traditional **subsistence farming** provides at least 1 unit of food energy and up to 10 units using traditional intensive farming.

What Growing Techniques Are Used in Traditional Agriculture? Low-Input Agrodiversity in Action

Many traditional farmers in developing countries use low-input agriculture to produce a variety of different crops on each plot of land.

Traditional farmers in developing countries grow about one-fifth of the world's food on about three-fourths of

---

INDIVIDUALS MATTER

Low-Tech Sustainable Agriculture in Africa

In 2003, Cuban-born soil scientist Pedro Sanchez was awarded the World Food Prize, the "Nobel Prize" of agriculture. He received it for developing a low-tech and sustainable form of agriculture that has increased crop yields fourfold, restored depleted soils, and helped more than 150 000 Africans (most in sub-Saharan Africa) escape from hunger and poverty.

Since 1992, Sanchez has been working with scientists in Kenya, Africa, to develop an effective cultivation system that grows crops and trees together.

A basic problem is that many African soils are thin and often depleted of nitrogen and phosphorus after several years of intense crop growing. Adding commercial inorganic fertilizers would help, but most African farmers cannot afford them.

Sanchez and his colleagues developed the following soil replenishment and crop-growth system to deal with these problems.

First, at the beginning of the rainy season farmers plant corn in rows between local varieties of fast-growing trees (Figure 14-14C, p. 313). The corn is harvested and the trees are allowed to grow for a year.

Second, just before the second corn-planting season the trees are cut down and their leaves are dug into the soil to add nitrogen. In addition, the trees can be used for firewood, which also helps prevent deforestation.

Third, phosphorus is added to the soil by crushing small deposits of phosphate rock found throughout much of Africa. Africa's mildly acidic soils help dissolve the phosphate fertilizer into the soluble form of phosphate needed by corn plants.

Fourth, farmers chop up the leaves and stems of a weedy shrub called the Mexican sunflower that is found along many roadside and farm boundaries. They place the plant pieces in planting holes with corn seed to provide micronutrients needed for healthy crop growth.

This four-part technologically simple system can then be used to provide food and restore depleted soil on a sustainable basis. The system also helps empower the women who raise most of the crops in Africa by bringing in extra income.

Recently, Pedro Sanchez cofounded the Millennium Villages Project, whereby villages are provided with: (1) seeds and fertilizers to improve their crops and (2) improved farming methods and knowledge to decrease their reliance on fertilizers and to increase plant diversity. Now villagers are eating better and they have products to sell for cash at the market. Sanchez says that all eight Millennium Development Goals are being addressed by his Millennium Villages Project (http://www .millenniumvillages.org).

its cultivated land. Many traditional farmers simultaneously grow several crops on the same plot, a practice known as **interplanting.** Such crop diversity reduces the chance of losing most or all of the year's food supply to pests, bad weather, and other misfortunes.

Interplanting strategies vary. One type, **polyvarietal cultivation,** involves planting a plot with several varieties of the same crop. Another is **intercropping**—growing two or more different crops at the same time on a plot (for example, a carbohydrate-rich grain that uses soil nitrogen and a protein-rich legume that puts it back). A third type is **agroforestry,** or **alley cropping,** in which crops and trees are grown together (see Individuals Matter).

A fourth type is **polyculture,** in which many different plants maturing at various times are planted together. Low-input polyculture has a number of advantages. There is less need for fertilizer and water because root systems at different depths in the soil capture nutrients and moisture efficiently. It provides more protection from wind and water erosion because the soil is covered with crops year-round. There is little or no need for insecticides because multiple habitats are created for natural predators of crop-eating insects. Also, there is little or no need for herbicides because weeds have trouble competing with the multitude of crop plants. The diversity of crops raised provides insurance against bad weather. This is a way of growing food by copying nature.

Recent ecological research found that on average, low-input polyculture produces higher yields per hectare of land than high-input monoculture. For example, a 2001 study by ecologists Peter Reich and David Tilman found that carefully controlled polyculture plots with 16 different species of plants consistently outproduced plots with 9, 4, or only 1 type of plant species.

Traditional farmers in arid and semi-arid areas with low natural soil fertility have developed innovative methods to boost crop production. For example, in the African countries of Niger and Burkina Faso, a farming innovation called *tassas* has tripled yields on at least 100 000 hectares (250 000 acres) of unproductive land. *Tassas* are small pits dug in the soil, filled with **manure,** and then planted with crops once they fill with infrequent rain.

14-3   SOIL EROSION AND DEGRADATION

What Causes Soil Erosion? The Big Three

Water, wind, and people cause soil erosion.

Most people in developed countries get their food from grocery stores, fast-food chains, and restaurants. But we need to remind ourselves that *all food comes from the soil*—the base of life. This explains why preserving the world's topsoil (Figure 4-24, p. 77) is the key to producing enough food to feed the world's growing population.

Land degradation occurs when natural or human-induced processes decrease the future ability of land to support crops, livestock, or wild species. One type of land degradation is **soil erosion:** the movement of soil components, especially surface litter and topsoil, from one place to another. The two main agents of erosion are *flowing water* and *wind,* with water causing most soil erosion.

Some soil erosion is natural, and some is caused or accelerated by human activities. In undisturbed vegetated ecosystems, the roots of plants help anchor the soil, and usually soil is not lost quicker than it forms. Soil becomes more vulnerable to erosion through human activities that destroy plant cover, including farming, logging, construction, overgrazing by livestock, off-road vehicle use, and deliberate burning of vegetation.

Soil erosion has two major harmful effects. One is *loss of soil fertility* through depletion of plant nutrients in topsoil. The other harmful effect occurs when eroded soil ends up as sediment in nearby surface waters, where it can pollute water, kill fish and shellfish, and clog irrigation ditches, boat channels, reservoirs, and lakes.

Soil, especially topsoil, is classified as a renewable resource because natural processes regenerate it. However, if topsoil erodes faster than it forms on a piece of land, it eventually becomes nonrenewable.

How Serious Is Global Soil Erosion? Mostly Bad News

Soil is eroding faster than it is forming on more than a third of the world's cropland, and much of this land also suffers from salt buildup and waterlogging.

A joint survey by the United Nations (UN) Environment Programme and the World Resources Institute estimated that topsoil is eroding faster than it forms on about 38% of the world's cropland. According to a study by the Consultative Group on International Agricultural Research, soil erosion and degradation has reduced food production on about 17% of the world's croplands. Soil expert David Pimentel estimates that worldwide soil erosion causes damages of at least $400 billion (U.S.) per year (an average of $46 million per hour), including direct damage to agricultural lands and indirect damage to waterways, infrastructure, and human health.

Some analysts contend that erosion estimates are overstated because they underestimate the abilities of some local farmers to restore degraded land. The UN Food and Agriculture Organization (FAO) also points out that much of the eroded topsoil does not go far and is deposited farther down a slope, valley, or plain. In some places, the loss in crop yields in one area could be offset by increased yields elsewhere.

Case Study: Soil Erosion in Canada

As in many countries, soil in Canada erodes faster than it can form.

Wherever soil is left exposed, it can be eroded by wind and water. This natural process can be accelerated by human activities such as forestry, construction, agriculture, and land management.

In Canada, wind erosion is most pronounced in the Prairies, affecting 36% of the region's cultivated land. A lack of sheltering vegetation and agricultural practices that involve plowing make an area especially susceptible to wind erosion. Soil conservation practices (p. 311; Case Study, p. 312) can do much to alleviate this problem.

Cultivated land that receives heavy precipitation is most likely to be affected by water erosion. About 80% of cultivated lands in the Maritimes, 75% of cultivated lands in British Columbia, and 50% of cultivated lands in Ontario are at high risk of water erosion. In addition to the obvious loss to agriculture it causes, the displaced soil resulting from water erosion transports pesticides and fertilizers, fills canals and dams, and destroys fish habitat. By compromising water quality, it increases the cost of water treatment.

Urban development also negatively impacts soil by exposing it to erosion or burying it under concrete. Since 1970, urban sprawl has consumed 12 000 square kilometres (4 600 square miles) of soil, much of it top-quality farmland. In southern Ontario, more than 18% of prime farmland (Class 1) has been lost to urban development.

Case Study: Environmental Lessons Learned from the Dust Bowl

During the "dirty thirties," a prolonged drought caused massive soil erosion in the Great Plains of North America.

Before settlers arrived in the late 1800s, the Great Plains of North America were covered in lush native grasses that were well adapted to the region's dry and windy conditions. During the periodic droughts that occurred in the area, the prairie grasses locked in moisture while preventing wind and water erosion.

The agricultural activities of the settlers set the stage for severe wind erosion and crop failures. Before settlers began planting crops in the prairies,

the deep and tangled root systems of native prairie grasses anchored the fertile topsoil firmly in place. But plowing the prairie tore up these roots, and the agricultural crops the settlers planted annually in their place had less extensive root systems. After each harvest, the land was plowed and left bare for several months, exposing it to high winds.

During the major drought that occurred between 1926 and 1937, the annual precipitation in the Great Plains dropped by almost two-thirds. By this time, much of the region was home to annual crops that lacked the drought-hardiness of native plants. The crops shrivelled and exposed the ground. The soil dried and started to blow. Moving dunes of soil buried fences and buildings. Dust clouds blocked the sun and choked animals. Journalists gave the worst-hit part of the Great Plains a new name: the *dust bowl*. An estimated 350 million tons of topsoil were lost from the region during the drought of the 1930s. Many families abandoned their dust-choked farms and moved elsewhere.

In the aftermath of the dust bowl experience, drought-alleviation programs were established in Canada and the United States. Measures to prevent further soil erosion included converting marginal farmland into pasture and planting hedgerows to serve as barriers against the wind. Despite these and other efforts, soil erosion remains a problem because the practice of conventional agriculture involves plowing the ground and leaving it exposed for much of the year.

What Is Desertification, and How Serious Is It? Decreasing Land Productivity

About one-third of the world's land has lost some of its productivity from a combination of drought and human activities that reduce or degrade topsoil.

In **desertification,** the productive potential of arid or semi-arid land falls by 10% or more because of a combination of natural climate change that causes prolonged drought and human activities that reduce or degrade topsoil. The process can be *moderate* (a 10–25% drop in productivity), *severe* (a 25–50% drop), or *very severe* (a drop of 50% or more, usually creating huge gullies and sand dunes). Note that only in extreme cases does desertification lead to what we call desert.

Over thousands of years the Earth's deserts have expanded and contracted, mostly because of natural climate changes. However, human activities can accelerate desertification in some parts of the world (Figure 14-8, p. 310). Study Figure 14-8 to find out the areas of the world most affected by desertification. Is it a problem where you live?

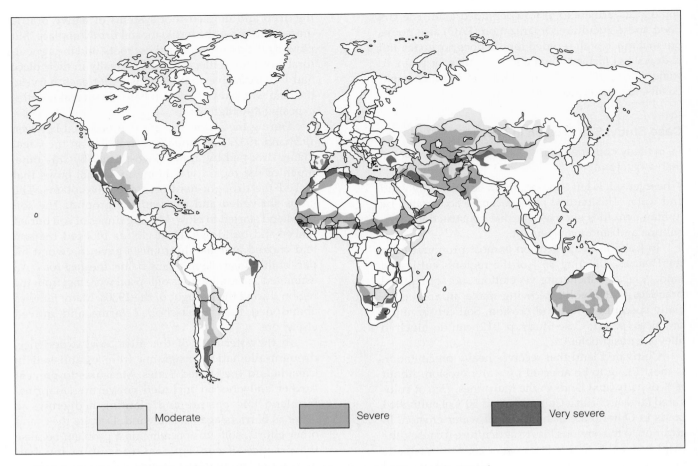

| Moderate | Severe | Very severe |

FIGURE 14-8 Natural capital degradation: desertification of arid and semi-arid lands. It is caused by a combination of prolonged drought and human activities that expose soil to erosion. (Data from UN Environment Programme and Harold E. Drengue)

According to a 2007 report by the FAO, about a third of the world's land and 70% of all drylands is suffering from the effects of desertification. UN officials estimate that this loss of soil productivity threatens the livelihoods of at least 250 million people in 110 countries (70 in Africa). China is facing serious desertification, as its portion of the Gobi Desert expanded by an area the size of Nova Scotia and Prince Edward Island combined between 1994 and 1999.

Figure 14-9 summarizes the major causes and consequences of desertification. We cannot control when or where prolonged droughts may occur, but we can reduce overgrazing, deforestation, and destructive

Causes

Overgrazing

Deforestation

Erosion

Salinization

Soil compaction

Natural climate change

Consequences

Worsening drought

Famine

Economic losses

Lower living standards

Environmental refugees

FIGURE 14-9 Causes and consequences of desertification.

forms of planting, irrigation, and mining that leave soil barren. We can also restore land suffering from desertification by planting trees and grasses that anchor soil and hold water.

How Do Excess Salts and Water Degrade Soils?
Crop Losses from Too Much Salt and Water

Repeated irrigation can cause loss of crop productivity by salt buildup in the soil and waterlogging of crop plants.

The one-fifth of the world's cropland that is irrigated produces almost 40% of the world's food. But irrigation has a downside. Most irrigation water is a dilute solution of various salts, picked up as the water flows over or through soil and rocks. Irrigation water not absorbed into the soil evaporates, leaving behind a thin crust of dissolved salts (such as sodium chloride) in the topsoil.

Repeated annual applications of irrigation water lead to the gradual accumulation of salts in the upper soil layers. This accumulation of salts is called **salinization** (Figure 14-10). It stunts crop growth, lowers crop yields, and eventually kills plants and ruins the land.

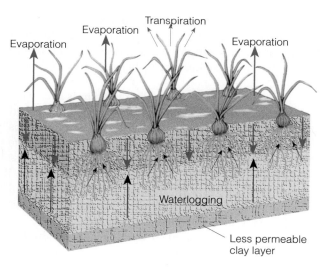

Salinization

1. Irrigation water contains small amounts of dissolved salts.

2. Evaporation and transpiration leave salts behind.

3. Salt builds up in soil.

Waterlogging

1. Precipitation and irrigation water percolate downward.

2. Water table rises.

FIGURE 14-10 Natural capital degradation: *salinization* and *waterlogging* of soil on irrigated land without adequate drainage can decrease crop yields.

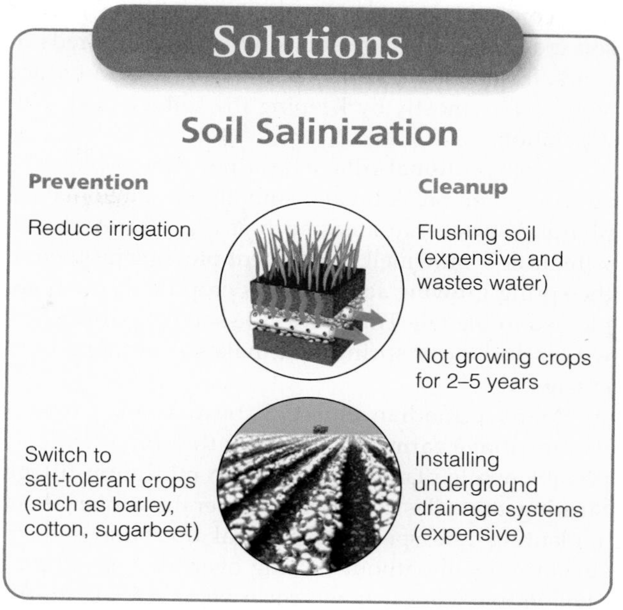

FIGURE 14-11 Solutions: methods for preventing and cleaning up soil salinization.

According to the United Nations, severe salinization has reduced yields on about 10% of the world's irrigated cropland, and almost another third has been moderately salinized. The most severe salinization occurs in warmer climates, such as China, India, and Pakistan, where rapid evaporation is a factor.

Relatively little cropland in Canada is affected by salinization; for instance, only 2% of Prairie cropland is thus affected. Salinization affects almost one-fourth of irrigated cropland in the United States.

We know how to prevent and deal with soil salinization, as summarized in Figure 14-11. But some of these remedies are expensive.

Another problem with irrigation is **waterlogging** (Figure 14-10). Farmers often apply large amounts of irrigation water to leach salts deeper into the soil. But without adequate drainage, water accumulates underground and gradually raises the water table. Saline water then envelops the deep roots of plants, lowering their productivity and killing them after prolonged exposure. At least one-tenth of the world's irrigated cropland suffers from waterlogging, and the problem is getting worse.

14-4 SOIL CONSERVATION

How Can Conservation Tillage Reduce Soil Erosion? Do Not Disturb the Soil

Modern farm machinery can plant crops without disturbing the soil.

Soil conservation involves using ways to reduce soil erosion and restore soil fertility. For hundreds of years, farmers have used various methods to reduce soil erosion, mostly by keeping the soil covered with vegetation.

In **conventional-tillage farming,** farmers plow the land and then break up and smooth the soil to make a planting surface. In areas such as the Prairies, harsh winters and snowmelt can prevent plowing just before the spring growing season. Thus crop fields often are plowed in the fall. This leaves the soil bare during the winter and early spring and makes it vulnerable to erosion.

Many Canadian and U.S. farmers use **conservation-tillage farming** to disturb the soil as little as possible while planting crops. With **minimum-tillage farming,** the soil is not disturbed over the winter. Then, at planting time, special tillers break up and loosen the subsurface soil without turning over the topsoil, previous crop residues, or any cover vegetation. In **no-till farming,** special planting machines inject seeds, fertilizers, and weed killers (herbicides) into thin slits made in the unplowed soil and then smooth over the cut. Figure 14-12 lists the advantages and disadvantages of conservation tillage.

By 2001, about 60% of Canadian farmers practised conservation tillage. This has led to reductions in soil erosion. Conservation tillage also has great potential to reduce soil erosion and raise crop yields in the Middle East and in Africa.

What Other Methods Can Reduce Soil Erosion? Several Tried and True Methods

Farmers have developed a number of ways to grow crops that reduce soil erosion.

Figure 14-14 (p. 313) shows some of the methods farmers have used to reduce soil erosion. One is **terracing,** which can reduce soil erosion on steep slopes by converting the land into a series of broad, nearly level terraces that run across the land contour (Figure 14-14A, p. 312). This retains water for crops at each level and reduces soil erosion by controlling runoff.

Another method is **contour farming,** which involves plowing and planting crops in rows across the slope of the land rather than up and down (Figure 14-14B). Each row acts as a small dam to help hold soil and to slow water runoff.

Farmers also use **strip cropping** to reduce soil erosion (Figure 14-14B). It involves planting alternating strips of a row crop (such as corn or cotton) and another crop that completely covers the soil (such as grass or a grass and legume mixture). The cover crop traps soil that erodes from the row crop, catches and reduces water runoff, and helps prevent the spread of pests and plant diseases.

One way to reduce erosion is to leave crop residues on the land after the crops are harvested. Another is to plant **cover crops** such as alfalfa, clover, or rye immediately after harvest to help protect and hold the soil.

Another method for slowing erosion is *alley cropping* or *agroforestry,* in which several crops are planted together in strips or alleys between trees and shrubs that decrease the effects of wind (Figure 14-14C). The trees or shrubs create shade (which reduces water loss by evaporation) and help retain and slowly release soil moisture. They also can provide fruit, fuelwood, and trimmings that can be used as mulch (green manure) for the crops and as fodder for livestock.

Some farmers establish **windbreaks,** or **shelterbelts,** of trees (Figure 14-14D) to reduce wind erosion, help retain soil moisture, supply wood for fuel, and provide habitats for birds, pest-eating and pollinating insects, and other animals.

Many governments use *land classification* to identify easily erodible (marginal) land that should be neither planted in crops nor cleared of vegetation.

Case Study: Soil Conservation on Prince Edward Island

Soil erosion has been a long-standing problem on Prince Edward Island. The sandy-loam soil, often

Trade-Offs

Conservation Tillage

Advantages	Disadvantages
Reduces erosion	Can increase herbicide use for some crops
Saves fuel	
Cuts costs	
Holds more soil water	
Reduces soil compaction	Leaves stalks that can harbour crop pests and fungal diseases and increase pesticide use
Allows several crops per season	
Does not reduce crop yields	Requires investment in expensive equipment
Reduces CO_2 release from soil	

FIGURE 14-12 Trade-offs: advantages and disadvantages of using *conservation tillage*. Pick the single advantage and disadvantage that you think are the most important.

on sloped land, is subject to water and wind erosion when plowed and left exposed by conventional agricultural methods. Soil losses of up to 20 tonnes/hectare per year have been recorded on P.E.I, which is clearly unsustainable considering that soil forms at 0.5–1.0 tonnes/hectare per year at this latitude (Pimentel et al., 1976). P.E.I had already lost about half its topsoil when a severe rain event in 2003 washed large quantities of soil from farmland into fish habitat. The government, farmers, and fishers of P.E.I were united in realizing that changes in agricultural practices were needed.

The government provided information, created an Alternate Land Use Services (ALUS) program that paid farmers to stabilize vulnerable soils, and established a number of awards to recognize soil conservation and environmental stewardship. The P.E.I Enhanced Environmental Farm Plan (EFP) was established. This program provides a voluntary, confidential self-assessment process through which farmers can evaluate and improve their operations in order to reduce soil erosion while increasing productivity.

Now on an increasing number of P.E.I farms (1) minimum or reduced tillage is used so that crops can be sown into the ground with little or no plowing (Figure 14-13); (2) crops are planted in strips along

FIGURE 14-13 Minimum-till methods sow seeds into the ground on this P.E.I farm without exposing the soil to erosion.

(a) Terracing

(c) Alley cropping

(b) Contour planting and strip cropping

(d) Windbreaks

FIGURE 14-14 Solutions: in addition to conservation tillage, soil conservation methods include (a) terracing, (b) contour planting and strip cropping, (c) alley cropping or agroforestry, and (d) windbreaks.

contours of hillsides to slow or prevent runoff; (3) over crops such as winter wheat are planted in the fall, or a mulch of hay is spread on the land, so that soil will not be left exposed in winter; (4) shelter belts of trees are planted to slow the wind; (5) crops such as potatoes are rotated with cereals or legumes so that the soil is always covered and so that soil nutrients are not depleted; (6) steep land is terraced and farm waterways are grassed to help control the flow of water; and (7) vegetated buffer zones are used to prevent soil from being washed into bodies of water. Farms that have adopted these types of changes are decreasing soil losses, saving costs, and increasing their productivity (Soil Conservation Council of Canada; http://www.soilcc.ca/).

How Can We Maintain and Restore Soil Fertility? Conservation and Fertilizers

Soil conservation can reduce loss of soil nutrients, and applying inorganic and organic fertilizers can help restore lost nutrients.

The best way to maintain soil fertility is through soil conservation. The next best thing to do is to restore some of the plant nutrients that have been washed, blown, or leached out of soil or removed by repeated crop harvesting.

Fertilizers can partially restore lost plant nutrients. Farmers can use **organic fertilizer** from plant and animal materials or **commercial inorganic fertilizer** produced from various minerals.

There are several types of *organic fertilizer*. One is **animal manure:** the dung and urine of cattle, horses, poultry, and other farm animals. It improves soil structure, adds organic nitrogen, and stimulates beneficial soil bacteria and fungi.

Manure use in many developed countries has decreased because most farmers no longer raise crops and livestock on the same farm, and it costs too much to transport animal manure from feedlots near urban areas to distant rural crop-growing areas. Also, tractors and other motorized farm machinery have largely replaced horses and other draft animals that added manure to the soil.

Burning poultry wastes to produce electricity leaves a phosphorus-rich ash. Researchers at the U.S. Department of Agriculture are evaluating its value as an organic fertilizer. Also, Canada-based International Bio-Recovery Corporation has developed a bacterial process that converts biodegradable human and animal wastes into pathogen-free, nutrient-rich organic fertilizer in only 72 hours.

A second type of organic fertilizer called **green manure** consists of freshly cut or growing green vegetation plowed into the soil to increase the organic matter and humus available to the next crop.

A third type is **compost,** produced when microorganisms in soil break down organic matter such as leaves, food wastes, paper, and wood in the presence of oxygen.

Crops such as corn, tobacco, and cotton can deplete nutrients (especially nitrogen) in the topsoil if planted on the same land several years in a row. One way to reduce such losses is **crop rotation.** Farmers plant areas or strips with nutrient-depleting crops one year. The next year they plant the same areas with legumes (whose root nodules add nitrogen to the soil). A typical rotation is corn → soybeans (a legume) → oats → alfalfa (a legume). In addition to helping restore soil nutrients, this method reduces erosion by keeping the soil covered with vegetation. It also helps reduce crop losses to insects by presenting them with a changing target.

Can Inorganic Fertilizers Save the Soil? A Partial Solution

Inorganic fertilizers can help restore soil fertility if they are used with organic fertilizers and their harmful environmental effects are controlled.

Many farmers (especially in developed countries) rely on *commercial inorganic fertilizers*. The active ingredients typically are inorganic compounds containing *nitrogen, phosphorus,* and *potassium.* Other plant nutrients may also be present in low or trace amounts. These fertilizers account for about one-fourth of the world's crop yield. According to Canadian geographer Vaclav Smil, much of the success of modern industrialized farming depends on the availability of inorganic fertilizers.

Figure 14-15 lists the advantages and disadvantages of using inorganic fertilizers to enhance or restore soil fertility. Inorganic chemical fertilizers can replace depleted inorganic nutrients, but they do not replace organic matter. Thus for healthy soil, both inorganic and organic fertilizers should be used.

14-5 FOOD PRODUCTION, NUTRITION, AND ENVIRONMENTAL EFFECTS

How Much Has Food Production Increased? Impressive Gains Nullified by Population Growth

The amount of food produced per person is affected by both food production and population growth.

Total world grain production has steadily increased since 1961 (Figure 14-16, left). However, population growth since 1961 has caused the *per capita* grain production to level off (Figure 14-16, right). Clearly population growth is an important part of the picture

Trade-Offs

Inorganic Commercial Fertilizers

Advantages	Disadvantages
Easy to transport	Do not add humus to soil
Easy to store	Reduce organic matter in soil
Easy to apply	Reduce ability of soils to hold water
Inexpensive to produce	Lower oxygen content of soil
Help feed one of every three people in the world	Supply only 2 or 3 of 20 or so nutrients needed by plants
	Require large amounts of energy to produce, transport, and apply
Without commercial inorganic fertilizers, world food output could drop by 40%	Release the greenhouse gas nitrous oxide (N_2O)
	Runoff can over-fertilize nearby lakes and kill fish

FIGURE 14-15 Trade-offs: advantages and disadvantages of using *inorganic commercial fertilizers* to enhance or restore soil fertility. Pick the single advantage and disadvantage that you think are the most important.

in terms of the amount of food that is theoretically available per person.

Good news. We produce enough food to meet the basic nutritional needs of every person on the Earth. *Bad news*: one out of six people in developing countries is not getting enough to eat because food is not distributed equally among the world's people. This occurs because of differences in soil, climate, political and economic power, and average per capita income.

Most agricultural experts agree that *the root causes of hunger and malnutrition are and will continue to be poverty and inequality,* which prevent poor people from growing or buying enough food regardless of how much is available. Other factors are war, corruption, and tariffs and subsidies that make it hard for poor people to acquire food they produce.

How Serious Are Undernutrition and Malnutrition? Some Progress

Some people cannot grow or buy enough food to meet their basic energy needs, and others do not get enough protein and other key nutrients.

To maintain good health and resist disease, we need fairly large amounts of *macronutrients* (such as protein, carbohydrates, and fats), and smaller amounts of *micronutrients* consisting of various vitamins (such as A, C, and E) and minerals (such as iron, iodine, and calcium).

People who cannot grow or buy enough food to meet their basic energy needs suffer from **chronic undernutrition.** Chronically undernourished children are likely to suffer from mental retardation and stunted growth. They are also susceptible to infectious diseases such as diarrhea and measles that rarely kill children in developed countries.

Many of the world's poor can only afford to live on a low-protein, high-carbohydrate diet consisting of grains such as wheat, rice, or corn. Many suffer from **malnutrition** resulting from deficiencies of protein and other key nutrients.

The two most common nutritional deficiency diseases are marasmus and kwashiorkor. **Marasmus**

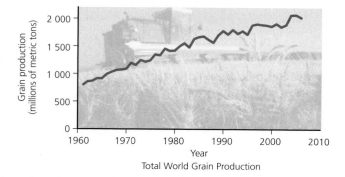

Total World Grain Production

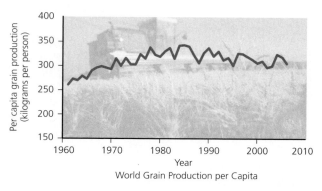

World Grain Production per Capita

FIGURE 14-16 Total worldwide grain production of wheat, corn, and rice (left), and per capita grain production (right), 1961–2009. In order, the world's three largest grain-producing countries are China, the United States, and India. (U.S. Department of Agriculture, Worldwatch Institute, UN Food and Agriculture Organization, and Earth Policy Institute)

(from the Greek word *marasmos,* "to waste away") occurs when a diet is low in both calories and protein. Most victims are either nursing infants of malnourished mothers or children who do not get enough food after being weaned from breast-feeding. A child suffering from severe marasmus is usually very thin and shrivelled and looks like a very old, miniature starving person (Figure 1-11, p. 13). *Good news.* If the child is treated in time with a balanced diet, most of these effects can be reversed.

Kwashiorkor (meaning "displaced child" in a West African dialect) is a severe protein deficiency occurring in infants and children ages 1–3, usually after the arrival of a new baby deprives them of breast milk. The displaced child's diet changes to grain or sweet potatoes, which provide enough calories but not enough protein. Such children typically have a bloated belly, reddish-orange hair, and discoloured and puffy skin. *Good news.* If caught soon enough, most of the harmful effects can be cured with a balanced diet. Otherwise, children who survive their first year or two suffer from stunted growth and mental retardation.

Good news. According to the FAO, the average daily food intake in calories per person in the world and in developing countries rose sharply between 1961 and 2003, and is projected to continue rising through 2030 (Figure 14-17). Also, the estimated number of chronically undernourished or malnourished people fell from 918 million in 1970 to 825 million in 2001, about 95% of them in developing countries.

Bad news. About one of every six people in developing countries (including about one of every three

children below age 5) is chronically undernourished or malnourished. The FAO estimates that at least 6 million children under the age of 5 die prematurely from a combination of poverty, undernutrition, malnutrition, and increased susceptibility to normally nonfatal infectious diseases (such as measles and diarrhea) because of their weakened condition. This means that each day an average of 16 400 children die prematurely from these causes related to poverty.

Studies by the United Nations Children's Fund (UNICEF) indicate that one-half to two-thirds of childhood deaths from nutrition-related causes could be prevented at an average annual cost of $5–$10 (U.S.) per child by taking the following measures:

- Immunizing children against childhood diseases such as measles

- Encouraging breast-feeding (except for mothers with AIDS)

- Preventing dehydration from diarrhea by giving infants a mixture of sugar and salt in a glass of water

- Preventing blindness by giving children a vitamin A capsule twice a year at a cost of about 75¢ per child or fortifying common foods with vitamin A and other micronutrients at a cost of about 10¢ per child annually

- Providing family planning services to help mothers space births at least two years apart

- Increasing education for women, with emphasis on nutrition, drinking water sterilization, and child care

Some people in developed countries also suffer from lack of access to enough food for good health. In Canada each month, more than 800 food banks distribute food to 900 000 hungry Canadians—a population the size of Nova Scotia's! In the United States, more than 11 million people (half of them children under age 5) do not have access to enough food on a regular basis for good health.

> **DID YOU KNOW**
> About 38% of the hungry Canadians who use food banks are children and youths. Other regular visitors include low-income single mothers and seniors.

How Serious Are Micronutrient Deficiencies? Important but Limited Progress

One of every three persons has a deficiency of one or more vitamins and minerals, especially vitamin A, iron, and iodine.

According to the World Health Organization (WHO), about one out of three people suffer from a deficiency of one or more vitamins and minerals. The most widespread micronutrient deficiencies in developing countries involve *vitamin A, iron,* and *iodine.*

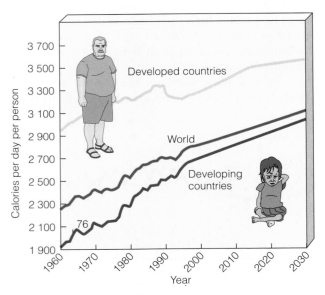

FIGURE 14-17 The average daily food intake in calories per person in the world, developing countries, and developed countries, with projected increases to 2030. The average adult male needs about 2 500 calories per day for good health. (Data from UN Food and Agriculture Organization)

According to the WHO, 120–140 million children in developing countries are deficient in vitamin A. Globally about 250 000 children under age 6 go blind each year from a lack of vitamin A and up to 80% of them die within a year.

Scientists recently spliced genes into rice to make it rich in beta-carotene, the source of vitamin A. Eating normal amounts of this vitamin-fortified rice—called golden rice—should provide 20–40% of the daily requirements of vitamin A (pp. 304–305).

Other nutritional deficiency diseases are caused by lack of minerals. Too little *iron*—a component of hemoglobin that transports oxygen in the blood—causes *anemia*. According to a 1999 survey by the WHO, one of every three people in the world, mostly women and children in tropical developing countries, suffers from too little iron. Iron deficiency causes fatigue, makes infection more likely, and increases a woman's chances of dying in childbirth and an infant's chances of dying of infection during its first year of life.

Elemental *iodine* is essential for proper functioning of the thyroid gland, which produces a hormone that controls the body's rate of **metabolism.** Chronic lack of iodine, found in seafood and crops grown in iodine-rich soils, can cause stunted growth, mental retardation, and goiter—an abnormal enlargement of the thyroid gland that can lead to deafness. According to the United Nations, about 26 million children suffer brain damage each year from lack of iodine and 600 million—mostly in South and Southeast Asia—suffer from goiter.

How Serious Is Overnutrition? Bad and Getting Worse

In developed countries, overnutrition is a major cause of preventable deaths.

Overnutrition occurs when food energy intake exceeds energy use and causes excess body fat. Overnourished people are classified as *overweight* if they have a body mass index (BMI) greater than 25 (roughly 4.5–14 kilograms or 10–30 pounds over a healthy weight) and *obese* if their BMI is more than 30 (roughly 14 kilograms or 30 pounds over a healthy weight). Too many calories, too little exercise, or both can cause overnutrition.

People who are underfed and underweight and those who are overfed and overweight face similar health problems: *lower life expectancy, greater susceptibility to disease and illness,* and *lower productivity and life quality.* We live in a world where more than 1 billion people have health problems because they do not get enough to eat and 1.2 billion worry about health problems from eating too much. According to a 2004 study by the International Obesity Task Force, about 1 of every 4 people in the world is overweight and 5% are obese.

In developed countries, overnutrition is the second leading cause of preventable deaths after smoking, mostly from heart disease, cancer, stroke, and diabetes. About one out of seven adults in developed countries suffers from overnutrition. The 2011 Canadian Community Health Survey revealed that 60% of adult Canadians are overweight and 24% are obese. A similar study by the Centers for Disease Prevention and Control found that about two-thirds of American adults are overweight and almost one-third are obese—the highest overnutrition rate of any developed country. The more than $40 billion (U.S.) that North Americans spend each year trying to lose weight is twice as much as the $19 billion per year needed to eliminate undernutrition and malnutrition in the world. More than half of all adults are overweight in Russia, the United Kingdom, and Germany compared to 15% in China.

In 2004, the WHO urged governments to discourage food and beverage ads that exploit children, to tax less healthy foods, and to limit high-fat and high-sugar foods in schools.

What Are the Environmental Effects of Producing Food? Agriculture Is Number One

Modern agriculture has a greater harmful environmental impact than any other human activity, and these effects may limit future food production.

Modern agriculture has significant harmful effects on air, soil, water, and biodiversity, as Figure 14-18 (p. 318) shows. According to many analysts, agriculture has a greater harmful environmental impact than any other human activity!

Some analysts believe these harmful environmental effects can be overcome and will not limit future food production. Other analysts disagree. For example, according to Norman Myers, a combination of environmental factors may limit future food production. They include *soil erosion, salt buildup, and waterlogging of soil on irrigated lands; water deficits and droughts;* and *loss of wild species* that provide the genetic resources for improved forms of foods.

According to a 2002 study by the UN Department for Economic and Social Affairs, close to 30% of the world's cropland has been degraded to some degree by soil erosion, salt buildup, and chemical pollution, and 17% has been seriously degraded. Such environmental factors may limit food production in India and China (Case Study, below), the world's two most populous countries.

Case Study: Can China's Population Be Fed? A Precarious Situation

Population growth, economic growth, limited agricultural potential, and the harmful environmental effects of food production must be balanced carefully by China.

Biodiversity Loss

Loss and degradation of habitat from clearing grasslands and forests and draining wetlands

Fish kills from pesticide runoff

Killing of wild predators to protect livestock

Loss of genetic diversity from replacing thousands of wild crop strains with a few monoculture varieties

Soil

Erosion

Loss of fertility

Salinization

Waterlogging

Desertification

Air Pollution

Greenhouse gas emissions from fossil fuel use

Other air pollutants from fossil fuel use

Pollution from pesticide sprays

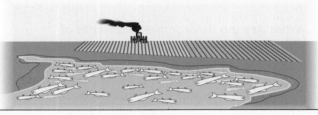

Water

Water waste

Aquifer depletion

Increased runoff and flooding from land cleared to grow crops

Sediment pollution from erosion

Fish kills from pesticide runoff

Surface and groundwater pollution from pesticides and fertilizers

Overfertilization of lakes and slow-moving rivers from runoff of nitrates and phosphates from fertilizers, livestock wastes, and food-processing wastes

Human Health

Nitrates in drinking water

Pesticide residues in drinking water, food, and air

Contamination of drinking and swimming water with disease organisms from livestock wastes

Bacterial contamination of meat

FIGURE 14-18 Natural capital degradation: major environmental effects of food production. According to a 2008 study by the FAO, more than 20% of the world's croplands have been degraded by soil erosion, salt accumulation, and chemical pollution.

Since 1970, China has made significant progress in feeding its people and slowing its rate of population growth. But there is concern that crop yields may not be able to keep up with demand because of China's growing population and economic development. A basic problem is that with about 20% of the world's people, China has only 7% of the world's cropland and fresh water, 4% of its forests, and 2% of its oil.

Between 1998 and 2003, China's grain production fell by 18%. This decline in grain production occurred mostly because of a drop in cropland owing to a loss of irrigation water, desert expansion, and conversion of cropland to nonfarm uses. Another factor was a decline in planting two crops a year because of a loss of farm labour as more Chinese migrated from rural areas to cities in search of jobs.

However, the Chinese government made food self-sufficiency and food security top national priorities. They changed national policies to reduce costs for farmers and to encourage farmers to plant more grain. They expanded irrigation. From 2003 to 2010, more cropland was planted and more grain was produced each year.

Good news. In 2011, China was the number one grain producer in the world and grew about 415 million tonnes of grain.

Bad news. China still needed to import 4.5 million tonnes of grain in 2011. As well, as China develops economically, people are eating more meat, milk, and eggs. This causes more demand for grain to be fed to animals.

Food analysts are concerned about China's ability to consistently grow sufficient grain to feed its huge population. Global grain stocks are low; if China has some poor grain harvests (through bad weather or climate change, for example), grain shortages and price shocks could affect many countries (http://www .earth-policy.org/indicators/C54).

The Chinese will have to carefully develop their food production plans and avoid any environmental damage to their agroecosystems (p. 289) if they want to steer clear of potential food shortages.

14-6 INCREASING CROP PRODUCTION

What Is the Gene Revolution? From Crossbreeding to Mixing Genes in a New Way

We can increase crop yields by using crossbreeding to mix the genes of similar types of organisms, and genetic engineering to mix those of different organisms.

For centuries, farmers and scientists have used *crossbreeding* through *artificial selection* to develop genetically improved varieties of crop strains (Figure 5-10, p. 104). Such selective breeding has had amazing results. Ancient ears of corn were about the size of your little finger and wild tomatoes were once the size of a grape.

But traditional crossbreeding is a slow process, typically taking 15 years or more to produce a commercially valuable new variety, and can combine traits only from species that are close to one another genetically. It also provides varieties that are useful for only about 5–10 years before pests and diseases reduce their effectiveness.

Scientists are creating a *third green revolution*— actually a *gene revolution*—by using genetic engineering to develop genetically improved strains of crops and livestock animals. It involves splicing a gene from one species and transplanting it into the DNA of another species (Figure 5-11, p. 105). Compared to traditional crossbreeding, gene splicing takes about half as long to develop a new crop, cuts costs, and allows the insertion of genes from almost any other organism into crop cells.

Ready or not, the world is entering the *age of genetic engineering*. About two-thirds of the food products on North American supermarket shelves contain ingredients made from genetically engineered crops, and the proportion is increasing rapidly. Currently, genetically engineered crops account for about 5% of the world's crop area. But by 2020, more cropland may be devoted to genetically engineered crops than to conventional crossbred crops.

Bioengineers are developing or plan to develop new varieties of crops resistant to heat, cold, herbicides, insect pests, parasites, viral diseases, drought, and salty or acidic soil. They also hope to develop crop plants that that can grow faster and survive with little or no irrigation and with less fertilizer and pesticides.

For example, bioengineers have altered citrus trees (that normally take six years to produce fruit) to yield fruit in only one year. They hope to go further and use *advanced tissue culture* techniques to mass-produce only orange juice sacs. This would eliminate the need for citrus orchards and would free large amounts of land for other purposes such as biodiversity protection.

However, new technologies can bring new problems. In 1998, a Saskatchewan canola farmer named Percy Schmeiser was sued by Monsanto Canada because herbicide-resistant canola plants developed by Monsanto were growing in his fields and he was gathering the seeds. Schmeiser claimed that the genetically modified canola plants were invading his fields, that he could not get rid of them, and that he could not avoid gathering their seeds since they were mixed in with his own crops. After a six-year legal battle, the Supreme Court ruled that Schmeiser had deprived Monsanto of the benefits of its biotechnology. This case gave the world a taste of the legal complications that biotechnology may give rise to. How can farmers keep genetically altered seeds and pollen from invading their crops? How can farmers be held liable for unwanted circumstances beyond their control?

A related issue is that some biotechnology companies are developing *genetic use restriction technology (GURT)* or *suicide seeds*. These are genetically altered seeds that will produce only sterile plants. The companies say that they wish to develop GURT in order to protect their investments in genetically altered plants. Critics fear that farmers will be at the mercy of seed companies forever after. Canada has joined a majority of other countries (the United States is a notable exception) in imposing a moratorium on the field testing of suicide seeds.

How Safe Are Genetically Modified Foods? Saviour or Frankenfood?

There is controversy over whether the benefits of genetically engineered food outweigh its unintended and potentially harmful effects.

Despite the promise, there is considerable controversy over the use of *genetically modified food (GMF)* and other forms of genetic engineering. Such food is seen by its producers and investors as a potentially sustainable way to solve world food problems, but critics consider it potentially dangerous "Frankenfood." Figure 14-19 summarizes the projected advantages and disadvantages of this new technology. Study this figure carefully.

Critics recognize the potential benefits of genetically modified crops. But they warn that we know too little about the potential harm to human health and ecosystems from widespread use of such crops. Also, genetically modified organisms cannot be recalled if they cause unintended harmful genetic and ecological effects—as some scientists expect to happen.

In 2002, biologist Barry Commoner warned, "The genetically engineered crops now being grown represent a massive uncontrolled experiment whose outcome is inherently unpredictable. The results could be catastrophic." Until we have more information, such critics call for more controlled field experiments, more research and long-term safety testing to better understand the risks, and stricter regulation of this technology. This is an example of the precautionary principle.

Most scientists and economists who have evaluated genetic engineering of crops believe that its potential benefits outweigh the potential risks. A statement signed in 2000 by over 2 100 scientists—including Nobel laureates James Watson (codiscoverer of DNA) and Norman Bourlag (founder of the second green revolution)—supported the use of food modified by genetic engineering. According to a 2004 report by the UN Food and Agriculture Organization, genetically modified (GM) crops hold great promise for farmers in developing countries. But the study pointed out that so far the technology has not been focused on developing GM crops for the poor. The report also called for more research and government regulation to assess any harmful environmental effects from this technology.

A 2004 study by the Ecological Society of America recommended more caution in releasing genetically engineered organisms into the environment. Also, agroecologists Miguel Altieri and Peter Rosset point out that the idea of using genetic engineering to provide enough food to feed everyone is based on two faulty assumptions. One is that world hunger is caused by a global shortage of food. The other is that genetic engineering is the only and best way to increase food production. The reality is that poverty and inequality, not food production, are currently the primary causes of hunger and malnutrition. Research also shows that polyculture using **perennial** crops can produce higher crop yields than current green revolution and genetic revolution techniques.

Trade-Offs

Genetically Modified Crops and Foods

Projected Advantages	Projected Disadvantages
Need less fertilizer	Irreversible and unpredictable genetic and ecological effects
Need less water	
More resistant to insects, plant disease, frost, and drought	Harmful toxins in food from possible plant cell mutations
Faster growth	New allergens in food
Can grow in slightly salty soils	Lower nutrition
Less spoilage	Increased evolution of pesticide-resistant insects and plant diseases
Better flavour	
Less use of conventional pesticides	Creation of herbicide-resistant weeds
Tolerate higher levels of herbicide use	Harm beneficial insects
Higher yields	Lower genetic diversity

FIGURE 14-19 Trade-offs: projected advantages and disadvantages of *genetically modified crops and foods*. Pick the single advantage and disadvantage that you think are the most important.

> **CONSIDER, DISCUSS, OR DEBATE**
>
> Do the potential advantages of genetically engineered foods outweigh their potential disadvantages? Give reasons for your answer.

Many analysts and consumer advocates believe governments should require mandatory labelling of genetically modified foods. This would provide consumers with information to help them make informed choices about the foods they buy. Such labelling is required in Japan, Europe, South Korea, Australia, and New Zealand.

The U.S. Department of Agriculture opposes this because they claim that genetically modified foods are not substantially different from foods developed by conventional crossbreeding methods. Also, they fear—probably correctly—that labelling such foods would hurt sales by arousing suspicion.

Can We Continue Expanding the Green Revolution? Maybe, Maybe Not

Lack of resources such as water and fertile soil, as well as environmental factors, may limit our ability to continue increasing crop yields.

Many analysts believe we can produce all the food we need in the future by spreading the use of existing high-yield green revolution crops and genetically engineered crops to more of the world.

Other analysts disagree. They point to several factors that have limited the success of the green and gene revolutions to date and may continue to do so. One problem is that without huge amounts of fertilizer and water, most green revolution crop varieties produce yields that are no higher (and are sometimes lower) than those from traditional strains. Another problem is that green revolution and genetically engineered crop strains and their high inputs of water, fertilizer, and pesticides cost too much for most subsistence farmers in developing countries. Scientists also point out that continuing to increase fertilizer, water, and pesticide inputs eventually produces no additional increase in crop yields—an example of the law of diminishing returns. For example, grain yields rose about 2.1% a year between 1950 and 1990, but the increase dropped to 1.1% per year between 1990 and 2000 and to 0.5% between 1997 and 2008. No one knows if and when the next agricultural break-through is coming that will reverse this slowing trend.

There is also concern that crop yields in some areas may start dropping as soil erodes and loses fertility, irrigated soil becomes salty and waterlogged, underground and surface water supplies become depleted and polluted with pesticides and nitrates from fertilizers, and populations of rapidly breeding pests develop genetic immunity to widely used pesticides. We do not know how close we are to such environmental limits.

Also, according to Indian economist Vandana Shiva, overall gains in crop yields from new green and gene revolution varieties may be much lower than claimed. The yields are based on comparisons between the output per hectare of old and new *monoculture* varieties rather than between the even higher yields per hectare for *polyculture* cropping systems and the new monoculture varieties that often replace polyculture crops.

There is also concern that the projected increased loss of biodiversity can limit the genetic raw material needed for future green and gene revolutions.

The FAO estimates that two-thirds of all seeds planted in developing countries are of uniform strains. Such genetic uniformity increases the vulnerability of food crops to pests, diseases, and harsh weather.

Will People Try New Foods? Changing Eating Habits Is Difficult

A variety of plants and insects could be used as sources of food, but most consumers are reluctant to try new foods.

Some analysts recommend greatly increased cultivation of less widely known plants to supplement or replace staples such as wheat, rice, and corn. One of many possibilities is the *winged bean* common in New Guinea and Southeast Asia. This fast-growing bean is a good source of protein and has so many edible parts it has been called a supermarket on a stalk. It also needs little fertilizer because of nitrogen-fixing nodules in its roots.

Some edible insects—called *microlivestock*—are also important potential sources of protein, vitamins, and minerals in many parts of the world. There are about 1 500 edible insect species. Examples include black ant larvae (served in tacos in Mexico); giant waterbugs (crushed into vegetable dip in Thailand); *Mopani*, or emperor moth caterpillars (eaten in South Africa); cockroaches (eaten by Kalahari desert dwellers); lightly toasted butterflies (a favourite food in Bali); and fried ants (sold on the streets of Bogota, Colombia). Most of these insects are 58–78% protein by weight—three to four times as protein-rich as beef, fish, or eggs. One problem is getting farmers to take the financial risk of cultivating new types of food crops. Another is convincing consumers to try new foods. Would you try a bug soup?

Some plant scientists believe we should rely more on *polycultures of perennial crops* (p. 308), which are better adapted to regional soil and climate conditions than most annual crops. Using perennials would also eliminate the need to till soil and replant seeds each year, greatly reducing energy use, saving water, and reducing soil erosion and water pollution from eroded sediment. Not surprisingly, large seed companies that make their money selling seeds each year for annual crops generally oppose this idea.

Is Irrigating More Land the Answer? A Limited Solution

The amount of irrigated land per person has been falling since 1978 and is projected to fall much more during the next few decades.

About 45% of the world's food production and two-thirds of the world's rice and wheat comes from the 20% of the world's cropland that is irrigated. *Good news.* Between 1950 and 2008, the world's irrigated area tripled, with most of the growth occurring from 1950 to 1978.

Bad news. The amount of irrigated land per person has been falling since 1978 and is projected to fall much more between 2004 and 2050. One reason is that since 1978 the world population has grown faster than irrigated agriculture. Other factors are depletion of underground water supplies (aquifers), inefficient use of irrigation water, and salt buildup in soil on irrigated cropland. In addition, the majority of the world's farmers do not have enough money to irrigate their crops, and the costs of energy are increasing.

Is Cultivating More Land the Answer? Another Limited Solution

Significant expansion of cropland is unlikely over the next few decades because of poor soils, limited water, high costs, and harmful environmental effects.

Theoretically, the world's cropland could be more than doubled by clearing tropical forests and irrigating arid land. But much of this is *marginal land* with poor soil fertility, steep slopes, or both. Cultivation of such land is unlikely to be sustainable.

Much of the world's potentially cultivable land lies in dry areas, especially in Australia and Africa. Large-scale irrigation in these areas would require expensive dam projects, use large inputs of fossil fuel to pump water long distances, and deplete groundwater supplies by removing water faster than it is replenished. It would also require expensive efforts to prevent erosion, groundwater contamination, salinization, and waterlogging, all of which reduce crop productivity.

Furthermore, these potential increases in cropland would not offset the projected loss of almost one-third of today's cultivated cropland caused by erosion, overgrazing, waterlogging, salinization, and urbanization.

Such expansion of cropland would also reduce wildlife habitats and thus the world's biodiversity. According to the FAO, cultivating all potential cropland in developing countries would reduce the areas of forests, woodlands, and permanent pasture by almost half. Clearing forests would also release a huge amount of carbon dioxide into the atmosphere and accelerate global warming, which is expected to cause shifts in the areas where some crops could be grown.

Bottom line: *Many analysts believe that significant expansion of cropland is unlikely over the next few decades.*

Can We Grow More Food in Urban Areas? Some Untapped Potential

People in urban areas could save money by growing more of their food.

According to the United Nations Development Programme, urban gardens provide about 15% of the world's food supply. Food experts believe that people in urban areas could live more sustainably and save money by growing more of their food. Such food could be grown in empty lots, in backyards, on rooftops and balconies, and by raising fish in tanks and sewage lagoons.

Growing food in urban areas reduces stresses on soil and biodiversity in nonurban areas. It can also provide food and jobs for low-income urban residents. However, it can lead to conflicts over how urban land should be used. And urban soil needs to be checked for traces of toxic pollutants such as lead and mercury.

A study by the UN Centre for Human Settlements estimated that up to half of the total area in many cities in developing countries is vacant public land that could be used to produce food. Is there a vacant lot or a rooftop (Figure 25-18, p. 632) in your neighbourhood that could be used to grow food?

How Much Food Is Wasted? Way Too Much

Up to 70% of the food we produce is wasted through spoilage, inefficient processing and preparation, and plate waste.

We have greatly increased the efficiency of food production, but the efficiency of food consumption is still low. According to the FAO, as much as 70% of the food produced in the world is lost through spoilage, inefficient processing and preparation, and plate waste. Even highly technological and affluent countries such as Canada, the United States, Switzerland, Italy, and Belgium waste nearly 60% of their food. Cutting such losses in half would go a long way toward meeting global food needs and reducing the environmental impact of agriculture. How much of the food on your plate is wasted?

14-7 PRODUCING MORE MEAT

How Are Rangelands Used to Produce Meat? Grass and Shrubs for Livestock

Much of the rangeland that makes up 40% of the world's ice-free land is used to raise livestock.

Most analysts call for an increase in meat production because we will need more meat to feed the projected increase in the world's population. Also, when incomes rise, meat consumption per person usually increases.

Rangelands are grasslands in temperate and tropical climates that supply forage or vegetation for grazing (grass-eating) and browsing (shrub-eating) animals. About 4 billion cattle, sheep, and goats graze on about 42% of the world's rangeland. Livestock also graze in **pastures:** managed grasslands or enclosed meadows usually planted with domesticated grasses or other forage.

Most rangeland grasses have a deep and complex network of roots (Figure 4-26, grassland soil, p. 79) that help anchor the plants. Blades of rangeland grass grow from the base, not the tip. Thus as long as only the upper half is eaten, rangeland grass is a renewable resource that can be grazed again and again.

Moderate levels of grazing are healthy for grasslands because removal of mature vegetation stimulates rapid regrowth and encourages greater plant diversity. If not overdone, disturbance of the soil surface by the hooves of grazing animals allows more rainfall to reach the roots of rangeland grasses. The key to the health of rangeland is to prevent both overgrazing and **undergrazing** by domesticated livestock and wild herbivores.

Is Producing More Meat the Answer? More Protein at the Expense of the Environment

Meat and meat products are important sources of protein, but meat production has many harmful environmental effects.

Meat and meat products are good sources of high-quality protein. Between 1961 and 2007, world meat production increased more than fourfold, and per capita meat production more than doubled. It is likely to more than double again by 2050 as affluence rises in middle-income developing countries and people begin consuming more meat.

Some analysts expect most future increases in meat production to come from densely populated *feedlots*, where animals are fattened for slaughter by feeding on grain grown on cropland or meal produced from fish. Feedlots account for about 43% of the world's beef production, half of pork production, and almost three-fourths of poultry production.

In North America, most production of cattle, pigs, and poultry is concentrated in increasingly large, factory-like production facilities in only a few areas. As many as 100 000 cattle may be confined to a single feedlot complex and 10 000 hogs may be crowded almost shoulder to shoulder in a giant barn.

This industrialized approach increases meat productivity. But it has a number of harmful environmental effects. Animal wastes from such facilities are typically stored in enormous open lagoons, which can rupture or leak and contaminate groundwater and nearby streams and rivers. In 1999, for example, torrential rains from Hurricane Floyd caused a number of hog and poultry waste lagoons in southeastern North Carolina to spill their wastes into local rivers.

CONNECTIONS

Some Environmental and Health Consequences of Meat Production

The meat-based diet of affluent people in developed and developing countries has a number of harmful environmental effects. More than half of the world's cropland is used to produce livestock feed grain (mostly field corn, sorghum, and soybeans). Livestock and fish raised for food also consume about 37% of the world's grain production.

Meat production uses more than half the water withdrawn from the world's rivers and aquifers each year. Most of this water is used to irrigate crops fed to livestock and to wash away animal wastes.

According to Canadian scientist Vaclav Smil, producing one calorie of energy in the flesh of a cow, pig, or chicken requires 11–15 calories of feed. The energy needed to produce a single hamburger is enough to drive a small car about 32 kilometres (20 miles).

About 14% of North American topsoil loss is directly associated with livestock grazing. Cattle belch out about 16% of the methane (a greenhouse gas about 25 times more potent than carbon dioxide) released into the atmosphere. Also, some of the nitrogen in commercial inorganic fertilizer used to grow livestock feed is converted to nitrous oxide, a greenhouse gas released from the soil into the atmosphere.

Chickens, pigs, and cows use about 70% of the antibiotics consumed in North America. According to the WHO and the FAO, widespread use of antibiotics in the livestock industry is increasing the development of microbes that are genetically resistant to widely used antibiotics. This makes it harder to fight infectious diseases in both humans and livestock animals.

A diet that relies heavily on meat can have negative health consequences. High intakes of animal fats are associated with high rates of heart disease, cancer, strokes, and obesity. Health Canada recommends a balanced diet that includes a variety of fruits, vegetables, whole grains, nuts, complex carbohydrates, dietary fibre, and dairy products. People who wish to consume meat as a source of protein are advised to eat smaller portions, and to favour fish, fowl, and leaner cuts of red meat.

Review the pyramid of energy flow (Figure 4-20, p. 74) and consider this: if we ate plants (producers) instead of animals (consumers), roughly 10 times more food energy would be available to us.

Critical Thinking

Can you see the benefits of eating lower on the food chain? Are you willing to eat less meat or not eat any meat? Explain.

Living near a feedlot or animal waste lagoon is also a nasal assault.

Expanding feedlot production of meat will increase pressure on the world's grain supply because feedlot livestock consume grain produced on cropland instead of feeding on natural grasses. It will also increase pressure on the world's fish supply because about one-third of the world's fish catch is used to feed livestock. Livestock production also has an enormous environmental impact (see Connections above).

What Are the Effects of Overgrazing? Eroding Soil and Fewer Livestock

Overgrazing can lead to soil erosion and limit livestock production.

Overgrazing occurs when too many animals graze too long and exceed the carrying capacity of a grassland area. It lowers the net primary productivity of grassland vegetation, reduces grass cover, and when combined with prolonged drought can cause desertification. It also exposes the soil to erosion by water and wind (Figure 14-20) and compacts the soil (which diminishes its capacity to hold water). Overgrazing also enhances invasion of exposed land by woody shrubs such as mesquite and prickly pear cactus. Finally, overgrazing can limit livestock production.

We do not know the condition of much of the world's rangeland because of a lack of detailed surveys. However, limited data from surveys in various countries by the FAO indicate that overgrazing by livestock has caused as much as a fifth of the world's rangeland to lose productivity, mostly by desertification (Figure 14-8, p. 310).

FIGURE 14-20 Rangeland: overgrazed (left) and lightly grazed (right).

USDA, Natural Resources Conservation Service

How Can Rangelands Be Managed More Sustainably to Produce More Meat? Control and Restore

We can sustain rangeland productivity by controlling the number and distribution of livestock and by restoring degraded rangeland.

The most widely used method for more sustainable management of rangeland is to control the number of grazing animals and the duration of their grazing in a given area so the carrying capacity of the area is not exceeded. However, determining the carrying capacity of a range site is difficult and costly.

Livestock tend to aggregate around natural water sources, especially thin strips of lush vegetation along streams or rivers known as **riparian zones** (Figure 14-21, left) and ponds established to provide water for livestock. As a result, areas around such water sources tend to be overgrazed and other areas can be undergrazed.

Bureau of Land Management

Bureau of Land Management

FIGURE 14-21 Solutions: cattle on a riparian zone of a public rangeland along Arizona's San Pedro River (left) in the mid-1980s, just before this section of waterway was protected by banning domestic livestock grazing for 15 years, eliminating sand and gravel operations and water pumping rights in nearby areas, and limiting access by off-highway vehicles. The right photo shows the recovery of this riparian area at the same time of year after 10 years of protection.

To help prevent the damage to stream and riparian ecosystems caused by livestock grazing, livestock can be moved from one grazing area to another and riparian areas can be fenced off. Sometimes protected areas can recover in a few years (Figure 14-21, right). Ranchers can also provide supplemental feed at selected sites and locate water holes as well as tanks and salt blocks in strategic places.

A more expensive and less widely used method of rangeland management is to suppress the growth of unwanted invader plants by herbicide spraying, mechanical removal, or **controlled burning.** A cheaper way to discourage unwanted vegetation is controlled, short-term trampling by large numbers of livestock.

Replanting barren areas with native grass seeds and applying fertilizer can increase growth of desirable vegetation and reduce soil erosion. But this is an expensive way to restore severely degraded rangeland.

How Can We Produce Meat More Sustainably? Shifting Our Meat Priorities

We can reduce the environmental impacts of meat production by relying more on fish and chicken and less on beef and pork.

Livestock and fish vary widely in the efficiency with which they convert grain into animal protein (Figure 14-22). A more sustainable form of meat production and consumption would involve shifting from less grain-efficient forms of animal protein, such as beef and pork, to more grain-efficient ones, such as poultry and farmed fish (Figure 14-22).

Some people argue that cattle and sheep that graze on rangeland use a resource (grass) that humans cannot eat, and most of this land is not suitable for growing crops. Moreover, because of poverty, insufficient economic aid, and the nature of global economic and food distribution systems, very little if any additional grain grown on land once used to raise livestock or livestock feed would reach the world's hungry people.

Kilograms of grain needed per kilogram of body weight

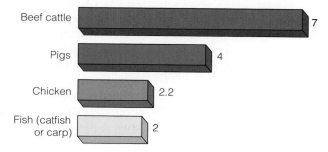

Beef cattle 7
Pigs 4
Chicken 2.2
Fish (catfish or carp) 2

FIGURE 14-22 Efficiency of converting grain into animal protein. Data in kilograms of grain per kilogram of body weight added. (U.S. Department of Agriculture)

Others argue that we can achieve a wholesome diet based on little or no meat; that consumption of meat has serious environmental impacts; and that overconsumption of meat has negative health impacts (Connections, p. 323).

14-8 CATCHING AND RAISING MORE FISH AND SHELLFISH

Where Do We Get the Fish and Shellfish We Eat? Ocean and Freshwater Ecosystems and Fish Farms

Most of the fish and shellfish we eat are still captured from wild ecosystems, but fish farming is growing at a steady rate.

The world's third major food-producing system consists of **fisheries:** concentrations of particular aquatic species suitable for commercial capture in ocean or freshwater ecosystems, or suitable for raising in ocean or freshwater fish farms. Comparing those four categories, in 2009 about 55% of the world's fish and shellfish were captured in wild ocean ecosystems, 14% were raised in ocean fish farms, 7% were captured in wild freshwater ecosystems, and 24% were raised in freshwater fish farms. In other words, most fish and shellfish are captured from wild ecosystems (62%), and of those most come from the ocean.

The remainder of the fish and shellfish (38%) are raised by means of aquaculture in ponds and underwater cages, in either fresh water or salt water. It surprises many people to note that more aquaculture takes place in fresh water than in salt water.

In recent years, the annual world harvest of fish and shellfish from natural ecosystems has remained about the same from year to year, but production from freshwater and saltwater fish farms has been increasing steadily (about 8% per year since 1970).

Some commercially important marine species of fish and shellfish are shown in Figure 14-23 (p. 326). Fish and shellfish supply about 7% of the global food supply and are the primary source of animal protein for about 1 billion people, mostly in developing countries.

How Are Fish and Shellfish Harvested? Hunt and Gather As Much As You Can

High-tech global fishing fleets roam the world's oceans to find and harvest most of the fish and shellfish we eat.

The world's commercial marine fishing industry is dominated by industrial fishing fleets using global satellite positioning equipment, sonar, huge nets and long fishing lines, spotter planes, and large factory

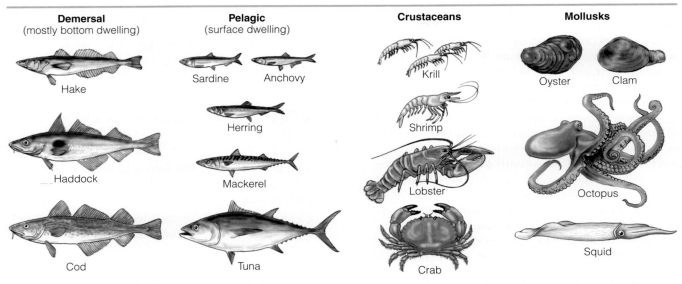

Fish			Shellfish	
Demersal (mostly bottom dwelling)	**Pelagic** (surface dwelling)		**Crustaceans**	**Mollusks**

Demersal (mostly bottom dwelling): Hake, Haddock, Cod

Pelagic (surface dwelling): Sardine, Anchovy, Herring, Mackerel, Tuna

Crustaceans: Krill, Shrimp, Lobster, Crab

Mollusks: Oyster, Clam, Octopus, Squid

FIGURE 14-23 Some major types of commercially harvested marine fish and shellfish.

ships that can process and freeze their catches. Figure 14-24 shows the major methods used for the commercial harvesting of various marine fish and shellfish.

Let us look at a few of these methods. *Trawler fishing* is used to catch fish and shellfish—especially shrimp, cod, flounder, and scallops—that live on or near the ocean floor. It involves dragging a funnel-shaped net held open at the neck along the ocean bottom and weighed down with chains or metal plates. This scrapes up almost everything that lies on the ocean floor and often destroys bottom habitats—somewhat like clear-cutting the ocean floor. Newer trawling nets are large enough to swallow 12 jumbo jets and even larger ones are on the way! The large mesh of the net allows most small fish to escape but can capture and kill other species such as seals and endangered and threatened sea turtles. Only the large fish are kept. Most of the fish and other aquatic species—called *bycatch*—are thrown back into the ocean, dead or dying.

Another method, *purse-seine fishing*, involves catching surface-dwelling species such as tuna, mackerel, anchovies, and herring, which tend to feed in schools near the surface or in shallow areas. After locating a school the fishing vessel surrounds it with a large net called a purse seine. Then they close the net like a drawstring purse to trap the fish. Nets used to capture yellowfin tuna in the eastern tropical Pacific Ocean have killed large numbers of dolphins that swim on the surface above schools of tuna.

Fishing vessels also use *longlining*. It involves putting out lines up to 130 kilometres (80 miles) long, hung with thousands of baited hooks. The depth of the lines can be adjusted to catch open-ocean fish species such as swordfish, tuna, and sharks or bottom fishes such as halibut and cod. Longlines also hook endangered sea turtles, sea-feeding albatross birds, and pilot whales and dolphins.

With **drift-net fishing**, fish are caught by huge drifting nets that can hang as much as 15 metres (50 feet) below the surface and be up to 64 kilometres (40 miles) long. This method can lead to overfishing of the desired species and may trap and kill large quantities of unwanted fish and marine mammals (such as dolphins, porpoises, and seals), marine turtles, and seabirds. Since 1992, a UN ban on the use of drift nets longer than 2.5 kilometres (1.6 miles) in international waters has sharply reduced use of this technique. But longer nets continue to be used because compliance is voluntary and it is difficult to monitor fishing fleets over vast ocean areas. Also, the decrease in drift nets has led to increased use of longlines, which often have similar effects on marine wildlife.

Figure 14-25 shows the effects of these now common efforts to increase the seafood harvest. After increasing fourfold between 1960 and 1982, the annual commercial fish catch (marine plus freshwater wild catch excluding aquaculture) has levelled off and slightly declined (Figure 14-25, left). It will likely continue to decline because of factors such as overfishing, pollution, and habitat loss. However, the total fish harvest has increased slightly because aquaculture has been growing each year and, for the moment at least, is compensating for the declining wild catch and the increasing population size and affluence of humans (Figure 14-25, right).

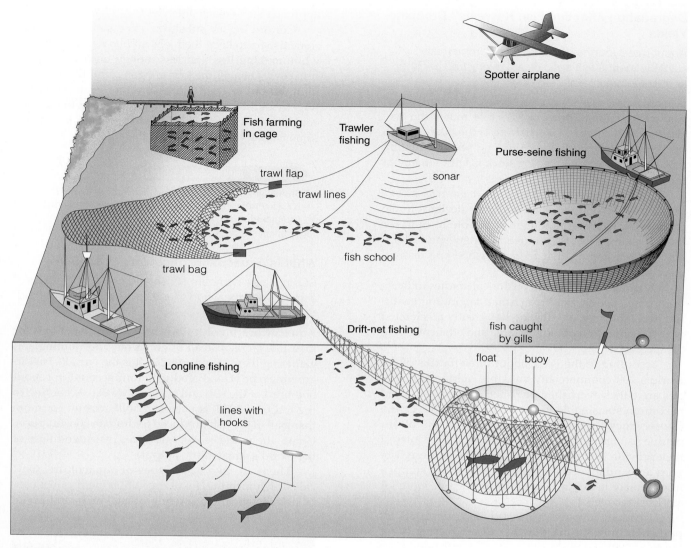

FIGURE 14-24 Major commercial fishing methods used to harvest various marine species. These methods have become so effective that many fish have become commercially extinct.

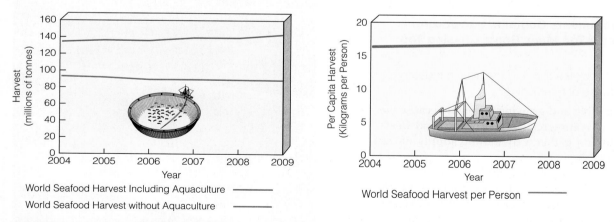

World Seafood Harvest Including Aquaculture ———

World Seafood Harvest without Aquaculture ———

World Seafood Harvest per Person ———

FIGURE 14-25 Natural capital degradation: the wild seafood catch has declined slightly since 2004 (left side, lower line). However, the growth of aquaculture has contributed to a growing total harvest (left side, upper line) of fish and shellfish and a slightly growing per capita seafood harvest (right side). (Data from FAO, 2010a)

Connections: How Are Overfishing and Habitat Degradation Affecting Fish Harvests? Dropping Yields

About three-fourths of the world's commercially valuable marine fish species are overfished or fished at their biological limit.

Fish are renewable resources as long as the annual harvest leaves enough breeding stock to renew the species for the next year. **Overfishing** is the taking of too many fish, particularly the larger and sexually mature fish, so that too little breeding stock is left to maintain numbers.

Prolonged overfishing leads to *commercial extinction,* when the population of a species declines to the point at which it is no longer profitable to hunt for them. Fishing fleets then move to a new species or a new region, hoping that the overfished species will recover.

Overfishing is not new. Historical studies indicate that some species were overfished beginning centuries ago. However, overfishing has greatly accelerated with the expansion of today's large and efficient global fishing fleets.

According to the FAO, about three-fourths of the world's 200 commercially valuable marine fish species are either overfished or fished to their estimated maximum sustainable yield. According to the Ocean Conservancy, "we are spending the principal of our marine fish resources rather than living off the interest they provide." Analysts warn that some of these fisheries are so depleted that even if all fishing stopped immediately it would take up to 20 years or more for stocks to recover.

Canadian fish stocks are also being depleted. Of particular concern are the East Coast fishery (Case Study, p. 289) and the West Coast salmon fishery (Case Study, p. 291).

Should Governments Continue Subsidizing Fishing Fleets? Too Many Boats Chasing Too Few Fish

Government subsidies given to the fishing industry are a major cause of overfishing.

Overfishing is a big and growing problem because we have too many commercial fishing boats and fleets trying to hunt and gather a dwindling supply of the most desirable fish.

It costs the global fishing industry about $120 billion (U.S.) a year to catch $70 billion worth of fish. Government subsidies such as fuel tax exemptions, price controls, low-interest loans, and grants for fishing gear make up most of the $50 billion annual deficit of the industry. Without such subsidies, some of the world's fishing boats and fleets would have to go

out of business and the number of fish caught would approach their sustainable yield.

Continuing to subsidize excess fishing allows some fishers to keep their jobs and boats a little longer while making less and less money until the fishery collapses. Then all the jobs are gone, and fishing communities suffer even more—another example of the tragedy of the commons in action. Some of the money could be shifted from subsidies to programs to buy out some fishing boats and retrain their crews.

> **CONSIDER, DISCUSS, OR DEBATE**
>
> Should governments eliminate all fishing subsidies? By what other means might governments support their fishing industries?

What Is Aquaculture? Feedlots of the Sea

Raising large numbers of fish and shellfish in ponds and cages is the world's fastest-growing type of food production.

Aquaculture involves raising fish and shellfish for food like crops instead of going out and hunting and gathering them (Figure 14-26). It is the world's fastest-growing type of food production and accounts for about one-third of the fish and shellfish we eat. According to the FAO, by 2030, aquaculture will account for more than half of the fish produced for human consumption. China, the world leader, produces over two-thirds of the world's aquaculture output.

There are two basic types of aquaculture. One, called **fish farming,** involves cultivating fish in a controlled environment (often a coastal or inland pond,

FIGURE 14-26 Rather than pursuing a diminishing stock of fish in a huge ocean, aquaculture aims to raise fish in a controlled and efficient manner.

lake, reservoir, or rice paddy) and harvesting them when they reach the desired size.

The other is **fish ranching.** It involves holding anadromous species such as salmon that live part of their lives in fresh water and part in salt water in captivity for the first few years of their lives, usually in fenced-in areas or floating cages in coastal lagoons and estuaries. Then the fish are released, and adults are harvested when they return to spawn (Figure 13-16, right, p. 292).

Figure 14-27 lists the major advantages and disadvantages of aquaculture. Some analysts project that freshwater and saltwater aquaculture production could provide at least half of the world's seafood by 2020. Some also propose increased use of aquaculture to grow single-cell algae such as *Spirulina,* which is 70% protein.

But other analysts warn that the harmful environmental effects of aquaculture (Figure 14-27, right) could limit future production. Also, some trends in aquaculture could harm ocean fisheries. For example, intensive farming of large carnivorous fish like salmon and trout is replacing traditional aquaculture in which farmed fish such as carp and tilapia eat plants and

Solutions

More Sustainable Aquaculture

- Use solid containment rather than open-net pens in order to have greater control over parasites, escapes, diseases, and wastes

- Improve pollution management of aquaculture wastes

- Reduce use of fishmeal as a feed to reduce depletion of other fish

- Improve pollution management of aquaculture wastes

- Reduce escape of aquaculture species into the wild

- Restrict location of fish farms to reduce loss of mangrove forests and other threatened areas

- Set up a system for certifying sustainable forms of aquaculture

FIGURE 14-28 Solutions: ways to make aquaculture more sustainable and reduce its harmful environmental effects.

detritus. This increases overfishing of smaller marine species used to feed farmed carnivorous species. If kept up, this depletion of the seas to feed aquaculture farms could cause the collapse of both marine fisheries and carnivorous aquaculture. Figure 14-28 lists some ways to make aquaculture more sustainable and to reduce its environmental effects.

What Is the State of Aquaculture in Canada? Healthy but Not Problem-Free

Aquaculture in Canada is a thriving and growing industry, but one that is susceptible to problems such as the salmon/PCB controversy.

Aquaculture is practised in all the provinces as well as the Yukon. British Columbia and New Brunswick are the largest producers, accounting for 75% of production (Figure 14-29, p. 330). More than 70 species of fish, shellfish, and plants are licensed for aquaculture in Canada. In 2011, the most common species were salmon (69%), mussels (17%), oysters (7%), and trout (5%). Where fish and plants are raised together, the term **aquaponics** is often used; the nutrient-rich pond water is used hydroponically to nourish the plants. The plants cleanse the water, which can then be returned to the fish ponds.

In 2011, the Canadian aquaculture industry generated more than 14 500 direct and indirect jobs and achieved sales of about $1 billion. The industry is projected to grow at 10–15% per year and could realize a potential of $2.8 billion per year.

Trade-Offs

Aquaculture

Advantages	Disadvantages
Highly efficient	Large inputs of land, feed, and water needed
High yield in small volume of water	Produces large and concentrated outputs of waste
Increased yields through crossbreeding and genetic engineering	Destroys mangrove forests
Can reduce harvesting pressure on conventional fisheries	Uses grain or large quantities of small fish to feed some species
Little use of fuel	Fish can be killed by pesticide runoff from nearby cropland
Profits not tied to price of oil	Dense populations vulnerable to disease
	Tanks too contaminated to use after about 5 years

FIGURE 14-27 Trade-offs: advantages and disadvantages of *aquaculture.* Pick the single advantage and disadvantage that you think are the most important.

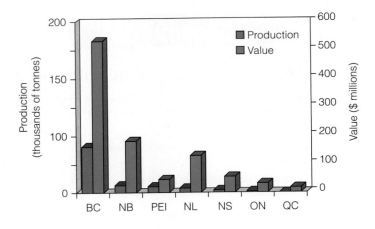

	BC	NB	PEI	NL	NS	ON	QC
Production	82.6	26.8	21.2	15.3	8.1	4.1	0.9
$ Value	533.8	168.3	30.2	116.3	41.3	17.1	2.4

FIGURE 14-29 Production (thousands of tonnes) and value ($ millions) of aquaculture in Canada in 2010. (Data from Statistics Canada, 2012a)

CONSIDER, DISCUSS, OR DEBATE

Do the advantages of aquaculture outweigh its disadvantages? Explain your answer.

In British Columbia, sales of farmed salmon have surpassed those of wild salmon, echoing a global trend as wild fish stocks decline and aquaculture continues to flourish (Figure 14-30). Farmed salmon is now the largest agricultural export of British Columbia and creates employment for at least 4 000 people.

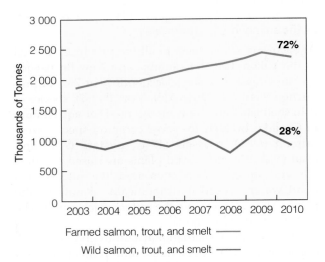

Farmed salmon, trout, and smelt ——

Wild salmon, trout, and smelt ——

FIGURE 14-30 Global production of farmed salmon, trout, and smelt is now more than twice as large as the catch of wild salmon, trout, and smelt. (Data from FAO, 2010b)

One problem associated with farming salmon has been the need to feed these predatory fish with food pellets made from small fish. This can deplete stocks of small fish. As well, the body oils of these small fish may contain PCBs and dioxins that can be passed on to the farmed salmon. A number of Canadian researchers have shown that much of the dietary fat of farmed salmon can be provided by canola oil (a common oilseed crop in Canada) rather than from small, potentially contaminated fish (Balfry et al., 2006; Farrell et al., 2007). This discovery will produce beneficial interactions with canola farmers and appeal to health-conscious consumers—including those in the huge U.S. market, which buys more than 90% of Canada's exported farmed salmon.

Another problem is that fish farming can have a variety of other impacts on wild fish populations, including transmission of disease from captive stocks; escapes of non-native and genetically altered fish from fish farms; and water quality issues such as excess wastes, antibiotics, and pesticides that build up in the waters surrounding fish farms.

An issue concerning wild salmon in the Broughton Archipelago region near Vancouver Island is that populations of pink salmon are on the decline, and many experts point at infestations of sea lice as the cause (see Spotlight, below). Sea lice (*Lepeophtheirus salmonis*) are naturally occurring parasites of wild salmon but they are found in greater concentrations near fish farms. Juvenile salmon are particularly vulnerable to infection because of their small size and thin skin. In the Broughton Archipelago, a concentration of fish farms coincides with a migration route that wild juvenile salmon must follow to reach the open ocean. Some researchers report that wild juvenile salmon are infected while swimming past fish farms and succumb to the effects of parasitism within a few weeks. Proposed solutions include moving fish farms away from the areas that are important to wild juvenile salmon, and requiring fish farms to use closed containment pens rather than open-net pens that are continuous with the sea.

The Canadian government is a strong supporter of the aquaculture industry. In 2000, the Department of Fisheries and Oceans (DFO) launched the Program for Sustainable Aquaculture, which invested $75 million over five years (followed by $15 million a year thereafter) to develop and sustain a thriving aquaculture industry.

CONSIDER, DISCUSS, OR DEBATE

Canada is the world's fourth-largest producer of farmed salmon, thanks largely to extensive aquaculture in British Columbia and New Brunswick.

Sea Lice

Sea lice are copepods that are *ectoparasites* (external parasites) of marine fish. There are about 600 species of sea lice; however, *Letheophtheirus salmonis* is of particular concern because of its association with farmed and wild salmon. Several researchers have pointed out that *L. salmonis* and other sea lice can build up to high concentrations in and near the open-net cages used to farm salmon (Johnson et al., 2004).

Since juvenile salmon are thin-skinned and can be damaged or killed if infested by only a few sea lice, some researchers suggest that sea lice may be having a major negative impact on wild juvenile salmon that must swim past salmon farms while migrating out to sea (Krkosek et al., 2007). Other researchers think that the sea lice problem has been overstated and that other factors may be involved (Riddell et al., 2008).

The potential impact of sea lice on wild salmon stocks is controversial; however, the precautionary principle would indicate that preventative steps should be taken. A number of solutions have been proposed. Salmon farms could be relocated away from the migration routes of juvenile salmon. Salmon farming could be modified to take place within impermeable enclosures rather than using open-net cage systems that are continuous with the sea. Salmon farmers could do a better job of using antiparasitic drugs and other measures to control sea lice (Living Oceans Society, 2012; Saksida et al., 2007).

14-9 SUSTAINABLE AGRICULTURE

What Is More Sustainable Agriculture? Learn from Nature

We can produce food more sustainably by reducing resource throughput and working with nature.

There are four main ways to reduce hunger and malnutrition and the harmful environmental effects of agriculture. One is to *slow population growth*. Another is to *reduce poverty* so people can grow or buy enough food for their survival and good health. A third way is to eat lower on the food chain in order to reduce energy loss, and to avoid environmental and health impacts (see Connections, p. 323).

A fourth way is to greatly improve our agro-ecosystems (introduced on p. 302). This would involve shifting to more **sustainable** or **low-input agriculture**—also called **organic farming** or **agroecology**—over the next few decades. Figure 14-31 lists the major components of more sustainable agriculture. This method of food production uses technologies based on ecological knowledge to increase yields, control pests, and build soil fertility. It relies more on a variety of perennial crops (polyculture) rather than monoculture of annual crops. It recognizes that it is unwise to overuse pesticides because this eliminates natural predators that help control pest populations and causes pest populations to become genetically resistant to widely used pesticides. Organic farmers or agroecologists also rely more or totally on manure and tilled-in crop residues to help maintain and build soil fertility by increasing its carbon content. This can help reduce runoff and improve water quality.

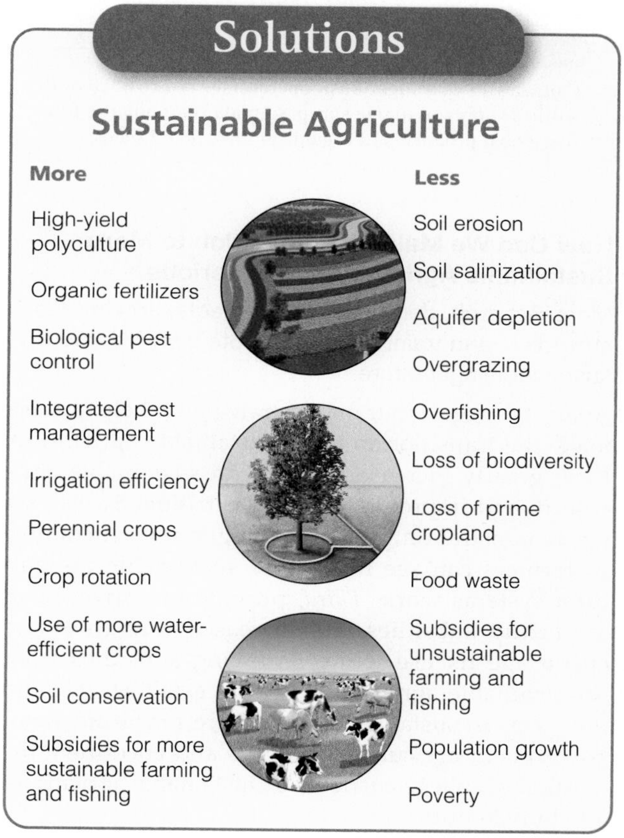

Solutions

Sustainable Agriculture

More	Less
High-yield polyculture	Soil erosion
Organic fertilizers	Soil salinization
Biological pest control	Aquifer depletion
Integrated pest management	Overgrazing
Irrigation efficiency	Overfishing
Perennial crops	Loss of biodiversity
Crop rotation	Loss of prime cropland
Use of more water-efficient crops	Food waste
Soil conservation	Subsidies for unsustainable farming and fishing
Subsidies for more sustainable farming and fishing	Population growth
	Poverty

FIGURE 14-31 Solutions: sustainable agriculture would involve using more of the items in the left column and avoiding the items in the right column.

In 2002, agricultural scientists Paul Mader and David Dubois reported the results of a 21-year study comparing organic and conventional farming. Their results and those from other studies have shown that for most crops low-input organic farming has a number of advantages over conventional high-input farming. They include use of up to 56% less energy per unit of yield, and improved soil health and fertility. Organic farming also provides more habitats for wild plant and animal species and generally is more profitable for the farmer than high-input farming.

Currently, organic farming is used on about 1% of the world's cropland (1.5% in Canada) but on 6–10% of the cropland in many European countries. In 2011, global sales of organic foods amounted to about $59 billion and such sales are growing rapidly in Canada, the United States, Japan, and much of Europe.

Most proponents of more sustainable agriculture are not opposed to high-yield agriculture. Instead, they see it as vital for protecting the Earth's biodiversity by reducing the need to cultivate new and often marginal land. They call for using environmentally sustainable forms of both high-yield polyculture (p. 308) and high-yield monoculture for growing crops.

> **DID YOU KNOW**
>
> Canada's 12 000 sugar bush operators produce 85% of the world's supply of maple syrup. Canada is among the top five global producers of organic grains and oil seeds.

How Can We Make the Transition to More Sustainable Agriculture? Get Serious

More research, demonstration projects, government subsidies, and training can promote a shift to more sustainable agriculture.

Analysts suggest four major strategies to help farmers make the transition to more sustainable agriculture. *First,* greatly increase research on sustainable agriculture and improving human nutrition. *Second,* set up demonstration projects throughout each country so farmers can see how more sustainable agricultural systems work. *Third,* provide incentives such as startup subsidies and increased foreign aid to encourage its use while removing subsidies from unsustainable agriculture. *Fourth,* establish training programs in sustainable agriculture for farmers and government agricultural officials and encourage the creation of college curricula in sustainable agriculture and human nutrition.

Phasing in more sustainable agriculture involves applying the four principles of sustainability (Figure 9-14, p. 191) to producing food. The goal is to feed the world's people while sustaining the Earth's natural capital and living off the natural income it provides. This will not be easy, but it can be done. Figure 14-32 lists some ways you can promote more sustainable agriculture.

What Can You Do?

Sustainable Agriculture

- Waste less food
- Reduce or eliminate meat consumption
- Feed pets balanced grain foods instead of meat
- Use organic farming to grow some of your food
- Buy organic food
- Compost or vermicompost (p. 594) your food wastes
- Support political parties that advocate sustainable agriculture

FIGURE 14-32 What can you do? Ways to promote more sustainable agriculture.

14-10 CHECKING OUR PROGRESS AT ERADICATING HUNGER

How Well Are We Proceeding with Millennium Goal 1? Slowly but with Signs of Hope

Our progress at eradicating hunger has been slow and varies regionally, but there are signs of hope.

The eight Millennium Development Goals were introduced in Chapter 1 and have been addressed in Chapters 9, 10, and 13 so far. Goal 1—aimed at eradicating hunger—includes Targets 1A and 1B, which address *poverty*; these will be covered in Chapter 26. Here, we will focus on Target 1C, which concerns the food-related topics we covered in Chapter 14. Target 1C is *to halve, between 1990 and 2015, the proportion of people who suffer from hunger.* It has two specific indicators used to monitor progress toward achieving the target (Figure 14-33).

Millennium Development Goal 1:

Eradicate Extreme Poverty and Hunger

Target 1C: Halve between 1990 and 2015, the proportion of people who suffer from hunger.

1.8 Prevalence of underweight children under five years of age.

1.9 Proportion of population below minimum level of dietary energy consumption.

FIGURE 14-33 Eradicating hunger: Millennium Development Goal 1 takes aim at poverty and hunger through specific targets and indicators. Target 1C addresses hunger, whereas Targets 1A and 1B focus on poverty, which will be considered in Chapter 26. Indicators 1.8 and 1.9 are used to assess progress toward achieving Target 1C. (http://www.undp.org/mdg/)

Progress has been mixed:

- Indicator 1.8, *the prevalence of underweight children under five years of age,* varies regionally. Half of the world's underweight children live in southern Asia, where little progress has been made. On the other hand, the percentage of underweight children has been halved in Eastern Asia including China. More must be done to help people improve their means of raising food and generating income.

- Indicator 1.9, *the proportion of population below a minimum level of dietary energy consumption,* has been decreasing. However, progress is hampered by high food and fuel prices, and by economic uncertainty in the world that affects the generosity of donor nations and corporations. Many developing countries will likely meet the 2015 target, but other regions such as sub-Saharan Africa are far behind. One sign of hope is that hybrid strains of rice such as NERICA (short for "New Rice for Africa"), which combine the drought-hardiness of African rice with the high productivity of Asian rice, have been

spreading across regions of Africa since the mid-1990s and those regions have shown higher rice production and improved nutrition. As well, recent microloans (Chapter 26) from governments and NGOs have been successful at improving agriculture and allowing people to start small businesses that generate income (http://www.undp.org/mdg/).

You can track progress in these areas by monitoring UN websites such as http://www.mdgmonitor.org/. Reflect on the complex nature of solving hunger problems, since a wide range of factors are involved including population growth (Chapter 10), food production (Chapter 14), and economics (Chapter 26).

The sector of the economy that seems likely to unravel first is food. Eroding soils, deteriorating rangelands, collapsing fisheries, falling water tables, and rising temperatures are converging to make it difficult to expand food production fast enough to keep up with the demand.

LESTER R. BROWN

CHAPTER REVIEW

1. Review the Key Questions for this chapter on p. 301. Describe the current importance and future prospects of *organic farming* relative to conventional agriculture.

2. Distinguish between *chronic undernutrition (hunger)* and *chronic malnutrition* and describe their harmful effects. Describe the effects of diet deficiencies in vitamin A, iron, and iodine. What is a *famine?* What is *overnutrition,* and what are its harmful effects?

3. What three systems supply most of the world's food? Distinguish among *industrialized agriculture (high-input agriculture), plantation agriculture, traditional subsistence agriculture, traditional intensive agriculture, polyculture,* and *slash-and-burn agriculture.* Define *soil* and describe its formation and the major layers in mature soils. What is a *green revolution?* Evaluate the positive and negative aspects of a green revolution.

4. Distinguish between *crossbreeding* and *genetic engineering.* Describe industrialized meat production. What is a *fishery?* What is *aquaculture?*

5. What are the major harmful environmental impacts of agriculture? What is *soil erosion* and what are its two major harmful environmental effects? What is *desertification* and what are its harmful environmental effects? Distinguish between *salinization* and *waterlogging* of soil and describe their harmful environmental effects.

6. What factors can limit green revolutions? Describe the use of energy in industrialized agriculture. Describe the advantages and disadvantages of genetically

engineered foods. Explain how most food production systems reduce biodiversity. Describe the advantages and disadvantages of industrialized meat production. Describe the advantages and disadvantages of aquaculture.

7. Describe three ways in which governments influence food production. How should national and international governments deal with issues affecting **(a)** wild fish in the ocean and **(b)** the fish involved in *fish farming* and *fish ranching?* What coordinated plans might be developed to balance the use of both groups of fish? How should the Canadian government settle issues concerning *aquaculture* and *sea lice* on the west coast of Canada?

8. What is *soil conservation?* Describe six ways to reduce soil erosion. Describe soil erosion and soil conservation in Canada. Distinguish among the use of *organic fertilizer, commercial inorganic fertilizer, animal manure, green manure,* and *compost* as ways to help restore soil fertility. Describe ways to prevent and clean up soil salinization.

9. Describe ways to produce meat more efficiently, humanely, and sustainably. How can we make aquaculture more sustainable? Define *organic agriculture* and describe its advantages over conventional agriculture. Describe the advantages of relying more on polycultures of perennial crops. What can individuals do to promote more sustainable agriculture?

10. Describe the relationships between organic farming and the four *principles of sustainability.*

CRITICAL THINKING

1. Summarize the major economic and ecological advantages and limitations of each of the following proposals for increasing world food supplies and reducing hunger over the next 30 years: **(a)** cultivating more land by clearing tropical forests and irrigating arid lands, **(b)** catching more fish in the open sea, **(c)** producing more fish and shellfish with aquaculture, and **(d)** increasing the yield per area of cropland.

2. List five ways in which your lifestyle directly or indirectly contributes to soil erosion.

3. What are the three most important actions you would take to reduce hunger **(a)** in the country where you live and **(b)** in the world?

4. Some have suggested that rangelands could be used to raise wild grazing animals for meat instead of conventional livestock. Others consider it unethical to raise and kill wild herbivores for food. What do you think? Explain.

5. Should governments phase in agricultural tax breaks and subsidies to encourage farmers to switch to more sustainable farming? Explain your answer.

6. Explain why you support or oppose greatly increased use of **(a)** genetically modified food, **(b)** perennial food crops, and **(c)** polyculture.

7. Suppose you live near a coastal area and a company wants to use a fairly large area of coastal marshland for an aquaculture operation. If you were an elected local official, would you support or oppose such a project? Explain. What safeguards or regulations would you impose on the operation?

8. Congratulations! You are in charge of the world. List the three most important features of **(a)** your agricultural policy, **(b)** your policy to reduce soil erosion, and **(c)** your policy for more sustainable harvesting and farming of fish and shellfish.

PROJECTS

1. Conduct a survey of soil erosion and soil conservation in and around your community on cropland, construction sites, mining sites, grazing land, and deforested land. Use these data to develop a plan for reducing soil erosion in your community.

2. If possible, visit both a conventional industrialized farm and an organic or low-input farm. Compare **(a)** soil erosion and other forms of land degradation, **(b)** use and costs of energy, **(c)** use and costs of pesticides and inorganic fertilizer, **(d)** use and costs of natural pest control and organic fertilizer, **(e)** yields per hectare for the same crops, and **(f)** overall profit per hectare for the same crops.

3. Try to gather data evaluating the harmful environmental effects of nearby agriculture on your local community. What is being done to reduce these effects?

4. Use health and other local government records to estimate how many people in your community suffer from undernutrition or malnutrition. Has this problem increased or decreased since 1980? What are the basic causes of this hunger problem, and what is being done to alleviate it? Share the results of your study with local officials, and present your own plan for improving efforts to reduce hunger in your community.

5. Make a list of all the food you eat in one day and look up the amount of calories, fat, protein, and carbohydrates in each food. Then determine how many calories you took in that day and the composition of your diet in terms of fat, proteins, and carbohydrates. Rate your diet as healthy, borderline healthy, or unhealthy. Compare your results with those of your classmates.

6. Use the library or the Internet to learn about the four types of vegetarians and the advantages and disadvantages of a vegetarian diet in terms of your health and the environment.

7. Use the library or the Internet to learn more about at least two of the following people mentioned in the chapter: *Colin Brauner, Lester Brown, Norman Bourlag, Barry Commoner, David Dubois, Dave Higgs, Aldo Leopold, Paul Mader, Norman Myers, David Pimental, Peter Reich, Vaclav Smil, David Tilman, James Watson, Percy Schmeiser.*

8. Use the library or the Internet to learn more about organic farming and aquaculture in the region where you live.

Water Resources

Water Conflicts in the Middle East

In the near future, water-short countries in the Middle East are likely to compete much more vigorously—not for oil, but for water (Figure 15-1). Most water in this dry region comes from three hotly contested river basins: the Nile, the Jordan, and the Tigris–Euphrates.

Three countries—Ethiopia, Sudan, and Egypt—use most of the water that flows in Africa's Nile River, with Egypt being last in line along the river.

To meet the water needs of its rapidly growing population, Ethiopia plans to divert more water from the Nile. So does Sudan. Such upstream diversions would reduce the amount of water available to Egypt, which cannot exist without irrigation water from the Nile.

Egypt must secure access to sufficient water. Otherwise, it must cut its population growth, drastically improve its irrigation efficiency, import expensive grain to reduce the need for irrigation water, or suffer the harsh human and economic consequences of hydrological poverty.

The Jordan basin is by far the most water-short region, with fierce competition for its water among Jordan, Syria, Palestine (Gaza and the West Bank), and Israel.

Syria plans to build dams and withdraw more water from the Jordan River, decreasing the downstream water supply for Jordan and Israel. Israel warns that it may destroy the largest dam that Syria plans to build.

Turkey, located at the headwaters of the Tigris and Euphrates rivers, controls how much water flows downstream to Syria and Iraq before emptying into the Persian Gulf. Turkey is building 24 dams along the upper Tigris and Euphrates to generate electricity and irrigate a large area of land.

If completed, these dams will reduce the flow of water downstream to Syria and Iraq by up to 35% in normal years and much more in dry years. Syria also plans to build a large dam along the Euphrates to divert water arriving from Turkey. This will leave little water for Iraq and could lead to intense water struggles between it and Syria.

Resolving these water issues peacefully will require a combination of regional cooperation in allocating water supplies, slowed population growth, improved efficiency in water use, higher water prices to help improve irrigation efficiency, and increased grain imports to reduce water needs. This will not be easy.

There are signs of rising tensions over water (Belt, 2010; Zeitoun, 2008), but so far diplomatic means such as appeals to the UN are being pursued (CounterCurrent, 2011).

To many analysts, emerging water shortages in many parts of the world and the related problems of biodiversity loss and climate change are the three most serious environmental problems the world faces during this century.

FIGURE 15-1 The Middle East is a volatile region with a history of religious and ethnic clashes, as well as armed conflict over resources like oil. Food production in these fast-growing countries depends on irrigation from a small number of increasingly contested water sources. Many experts consider that rising tensions over water may reach a boiling point in the near future. In the photo, some women and children are rolling a precious barrel of water past some soldiers. (Photo from Zeitoun, 2008)

The availability and management of fresh water are becoming one of the greatest environmental, social, and political challenges of the 21st century.

JOHANNE GELINAS, CANADIAN COMMISSIONER OF THE ENVIRONMENT AND SUSTAINABLE DEVELOPMENT

CHAPTER PURPOSE AND QUESTIONS

Chapter 15 discusses the water problems we face and ways to use this irreplaceable resource more sustainably. The chapter addresses the following questions:

15-1   What are water's unusual physical properties?

15-2   What is the status of fresh water in Canada?

15-3   What causes shortages of fresh water, and what can be done about this problem?

15-4   What are the advantages and disadvantages of using dams and reservoirs to supply more water?

15-5   What are the advantages and disadvantages of transferring large amounts of water from one place to another?

15-6   What are the advantages and disadvantages of withdrawing groundwater and converting salt water to fresh water?

15-7   What are the benefits of reducing water waste?

15-8   What are the causes of flooding, and what can be done to reduce the risk of flooding and flood damage?

15-9   How can we use the Earth's fresh water more sustainably?

15-10   How well are we proceeding at ensuring environmental sustainability?

15-1   WATER'S IMPORTANCE AND UNIQUE PROPERTIES

Why Is Water So Important? Liquid Natural Capital

Water keeps us alive, moderates climate, sculpts the land, and removes and dilutes wastes and pollutants.

We live on the water planet, with a precious film of water—most of it salt water—covering about 71% of the Earth's surface. Look in the mirror. What you see is about 60% water, most of it inside your cells.

No species can do without water. You could survive several weeks without food but only a few days without water. It takes huge amounts of water to supply you with food, shelter, and other needs and wants. Water also plays a key role in sculpting the Earth's surface, moderating climate, and removing and diluting wastes and pollutants.

What Are Some Important Properties of Water? An Amazing Molecule

Water's unique and important properties arise mostly from attractive forces between its molecules.

Water is a remarkable substance with a unique combination of properties:

- *There are strong forces of attraction* (called *hydrogen bonds*, Appendix 3, Figure 4) *between molecules of water.* These attractive forces are the major factor determining water's distinctive properties.

- *Water exists as a liquid over a wide temperature range because of the strong forces of attraction between water molecules.* Without its high boiling point the oceans would have evaporated a long time ago.

- *Liquid water changes temperature slowly because it can store a large amount of heat without a large change in temperature.* This high heat capacity helps protect living organisms from temperature fluctuations. It also moderates the Earth's climate and makes water an excellent coolant for car engines and power plants.

- *Evaporating liquid water takes large amounts of energy because of the strong forces of attraction between its molecules.* Water absorbs large amounts of heat as it changes into water vapour and releases this heat as the vapour condenses back to liquid water. This helps distribute heat throughout the world and determine the climates of various areas (Figures 6-11 and 6-12, p. 117). This property also causes the evaporation cooling process—explaining why you feel cooler when perspiration evaporates from your skin.

- *Liquid water can dissolve a variety of compounds.* This enables it to carry dissolved nutrients into the tissues of living organisms, flush waste products out of those tissues, serve as an all-purpose cleanser, and help remove and dilute the water-soluble wastes of civilization. This property also means that water-soluble wastes can easily pollute water.

- *Water filters out wavelengths of the sun's ultraviolet (UV) radiation that would harm some aquatic organisms.*

- *Attractive forces between the molecules of liquid water cause its surface to contract and to adhere to and coat a solid.* These strong cohesive forces allow narrow columns of water to rise through a plant from its roots to its leaves (capillary action).

- *Unlike most liquids, water expands when it freezes.* This means that ice floats on water because it has a lower density (mass per unit of volume) than liquid water. Otherwise lakes and streams in cold climates would freeze solid and lose most of their current forms of aquatic life. Because water expands upon freezing, it can break pipes, crack a car's engine block (which is why we use antifreeze), break up streets, and fracture rocks that end up as soil particles.

Without these unique properties of water, you and most other forms of life on this planet would not exist. As water endlessly recycles through the biosphere, it physically connects us to one another, to other forms of life, and to the entire planet.

Despite its importance, water is one of our most poorly managed resources. We waste it and pollute it. We also charge too little for making it available. This encourages still greater waste and pollution of this resource, for which we have no substitute. As Benjamin Franklin said many decades ago: "It is not until the well runs dry that we know the worth of water."

15-2 SUPPLY, RENEWAL, AND USE OF WATER RESOURCES

How Much Fresh Water Is Available? Natural Recycling to the Rescue

Only about 0.01% of the Earth's water supply is available to us as fresh water, but this supply is recycled.

Only a tiny fraction of the planet's abundant water is available to us as fresh water (Figure 15-2). Study this figure carefully to see where the world's water is found. About 97.4% of the world's total volume of water is found in oceans and saline lakes and is too salty for drinking, irrigation, or industry (except as a coolant). Most of the remaining 2.6% that is fresh water is locked up in ice caps or glaciers or in groundwater too deep or salty to be used.

Thus only about 0.014% of the Earth's total volume of water is easily available to us as soil moisture, usable groundwater, water vapour, and lakes and streams. If the world's water supply were only 100 litres (26 gallons), our usable supply of fresh water would be only 0.014 litre, or 2.5 teaspoons!

Fortunately, the world's fresh water supply is continuously collected, purified, recycled, and distributed in the solar-powered *hydrologic cycle* (Figure 4-27, p. 80). You might want to review this figure to trace the circulation of the Earth's water as it evaporates from water, land, and organisms into the atmosphere; condenses and falls as precipitation back to the Earth's land and water; and flows across the Earth's surfaces as runoff into streams, rivers, lakes, wetlands, and the seas and infiltrates underground.

This magnificent water recycling and purification system works only as long as we do not overload water systems with slowly degradable and nondegradable wastes or withdraw water from underground supplies faster than it is replenished. *Bad news.* In parts of the world, we are doing both of these things.

Differences in average annual precipitation divide the world's continents, countries, and people into water *haves* and *have-nots*. Some places get lots of rain (the dark green and light green areas in Figure 6-8, p. 116) and others very little (the yellow areas in Figure 6-8). For example, Canada, with only 0.5% of the world's population, has 20% of the world's fresh water, whereas China, with 21% of the world's people, has only 7% of the supply.

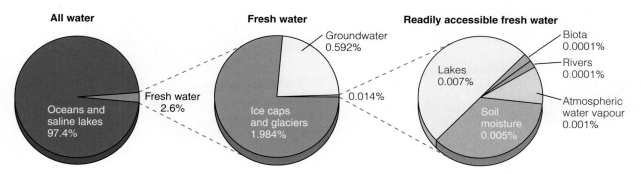

FIGURE 15-2 Natural capital: the planet's water budget. Only a tiny fraction by volume of the world's water supply is fresh water available for human use.

What Is Surface Water? Water on Top

Water that does not sink into the ground or evaporate into the air runs off into bodies of water.

One of our most precious resources is fresh water that flows across the Earth's land surface and into the world's rivers, streams, lakes, wetlands, and estuaries. The precipitation that does not infiltrate the ground or return to the atmosphere by evaporation (including transpiration from plants) is called **surface runoff.** The region from which surface water drains into a river, lake, wetland, or other body of water is called its **watershed** or **drainage basin.**

The renewable supplies of fresh water we depend on consist of accessible surface runoff and fresh water that infiltrates into aquifers found fairly near the Earth's surface. About two-thirds of the world's annual runoff is lost by seasonal floods and is not available for human use. The remaining one-third

is **reliable runoff:** the amount of runoff that we can generally count on as a stable source of water from year to year.

What Is Groundwater? Water Down Below

Some precipitation infiltrates the ground and is stored in spaces in soil and rock.

Some precipitation infiltrates the ground and percolates downward through voids (pores, fractures, crevices, and other spaces) in soil and rock (Figure 15-3). The water in these spaces is called **groundwater**—one of our most important sources of fresh water. Groundwater found within 1 kilometre (0.6 miles) of the Earth's surface contains more than 100 times all the water found in the world's rivers, streams, freshwater lakes, and reservoirs combined.

Close to the surface in the **zone of aeration,** the pores of the soil contain a mixture of air and

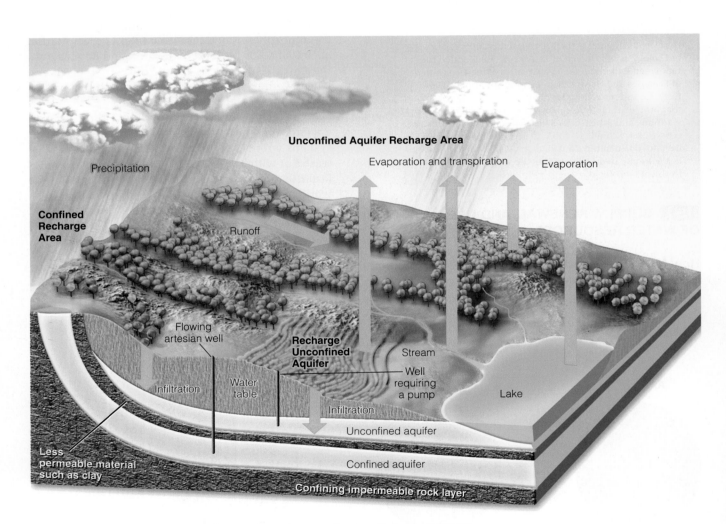

FIGURE 15-3 Natural capital: groundwater system. An *unconfined aquifer* is an aquifer with a water table. A *confined aquifer* is bounded above and below by less permeable beds of rock. Groundwater in this type of aquifer is confined under pressure. Some aquifers are replenished by precipitation and others are not.

some water. Lower layers of soil where the spaces are completely filled with water make up the **zone of saturation.** We drill shallow wells to tap into groundwater in this zone. The **water table** is located at the top of the zone of saturation. It falls in dry weather or when we remove groundwater faster than it is replenished, and rises in wet weather.

Deeper down are geological layers called **aquifers:** porous, water-saturated layers of sand, gravel, or bedrock through which groundwater flows. They are like large elongated sponges through which groundwater seeps. Fairly watertight layers of rock or clay below an aquifer keep the water from seeping out. An aquifer that is bounded only by the impermeable layer below it is called an **unconfined aquifer;** the water is not under pressure and a well drawing water from such an aquifer would have to lift or pump the water to the surface. An aquifer that is bounded by both upper and lower layers of impermeable material is called a **confined aquifer;** the water is often under high pressure and drilling through the uppermost impermeable layer will result in a self-flowing artesian well. About one of every three people on the Earth depends on water from aquifers for drinking and other uses.

Most aquifers are replenished naturally by precipitation that percolates downward through soil and rock in what is called **natural recharge.** But some are recharged from the side by *lateral recharge* from nearby streams. Most aquifers recharge extremely slowly.

Groundwater normally moves from points of high elevation and pressure to points of lower elevation and pressure. This movement is quite slow, typically only a metre or so (about 3 feet) per year and rarely more than 0.3 metre (1 foot) per day.

There is a *hydrological connection* between groundwater and surface water because eventually most groundwater flows into rivers, lakes, estuaries, and wetlands. Thus if we disrupt the hydrological cycle by removing groundwater faster than it is replenished, some nearby streams, lakes, and wetlands can dry up.

Some aquifers get very little, if any, recharge and on a human time scale are nonrenewable resources. Typically these *nonreplenishable aquifers*—also called *fossil aquifers*—are found fairly deep underground and were formed tens of thousands of years ago. Withdrawals from them amount to *water mining* that, if kept up, will deplete these ancient deposits.

How Much of the World's Reliable Water Supply Are We Withdrawing? Taking Half Now and More Later

We are using more than half of the world's reliable runoff of surface water and could be using 70–90% by 2025.

Withdrawal is the total amount of water we remove from a river, lake, or aquifer for any purpose. Some of this water may be returned to its source. For example, most water withdrawn from a river or lake to help cool power plants may be returned to its source. However, this input of heated water can disrupt aquatic life, a phenomenon known as *thermal pollution.*

Some of the water withdrawn from a source may be returned to that source for reuse. *Consumptive water use* occurs when water withdrawn is not available for reuse in the basin from which it was removed—mostly because of losses such as evaporation, seepage into the ground, transport to another area, or contamination.

During the last century, the human population tripled, global water withdrawal increased sevenfold, and per capita withdrawal quadrupled. As a result, we now withdraw about 34% of the world's reliable runoff. We leave another 20% in streams to transport goods by boats, dilute pollution, and sustain fisheries and wildlife. Thus *we directly or indirectly use about 54% of the world's reliable runoff of surface water.*

Because of increased population growth alone, global withdrawal rates of surface water could reach more than 70% of the reliable surface runoff by 2025— 90% if per capita withdrawal of water continues rising at the current rate. This is a global average, with withdrawal rates already exceeding the reliable runoff in a growing number of areas.

How Do We Use the World's Fresh Water? Watering Crops Is Number One

Worldwide, irrigation is the biggest user of water (70%), followed by industries (19%), and cities and residences (11%).

Worldwide, we use about 70% of the water we withdraw each year from surface waters and aquifers to irrigate one-fifth of the world's cropland. This produces about 40% of the world's food, including two-thirds of the rice and wheat. About 85% of the water withdrawn for irrigation is consumed and not returned to its water basin, mostly because of evaporation and seepage into the ground. Some of this water is also contaminated with salts and pesticides. Industry uses about 19% of the water withdrawn each year, and cities and residences use the remaining 11%.

Uses of withdrawn water vary from one region or country to another (Figure 15-4, p. 340). Canada uses relatively little irrigation for agriculture, choosing instead to grow crops such as wheat and sunflowers that are well suited to the dry Prairies. The United States, on the other hand, has elected to use extensive irrigation to grow crops such as corn and soybeans in the arid Midwest. China uses widespread irrigation for water-intensive crops such as rice. Both Canada and the United States use large amounts of water for industry; more than three-quarters of this water is used for coding power plants.

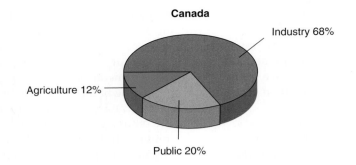

Canada

Industry 68%

Agriculture 12%

Public 20%

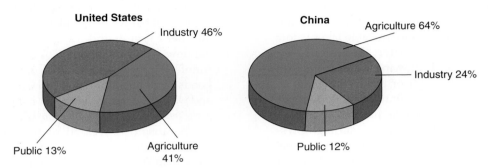

United States

Industry 46%

Public 13%

Agriculture 41%

China

Agriculture 64%

Industry 24%

Public 12%

FIGURE 15-4 Use of water withdrawn in Canada, the United States, and China. (Data from Gleick et al., 2011)

Just about anything you do uses water. Reading a newspaper, driving a car, eating a hamburger or a bowl of rice, wearing cotton clothing, or drinking a beverage out of an aluminium can involve processes or products that require large amounts of water. For instance, it takes 7 000 litres of water to produce 1 kilogram of grain-fed beef, and 5 000 litres of water to grow 1 kilogram of rice.

There is also a difference in water priorities between developed and developing nations. According to the United Nations, for example, the daily minimum amount of water needed to support three-fourths of the world's people is equal to the amount of water used each day to irrigate the world's golf courses.

Case Study: Water Resources in Canada— Abundant but Not Problem-Free

Canada has plenty of fresh water, but supplies are distributed unevenly and our per capita consumption is very high.

Water has played an important role in Canadian history. Native people, explorers, and pioneers travelled by water. Lakes and rivers were the highways that cut through difficult terrain and allowed relatively easy transportation of people and goods. Water was a crucial factor in determining the location of settlements, including North Battleford (ford), Winnipeg (strategic fork in a river), Portage la Prairie (portage), and Toronto (harbour). Today, Canada uses water to generate hydroelectric power,

and our lakes and rivers are a major tourist attraction (Figure 15-5).

Canada has relatively abundant supplies of water (Figure 15-6). Our water supply begins as precipitation that is distributed unevenly across the country. Precipitation is highest in the western and eastern parts of the country, and lowest in the Arctic and in the southern Prairies (Figure 15-7A). About two-thirds of the precipitation falls as rain. Most of the one-third that falls as snow accumulates over winter and is released during spring melt, which can lead to flooding problems (p. 356). Snow that falls on glaciers and in the High Arctic may remain frozen for many thousands of years.

FIGURE 15-5 Canada's beautiful lakes and rivers are a celebrated tourist destination.

© Chris Cheadle/Alamy

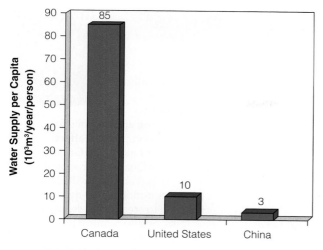

FIGURE 15-6 Canada has a large per capita supply of water compared with other countries. (FAO, 2012)

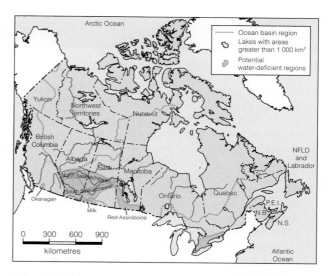

FIGURE 15-7B Main rivers, lakes, drainage basins (green), and water-deficient areas (yellow) of Canada. (Statistics Canada, *Atlas of Canada* (http://atlas.gc.ca), and Draper and Reed, 2005)

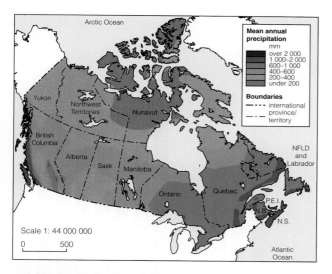

FIGURE 15-7A Mean annual precipitation in Canada. (Modified from Stanford, 1992)

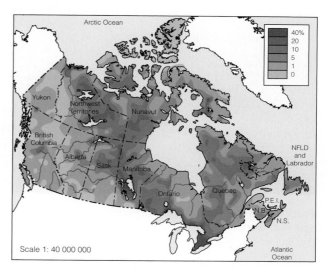

FIGURE 15-7C Freshwater surfaces as a percentage of total land area. This map shows areas that are relatively dense with lakes and wetlands. (Matthews and Morrow, 1985)

Once water meets the ground, it may infiltrate into soil, or it may drain from the land through streams, rivers, lakes, and wetlands. Streams are small but important water systems that finely divide the landscape into drainage areas. Rivers range from meandering giants like the Saskatchewan River to rushing torrents like the Niagara River. Canada has millions of lakes, including the myriad rocky lakes that dot the Canadian Shield, the icy green lakes of British Columbia, and the Great Lakes (see Spotlight). Figure 15-7B illustrates the main lakes and rivers that carry runoff from Canada's land surfaces to the surrounding oceans.

About 7.6% of Canada consists of lakes and rivers, and another 14% of wetlands. Canada has about 25% of the world's wetlands, the largest proportion of

wetlands in any one country (see Chapter 7 for more information about wetlands). These, in combination with lakes and rivers, form the system of surface water that is so visually obvious in many parts of the country (Figures 15-7C and 15-8, p. 342).

Canada also has an abundant supply of groundwater—estimated at more than 30 times the amount of surface water! About 30% of Canadians use groundwater. About 85% of rural people depend on groundwater, and its use varies by region; for example, P.E.I. (a small island) uses 100% groundwater whereas Nunavut (on permafrost) uses 0%. About 90% of the

The Great Lakes Water Supply

The Great Lakes span more than 1 200 kilometres (745 miles) from east to west and make up the largest system of fresh surface water on the planet—roughly 18% of the world's supply. The area is inhabited by 9 million Canadians and 33 million Americans. Approximately one in three Canadians and one in seven Americans depend on the Great Lakes for drinking water.

These concentrations of people are having an impact on the Great Lakes. Industry and agriculture surround the lakes. Pollutants generated throughout the entire basin can end up in the lakes. Since outflow from the system is less than 1% per year, there is great potential for pollutants to become concentrated. Also, there is concern that falling water levels can impact shipping, fish habitat, and real-estate values.

Management of the Great Lakes is shared between Canada and the United States. The Boundary Waters Treaty, signed in 1909, focuses on boundary issues, initiating studies, and approving applications for water diversion projects affecting the Great Lakes. The Great Lakes Water Quality Agreement (GLWQA) was signed in 1972 to establish common water-quality objectives, to create joint research programs, and to monitor and control pollutants. For more information on pollution in the Great Lakes, see Chapter 22.

FIGURE 15-8 Parts of the Canadian North are home to countless lakes, streams, rivers, and wetlands.

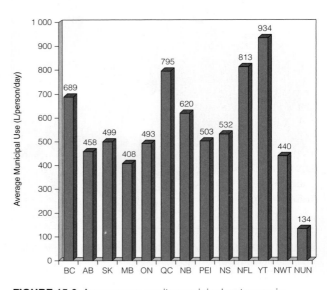

FIGURE 15-9 Average per capita municipal water use in different regions of Canada. (Data from Table 1, p. 4 of 2010 Municipal Water Use Report, Environment Canada, 2010.)

water used in agriculture is supplied by groundwater; of this amount, 85% is used for irrigation and 15% is used for watering livestock.

Although Canada has only 0.5% of the world's population, we have 20% of the planet's supply of available fresh water and the second-highest per capita use of water (1 494 metres^3/year) after Americans (1 682 metres^3/year). Water use within Canada varies by region, with Nunavut being the most frugal and Yukon Territory being the most extravagant (Figure 15-9). About 65% of the water in a Canadian household is used just for flushing toilets and taking showers (Figure 15-10, p. 343).

The water that comes to your home is managed municipally in terms of water treatment and delivery through the local infrastructure of pipes and pumps. The provincial and territorial governments have a major hand in water management through ministries that regulate water use, water quality, and fish habitat, among other areas. The federal government, through agencies such as Environment Canada and Health Canada, ensures that water management is undertaken in the best national interest.

The management of specific bodies of water is carried out by groups such as the Lake Winnipeg Stewardship Board, the Fraser Basin Council, and various Conservation authorities. Wetlands are evaluated by local and provincial governments, and often managed by their own groups such as Friends of Laurier Marsh in North Bay, Ontario. Canada is a supporter of the 1981 Convention on Wetlands of

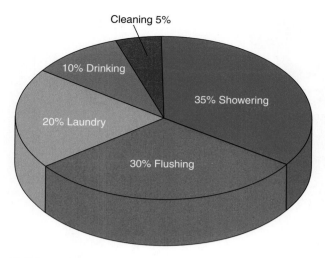

FIGURE 15-10 Average water use in Canadian homes. (Environment Canada, 2011)

International Importance (also known as the Ramsar Convention), which acts to conserve the world's most significant wetland habitats.

Despite its relatively abundant water supply, Canada faces problems related to distribution of water, water pollution, and impacts of water use. As noted previously, precipitation falls unevenly across the country, and many of the rivers flow north. Most Canadians live in the southern parts of the country within 300 kilometres of the U.S. border. Thus the majority of the population overlaps with only the southern portion of Canada's water supply, and populations can be quite dense in developed areas. This makes it possible for Canadians to overburden the water resources that are locally available to them (see the spotlight on renewable water).

Much of the best soil for agriculture is in the Prairies; yet there is relatively little water there and the region is subject to periodic droughts. Crops can be aided by irrigation, but overuse of groundwater can deplete aquifers, cause soil subsidence, and lead to soil salinization when the water evaporates leaving salts behind (Chapter 14).

Our cities were originally small settlements founded near suitable water sources. In expanding to become urban centres, they have become focal points for large concentrations of people. This places increasing demands on water sources to provide for the growing needs of these people without becoming depleted, polluted, or ecologically disrupted. Many urban and rural communities have experienced at least temporary seasonal water shortages as local demands have grown and summers have become warmer. This will certainly increase in the future with both population growth and global warming (Chapters 10 and 21).

15-3 TOO LITTLE WATER

What Causes Shortage of Fresh Water? Climate and Demand

Dry climate, drought, dry soil, and too many people using the reliable supply cause water scarcity.

According to Swedish hydrologist Malin Falkenmark, there are four causes of water scarcity: *dry climate*, **drought** (a prolonged period in which precipitation is at least 70% lower and evaporation is higher than normal), *desiccation* (drying of exposed soil because of activities such as deforestation and overgrazing by livestock), and *water stress* (low per capita availability of water caused by increasing numbers of people relying on limited runoff).

Figure 15-11 shows the degree of stress on the world's major river systems, based on the amount of water available compared to the amount used by humans. A country is said to be *water stressed* when the volume of reliable runoff per person drops below about 1 700 cubic metres (60 000 cubic feet) per year. This usually occurs when water withdrawal is more than 20% higher than the reliable supply. A country suffers from *water scarcity* when per capita water

---

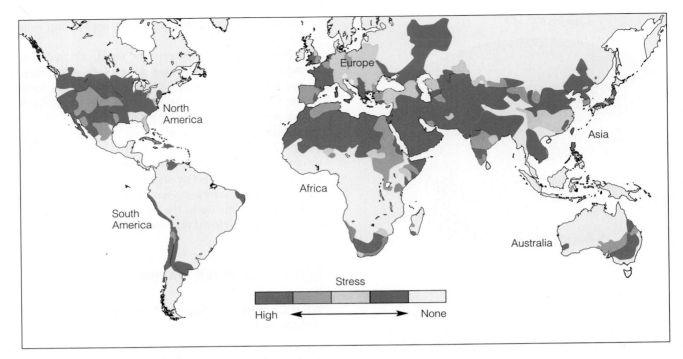

FIGURE 15-11 Natural capital degradation: stress on the world's major river basins, based on a comparison of the amount of water available with the amount used by humans. (Data from World Commission on Water Use in the 21st Century)

availability falls below 1 000 cubic metres (35 000 cubic feet) per year.

According to the United Nations, about 41% of the world's population lives in river basins located in 20 countries that suffer from water stress or water scarcity. Look at the red and orange areas in Figure 15-11 to see where these areas are located. The number of countries suffering from water stress or water scarcity could grow to 40 countries by 2020 and 60 countries by 2050.

Some areas have lots of water, but the largest rivers carrying most of the runoff are far from agricultural and population centres. For example, South America has the largest annual water runoff of any continent, but 60% of the runoff flows through the Amazon River in remote areas where few people live.

In some areas, overall precipitation is plentiful but arrives mostly during short periods or cannot be collected and stored because of a lack of storage capacity. For example, only a few hours of rain provide over half of India's rainfall during a four-month monsoon season.

The volumes of some of the world's lakes and rivers have shrunk drastically, mostly because of human withdrawals of water for irrigation and industry. Siberia's Aral Sea, once the world's fourth-largest freshwater lake, has shrunk in area to less than half its former size and lost 83% of its volume of water since 1960. The area of West Africa's Lake Chad, once

the world's sixth-largest lake, has shrunk by 92% since 1960 because of a combination of water diversion for irrigation and periods of prolonged drought. In the dry season, water flowing in the Colorado River and a number of other rivers throughout the world rarely reaches the ocean.

How Many of the World's People Do Not Have Access to Enough Fresh Water? Aquatic Inequality

About one out of seven people do not have regular access to an adequate and affordable supply of clean water, and many more lack access to sanitation.

About a billion people still lack access to safe drinking water and about 2.5 billion people are without access to improved sanitation facilities. These are serious deficits that leave people vulnerable to water-borne diseases.

There is *aquatic inequality* in the sense that water is not equally available in all geographical locations, and on a smaller scale, rural people tend to be disadvantaged compared to urban people.

Even when a sufficient supply of water exists, many cannot afford a safe supply of drinking water and must live in *hydrological poverty*. Many are cut off from municipal water supplies and must collect water from unsafe sources or buy water—often coming

FIGURE 15-12 In many places in the world, people work hard every day to find enough water to meet their needs. They are often in danger of contracting diseases or parasites through the water they drink.

from polluted rivers—from private vendors at high prices. In water-short rural areas in developing countries, many women and children must walk long distances each day, carrying heavy jars or cans, to get a meagre and sometimes contaminated supply of water (Figure 15-12).

How Can We Increase Freshwater Supplies? Withdraw More and Waste Less

We can increase water supplies by building dams, bringing in water from elsewhere, withdrawing groundwater, converting salt water to fresh water, wasting less water, and importing food.

There are several ways to increase the supply of fresh water in a particular area. One is to build dams and reservoirs to store runoff for release as needed. Another is to bring in surface water from another area. We can also withdraw groundwater and convert salt water to fresh water (desalination). Other strategies are to reduce water waste and import food to reduce water use in growing crops and raising livestock.

In *developed countries,* people tend to live where the climate is favourable and bring in water from another watershed. In *developing countries,* most people (especially the rural poor) must settle where the water is and try to capture the precipitation they need.

In developed countries, we tend to think of golf as a pleasant outdoor game to play in a spacious, grass-green setting. What could be nicer? Yet in developing countries, golf courses have a more sinister side to them. They occupy space that could be used for

growing food. Somebody is making money from them, but not the people who may have been displaced from this land. The runoff from the golf course—polluted with herbicides, fungicides, and insecticides and enriched by fertilizers intended to grow grass—can kill off local fish populations.

But the greatest impact is that large amounts of scarce water are used for keeping the grass green rather than providing local people with food and drink. According to the World Watch Institute, more than 9.5 million cubic metres of water are used daily for the golf courses of the world. This would provide 4.7 billion people with the minimum amount of drinking water that is set out by UN requirements, rather than just keeping the grass green for a game (Platt, 1994; Wheeler and Nauright, 2006).

Who Should Own and Manage Freshwater Resources? Government versus Private Ownership

There is controversy over whether water supplies should be owned and managed by governments or by private corporations.

Is access to enough clean water to meet one's basic needs a basic human right, or is water a commodity to be sold in the marketplace? Most people would say that everyone should have a right to clean water. The problem is, who will pay for making water available to everyone?

Most water resources are owned by governments and managed as publicly owned resources for their citizens. However, an increasing number of governments are retaining ownership of these public resources but hiring private companies to manage them. In addition, three large transnational companies—Vivendi, Suez, and RWE—based in Europe have a long-range strategy to buy up as much of the world's water supplies as possible, especially in Europe and North America.

The argument is that private companies have the money and expertise to manage these resources better and more efficiently than government bureaucracies. Experience with this *public–private partnership* approach is mixed. Some companies hired to manage water resources have improved efficiency, done a good job, and in a few cases lowered rates.

But in the late 1980s, Prime Minister Margaret Thatcher placed England's water management in private hands. The result was financial mismanagement, skyrocketing water rates, deteriorating water quality, and company executives giving themselves generous financial compensation packages. In the late 1990s, Prime Minister Tony Blair brought the system under control by imposing much stricter government oversight. *The message:* Governments hiring private companies to manage water resources must set standards and maintain strict oversight of such contracts.

Some government officials want to go further and sell public water resources to private companies. Many people oppose full privatization of water resources because they believe that water is a public resource too important to be left solely in private hands. Also, once a city's water systems have been taken over by a foreign-based corporation, efforts to return the systems to public control can lead to severe economic penalties under the rules of the World Trade Organization (WTO).

CONSIDER, DISCUSS, OR DEBATE

Should private companies own and manage most of the world's water resources? What will happen if water companies form a cartel that raises prices, or if one large water company gains a monopoly?

15-4 USING DAMS AND RESERVOIRS TO SUPPLY MORE WATER

What Are the Advantages and Disadvantages of Large Dams and Reservoirs? Mixed Blessings

Large dams and reservoirs can produce cheap electricity, reduce downstream flooding, and provide year-round water for irrigating cropland, but they also displace people and disrupt aquatic systems.

An estimated 800 000 dams of all sizes now restrict the flow of the world's rivers. Large dams and reservoirs have benefits and drawbacks (Figure 15-13).

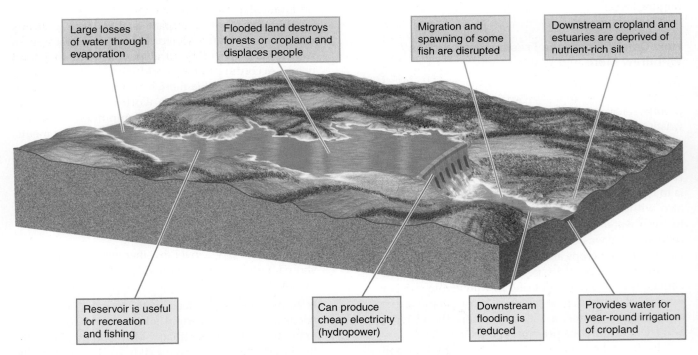

Large losses of water through evaporation

Flooded land destroys forests or cropland and displaces people

Migration and spawning of some fish are disrupted

Downstream cropland and estuaries are deprived of nutrient-rich silt

Reservoir is useful for recreation and fishing

Can produce cheap electricity (hydropower)

Downstream flooding is reduced

Provides water for year-round irrigation of cropland

FIGURE 15-13 Trade-offs: advantages (green) and disadvantages (orange) of large dams and reservoirs. The world's 45 000 large dams (higher than 15 metres, or 50 feet) capture and store about 14% of the world's runoff, provide water for about 45% of irrigated cropland, and supply more than half the electricity used by 65 countries. Pick the single advantage and disadvantage that you think are the most important.

Their main purpose is to capture and store runoff and release it as needed to control floods; to generate electricity; and to supply water for irrigation and for towns and cities. Reservoirs also provide recreational activities such as swimming, fishing, and boating.

The more than 45 000 large dams (22 000 of them in China) built on the world's 227 largest rivers have increased the annual reliable runoff available for human use by nearly one-third. But a series of dams on a river, especially in arid areas, can reduce downstream flow to a trickle and prevent it from reaching the sea as a part of the hydrologic cycle. According to the World Commission on Water in the 21st Century, half of the world's major rivers are going dry part of the year because of flow reduction by dams.

This engineering approach to river management has displaced between 40 and 80 million people from their homes and has flooded an area of mostly productive land about half the size of British Columbia or Ontario. In addition, this approach often impairs some of the important ecological and economic services rivers provide (Figure 13-15, p. 291). In 2003, the World Resources Institute estimated that dams and reservoirs have strongly or moderately fragmented and disturbed 60% of the world's major river basins. According to water-resource expert Peter H. Gleck, at least a fourth of the world's freshwater fish species are threatened or endangered, primarily because dams and water withdrawals have destroyed many free-flowing rivers.

Because of evaporation and seepage from their reservoirs, some dams lose more water than they provide. The reservoirs behind dams also eventually fill up with silt, which makes the dams useless for storing water or producing electricity.

When the Aswan High Dam was built in Egypt in 1970, it slowed the waters of the Nile River into man-made Lake Nassar, creating a large reservoir for power generation and irrigation. Unfortunately, it also contributed to the spread of **schistosomiasis** (also known as **bilhartzia**). This disease is caused by a trematode worm that invades the bodies of people and domestic animals that come into contact with water. The outbreak was facilitated by slower water and an increase in water plants that allowed the intermediate hosts—snails—to thrive.

The Columbia River originates in British Columbia and flows for 2 000 kilometres (1 240 miles), often steeply, passing through Washington and Oregon before emptying into the Pacific Ocean. The Columbia is the largest river on the west side of North America, and it generates more hydroelectric power than any other river in North America. This international river has more than 150 dams, including 14 major hydroelectric dams. It also supplies water for irrigation, municipal, and industrial uses, and is an example of

international cooperation since Canada and the United States govern the use of the river through the Columbia River Treaty. In brief, Canada built dams in the upper part of the river to generate electric power and to avert flood problems in the lower part of the river. Canada gets a portion of the power generated at U.S. dams as well as one-half of the estimated savings in terms of averted flood damage costs (http://www.ccrh.org/comm/river/docs/cotreaty.htm).

The unfortunate part of this story is that the Columbia River was a major salmon river, and the salmon spawned in the upper reaches of the river. Since the dams were built, the Columbia River's wild salmon population has diminished by 94%, and no amount of money spent on fish ladders or other conservation practices has remedied the situation. Some hydro dams, such as the Chief Joseph, have no fish ladders and are a complete barrier to fish migration. Even dams that have fish ladders present problems in that they restrict water release downstream, and they alter the water upstream from a turbulent river to a quiet reservoir. These changes in the river have posed severe challenges for migrating salmon, and several species that use the river are now listed as endangered or threatened.

The original treaty was signed in 1964, with the condition that either country could withdraw from the treaty in 60 years (2024), after ten years' notice (2014). People are now becoming aware that the chance to "rethink" the water management plan of the Columbia River is fast approaching. Those with a strong interest in renegotiating the Columbia River Treaty will be Native groups who had rights to the salmon in the river, conservationists, academics, recreationists, farmers, dam operators, industry leaders, and politicians from both countries (Kramer, 2009). Further information about the declining West Coast salmon fishery can be found in Section 13-4.

Case Study: China's Three Gorges Dam— A Controversial Project

There is debate over whether the advantages of the world's largest dam and reservoir outweigh its disadvantages.

Completed in May 2012, China's Three Gorges Dam on the mountainous upper reaches of the Yangtze River is currently the world's largest hydroelectric dam and reservoir. The dam is 2 kilometres (1.2 miles) long and has 32 main turbines with a combined generating capacity of 22 500 megawatts. Figure 15-14 lists major advantages and disadvantages of this controversial project.

Bad news. More than a million people were relocated from the area that was flooded to form a gigantic 600-kilometre-long (385-mile-long) reservoir behind

Trade-Offs

China's Three Gorges Dam

Advantages	Disadvantages
Will generate about 10% of China's electricity	Floods large areas of cropland and forests
Reduces dependence on coal	Displaces more than 13 million people
Reduces air pollution	Increases water pollution because of reduced water flow
Reduces CO_2 emissions	Reduces deposits of nutrient-rich sediments below dam
Reduces chances of downstream flooding for 15 million people	Increases salt water introduced into drinking water near mouth of river because of decreased water flow
Reduces river silting below dam by eroded soil	Disrupts spawning and migration of some fish below dam
Increases irrigation water for cropland below dam	High cost

FIGURE 15-14 Trade-offs: advantages and disadvantages of the Three Gorges Dam the Yangtze River in China. Pick the single advantage and disadvantage that you think are the most important.

the dam. Roughly 1 300 cities and villages, and thousands of archeological and cultural sites, had to be abandoned. There have been some large landslides above the dam, associated with the higher water levels in the reservoir. Some critically endangered wildlife such as the Siberian crane and the Baiji Yangtze river dolphin have been negatively impacted by the dam.

Good news. The dam has the electrical output of 18 large coal-burning or nuclear power plants and will help reduce China's dependence on coal and its emissions of the greenhouse gas CO_2. It will also help hold back the Yangtze River's floodwaters, which have killed more than 500 000 people during the past 100 years—including 4 000 people in 1998. In addition, it will release water to downstream cities during the dry season and will enable large cargo-carrying ships to travel deep into China's interior, greatly reducing transportation costs.

Mixed news. Because the dam is built over a seismic fault, geologists worry that the dam might collapse and cause a major flood that would kill millions of people. Engineers claim that the dam can

withstand the maximum projected earthquake. Others are not so confident, noting that since 1949 more than 3 200 dams in China have collapsed and killed several hundred thousand people. About 80 small cracks have already been discovered in the dam. Critics claim that it would have been cheaper, less disruptive, and safer to build a series of smaller dams. The Chinese government views the project as an engineering, social, and economic success.

CONSIDER, DISCUSS, OR DEBATE

Do the advantages of large dams outweigh their disadvantages? How can the negative aspects of dams be remedied?

15-5 TRANSFERRING WATER FROM ONE PLACE TO ANOTHER

Case Study: The Aral Sea Disaster—A Glaring Example of Unintended Consequences

Diverting water from the Aral Sea and its two feeder rivers mostly for irrigation has created a major ecological, economic, and health disaster.

Tunnels, aqueducts, and underground pipes can transfer stream runoff collected by dams and reservoirs from water-rich areas to water-poor areas. However, they also create environmental problems. Indeed, most of the world's dam projects and large-scale water transfers illustrate the important ecological principle that *you cannot do just one thing*. There are almost always a number of unintended environmental consequences (Figure 3-4, p. 40).

An example is the shrinking of the Aral Sea (Figure 15-15). It is a result of a large-scale water transfer project in an area of the former Soviet Union with the driest climate in central Asia. Since 1960, enormous amounts of irrigation water have been diverted from the inland Aral Sea and its two feeder rivers to create one of the world's largest irrigated areas, mostly for raising cotton and rice. The irrigation canal, the world's longest, stretches over 1 300 kilometres (800 miles)—equivalent to one-third the width of Canada.

This large-scale water diversion project, coupled with droughts and high evaporation rates in this area's hot and dry climate, has caused a regional ecological, economic, and health disaster. Since 1960, the sea's salinity has more than tripled and its surface area has decreased by about 90%. In effect, it has been transformed from a single large lake (Figure 15-15, left) into a number of smaller lakes (Figure 15-15, right). Water withdrawal for agriculture has reduced the sea's two supply rivers to mere trickles.

More than 85% of the area's wetlands have been eliminated, and roughly half the area's bird and

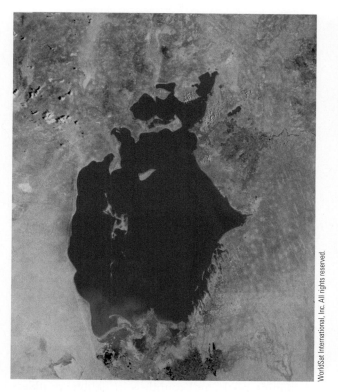

FIGURE 15-15 Natural capital degradation: the *Aral Sea* was once the world's fourth-largest fresh-water lake. Since 1960, it has been shrinking and getting saltier because most of the water from the rivers that replenish it has been diverted to grow cotton and food crops. These satellite photos show the sea in 1976 and in 2009. As the lake shrinks, it leaves behind a salty desert, economic ruin, increasing health problems, and severe ecological disruption.

mammal species have disappeared. In addition, a huge area of former lake bottom has been converted to a human-made desert covered with glistening white salt. The increased salt concentration caused the presumed extinction of 26 of the area's 32 native fish species. This has devastated the area's fishing industry, which once provided work for more than 60 000 people. Fishing villages and boats once on the sea's coastline now are abandoned in the middle of a salt desert.

Shrinkage of the Aral Sea has altered the area's climate. The once-huge sea acted as a thermal buffer that moderated the heat of summer and the extreme cold of winter. Now there is less rain, summers are hotter and drier, winters are colder, and the growing season is shorter. The combination of such climate change and severe salinization has reduced crop yields by 20–50% on almost a third of the area's cropland.

Finally, there have been increasing health problems from a combination of toxic dust, salt, and contaminated water for many of the 45 million people living in the Aral Sea's watershed.

Can the Aral Sea be saved, and can the area's serious ecological and human health problems be reduced? There is agreement that the sea will never return to its former volume. Efforts have focused primarily on stopping further shrinkage and undoing some of the ecological and health damage caused by its shrinkage.

15-6 TAPPING GROUNDWATER, CONVERTING SALT WATER TO FRESH WATER, SEEDING CLOUDS, AND TOWING ICEBERGS

What Are the Advantages and Disadvantages of Withdrawing Groundwater? Avoid Too Many Straws in the Glass

Most aquifers are renewable sources unless the water is removed faster than it is replenished or it becomes contaminated.

Aquifers provide drinking water for about one-fourth of the world's people. In Canada and the United States, water pumped from aquifers supplies almost all of the drinking water in rural areas as well as most of the water used in agriculture.

Relying more on groundwater has advantages and disadvantages (Figure 15-16, p. 350). The *good news* is that aquifers are widely available and are renewable

Trade-Offs

Withdrawing Groundwater

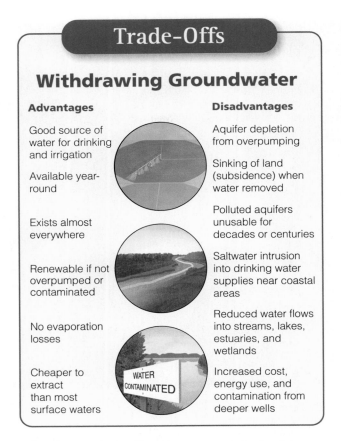

Advantages	Disadvantages
Good source of water for drinking and irrigation	Aquifer depletion from overpumping
Available year-round	Sinking of land (subsidence) when water removed
Exists almost everywhere	Polluted aquifers unusable for decades or centuries
Renewable if not overpumped or contaminated	Saltwater intrusion into drinking water supplies near coastal areas
No evaporation losses	Reduced water flows into streams, lakes, estuaries, and wetlands
Cheaper to extract than most surface waters	Increased cost, energy use, and contamination from deeper wells

FIGURE 15-16 Trade-offs: advantages and disadvantages of withdrawing groundwater. Pick the single advantage and disadvantage that you think are the most important.

sources of water as long as the water is not withdrawn faster than it is replaced and as long as the aquifers do not become contaminated.

The *bad news* is that water tables are falling in many areas of the world as the rate of pumping out water (mostly to irrigate crops) exceeds the rate of natural recharge from precipitation. The problem of falling water tables sneaks up on us because we cannot see it happening. The first sign is shallow wells going dry, followed by loss of water from deeper wells if the water mining process continues. Covering aquifer **recharge areas** with urban development also contributes to aquifer depletion.

The world's three largest grain-producing countries—China, India, and the United States—are overpumping many of their aquifers. In 2002, China announced a massive project to pump surface water through three huge aqueducts from the Yangtze River in China's water-rich south to the country's arid north. The water will help grow more food and slow aquifer depletion in the North China Plain. This project began in 2005 but will not be completed until 2050. Environmentalists are concerned about its potentially harmful ecological impacts.

In the United States, groundwater is being withdrawn at four times its replacement rate. The most serious overdrafts are in parts of the huge Ogallala Aquifer, underlying eight states in the arid high plains from southern South Dakota to central Texas and in parts of the arid Southwest (Figure 15-17). Serious groundwater depletion is also taking place in California's water-short Central Valley, which supplies about half the country's vegetables and fruits (see the Spotlight on the next page).

Saudi Arabia is as water-poor as it is oil-rich. It gets about 70% of its drinking water at a high cost from the world's largest desalination complex on its eastern coast. The rest of the country's water is pumped from deep aquifers, most as nonrenewable as the country's oil. Yet this water-short nation wastes much of its scarcest resource with large numbers of fountains, swimming pools, and countless irrigation sprinklers that suck nonrenewable water from deep underground and let precious water evaporate into the hot, dry desert air. Hydrologists estimate that because of the rapid depletion of its fossil aquifers, most irrigated agriculture in Saudi Arabia may disappear within 10 to 20 years.

According to water resource expert Sandra Postel, about 480 million people are being fed with grain produced with eventually unsustainable water mining from aquifers. This example of the tragedy of the commons is expected to increase as irrigated areas are expanded to help feed 2.5 billion more people projected to join the ranks of humanity by 2050.

CENGAGENOW ACTIVE FIGURE 15-17 Natural capital degradation: areas of greatest aquifer depletion from groundwater overdraft in the continental United States. Will American politicians be tempted to solve their problems by pumping large amounts of water from Lake Michigan? (U.S. Water Resources Council and U.S. Geological Survey). *See an animation based on this figure at* CengageNOW.

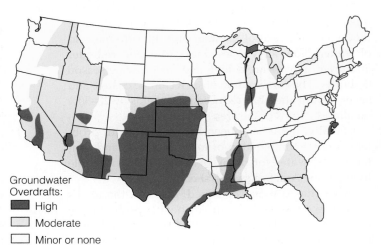

Groundwater Overdrafts:
- High
- Moderate
- Minor or none

Should Canada Sell Water to the United States?

As intensive industrial and agricultural activities deplete and pollute their water supply, Americans have been contemplating Canada's potential role as a major supplier. Before the Canadian Parliament ratified the North American Free Trade Agreement (NAFTA) in 1993, many politicians argued that Canada must retain sovereignty over its water resources: water, therefore, was not on the table.

In fact, the status of Canada's water supply is not so clear. Canadian companies sell billions of litres of bottled water to the United States every year. Under a longstanding arrangement, Chicago pumps 9.1 billion litres of water a day from the Great Lakes basin—which is shared by Canada and the United States—and injects the water into the Mississippi River system where it can be used for other purposes. There has been talk that the United States might sidestep the thorny issue of buying water from Canada by simply pumping larger volumes of water directly from Lake Michigan.

Those who advocate selling water to the Americans argue that Canada should treat water like any other resource and sell it for profit. Doing so might even encourage the United States to cooperate with Canadians in creating mega-projects that will bring water from farther north to the places where we need it.

Opponents counter that water is no ordinary commodity. Like air—and unlike other commodities we choose to buy—water is essential for life. Once we begin selling this precious and limited resource to the Americans, we will be committed by NAFTA to continue doing so regardless of any future water shortages in Canada. Furthermore, water mega-projects will displace local residents and cause large-scale ecological problems.

While Canadians reflect on these issues, the rest of the world is not standing still. The Great Lakes Annex Implementing Agreements have been amended to allow (in addition to Chicago) any counties straddling the Great Lakes basin to pump water from the basin. American and European water companies have been aggressively pursuing new sources and markets as privatizing and selling water becomes big business. Against this backdrop, the Fourth, Fifth, and Sixth World Water Forums—which convened in Mexico City in 2006, Istanbul in 2009, and Marseille in 2012—focused international attention on growing water supply problems around the world. Canadian activist Maude Barlow (2009) has repeatedly warned Canadians and the world about the need to value and guard our ownership of water.

Critical Thinking

Do you think that Canada should sell bulk quantities of fresh water to the United States? What would be the ecological, ethical, economic, political, and military implications of saying yes? Of saying no?

In addition to limiting future food production, over-pumping aquifers is increasing the gap between the rich and poor in some areas. As water tables drop, farmers must drill deeper wells, buy larger pumps, and use more electricity to run the pumps. Poor farmers cannot afford to do this and end up losing their land and either working for richer farmers or migrating to cities already crowded with poor people struggling to survive.

Withdrawing lots of water sometimes allows the sand and rock in aquifers to collapse, causing the land above the aquifer to **subside** or sink. Once an aquifer becomes compressed, recharge is impossible. Since 1950, some spots above aquifers in California's heavily farmed San Joaquin Valley have sunk or subsided more than 50 metres (160 feet).

Mexico City, built on a lakebed, has one of the world's worst subsidence problems because of an increase in groundwater overdrafts from rapid population growth and urbanization. In recent years, some parts of the city have sunk as much as 8 metres (26 feet).

Excessive withdrawal of groundwater can cause the roof of a cavern or underground conduit to collapse suddenly and create a large crater. Such *sinkholes* can form suddenly without warning and swallow houses, cars, and trees. Subsidence and the formation of sinkholes usually compress the rock particles in aquifers and thus lead to a permanent loss of the aquifer.

Finally, groundwater overdrafts near coastal areas can contaminate groundwater supplies by causing intrusion of salt water into freshwater aquifers used to supply water for irrigation and domestic purposes (Figure 15-18). This is an especially serious problem in coastal areas of Florida, California, South Carolina, and Texas.

Figure 15-19 lists ways to prevent or slow the problem of groundwater depletion. Study this figure carefully.

Can Deep Aquifers Supply More Water? Solution or Pipe Dream

Scientists are evaluating huge, deep aquifers as a source of water.

With global water shortages looming, scientists are evaluating deep aquifers—found at depths of

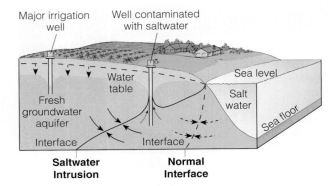

FIGURE 15-18 **Natural capital degradation:** *saltwater intrusion* along a coastal region. When the water table is lowered, the normal interface (dashed line) between fresh and saline groundwater moves inland (solid line), making groundwater supplies unusable for irrigation and domestic purposes.

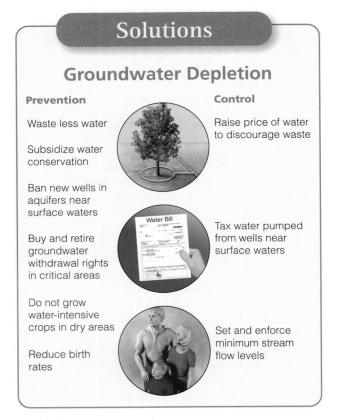

Solutions

Groundwater Depletion

Prevention

Waste less water

Subsidize water conservation

Ban new wells in aquifers near surface waters

Buy and retire groundwater withdrawal rights in critical areas

Do not grow water-intensive crops in dry areas

Reduce birth rates

Control

Raise price of water to discourage waste

Tax water pumped from wells near surface waters

Set and enforce minimum stream flow levels

FIGURE 15-19 **Solutions:** ways to prevent or slow groundwater depletion. Which two of these solutions do you believe are the most important?

0.8 kilometre (0.5 mile) or more—as future water sources. Some of these are gigantic nonrenewable aquifers containing deposits of water as much as a million years old.

Seismic and core-drilling technologies used by the oil industry are being used to locate and evaluate the largest of these deep aquifers, some of which run underneath several countries. Preliminary results suggest that some of these aquifers hold enough water to support billions of people for centuries. They also indicate that the water quality is much higher than that in most of the world's rivers and lakes.

There are two major concerns about tapping these mostly one-time deposits. One is that we know little about the geological and ecological impacts of pumping from deep aquifers. The other is that no international water treaties govern the rights to and ownership of water that underlies several countries. Without such treaties, there could be legal and physical conflicts over who has the right to tap into and use these resources.

How Useful Is Desalination? A Costly Option

Removing salt from seawater will probably not be done widely because of high costs and the question of what to do with the resulting salt.

Desalination involves removing dissolved salts from ocean water or from brackish (slightly salty) water in aquifers or lakes. It is another way to increase supplies of fresh water.

One method for desalinating water is *distillation*—heating salt water until it evaporates, leaves behind salts in solid form, and condenses as fresh water. Another method is *reverse osmosis*—pumping salt water at high pressure through a thin membrane with pores that allow water molecules, but not most dissolved salts, to pass through. In effect, high pressure pushes fresh water out of salt water.

There are about 14 500 desalination plants in 125 countries, mostly the desert nations of the Middle East, North Africa, the Caribbean, and the Mediterranean. These plants meet less than 0.3% of the world's water needs.

Oil-rich and water-short Middle Eastern countries produce about 60% of the world's desalinated water. Saudi Arabia is the largest producer and accounts for more than a third of the world's output, followed by the United States, which produces about a fifth of the world's desalinated water.

Water-short Israel aims to get half of its water from desalination; Israel currently treats and uses 75% of its sewage water for watering crops. Some water-short coastal cities in the United States, such as Tampa, Florida, have built desalination plants to supplement water supplies. In California, coastal cities such as Los Angeles, San Diego, and Monterey may build such plants.

There are two major problems with the widespread use of desalination. One is the high cost because it takes a lot of energy to desalinate water. Currently, desalinating water costs two to three times as much as the conventional purification of fresh water, although recent advances in reverse osmosis have brought the energy costs down somewhat.

The second problem is that desalination produces large quantities of briny wastewater that contains lots of salt and other minerals. Dumping concentrated brine into a nearby ocean increases the salinity of the ocean water, which threatens food resources and aquatic life in the vicinity. Dumping it on land could contaminate groundwater and surface water.

Bottom line: Currently, significant desalination is practical only for water-short wealthy countries and cities that can afford its high cost.

Scientists are working to develop new membranes for reverse osmosis that can separate water from salt more efficiently and under less pressure. If successful, this strategy could bring down the cost of desalination. Even so, it probably will not be cheap enough to irrigate conventional crops or meet much of the world's demand for fresh water unless scientists can figure out how to use solar energy or other means to desalinate seawater cheaply and how to safely dispose of the salt left behind.

Can Cloud Seeding and Towing Icebergs or Gigantic Water Bags Improve Water Supplies? Solutions or Pipe Dreams?

Seeding clouds with tiny particles of chemicals to increase rainfall, or towing icebergs or huge bags filled with fresh water to dry coastal areas, probably will not provide significant amounts of fresh water in the future.

For decades, 10 states, mostly in the water-short western United States, and 24 other countries have experimented with seeding clouds with dry ice or tiny particles of chemicals such as silver iodide. The hypothesis is that the particles become nuclei around which raindrops form and thus produce more rain or snow over dry regions and more snow over mountains.

Bad news. First, cloud seeding does not work well in very dry areas where rain is needed most, because there are few clouds to seed. *Second,* although some proponents in the multimillion-dollar cloud-seeding industry say the technology works, a 2003 report by the U.S. National Academy of Sciences says there is no compelling scientific evidence that it does. *Third,* it introduces large amounts of the cloud-seeding chemicals into soil and water systems, possibly harming people, wildlife, and agricultural productivity.

Fourth, seeding has led to legal disputes over the ownership of cloud water. For example, during a 1977 drought the attorney general of Idaho accused officials in neighbouring Washington State of "cloud rustling" and threatened to file suit in federal court.

Some analysts have proposed towing huge icebergs from Antarctic or Arctic waters to arid coastal areas such as Saudi Arabia and southern California and pumping fresh water from the melting bergs

ashore. But nobody is sure how to do it, and even if they did it might cost too much, especially for water-short developing countries.

15-7 REDUCING WATER WASTE

What Are the Benefits of Reducing Water Waste? A Win-Win Solution

We waste about two-thirds of the water we use, but using water more efficiently could reduce wastage to about 15%.

Mohamed El-Ashry of the World Resources Institute estimates that *65–70% of the water people use throughout the world is wasted through evaporation, leaks, and other losses.* The United States, the world's largest user of water, does slightly better but still loses about half of the water it withdraws. El-Ashry believes it is economically and technically feasible to reduce such water losses to 15%, thereby meeting most of the world's water needs for the foreseeable future.

This win-win solution will also decrease the burden on wastewater plants and reduce the need for expensive dams and water transfer projects that destroy wildlife habitats and displace people. It will also slow depletion of groundwater aquifers and save energy and money.

According to water-resource experts, the main cause of water waste is that *we charge too little for water.* Such *underpricing* is mostly the result of government subsidies that provide irrigation water, electricity, and diesel fuel for farmers to pump water from rivers and aquifers at below-market prices.

Subsidies keep the price of water so low that users have little or no financial incentive to invest in well-known water-saving technologies. According to water-resource expert Sandra Postel, "By heavily subsidizing water, governments give out the false message that it is abundant and can afford to be wasted—even as rivers are drying up, aquifers are being depleted, fisheries are collapsing, and species are going extinct."

The second major cause of water waste is *lack of government subsidies for improving the efficiency of water use.* A basic rule of economics is that you get more of what you reward. Subsidies for efficient water use would sharply reduce water waste.

Solutions: How Can We Waste Less Irrigation Water? Deliver Water Precisely When and Where Needed

About 60% of the world's irrigation water is wasted, but several irrigation techniques could reduce the waste to 5–20%.

About 60% of the irrigation water applied throughout the world does not reach targeted crops and does not contribute to food production. Most irrigation water comes from groundwater wells or surface water sources and flows by gravity through unlined ditches in crop fields so the water can be absorbed by crops (Figure 15-20, left). This *flood irrigation* method delivers far more water than the crops need and typically loses 40% of the water through evaporation, seepage, and runoff.

More efficient and environmentally sound irrigation technologies exist that can greatly reduce water demands and waste by delivering water more precisely to crops. One of these technologies is a *centre-pivot low-pressure sprinkler* (Figure 15-20, right), which uses pumps to spray water on crops. Typically, it allows 80% of the water to reach crops and thus cuts water use by one-fourth compared to conventional gravity-flow systems.

Another method is *low-energy precision application (LEPA) sprinklers*, a form of centre-pivot irrigation that puts 90–95% of the water where crops need it by spraying the water closer to the ground and in larger droplets than the centre-pivot low-pressure system. LEPA sprinklers use 20–30% less energy than low-pressure sprinklers and typically use 37% less water than conventional gravity-flow systems.

Farmers also use *surge valves* or *time-controlled valves* on conventional gravity flow irrigation systems (Figure 15-20, left). These valves send water down irrigation ditches in pulses instead of a continuous

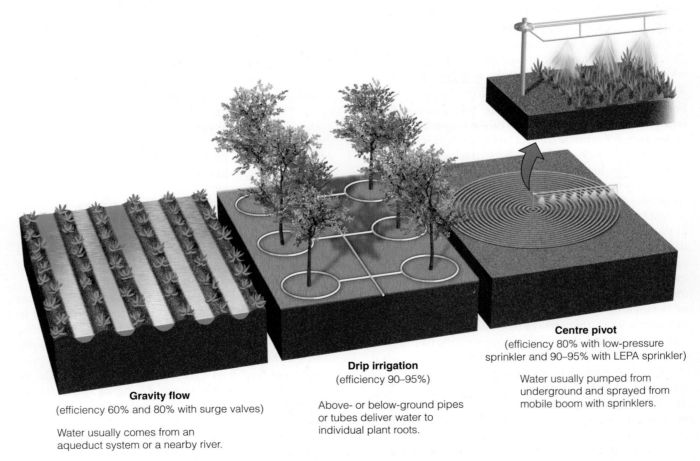

Gravity flow
(efficiency 60% and 80% with surge valves)

Water usually comes from an aqueduct system or a nearby river.

Drip irrigation
(efficiency 90–95%)

Above- or below-ground pipes or tubes deliver water to individual plant roots.

Centre pivot
(efficiency 80% with low-pressure sprinkler and 90–95% with LEPA sprinkler)

Water usually pumped from underground and sprayed from mobile boom with sprinklers.

FIGURE 15-20 Major *irrigation systems*. Because of high initial costs, centre-pivot irrigation and drip irrigation are not widely used. This may change because of the development of new, low-cost drip irrigation systems.

Solutions

Reducing Irrigation Water Waste

- Lining canals that transport water to fields
- Levelling fields with lasers
- Irrigating at night to reduce evaporation
- Using soil and satellite sensors and computer systems to monitor soil moisture and add water only when necessary
- Polyculture
- Organic farming
- Growing water-efficient crops using drought-resistant and salt-tolerant crop varieties
- Irrigating with treated urban wastewater
- Importing water-intensive crops and meat

FIGURE 15-21 Solutions: methods for reducing water waste in irrigation. Which two of these solutions do you believe are the most important?

stream. This can raise irrigation efficiency to 80% and cut water use by a fourth.

Drip irrigation or *microirrigation systems* (Figure 15-20, centre) are the most efficient ways to deliver small amounts of water precisely to crops. These systems consist of a network of perforated plastic tubing installed at or below the ground level. Small holes or emitters in the tubing deliver drops of water at a slow and steady rate close to the plant roots.

Drip irrigation is very efficient, with 90–95% of the water reaching the crops. It is also adaptable because the flexible and lightweight plastic tubing can be fitted to match the patterns of crops in a field and left in place or moved around. Figure 15-21 lists other ways to reduce water waste in irrigating crops.

Many of the world's poor farmers cannot afford to use most of the modern technological methods for increasing irrigation and its efficiency. Instead they use small-scale and low-cost traditional technologies.

Some (in Bangladesh, for example) use pedal-powered treadle pumps to move water through irrigation ditches. Others use buckets or small tanks with holes for drip irrigation.

How Can We Waste Less Water in Industry, Homes, and Businesses? Copy Nature, Raise Prices, Improve Efficiency

We can save water by using yard plants that need little water, using drip irrigation, raising water prices, fixing leaks, and using water-saving toilets and other appliances.

Figure 15-22 lists ways to use water more efficiently in industries, homes, and businesses. Many homeowners and businesses in water-short areas are copying nature by replacing green lawns with vegetation adapted to the local climate (Figure 15-23, p. 356). This **natural landscaping** reduces water use by 30–85% and sharply reduces the need for labour, fertilizer, and fuel. It also reduces polluted runoff, air pollution, and yard wastes. In particularly dry areas, people may practise **Xeriscaping** in which they plant only drought-resistant species. Some people in dry regions collect rainwater from gutters in large plastic barrels on wheels and use it to water their flowers and gardens.

In North America, flushing toilets with water clean enough to drink is the single largest use of domestic water. It accounts for about 38% of domestic water use, followed by bathing (32%), and washing clothes and dishes (20%). New models of low-flush toilets can remove the equivalent of two dozen golf balls in one flush without clogging and use fewer than 6.1 litres (1.6 gallons) of water—much less than the current standard of about 20 litres (5 gallons).

Solutions

Reducing Water Waste

- Redesign manufacturing processes
- Landscape yards with plants that require little water
- Use drip irrigation
- Fix water leaks
- Use water meters and charge for all municipal water use
- Raise water prices
- Use waterless composting toilets
- Require water conservation in water-short cities
- Use water-saving toilets, showerheads, and front-loading clothes washers
- Collect and reuse household water to irrigate lawns and nonedible plants
- Purify and reuse water for houses, apartments, and office buildings

FIGURE 15-22 Solutions: methods of reducing water waste in industries, homes, and businesses. Which two of these solutions do you believe are the most important?

FIGURE 15-23 Solutions: natural landscaping or xeriscaping can reduce water use by as much as 85% by using rocks and plants that need little water and are adapted to local growing conditions.

About 50–75% of the water from bathtubs, showers, bathroom sinks, and clothes washers in a typical house could be stored and reused as *grey water* for irrigating lawns and nonedible plants. About two-thirds of the wastewater in Israel is reused this way. All of Singapore's sewage is treated at reclamation plants to allow reuse of the water by industry.

Another problem is leakage and other losses from systems that supply water to homes, businesses, and industries. According to UN studies, 15–40% of the water supplied in urban areas is lost, mostly through leakage of water mains, pipes, pumps and valves, and illegal water hook-ups. In some parts of Africa, such losses can reach 50–70% of the water extracted from surface waters and aquifers. Even in advanced industrialized countries like Canada and the United States such losses average 10–30%. However, losses have been reduced to about 3% in Copenhagen and Denmark and 5% in Fukuoka, Japan.

How Can We Reduce the Use of Water in Removing Industrial and Household Wastes? Changing the Way We Deal with Wastes

We can mimic the way nature deals with wastes instead of using large amounts of high-quality water to wash away and dilute our industrial and animal wastes.

Industrialized countries use large amounts of water good enough to drink to dilute and wash or flush away industrial, animal, and household wastes. Sewage treatment plants remove valuable plant nutrients and dump most of them into rivers, lakes, and oceans. This overloads aquatic systems with plant nutrients that should be recycled to the soil, as nature does.

We also use high-quality water to flush toxic industrial wastes into sewers and send them to treatment plants that do not remove most of the harmful chemicals. The FAO estimates that if current trends continue, within 40 years we will need the world's entire reliable flow of river water just to dilute and transport the wastes we produce.

We can use five principles to redesign the way we manage sewage and industrial wastes while saving enormous amounts of water.

- Use pollution prevention and waste reduction to sharply decrease the amount of industrial wastes we produce.
- Ban discharge of industrial toxic wastes into municipal sewer systems.
- Rely more on waterless composting toilets that convert human fecal matter to a small amount of dry and odourless soil-like humus material that can be removed from a composting chamber every year or so and returned to the soil as fertilizer (pp. 562–563).
- Return the nutrient-rich sludge produced by conventional waste treatment plants to the soil as a fertilizer. Banning the input of toxic industrial chemicals into sewage treatment plants will make this feasible.
- Shift to new ways to treat sewage that mimic the way nature breaks down and recycles the nutrients in organic waste material. Examples include solar-powered waste treatment systems and using wetlands to treat sewage, as discussed in Chapter 22.

SELF CHECK

How do *you* use water? Do you blast your driveway clean with a hose and maintain a lush green lawn all summer? Do you have good water habits and efficient devices at your home? Do you plan to try some water-smart landscaping if and when you own a home? What changes would you be willing to make that would improve how you use Canada's water supply?

Why not return to the Self Check box on p. 353 and recalculate the water footprint *you could have* with your new water strategies!

15-8 TOO MUCH WATER

What Causes Flooding? Rain and People

Heavy rainfall, rapid melting of snow, removing vegetation, and destroying wetlands cause flooding.

Heavy rain and rapid snowmelt are the major causes of natural flooding by streams. A flood happens when water in a stream overflows its normal channel and spills into the adjacent area, called a **floodplain** (Figure 15-24).

People settle on floodplains because of their many advantages: fertile soil, ample water for irrigation, availability of nearby rivers for transportation and recreation, and flat land suitable for crops, buildings, highways, and railroads.

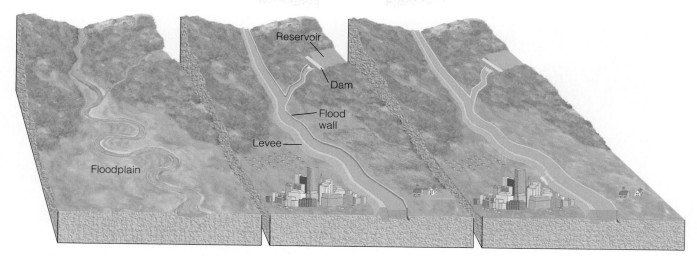

FIGURE 15-24 Land in a natural floodplain (left) often is flooded after prolonged rains. When the floodwaters recede, deposits of silt are left behind, creating a nutrient-rich soil. In an attempt to remove the threat of flooding and thus to allow people to live in floodplains, rivers have been narrowed and straightened (channelized), equipped with protective levees and walls, and dammed to create reservoirs that store and release water as needed. These alterations can give a false sense of security to floodplain dwellers. Such measures would greatly increase flood damage were they to catastrophically and unexpectedly fail at the height of an exceptional flood event. Furthermore, these alterations often destroy important fish habitat, and they eliminate the opportunity for soil to be enriched by deposits of silt.

Floods have several benefits. They provide the world's most productive farmland because the land is regularly covered with nutrient-rich silt left after floodwaters recede. They also recharge groundwater and help refill wetlands.

But each year, floods kill up to 25 000 people and cause tens of billions of dollars in property damage. Floods, like droughts, are usually considered natural disasters.

Since the 1960s, several types of human activities have contributed to the sharp rise in flood deaths and damages. One is *removal of water-absorbing vegetation,* especially on hillsides (Figure 15-25, p. 358). Another is *draining wetlands* that absorb floodwaters and reduce the severity of flooding. *Living on floodplains* also increases the threat of damage from flooding. Flooding also increases when we *pave or build* and replace water-absorbing vegetation, soil, and wetlands with highways, parking lots, and buildings that cannot absorb rainwater.

In developed countries, people deliberately settle on floodplains and then expect dams, levees, and other devices to protect them from floodwaters. However, when heavier-than-normal rains occur, these devices can be overwhelmed. In many developing countries, the poor have little choice but to try to survive in flood-prone areas (see the following Case Study).

Red River, which flows northward to Manitoba, regularly overflows its shallow banks when swollen with rain and spring meltwater. The city of Winnipeg, founded at the forks of the Red and Assiniboine Rivers, has been flooded many times; floods in 1948 and 1950 caused damage in excess of $600 million. In 1968, a 50-kilometre (30-mile) system of channels called the Red River Floodway was built to divert floodwaters around Winnipeg. The floodway has successfully diverted many potential floods. However, in 1997, record levels of winter snow accumulation and a major spring storm resulted in 5% of Manitoba's farmland being flooded and 6 000 people being evacuated from Winnipeg. No human engineering project, however ingenious, can make settlements built on floodplains immune to the threat of flooding.

Case Study: Living on Floodplains in Bangladesh—Danger for the Poor

Bangladesh has increased flooding because of upstream deforestation of Himalayan mountain slopes and the clearing of mangrove forests on its coastal floodplains.

Bangladesh is one of the world's most densely populated countries, with 162 million people (currently more than four times Canada's population and projected to reach 222 million by 2050) packed into an area roughly the size of the Maritime provinces. It is also one of the world's poorest countries.

The people of Bangladesh depend on moderate annual flooding during the summer monsoon season to grow rice and help maintain soil fertility in the delta

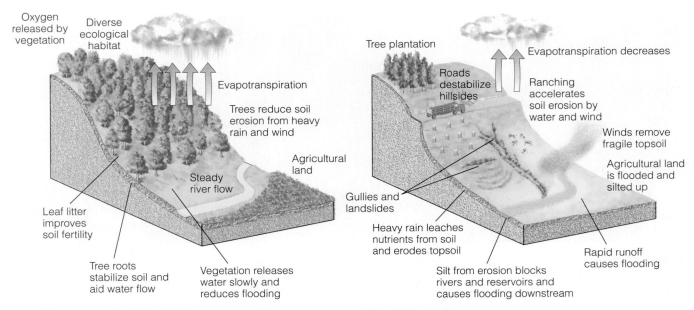

Oxygen released by vegetation

Diverse ecological habitat

Evapotranspiration

Trees reduce soil erosion from heavy rain and wind

Agricultural land

Steady river flow

Leaf litter improves soil fertility

Tree roots stabilize soil and aid water flow

Vegetation releases water slowly and reduces flooding

Forested Hillside Before Deforestation

Tree plantation

Roads destabilize hillsides

Evapotranspiration decreases

Ranching accelerates soil erosion by water and wind

Winds remove fragile topsoil

Agricultural land is flooded and silted up

Gullies and landslides

Heavy rain leaches nutrients from soil and erodes topsoil

Silt from erosion blocks rivers and reservoirs and causes flooding downstream

Rapid runoff causes flooding

After Deforestation

CENGAGENOW **ACTIVE FIGURE 15-25 Natural capital degradation:** hillside before and after deforestation. Once a hillside has been deforested for timber and fuelwood, livestock grazing, or unsustainable farming, water from precipitation rushes down the denuded slopes, erodes precious topsoil, and floods downstream areas. A 3 000-year-old Chinese proverb says, "To protect your rivers, protect your mountains." *See an animation based on this figure at* CengageNOW.

basin. The annual floods deposit eroded Himalayan soil on the country's crop fields.

In the past, great floods occurred every 50 years or so. But since the 1970s they have come about every four years. Bangladesh's increased flood problems begin in the Himalayan watershed, where several factors—rapid population growth, deforestation, overgrazing, and unsustainable farming on steep and easily erodible mountain slopes—have greatly diminished the ability of its mountain soils to absorb water (Figure 15-25, right).

The increased runoff of soil, combined with heavier-than-normal monsoon rains, has increased the severity of flooding along Himalayan rivers and downstream in Bangladesh. A disastrous flood in 1998 covered two-thirds of Bangladesh's land area for 9 months, levelled 2 million homes, drowned at least 2 000 people, and left 30 million people homeless. It also destroyed more than one-fourth of the country's crops, which caused thousands of people to die of starvation. In 2002, another flood left 5 million people homeless and inundated large areas of rice fields.

How Can We Reduce Flood Risks? Think about Where You Want to Live

We can reduce flooding risks by controlling river water flows, preserving and restoring wetlands,

identifying and managing flood-prone areas, and if possible choosing not to live in such areas.

Several methods can be used to deal with the risk from flooding. One is to *straighten and deepen streams*, a process called *channelization* (Figure 15-24, middle). Channelization can reduce upstream flooding, but it removes bank vegetation and increases stream velocity. This increased flow of water can promote upstream bank erosion, increase downstream flooding and sediment deposition, and reduce habitats for aquatic wildlife.

Another approach is to *build levees or floodwalls* along the sides of streams (Figure 15-24, middle). Levees contain and accelerate stream flow, but this increases the water's capacity for doing damage downstream. They also do not protect against unusually high and powerful floodwaters, as occurred in 1993 when two-thirds of the levees built along the Mississippi River in the United States were damaged or destroyed. A more recent case of floodwalls failing happened in 2005 when Hurricane Katrina caused 80% of New Orleans to be flooded.

Building dams can also reduce the threat of flooding by storing water in a reservoir and releasing it gradually. We can also construct a floodway, like the one in Winnipeg, designed to direct the water around a community with minimal damage.

All of the above are engineering solutions, and all of these can fail—sometimes catastrophically—when people place false confidence in them and are caught completely unprepared.

Some sensible and natural solutions would be to zone floodplains as parks, greenbelts, wildlife corridors, and recreational areas, where flooding causes no damage and can be seen as a natural event. Restored wetlands and vegetation buffers fulfill important roles in flood control while providing ecological, recreational, and educational benefits. In fact, if forests and other forms of plant cover within the watershed are left relatively intact, rainwater will be released slowly (Figure 15-25), preventing or greatly reducing flooding and soil erosion.

On a personal level, we can use the precautionary approach to *think carefully about where we live.* Many of the poor live in flood-prone areas because they have nowhere else to go. But most people can do some research and choose not to live in areas subject to flooding.

15-9 A MORE SUSTAINABLE WATER FUTURE

How Can We Use Water More Sustainably? A Blue Revolution

We can use water more sustainably by cutting waste, raising water prices, preserving forests on water basins, and slowing population growth.

Sustainable water use is based on the commonsense principle stated in an old Inca proverb: "The frog does not drink up the pond in which it lives." Figure 15-26 lists ways to implement this principle.

Historically, our response to water scarcity has been to expand the supply by building more dams, transporting water from one area to another, and drilling more wells. These measures will continue to some degree, but water resource experts project that the emphasis will begin shifting from increasing the water supply to reducing the water demand by using water more efficiently and stabilizing population.

The challenge in developing such a *blue revolution* is to implement a mix of strategies. One involves using technology to irrigate crops more efficiently and to save water in industries and homes. A second approach uses economic and political decisions to remove subsidies that cause water to be underpriced and thus wasted while guaranteeing low prices for low-income consumers, and adding subsidies that reward reduced water waste.

A third component is to switch to new waste production and treatment systems that accept only non-toxic wastes, use less or no water to treat wastes, return nutrients in plant and animal wastes to the soil, and mimic the ways that nature decomposes and recycles organic wastes.

Solutions

Sustainable Water Use

- Not depleting aquifers
- Preserving ecological health of aquatic systems
- Preserving water quality
- Integrated watershed management

- Agreements among regions and countries sharing surface water resources
- Outside party mediation of water disputes between nations
- Marketing of water rights
- Raising water prices
- Wasting less water

- Decreasing government subsidies for supplying water
- Increasing government subsidies for reducing water waste
- Slowing population growth

FIGURE 15-26 Solutions: methods for achieving more sustainable use of the Earth's water resources.

A fourth strategy is to leave enough water in rivers to protect wildlife, ecological processes, and the natural ecological services provided by rivers (Figure 13-15, p. 291). We now control the flow rates of most rivers. As a result, some analysts say that we have an ethical and ecological responsibility to manage rivers for wildlife and restore those we have damaged. Ecological restoration efforts show that when we restore a river's flow and reconnect it with its floodplain its wildlife and ecological health can return. One way to do this is to follow South Africa's lead in legally establishing a freshwater reserve for all rivers designed to sustain their biodiversity and the valuable ecosystem services they provide for other species and society.

Each of us can help bring about this blue revolution by using and wasting less water. We can also support government policies that result in more sustainable use of the world's water and better ways to treat our industrial and household wastes. Figure 15-27 lists ways you can reduce your water use and waste. Since virtually everything we use requires water to produce, cutting down on unnecessary consumption is a key

What Can You Do?

Water Use and Waste

- Use water-saving toilets, showerheads, and faucet aerators.
- Shower instead of taking baths, and take short showers.
- Repair water leaks.
- Turn off sink faucets while brushing teeth, shaving, or washing.
- Wash only full loads of clothes or use the lowest possible water-level setting for smaller loads.
- Wash a car from a bucket of soapy water, and use the hose for rinsing only.
- If you use a commercial car wash, try to find one that recycles its water.
- Replace your lawn with native plants that need little if any watering.
- Water lawns and gardens in the early morning or evening.
- Use drip irrigation and mulch for gardens and flowerbeds.
- Use recycled (grey) water for watering lawns and houseplants and for washing cars.

FIGURE 15-27 What can you do? Ways you can reduce your use and waste of water.

to reducing water use and water pollution. Reducing meat consumption is another way to lower water use and waste. The typical meat-intensive North American diet requires about twice as much water per person as a nutritious vegetarian diet.

15-10 CHECKING OUR PROGRESS AT ENSURING ENVIRONMENTAL SUSTAINABILITY

How Well Are We Proceeding with Millennium Goal 7?

Our progress at meeting the water-related goals of Goal 7 has varied regionally, but in general we can be pleased with progress in improving drinking water supply and less optimistic about sanitation.

The eight Millennium Development Goals were introduced in Chapter 1 and so far have been addressed in Chapters 9, 10, 13, and 14. Goal 7—aimed at ensuring environmental sustainability—has two targets that relate specifically to our use of water. Other Goal 7 targets and indicators are discussed in Chapters 9 and 13.

Target 7B is *to reduce biodiversity loss, achieving by 2010, a significant reduction in the rate of loss* (Figure 15-28). There is one water-based indicator for assessing progress toward this target:

- Indicator 7.5, *the proportion of total water resources used,* recognizes that water that is withdrawn for one use may be unavailable for other uses. For example, water that is withdrawn from a river for irrigating a crop may be unlikely to return to that river to support biodiversity there. Where human uses are competing for scarce water supplies and river levels are falling (pp. 343–345), biodiversity is bound to take a back seat to human concerns. As mentioned on pp. 297–298, biodiversity continues to diminish with no sign of a significant reduction in the rate of loss. Target B remains elusive in the near future.

Target C is *to halve, by 2015, the proportion of people without sustainable access to safe drinking water and basic sanitation.* It has two indicators:

- Indicator 7.8, *the proportion of population using an improved drinking water source,* has improved greatly. In fact, the Millennium Development Goal of *halving* the number of people without sustainable access to safe drinking water was met by 2010, and the situation continues to improve. Still, there will probably be more than 600 million people still lacking access to safe drinking water by 2015, and they are most likely to be poor rural people living in water-strapped regions such as sub-Saharan Africa.
- Indicator 7.9, *the proportion of population using an improved sanitary facility,* is progressing slowly. These facilities can be expensive and parts of African and

Millennium Development Goal 7:

ENSURE ENVIRONMENTAL SUSTAINABILITY

Ensure Environmental Sustainability

Target 7B: Reduce biodiversity loss, achieving, by 2010, a significant reduction in the rate of loss.

7.5 Proportion of total water resources used.

Target 7C: Halve, by 2015, the proportion of people without sustainable access to safe drinking water and basic sanitation.

7.8 Proportion of population using an improved drinking water source.

7.9 Proportion of population using an improved sanitary facility.

FIGURE 15-28 Ensuring environmental sustainability: Millennium Development Goal 7, aimed at ensuring environmental sustainability, has some targets and indicators that are specific to the use of water in addition to the other targets and indicators we encountered at the end of Chapters 9 and 13. (http://www.undp.org/mdg). (Courtesy of the UNDP)

Asia are lagging far behind. Currently 2.5 billion people lack access to basic sanitation facilities, which has implications regarding diseases that can be spread by means of human wastes (p. 542). The UN calculates that an extra $10 billion per year is necessary to meet the target on time (http://www.undp.org/mdg/).

You can continue to monitor progress toward these goals at websites such as http://www.mdgmonitor.org/.

As air is a sacred gas, so is water a sacred liquid that links us to all the oceans of the world and ties us back in time to the very birthplace of life.
DAVID SUZUKI

Water will become Canada's foremost ecological crisis early in this century.
DAVID SCHINDLER

CHAPTER REVIEW

1. Review the Key Questions for this chapter on p. 336. Describe water conflicts in the Middle East and suggest possible solutions to these problems.

2. What percentage of the Earth's fresh water is available to us? Define *groundwater, zone of saturation, water table, confined aquifer,* and *unconfined aquifer.* Define *surface water, surface runoff,* and *watershed (drainage basin).* Distinguish between surface runoff and *reliable surface runoff.* What is an *artesian well*?

3. How is most of the world's water used? Describe the availability and use of freshwater resources in Canada. How many people in the world lack regular access to safe drinking water, and how many do not have access to basic sanitation? What is *drought* and what are its causes and harmful effects? Discuss the question of who should own and manage freshwater resources.

4. What are the advantages and disadvantages of withdrawing groundwater? Describe the problem of groundwater depletion in the world and Canada. Describe ways to prevent or slow groundwater depletion.

5. What is a *dam*? What is a *reservoir*? What are the advantages and disadvantages of large dams and reservoirs? What are the advantages and disadvantages of China's Three Gorges Dam?

6. Describe the Aral Sea disaster. Describe China's South–North Water Transfer Project. Compare the pros and cons of seeding clouds, towing icebergs, and moving giant plastic bags of fresh water with tugboats, versus the idea of simply improving the efficiency of our water use.

7. Define *desalination* and distinguish between distillation and reverse osmosis as methods for desalinating water. What are the limitations of desalination and how might they be overcome?

8. What percentage of the world's water is unnecessarily wasted and what are two causes of such waste? Describe four irrigation methods and describe ways to reduce water waste in irrigation in developed and developing countries. List ways to reduce water waste in industry and homes. List ways to use water more sustainably. Describe ways in which you can reduce your own use and waste of water.

9. What is a *floodplain*? Why do people like to live on floodplains? What are the benefits and drawbacks of floods? List three human activities that increase the risk of flooding. Describe the increased risk that people in Winnipeg and in Bangladesh face. How can we reduce the risks of flooding?

10. Describe relationships between water conflicts in the Middle East (**Core Case Study**) and the four *scientific principles of sustainability*.

CRITICAL THINKING

1. How do human activities increase the harmful effects of prolonged drought? How can we reduce these effects?

2. What role does population growth play in water supply problems?

3. Calculate how many litres of water are wasted in 1 month by a toilet that leaks 2 drops of water per second (1 litre of water equals about 3 500 drops).

4. How do human activities contribute to flooding and flood damage? How can these effects be reduced?

5. Congratulations! You are in charge of managing the world's water resources. What are the three most important things you would do?

PROJECTS

1. In your community,

   a. What are the major sources of the water supply?

   b. How is water use divided among agricultural, industrial, power plant cooling, and public uses?

   c. Who are the biggest consumers of water?

   d. What has happened to water prices (adjusted for inflation) during the past 20 years? Are they too low to encourage water conservation and reuse?

   e. What water supply problems are projected?

2. Develop a water conservation plan for your school and submit it to school officials.

3. Consult with local officials to identify any floodplain areas in your community. Develop a map showing these areas and the types of activities (such as housing, manufacturing, roads, and recreational use) found on these lands. Evaluate management of such floodplains in your community and come up with suggestions for improvement.

4. Use the library or the Internet to learn more about at least two of the following people mentioned in the chapter: *Tony Blair, Mohamed El-Ashry, Malin Falkenmark, Benjamin Franklin, Peter Gleck, Sandra Postel, David Schindler, David Suzuki, Margaret Thatcher.*

ECOLOGICAL FOOTPRINT ANALYSIS

Imagine a region that uses 24.5 billion litres of fresh water daily. Suppose projections are that daily consumption will increase to 32.1 billion litres per day by 2025. Given that the population is projected to increase from 17.5 million to 25.9 million by 2025:

   a. Calculate the current per capita consumption of water *per day*, and the projected per capita consumption *per day* for 2025.

   b. Calculate the current per capita consumption of water *per year*, and the projected per capita consumption *per year* for 2025.

   c. Compare the *average water footprint* (consumption per person per year) of this region with the average North American water footprint of approximately 249 000 litres per person per year, and the global average water footprint of 123 770 litres per person per year.

   d. What can you conclude about water use in this region?

Geology and Nonrenewable Mineral Resources

Diamonds of the North

In 1980, while working in the Northwest Territories, Canadian geologists Chuck Fipke and Stewart Blusson discovered pyrope garnets and other minerals that are often associated with diamonds. Until then, diamonds had never been found in North America. Applying their knowledge of glacial movements (see Figure 16-4, p. 367), the two back-tracked across the Canadian North until they found evidence of ancient volcanic plumes (p. 365), called kimberlite pipes, that had swept columns of potentially diamond-bearing rocks to the Earth's surface. They staked their claims in 1989.

The two geologists established a partnership with BHP World Minerals (now called BHP Billiton Diamonds Inc.), an Australian mining company that had experience drilling for diamonds. By 1991, the first diamonds had been discovered. BHP staked a large area around the find, which was located about 300 kilometres (185 miles) northeast of Yellowknife.

Working in a tundra region with permafrost underfoot and a delicate ecosystem that would be readily affected by disturbance was just one of the challenges BHP faced as it began preparing for an environmental impact assessment. Other considerations included the four groups of Aboriginal people that used the area, two ongoing land claims, and vulnerable populations of grizzly bears and migratory

caribou. Could large-scale mining be done without major impacts affecting Aboriginal people, the wildlife, the water quality, and other aspects of a delicate environment?

BHP took quick and decisive action. The company sought traditional knowledge about the area from all four groups of Aboriginal people. It studied the caribou and grizzly bears. It developed a strategy for extracting diamonds and managing mine tailings with minimum impact on wildlife, water quality, and fish habitat. For example, it proposed using air transport and winter ice roads rather than impacting the ground with typical all-season roads.

BHP submitted its environmental impact statement in 1995. After an extensive review, the Ekati Diamond mine received official approval in 1997 and operations began in 1998. The company hired Aboriginal people, provided them with training and education, and established good relations with local communities.

In January 1999, the first Canadian diamonds were sold in Holland. By 2003, a nearby second mine—Diavik Diamond Mines Inc.—was in operation. By 2004, the two mines were extracting large numbers of high-quality diamonds valued at $1.9 billion Canadian (Figure 16-1). In 2006, the Jericho Diamond Project began extracting

(continued)

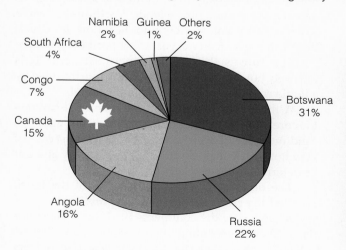

Figure 16-1A Canada is the fourth-largest producer of diamonds. (Data from USGS Mineral Commodity Summaries, 2010, http://www.geology.com)

Figure 16-1B Diamonds are playing an increasingly important role in the economy of the Canadian North.

diamonds near Contwoyto Lake in Nunavut. Mines at Snap Lake in the Northwest Territories and Victor, near Attawapiskat, Ontario, began production in 2008. Canada's diamond mines now produce about 15% of the diamonds in the world by value. Meanwhile, the federal and territorial governments, the World Wildlife Federation, and other groups are monitoring events closely to ensure these mining companies develop Canada's diamond resources in an appropriate and sustainable manner. The subject of diamond mining will be explored in greater depth on this textbook's website, at http://www.nelson.com/livingintheenvironment3e.com.

Civilization exists by geological consent, subject to change without notice.

WILL DURANT

CHAPTER PURPOSE AND QUESTIONS

Chapter 16 describes the Earth's basic geological processes and the nonrenewable mineral resources we use. The chapter addresses the following questions:

16-1   Is the Earth a stable or a dynamic planet?

16-2   What geological processes occur within the Earth's interior?

16-3   What are earthquakes?

16-4   What are minerals and rocks?

16-5   How are buried mineral deposits found?

16-6   What are the environmental impacts of using mineral resources?

16-7   What is the state of mineral resources in Canada?

16-1   GEOLOGIC PROCESSES

Is the Earth a Stable or a Dynamic Planet? Change Is the Norm

The planet we live on is constantly changing as a result of processes taking place on and below its surface.

Geology, the subject of this chapter, is the science devoted to the study of dynamic processes occurring on the Earth's surface and in its interior. Geologists study and analyze rocks and the features and processes of the Earth's interior and surface. Some of these processes lead to geologic hazards such as earthquakes and volcanic eruptions, and others produce the renewable soil and nonrenewable mineral and energy resources that support life and economies.

You probably think of the ground you stand on as stable and unmoving. Wrong. It is part of a dynamic planet whose surface and interior are constantly changing. Fortunately, most of these geologic changes take place very slowly on our short human time scale and most occur out of sight within the Earth's interior.

Over eons continents have moved to new positions, breaking apart and crunching into one another (Figure 5-9, p. 103). Inside the Earth, huge cyclical flows of molten rock break the Earth's surface into a series of gigantic plates that move very slowly across the planet's surface. Go outside and you are standing on one of these moving plates. Hard to believe, isn't it?

Energy from the sun and from the Earth's interior, coupled with the erosive power of flowing water, have created continents, mountains, valleys, plains, and ocean basins in an ongoing process that continues to change the landscape. And every now and then the solid Earth under our feet shakes, rattles, and rolls during an earthquake, or erupts like a punctured boil when a volcano forms or awakens after a long geological sleep.

What Is the Earth's Structure? Living on a Layered Sphere

The Earth's three major zones are its core, mantle, and crust.

As the primitive Earth cooled over eons, its interior separated into three major concentric zones, layers which geologists identify as the *core,* the *mantle,* and the *crust* (Figure 4-7, p. 64). In other words, beneath your feet is a crust of soil and rock floating on a mantle of partly melted and solid rock, which surrounds an intensely hot core. What we know about the Earth's interior comes mostly from indirect evidence such as density measurements, seismic (earthquake) wave studies, measurements of interior heat flow, lava analyses, and research on meteorite composition.

The **core** is the Earth's innermost zone. It is intensely hot and has a solid inner part, surrounded by a liquid core of molten or semisolid material.

A thick solid zone called the **mantle** surrounds the core. Most of the mantle is solid rock, but under its rigid outermost part is a zone—the *asthenosphere*—of very hot, partly melted rock that flows slowly and can be deformed like soft plastic.

The outermost and thinnest zone of the Earth is called the **crust.** It consists of the *continental crust,* which underlies the continents (including the continental shelves extending into the oceans), and the *oceanic crust,* which underlies the ocean basins and covers 71% of the Earth's surface (Figure 16-2).

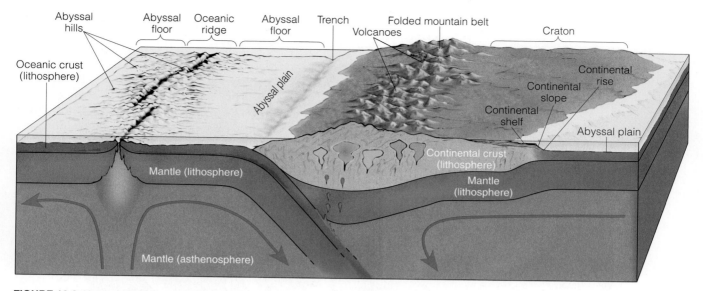

FIGURE 16-2 Natural capital: major features of the Earth's crust and upper mantle. The *lithosphere*, composed of the crust and outermost mantle, is rigid and brittle. The *asthenosphere*, a zone in the mantle, can be deformed by heat and pressure.

16-2 INTERNAL AND EXTERNAL GEOLOGIC PROCESSES

What Geologic Processes Occur within the Earth's Interior? Welcome to the Hot Zone

Huge volumes of heated and molten rock move around within the Earth's interior.

We tend to think of the Earth's crust, mantle, and core as fairly static. But geologic processes taking place within the Earth and on its surface, mostly over thousands to millions of years, bring about changes in these components (Figure 16-3, p. 366).

Geologic changes originating from the Earth's interior, called *internal processes*, generally build up the planet's surface. Heat from the Earth's interior provides the energy for these processes, but gravity also plays a role.

Residual heat from the Earth's formation is still being given off as the inner core cools and the outer core cools and solidifies. Continued decay of radioactive elements in the crust, especially the continental crust, provides much of this heat flow from within. Heat from the core causes much of the mantle to deform and flow slowly like heated plastic.

Measurements of heat flow within the Earth suggest that two kinds of movement occur in the mantle's asthenosphere. One is *convection cells* or *currents* that move large volumes of rock and heat in loops within the mantle like a giant conveyer belt (Figure 16-3). Internal heat pushes soft rock in the mantle's asthenosphere upward, then downward as the rock cools. This pattern resembles convection in the atmosphere (Figure 6-11, p. 117) or in a pot of boiling water (Figure 3-11, left, p. 48).

The second type of movement involves *mantle plumes*, in which mantle rock flows slowly upward in a column (Figure 16-3), like smoke from a chimney on a cold, calm morning. When the moving rock reaches the top of the plume, it moves out in a radial pattern, as if it were flowing up an umbrella through the handle and then spreading out in all directions from the tip of the umbrella to the rim. There is a lot going on beneath your feet.

What Is Plate Tectonics? The Earth Is Moving

Huge solid plates—called tectonic plates—move extremely slowly across the Earth's surface.

The flows of energy and heated material in the mantle convection cells cause about 15 huge rigid **plates**, called **tectonic plates,** to move extremely slowly across the Earth's surface (Figure 16-3). These plates are about 100 kilometres (60 miles) thick. They are composed of the continental and oceanic crust and the rigid, outermost part of the mantle (above the asthenosphere), a combination called the **lithosphere.**

These plates move constantly, supported by the slowly flowing asthenosphere. They are somewhat like large icebergs floating extremely slowly on the surface of an ocean. Some plates move about 1 centimetre a year. Others at a seafloor spreading zone can move as much as 18 centimetres a year. You are riding on one of these plates throughout your entire life, but the motion is too slow for you to notice.

The theory explaining the movements of the plates and the processes that occur at their boundaries is called **plate tectonics.** The concept, which was advanced by the work of Canadian geophysicist Tuzo

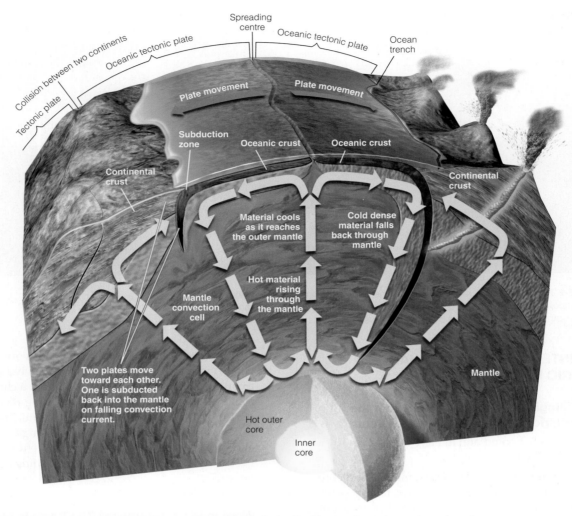

Collision between two continents
Oceanic tectonic plate
Spreading centre
Oceanic tectonic plate
Ocean trench
Tectonic plate
Plate movement
Plate movement
Subduction zone
Oceanic crust
Oceanic crust
Continental crust
Continental crust
Material cools as it reaches the outer mantle
Cold dense material falls back through mantle
Hot material rising through the mantle
Mantle convection cell
Two plates move toward each other. One is subducted back into the mantle on falling convection current.
Mantle
Hot outer core
Inner core

CENGAGENOW **ACTIVE FIGURE 16-3 Natural capital:** the Earth's crust is made up of a series of rigid plates, called *tectonic plates*, which move around in response to forces in the mantle. *See an animation based on this figure at* CengageNOW.

Wilson (p. 102), was developed from an earlier idea called *continental drift*. Throughout the Earth's history, continents have split and joined as plates have very slowly drifted thousands of kilometres back and forth across the planet's surface (Figure 5-9, p. 103).

As these plates collide, break apart, and slide by one another over millions of years, they produce mountains on land (such as the Himalayas and the Rocky Mountains), huge ridges and trenches on the ocean floor, and other features of the Earth's surface (Figures 16-2 and 16-3). These movements and geological processes continue today. Natural hazards such as volcanoes and earthquakes are likely to be found at plate boundaries. In addition, plate movements and interactions affect the Earth's climate and concentrate many of the minerals we extract and use.

The theory of plate tectonics also helps explain how certain patterns of biological evolution occurred. By reconstructing the course of continental drift over millions

of years, scientists can trace how species migrated from one area to another when continents that are now far apart were still joined together. As the continents separated, populations became geographically and reproductively isolated, and speciation occurred. In other words, tectonic plates have played a major role in the drama of life that continues to unfold on our planetary home.

What Geologic Processes Occur on the Earth's Surface? Erosion and Weathering

Water, wind, and glaciers move large amounts of soil and broken-down pieces of rock from one place to another.

Geologic changes based directly or indirectly on energy from the sun and on gravity (rather than on heat in the Earth's interior) are called *external processes*. Internal processes generally build up the Earth's surface. In contrast, external processes tend to wear it down and produce a variety of landforms and environments formed by the buildup of eroded sediment.

A major external process is **erosion**: the process by which material is dissolved, loosened, or worn away from one part of the Earth's surface and deposited elsewhere. Flowing streams cause most erosion. Wind blowing particles of soil from one area to another is another cause. Human activities, particularly those that destroy vegetation that holds soil in place, accelerate erosion, as discussed in Section 14-3 (p. 308).

The Canadian landscape has been greatly affected by *glaciation*. On four occasions over the past 2 million years, continental ice sheets several kilometres thick scraped back and forth across Canada. They ground down the crust and shifted vast amounts of rock and soil while advancing. Then, in retreat, they deposited and sorted glacial materials, creating many of the landforms and drainage patterns that we see today. The Wisconsin ice sheet retreated from southern Canada about 13 000 years ago. The extent of that ice sheet and the locations of present-day glaciers are shown in Figure 16-4.

Weathering consists of the physical, chemical, and biological processes that break down rocks and minerals into smaller particles that can be eroded. There are three types of weathering processes. One is *physical* or *mechanical weathering*, in which a large rock mass is broken into smaller fragments. This is similar to what happens when you hammer a rock into pieces. The most important agent of mechanical weathering is *frost wedging*, in which water collects in pores and cracks of

rock, expands upon freezing, and splits off pieces of the rock. This is also what causes most of the potholes we complain about in our roads and streets.

A second process is *chemical weathering*, in which one or more chemical reactions decompose a mass of rock. Most chemical weathering involves a reaction of rock material with oxygen, carbon dioxide, and moisture in the atmosphere and on the ground.

A third process is *biological weathering*, the conversion of rock or minerals into smaller particles through the action of living things. For example, lichens produce acids that can chemically weather rocks. And roots growing into and rubbing against rock can physically break it into small pieces.

Websites such as http://dsc.discovery.com/ have videos and other active features that illustrate the dynamic nature of the Earth's crust and mantle.

16-3 NATURAL GEOLOGIC HAZARDS: EARTHQUAKES AND VOLCANIC ERUPTIONS

What Are Earthquakes? Shake, Rattle, and Roll

Earthquakes occur when a part of the Earth's crust suddenly fractures, shifts to relieve stress, and releases energy as shock waves.

Stress in the Earth's crust can cause solid rock to deform until it suddenly fractures and shifts along the fracture, producing a fault. The faulting or a later abrupt movement on an existing fault causes an **earthquake** that has certain features and effects (Figure 16-5).

Relief of the Earth's internal stress releases energy as shock waves, which move outward from the earthquake's focus like ripples in a pool of water. Scientists measure the severity of an earthquake by the *magnitude* of its shock waves. The magnitude is a measure of the amount of energy released in the earthquake, as

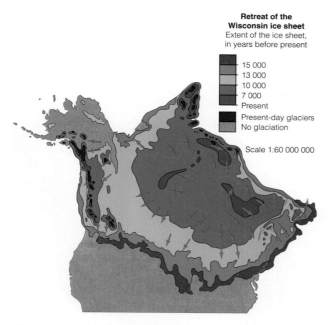

Retreat of the Wisconsin ice sheet
Extent of the ice sheet, in years before present

- 15 000
- 13 000
- 10 000
- 7 000
- Present
- Present-day glaciers
- No glaciation

Scale 1:60 000 000

FIGURE 16-4 Retreat of the Wisconsin ice sheet. This map shows the extent of ice coverage over time and the locations of present-day glaciers. Arrows indicate the direction of advance of the Wisconsin ice sheet. (Livingston, 1970; Matthews and Morrow, 1995)

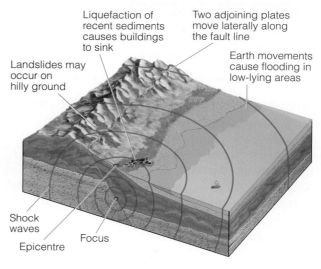

Liquefaction of recent sediments causes buildings to sink

Two adjoining plates move laterally along the fault line

Earth movements cause flooding in low-lying areas

Landslides may occur on hilly ground

Shock waves

Epicentre

Focus

FIGURE 16-5 Major features and effects of an *earthquake*.

indicated by the amplitude (size) of the vibrations when they reach a recording instrument (seismograph).

Scientists use the **Richter scale,** on which each unit represents an amplitude 10 times greater than the next smaller unit. Thus a magnitude 5.0 earthquake is 10 times greater than a magnitude 4.0, and a magnitude 6.0 quake is 100 times greater than a magnitude 4.0 quake. Seismologists rate earthquakes as *insignificant* (less than 4.0 on the Richter scale), *minor* (4.0–4.9), *damaging* (5.0–5.9), *destructive* (6.0–6.9), *major* (7.0–7.9), and *great* (over 8.0).

Earthquakes often have *aftershocks* that gradually decrease in frequency over a period of up to several months, and some have *foreshocks* from seconds to weeks before the main shock.

The *primary effects of earthquakes* include shaking and sometimes a permanent vertical or horizontal displacement of the ground. These effects may have serious consequences for people and for buildings, bridges, freeway overpasses, dams, and pipelines.

Secondary effects of earthquakes include rock-slides, urban fires, and flooding caused by *subsidence* (sinking) of land. Coastal areas can be severely damaged by earthquakes at sea that can generate huge water waves, called **tsunamis** (also called tidal waves, although they have nothing to do with tides) that travel as fast as 950 kilometres (590 miles) per hour and give little warning of their approach.

One way to reduce loss of life and property from earthquakes is to examine historical records and make geologic measurements to locate active fault zones. We can also map high-risk areas (Figure 16-6), establish building codes that regulate the placement and design of buildings in areas of high risk, and increase research on projecting when and where earthquakes will occur. Then people can decide how high the risk might be and whether they want to accept the risk and live in areas subject to earthquakes.

CONSIDER, DISCUSS, OR DEBATE

Study Figure 16-6 closely. Should planners and developers consider potential earthquake damage when determining the location of tall buildings, bridges, and nuclear power plants? Do they?

What Are Volcanoes? Popping an Earth Cork

Some volcanoes erupt quietly and release flows of molten rock, but others erupt explosively and spew large chunks of lava rock, ash, and harmful gases into the atmosphere.

An active **volcano** occurs where **magma** (molten rock) reaches the Earth's surface through a

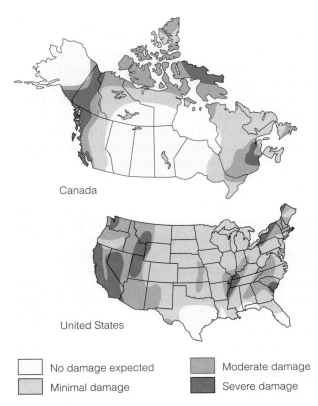

Canada

United States

☐ No damage expected   ▨ Moderate damage
▨ Minimal damage   ▧ Severe damage

FIGURE 16-6 Expected damage from earthquakes in Canada and the contiguous United States. This map is based on earthquake records. (U.S. Geological Survey)

central vent or a long crack (*fissure*; Figure 16-7). Volcanic activity can release *ejecta* (debris ranging from large chunks of lava rock to ash that may be glowing hot), liquid lava, and gases (such as water vapour, carbon dioxide, and sulphur dioxide) into the environment.

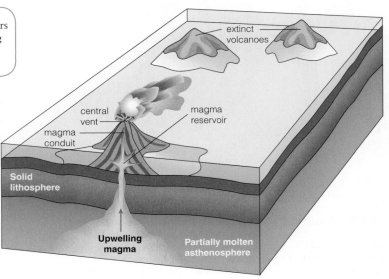

FIGURE 16-7 A *volcano* erupts when molten magma rises in a plume through the lithosphere to erupt on the surface as lava. Chains of islands can be created by eruptions of volcanoes that then become inactive.

Volcanic activity is concentrated for the most part in the same areas as seismic activity. Some volcanoes erupt explosively and eject large quantities of gases and particulate matter (soot and mineral ash) high into the troposphere. Most of the particles of soot and ash soon fall back to the Earth's surface. But gases such as sulphur dioxide remain in the atmosphere and are converted to tiny droplets of sulphuric acid, many of which stay above the clouds and may not be washed out by rain for up to three years. These tiny droplets reflect some of the sun's energy and can cool the atmosphere for 1–4 years.

Other volcanoes erupt more quietly. They involve primarily lava flows, which can cover roads and villages and ignite brush, trees, and homes.

We tend to think negatively of volcanic activity, but it also provides some benefits. One is outstanding scenery in the form of majestic mountains, some lakes, and other landforms. Perhaps the most important benefit of volcanism is the highly fertile soils produced by the weathering of lava.

We can reduce the loss of human life and sometimes property from volcanic eruptions. One way is to use historical records and geologic measurements to identify high-risk areas so that people can try to avoid living in them. Other methods involve developing effective evacuation plans and trying to develop measurements that warn us when volcanoes are likely to erupt.

Scientists are studying phenomena that precede an eruption. Examples include tilting or swelling of the cone, changes in magnetic and thermal properties of the volcano, changes in gas composition, and increased seismic activity.

16-4 MINERALS, ROCKS, AND THE ROCK CYCLE

What Are Minerals and Rocks? Hard Stuff

The Earth's crust consists of solid inorganic elements and compounds called minerals, and masses of one or more minerals called rock.

The Earth's crust, still forming in various places, is composed of minerals and rocks. It is the source of almost all the nonrenewable **mineral resources** we use: fossil fuels, metallic minerals, and nonmetallic minerals (Figure 1-6, p. 7). It is also the source of soil (Figure 4-24, p. 77) and of the elements that make up your body and the bodies of other living organisms. You are mostly water mixed with chemically transformed particles of minerals and rock and a small amount of air.

A **mineral** is an element or inorganic compound that occurs naturally and is solid with a regular internal crystalline structure. Some minerals consist of a single element, such as gold, silver, diamond (carbon), and sulphur. But most of the more than 2 000 identified minerals occur as inorganic compounds formed by various combinations of elements. Examples are salt, mica, and quartz.

Rock is a solid combination of one or more minerals that is part of the Earth's crust. Some kinds of rock, such as limestone (calcium carbonate, or $CaCO_3$) and quartzite (silicon dioxide, or SiO_2), contain only one mineral, but most rocks consist of two or more minerals.

What Are the Major Rock Types, and How Are They Recycled? Really Slow Recycling

The Earth's crust contains igneous, sedimentary, and metamorphic rocks that are recycled by the rock cycle.

Based on the way it forms, rock is placed in three broad classes. One is **igneous rock,** formed below or on the Earth's surface when molten rock (magma) wells up from the Earth's upper mantle or deep crust, cools, and hardens. Examples are granite (formed underground) and lava rock (formed above ground when molten lava cools and hardens). Although often covered by sedimentary rocks or soil, igneous rocks form the bulk of the Earth's crust. They also are the main source of many nonfuel mineral resources.

A second type is **sedimentary rock.** It is formed from sediment produced when existing rocks are weathered and eroded into small pieces, and transported from their sources by water, wind, or gravity to downstream, downwind, or downhill sites. These sediments are deposited in layers that accumulate over time and increase the weight and pressure on underlying layers. A combination of pressure and dissolved minerals seeping through the layers of sediment crystallizes and binds sediment particles together to form *sedimentary rock.*

Examples are sandstone and shale (formed from pressure created by deposited layers of sediment), dolomite and limestone (formed from the compacted shells, skeletons, and other remains of dead organisms), and lignite and bituminous coal (derived from plant remains). Some types of sedimentary rock are the result of crystals precipitating out of or growing in solutions and then being compacted in layers or drying out to leave crystals behind. An example is rock salt, which we know as table salt or sodium chloride (NaCl).

The third type is **metamorphic rock,** produced when a pre-existing rock is subjected to high temperatures (which may cause it to melt partially), high pressures, chemically active fluids, or a combination of these agents. These forces can change or transform a rock by reshaping its internal crystalline structure and its physical properties and appearance. Examples are anthracite (a form of coal), slate (formed when shale and mudstone are heated), and marble (produced when limestone is exposed to heat and pressure).

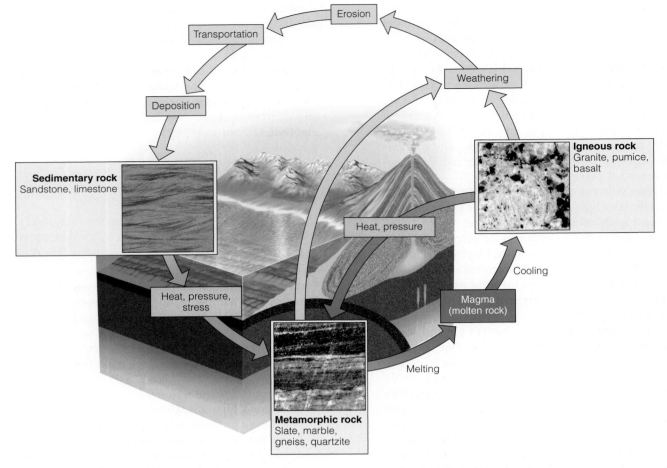

FIGURE 16-8 Natural capital: the *rock cycle* is the slowest of the Earth's cyclic processes. The Earth's materials are recycled over millions of years by three processes: *melting, erosion,* and *metamorphism,* which produce *igneous, sedimentary,* and *metamorphic* rocks. Rock of any of the three classes can be converted to rock of either of the other two classes, or can be recycled within its own class.

The interaction of physical and chemical processes that changes rocks from one type to another is called the **rock cycle** (Figure 16-8). It recycles the Earth's three types of rocks over millions of years and is the slowest of the Earth's cyclic processes. It also concentrates the planet's nonrenewable mineral resources on which we depend. Without the incredibly slow rock cycle you would not exist.

What Are Nonrenewable Mineral Resources? Useful Rock Resources

Mineral resources are nonrenewable materials that we can extract from the Earth's crust.

A **nonrenewable mineral resource** is a concentration of naturally occurring material in or on the Earth's crust that can be extracted and processed into useful materials at an affordable cost. Over millions to billions of years the Earth's internal and external geologic processes have produced numerous nonfuel mineral resources and fossil fuel energy resources. Because

they take so long to produce, they are classified as *nonrenewable resources.*

We know how to find and extract more than 100 nonrenewable minerals from the Earth's crust. They include *metallic mineral resources* (iron, copper, aluminum), *nonmetallic mineral resources* (salt, clay, sand, phosphates, and soil), and *energy resources* (coal, oil, natural gas, and uranium).

Ore is rock containing enough of one or more metallic minerals to be mined profitably. We convert about 40 metals extracted from ores into many everyday items that we either use and discard (Figure 3-18, p. 56) or learn to reuse, recycle, or use less wastefully (Figure 3-19, p. 56).

Geologists often divide nonrenewable mineral resources into four major categories (Figure 16-9):

■ **Identified resources**: deposits of a nonrenewable mineral resource with a *known* location, quantity, and quality, or whose existence is based on direct geologic evidence and measurements

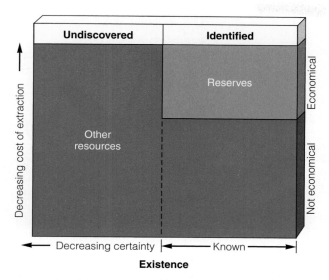

FIGURE 16-9 Categories of natural capital: geologists tend to focus on reserves of minerals that have already been identified and that occur in concentrations that make them economically viable. Reserves can be depleted through use, but they can also be increased if new high-quality discoveries are made or if improvements in technology allow lower grades of ores to be mined economically.

- **Reserves:** identified resources from which a usable nonrenewable mineral can be extracted profitably at current prices

- **Undiscovered resources:** potential supplies of a nonrenewable mineral resource assumed to exist on the basis of geologic knowledge and theory but with unknown specific locations, quality, and amounts

- **Other resources:** undiscovered resources and identified resources not classified as reserves

Most published estimates of the supply of a given nonrenewable resource refer to *reserves.* Reserves can increase when new deposits are found or when higher prices or improved mining technology make it profitable to extract deposits that previously were too expensive to extract. Theoretically, all *other resources* could eventually be converted to reserves, but this is highly unlikely.

16-5 FINDING, REMOVING, AND PROCESSING NONRENEWABLE MINERAL RESOURCES

How Are Buried Mineral Deposits Found? Underground Detective Work

Promising underground deposits of minerals are located by a variety of physical and chemical methods.

Mining companies use several methods to find promising mineral deposits. One is using aerial photos and satellite images to reveal protruding rock formations (outcrops) associated with certain minerals. Also, planes can be equipped with *radiation-measuring equipment* to detect deposits of radioactive minerals such as uranium ore, and a *magnetometer* to measure changes in the Earth's magnetic field caused by magnetic minerals such as iron ore. Another method uses a *gravimeter* to measure differences in gravity caused by differences in density between an ore deposit and the surrounding rock.

Underground methods include drilling a deep well and extracting core samples. Scientists can also put sensors in existing wells to detect electrical resistance or radioactivity to pinpoint the location of oil and natural gas. Scientists also make *seismic surveys* on land and at sea by detonating explosive charges and analyzing the resulting shock waves to get information about the makeup of buried rock layers. Yet another method is to perform *chemical analysis* of water and plants to detect deposits of underground minerals that have leached into nearby bodies of water or have been absorbed by plant tissues.

How Are Buried Mineral Deposits Removed? Heavy Digging and Lifting

Shallow deposits of mineral deposits are removed by surface mining, and deep deposits are removed by subsurface mining.

After suitable mineral deposits are located, several different types of mining techniques are used to remove them, depending on their location and type. Shallow deposits are removed by **surface mining,** and deep deposits are removed by **subsurface mining.**

In surface mining, mechanized equipment strips away the **overburden** of soil and rock and usually discards it as waste material called **spoils.** Surface mining extracts about 90% of the nonfuel mineral and rock resources and 60% of the coal (by weight) that are used in North America.

The type of surface mining used depends on the resource being sought and on local topography. There are several types of surface mining. One is **open-pit mining** (Figure 16-10a, p. 372), in which machines dig holes and remove ores (such as iron and copper), sand, gravel, and stone (such as limestone and marble). A second method is **dredging** (Figure 16-10b), in which chain buckets and draglines scrape up underwater mineral deposits.

A third method used where the terrain is fairly flat is **area strip mining** (Figure 16-10c). A gigantic earthmover strips away the overburden, and a huge power shovel digs a cut to remove the mineral deposit. Then the trench is filled with overburden and a new cut is made parallel to the previous one. The process is repeated over the entire site. If filling it does not restore the land, area strip mining leaves a wavy series of highly erodible hills of rubble called *spoil banks.*

(a) Open–Pit Mine

(b) Dredging

(c) Area Strip Mining

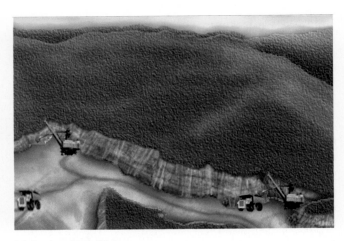

(d) Contour Strip Mining

FIGURE 16-10 Major mining methods used to extract *surface deposits* of solid mineral and energy resources.

Contour strip mining (Figure 16-10d) is used on hilly or mountainous terrain. A power shovel cuts a series of terraces into the side of a hill. An earthmover removes the overburden, a power shovel extracts the coal, and the overburden from each new terrace is dumped onto the one below. Unless the land is restored, a wall of dirt is left in front of a highly erodible bank of soil and rock called a *highwall*.

Another method is **mountaintop removal.** It uses explosives, massive shovels, and huge machinery called draglines to remove the top of a mountain and expose seams of coal underneath. The resulting waste rock and dirt is pushed down into the nearest streams and valleys below. This form of surface mining causes considerable environmental damage. The topic of mountaintop removal will be expanded upon in this textbook's website at http:// www.nelson.com/livingintheenvironment3e.com.

Subsurface mining (Figure 16-11, p. 373) removes coal and various metal ores that are too deep to be extracted by surface mining. Miners dig a deep vertical shaft, blast subsurface tunnels and chambers to get to the deposit, and use machinery to remove the ore or coal and transport it to the surface.

Subsurface mining disturbs less than one-tenth as much land as surface mining and usually produces less waste material. But it leaves much of the resource in the ground and is more dangerous and expensive than surface mining. Hazards include cave-ins, explosions, and lung diseases (such as black lung) caused by prolonged inhalation of mining dust.

16-6 ENVIRONMENTAL EFFECTS OF USING MINERAL RESOURCES

What Are the Environmental Impacts of Using Nonrenewable Mineral Resources? Degradation, Waste, and Pollution

Extracting, processing, and using mineral resources can disturb the land, kill miners, erode soils, produce large amounts of solid waste, and pollute the air, water, and soil.

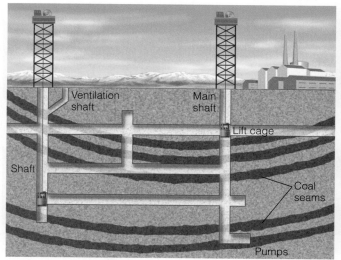

(a) Underground Coal Mine

(b) Room-and-Pillar

(c) Longwall Mining of Coal

FIGURE 16-11 Major mining methods used to extract *underground deposits* of solid mineral and energy resources (primarily coal). (a) Mine shafts and tunnels are dug and blasted out. (b) In *room-and-pillar* mining, machinery is used to gouge out coal and load it onto a shuttle car in one operation, and pillars of coal are left to support the mine roof. (c) In *longwall coal mining*, movable steel props support the roof and cutting machines shear off the coal onto a conveyor belt. As the mining proceeds, roof supports are moved forward and the roof behind is allowed to fall (often causing the land above to sink or subside).

The mining, processing, and use of mineral resources take enormous amounts of energy and often cause land disturbance, soil erosion, and air and water pollution (Figure 16-12, p. 374).

Mining can harm the environment in a number of ways. One is *scarring and disruption of the land surface*. Another problem is collapse of land above underground mines. This *subsidence* can cause houses to tilt, sewer lines to crack, gas mains to break, and groundwater systems to be disrupted.

Toxin-laced mining wastes can be blown or deposited elsewhere by wind or water erosion. Another problem is *acid mine drainage*. It occurs when rainwater seeping through a mine or mine wastes carries sulphuric acid (H_2SO_4, produced when aerobic bacteria act on iron sulphide minerals in spoils) to nearby streams and groundwater (Figures 16-12 and 16-13, p. 374). This contaminates water supplies and can destroy some forms of aquatic life. Mining can also result in emission of toxic chemicals into the atmosphere (Chapter 20). Finally, some forms of wildlife can be exposed to toxic mining wastes stored in holding ponds and leaking from such ponds.

What Is the Typical Life Cycle of a Nonrenewable Metal Resource? Going Around in Circles

Metal ores are extracted from the Earth's crust, purified, smelted to extract the desired metal, and converted to the desired products.

Figure 16-14 (p. 375) depicts the typical life cycle of a metal resource. It begins with extracting ore from the Earth's crust.

Ore typically has two components. One is the *ore mineral* containing the desired metal and the other is

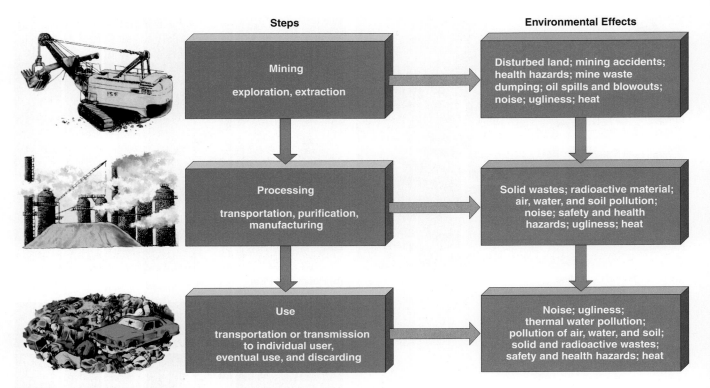

Steps	Environmental Effects
Mining exploration, extraction	Disturbed land; mining accidents; health hazards; mine waste dumping; oil spills and blowouts; noise; ugliness; heat
Processing transportation, purification, manufacturing	Solid wastes; radioactive material; air, water, and soil pollution; noise; safety and health hazards; ugliness; heat
Use transportation or transmission to individual user, eventual use, and discarding	Noise; ugliness; thermal water pollution; pollution of air, water, and soil; solid and radioactive wastes; safety and health hazards; heat

FIGURE 16-12 Natural capital degradation: some harmful environmental effects of extracting, processing, and using nonrenewable mineral and energy resources. The energy used to carry out each step causes additional pollution and environmental degradation.

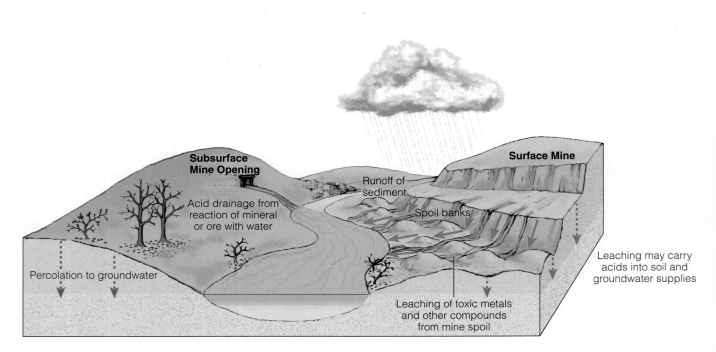

FIGURE 16-13 Natural capital degradation: pollution and degradation of a stream and groundwater by runoff of acids—called *acid mine drainage*—and by toxic chemicals from surface and subsurface mining. These substances can kill fish and other aquatic life.

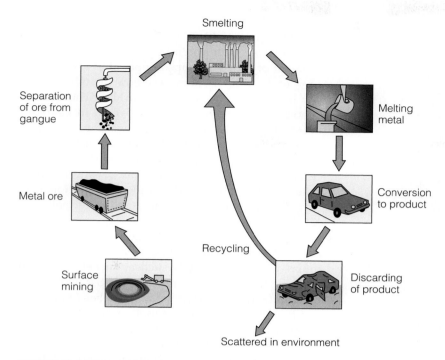

Smelting

Separation of ore from gangue

Melting metal

Metal ore

Conversion to product

Surface mining

Recycling

Discarding of product

Scattered in environment

FIGURE 16-14 Typical *life cycle of a metal resource.* Each step in this process uses energy and produces some pollution and waste heat.

waste material called **gangue** (pronounced "gang"). Removing the gangue from ores produces piles of waste called **tailings.** Particles of toxic metals blown by the wind or leached from tailings by rainfall can contaminate surface water and groundwater.

After gangue has been removed, **smelting** is used to separate the metal from the other elements in the ore mineral. Without effective pollution control equipment, smelters emit enormous quantities of air pollutants, which damage vegetation and soils in the surrounding area. They also cause water pollution and produce liquid and solid hazardous wastes that must be disposed of safely.

Some companies are using improved technology to reduce pollution from smelting, thereby lowering production costs, saving costly cleanup bills, and decreasing liability for damages.

Once smelting has produced the pure metal, it is usually melted and converted to desired products, which are then used and discarded or recycled.

Are There Environmental Limits to Resource Extraction and Use? A Serious Problem

Environmental damage caused by extraction, processing, and use of mineral resources can limit their availability.

Some environmentalists and resource experts do not believe that exhaustion of supplies is the greatest danger from continually increasing consumption of nonrenewable mineral resources. Instead, it is more likely to be the environmental damage caused by their extraction, processing, and conversion to products (Figure 16-12).

The environmental impacts from mining an ore are affected by its percentage of metal content, or *grade*. The more accessible and higher-grade ores are usually exploited first. As they are depleted, it takes more money, energy, water, and other materials to exploit lower-grade ores. This in turn increases land disruption, mining waste, and pollution.

For example, gold miners typically remove an amount of ore equal to the weight of 50 automobiles to extract a piece of gold that would fit inside your clenched fist. Most newlyweds would be surprised to know that about 5.5 metric tons (6 tons) of mining waste was created to make their two gold wedding rings. In Australia and North America, a mining technology called *cyanide heap leaching* is cheap enough to allow mining companies to level entire mountains containing very low-grade gold ore. Cyanide—a highly toxic chemical—is used to separate about 85% of the world's gold from waste ore.

Currently, most of the harmful environmental costs of mining and processing minerals are not included in the prices for processed metals and the resulting consumer products. Instead, these costs are passed on to society and future generations, which gives mining companies and manufacturers little incentive to reduce resource waste and pollution. Environmentalists and some economists call for phasing in *full-cost pricing*—including the cost of environmental harm done in the price of goods made from minerals.

CONSIDER, DISCUSS, OR DEBATE

Should market prices of goods made from minerals include their harmful environmental costs?

16-7 SUPPLIES OF MINERAL RESOURCES

What Is the State of Mineral Resources in Canada? Strong but Not Problem-Free

As Canada continues to exploit its abundant supply of mineral resources, it must address the negative impacts that arise from acquiring and processing minerals.

Minerals are widely distributed across Canada. Metallic minerals are concentrated in the Canadian Shield and in the mountains, whereas nonmetallic minerals

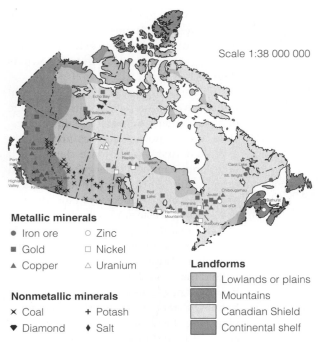

Scale 1:38 000 000

Metallic minerals

- Iron ore   ○ Zinc
- Gold   □ Nickel
- Copper   △ Uranium

Nonmetallic minerals

× Coal   + Potash
♥ Diamond   ♦ Salt

Landforms

Lowlands or plains
Mountains
Canadian Shield
Continental shelf

FIGURE 16-15 Canada's landforms and selected minerals. Metallic minerals such as copper, gold, iron, nickel, uranium, and zinc are found in the mountains or in the Canadian Shield. Fuels such as coal and nonmetallic minerals such as potash and salt are found in the lowlands. The locations of Canada's diamond mines north of Yellowknife are shown. (Matthews and Morrow, 1995; Diamonds North Resources Ltd., http://www.diamondsnorthresources.com)

are commonly found in the lowlands (Figure 16-15). According to National Resource Canada, in 2009 the metallic minerals mined in Canada were valued at $16.2 billion, followed by nonmetallic minerals ($11.5 billion) and coal ($4.5 billion). About 150 communities across Canada are economically dependent on mining. Many Canadian mining companies have operations all over the world.

Mining has played an important role in Canadian history. The *Klondike gold rush* of 1897–98 led to the establishment of Dawson and sparked a boom as gold-seekers staked every creek in the Klondike. Today most of Canada's gold is mined underground or in open pits in Ontario, Quebec, and British Columbia. Gold mining normally involves displacing large amounts of rock in order to find a small amount of gold. Cyanide used in the extraction process poses a health risk for people and fish.

In 1901, the first *nickel* ore was shipped from the Creighton mine in the now-famous mining district of Sudbury. Here, rich subterranean deposits of nickel and other metals are mined by the International Nickel Company (Inco) and Falconbridge. This area has deep shafts (once the deepest in the western hemisphere at 2 196 metres 7 205 feet) and the second-tallest

free-standing chimney in the world (the 381-metre/1251-feet superstack). In 1956, the discovery of a rich nickel deposit in northern Manitoba led to the establishment of Inco's Thompson operation and the creation of the City of Thompson, now the third-largest city in Manitoba. One of the world's richest nickel deposits, Voisey's Bay, was discovered in Labrador in late 1993, but production is awaiting the settlement of Aboriginal land claims. Mined nickel is used to make stainless steel, metal alloys, batteries, fuel cells, and coins (Figure 16-16). Special concerns associated with mining nickel include air pollution, acid rain, the release of heavy metals, and water pollution (Chapters 20 and 22).

Copper was discovered in Quebec in 1859, and the first mine opened in Ascot, Quebec. Copper is often found with other metals such as nickel, zinc, and gold. Today, copper is mined in British Columbia, Ontario (Sudbury and Timmins), Quebec (Noranda), and Manitoba (Flin Flon). More than 50% of Canada's copper is used to produce wire. Mining problems associated with this metal include preventing copper from contaminating drinking water and aquatic habitats.

Iron is mined for the steel industry, usually from open-pit mines in Newfoundland and Labrador, Quebec, and British Columbia. The steel industry is associated with high levels of air pollution because of its reliance on coal for high-temperature heat. On a positive note, increasing amounts of iron and steel are being recycled (Chapter 17).

Zinc is often found in conjunction with copper. Most zinc is extracted underground or from open-pit mines in New Brunswick, Quebec, Ontario, and Manitoba. About 50% of zinc is used to galvanize steel and iron to prevent rusting.

Uranium is a radioactive element found in rock; it can be used as fuel for nuclear reactors and as an

FIGURE 16-16 What's in a coin? Except during the war years when supplies of the metal were limited, the Canadian nickel consisted of 100% nickel. As the price of nickel increased, the Royal Canadian Mint responded by producing a coin that was only 2% nickel (plated on steel). Similarly, a penny was 98% copper until 1997, when it was reduced to 4.5% copper; the penny was dropped entirely in 2012 because it cost 1.6 cents to produce each coin! (Royal Canadian Mint, 2012)

Potentially Conflicting Uses of the Niagara Escarpment

The Niagara Escarpment is a towering rocky ridge that stretches 725 kilometres (450 miles) through southern Ontario from the Niagara River to the tip of Lake Huron's Bruce Peninsula. It is home to many fascinating species including unique orchids, the most ancient trees in eastern North America (1 000 years old), and numerous species at risk (Chapter 12). The escarpment has spectacular scenic vistas, caves, waterfalls, and more than 100 sites of geological significance. The famous 762-kilometre (473-mile) Bruce Trail, the longest natural corridor in south-central Ontario, runs through this area. For all of these values, the Niagara Escarpment was recognized as a world biosphere reserve (p. 242) by the United Nations Educational, Scientific and Cultural Organization (UNESCO) in 1990.

The area is also recognized for other values. For example, the escarpment is viewed as a potential source of lucrative sedimentary rocks such as sandstone, shale, limestone, and dolomite rock (also known as dolostone). Rocks such as these are in great demand for many construction and decorative purposes, and the highly populated market of

Ontario's "Golden Horseshoe" area is a short distance away.

As well, there are developers who would like to create new housing projects ranging from single dwellings to subdivisions. There are farmers who wish to operate vineyards and orchards. There are cottagers, tourism businesses, and lumbering operations with interests in the Niagara Escarpment area. There are advocates of using the escarpment to generate power by building a series of windmills along the high ridges.

How are the potentially conflicting issues of the Niagara Escarpment resolved? The Niagara Escarpment Commission (NEC), an agency of Ontario's Ministry of Natural Resources, consists of 17 members appointed by the Ontario cabinet to make decisions about the sustainable development of the escarpment. The NEC is guided by the Niagara Escarpment Plan (NEP), which is considered to be Canada's first large-scale environmental land-use plan.

Biosphere reserves include zones that can be developed for a variety of compatible purposes, and the NEP does contain provisions for extraction of *aggregates* (rock, gravel, and sand) from designated

zones "subject to development criteria" (http://www.escarpment.org/landplanning/plan/index.php). The NEC meets monthly to consider appeals from groups that are promoting or resisting various types of development.

If you read the reports from some of the NEC's meetings (http://www.escarpment.org/commission/meeting/index.php) and visit the sites of various interest groups such as Walker Aggregates Inc. (http://www.walkerind.com/walker-aggregates/vineland-quarries.html) and the watchdog group Coalition on the Niagara Escarpment (CONE; http://www.niagaraescarpment.org/), you will develop a sense of the potentially conflicting demands that are being placed on the Niagara Escarpment.

© All Canada Photos/Alamy

---

explosive in nuclear weapons. Canada is the largest producer and exporter of uranium ore. There are currently four active mines in northern Saskatchewan: Key Lake, McArthur River, McClean Lake, and Rabbit Lake. Special dangers of mining uranium include exposure to radioactivity, air pollution associated with radioactive dust and radon gas, and groundwater contamination resulting from chemicals used to mine uranium.

Potash is an impure form of potassium carbonate (K_2CO_3) found mixed with other potassium salts in subterranean deposits. It is largely used in making fertilizers but can also be used to manufacture products such as glass and soap. Extraction typically involves underground mining of horizontal layers. There are nine mines in Saskatchewan and two in New Brunswick.

Sand, *gravel*, and *stone* are structural minerals. They have broad applications as building materials and are extracted from quarries widely distributed across all

provinces and territories. These materials are used in large volumes and so collectively have a high economic value. On the other hand, quarries have a lasting effect on the landscape and can negatively impact other values of the area. See the following Spotlight on potentially conflicting uses of the Niagara Escarpment.

The first *salt* bed discovered in North America was found at Goderich, near Lake Huron, in 1866. This led to the creation of the Sifto Salt Company, one of the world's largest suppliers of salt. Salt is usually extracted from underground mines. It occurs in 180- to 1 830-metre-thick (590- to 6 004-feet-thick) beds under the prairies, 275- to 825-metre-thick (902- to 2 707-feet-thick) beds in southwestern Ontario, and in folded salt beds in the Maritimes. Elevated salinity in groundwater can prevent its use for drinking water or irrigation.

Many *gems* and *precious stones* are mined in Canada. Diamonds are a recent and highly lucrative

FIGURE 16-17 Nephrite jade, a silicate of calcium and magnesium, is a hard translucent stone that ranges in colour from green to pure white. It is extracted from boulder-filled quarries in the mountains of British Columbia and, depending on quality, sold as gemstones, carving rocks, or ornamental stone. The hardest grades must be cut by diamonds.

find in the Canadian North (p. 364). Jade is found in more than 50 locations in the mountains of British Columbia (Figure 16-17).

Coal is mined and used to produce high-temperature heat for industrial processes and for generating electricity. For more than 100 years, coal was extracted from subterranean tunnels that reached out under the sea near Cape Breton Island. These days, 95% of coal comes from surface mines. The Fording River Mine is a huge open-pit mine in British Columbia that has received positive recognition for mine reclamation. The Cheviot Mine in Alberta is a huge open-pit mine that is at the centre of controversy because it is less than 3 kilometres (1.9 miles) from the edge of Jasper National Park; opponents feel that the mine jeopardizes grizzly bear populations as well the sanctity of the park as a World Heritage Site. Special concerns associated with coal mines include dangers of cave-ins and poison gases in underground mines; ecosystem disturbance and land erosion in open-pit mines; and air pollution and global warming (Chapters 20 and 21) resulting from burning coal.

DID YOU KNOW

• The largest known discovery of silver—in Cobalt, Ontario—sparked the world's biggest silver rush.
• The new hybrid electric vehicles (HEVs) being produced by Ford, Honda, Toyota, and Lexus, among others, use nickel-based rechargeable batteries.
• Canada is the world's largest producer of potash, with two-thirds of the world's recoverable supply found in Saskatchewan.
• Our need to use salt on winter roads makes Canadians the largest per capita users of salt in the world.
• Canada supplies 75% of the world's production of nephrite jade, "the stone of heaven" revered by the Chinese throughout history.

Will We Have Enough Nonrenewable Mineral Resources? Making Educated Guesses

The future supply of a resource depends on its available and affordable supply and how rapidly that supply is used.

The future supply of nonrenewable minerals depends on two factors. One is the actual or potential supply of the mineral and the other is the rate at which we use it.

We never completely run out of any mineral. However, a mineral becomes *economically depleted* when it costs more to find, extract, transport, and process the remaining deposit than it is worth. At that point, there are five choices: *recycle or reuse existing supplies, waste less, use less, find a substitute,* or *do without*.

Depletion time is how long it takes to use up a certain proportion—usually 80%—of the reserves of a mineral at a given rate of use. When experts disagree about depletion times, they are often using different assumptions about supply and rate of use (Figure 16-18).

The shortest depletion time assumes no recycling or reuse and no increase in reserves (curve A, Figure 16-18). A longer depletion time assumes that recycling will stretch existing reserves and that better mining technology, higher prices, and new discoveries will increase reserves (curve B, Figure 16-18).

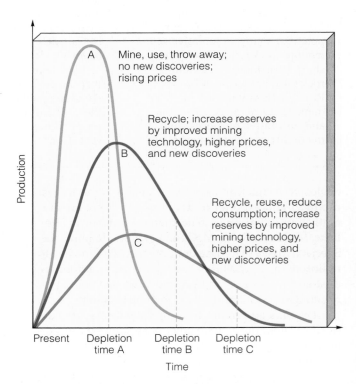

FIGURE 16-18 **Extending natural capital:** these are *depletion curves* for nonrenewable resources (such as aluminum or copper or other minerals) based on three sets of assumptions. Dashed vertical lines represent times when 80% depletion occurs. Note that actions such as recycling, reusing, and reducing can greatly extend the life of a nonrenewable resource.

An even longer depletion time assumes that new discoveries will further expand reserves and that recycling, reuse, and reduced consumption will extend supplies (curve C, Figure 16-18). Finding a substitute for a resource leads to a new set of depletion curves for the new resource.

We can use geological methods to make fairly good estimates of the reserves of most resources (Figure 16-9, blue) and less accurate measurements of potential other supplies of mineral resources (Figure 16-9, red). Rising prices and improved mining technology can convert some of the other resources to reserves, but it is difficult to make accurate projections of how much this will add to the usable supply.

We do know that the demand for mineral resources is increasing at a rapid rate as more people consume more and more stuff. For example, since 1940 North Americans alone have used up more of the Earth's mineral resources than all previous generations put together, and this resource-use treadmill is speeding up.

Will we run out of affordable supplies of a particular mineral resource? No one knows. If we do, can we find an acceptable substitute? Some think we can. Are there environmental limits to the use of mineral resources? Many environmentalists think so unless we can use microorganisms, or other less environmentally harmful ways, to extract and process minerals, or nanotechnology to construct materials we need from atoms and molecules.

How Does Economics Affect Supplies of Nonrenewable Minerals? Prices Can Make a Difference If the Market Is Truly Free

A rising price for a scarce mineral resource can increase supplies and encourage more efficient use.

Geologic processes determine the quantity and location of a mineral resource in the Earth's crust. But economics determines what part of the known supply is extracted and used.

According to standard economic theory, in a competitive free market a plentiful mineral resource is cheap when its supply exceeds demand. And when a resource becomes scarce its price rises. This can encourage exploration for new deposits, stimulate development of better mining technology, and make it profitable to mine lower-grade ores. It can also encourage a search for substitutes and promote resource conservation.

But according to some economists, this price effect may no longer apply very well in most developed countries. One reason is that industry and government in such countries often control the supply, demand, and prices of minerals to such an extent that a truly competitive free market does not exist. Another reason

is that governments subsidize development of their domestic mineral resources to help promote economic growth and national security.

Critics argue that taxing rather than subsidizing the extraction of nonfuel mineral resources would provide governments with revenue, create incentives for more efficient resource use, promote waste reduction and pollution prevention, and encourage recycling and reuse of mineral resources.

Mining company representatives say they need subsidies and low taxes to keep the prices of minerals low for consumers and to encourage the companies not to move their mining operations to other countries with no such taxes and less stringent mining regulations. As well, locating and extracting mineral resources involves time, money, and risk. Typically, if geologists identify 10 000 possible deposits of a given resource, only 1 000 sites are worth exploring; only 100 justify drilling, trenching, or tunnelling; and only 1 becomes a producing mine or well.

Can We Get Enough Minerals by Mining Lower-Grade Ores? Taking It to the Limit

New technologies can increase the mining of low-grade ores at affordable prices, but harmful environmental effects can limit this.

Some analysts contend that all we need to do to increase supplies of a mineral is to extract lower grades of ore. They point to the development of new earth-moving equipment, improved techniques for removing impurities from ores, and other technological advances in mineral extraction and processing.

In 1900, the average copper ore mined in North America was about 5% copper by weight. Today it is 0.5%, and copper costs less (adjusted for inflation). New methods of mineral extraction may allow even lower-grade ores of some metals to be used.

But several factors can limit the mining of lower-grade ores. One is the increased cost of mining and processing larger volumes of ore. Another is the availability of fresh water needed to mine and process some minerals—especially in arid and semiarid areas. A third limiting factor is the environmental impact of the increased land disruption, waste material, and pollution produced during mining and processing (Figure 16-12).

One way to improve mining technology is to use microorganisms for in-place (in situ, pronounced "in-SY-too") mining. This biological approach removes desired metals from ores while leaving the surrounding environment undisturbed. It also reduces air pollution associated with the smelting of metal ores and reduces water pollution associated with using hazardous chemicals such as cyanides and mercury to extract gold.

Once a commercially viable ore deposit has been identified, wells are drilled into it and the ore is fractured. Then the ore is inoculated with natural or genetically engineered bacteria to extract the desired metal. Next the well is flooded with water, which is pumped to the surface, where the desired metal is removed. Then the water is recycled.

This technique permits economical extraction from low-grade ores that are used more as high-grade ores are depleted. Currently, more than 25% of all copper produced worldwide, worth more than $1 billion (U.S.) a year, comes from such *biomining*. If naturally occurring bacteria cannot be found to extract a particular metal, genetic engineering techniques could be used to produce such bacteria.

However, microbiological ore processing is slow. It can take decades to remove the same amount of material that conventional methods can remove within months or years. So far, biological mining methods are economically feasible only with low-grade ore for which conventional techniques are too expensive.

Can We Find Substitutes for Scarce Nonrenewable Mineral Resources? The Materials Revolution

Scientists and engineers are developing new types of materials that can serve as substitutes for many metals.

Some analysts believe that even if supplies of key minerals become too expensive or scarce, human ingenuity will find substitutes. They point to the current *materials revolution* in which silicon and new materials, particularly ceramics and plastics, are being developed and used as replacements for metals.

Ceramics have many advantages over conventional metals. They are harder, stronger, lighter, and longer lasting than many metals, and they withstand intense heat and do not corrode. Within a few decades we may have high-temperature ceramic superconductors in which electricity flows without resistance. Such a development may lead to faster computers, more efficient power transmission, and affordable electromagnets for propelling high-speed magnetic levitation trains.

High-strength plastics and composite materials strengthened by lightweight carbon and glass fibres are beginning to transform the automobile and aerospace industries. They cost less to produce than metals because they take less energy, do not need painting, and can be moulded into any shape. New plastics and gels are also being developed to provide superinsulation without taking up much space. And nanotechnology may result in many new materials.

Substitutes can be found for many scarce mineral resources. But finding substitutes for some key materials may be difficult or impossible. Examples are helium, phosphorus for phosphate fertilizers, manganese for making steel, and copper for wiring motors and generators.

In addition, some substitutes are inferior to the minerals they replace. For example, aluminum could replace copper in electrical wiring. But producing aluminum takes much more energy than producing copper, and aluminum wiring is a greater fire hazard than copper wiring.

Mineral resources are the building blocks on which modern society depends. Knowledge of their physical nature and origins, the web they weave between all aspects of human society and the physical Earth, can lay the foundations for a sustainable society.

Ann Dorr and Alma Hale Paty

CHAPTER REVIEW

1. Review the Key Questions for this chapter on p. 364. Describe the pros and cons of mining diamonds in the Canadian north.

2. Define *geology, core, mantle, crust, tectonic plate,* and *lithosphere.* What is *weathering* and why is it important? Define *volcano* and describe the nature and effects of a volcanic eruption. Define and describe the nature and effects of an *earthquake.* What is a *tsunami* and what are its effects?

3. Define *mineral, rock, sedimentary rock, igneous rock,* and *metamorphic rock* and give an example of each. Describe the nature and importance of the *rock cycle.*

4. Define *mineral resource* and list three types of such resources. Define *ore* and distinguish between a *high-grade ore* and a *low-grade ore.* What are *reserves*? Describe the life cycle of a metal resource. Describe the major harmful environmental effects of extracting, processing, and using nonrenewable mineral resources.

5. Distinguish between *surface mining* and *subsurface mining.* Define *overburden, spoils,* and *open-pit mining.* Define *strip mining* and distinguish among *area strip mining, contour strip mining,* and *mountaintop removal.* What is *smelting* and what are its major harmful environmental effects? What five nations supply most of the world's nonrenewable mineral resources?

6. What are five possible options when a mineral becomes economically depleted? Define *depletion time* and describe three types of depletion curves for a mineral resource. Describe the conventional view of the relationship between the supply of a mineral resource and its market price.

7. Describe the opportunities and limitations of increasing mineral supplies by mining lower-grade ores. What are the advantages and disadvantages of biomining?

8. Describe the opportunities and limitations of getting more minerals from the ocean.

9. Describe the opportunities and limitations of finding substitutes for scarce mineral resources and recycling and reusing valuable metals. Describe ways of using nonrenewable mineral resources more sustainably.

10. Describe how the four *scientific principles of sustainability* could be applied to diamond mining in the north to help ensure the operation is sustainable and that it has minimal environmental impact.

CRITICAL THINKING

1. Debate the pros and cons of mining. What would you do to improve mining techniques?

2. Under what circumstances, and in pursuit of which minerals, would the mining techniques shown on pp. 372–373 likely be used? What are the pros and cons of each technique?

3. Discuss the pros and cons of the mining industry having to pay for the full costs of mining, including all costs incurred by damaging the environment.

4. Congratulations! You are in charge of the world. What are the three most important features of your policy for developing and sustaining the world's nonrenewable mineral resources?

PROJECTS

1. Use the library or the Internet to research the Cheviot Mine controversy. Which side (pro-mine or pro-park) makes the most compelling arguments?

2. What mineral resources are extracted in your area? What mining methods are used, and what have been their harmful environmental impacts? How has mining these resources affected the local economy and ecosystem?

3. Use the library or the Internet to find out where earthquakes and volcanic eruptions have occurred during the past 30 years. Consider the vulnerabilities of cities and nuclear power plants in these areas.

4. Choose a mineral. Use the library or the Internet to learn more about specific mines, processes, products, and impacts related to that mineral.

Chernobyl is known around the globe as the site of the world's most serious nuclear power plant accident (Figure 17-1). On April 26, 1986, a series of explosions in one of the reactors in a nuclear power plant in Ukraine—then part of the Soviet Union—blew the massive roof off a reactor building and flung radioactive debris and dust high into the atmosphere. A huge radioactive cloud spread over much of Belarus, Russia, Ukraine, and other parts of Europe and eventually encircled the planet. To see a Flash simulation of the radioactive cloud, visit http://www.ratical.org/radiation/chernobyl/IRSN14dayPlume.html. Clouds of radioactive material escaped into the atmosphere for 10 days. The surrounding environment and people were exposed to radiation levels about 100 times higher than those caused by the atomic bomb the United States dropped on Hiroshima, Japan, near the end of World War II.

According to various UN studies, the disaster was caused by poor reactor design and human error. Around 30 people near the accident site died from radiation exposure and approximately 4 000 children developed thyroid cancer. Thousands of others may have also developed various cancers and died. But because of poor record-keeping no one knows the exact death toll, with the estimated number of premature deaths ranging from 8 000 to 15 000. Regardless of numbers, this was a major human-caused tragedy.

More than 100 000 people had to leave their homes. Most were not evacuated until at least 10 days after the accident. These environmental refugees had to

(continued)

FIGURE 17-1A On April 26, 1986, the Chernobyl nuclear power plant was rocked with an explosion that released massive clouds of radiation.

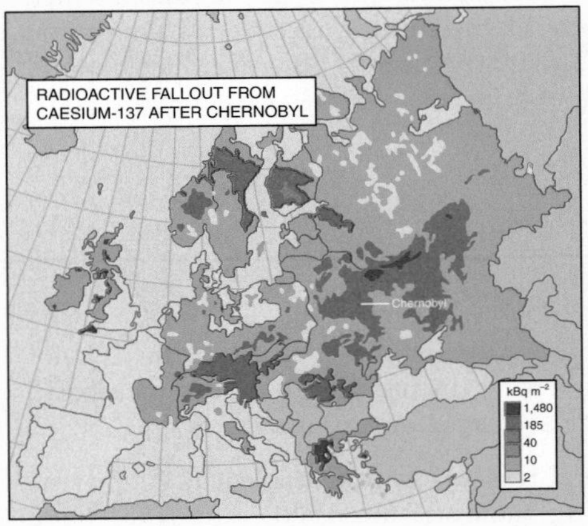

Novosti / Photo Researchers, Inc.

RADIOACTIVE FALLOUT FROM CAESIUM-137 AFTER CHERNOBYL

Chernobyl

kBq m^{-2}
1,480
185
40
10
2

FIGURE 17-1B Radioactive fallout from Chernobyl contaminated much of Europe with caesium-137 and other radioactive isotopes. The legend shows activity of the radiation per square metre of ground (kBqm^{-2}). (*Chernobyl: Catastrophe and Consequences,* 1998, J. Smith & N. A. Beresford. With kind permission of Springer Science+Business Media. Adapted from M. De Cort, G. Dubois, Sh. D. Fridman, M. G. Germenchuk, Yu. A. Izrael, A. Janssens, A. R. Jones, G. N. Kelly, E. V. Kvasnikova, I. I. Matveenko, I. M. Nazarov, Yu. M. Pokumeiko, V. A. Sitak, E. D. Stukin, L.Ya. Tabachny, Yu. S. Tsaturov and S. I. Avdyushin, "Atlas of Caesium Deposition on Europe after the Chernobyl Accident," EUR report nr. 16733, EC, Office for Official Publications of the European Communities, Luxembourg (1998))

FIGURE 17-1C Animals such as reindeer in Russia and Scandinavia carried high body burdens of radioactivity.

Farrell Grehan / Photo Researchers, Inc.

leave their possessions behind. They also had to say goodbye to lush green wheat fields and blossoming apple trees, land their families had farmed for generations. Many reindeer throughout Russia and as far away as Scandinavia became contaminated when they ate radioactive lichens and mushrooms; this posed a major problem for people who depended on the animals for meat. Sheep and cows from as far away as the British Isles became contaminated when they ate radioactive grass. More than 20 years later, there are regions in Russia, Scandinavia, the British Isles, and other parts of Europe where the meat of these animals is still too radioactive for human consumption (OECD, 2006).

The total cost of the accident is at least $140 billion (U.S.) according to the U.S. Department of Energy and could eventually reach at least $358 billion (U.S.) according to Ukrainian officials—many times more than the value of all nuclear electricity ever generated in the former Soviet Union.

Chernobyl taught us that *a major nuclear accident anywhere has effects that reverberate throughout much of the world.*

Typical citizens of advanced industrialized nations each consume as much energy in six months as typical citizens in developing countries consume during their entire life.

MAURICE STRONG

CHAPTER PURPOSE AND QUESTIONS

Chapter 17 discusses the advantages and disadvantages of various nonrenewable energy resources. The chapter addresses the following questions:

17-1 How should we evaluate energy alternatives?

17-2 What are the advantages and disadvantages of conventional and nonconventional oil?

17-3 What are the advantages and disadvantages of natural gas?

17-4 What are the advantages and disadvantages of coal and converting coal to gaseous and liquid fuels?

17-5 What are the advantages and disadvantages of conventional nuclear fission, breeder nuclear fission, and nuclear fusion?

17-1 EVALUATING ENERGY RESOURCES

What Types of Energy Do We Use? Supplementing Free Solar Capital

About 99% of the energy that heats the Earth and our homes comes from the sun, and the remaining 1% comes mostly from burning fossil fuels.

Some 99% of the energy that heats the Earth and all of our buildings comes directly from the sun at no cost to us. Without this essentially inexhaustible solar energy (*solar capital*), the Earth's average temperature would be –240°C (heat from the core and mantle would keep Earth's surface from dropping to –273°C), and life as we know it would not exist.

Solar energy comes from the nuclear fusion of hydrogen atoms that make up the sun's mass. Thus *life on Earth is made possible by a gigantic nuclear fusion reactor safely located in space about 150 million kilometres (93 million miles) away.*

This direct input of solar energy also produces several other *indirect forms of renewable solar energy.* Examples are wind, falling and flowing water (hydropower), and biomass (solar energy converted to chemical energy stored in chemical bonds of organic compounds in trees and other plants).

Commercial energy sold in the marketplace makes up the remaining 1% of the energy we use. Most commercial energy comes from extracting and burning *nonrenewable mineral resources* obtained from the Earth's crust, primarily carbon-containing **fossil fuels**—oil, natural gas, and coal—as shown in Figure 17-2.

What Types of Commercial Energy Does the World Depend On? The Fossil Fuel Era

About 79% of the commercial energy used worldwide comes from nonrenewable fossil fuels.

About 85% of the commercial energy consumed in the world comes from *nonrenewable* energy resources (79% from fossil fuels and 6% from nuclear power; Figure 17-3, top, p. 385). The remaining 15% comes from *renewable* energy resources—biomass (11%), hydropower (3%), and a combination of geothermal, wind, and solar energy (1%).

Figure 17-4 (p. 385) shows the global consumption of energy by fuel type between 1970 and 2009, with projections to 2020. Note that oil predominates, followed by natural gas and coal. Figure 17-5 (p. 385) shows Canadian energy use by sector.

Roughly half the world's people in developing countries burn wood and charcoal to heat their dwellings and cook their food. This *biomass energy* is renewable as long as wood supplies are not harvested faster than they are replenished. Most of this biomass is collected by users and not sold in the marketplace. Thus

Nonrenewable Energy Resources **383**

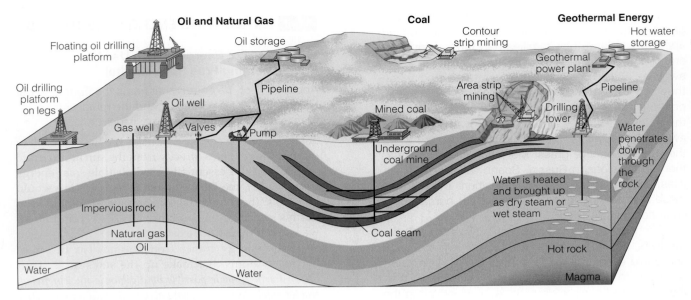

Oil and Natural Gas

Floating oil drilling platform

Oil storage

Oil drilling platform on legs

Gas well

Oil well

Valves

Pipeline

Pump

Impervious rock

Natural gas

Oil

Water

Water

Coal

Contour strip mining

Area strip mining

Mined coal

Underground coal mine

Coal seam

Geothermal Energy

Hot water storage

Geothermal power plant

Drilling tower

Pipeline

Water penetrates down through the rock

Water is heated and brought up as dry steam or wet steam

Hot rock

Magma

FIGURE 17-2 Natural capital: important nonrenewable energy resources that can be removed from the Earth's crust are coal, oil, natural gas, and some forms of geothermal energy. Nonrenewable uranium ore is also extracted from the Earth's crust and then processed to increase its concentration of uranium-235, which can be used as a fuel in nuclear reactors to produce electricity.

the actual percentage of renewable biomass energy used in the world is higher than the 11% figure shown in Figure 17-3 (top).

Bad news. Many people in developing countries face a *fuelwood shortage* that is expected to get worse because of unsustainable harvesting of fuelwood. Also, people die prematurely from breathing particles emitted by burning wood indoors in open fires and poorly designed primitive stoves.

> **CONSIDER, DISCUSS, OR DEBATE**
>
> Study Figure 17-3 closely. Can you explain why the energy pie charts of the world, Canada, and the United States are not the same? How should governments be attempting to change these pie charts in the future? What types of decisions and choices would have to be made for the pie charts to change in the ways you have suggested?

Why Is the Energy Future of the United States Important to Canada? Environmental and Economic Impacts

The future direction of U.S. energy policy will have important environmental and economic consequences for Canada.

In addition to being an industrial giant and a military superpower with 10 times our population, the United States is Canada's largest trading partner. Thus the energy choices it makes will have enormous implications for its northern neighbour.

The United States is the world's largest energy user, with the average American consuming as much energy in one day as a person in the poorest countries consumes in a year. In 2011, with only 4.5% of the population,

the United States used 24% of the world's commercial energy. In contrast, India, with 17% of the world's people, used about 3% of the world's commercial energy.

The United States is out of step with Canada and the rest of the world in terms of the energy resources it uses (Figure 17-3). About 93% of its commercial energy comes from nonrenewable energy resources (oil, coal, natural gas, and nuclear power), whereas the remaining 7% comes mostly from renewable biomass and hydropower. In comparison, only 73% of commercial energy used in Canada and 85% of the energy used in the world comes from nonrenewable energy resources, with renewable biomass and hydropower accounting for most of the remainder. Canada and the United States use about the same percentage of nuclear energy. However, the United States uses more than twice as much coal—an especially polluting technology.

How Can We Decide Which Energy Resources to Use? Evaluating Alternative Resources

Each country needs to answer several questions in deciding which energy resources to promote.

Energy policies must be developed with the future in mind because experience shows that it usually takes at least 50 years and huge investments to phase in new energy alternatives to the point where they provide 10–20% of total energy use. Making these decisions and converting them into energy policy involves answering the following questions for *each* alternative:

- What is the intended use for that energy? All sources of energy do not lend themselves to the same applications. On a personal level, you are probably

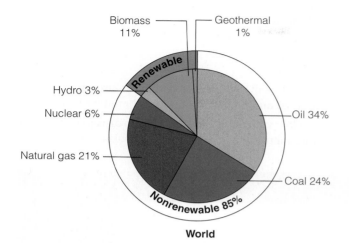

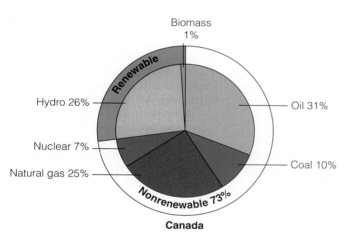

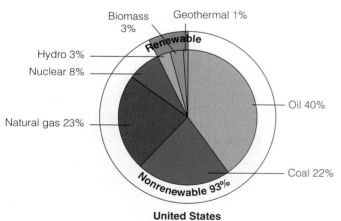

FIGURE 17-3 Commercial energy use for the world (top), Canada (middle), and the United States in 2009. Commercial energy amounts to only 1% of the energy used in the world; the other 99% is direct solar energy received from the sun and is not sold in the marketplace. (Data from the International Energy Agency and the Energy Information Agency)

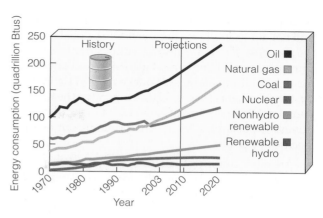

FIGURE 17-4 Global energy consumption by fuel type, 1970–2009, with projections to 2020. (A Btu is a British thermal unit, a standard measure of heat for value comparison of various fuels.) (Data from International Energy Annual 2010, International Energy Outlook 2011)

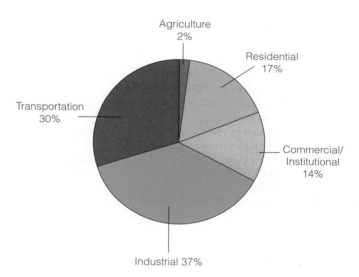

FIGURE 17-5 Canadian energy use by sector. (Data from Natural Resources Canada, 2012)

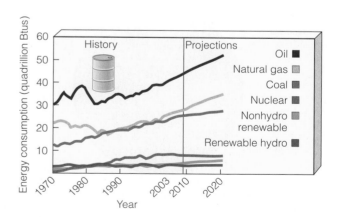

FIGURE 17-6 Energy consumption by fuel in the United States, 1970–2009, with projections to 2020. (International Energy Annual 2010, International Energy Outlook 2011)

quite pleased that your cell phone runs on electricity and not, for example, on kerosene. On a global level, we use most of our oil (62%) for various transportation purposes, most of our natural gas (84%) for various heating applications, most of our coal (77%) for industrial requirements such as high-temperature heat, and most of our electricity (60%) for a huge variety of nonindustrial applications such as running our many electric devices.

- Are other considerations, such as convenience, important? It might be a priority to secure plentiful supplies of an energy source that could easily be adapted to many products and services, or could easily be transported. Oil, for example, is valued for these properties.

- How much of the energy resource is likely to be available in the near future (the next 15–25 years) and the long term (the next 25–50 years)?

- What is the net energy yield for the resource?

- How much will it cost to develop, phase in, and use the resource?

- What government research and development subsidies and tax breaks will be used to help develop the resource?

- How will dependence on the resource affect national and global economic and military security?

- How vulnerable is the resource to disruption through wars, natural disasters, economic problems, or terrorism?

SPOTLIGHT

Making Energy Choices

As an illustration of making energy choices, consider that various technologies could be used to generate electricity. Which one, or ones, should be chosen? Many considerations were listed in the previous section, but let's focus on an aspect of air pollution—the generation of greenhouse gases.

Technologies such as hydropower, solar power, wind power, and nuclear power have a very small impact in terms of greenhouse gases. Among fossil fuels, the use of coal to generate electricity produces by far the highest emissions of CO_2 (see Figure 17-16, p. 395). Many energy experts assert that while coal

may have its useful attributes in terms of creating high-temperature heat for industrial purposes, it is a relatively poor choice for generating electricity, at least from the perspective of greenhouse gases.

What energy choices were made for generating electricity in Canada in 2010? As depicted in Figure 17-7 (left side), hydropower supplied most of our electricity (62%), while each of the various fossil fuel technologies supplied a relatively small amount (21% in total).

What were the consequences of our energy choices? As shown in Figure 17-7 (right side), all of the

"noncombustion" technologies such as hydropower, nuclear power, solar power, and wind power contributed only 2% of the CO_2 associated with generating our electricity. The remaining 98% came from our use of fossil fuels.

Of course, many factors—including costs, convenience, needs of industry, and public opinion—must be considered when making energy choices. What choices would you make if you were a politician charged with supplying electricity while avoiding climate change and keeping your government in office?

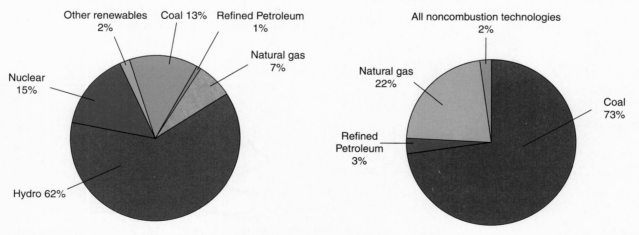

FIGURE 17-7 Energy choices used to generate electricity in Canada in 2010 (left side). Note that hydropower supplied the largest portion of our electricity (62%), while thermal generation using coal, for example, supplied 13%. Consequences of energy choices (right side): all of the noncombustion technologies, including hydropower and nuclear power, accounted for only 2% of the CO_2 produced. Thermal generation of electricity using coal, for example, was responsible for 73% of the CO_2 produced. (Data from Environment Canada, 2011)

- How will extracting, transporting, and using the resource affect the environment, human health, and the Earth's climate? Should these harmful costs be included in the market price of the resource through a combination of taxes and phasing out environmentally harmful subsidies (full-cost pricing)? Further considerations about making energy choices are outlined in the following Spotlight.

What Is Net Energy? An Important Consideration

Net energy is the amount of high-quality usable energy available from a resource after subtracting the energy needed to make it available for use.

It takes energy to get energy. For example, before oil is useful to us it must be found, pumped from beneath the ground or ocean floor, transferred to a refinery and converted to useful fuels (such as gasoline, diesel fuel, and heating oil), transported to users, and burned in furnaces and cars. Each step uses high-quality energy. The second law of thermodynamics tells us that some of it will always be wasted and degraded to lower-quality energy.

The usable amount of *high-quality energy* available from a given quantity of a resource is its **net energy**. It is the total amount of energy available from the resource minus the energy needed to find, extract, process, and get it to consumers. It is calculated by estimating the total energy available from the resource over its lifetime minus the amount of energy *used* (the first law of thermodynamics), *automatically wasted* (the second law of thermodynamics), and *unnecessarily wasted* in finding, processing, concentrating, and transporting the useful energy to users.

Net energy is like your net spendable income—your wages minus taxes and job-related expenses. For example, suppose that for every 10 units of energy in oil in the ground we have to use and waste 8 units of energy to find, extract, process, and transport the oil to users. Then we have only 2 units of *useful energy* available from every 10 units of energy in the oil.

We can express net energy as the ratio of useful energy produced to the useful energy used to produce it. In the example just given, the *net energy ratio* would be 10/8, or 1.25. The higher the ratio, the greater the net energy. When the ratio is less than 1, there is a net energy loss.

Figure 17-8 shows estimated net energy ratios for various types of space heating, high-temperature heat

Space Heating

Passive solar	5.8
Natural gas	4.9
Oil	4.5
Active solar	1.9
Coal gasification	1.5
Electric resistance heating (coal-fired plant)	0.4
Electric resistance heating (natural gas–fired plant)	0.4
Electric resistance heating (nuclear plant)	0.3

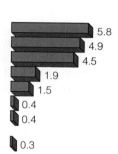

High-Temperature Industrial Heat

Surface-mined coal	28.2
Underground-mined coal	25.8
Natural gas	4.9
Oil	4.7
Coal gasification	1.5
Direct solar (highly concentrated by mirrors, heliostats, or other devices)	0.9

Transportation

Natural gas	4.9
Gasoline (refined crude oil)	4.1
Biofuel (ethyl alcohol)	1.9
Coal liquefaction	1.4
Oil shale	1.2

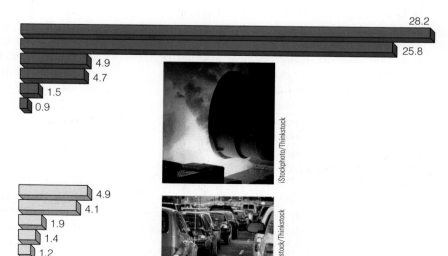

FIGURE 17-8 *Net energy ratios* for various energy systems over their estimated lifetimes. The higher the net energy ratio, the greater the net energy available. (Data from the U.S. Department of Energy; U.S. Department of Agriculture; Colorado Energy Research Institute, *Net Energy Analysis*, 1976; and Howard T. Odum and Elisabeth C. Odum, *Energy Basis for Man and Nature*, 3rd ed., New York: McGraw-Hill, 1981)

for industrial processes, and transportation. In terms of net energy, how do the energy resources used to heat your home and propel your car (if you have one) stack up compared to other alternatives?

Currently, oil has a high net energy ratio because much of it comes from large, accessible, and cheap-to-extract deposits such as those in the Middle East. When those are depleted, the net energy ratio of oil will decline and prices will rise.

Conventional nuclear energy has a low net energy ratio because of the large amounts of energy needed to make it available. We have to extract and process uranium ore, convert it into nuclear fuel, build and operate nuclear power plants, dismantle the highly radioactive plants after their 15–60 years of useful life, and store the resulting highly radioactive wastes safely for 10 000–240 000 years depending on the types of radioisotopes they contain. Each of these steps in what is called the *nuclear fuel cycle* uses energy and costs money. Some analysts estimate that ultimately the conventional nuclear fuel cycle will lead to a net energy loss; we will have to put more energy into it than we will ever get out of it.

17-2 OIL

What Is Crude Oil, and How Is It Extracted and Processed? Gooey Stuff to Which We Are Addicted

Crude oil is a thick liquid containing hydrocarbons that we extract from underground deposits and separate into products such as gasoline, heating oil, and asphalt.

Petroleum, or **crude oil** (oil as it comes out of the ground), is a thick and gooey liquid consisting of hundreds of combustible hydrocarbons along with small amounts of sulphur, oxygen, and nitrogen impurities. We have oil today because of a series of three geological events taking place over millions of years. The first event occurred when sediments buried dead organic material raining down onto seafloors faster than it could decay. The next event took place eons later when the seafloor sediments ended up with the right depth for pressure and heat to slowly "cook" or convert the buried organic material into *oil*. The third geological break came about because the oil was able to collect in porous limestone or sandstone rock covered by an impermeable cap of shale or silt to keep it from escaping (Figure 17-2) and thus making it and other fossil fuels part of the carbon cycle (Figure 4-28, p. 82).

All three events had to happen to result in the formation of oil, which provides about a third of the energy we use today to heat our homes and other buildings and to run our motor vehicles. Oil and its chemical cousin natural gas also provide us with food grown with the help of hydrocarbon-based fertilizers and pesticides. This type of oil is also known as *conventional oil.*

Today's global oil industry is a marvel of technology and management skills. Satellites help find promising oil deposits. Sophisticated computers and software programs analyze seismic data to create 3-D images of the Earth's interior. High-tech equipment can drill oil and natural gas wells to a depth of almost 11 kilometres (7 miles). Drilling platforms on the high seas are engineering marvels that can withstand major hurricanes. The incredibly complex process of managing and coordinating the discovery, production, marketing, and distribution of oil throughout the world to billions of users is an amazing process.

Deposits of crude oil and natural gas often are trapped together under a dome deep within the Earth's crust on land or under the seafloor (Figure 17-2). The crude oil is dispersed in pores and cracks in underground rock formations, somewhat like water saturating a sponge. To extract the oil, a well is drilled into the deposit. Then oil drawn by gravity out of the rock pores and into the bottom of the well is pumped to the surface.

On average, producers get only about 35–50% of the oil out of an oil deposit—although some believe that improved drilling technology may increase the recovery rate to 75%. The remaining *heavy crude oil* is too difficult or expensive to recover. As oil prices rise, it can become economical to remove about 10–25% of this remaining heavy oil by flushing the well with steam and water. But this lowers the net energy yield for the recovered oil.

Drilling for oil causes only moderate damage to the Earth's land because the wells occupy fairly little land area. But drilling for oil and transporting it around the world carries with it the risk of oil spills (pp. 557–559) on land and in aquatic systems. In addition, harmful environmental effects are associated with the extraction, processing, and use of any nonrenewable resource from the Earth's crust (Figure 16-12, p. 374).

According to oil producers, improved extraction technologies can increase oil production without serious damage to environmentally sensitive areas. One method allows oil and natural gas producers to drill deeper in most locations. In addition, oil producers can now use one drilling rig (derrick) on a pad to drill several gas or oil pockets at the same time. Another new technology allows oil or gas extraction from distances as far away as 8 kilometres (5 miles) by drilling at angles (slant drilling).

After it is extracted, crude oil is transported to a *refinery* by pipeline, truck, or ship (oil tanker). There it is heated and distilled in gigantic columns to separate it into components with different boiling points (Figure 17-9)—another technological marvel based on complex chemistry and chemical engineering. However, refining oil decreases its net energy yield.

Some products of oil distillation, called **petrochemicals,** are used as raw materials in manufacturing pesticides, plastics, synthetic fibres, paints, medicines, and many other products. Look at your clothes and other items around you and try to figure out how many of these things were made from chemicals produced by distilling oil.

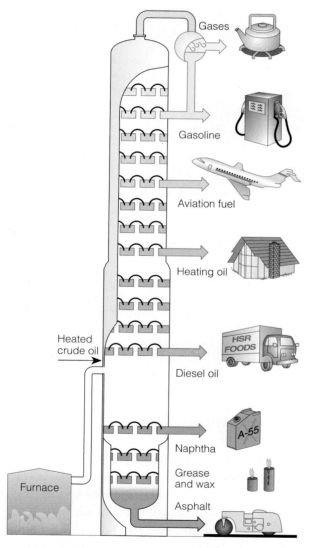

FIGURE 17-9 Refining crude oil. Based on their boiling points, components are removed at various levels in a giant distillation column. The most volatile components with the lowest boiling points are removed at the top of the column.

Who Has the World's Oil Supplies? OPEC Rules

Twelve OPEC countries—most of them in the Middle East—have at least 71% of the world's proven oil reserves and most of the world's unproven reserves.

The oil industry is the world's largest business. Thus control of current and future oil reserves is the single greatest source of global economic and political power.

The 12 countries that make up the Organization of the Petroleum Exporting Countries (OPEC) have at least 71% of the world's estimated crude oil reserves. This explains why OPEC is expected to have long-term control over the supplies and prices of the world's conventional oil. Today OPEC's members are Algeria, Angola, Ecuador, Iran, Iraq, Kuwait, Libya, Nigeria, Qatar, Saudi Arabia, United Arab Emirates, and Venezuela.

The proven oil reserves of each country change from year to year. According to the CIA (2012), in 2011 Saudi Arabia, with 18%, had the largest portion of the world's proven oil reserves, followed by Venezuela, with 14%. Canada was in third place, with 12%, because of its huge supply of oil sand. Other countries with large proven reserves include Iran (9%), Iraq (8%), Kuwait (7%), and the United Arab Emirates (7%).

Most analysts say it is only a matter of time before the Middle Eastern share of global oil production increases from its current 44% to at least 50%. This is why the world's other nations have such vital economic and military security interests in helping preserve political stability in the often-volatile Middle East.

Here is the problem in a nutshell. Oil is the most widely used energy resource in the world and in North America. Some call the people in developed countries *oilaholics,* and the world's largest suppliers to them are Canada, Saudi Arabia, and several other Persian Gulf Middle Eastern countries. Yet the current importance of oil to the transportation system, in particular, means that oil is likely to remain a crucial resource for many years. To some, the stability of the world economy depends largely on how long Saudi Arabia's House of Saud rulers can continue. There is also concern that terrorist assaults on a few key parts of the country's oil system, or a war close to the oil fields, could put the Saudis out of the oil business for up to two years and create global economic chaos.

Case Study: How Much Oil Do Canada and the United States Have? Have and Have-Not

Whereas Canada is a net exporter of oil, the United States—the world's largest oil user—has only 1.4% of the world's proven oil reserves.

Figure 17-10 shows the locations of the major known deposits of oil and natural gas in Canada. Canada's oil reserves are concentrated in Alberta. Large areas of *oil sands* in this province are being developed. Another area of growing importance is the East Coast Hibernia

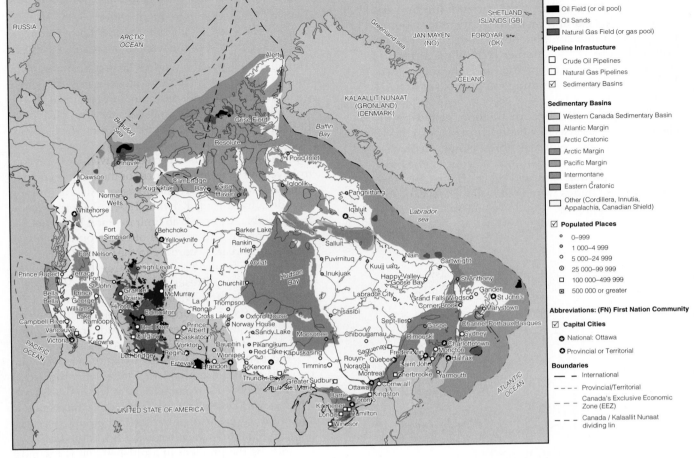

FIGURE 17-10 Map of the locations of the major known deposits of oil fields, oil sands, and natural gas fields, as well as the sedimentary basins, of Canada. (The Atlas of Canada, http://atlas.nrcan.gc.ca/site/english/maps/economic/energy/oilgas, Natural Resources Canada. Reproduced with the permission of the Minister of Public Works and Government Services, 2012.)

oil field (Spotlight, p. 393) and the nearby White Rose and Terra Nova oil fields. Canada is a net exporter of oil, shipping 30% of its production to the United States every year and keeping 70% for domestic use. As well, Canada has surplus natural gas. Some of the natural gas is used for heating and transportation purposes formerly supplied by oil, freeing up additional oil for potential export (http://www.eia.doe.gov).

The United States has only 1.6% of the world's oil reserves. But it uses about 24% of the crude oil extracted worldwide each year (over two-thirds of that for transportation), mostly because oil is usually an abundant, convenient, and cheap fuel (Figure 17-11). Despite an upsurge in exploration and test drilling, U.S. oil extraction has declined since 1985, and most geologists do not expect a significant increase in domestic supplies. And the United States produces most of its dwindling supply of oil at a high cost of $7.50–$10 per barrel compared to about $2.50 in Saudi Arabia.

Bottom line: If you think of U.S. oil reserves as a six-pack of oil, four of the cans are empty. Geologists estimate that if the country opens up virtually all of its public lands and coastal regions to oil exploration, it may find at best about half a can of new oil at a high economic and environmental cost.

In 2009, the United States imported about 52% of the oil it used (up from 36% in 1973 when OPEC imposed an oil embargo against the United States and other nations). According to the U.S. Department of Energy (DOE), the United States could be importing 64–70% of the oil it uses by 2020.

How Long Will Conventional Oil Supplies Last? The End of the Oil Era Is in Sight

Known and projected global oil reserves should last for 42–93 years depending on how rapidly we use oil.

According to various experts, production of the world's estimated oil reserves is nearing its peak or has already passed its peak. Canada's oil peak is difficult to predict; the Alberta Energy and Utilities Board estimates that Canada's oil sands could yield oil for

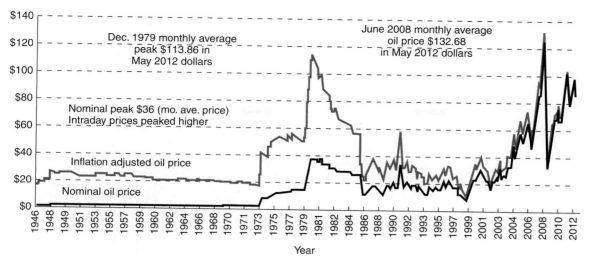

FIGURE 17-11 The nominal (face value) price of oil is deceptive; when the cost of crude oil is translated to May 2012 dollars (adjusted for inflation), it is clear that crude oil has often been at a price of $20 to $30 per barrel. The 1979 spike of the famous "energy crisis" was surpassed in 2008, driven by market uncertainties about oil. Analysts predict rising trends and more spikes as oil supplies are depleted. (© InflationData.com)

several hundred years at current rates of extraction, but much depends on the price of oil and on advances in mining technology. U.S. oil reserves in Texas and the lower 48 states already peaked in 1971.

There have been many attempts to predict when oil reserves will peak and begin to decline. Two of the most famous attempts were made by M. King Hubbert, a geologist. In 1956, Hubbert predicted that U.S. oil production would peak in the 1970s. His model, known as "Hubbert's Peak," looked like a bell-shaped curve that centred on the '70s. He was ridiculed for his prediction until it turned out that he was correct. In 1974, he used Hubbert's Peak methods again to predict that, if current trends continued, world oil production would peak around 1995 and decline thereafter. Many variables could affect such a prediction—such as new discoveries of oil and more efficient techniques—however, some analysts believe that the peak of world oil production occurred in 2006 (Figure 17-12, p. 392; Schindler and Zittel, 2008).

We are not yet running out of oil. But once oil production peaks, we will begin sliding down the bell-shaped oil production curve of a nonrenewable resource from 50% depletion toward 80% depletion when it costs too much to extract what is left. At some point during this slide, we will shift from an abundant supply of cheap oil (Figure 17-11) to a dwindling supply of increasingly expensive oil (Figure 17-12).

According to geologists, known and projected global reserves of oil are expected to be 80% depleted within 42–93 years depending on how rapidly we use oil. If these estimates are correct, oil should be reaching its sunset years sometime this century. Appendix 6 (p. A-15) summarizes milestones in the Age of Oil.

CONSIDER, DISCUSS, OR DEBATE

Will oil shortages act to encourage the development of new technologies or merely increase the potential for political tension, war, and terrorism in the world? Explain.

Can We Meet the World's Growing Demand for Oil? Rapid Exponential Growth Is a Hungry Beast

Just to keep using conventional oil at the current rate, we must discover global oil reserves equivalent to a new Saudi Arabian supply every 10 years.

Even if much more oil is somehow found, we are ignoring the consequences of the high (1–5% per year) exponential growth in oil consumption in the world, especially in developing countries (Figure 17-13). It is hard to get a grip on the incredible amount of oil we consume. Maybe this will help. *Stretched end to end, the number of barrels of oil the world used in 2011 would wrap around the Earth's equator more than 700 times, and projected oil use in 2030 would circle the equator approximately 900 times!*

Suppose we continue to use oil at the current rate with no increase in oil consumption—a highly unlikely assumption. Even under this conservative no-growth estimate:

- Saudi Arabia, with the world's largest crude oil reserves, could supply world oil needs for about 10 years.

- Canada, with the world's second-largest crude oil reserves, could supply world oil needs for about six years.

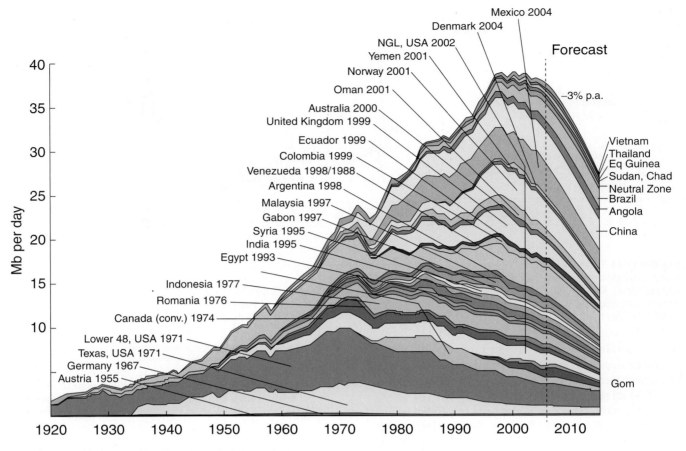

FIGURE 17-12 Many people have attempted various forms of analysis extending the ideas of Hubbert's Peak. This example shows when the conventional oil supplies of various countries peaked and began to decline. Note that Canada's conventional supplies began to decline in 1974; our oil sands are not included in this diagram. Schindler and Zittel (2008) analyzed the OPEC countries separately, but concluded that their oil production had also peaked in 2006. (© Energy Watch Group/ Ludwig-Boelkow-Foundation)

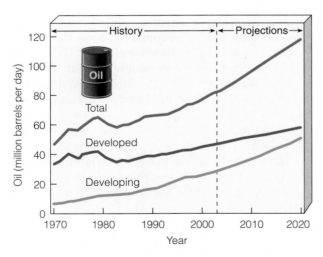

FIGURE 17-13 Oil consumption globally and in developed and developing regions, with projections to 2020. In order, the world's three largest consumers of oil are the United States, China, and Japan—all with limited domestic oil supplies. (International Energy Agency, *World Energy Outlook 2011*)

■ The estimated reserves in Alaska's Arctic National Wildlife Refuge, an area that is hotly contested as a potential site for fossil fuel extraction, would meet the world's current oil demand for only 1–5 months or U.S. oil demand for 7–24 months. (Critics have pointed out that an improvement in motor vehicle fuel efficiency of only 0.4 kilometres per litre would yield more oil than lies under the wildlife refuge.)

Thus for the world just to keep using conventional oil at the current rate, we must discover reserves equivalent to a new Saudi Arabian supply every 10 years. According to most geologists, this is highly unlikely.

And many developing countries such as China and India are rapidly expanding their use of oil. China is now the world's second-largest oil importer and is competing with the United States for an increasing share of the world's diminishing supply of oil. Indeed,

The Hibernia Oil Field

Discovered on December 11, 1979, the Hibernia oil field is located on the Grand Banks, 315 kilometres east of St. John's, Newfoundland and Labrador, in about 90 metres (295 feet) of water. With an estimated 874 million barrels of light high-grade crude oil, Hibernia is the fifth-largest find in Canadian history.

Hibernia's location in an iceberg lane makes oil extraction a particular challenge. A special rig was built to access the oil. The 224-metre-tall (735-foot) drilling platform was floated to the site and then anchored to the seafloor.

It was built to withstand the force of collision with a 6-million-tonne iceberg travelling at one knot. The drilling rig is defended by tugboats that can intercept and move incoming icebergs. If all else fails, the rig can be released from the ocean floor and floated to safety. Skeptics warn that a massive oil spill here would be disastrous for the fishery, for marine life, and for tourism.

Hibernia has been producing oil and natural gas since November 17, 1997. The project employs more than 700 people directly and creates spinoff employment for at least 3 000 others. The Hibernia oil field

is expected to have a 25-year lifespan and to provide substantial economic benefits that will help compensate for the declining East Coast fishery.

---

if everyone in the world consumed as much oil as the average American, the world's proven oil reserves would be gone in a decade. Exponential growth is an incredibly powerful force.

Case Study: Why Has the Arctic Suddenly Gained World Attention? New Potential for Oil and Gas Discovery

In recent years, the Arctic sea ice has melted to unprecedented levels, opening one of the world's least explored regions to oil and gas discovery.

With Arctic sea ice melting back in response to warmer temperatures (Chapter 21), many countries have been showing keen interest in exploring the continental shelf areas of the Arctic for oil and gas potential. In May 2008, a team of scientists from the U.S. Geological Survey completed an assessment of the oil and gas potential of all areas north of the Arctic Circle (Panel a of Figure 17-14). Because there was a lack of seismic and drilling information for the region, they used newly compiled maps of Arctic sedimentary basins and probability-based computer models that estimated oil and gas potential based on the types, ages, and formations of the rocks.

The team concluded that approximately 90 billion barrels of oil, 47 trillion cubic metres (1 669 trillion cubic feet) of natural gas, and 44 billion barrels of natural gas liquids may await discovery in the Arctic. About 84% of this is expected to be found offshore on the shallow continental shelf. Panels b and c of Figure 17-14 show where the oil and gas are predicted to occur on the basis of their analysis. Panel d of Figure 17-14 illustrates the probabilities of finding at least one undiscovered oil

and/or gas field with recoverable resources greater than 50 million barrels of oil equivalent (http://energy .usgs.gov/RegionalStudies/Arctic.aspx/). Note that many of the most promising areas are in and around parts of the Arctic long considered by us to be Canadian.

The government of Canada will have to be prepared to deal with an unprecedented wave of fossil fuel exploration, geological claims, sovereignty challenges, political friction, and environmental impact (see also p. 506 and http://www.nelson.com/livinginthe environment3e.com).

CONSIDER, DISCUSS, OR DEBATE

How should the government of Canada prepare itself for the anticipated challenges to its sovereignty in the Arctic? Which countries are most likely to challenge us, and how should Canada react?

What Are the Major Advantages and Disadvantages of Conventional Oil? A Difficult Choice

Conventional oil is versatile fuel, and reserves can last for at least 50 years, but burning it produces air pollution and releases the greenhouse gas carbon dioxide.

Figure 17-15 (p. 395) lists the advantages and disadvantages of using conventional crude oil as an energy resource. A serious problem is that burning oil or any fossil fuel releases CO_2 into the atmosphere and thus can help promote climate change through global warming. Currently, burning oil mostly as gasoline and diesel fuel for transportation accounts for about 43% of global CO_2 emissions. Figure 17-16 (p. 395)

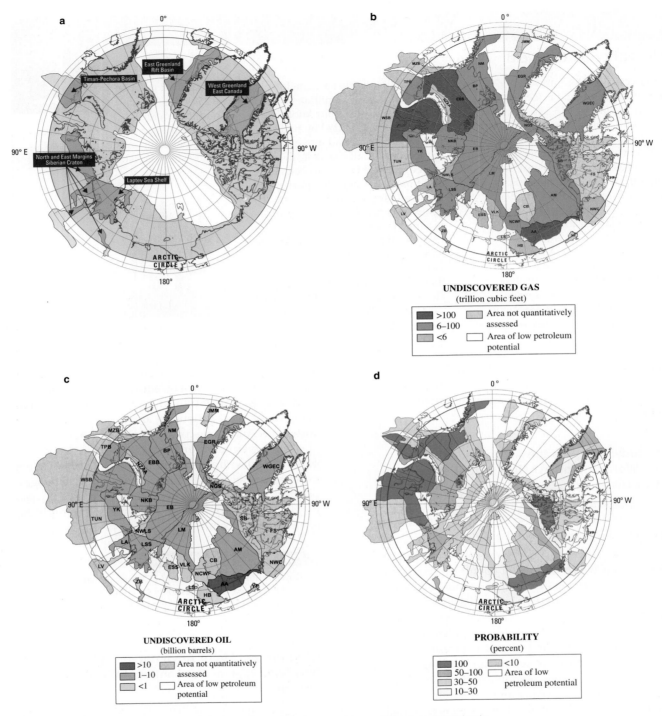

FIGURE 17-14 Panel "a" illustrates the land, continental shelves, and some of the more completely assessed geological provinces (regions delineated by the rocks found there) of the Arctic. Panel "b" and "c" predict where the greatest concentrations of gas and oil, respectively, will be located; the small numbers are short forms for the names of geological provinces. Panel "d" illustrates the probability of finding a large oil and/or gas deposit in each geological province. (U.S. Geological Survey, http://energy.usgs.gov/RegionalStudies/Arctic.aspx/)

compares the relative amounts of CO_2 emitted per unit of energy by the major fossil fuels and nuclear power.

In 1999 Mike Bowling, CEO of ARCO Oil, said, "We are embarked on the beginning of the last days of the Age of Oil." He went on to discuss the need for the world to shift from a carbon-based to a hydrogen-based energy economy during this century.

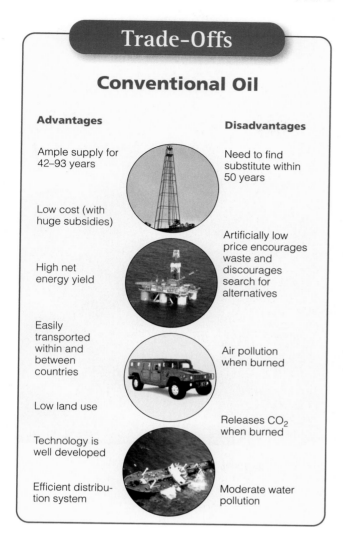

Trade-Offs

Conventional Oil

Advantages	Disadvantages
Ample supply for 42–93 years	Need to find substitute within 50 years
Low cost (with huge subsidies)	Artificially low price encourages waste and discourages search for alternatives
High net energy yield	
Easily transported within and between countries	Air pollution when burned
Low land use	Releases CO_2 when burned
Technology is well developed	
Efficient distribution system	Moderate water pollution

FIGURE 17-15 Trade-offs: advantages and disadvantages of using conventional crude oil as an energy resource. Pick the single advantage and disadvantage that you think are the most important.

How Useful Are Heavy Oils from Oil Sand and Oil Shale? Can Heavier Substitutes Save the Day?

Heavy oils from oil sand and oil shale could supplement conventional oil, but there are environmental problems.

So far we have been considering conventional oil—in other words, liquid crude oil that is pumped from oil wells. Oil that must be extracted from substrate such as sand or rock by means of specialized processes is termed **unconventional oil. Oil sand,** is a mixture of clay, sand, water, and a combustible organic material called **bitumen**—a thick and sticky heavy oil with a high sulphur content.

Oil sands nearest the surface are dug up with tremendous disturbance to the area (see surface mining on pp. 371–372) by gigantic electric shovels and loaded

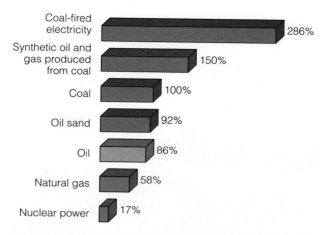

FIGURE 17-16 CO_2 emissions per unit of energy produced by various fuels, expressed as percentages of emissions produced by burning coal directly. (Data from U.S. Department of Energy)

into house-sized trucks that carry them to upgrading plants (Figure 17-17, p. 396). There they are mixed with hot water and steam to extract the bitumen, which is heated in huge cookers to convert it into a low-sulphur synthetic crude oil suitable for refining. Heating the cookers requires vast amounts of natural gas that reduces the net energy yield for the oil. Two tons of oil sand are strip-mined for each barrel of oil and three barrels of water are needed to extract each barrel of bitumen.

About 80% of Alberta's oil sands are too deep to permit open-pit surface mining. In this case, the bitumen can be extracted by one of several in situ methods that cause relatively little disturbance compared to surface mining. Cyclic steam stimulation involves softening the bitumen with steam and then extracting it (Figure 17-18, p. 396); this method uses a vertical well to inject steam and extract bitumen, so it works best where the bitumen deposits run vertically. Steam-assisted gravity drainage involves two horizontal wells; the upper well injects steam while the lower well extracts the condensed steam and softened bitumen (Figure 17-19, p. 396). This works best if the bitumen runs in horizontal seams.

A relatively new method called vapour extraction uses solvents such as butane to dilute and extract the bitumen without the need for energy-expensive steam. Yet another new method called toe-to-heel air injection involves igniting bitumen underground in order to soften the surrounding bitumen enough to pump.

To date the largest oil sands projects, operated by Syncrude and Suncor, have been surface mines. In situ projects have been smaller but gaining in numbers. A 50:50 balance between the two types of projects was reached in 2007, and future expansion is expected to favour in situ projects.

FIGURE 17-17 Canada's oil sands are typically mined near the surface using gigantic equipment. The technology used to separate oil from sand has been improving rapidly.

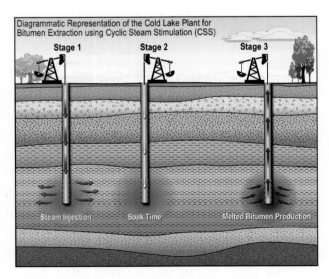

FIGURE 17-18 Cyclic steam stimulation involves using steam to heat the bitumen, making it easier to pump. A vertical well is used, so this method works best in bitumen deposits that are thick or that run vertically. (Energy Resources Conservation Board/Alberta Geological Survey)

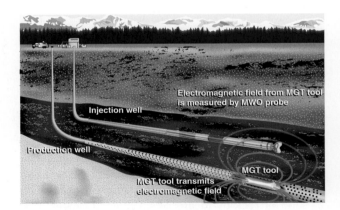

FIGURE 17-19 Steam-assisted gravity drainage involves drilling two parallel horizontal wells, guided by special probes; the magnetic guidance tool (MGT) in the first well generates a magnetic field that guides the measurement-while-drilling (MWD) probe as the second well is drilled. Steam is injected in the top well, and softened bitumen is extracted through the bottom well. This method works best where the bitumen deposits run horizontally. (Courtesy of Halliburton)

Environmental Impacts of Mining and Processing Oil Sands

Although the development of Canada's oil sands is associated with many positive outcomes such as the generation of income, the creation of jobs, and security from dependence on foreign oil sources, there are also many negatives. According to Dyer et al. (2008) of the Pembina Institute, the technologies involved in mining and processing oil sands "make the product among the most environmentally costly sources of transport fuel in the world." The mining of oil sands calls for massive disruption of forests and soils over a huge area of boreal forest in Northern Alberta. Approximately 2 tonnes of oil sands must be mined and processed to create a single barrel of oil. Overall, about 3 000 square kilometres (1 158 square miles) of boreal forest is slated to be cleared. The result will be a change from a landscape of wild forests to a terrain of open-pit mines, huge waste storage ponds, and other disturbed spaces (Figure 17-17).

The mining and processing of oil sands is very energy-intensive. Various fossil fuels are used to power the oversize mining equipment. Natural gas supplies the energy to separate oil from the oil sands. It takes 34 cubic metres (1 201 cubic feet) of natural gas for each barrel of bitumen produced. This means that the net energy

yield is very low (the equivalent of 0.7 barrels of oil must be invested to gain a barrel of oil). Furthermore, this massive use of fuel hastens the end of our natural gas supplies and produces large amounts of greenhouse gases such as CO_2. The oil sands are predicted to account for about half of the increase in national CO_2 emissions since 2003. Other forms of air pollution include the release of sulphur dioxide (SO_2), nitrogen oxides (NO_x), and volatile organic compounds (VOCs).

Typically, 2 to 5 cubic metres (70 to 177 cubic feet) of water are used to make each cubic metre of synthetic crude oil. Overall, about 550 million cubic metres (19 423 million cubic feet) of water per year are drawn from the Athabasca River, more than the amount used by a city of 2 million people over a year. Furthermore, the water is taken even when the water levels are low, potentially impacting fish habitat. Critics fear that the projected expansion of the oil sands operations will quickly surpass the ability of the area to provide water without creating serious water shortages affecting humans and wildlife.

Water that is used in oil sands production is now contaminated and cannot be returned to the river. It is stored in large holding

ponds where some of it may leak into surface water and groundwater. People downstream of the oil sands operations complain about decreased water quality, toxins in fish (arsenic, mercury, and polycyclic aromatic hydrocarbons), and health issues they attribute to the oil sands operations.

The government and the industry both have poor records of ensuring that environmental considerations are top priorities. For example, the Government of Alberta is supposed to ensure that mining companies rehabilitate disturbed lands, and the companies are supposed to comply and receive certification that the land has been reclaimed appropriately. Yet after 40 years of oil sands operations in the area, no lands were certified until 2008; at present, only about 3% of the 33 000 hectares (81 544 acres) of disturbed lands have been reclaimed.

The Pembina Report Card says that 9 out of 10 oil sands companies receive a failing grade for their operations. The report makes a series of recommendations to government and to industry in terms of improving on the environmental problems described above. For further details, visit http://www.pembina.org.pub.1571.

Currently these deposits supply about a half of Canada's oil needs and this proportion is expected to increase. Because of the dramatic reductions in development and production costs, the oil industry has begun counting Canada's oil sands as reserves of conventional oil. This means that Canada has 12% of the world's oil reserves, making it number three after Saudi Arabia and Venezuela.

If a pipeline is built to transfer some of this synthetic crude oil from Western Canada to the northwestern United States, Canada could greatly reduce future U.S. dependence on oil imports from the Middle East and add to its income. On the other hand, there

are many issue involved with such pipelines. The topic will be handled in depth on the book's website.

Bad news. Extracting and producing oil sands has a severe impact on the land and produces more water pollution, much more air pollution (especially sulphur dioxide), and more CO_2 per unit of energy than conventional crude oil. Environmentalists have been concerned that large areas of Alberta's boreal forests will be affected by surface disturbance and other impacts of the oil sands projects. As well, the large amounts of CO_2 produced by these projects will frustrate Canada's attempts to combat climate change by reducing greenhouse gas emissions (Spotlight and Chapter 21).

FIGURE 17-20 **Natural capital:** oil shale rock (left) and the shale oil (right) extracted from it. Big oil shale projects have been cancelled because of high costs associated with mining and processing oil shale.

Another potential source of oil is deposits of **oil shale,** which is neither oil nor shale rock. Instead, *oil shales* are fine-grained sedimentary rocks (Figure 17-20, left) containing a solid combustible mixture of hydrocarbons called **kerogen.** It can be distilled from crushed oil shale rock by heating it in a large container to yield **shale oil** (Figure 17-20, right). Before the thick shale oil can be sent by pipeline to a refinery, it must be heated to increase its flow rate and processed to remove sulphur, nitrogen, and other impurities.

Estimated potential global supplies of shale oil are about 240 times larger than estimated global supplies of conventional oil. But most deposits are of such a low grade that with current oil prices and technology it takes more energy and money to mine and convert kerogen to crude oil than the resulting fuel is worth. Producing and using shale oil also has a much higher environmental impact than conventional oil.

Figure 17-21 lists the advantages and disadvantages of using heavy oil from oil sand and oil shale as energy resources. Overall, do you believe the advantages outweigh the disadvantages?

17-3 NATURAL GAS

What Is Natural Gas? Mostly Methane

Natural gas, consisting mostly of methane, is often found above reservoirs of crude oil.

In its underground gaseous state, **natural gas** is a mixture of 50–90% by volume of methane (CH_4), the simplest **hydrocarbon**. It also contains smaller amounts of heavier gaseous hydrocarbons such as ethane (C_2H_6), propane (C_3H_8), and butane (C_4H_{10}), and small amounts of highly toxic hydrogen sulphide (H_2S).

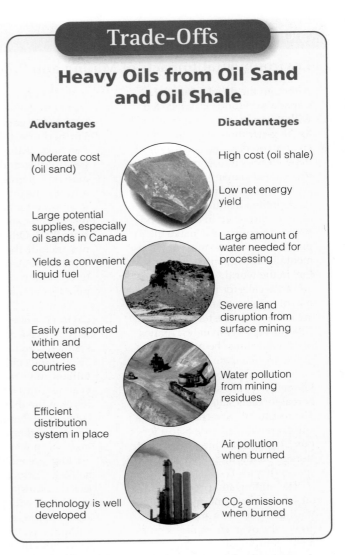

Trade-Offs

Heavy Oils from Oil Sand and Oil Shale

Advantages	Disadvantages
Moderate cost (oil sand)	High cost (oil shale)
	Low net energy yield
Large potential supplies, especially oil sands in Canada	Large amount of water needed for processing
Yields a convenient liquid fuel	
	Severe land disruption from surface mining
Easily transported within and between countries	
	Water pollution from mining residues
Efficient distribution system in place	
	Air pollution when burned
Technology is well developed	CO_2 emissions when burned

FIGURE 17-21 **Trade-offs:** advantages and disadvantages of using heavy oils from oil sand and oil shale as energy resources. Pick the single advantage and disadvantage that you think are the most important.

Conventional natural gas lies above most reservoirs of crude oil (Figure 17-2). Like oil, natural gas was formed from fossil deposits of phytoplankton and animals buried on the seafloor for millions of years and subjected to high temperatures and pressures.

However, unless a natural gas pipeline has been built, deposits of natural gas found above oil deposits (Figure 17-2) cannot be used. Indeed, the natural gas found above oil reservoirs in deep-sea and remote land areas is often viewed as an unwanted by-product and is burned off. This wastes a valuable energy resource and releases carbon dioxide into the atmosphere.

Unconventional natural gas is found in other underground sources. One example is *shale gas*, which is associated with certain rock formations (see the following Spotlight on shale gas).

Another example is *methane hydrate,* in which small bubbles of natural gas are trapped in ice crystals deep under the Arctic permafrost and beneath deep-ocean sediments. Globally the amount of energy in methane hydrates is about twice that in the Earth's oil, natural gas, and coal resources combined.

So far it costs too much to get natural gas from methane hydrates, but the extraction technology is being developed rapidly, especially in Japan, which has large deposits off its coast and few deposits of conventional oil and natural gas. One problem is that when methane hydrate is brought to the surface it warms up and releases methane (a greenhouse gas) into the atmosphere.

When a natural gas field is tapped, propane and butane gases are liquefied and removed as **liquefied petroleum gas (LPG).** LPG is stored in pressurized tanks for use mostly in rural areas not served by natural gas pipelines. The rest of the gas (mostly methane) is dried to remove water vapour. Then it is cleansed of poisonous hydrogen sulphide and other impurities and pumped into pressurized pipelines for distribution.

At a very low temperature natural gas can be converted to **liquefied natural gas (LNG).** This highly flammable liquid can then be shipped to other countries in refrigerated tanker ships.

How Is Natural Gas Used? A Versatile Fuel

Natural gas can be burned to heat space and water, generate electricity, and propel vehicles.

Natural gas is a versatile fuel that can be burned to heat water and buildings and to generate electricity. It can also be used as a fuel for cars and trucks with fairly inexpensive engine modifications. Natural gas is especially useful for running fleets of taxis and delivery and work vehicles operating from garages and maintenance facilities that can be used to supply them with this fuel.

Increasingly, natural gas is used to run medium-sized turbines that produce electricity. These clean-burning turbines have a much higher energy efficiency (50–60%) than coal-burning power plants (24–35%). They are cheaper to build per kilowatt-hour, require less time to install, and are easier and cheaper to maintain than large-scale coal and nuclear power plants. Burning natural gas emits CO_2 but at a lower rate per unit of energy than other fossil fuels (Figure 17-16). For these reasons, natural gas use is expected to grow worldwide (Figure 17-4) and in the United States (Figure 17-6).

Shale Gas

Shale gas is natural gas that has been collected from where it was trapped in fine-grain sedimentary rocks. The gas is released by a process called *hydraulic fracturing* (or *fracking*). First a well is drilled and a pressurized fluid or gas is pumped down the well to fracture the sedimentary rocks. Then a fluid (usually water mixed with sand and special additives) is pumped into the cracks. When the pumping pressure stops, the sand keeps the cracks open so that the natural gas can escape and be collected (Alberta Energy, 2012).

Commercial production of shale gas is in its early stages in Canada; however, this practice has been expanding in the United States over the past decade, driven by the declining potential of conventional gas deposits. In fact, shale gas has been the fastest-growing segment of primary energy production in the United States.

On the positive side, this is a way to collect natural gas that would otherwise be trapped in the rocks. Proponents argue that it will double the supplies of natural gas, and that it will help to slow global warming since natural gas can be burned with fewer greenhouse gas emissions than other fossil fuels such as coal.

Opponents argue that the industry is greatly exaggerating the amount of shale gas that exists to be collected. They point out that shale gas contains more methane (a potent greenhouse gas) than natural gas and will therefore have a greater potential to contribute to climate change than natural gas (though not as much as coal).

The main issue about shale gas is its potential to create water pollution. As mentioned above, special additives—such as lubricants, anti-rust agents, and antimicrobial agents—are in the water-and-sand mixture that is pumped down the well. Since only about 50–70% of that water is recovered from the well, large quantities of chemicals are being injected into the ground, potentially finding their way into aquifers and drinking water supplies.

There have been a number of disputes about whether or not shale gas production has been responsible for water pollution (Energy Institute, 2011; MIT Energy Initiative, 2011). A Canadian company has developed a method of fracking shale, using liquefied petroleum gas, that they claim has much less environmental impact than other methods (Brino and Nearing, 2011). However, public opposition to fracking is increasing (Seguin, 2011). This is a topic to watch closely as companies attempt to gear up shale gas production in Canada!

Who Has the World's Natural Gas Supplies, and How Long Will the Supplies Last? More Abundant Than Oil

Russia and Iran have almost half of the world's reserves of conventional natural gas, and global reserves should last 62–125 years.

Russia has about 25% of the world's proven natural gas reserves, followed by Iran (15%) and Qatar (14%). About 41% of the world's natural gas reserves are in Middle Eastern countries. Geologists expect to find more natural gas, especially in unexplored developing countries.

The long-term global outlook for natural gas supplies is better than for conventional oil. At the current consumption rate, geologists estimate that known reserves and undiscovered potential reserves of conventional natural gas should last the world for 62–125 years depending on how rapidly it is used.

They project that *conventional* and *unconventional* supplies of natural gas (the latter available at higher prices) should last at least 200 years at the current consumption rate and 80 years if consumption rates rise 2% per year.

Figure 17-22 lists the advantages and disadvantages of natural gas as an energy resource. Energy experts project greatly increased global use of natural gas during this century because of its fairly abundant supply, and lower pollution and CO_2 rates per unit of energy compared to other fossil fuels (Figure 17-16).

Because of its advantages over oil, coal, and nuclear energy, some analysts see natural gas as the best fuel to help make the transition to improved energy efficiency and greater use of solar energy and hydrogen over the next 50 years.

Trade-Offs

Conventional Natural Gas

Advantages	Disadvantages
Ample supplies (125 years)	Nonrenewable resource
High net energy yield	Releases CO_2 when burned
Low cost (with huge subsidies)	Methane (a greenhouse gas) can leak from pipelines
Less air pollution than other fossil fuels	
Lower CO_2 emissions than other fossil fuels	Difficult to transfer from one country to another
Moderate environmental impact	Shipped across ocean as highly explosive LNG
Easily transported by pipeline	
Low land use	Sometimes burned off and wasted at wells because of low price
Good fuel for fuel cells and gas turbines	Requires pipelines

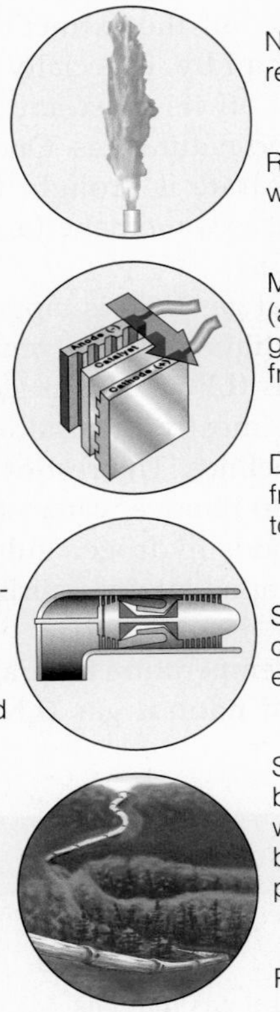

FIGURE 17-22 Trade-offs: advantages and disadvantages of using conventional natural gas as an energy resource. Pick the single advantage and disadvantage that you think are the most important.

What Is the Future of Natural Gas in Canada and the United States? Declining Supplies

Natural gas production in the United States is expected to continue declining, whereas Canadian production is expected to peak between 2020 and 2030.

Today Canada has surplus natural gas and exports 58% of its annual production to the United States. Both countries use natural gas to heat homes, and the United States burns natural gas to produce 16% of the country's electricity.

Bad news. U.S. production of natural gas has been declining for a long time, and most geologists do not believe this situation will be reversed. The United States could import more natural gas from Canada, but this would require building a major pipeline between the two countries. Also, production in Canada is expected to peak between 2020 and 2030. Then Canada, the United States, and the rest of the world will have to rely increasingly on Russia and the Middle East for supplies of natural gas.

More liquefied natural gas could be imported by ship. But this requires cooling the gas to a very low temperature to liquefy it, shipping it in special tankers, and building special LNG receiving terminals. This is quite expensive and reduces the net energy yield for natural gas. Also, LNG is highly flammable and could lead to large-scale fires at receiving terminals.

17-4 COAL

What Is Coal, and How Is It Extracted? A Mostly Carbon Fuel

Coal, which can be extracted by surface and underground mining, consists mostly of carbon plus small amounts of sulphur and trace amounts of mercury and radioactive material.

Coal is a solid fossil fuel formed in several stages as buried remains of land plants that lived 300–400 million years ago were subjected to intense heat and pressure over many millions of years (Figure 17-23). Coal is mostly carbon and contains small amounts of sulphur, released into the atmosphere as SO_2 when coal is burned. Burning coal also releases trace amounts of toxic mercury and radioactive materials.

Anthracite (which is about 98% carbon) is the most desirable type of coal because of its high heat content and low sulphur content. However, because it takes much longer to form, it is less common and therefore more expensive than other types of coal.

Some coal is extracted underground by miners working in tunnels and shafts (Figure 16-11, p. 373). This is one of the world's most dangerous occupations because of accidents and black lung disease caused by prolonged inhalation of coal dust particles. *Area strip mining* (Figure 16-10c, p. 372) is used to extract coal found close to the Earth's surface on flat terrain, and *contour strip mining* (Figure 16-10d) is used on hilly or mountainous terrain. In some cases, entire mountaintops are removed and dumped into the valleys below to expose seams of coal. The scarred land from the surface mining of coal is not restored in most countries and only partially restored in parts of Canada and the United States.

After coal is removed, trains usually transport it to a processing plant, where it is broken up, crushed, and washed to remove impurities. After the coal is dried it is shipped (again usually by train) to users, mostly power plants and industrial plants.

How Is Coal Used, and How Long Will Supplies Last?

Coal is burned mostly to produce electricity and steel, and reserves in the United States, Russia, and China could last for hundreds of years.

Coal is burned to generate 40% of the world's electricity and make three-fourths of its steel. Coal is by far the world's most abundant fossil fuel, with deposits containing 10 times more energy than oil and natural gas resources combined. Identified and unidentified supplies of coal could last the world for 200–1 000 years, depending on the rate of usage.

Canada has only 1% of the world's proven reserves of coal. However, with only 0.5% of the world's population, Canada can still export 14% of its annual coal production to the United States. The United States has one-fourth of the world's proven coal reserves. Russia has 19% and China 14%.

In 2006, the largest consumers of coal were China (38%), the United States (16%), and India (8%).

China has enough proven coal reserves to last 100 years at its current rate of consumption. U.S. coal reserves could last about 250 years at the current consumption rate. However, if U.S. coal use should increase by 4% a year—as the coal industry projects—the country's proven coal reserves would last only 64 years.

Figure 17-24 lists the advantages and disadvantages of using coal as an energy resource. *Bottom line.* Coal is the world's most abundant fossil fuel, but

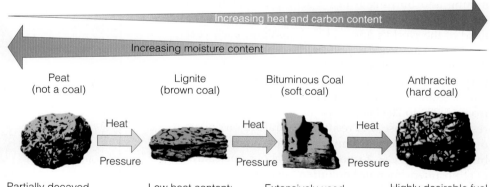

FIGURE 17-23 Natural capital: stages in coal formation over millions of years. Peat is a soil material made of moist, partially decomposed organic matter. Lignite and bituminous coal are sedimentary rocks, whereas anthracite is a metamorphic rock (Figure 16-8, p. 370).

Increasing heat and carbon content

Increasing moisture content

Peat (not a coal)
Partially decayed plant matter in swamps and bogs; low heat content

Heat / Pressure

Lignite (brown coal)
Low heat content; low sulphur content; limited supplies in most areas

Heat / Pressure

Bituminous Coal (soft coal)
Extensively used as a fuel because of its high heat content and large supplies; normally has a high sulphur content

Heat / Pressure

Anthracite (hard coal)
Highly desirable fuel because of its high heat content and low sulphur content; supplies are limited in most areas

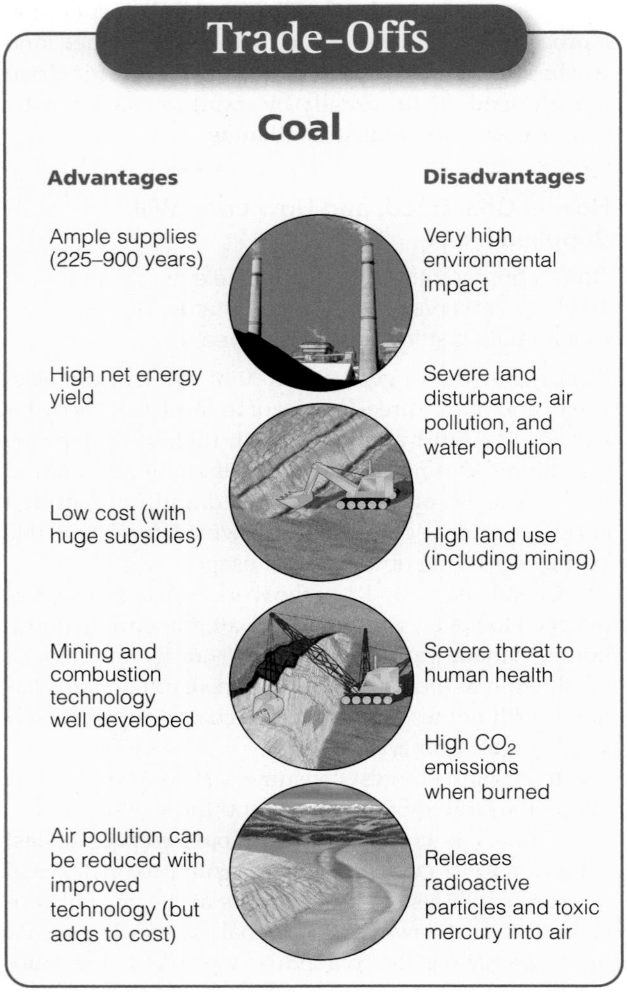

Trade-Offs

Coal

Advantages		Disadvantages
Ample supplies (225–900 years)		Very high environmental impact
High net energy yield		Severe land disturbance, air pollution, and water pollution
Low cost (with huge subsidies)		High land use (including mining)
Mining and combustion technology well developed		Severe threat to human health
		High CO_2 emissions when burned
Air pollution can be reduced with improved technology (but adds to cost)		Releases radioactive particles and toxic mercury into air

FIGURE 17-24 **Trade-offs:** advantages and disadvantages of using coal as an energy resource. Pick the single advantage and disadvantage that you think are the most important.

mining and burning it has a severe environmental impact on air, water, and land and accounts for over a third of the world's annual CO_2 emissions. Each year in North America, air pollutants—such as sulphur dioxide, particulates, and toxic metals such as mercury, arsenic, and lead—released when coal is burned kill thousands of people prematurely (estimates range from 65 000 to 200 000), cause at least 50 000 cases of respiratory disease, and result in several billion dollars of property damage. Many people are unaware that burning coal is also responsible for about one-fourth of atmospheric mercury pollution in North America.

In China, millions of people burning coal in unvented stoves for heat and cooking are exposed to dangerous levels of particulate matter and toxic metals such as mercury and arsenic. On the other hand, there are new "clean coal" technologies. We will discuss these in detail on the website.

CONSIDER, DISCUSS, OR DEBATE

Is coal likely to be phased out given the powerful industries that support its continued use? What is your viewpoint about coal?

What Are the Advantages and Disadvantages of Converting Solid Coal into Gaseous and Liquid Fuels? Better for the Air, Worse for the Climate

Coal can be converted to gaseous and liquid fuels that burn cleaner than coal, but costs are high, and producing and burning them add more carbon dioxide to the atmosphere than burning coal.

Solid coal can be converted into **synthetic natural gas (SNG)** by **coal gasification** or into a liquid fuel such as methanol or synthetic gasoline by **coal liquefaction.** Figure 17-25 lists the advantages and disadvantages of using these *synfuels*.

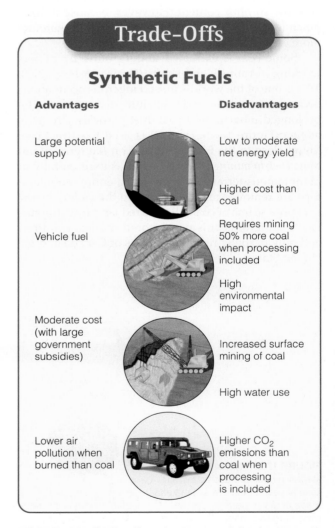

Trade-Offs

Synthetic Fuels

Advantages		Disadvantages
Large potential supply		Low to moderate net energy yield
		Higher cost than coal
Vehicle fuel		Requires mining 50% more coal when processing included
		High environmental impact
Moderate cost (with large government subsidies)		Increased surface mining of coal
		High water use
Lower air pollution when burned than coal		Higher CO_2 emissions than coal when processing is included

FIGURE 17-25 **Trade-offs:** advantages and disadvantages of using synthetic natural gas (SNG) and liquid synfuels produced from coal. Pick the single advantage and disadvantage that you think are the most important.

Without huge government subsidies, most analysts expect these synthetic fuels to play only a minor role as energy resources in the next 20–50 years. Compared with burning conventional coals, they require mining 50% more coal and their production and burning add 50% more carbon dioxide to the atmosphere. Also, they cost more to produce.

However, researchers are working on ways to reduce CO_2 emissions during the coal gasification process. They hope to develop metal-ceramic membranes that trap carbon dioxide gas. The CO_2 could then be compressed and piped off to underground repositories or other permanent storage sites. If this works, burning gasified coal could be a cleaner way to produce electricity than burning coal, oil, or natural gas. Stay tuned.

17-5 NUCLEAR ENERGY

How Does a Nuclear Fission Reactor Work? Splitting Nuclei to Produce Electricity

In a conventional nuclear reactor, isotopes of uranium undergo controlled nuclear fission, and the resulting heat is used to produce steam that spins turbines to generate electricity.

To evaluate the advantages and disadvantages of nuclear power, we must know how a conventional nuclear power plant and its accompanying nuclear fuel cycle work. As shown in Section 3-6, a nuclear fission reaction occurs when slow-moving neutrons are absorbed by nuclei such as those of uranium-235 and plutonium-239. (Fast-moving neutrons, in contrast, are not easily absorbed.) The products of the reaction are smaller fragments of the original nucleus, a few fast-moving neutrons, and heat. In a nuclear reactor, a material known as a *moderator* slows down enough of the fast-moving fission neutrons so that the neutrons from one fission reaction subsequently cause additional fission reactions—a process called a *chain reaction*. The high-temperature heat resulting from the chain reaction is carried away from the reactor by a *coolant* and is used to produce high-pressure steam, which spins turbines that generate electricity.

There are many different designs of nuclear reactors, almost all of which share these basic features. The most common type of reactor is one that uses water both as coolant and moderator. The Canadian design is called a CANDU reactor, an acronym derived from the words "Canada," "deuterium," and "uranium" (see Figure 17-26).

Unlike other water-cooled reactors, the CANDU design uses *heavy water* as coolant and moderator. In heavy water, the hydrogen atoms are replaced with atoms of *deuterium*, which is an isotope of hydrogen having one extra neutron. The result is water that is about 11% heavier that normal and has a greater ability to slow down fast-moving fission neutrons

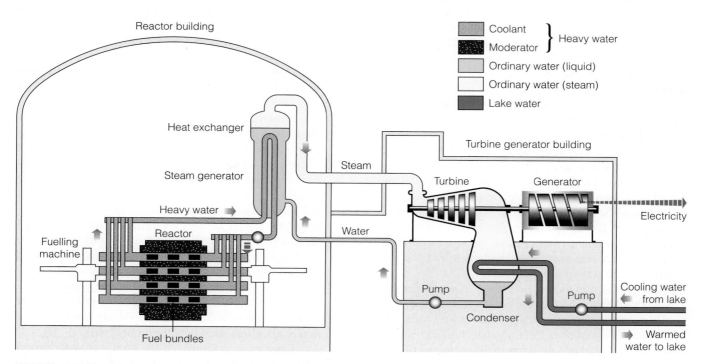

FIGURE 17-26 CANDU reactors employ three loops of water. The innermost loop carries heavy water reactor coolant. The middle loop is ordinary water/steam spinning a turbine. The outermost loop connects to an outside water source for cooling purposes. (© 2007 Jeremy Whitlock)

(i.e., it is a more effective moderator). The end result is that a CANDU reactor can use uranium oxides with a concentration of only 0.7% fissionable uranium-235 (a concentration that could be found in natural ore), whereas most other reactors require an extra step to enrich uranium oxides to uranium hexafluoride with a concentration of 3% fissionable uranium-235.

The fuel for a CANDU reactor is placed into 50-centimetre-long tubes made of a zirconium alloy, since this material does not absorb neutrons well. There are 37 of these tubes in a fuel bundle, and 12 or 13 fuel bundles in a pressure tube. The entire reactor core has several hundred pressure tubes. Pressurized heavy water flows through these tubes carrying thermal energy created by fission to the heat exchanger. Here the thermal energy is transferred to a second closed loop; this one contains normal or "light" water that, when converted to steam, spins a turbine to create electricity. The water condenses and is pumped back to the heat exchanger to be converted to steam again.

A third loop of water comes from an outside source such as a lake, river, or cooling tower and brings cool water to condense the steam of the central loop back into water. Note that none of these loops is continuous with the others; the heavy water, for instance, would only be found in the inner loop.

The CANDU reactor is shielded inside a reinforced concrete containment vessel. The entire system is further isolated within a specially designed reactor building. Multiple safety features backing up all the systems greatly reduce the chance of a serious nuclear accident.

We will give more details about the operation of Candu reactors, including a new design of Candu reactor, on the website.

Fuel bundles are used for 12–18 months, then removed from the reactor core and placed into *wet storage* in pools of water on site. After six or seven years, the heat and radiation have subsided sufficiently that fuel bundles are less dangerous to handle. They are then moved to *dry storage* in concrete containers, usually at a reactor site.

There are 22 large reactors in Canada—all of CANDU design. Twenty are in Ontario; Quebec and New Brunswick have one each. Together, the reactors produce 12% of Canada's electricity. Ontario is Canada's "nuclear province" and produces 30–50% of its electricity this way. The locations of radioactive waste sites are shown in Figure 17-27.

The production of nuclear energy is controlled by three federal acts. The Nuclear Safety and Control Act (1997) regulates the activities of the nuclear industry in Canada; it establishes the Canadian Nuclear Safety Commission as the body in charge of the nuclear industry. The Nuclear Liability Act (1970) limits the liability of the nuclear industry should there be a serious accident. The Nuclear Fuel Waste Act (2002) regulates the management and disposal of nuclear wastes in Canada; it establishes the Nuclear Waste Management Organization as the body overseeing nuclear wastes in Canada.

DID YOU KNOW

Each fuel bundle produces about as much energy as 500 tonnes of coal. If a CANDU reactor has 300 pressure tubes, each loaded with 12 fuel bundles, how much energy will be produced in terms of tonnes of coal?

CONSIDER, DISCUSS, OR DEBATE

Why do property insurance policies not insure against nuclear accidents? Is it because the probability of such an accident is so remote that it doesn't warrant consideration? Or would the costs of a nuclear accident be so high that no insurance company would risk paying out the potential claims?

What Went Wrong at Chernobyl? Human Error Was at the Root of the Problem

Operators made some poor judgments and then were unable to control the surge of nuclear power that resulted.

There are several versions of the Chernobyl story that differ in details; however, all versions agree that on April 25, 1986, the reactor crew at Chernobyl Unit-4 was scheduled to shut down the reactor. Instead of simply shutting it down, they performed an experiment to determine how long the turbines would continue to spin and generate electricity following the loss of the main power supply. This experiment had already been performed successfully at Chernobyl and other power plants.

Operators made a number of adjustments to disable the automatic shut-down mechanisms (Figure 17-28), which would have interfered with their experiment. As the flow of coolant water decreased, there was a sudden surge of power. The fuel elements ruptured and an explosion of steam blew the cover plate off the reactor. A second explosion threw burning fuel and graphite into the air. The graphite moderator ignited and burned for 9 to 10 days, releasing large amounts of radioactivity into the environment. Soviet authorities initially tried to cover up the disaster, but Swedish monitoring stations detected high levels of wind-transported radioactivity and sounded the alarm. More than 200 000 square kilometres (77 000 square miles) of Europe was contaminated (p. 383; see also http://www.ens-newswire.com/ens/sep2005/2005-09-06-04.asp and http://www.aztechresearch.net/chernobyl.htm).

Chernobyl is known as the largest nuclear power plant disaster, but it is by no means the only one. Visit http://www.nelson.com/livingintheenvironment3e.com for more information on this topic.

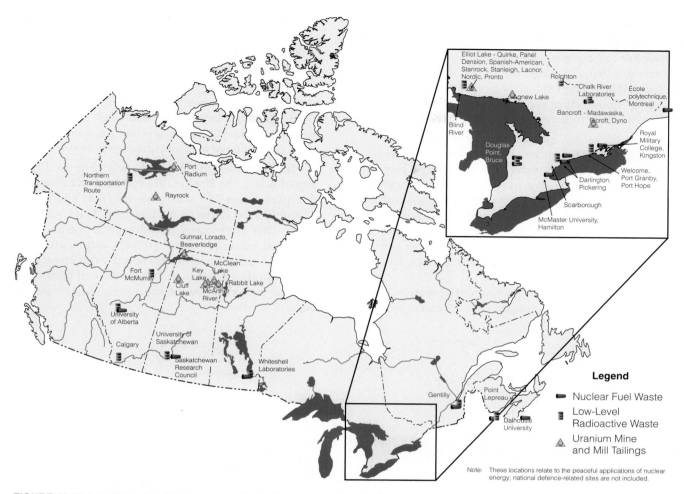

FIGURE 17-27 Locations of radioactive waste sites in Canada. Nuclear fuel wastes are stored at commercial reactor sites (Douglas Point, Bruce, Darlington, Pickering, Gentilly, and Point Lepreau) and at research reactors. (Natural Resources Canada)

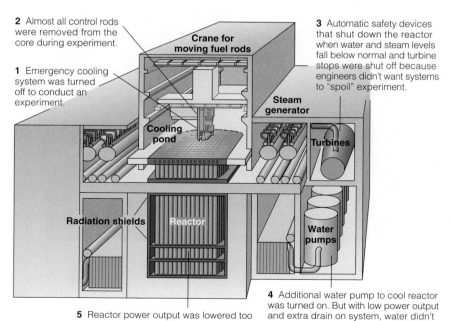

2 Almost all control rods were removed from the core during experiment.

Crane for moving fuel rods

3 Automatic safety devices that shut down the reactor when water and steam levels fall below normal and turbine stops were shut off because engineers didn't want systems to "spoil" experiment.

1 Emergency cooling system was turned off to conduct an experiment.

Steam generator

Cooling pond

Turbines

Radiation shields

Reactor

Water pumps

5 Reactor power output was lowered too much, making it too difficult to control.

4 Additional water pump to cool reactor was turned on. But with low power output and extra drain on system, water didn't actually reach reactor.

FIGURE 17-28 Five key points that contributed to the nuclear power plant disaster at Chernobyl.

What Is the Nuclear Fuel Cycle? Looking at the Whole Picture

The nuclear fuel cycle includes the mining of uranium, processing it to make a satisfactory fuel, using it in a reactor, safely storing the resulting highly radioactive wastes for thousands of years, and dealing with the highly radioactive reactor after its useful life.

Nuclear power plants, each with one or more reactors, are only one part of the nuclear fuel cycle (Figure 17-29). Unlike other energy resources, nuclear energy produces high-level **radioactive wastes** that give off large amounts of harmful ionizing radiation for a short time and small amounts for a long time. Such wastes, consisting mainly of spent fuel rods from commercial nuclear power plants and assorted wastes from the production of nuclear weapons, must be stored safely for thousands of years.

After approximately 15–60 years of operation, a nuclear reactor becomes dangerously contaminated with radioactive materials, and many of its parts become brittle or corroded and worn out. Unless the plant's life can be extended by expensive renovation, it must be **decommissioned** or retired.

Once a nuclear reactor comes to the end of its useful life it cannot be shut down and abandoned like a coal-burning plant. It contains large quantities of intensely radioactive materials that must be kept out of the environment for many thousands of years.

In the *closed nuclear fuel cycle* (Figure 17-29, dotted lines), the **fissionable isotopes** uranium-235 and plutonium-239 are removed from spent fuel assemblies for reuse as nuclear fuel. Their removal means that the remaining radioactive wastes must be stored safely for about 10 000 years. Currently, these isotopes are rarely removed from spent fuel rods and other nuclear wastes because of high costs and the potential use of the removed isotopes in nuclear weapons.

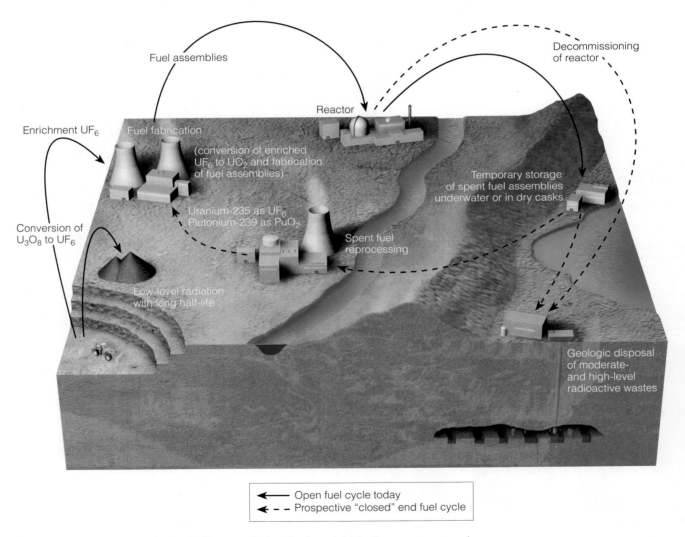

FIGURE 17-29 The nuclear fuel cycle. To see a Flash animation, visit http://www.cameco.com/common/flash/fuelcycle/index.html.

In the *open nuclear fuel cycle* (solid lines, Figure 17-29) the isotopes are not removed by reprocessing the nuclear wastes and are eventually buried in an underground disposal facility. These wastes must be stored safely for about 240 000 years—several times longer than the latest version of our species has been around. *In evaluating the safety, economic feasibility, and overall environmental impact of nuclear power, energy experts and economists caution us to look at this entire cycle, not just the nuclear plant itself.*

How Did We Get into Nuclear Power, and How Successful Has It Been? A Technology in Question

After more than 50 years of development and enormous government subsidies, nuclear power has not lived up to its promise.

When commercial nuclear plants were being built in the 1950s, there was great optimism about the future of this technology. The power of the atom seemed limitless. The idea of gaining high-tech energy from uranium ore (rocks!) must have seemed nothing short of miraculous. Another prevailing notion was that the power produced would be too cheap to merit the costs of metering.

In the 1950s, researchers projected that by the year 2000 at least 1 800 nuclear power plants would supply 21% of the world's commercial energy and most of the world's electricity.

After almost 60 years of development, enormous government subsidies, and an investment of more than $2 trillion (U.S.) worldwide, these goals have not been met. Instead, by 2010, 436 commercial nuclear reactors in 31 countries were producing only 6% of the world's commercial energy and 14% of its electricity.

Since 1989, electricity production from nuclear power has increased only slightly and is now the world's slowest-growing energy source. According to the U.S. Department of Energy, the percentage of the world's electricity produced by nuclear power will fall to 12% by 2025 because the retirement of aging existing reactors is expected to exceed construction of new ones.

According to energy analysts and economists, there are several major reasons for the failure of nuclear power to grow as projected. They include multibillion-dollar construction cost overruns, higher operating costs and more malfunctions than expected, and poor management. Two other major setbacks have been public concerns about safety and stricter government safety regulations, especially after the accidents in 1979 at the Three Mile Island nuclear plant in Pennsylvania and in 1986 at Chernobyl (p. 382).

Another problem is investor concerns about the economic feasibility of nuclear power that take into account the entire nuclear fuel cycle. At Three Mile Island, investors lost over a billion dollars in one hour from damaged equipment and repair, even though the reactor core had only a partial meltdown and no human lives were lost. Also, concern has risen about the vulnerability of nuclear power plants to terrorist attacks after the events of September 11, 2001, in the United States. Experts are especially concerned about the vulnerability of poorly protected and intensely radioactive spent fuel rods stored in pools or casks outside of reactor buildings.

However, according to a 2008 report by the International Atomic Energy Agency, interest in nuclear power is increasing as countries strive to lower their greenhouse gas emissions by phasing out power plants based on fossil fuels (http://www.iaea.org/Publications/Booklets/NuclearPower/np08.pdf).

What Are the Advantages and Disadvantages of the Conventional Nuclear Fuel Cycle? Better Than Coal, but There Are Other Problems

The nuclear fuel cycle has a fairly low environmental impact and a very low risk of an accident, but costs are high, radioactive wastes must be stored safely for thousands of years, and the facilities have some vulnerabilities.

Figure 17-30 lists the major advantages and disadvantages of the conventional nuclear fuel cycle. Using nuclear power to produce electricity has some important advantages over coal-burning power plants (Figure 17-31).

Some proponents of nuclear power claim it will help reduce dependence on imported oil. But other analysts point out that nuclear power has little effect on oil use because burning oil typically produces only a small amount of electricity. The major use for oil is to produce gasoline and diesel fuel for transportation, which would not be affected by nuclear power unless we switch to electric cars in the future.

Proponents say we should increase the use of nuclear power because its use does not release the greenhouse gas carbon dioxide into the atmosphere. It is true that nuclear power plants do not release carbon dioxide. However, the nuclear fuel cycle does release this gas into the atmosphere, although emissions are about one-sixth per unit of energy compared to burning fossil fuels (Figure 17-16).

Because of multiple built-in safety features, the risk of exposure to radioactivity from nuclear power plants in Canada and most other developed countries is extremely low. However, a partial or complete **meltdown** or explosion is possible, as the Chernobyl and Three Mile Island accidents have taught us.

Conventional Nuclear Fuel Cycle

Advantages	Disadvantages
Large fuel supply	High cost even with large subsidies
Low environmental impact (without accidents)	Low net energy yield
Emits 1/6 as much CO_2 as coal	High environmental impact (with major accidents)
Moderate land disruption and water pollution (without accidents)	Catastrophic accidents can happen (Chernobyl)
Moderate land use	No widely acceptable solution for long-term storage of radioactive wastes and decommissioning worn-out plants
Low risk of accidents because of multiple safety systems (except in 35 poorly designed and run reactors in former Soviet Union and eastern Europe)	Subject to terrorist attacks
	Spreads knowledge and technology for building nuclear weapons

FIGURE 17-30 Trade-offs: advantages and disadvantages of using the conventional nuclear fuel cycle (Figure 17-29) to produce electricity. Pick the single advantage and disadvantage that you think are the most important.

The U.S. Nuclear Regulatory Commission (NRC) estimates there is a 15–45% chance of a complete core meltdown at a U.S. reactor during the next 20 years. The NRC also found that 39 U.S. reactors have an 80% chance of failure in the containment shell from a meltdown or an explosion of gases inside containment structures.

Throughout the world, nuclear scientists and government officials urge the shutdown of 35 poorly designed and poorly operated nuclear reactors in some republics of the former Soviet Union and in eastern Europe. This is unlikely without economic aid from developed countries.

Many nuclear reactors throughout the world began to show problems after 20 to 30 years, when reactor cores became dangerously reactive, and cooling pipes and pressure tubes became brittle and started leaking. New Brunswick's Point Lepreau plant had to be shut down for costly repairs after only

Coal vs. Nuclear

Coal	Nuclear
Ample supply	Ample supply of uranium
High net energy yield	Low net energy yield
Very high air pollution	Low air pollution (mostly from fuel reprocessing)
High CO_2 emissions	Low CO_2 emissions (mostly from fuel reprocessing)
High land disruption from surface mining	Much lower land disruption from surface mining
High land use	Moderate land use
Low cost (with huge subsidies)	High cost (with huge subsidies)

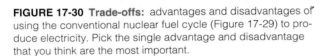

FIGURE 17-31 Trade-offs: comparison of the risks of using nuclear power (based on the nuclear fuel cycle) and coal-burning plants to produce electricity. If you had to choose, would you rather live next door to a coal-fired power plant or a nuclear power plant?

15 years of operation. A nuclear plant near Toledo, Ohio, was found to have a thinning reactor lid that was only 1 centimetre away from the rupture of a high-pressure reactor vessel that could have led to a meltdown.

How Vulnerable Are Nuclear Power Plants to Disasters of Various Kinds? A Serious Concern

There is great concern about the vulnerability of nuclear power plants and the nuclear wastes they store.

The 2001 destruction of New York City's World Trade Center towers has raised fears that a similar attack could break open a reactor's containment shell and set off a reactor meltdown that could create a major radioactive disaster.

Nuclear officials say such concerns are overblown and that nuclear plants could survive such an attack because of the thickness and strength of the containment walls. But a 2002 study by the Nuclear Control Institute found that the plants were not designed to withstand the crash of a large jet travelling at the impact speed of the two hijacked airliners that hit the World Trade Center. While it is true that a large dam would also cause great damage if destroyed by an attack or a natural disaster, the public seems more concerned about the long-term problems associated with a release of radioactivity.

Further tests revealed that there is insufficient security at nuclear plants to withstand ground-level attacks by terrorists. Nuclear industry officials contend that the security weaknesses exposed by these mock tests have been corrected. According to critics, the nuclear industry is reluctant to upgrade plant security because this would increase the costs of nuclear power significantly.

A particular vulnerability is that the spent fuel rods, which are high-level radioactive wastes, are stored at nuclear power plants. The spent fuel rods are kept underwater in pools or in dry casks outside of the Containment Shells. A spent-fuel storage pool typically holds 5–10 times more long-lived radioactivity than the radioactive core inside a plant's reactor.

Suppose that water drains out of a spent-fuel pool or a dry storage cask ruptures because of unlikely but possible events such as earthquake (see the following Spotlight on Fukushima), airplane impact, or terrorist act.

SPOTLIGHT

Fukushima, Japan

On March 11, 2011, a magnitude 9.0 earthquake centred off the east coast of Japan caused a 15-metre (50-foot) tsunami wave that precipitated the most serious nuclear accident since Chernobyl. Many nuclear reactors in Japan automatically shut down when the earthquake hit, but the four reactors at the Fukushima Daiichi complex were severely damaged. Specifically, the tsunami destroyed seawater pumps and backup generators and flooded power rooms, compromising core cooling at three of the four reactors. (The fourth was de-fuelled at the time, though that facility would later become cause for concern.)

Even when shut down, the core of a nuclear reactor remains extremely hot as a result of the rapid decay of fission waste products, and requires constant cooling. The backup cooling mechanisms in place at Fukushima were only designed to operate for a short time. When they failed, the fuel elements in the reactor core as well as their support structures began to melt. Measures taken to relieve dangerously high pressure in the reactor vessels resulted in the release of some radioactive material to the surroundings, as well as hydrogen gas, which detonated, severely damaging surface buildings. Efforts to restore some measure of core cooling using fire pumps to inject seawater were largely successful in avoiding a larger catastrophe. Concern focused not only on the

three reactor cores, but also on the spent fuel cooling ponds, which also require constant cooling. At this time, the cooling pond of the fourth (de-fuelled) reactor became a particular problem because it contained more fuel rods, resulting in a higher heat load; by March 15, it was losing roughly 100 cubic metres (3 530 cubic feet) of water per day, which had to be replaced (in part with seawater). It was roughly two weeks before reliable cooling was re-established.

In the hours after the tsunami hit, a radius of 20 kilometres (12 miles) around the power plant was evacuated; many have yet to return to their homes. Precise estimates of the amount of radioactivity released are difficult to determine because of damaged equipment and because much was released to the sea. However, one estimate has suggested the accident resulted in the release of about one-tenth the amount of radioactivity that was released at Chernobyl. In the aftermath, it was found that the design of the reactor site was partly to blame, with backup generators being sited in much too vulnerable a location. Institutional complacency about safety was also cited as a contributing factor. But some have observed that the technology of these three old reactors proved remarkably robust given the conditions. Nevertheless, all three machines are write-offs and the site will have to be decontaminated

and, eventually, decommissioned.

It is difficult to get a full grasp of the situation in Japan because, even while the disaster was unfolding under the scrutiny of TV cameras, there were considerable differences in the reports of government officials, international experts, and local bystanders. The Internet has a vast amount of information about Fukushima, but much of it seems highly polarized either for or against nuclear energy.

If you visit the *New York Times* website, you will be able to see satellite photos of the Fukushima Daiichi Nuclear Plant before and after the disaster (http://www.nytimes.com/interactive/2011/03/13/world/asia/satellite-photos-japan-before-and-after-tsunami.html?ref=japan). You can look through the International Atomic Energy Agency's accident update log and see what has been happening at the Fukushima Plant almost every day since the disaster (http://www.iaea.org/newscenter/news/2011/fukushima110311.html). You can discover what the World Health Organization said about eating seafood in the area (http://www.who.int/hac/crises/jpn/faqs/en/index7.html). You can read the International Atomic Energy Agency's report of June 28, 2012 (http://www.iaea.org/newscenter/focus/fukushima/

(continued)

Fukushima, Japan (*continued*)

statusreport280612.pdf) and see that in April 2012 some people were being allowed to return to their homes (Figure 17-32). Finally, you can read a *New York Times* article that summarizes events up to June 29, 2012 (http://topics.nytimes.com/top/news/international/countriesandterritories/japan/index.html). Be sure to note the titles of related articles on the same web page because they provide stories of the Japanese people striving to put their lives back in order in various ways.

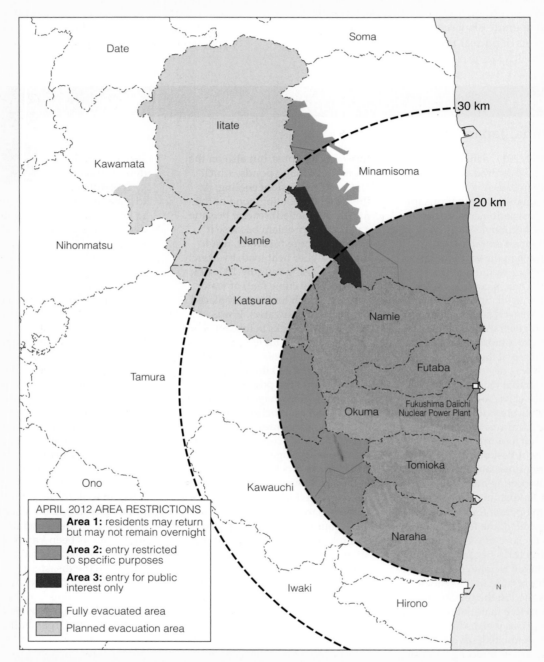

FIGURE 17-32 Fukushima, Japan: the map shows the half-circle of the 20-kilometre-radius (12-mile-radius) evacuation zone (most of which is still a restricted area), plus another evacuation zone (yellow) that was downwind from the nuclear power plant. In April 2012, after more than a year, people were being allowed to return to their homes in the zones marked "Area 1" (green). People will not be allowed to return to the zones marked "Area 2" (orange) or "Area 3" (red) for a long time. (International Atomic Energy Agency, 2012). (Based on http://www.cnn.com/2011/WORLD/asiapcf/03/16/japan.nuclear.reactors/index.html; http://www.world-nuclear.org/info/fukushima_accident_inf129.html; http://www.ndreport.com/wp-content/uploads/2011/07/table3.gif)

Then the highly radioactive and thermally hot fuel would be exposed to air and steam. This would cause the zirconium outer cover of the fuel assemblies to catch fire and burn fiercely. Such a fire could not be extinguished and would burn for days. This would release significant amounts of radioactive materials into the atmosphere, contaminate large areas for many decades, and create economic and psychological havoc.

Unlike the reactor core with its thick concrete protective dome, spent-fuel pools have little protective cover. The pools have backup cooling systems to help prevent a fire, but these could malfunction or be destroyed by an attack, an accident, or a natural disaster. Nuclear power officials contend that nuclear power facilities are safe. Critics are not convinced and call for more secure structures to protect spent-fuel storage sites.

> **CONSIDER, DISCUSS, OR DEBATE**
>
> Would you build a nuclear power plant in an earthquake-prone area? If so, what precautions would you take? If not, what alternatives would you choose to supply electricity? Will the world change in any ways as a result of what happened at Fukushima?

How Do We Dispose of Low-Level Radioactive Waste? Manage It on Site or Store It Safely

The nuclear fuel cycle and other nuclear facility processes produce low-level radioactive wastes that must be stored safely for 100–500 years before they decay to safe levels.

Each part of the nuclear fuel cycle (Figure 17-29) produces low-level and high-level solid, liquid, and gaseous radioactive wastes with various half-lives (Table 3-1, p. 51). There are huge volumes of low-radioactivity tailings produced while mining uranium, which are left on site but managed in such a way as to prevent them from being transported from the site; for example, they may be returned to mined-out pits. There are also large quantities of mill tailings produced while processing uranium into fuels for reactors; these are managed on site.

Wastes classified as *low-level radioactive wastes* give off small amounts of ionizing radiation and must be stored safely for 100–500 years before decaying to safe levels. Such wastes include tools, building materials, clothing, glassware, and other items that have been contaminated by radioactivity.

According to Natural Resources Canada, the nuclear and other industries have produced 2.3 million m^3 of low-level wastes in Canada (as of 2004). These waste materials are stored in specially designed aboveground buildings while awaiting a more permanent disposal option. There are plans to build a deep-disposal site at the Bruce Nuclear Plant for low-level and medium-level wastes.

How Do We Dispose of High-Level Radioactive Waste? An Unresolved Issue

There is disagreement among scientists over methods for the long-term storage of high-level radioactive waste.

After more than 50 years of research, scientists still do not agree on whether there is a safe, permanent solution for dealing with high-level radioactive waste. Some believe the long-term safe storage or disposal of high-level radioactive wastes is technically possible. Others disagree, pointing out that it is impossible to demonstrate that any method will work for 10 000–240 000 years.

Here are some of the proposed methods and their possible drawbacks.

Shoot it into space or into the sun. Costs would be very high, and a launch accident—like the explosion of the space shuttle *Challenger*—could disperse high-level radioactive wastes over large areas of the Earth's surface. This strategy has been abandoned for now.

Bury it under the Antarctic ice sheet or the Greenland ice cap. The long-term stability of the ice sheets is not known. They could be destabilized by heat from the wastes, and retrieving the wastes would be difficult or impossible if the method failed. This strategy is prohibited by international law.

Dump it into descending subduction zones in the deep ocean. But wastes eventually might be spewed out somewhere else by volcanic activity, and containers might leak and contaminate the ocean before being carried downward. Also, retrieval would be impossible if the method did not work. This strategy is prohibited by international law.

Bury it in thick deposits of mud on the deep-ocean floor in areas that tests show have been geologically stable for 65 million years. The waste containers eventually would corrode and release their radioactive contents. This approach is prohibited by international law.

Change it into harmless, or less harmful, isotopes. Scientists are investigating the use of a particle accelerator to transform long-lived fission wastes into other shorter-lived radioisotopes (by proton absorption, for example), thereby reducing the amount of time for which wastes must be safely stored. However, there is currently no efficient way to do this.

Bury it deep underground. This favoured strategy is under study by all countries producing nuclear waste. Many experts feel that the geologic repository option is the only scientifically credible long-term solution for safely isolating such wastes. This option raises a number of issues: where to locate such a site, how to safely transport the radioactive waste, how to avoid unforeseen long-term problems (such as geological activity or unexpected behaviour of the radioactive fuel), and how to gain public acceptance.

Case Study: Deep Disposal of High-Level Nuclear Wastes

Deep disposal of high-level nuclear wastes in stable rock formations has been proposed in both Canada and the United States, but there is little public support for this option.

In Canada, one solution to the problem of high-level nuclear waste that has been proposed is *deep disposal* (500–1 000 metres/1 640–3 280 feet beneath the surface) in stable granite rocks of the Canadian Shield. The search for a potential disposal site began in the late 1970s. A test site was established at Lac du Bonnet, Manitoba, and a 500-metre shaft was sunk. The Seaborn Panel, named after chairman Blair Seaborn, spent 10 years assessing the merits of deep disposal. In the end, the panel concluded that the method was technically safe, but tremendous public opposition convinced them that societal consent was lacking.

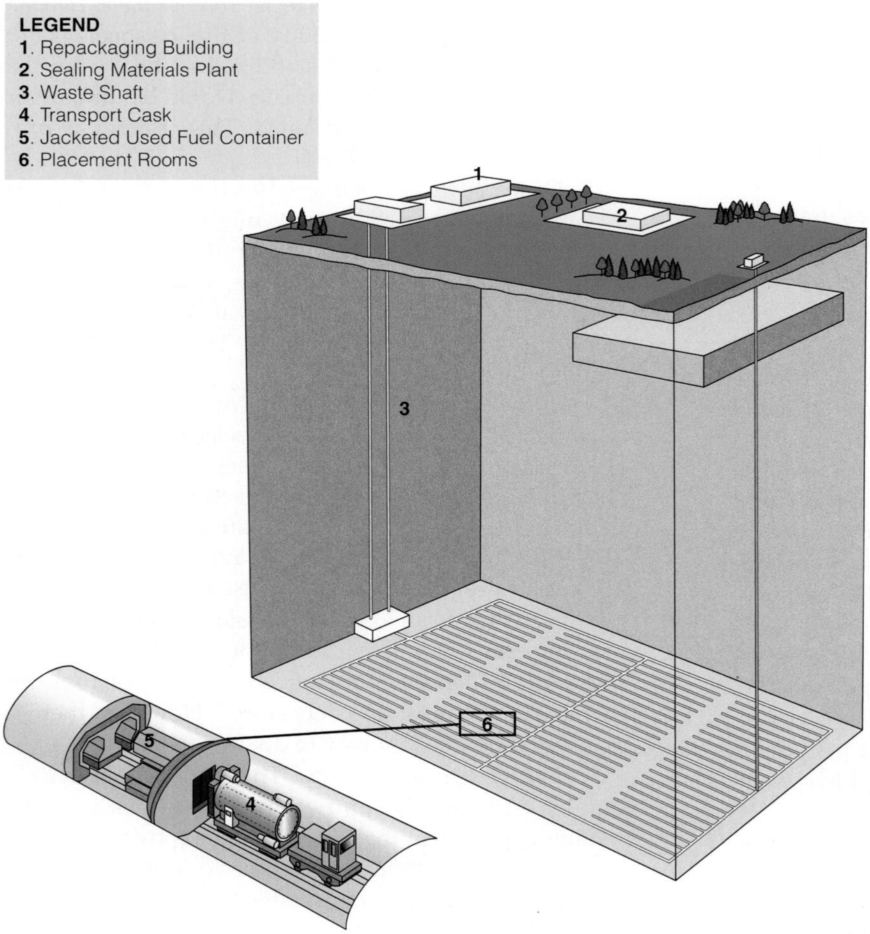

Figure 17-33 illustrates the steps that would be taken to secure the nuclear material into special chambers 500–1 000 metres below the surface. Critics have expressed concerns about issues of hydrology, geological activity, and fuel behaviour. Citizens are unhappy about having dangerous wastes transported past their homes or buried nearby. Deep disposal will likely not be practised until the public becomes more accepting of this option.

A similar situation has been unfolding in the United States. In 1985, the U.S. Department of Energy (DOE) announced plans to build a repository for underground storage of high-level radioactive wastes from commercial nuclear reactors and some nuclear weapons facilities. The site is to be built on federal land in the Yucca Mountain desert region, 160 kilometres (100 miles) northwest of Las Vegas, Nevada.

A number of scientists and energy analysts have serious concerns about the safety of this site. For one, they are concerned that rock fractures and tiny cracks may allow water to leak into the site and eventually corrode casks holding radioactive waste. In 1998, Jerry Szymanski, formerly the DOE's top geologist at Yucca Mountain and now an outspoken opponent of the site, said that if water flooded the site it could cause an explosion so large that "Chernobyl would be small potatoes."

In 2004, physicist Paul Craig resigned from a federal panel of experts evaluating the Yucca Mountain project so he could speak more freely about the project. He said that the metal canisters used to store the waste and their protective drip shields are badly designed and that they "would corrode and that would eventually lead to leakage of nuclear waste."

In 2002, the U.S. National Academy of Sciences, in collaboration with Harvard and University of Tokyo scientists, urged the U.S. government to slow down and rethink the nuclear waste storage process. They contend that storing spent-fuel rods in dry-storage casks in well-protected buildings at nuclear plant sites is an adequate solution for at least 100 years in terms of safety and national security. This would buy time to carry out more research on this complex problem and to evaluate other sites and storage methods that might be more acceptable scientifically and politically.

LEGEND
1. Repackaging Building
2. Sealing Materials Plant
3. Waste Shaft
4. Transport Cask
5. Jacketed Used Fuel Container
6. Placement Rooms

FIGURE 17-33 Solutions: deep disposal of high-level nuclear wastes in the Canadian Shield. In special-purpose buildings, high-level nuclear wastes would be repackaged (1) and sealed (2) into corrosion-resistant containers (5). These would be moved down a 500–1 000-metre shaft (3), using a special transport cask (4), and taken to a radiation-resistant placement room (6). (Nuclear Waste Management Organization)

Despite these suggestions and many objections from scientists and citizens, in 2002 the U.S. Congress approved Yucca Mountain as the official site for storing the country's commercial nuclear wastes. Then President Obama removed almost all budget from the Yucca Mountain project in 2009, and cancelled the project in 2010. This story illustrates how science, politics, and economics can interact as people attempt to solve a difficult and controversial problem.

CONSIDER, DISCUSS, OR DEBATE

Should people in large urban centres who benefit most from nuclear power be able to pass the risks associated with nuclear waste to those who reside along the disposal route or near the permanent-disposal site? View this issue from as many perspectives as possible.

What Can We Do with Worn-Out Nuclear Plants? A Hidden Cost

When a nuclear reactor reaches the end of its useful life we have to keep its highly radioactive materials from reaching the environment for thousands of years.

When a nuclear plant comes to the end of its useful life, it must be *decommissioned*. Scientists have proposed three ways to do this.

One is to *dismantle* the plant and store its large volume of highly radioactive materials in a high-level nuclear waste storage facility (Figure 17-33). The safety of this option is questioned by a number of scientists. How can a nuclear plant be safely dismantled when the plant itself will be radioactive, and when every tool used—and even the water used in the cleanup—will become radioactive waste? How can the radioactive dust be contained while the building is being demolished?

A second approach is to *mothball* the plant by erecting a physical barrier and setting up full-time security for 30–100 years before the plant is dismantled. This allows time for some of the radioactive material to decay to levels that make dismantlement safer.

A third option is *entombment*, which involves enclosing the entire plant in a concrete tomb that must last and be monitored for several thousand years. A drawback of this option is that concrete breaks down after a comparatively short period.

Regardless of the method chosen, decommissioning adds to the total costs of nuclear power as an energy option. So far, only a few plants have been torn down. But doing this costs 2–10 times as much as it did to build them. Decommissioning the remaining reactors now in operation would further decrease the net energy yield of nuclear power and add to its already high cost.

At least 228 large commercial reactors worldwide are scheduled for retirement by 2012. However, the Nuclear Regulatory Commission has approved extending the life of at least 50 reactors to 60 years. Opponents contend that this could increase the risk of nuclear accidents in aging reactors (p. 408).

Can We Afford Nuclear Power? Financial Considerations

Even with massive government subsidies, the nuclear power fuel cycle is an expensive way to produce electricity compared with a number of other energy alternatives.

Experience has shown that the nuclear power fuel cycle is an expensive way to produce electricity, even when huge government subsidies partially shield it from free-market competition with other energy sources.

Costs associated with nuclear power rose dramatically in the 1970s and 1980s because of unanticipated safety problems and stricter regulations after the Three Mile Island and Chernobyl accidents. In 1995, the World Bank said that nuclear power is too costly and risky. *Forbes* business magazine has called the failure of the U.S. nuclear power program "the largest managerial disaster in U.S. business history, involving $1 trillion in wasted investment and $10 billion in direct losses to stockholders." And the *Economist* says, "Not one [nuclear power plant], anywhere in the world, makes commercial sense."

In Canada, by contrast, nuclear power plants are under no pressure to be profitable or to break even. The costs of this historically money-losing industry have to date been assumed by Canadian taxpayers.

In recent years, the operating costs of nuclear power plants have dropped, mostly because of less downtime. But environmentalists and economists point out that the true cost of nuclear power must be based on the entire nuclear power fuel cycle, not merely the operating cost of individual plants. According to them, when these costs are included the overall cost of nuclear power is very high (even with huge government subsidies) compared to many other energy alternatives.

Partly to address cost concerns, the nuclear industry plans to build smaller second-generation plants using standardized designs, which it claims are safer and can be built more quickly (in 3–6 years).

These new designs would have built-in *passive safety features* designed to make explosions or the release of radioactive emissions highly unlikely. However, according to *Nucleonics Week,* an important nuclear industry publication, "Experts are flatly unconvinced that safety has been achieved—or even substantially increased—by the new designs." In addition, these new designs do not eliminate the threats and the expense and hazards of long-term radioactive waste storage and power plant decommissioning.

Is Breeder Nuclear Fission a Feasible Alternative? An Uncertain Technology

Because of very high costs and bad safety experiences with several nuclear breeder reactors, this technology has been put aside by most nations.

Some nuclear power proponents urge the development and widespread use of **breeder nuclear fission reactors,** which generate more nuclear fuel than they consume by converting nonfissionable uranium-238 into fissionable plutonium-239. Because breeders would use more than 99% of the uranium in ore deposits, the world's known uranium reserves would last at least 1 000 years, and perhaps several thousand years.

However, if the safety system of a breeder reactor fails, the reactor could lose some of its liquid sodium coolant, which ignites when exposed to air and reacts explosively if it comes into contact with water. This could cause a runaway fission chain reaction and perhaps a nuclear explosion powerful enough to blast open the containment building and release a cloud of highly radioactive gases and particulate matter. Leaks of flammable liquid sodium have caused fires at many of the experimental breeder reactors built so far. Besides high costs, there have been serious problems at breeder reactors including partial meltdowns. In addition, existing experimental breeder reactors produce plutonium so slowly that they cannot compete with conventional nuclear reactors.

In December 1986, France opened a commercial-size breeder reactor. It was so expensive to build and operate that after spending $13 billion (U.S.), the government spent another $2.75 billion to shut it down permanently in 1998. Because of this experience, most other countries have abandoned their plans to build full-size commercial breeder reactors.

However, a number of countries, including Russia, Japan, India, and China, are continuing to experiment with breeder reactors in hopes of developing this technology (Jain, 2008; "China's Experimental," 2011).

Is Nuclear Fusion a Feasible Alternative? We May Know by 2020

Nuclear fusion has a number of advantages, but after more than five decades of research and billions of dollars in government research and development subsidies, this technology still consumes more energy than it produces.

For decades, scientists have hoped that controlled nuclear fusion will provide an almost limitless source of high-temperature heat and electricity to supply most of the world's commercial energy. Research has focused on the D–T nuclear fusion reaction, in which two isotopes of hydrogen—deuterium (D) and tritium (T)—fuse at about 100 million °C (180 million °F; Figure 3-16, p. 53).

Fusion energy has a number of important advantages. They include no emissions of conventional air pollutants or carbon dioxide, an almost infinite fuel supply (water), and wastes that are much less radioactive so they would need to be stored for only about 100 years.

There would be no risk of meltdown or release of large amounts of radioactive materials from a disaster, and little risk from additional proliferation of nuclear weapons because bomb-grade materials (such as enriched uranium-235 and plutonium-239) are not required for fusion energy.

Fusion power might also be used to destroy toxic wastes, supply electricity for ordinary use, and decompose water and produce the hydrogen gas needed to run a hydrogen economy by the end of this century.

This sounds great. So what is holding up fusion energy? After more than 50 years of research and expenditures of more than $25 billion, controlled nuclear fusion projects have always consumed more energy than they produced.

All of that might be about to change! The ITER project is a cooperative venture aimed at building a nuclear fusion reactor that will produce 10 times the amount of energy it consumes. The name ITER was originally an acronym for international thermonuclear experimental reactor, although it is now being described in terms of the Latin word *iter,* meaning "direction," since this project is intended to lead the way toward harnessing controlled nuclear fusion. Seven partners—the European Union, India, Japan, China, Russia, South Korea, and the United States—are involved in funding and directing the venture. Construction began in 2007 in Cadarache, France. ITER should be operational by 2020 and is designed to last for 20 years. The project is considered an experiment and won't actually be used to generate commercial electricity. However, it will be followed by DEMO, a demonstration fusion power plant that is intended to bring controlled fusion energy to the commercial market (http://www.iter.org).

What Should Be the Future of Nuclear Power? Phase Out or Keep Options Open

There is disagreement over whether nuclear power should be phased out or kept open as an option.

To many analysts, nuclear power is a complex, expensive, inflexible, and centralized way to produce electricity that is too vulnerable to large-scale failures. They believe it is a technology whose time has passed in a world where electricity will increasingly be provided by small, decentralized, easily expandable power plants such as natural gas turbines, farms of wind turbines on land and at sea, arrays of solar cells, and hydrogen-powered fuel cells. According to investors and World Bank economic analysts, conventional nuclear power simply cannot compete in today's increasingly open, decentralized, and unregulated energy market unless it is artificially shielded from free-market competition by huge government subsidies.

Proponents of nuclear power argue that governments should continue funding research and development and pilot plant testing of smaller and potentially safer and cheaper reactor designs along with breeder fission and nuclear fusion. They say we need to keep nuclear options available for use in the future if various renewable energy options fail to keep up with electricity demands and reduce CO_2 emissions to acceptable levels.

Mounting concerns about global warming have caused governments to re-weigh the potential pros and cons of all energy technologies that can help to reduce greenhouse gas emissions. Some countries, such as Germany, have moved away from nuclear energy and are focusing on developing renewable technologies like solar energy.

France, on the other hand, has invested greatly in nuclear technology and generates about 80% of its electricity using nuclear energy. Canada is keeping its nuclear options open. At least four provinces—Ontario, Saskatchewan, New Brunswick, and Alberta—are planning or considering new nuclear power plants.

What happens next will likely depend on the rate at which greenhouse gases are added to the atmosphere by various countries around the world, and the rate at which certain technologies—nuclear technology and the renewable energy technologies discussed in the next chapter—can develop and become economically competitive with fossil fuels.

Civilization as we know it will not survive unless we can find a way to live without fossil fuels.
DAVID GOLDSTEIN

CHAPTER REVIEW

1. Review the Key Questions for this chapter on p. 383. Summarize the issue of when we are likely to run out of affordable oil.

2. What major energy resources do the world and Canada rely on? Give a brief history of human energy use. What is *net energy* and why is it important in evaluating energy resources? Why does the nuclear power fuel cycle have a low net energy yield?

3. What is *crude oil (petroleum)* and how is it extracted from the ground and refined? What is a *petrochemical* and why are such chemicals important? Who controls most of the world's oil supply? What percentage of the world's proven oil reserves does Canada have? How much does the United States have? How much of the world's annual oil production does the United States use and what percentage of it is imported? Describe the relationships between oil, prosperity, and world peace. Discuss the pros and cons of drilling for oil in the Arctic. What specific problems may occur in the Arctic? What are the major advantages and disadvantages of using conventional oil as an energy resource?

4. What is *oil sand* and how is it extracted and converted to heavy oil? What is *shale oil* and how is it produced? Should Canada continue with large-scale oil sands operations? List arguments for and against this course of action. What alternatives are there?

5. Define *natural gas, liquefied petroleum gas (LPG)*, and *liquefied natural gas (LNG)*. What are the major advantages and disadvantages of using natural gas as an energy resource? What are some problems involved with increasing our use of LNG?

6. What is *coal* and how is it formed? Compare the use of coal in Canada, the United States, and China. What are the major advantages and disadvantages of using coal as an energy resource?

7. What is *synthetic natural gas (SNG)*? What is coal liquefaction and how can liquid fuels be produced from coal? What are the major advantages and disadvantages of using liquid and gaseous synfuels produced from coal?

8. How does a nuclear fission reactor work and what are its major safety features? Describe the *nuclear fuel cycle*. What factors have hindered the development of nuclear power? Describe the nuclear power plant disaster at Chernobyl. What are the major advantages and disadvantages of relying on nuclear power as a way to produce electricity?

9. How can we deal with the highly radioactive wastes produced by nuclear power plants? What are our options for safely retiring worn-out nuclear power plants? Discuss the degree to which nuclear power can reduce dependence on imported oil. Discuss the question of whether using nuclear power can help to significantly slow projected global warming. Discuss the pros and cons of building safer nuclear reactors. List the problems encountered in using breeder reactors. What is *nuclear fusion* and what is its potential as an energy resource? Overall, what future do you see for the nuclear power industry?

10. Discuss the relationship between relying on oil as our major source of energy and the four *principles of sustainability*.

CRITICAL THINKING

1. Just to continue using oil at the current rate (not the projected higher exponential rate), we must discover and add to global oil reserves the equivalent of a new Saudi Arabian supply (the world's largest) *every 10 years*. Do you believe this is possible? If not, what effects might this have on your life and on the life of a child or grandchild you might have?

2. List five actions you could take to reduce your dependence on oil and gasoline derived from it. Which do you actually plan to do?

3. Explain why you are for or against continuing an energy policy that is heavily reliant on oil. If you favour reducing dependence on oil, list the three best ways to do this.

4. Explain why you agree or disagree with the following proposals by various energy analysts to help solve North America's energy problems: **(a)** find and develop more domestic supplies of oil, **(b)** place a heavy federal tax on gasoline and imported oil to help reduce the waste of oil resources, **(c)** increase dependence on nuclear power, and **(d)** phase out all nuclear power plants by 2025.

5. What do you believe should be done with high-level radioactive wastes? Explain.

6. Would you favour having high-level nuclear waste transported by truck or train through the area where you live to a centralized underground storage site? Explain. What are the options?

7. Should Canada and other developed countries provide economic and technical aid for closing 35 poorly designed and poorly operated nuclear reactors in some republics of the former Soviet Union and in eastern Europe? Explain.

8. Congratulations! You are in charge of the world. List the three most important features of your policy to develop nonrenewable energy resources during the next 50 years.

PROJECTS

1. How is the electricity in your community produced? How has the inflation-adjusted cost of that electricity changed since 1970?

2. Write a two-page scenario of what your life might be like without oil. Compare and discuss the scenarios developed by members of your class.

3. Use the library or the Internet to find information about nuclear accidents that took place at Chalk River, Canada (1952); Kyshtym, U.S.S.R. (1957); Windsale, Britain (1957); Three Mile Island, United States (1979); and Hanford, United States (1986). Use the results of your research to consider whether or not governments might withhold information from the public to protect the nuclear industry.

ECOLOGICAL FOOTPRINT ANALYSIS

In 2008, the average fleet-wide fuel economy of new cars, light trucks, and SUVs in Canada was 11.4 kilometres per litre (kpL) or 26.6 miles per gallon (mpg), and the average motor vehicle was driven 19 300 kilometres (12 000 miles). There were about 20 million motor vehicles in Canada in 2008. Use these data to calculate the *gasoline consumption* and *carbon dioxide* (CO_2) *footprints* of individual motor vehicles with different fuel efficiencies and for all of the motor vehicles in Canada by answering the following questions.

1. Suppose a car has an average fuel efficiency of 8.5 kpL (20 mpg) and is driven 19 300 kilometres (12 000 miles) a year. **(a)** How many litres (and gallons) of gasoline does this vehicle consume in a year? **(b)** If gasoline costs $1.05 per litre ($4.00 per gallon), how much will the owner spend on fuel in a year? **(c)** How many litres (and gallons) of gasoline would be consumed by a fleet of 250 million such vehicles in a year? (*Note:* 1 litre = 0.265 gallons and 1 kilometre = 0.621 miles.)

2. Recalculate the values in Question 1, assuming that a car has an average fuel efficiency of 19.6 kpL (46 mpg).

3. Approximately 2.4 kilograms of CO_2 are released when 1 litre of gasoline is burned. Use this information to determine the number of metric tons of CO_2 emitted annually by **(a)** the car described in Question 1 with a low fuel efficiency, **(b)** a fleet of 20 million vehicles

with this same fuel efficiency, **(c)** the car described in Question 2 with a high fuel efficiency, and **(d)** a fleet of 20 million vehicles with this same high fuel efficiency. These calculations provide a rough estimate of the CO_2 *footprints* for individual cars and for the entire Canadian fleet with low- and high-efficiency cars.

(*Note:* 1 kilogram = 2.20 pounds; 1 metric ton = 1 000 kilograms = 220 pounds = 1.1 tons; 1 ton = 2 000 pounds. See Appendix 1.)

4. If the average fuel efficiency of the Canadian fleet increased from 8.5 kpL (20 mpg) to 19.6 kpL (46 mpg), by what percentage would this reduce the CO_2 emissions from the entire fleet per year? Think of this as the percentage reduction in the carbon footprint of the Canadian motor vehicle fleet.

CASE STUDY | Tidal Power Comes of Age

Tidal power is a form of hydropower that takes advantage of the vast quantities of water being moved twice daily by gravitational interplay among the Earth, the moon, and the sun (http://fundyforce.ca/renewable-and-predictable/understanding-tides/). Its advantages are that it is renewable, it produces no greenhouse gases, it is more reliable than wind or solar, and it is absolutely predictable in terms of its peaks and flows of energy.

Its disadvantages are that it will work only in certain locations, the timing of tidal power does not coincide well with peaks of human demand, tidal equipment that is installed in the ocean is difficult to maintain, and such systems can be expensive and even experimental to establish because each circumstance tends to be unique.

However, where conditions are suitable, tidal power is increasingly viewed as a viable energy option. The equipment is becoming more efficient, less expensive, more durable, and easier to maintain. The periodic nature of tides can be accommodated so that the use of tidal power is coordinated with other forms of power. As well, there are Canadian and other companies that now specialize in developing tidal power.

Canada's Bay of Fundy provides an ideal circumstance for capturing tidal energy. The area is famous for its tides, which can rise and fall a vertical distance of 16 metres (52 feet). Twice per day, 100 billion tonnes of seawater (a greater volume of water than all the freshwater rivers and streams on Earth) rushes in and out of the Bay of Fundy at velocities of up to 10 metres (32 feet) per second.

In the past, *tidal barrage* projects worked by capturing some of the high tide behind a dam-like structure and then releasing the trapped water through turbines after the tide retreated. A tidal project of this design, the Annapolis Royal Generating Station, has been operating on an inlet of the Bay of Fundy since 1985.

The excitement about tidal power these days comes from the fact that innovative new designs of *tidal stream generators* have been created that can be placed out in the ocean in the fastest and most powerful *tidal streams* (currents). These generators are extremely robust to be able to deal with the power of flowing water and the challenging environment that includes water pressure and salt corrosion. They have been described as "windmills on steroids." Figure 18-1 shows four different designs that are being tested in the Bay of Fundy.

(continued)

The Canadian Press/Andrew Vaughan

Courtesy of Alstom

Courtesy of Atlantis Resources Corporation

Marine Current Turbines Ltd

FIGURE 18-1 Four types of tidal power technology being deployed in Canada's Bay of Fundy.

The Fundy Ocean Research Centre for Energy (FORCE) is working with the government of Nova Scotia, Natural Resources Canada, industrial partners, academics, and fishermen to sort out how tidal power, with the potential to provide all the electricity needed by Nova Scotia, can be developed without damaging other values in the area such as fishing and tourism. To learn more, see the short video at http://vimeo.com/42384818 that summarizes the Bay of Fundy tidal project, and look into other videos and reports available at sites such as http://fundyforce.ca/.

We're on the cusp of a new energy revolution.
DAVID SUZUKI

CHAPTER PURPOSE AND QUESTIONS

Chapter 18 evaluates the potential of energy efficiency and renewable energy as solutions to our energy problems. The chapter addresses the following questions:

18-1   What is energy efficiency and how much energy do we waste?

18-2   How can we save energy in industry?

18-3   What are the main types of renewable energy?

18-4   How can we produce electricity from flowing water?

18-5   What is the status of wind power?

18-6   How is biomass used to produce energy?

18-7   What is geothermal energy?

18-8   Can hydrogen replace oil?

18-9   What is micropower?

18-10 What roles will economics and politics play in our energy future?

18-1   THE IMPORTANCE OF IMPROVING ENERGY EFFICIENCY

What Is Energy Efficiency, and How Much Energy Do We Waste? Saving Money by Not Wasting Energy

Using less energy to do useful work reduces the environmental impact of energy use and saves money.

Energy efficiency is a measure of the useful energy produced by an energy conversion device compared to the energy that ends up being converted to low-quality, essentially useless heat. For example, the light produced by a light bulb is useful energy, whereas the heat it produces is wasted energy.

If you replace an incandescent bulb that is only 5% efficient with a compact fluorescent bulb that is 20% efficient, you get the same amount of light using one-fourth as much energy. This reduces pollution and carbon dioxide emissions and saves money on your electric bill—a win-win solution for you and the Earth. Figure 18-2 lists major economic and environmental advantages of reducing energy waste.

Some critics like to paint proponents of conserving energy as calling for personal sacrifice, giving up cars, freezing in winter, wearing sweaters, and burning up in the summer. This is an incorrect and misleading view of energy conservation, which is implemented mainly by using existing technologies and developing new ones that waste less energy.

You may be surprised to learn that about 84% of all commercial energy used in North America is wasted (Figure 18-3, p. 420). About 41% of the energy used is wasted automatically because of the degradation of energy quality imposed by the second law of thermodynamics. But about 43% of the energy is wasted unnecessarily, mostly by using fuel-wasting motor

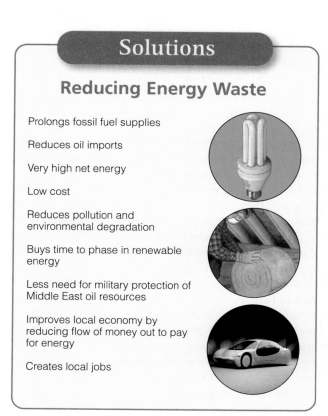

Solutions

Reducing Energy Waste

Prolongs fossil fuel supplies

Reduces oil imports

Very high net energy

Low cost

Reduces pollution and environmental degradation

Buys time to phase in renewable energy

Less need for military protection of Middle East oil resources

Improves local economy by reducing flow of money out to pay for energy

Creates local jobs

FIGURE 18-2 Solutions: advantages of reducing energy waste. Global improvements in energy efficiency could save the world about $1 trillion (U.S.) per year—an average of $114 million per hour!

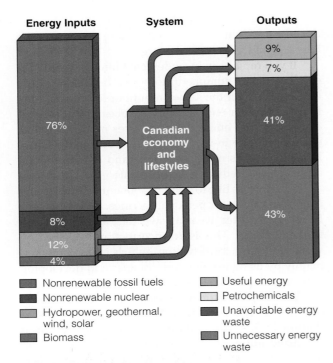

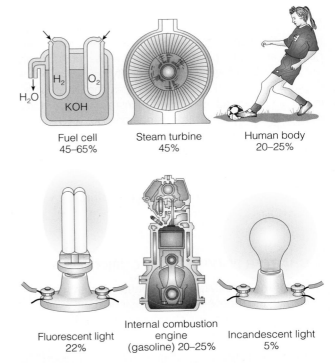

FIGURE 18-4 Energy efficiency of some common energy conversion devices.

FIGURE 18-3 Flow of commercial energy through the Canadian economy. Note that only 16% of all commercial energy used in Canada ends up performing useful tasks or being converted to petrochemicals; the rest is unavoidably wasted because of the second law of thermodynamics (41%) or is wasted unnecessarily through the use of inefficient devices (43%). (Energy Consumption by Sector 2005 (2001 data); International Energy Association (IEA))

vehicles, furnaces, and other devices and living and working in leaky, poorly insulated, poorly designed buildings.

We can save energy and money by buying more energy-efficient cars, lighting, heating systems, water heaters, air conditioners, and appliances. Some energy-efficient models may cost more initially, but in the long run they usually save money by having a lower **life-cycle cost**: initial cost plus lifetime operating costs.

The energy conversion devices we use vary in their energy efficiencies (Figure 18-4). Three widely used devices waste large amounts of energy. One is the *incandescent light bulb*, which wastes 95% of its energy input of electricity. In other words, it is a *heat bulb*. The second is a *thermal power plant* (using a coal- or oil-fired boiler or a nuclear reactor) producing electricity for space or water heating. Such a plant typically wastes two-thirds of the energy released from its fuel. *Nuclear power plants* have the added burden that the processing of uranium ore into reactor fuel is very energy intensive, bringing the overall efficiency down to the 15–20% level. (Add in unknown costs to deal with radioactive wastes for thousands of years and to retire the plant, and the efficiency plummets further.) Third is a motor vehicle with an *internal combustion engine*,

which wastes 75–80% of the energy in its fuel. Energy experts call for us to replace these energy-wasting technologies or greatly improve their energy efficiency over the next few decades.

What Is Net Energy Efficiency? Honest Energy Accounting

Net energy efficiency is a measure of how much useful energy we get from an energy resource after subtracting the energy used and wasted in making the energy available.

Recall that the only energy that really counts is *net energy* (p. 387). The *net energy efficiency* of a system used to heat your house, for example, is determined by the efficiency of each step in the energy conversion for the entire system.

Figure 18-5 (p. 421) shows the net energy efficiency for heating two well-insulated homes. One is heated with electricity produced at a nuclear power plant, transported by wire to the home, and converted to heat (electric resistance heating). The other is heated passively: direct solar energy enters through high-efficiency windows facing the sun and strikes heat-absorbing materials that store the heat for slow release.

This analysis shows that converting the high-quality energy in nuclear fuel to high-quality heat at several thousand degrees in the power plant,

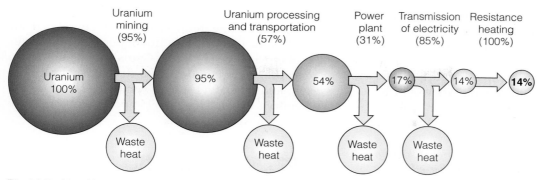

Electricity from Nuclear Power Plant

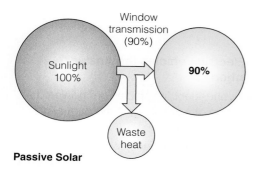

Passive Solar

FIGURE 18-5 Comparison of net energy efficiency for two types of space heating. The cumulative net efficiency is obtained by multiplying the percentage shown inside the circle before each step by the energy efficiency for that step (shown in parentheses). So 100 × 0.95 = 95%; 95 × 0.57 = 54%; and so on. Because of the second law of thermodynamics, in most cases the greater the number of steps in an energy conversion process, the lower its net energy efficiency. About 86% of the energy used to provide space heating by electricity produced at a nuclear power plant is wasted. If the additional energy needed to deal with nuclear wastes and to retire highly radioactive nuclear plants after their useful life is included, then the net energy yield for a nuclear plant is only about 8% (or 92% waste). By contrast, with passive solar heating, only about 10% of incoming solar energy is wasted.

converting this heat to high-quality electricity, transmitting the electricity to users, and using the electricity to provide low-quality heat for warming a house to only about 20°C (68°F) is very wasteful of high-quality energy. Although the last step of using the incoming electricity to produce heat is 100% efficient, the numerous steps needed to get the electricity to the house waste enormous amounts of energy. Burning coal or oil at a power plant to supply electricity and transmitting it long distances to heat water or space suffers from the same limited efficiency as nuclear (but without the latter's high fuel-processing energy cost). At the power plant this is due mainly to the unavoidably limited efficiency of steam turbines (roughly 35%). Natural gas turbines have a higher efficiency because there is no fuel-to-steam conversion. The transmission losses depend on distance and are unavoidable no matter what resource is used to produce the electricity. For space and water heating it is more efficient to burn the fuel (gas or oil) in the home.

The above examples illustrate two general principles for saving energy. First, *keep the number of steps in an energy conversion process as low as possible.* Each time we convert energy from one form to another or transmit it, some useful energy is almost always lost. Second, *strive to have the highest possible energy efficiency for each step in an energy conversion process.*

18-2 WAYS TO IMPROVE ENERGY EFFICIENCY

How Can We Save Energy in Industry? Cogenerate, Buy New Motors, and Use Efficient Lighting

Industries can save energy and money by producing both heat and electricity from an energy source and by using energy-efficient electric motors and lighting.

Some industries save energy and money by using **cogeneration,** or *combined heat and power (CHP)* systems. In such a system two useful forms of energy (such as steam and electricity) are produced from the same fuel source. These systems have an energy efficiency of 80–90% (compared to about 30–40% for coal-fired boilers and nuclear power plants) and emit two-thirds less CO_2 per unit of energy produced than conventional coal-fired boilers do. Cogeneration has been widely used in western Europe for years. Its use in North America and China is growing.

Another way to save energy and money in industry is to *replace energy-wasting electric motors,* which consume about one-fourth of the electricity produced in North America. Most of these motors are inefficient because they run only at full speed with their output throttled to match the task—somewhat like driving a car fast with your foot on the brake pedal. Each year a heavily used electric motor consumes 10 times its purchase cost in electricity—equivalent to using $200 000 worth of gasoline each year to fuel a $20 000 car! The costs of replacing such motors with new adjustable-speed drive motors would be paid back in about one year and save an amount of energy equal to that generated by 150 large (1 000-megawatt) power plants.

A third way to save energy is to *switch from low-efficiency incandescent lighting to higher-efficiency fluorescent lighting* and light-emitting diode (LED) lighting.

How Can We Save Energy in Transportation? Replace Gas Guzzlers with Gas Sippers

The best way to save energy in transportation is to increase the fuel efficiency of motor vehicles.

Good news. Between 1973 and 1985, the average fuel efficiency rose sharply for new cars sold in Canada and the United States and to a lesser degree for pickup trucks, minivans, and sport utility vehicles (SUVs). This occurred primarily because of government-mandated *Corporate Average Fuel Economy* (*CAFE*) standards. *Bad news.* After 1985, the average fuel efficiency for new passenger cars sold in North America levelled off for about 20 years (Figure 18-6). Fuel economy has been increasing recently as the public pays more attention to environmental considerations and fuel costs, as car companies compete to market more fuel-efficient cars, and as governments consider the greenhouse gas savings that can be achieved through efficiencies in the transportation sector.

What would happen if the Canadian and U.S. governments required the average vehicle to get 17 kilometres per litre (kpL) /40 miles per gallon (mpg) within 10 years? According to energy analysts, this would cut gasoline consumption in half, with a corresponding reduction in vehicle-related air pollution. China plans to impose even stricter fuel-efficiency standards. China's goals are (1) to encourage car companies to develop hybrid, fuel cell, and other fuel-saving vehicles; (2) reduce the country's dependence on oil imports; and (3) reduce carbon dioxide emissions.

Are Hybrid-Electric Vehicles the Answer? A Current Option

Fuel-efficient hybrid-electric vehicles are powered by the combination of a small internal combustion engine and an electric motor.

Interest has been growing in developing *superefficient cars* that could eventually get 34–128 kpL (80–300 mpg). This concept was pioneered and developed in detail in the 1980s by physicist Amory Lovins. Note that by 1983 Volvo had developed a prototype car called the LCP2000 that could achieve a fuel efficiency of 35 kilometres per litre (100 mpg) using lightweight components and a small internal combustion engine; this car was not placed on the market because the energy crisis (p. 391) ended and gasoline prices became very inexpensive again. Efficient cars that you can buy (Figure 18-7, p. 423) include the highly recognizable and easy-to-park Smart Car (gasoline engine; 17 kpL in the city or 21 kpL on the highway), as well as the Volkswagen Jetta (diesel engine; 12.8 kpL city or 17.5 kpL highway).

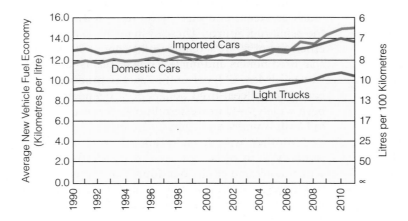

FIGURE 18-6 Average fuel economy of new cars sold in North America from 1990 to 2011. (Data from the Research and Innovative Technology Administration, 2012)

FIGURE 18-7 The Smart Car (upper left) is one example of a small efficient car. The Toyota Prius (upper right) and the Ford Escape (lower left) are hybrid-electric vehicles. The Chevy Volt (lower right) is a "plug-in" hybrid-electric vehicle.

One type of energy-efficient car uses a *hybrid-electric internal combustion engine*. It runs on gasoline, diesel fuel, or natural gas and uses an electric motor and battery (recharged by the internal combustion engine) to provide the energy needed for acceleration, for hill climbing, and for driving at city speeds without adding to air pollution. The electric motor is well suited for stop-and-go city driving, and hybrid vehicles are being used as taxis on the crowded streets of New York City.

Toyota introduced the first electric-hybrid vehicle, the Prius, to Canada in 1997 (Figure 18-7). The Prius offered impressive efficiency (20.4 kpL city or 19.2 kpL highway), but it was a small car by North American standards and the idea of a hybrid engine took some time to gain wide appeal. Ford entered the market with its Escape in 2004, providing a larger electric-hybrid vehicle with the fuel economy of a compact car (14.5 kpL city or 13.2 kpL highway). Now, Canadian consumers are aware of the advantages of electric-hybrid engines, and every car manufacturer is offering a range of models.

Some of the latest choices are "plug-in" electric hybrids, such as the Chevy Volt (Figure 18-7). This car has an extra-large battery that can be charged overnight by plugging it into an ordinary household circuit; it can then be driven for the first 60 kilometres (37 miles) using the electric motor alone. As the battery begins to de-charge, a small gasoline motor runs a generator to recharge the battery. In terms of cost and efficiency, the first 60 kilometres are provided for the price of overnight electric-charging at your home (perhaps 80 cents, assuming 10 cents per kwh); thereafter, the small gasoline motor that runs the generator is rated at 20.8 kpL (http://gm-volt.com/chevy-volt-faqs/).

Some automotive experts see hybrid cars as an intermediate step toward cars that are completely electric. Such cars will become more practical once better batteries have been developed. The issue then will be whether the electricity used to charge the car comes from renewable energy (such as hydro, solar, or wind), from fossil fuel energy (such as coal or natural gas), or from nuclear energy.

Are Fuel-Cell Cars the Answer? Possible Star of the Future

Automakers are developing fuel-efficient cars powered by fuel cells running on hydrogen and producing little pollution.

Another type of superefficient car is an electric vehicle that uses a *fuel cell*—a device that combines hydrogen gas (H_2) and oxygen gas (O_2) fuel to produce electricity and water vapour ($2\,H_2 + O_2 \rightarrow 2\,H_2O$) (Figure 18-8).

Fuel cells are at least twice as efficient as internal combustion engines, have no moving parts, require little maintenance, and produce little or no pollution depending on how their hydrogen fuel is produced. Most major automobile companies have developed prototype fuel-cell cars. They hope to have a variety of affordable fuel-cell vehicles on the market by 2020 and greatly increase their use by 2050. Until then hybrids will probably have an advantage because they are available now and get their fuel from regular filling stations instead of having to depend on building a new network of hydrogen filling stations.

In 2001, Bill Ford, grandson of Henry Ford and chairman of the Ford Motor Company, said, "I believe fuel cells will finally end the 100-year reign of the internal combustion engine."

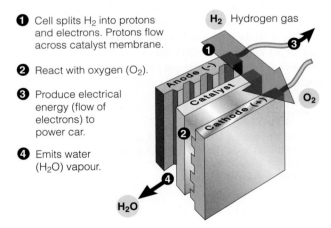

1 Cell splits H_2 into protons and electrons. Protons flow across catalyst membrane.

2 React with oxygen (O_2).

3 Produce electrical energy (flow of electrons) to power car.

4 Emits water (H_2O) vapour.

FIGURE 18-8 Solutions: general features of an electric car powered by a *fuel cell* running on hydrogen gas. Prototype models are on the road now, and manufacturers hope to have some models of such cars on the market within a decade. (Concept information from DaimlerChrysler, Ford, Ballard, Toyota, and Honda)

A **Fuel cell stack:** Hydrogen and oxygen combine chemically to produce electricity.

B **Fuel tank:** Hydrogen gas or liquid or solid metal hydride stored on board or made from gasoline or methanol.

C **Turbo compressor:** Sends pressurized air to fuel cell.

D **Traction inverter:** Module converts DC electricity from fuel cell to AC for use in electric motor.

E **Electric motor / transaxle:** Converts electrical energy to mechanical energy to turn wheels.

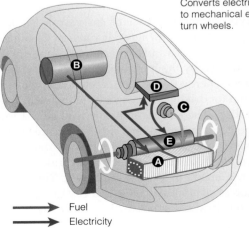

→ Fuel

→ Electricity

If fuel-cell cars become the choice of the future, the question will be, "What is the source of the energy that is used to split water into hydrogen gas and oxygen gas ($2 H_2O \rightarrow 2 H_2 + O_2$)?" Will that be accomplished by increasing our use of renewable energy, fossil fuel energy, nuclear energy, or some combination of these? This decision will have environmental, health, and economic impacts to consider.

How Can We Design Buildings to Save Energy? Work with Nature

We can save energy in buildings by getting heat from the sun, superinsulating them, and using plant-covered ecoroofs.

The design of energy-efficient buildings has become a growth industry throughout the world as occupants seek to reduce their energy costs. The *National Green Building Conference and Exposition 2006*, held in Ottawa, focused attention on the benefits of green architecture. A prime example is the University of Ottawa's biology building, which uses 73% less energy than conventional structures of the same size. In addition to insulated curtain-wall construction, the building features ultra-efficient lighting, recovery and collection of heat from exhaust air and growth chambers in the building, and a circulation system that vents dry air into rooms to be heated locally as needed. The 22-story Manitoba Hydro building in Winnipeg uses cutting-edge technology to achieve a 60% reduction in energy costs.

Another energy-efficient design is a **superinsulated house** (Figure 18-9). Such houses typically cost 5% more to build than conventional houses of the same size. But this extra cost is paid back by energy savings within about five years and can save a homeowner $50 000–$100 000 over a 40-year period. Superinsulated houses in Sweden use 90% less energy for heating and cooling than the typical North American home.

FIGURE 18-9 Solutions: major features of a *superinsulated house*. Such a house is so heavily insulated and so airtight that heat from direct sunlight, appliances, and human bodies can warm it with little or no need for a backup heating system. An air-to-air heat exchanger prevents buildup of indoor air pollution.

Superinsulated houses are especially well suited to Canadian winters. There are more than 3 000 superinsulated houses in Saskatchewan, where winter temperatures can fall to −40°C. Virtually all of the heating in a well-designed superinsulated house comes from passive solar energy, waste heat generated by appliances, and the body heat of occupants. A small auxiliary heater is typically added to smooth out the fluctuations of temperature that would otherwise occur.

Since the mid-1980s, there has been growing interest in building one particular type of superinsulated house called a *strawbale house* (Figure 18-10). The walls are made by stacking compacted bales of low-cost straw and then covering the bales on the outside and inside with plaster or adobe. The main problem is getting banks and other moneylenders to recognize the potential of this and

FIGURE 18-10 Solutions: an energy-efficient, environmentally healthy, and affordable *strawbale house*. Depending on the thickness of the bales, plastered strawbale walls have an insulating value of R-35 to R-60, compared with R-12 to R-19 in a conventional house. (The R-value is a measure of resistance to heat flow.) Such houses are also great sound insulators.

other unconventional types of housing and to provide homeowners with construction loans.

Ecoroofs or *green roofs* covered with plants have been used in Germany, in other parts of Europe, and in Iceland for decades and are becoming an increasingly common feature of tall buildings in North America (Chapter 25). With proper design, these plant-covered roof gardens provide good insulation, absorb storm water and release it slowly, outlast conventional roofs, and make a building or home more energy efficient. Designing and installing such systems could be an interesting career.

The Earth Rangers Centre in Woodbridge, Ontario, has won awards for its innovative design. For example, it features extensive use of rainwater harvesting and water reuse. Heating and cooling are made energy efficient by moving air through earth tubes similar to those shown in Figure 18-15 (p. 430). The windows have been carefully chosen and placed to minimize the need for artificial lighting. Insulation and oxygen are supplied by the green roof of living plants. And many parts of the building are made of recycled materials.

One energy-efficient house that exemplifies the long-term benefits of green architecture is Toronto's Healthy House, which was constructed in 1996 as part of a Canada Mortgage and Housing Corporation (CMHC) project (Figure 18-11). This house uses solar heating, radiant floors, superinsulation, superefficient windows, and landscaping. The residents of Healthy House pay little for electricity, heating, or cooling because of these efficiency features.

How Can We Save Energy in Existing Buildings? Stop Leaks and Use Energy-Efficient Devices

We can save energy in existing buildings by insulating them, plugging leaks, and using energy-efficient heating and cooling systems, appliances, and lighting.

Here are some ways to save energy in existing buildings.

- *Insulate and plug leaks.* About one-third of heated air in North American homes and buildings escapes through closed windows and holes and cracks (Figure 18-12)—roughly equal to the energy in all the oil flowing through the Alaska pipeline every year. During hot weather these windows and cracks also let heat in, increasing the use of air conditioning. People often overlook the fact that adding readily available insulation and plugging leaks in a house are two of the quickest, cheapest, and best ways to save energy and money.

- *Use energy-efficient windows.* Replacing all windows with low-E (low-emissivity) windows would cut expensive heat losses from houses by two-thirds and reduce CO_2 emissions. Widely available superinsulating windows insulate as well as 8–12 sheets of glass. Although they cost 10–15% more than double-glazed windows, this cost is paid back rapidly by the energy they save. Even better windows will reach the market soon.

FIGURE 18-11 CHMC's family-occupied Healthy House in Toronto serves as a living demonstration of comfortable and efficient housing. (Canada Mortgage and Housing Corporation (CMHC). CMHC's Family-Occupied Healthy House in Toronto, 2010. All rights reserved. Reproduced with the consent of CMHC. All other uses and reproductions of this material are expressly prohibited.)

thieury/Shutterstock.com

FIGURE 18-12 An infrared photo (thermogram) shows heat loss (red, white, and orange) around the windows, doors, roofs, and foundations of houses and stores at night. Many homes and buildings are so full of leaks that their heat loss in cold weather and heat gain in hot weather are equivalent to having a large, window-sized hole in the wall of the house.

- *Stop other heating and cooling losses.* Leaky heating and cooling ducts in attics and unheated basements allow 20–30% of a home's heating and cooling energy to escape and draw unwanted moisture and heat into the home. Careful sealing can reduce this loss. Some designs for new homes keep the ducts inside the home's thermal envelope so that escaping hot or cool air feeds back into the living space.

- *Heat houses more efficiently* (Figure 18-13). In order, the most energy-efficient ways to heat a space are superinsulation, a geothermal heat pump, passive solar heating, a conventional heat pump (in warm climates only), small cogenerating microturbines, and a high-efficiency (85–98%) natural gas furnace. The most wasteful and expensive way is to use electric resistance heating with the electricity produced by a coal-fired or nuclear power plant (Figure 18-13). One option that is gaining in popularity is the use of cogeneration units or *microturbines* about the size of a refrigerator. They run on natural gas or liquefied petroleum gas (LPG) to produce heat and electricity for businesses, small apartment buildings, neighbourhood groups of four or five energy-efficient houses, and small government facilities such as police stations. In 6–8 years, they pay for themselves in saved fuel and electricity.

- *Heat water more efficiently.* One way to do this is to use a *tankless instant water heater* (about the size of a small suitcase) fired by natural gas or LPG but not by electricity. These devices, widely used in many parts of Europe, heat water instantly as it flows through a small burner chamber, provide hot water only when it is needed, and cost 30–50% less to heat water than traditional heaters. They cost 2–4 times more than conventional water heaters, but save money because they last 3–4 times longer and cost less to operate than conventional tank heaters.

A well-insulated, conventional natural gas or LPG water heater is also fairly efficient. But all conventional natural gas and electric resistance heaters waste energy by keeping a large tank of water hot all day and night and can run out after a long shower or two—like running your car all night until you drive it.

- *Use energy-efficient appliances.* In most countries, appliances are rated in terms of their energy efficiency. Choosing a more efficient appliance will pay big dividends in energy savings over the life of the appliance. If all households in North America used the most efficient frost-free refrigerator now available, 20 large (1 000-megawatt) power plants could

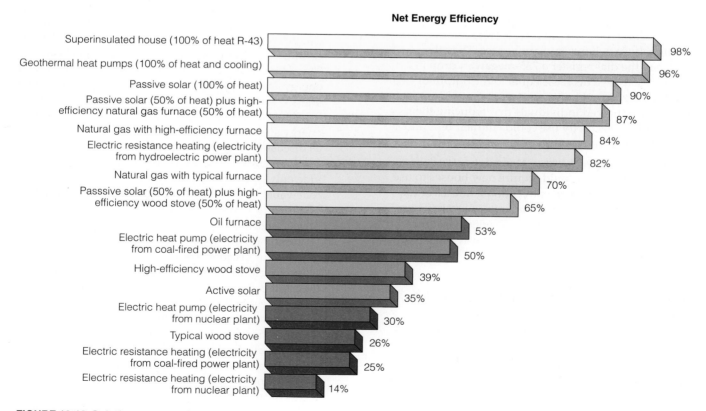

Net Energy Efficiency

Method	Efficiency
Superinsulated house (100% of heat R-43)	98%
Geothermal heat pumps (100% of heat and cooling)	96%
Passive solar (100% of heat)	90%
Passive solar (50% of heat) plus high-efficiency natural gas furnace (50% of heat)	87%
Natural gas with high-efficiency furnace	84%
Electric resistance heating (electricity from hydroelectric power plant)	82%
Natural gas with typical furnace	70%
Passsive solar (50% of heat) plus high-efficiency wood stove (50% of heat)	65%
Oil furnace	53%
Electric heat pump (electricity from coal-fired power plant)	50%
High-efficiency wood stove	39%
Active solar	35%
Electric heat pump (electricity from nuclear plant)	30%
Typical wood stove	26%
Electric resistance heating (electricity from coal-fired power plant)	25%
Electric resistance heating (electricity from nuclear plant)	14%

FIGURE 18-13 Solutions: ways to heat an enclosed space such as a house, ranked by net energy efficiency. (Data from Howard T. Odum)

close. Microwave ovens can cut electricity use for cooking by 25–50% (but not if used for defrosting food). Clothes dryers with moisture sensors cut energy use by 15%, and front-loading washers use 50% less energy than top-loading models but cost about the same.

- *Use energy-efficient lighting.* North Americans spend about a quarter of their electricity budget on lighting. But many do not realize that they could cut these costs 30–60% by replacing energy-wasting incandescent bulbs and halogen torchiere bulbs (which because of their high heat output have caused fires and increased air conditioning costs) with much more efficient *compact fluorescent* bulbs and *light-emitting diode (LED)* bulbs. A compact fluorescent bulb uses one-quarter as much electricity as an incandescent bulb and typically lasts 10 times as long. An LED bulb uses about one-seventh the electricity required by an incandescent bulb and can last about 100 times longer. These two efficient bulbs are more expensive to purchase but they more than pay for themselves through energy savings.

- *Cut off electrical devices when not using them.* Cutting off lights, computers, TVs, and other appliances when they are not needed and cutting off their instant-on feature can make a big difference in energy use and bills. At 9 p.m. one weekday evening, major TV stations in Bangkok, Thailand, cooperated with the government in showing a dial that gave the city's current use of electricity. Viewers were asked to turn off unnecessary lights and appliances. They then watched the dial register a 735-megawatt drop in electricity use—a decrease equal to the output of two medium-sized coal-burning power plants. This visual experience showed individuals that reducing their unnecessary electricity use could cut their bills and close down power plants.

- *Set strict energy-efficiency standards for new buildings.* Building codes could require new houses to use 60–80% less energy than conventional houses of the same size. Because of tough national energy-efficiency standards, the average home in Sweden consumes about one-third as much energy as the average North American home of the same size.

Why Are We Still Wasting So Much Energy? We Get What We Reward

Low-priced oil and gasoline and lack of government tax breaks for saving energy promote energy waste.

With such an impressive array of benefits (Figure 18-2), why is there so little emphasis on improving energy efficiency? One reason is the relatively low price of oil and gasoline. As long as energy is artificially cheap because its market price does not include its harmful

costs, people are more likely to waste it and not make investments in improving energy efficiency.

Another reason is a lack of sufficient government tax breaks and other economic incentives for consumers and businesses to invest in improving energy efficiency.

Would you like to earn about 20% a year on your money, tax-free and risk-free? Invest it in improving the energy efficiency of your home and in energy-efficient lights and appliances. You get your investment back in a few years and then make about 20% a year by having lower heating, cooling, and electricity bills. This is a win-win deal for you and the Earth.

> **CONSIDER, DISCUSS, OR DEBATE**
>
> If you were responsible for improving Canada's energy efficiency, what would be your multi-pronged approach to the problem?

18-3 USING RENEWABLE ENERGY TO PROVIDE HEAT AND ELECTRICITY

What Are the Main Types of Renewable Energy? Solar Capital

Six types of renewable energy are solar, flowing water, wind, biomass, geothermal, and hydrogen.

One of the four keys to sustainability based on learning from nature is to *rely mostly on renewable solar energy*. We can get renewable solar energy directly from the sun or indirectly from moving water, wind, and biomass. Two other forms of renewable energy are geothermal energy from the Earth's interior and using renewable energy to produce hydrogen fuel from water. Like fossil fuels and nuclear power, each of these renewable energy alternatives has advantages and disadvantages, as discussed in the remainder of this chapter.

If renewable energy is so great, why does it provide only 16% of the world's energy? One reason is that renewable energy resources have received and generally continue to receive much lower government tax breaks, subsidies, and research and development (R & D) funding than fossil fuels and nuclear power have received for decades. The other reason is that the prices we pay for fossil fuels and nuclear power do not include their full costs, such as harm to human health and the environment in the case of fossil fuels, and hidden costs of decommissioning (p. 413) in the case of nuclear energy.

In other words, the economic dice have been loaded against solar, wind, and other forms of renewable energy. If the economic playing field was made more even, energy analysts say that many of these forms of renewable energy would take over—another example of the *you-get-what-you-reward* economic principle in action.

A key advantage of renewable energy, aside from low environmental impact, is that it allows energy problems to be solved in so many versatile ways depending on the combination of renewable energy sources (such as solar, wind, hydro, microhydro, geothermal, biomass, and efficiency) that are available locally. Consider the opening Case Study (p. 418) about tidal power that is being developed in the Bay of Fundy area. Renewable energy installations can be large or small, and can allow communities and individuals to be more directly involved with their energy options. For example, homeowners might decide to take advantage of renewable energy options on their properties out of concern for the environment, in order to have their own supply of energy during emergencies, and in order to sell surplus energy to the grid.

How Can We Use Direct Solar Energy to Heat Houses and Water? Face the Sun and Store Its Heat

We can heat buildings by orienting them toward the sun (passive solar heating) or by pumping a liquid such as water through rooftop collectors (active solar heating).

Buildings and water can be heated by direct solar energy using two methods: passive and active (Figure 18-14). A **passive solar heating system** absorbs and stores heat from the sun directly within a structure (Figures 18-1, 18-14 (left), and 18-15, p. 430).

Using passive solar energy is not new. For thousands of years, many people have intuitively followed the first principle of sustainability. They have oriented their dwellings to take advantage of heat from the sun and used adobe and thick stone walls to collect and store heat during the day and gradually release it at night.

In today's passively heated buildings, energy-efficient windows and attached greenhouses face the sun to collect solar energy by direct gain. Walls and floors of concrete, adobe, brick, stone, salt-treated timber, and water in metal or plastic containers store much of the collected solar energy as heat and release it slowly throughout the day and night. A small backup heating system such as a vented natural gas or propane heater may be used but is not necessary in many climates.

On a life-cycle-cost basis, good passive solar and superinsulated design is the cheapest way to heat a home or small building in regions with access to ample sunlight. Such a system usually adds 5–10% to the construction cost, but the life-cycle cost of operating such a house is 30–40% lower. The typical payback time for passive solar features is 3–7 years.

An **active solar heating system** absorbs energy from the sun by pumping a heat-absorbing fluid (such as water or antifreeze solution) through special **solar collectors** usually mounted on a roof or on special racks to face the sun (Figure 18-14, right). A typical active collector has a flat black surface, a coil through which the heat-absorbing medium such as water is pumped, and a cover consisting of two or three layers of glass.

Some of the collected heat can be used directly. The rest can be stored in a large insulated container filled with gravel, water, clay, or a heat-absorbing chemical for release as needed. Often these insulated heat storage containers are located under a house.

Active solar collectors can also supply hot water and are widely used in areas of the world with sunny

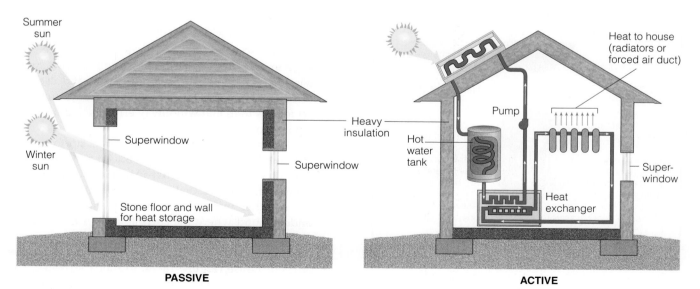

FIGURE 18-14 Solutions: passive and active solar heating for a home.

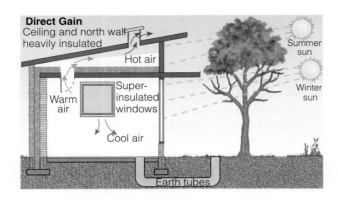

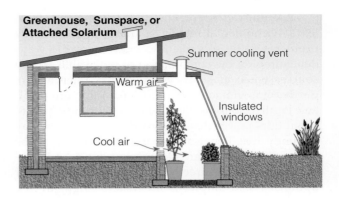

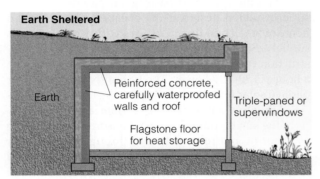

FIGURE 18-15 **Solutions:** three examples of *passive solar design* for houses.

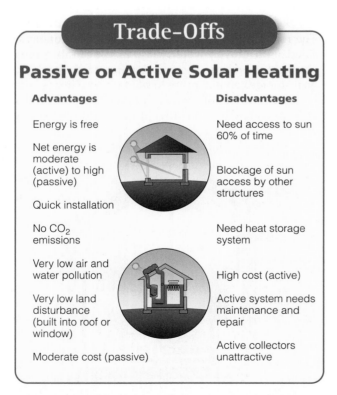

FIGURE 18-16 **Trade-offs:** advantages and disadvantages of heating a house with passive or active solar energy. Pick the single advantage and the single disadvantage that you think are the most important.

climates. More than 1 million homes in Florida and California heat all or some of their water with one or more active solar collectors. Many houses in the Caribbean heat their water passively by placing large black water containers on the roof where they are exposed to direct sunlight.

Figure 18-16 lists the major advantages and disadvantages of using passive or active solar energy for heating buildings. Passive solar energy is great for new homes in sunny areas but cannot be used to heat existing homes and buildings not oriented to receive sunlight or where trees or other buildings block access to sunlight. Active solar collectors are good for heating water in sunny areas. But most analysts do not expect widespread use of active solar collectors for heating houses because of their high costs, maintenance requirements, and unappealing appearance.

How Can We Cool Houses Naturally? Insulate and Work with Nature

We can cool houses by superinsulating them, taking advantage of breezes, shading them, having light-coloured roofs, and using geothermal cooling.

Here are some ways to have a cooler house. Use superinsulation and superinsulating windows, open windows to take advantage of breezes, and use fans to keep air moving. Block the high summer sun with deciduous trees and window overhangs (Figure 18-15, top left), or awnings.

Use a light-coloured roof to reflect up to 80% of the sun's heat, compared to only 8% for a roof coloured dark grey. Suspend reflective insulating foil in an attic to block heat from radiating down into the house.

Another option is to place plastic *earth tubes* underground where the earth is cool year-round. In this geothermal cooling system, a tiny fan can pipe cool and partially dehumidified air into an energy-efficient house (Figure 18-15, top left). In warm climates you can also use high-efficiency heat pumps for air conditioning.

Toronto, Canada's largest city, cools downtown buildings by pumping cold water from the depths of Lake Ontario and passing it through building air conditioning systems. This reduces the use of coal for producing electricity, cuts greenhouse gas emissions, and slashes summer use of electricity for air conditioning by 90%.

How Can We Use Solar Energy to Generate High-Temperature Heat and Electricity? Desert Power

Large arrays of solar collectors in sunny deserts can produce high-temperature heat to spin turbines and produce electricity, but costs are high.

Several *solar thermal systems* can collect and transform radiant energy from the sun into high-temperature thermal energy (heat), which can be used directly or converted to electricity. These systems are used mostly in desert areas with ample sunlight.

One method uses a *central receiver system,* called a *power tower.* Huge arrays of computer-controlled mirrors called *heliostats* track the sun and focus sunlight on a central heat collection tower (top drawing in Figure 18-17).

Australia is building a different type of power tower in its sunny outback. It will consist of a concrete thermal chimney twice the height of the world's tallest building surrounded by a gigantic sloped solar greenhouse with a diameter of 5 kilometres (3 miles).

As the hot air collected by the huge greenhouse flows up into the tower it will spin 32 giant turbines and produce enough electricity to serve 200 000 homes. Some of the heat collected during the day will be stored in tubes filled with water. The heat released from this water after dark should keep the power plant working throughout the night. This project is a miniature version of how the Earth makes wind from solar energy.

Another approach is a *solar thermal plant* in which sunlight is collected and focused on arrays of oil-filled pipes running through the middle of a large area of curved solar collectors (bottom drawing in Figure 18-17). This concentrated sunlight can generate temperatures high enough for producing steam to run turbines and generate electricity. At night or on cloudy days, high-efficiency combined-cycle natural gas turbines can supply backup electricity as needed.

On an individual scale, inexpensive *solar cookers* can focus and concentrate sunlight and cook food, especially in rural villages in sunny developing countries. They can be made by fitting an insulated box big enough to hold three or four pots with a transparent, removable top. Solar cookers reduce deforestation for fuelwood and the time and labour needed to collect firewood. They also reduce indoor air pollution from smoky fires.

Figure 18-17 lists the advantages and disadvantages of concentrating solar energy to produce high-temperature heat or electricity. Most analysts do not expect widespread use of such technologies over the next few decades because of high costs, limited suitable sites, and availability of cheaper ways to produce electricity such as combined-cycle natural gas and wind turbines.

> **DID YOU KNOW**
>
> The amount of solar energy falling on 15 square kilometres 4 square miles of Canadian surface equals the entire energy capacity of all the nuclear power plants in Canada. (Canadian Solar Industries Association, http://www.cansia.ca)

How Can We Produce Electricity with Solar Cells? Use Your Roof or Windows as a Power Plant

Solar cells that convert sunlight to electricity can be incorporated into roofing materials or windows, and the high costs of doing this are expected to fall.

Solar energy can be converted directly into electrical energy by **photovoltaic (PV) cells,** commonly called **solar cells** (Figure 18-18, p. 432). A typical solar cell is a transparent wafer containing a semiconductor material with a thickness ranging from less than that of a human hair to a sheet of paper. Sunlight energizes and causes electrons in the semiconductor to flow, creating an electrical current. These devices have no moving

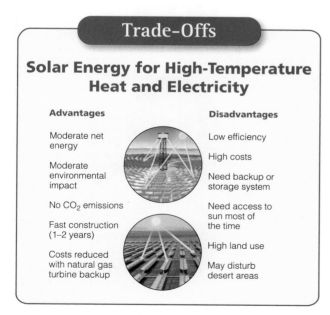

FIGURE 18-17 Trade-offs: advantages and disadvantages of using solar energy to generate high-temperature heat and electricity. Pick the single advantage and the single disadvantage that you think are the most important.

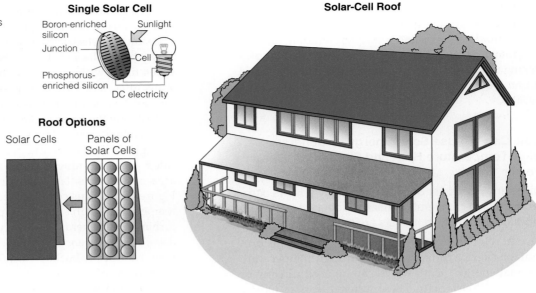

FIGURE 18-18 Solutions: photovoltaic (PV) (solar) cells can provide electricity for a house or building using new solar-cell roof shingles or PV panel roof systems that look like a blue metal roof. Arrays of such cells can also produce electricity for a village or at a small power plant.

Single Solar Cell

Boron-enriched silicon
Junction
Cell
Phosphorus-enriched silicon
Sunlight
DC electricity

Solar-Cell Roof

Roof Options

Solar Cells   Panels of Solar Cells

parts, require little maintenance, produce no pollution during operation, and last as long as a conventional fossil fuel or nuclear power plant.

The semiconductor material used in solar cells can be made into lightweight paper-thin rigid or flexible sheets and incorporated into traditional-looking roofing materials (blue in Figure 18-18). Glass walls and windows of buildings can also have built-in solar cells. In 2004, energy giant British Petroleum (BP) began building the world's largest factory to produce windows and siding and roofing materials that will incorporate BP's power-producing solar cells.

Easily expandable banks of solar cells can be used to provide electricity in developing countries for 1.7 billion people in rural villages without electricity. Such banks of cells can also produce electricity at a small power plant (bottom drawing in Figure 18-19), using combined-cycle natural gas turbines to provide backup power when the sun is not shining. Another possibility is to use arrays of solar cells to convert water to hydrogen gas that can be distributed to energy users by pipeline, as natural gas is. With financing from the World Bank, India (the world's number-one market for solar cells) is installing solar-cell systems in 38 000 villages, and Zimbabwe is bringing solar electricity to 2 500 villages. By 2004, more than 1 million homes in the world, many of them in villages in developing countries, were getting some or all of their electricity from solar cells mostly because they were long distances from a power grid. Solar energy is becoming an increasingly popular choice for people in developed countries who wish to reduce their dependence on conventional sources of energy.

Trade-Offs

Solar Cells

Advantages	Disadvantages
Fairly high net energy	Need access to sun
Work on cloudy days	Low efficiency
Quick installation	Need electricity storage system or backup
Easily expanded or moved	
No CO_2 emissions	High land use (solar-cell power plants) could disrupt desert areas
Low environmental impact	
Last 20–40 years	
Low land use (if on roof or built into walls or windows)	High costs (but should be competitive in 5–15 years)
Reduce dependence on fossil fuels	DC current must be converted to AC

FIGURE 18-19 Trade-offs: advantages and disadvantages of using solar cells to produce electricity. Pick the single advantage and the single disadvantage that you think are the most important.

Figure 18-19 lists the advantages and disadvantages of solar cells. Current costs of producing electricity from solar cells are high but are expected to drop because of savings from mass production and new designs. Solar cells can also be incorporated into carbon-based polymers similar to Teflon that can be applied to surfaces in thin layers. The first generation of such *organic solar cells* that can convert 20–35% of the sun's energy into electricity could enter the marketplace within a few years. These solar cells could be printed on a sheet of paper, stuck onto your house or car windows, painted on your house, or even incorporated into your clothing—making you a tiny walking power plant.

Some envision incorporating minuscule rods of semiconductors with a thickness of several nanometres (a tiny fraction of the thickness of a hair on your head) in plastic materials. Such *nano solar cells* can be manufactured in extremely high volumes at a very low cost. Stay tuned.

Currently solar cells supply only about 0.05% of the world's electricity. But with increased government and private R & D and greater government tax breaks and other subsidies they could provide over a quarter of the world's electricity by 2040. If such projections are correct, the production, sale, and installation of solar cells could become one of the world's largest and fastest-growing businesses. This is another exciting field to consider as a career choice.

18-4 PRODUCING ELECTRICITY FROM THE WATER CYCLE

How Can We Produce Electricity from Flowing Water? Renewable Hydropower

Water flowing in rivers and streams can be trapped in reservoirs behind dams and released as needed to spin turbines and produce electricity.

Solar energy evaporates water and deposits it as water and snow in other areas as part of the water cycle (Figure 4-27, p. 80). Water flowing from high elevations to lower elevations in rivers and streams can be controlled by dams and reservoirs and used to produce electricity. This indirect form of renewable solar energy is called **hydropower** (Figure 15-13, p. 346).

Three methods are used to produce such electricity. One is *large-scale hydropower*, in which a high dam is built across a large river to create a reservoir. Some of the water stored in the reservoir is allowed to flow through huge pipes at controlled rates, spinning turbines and producing electricity. At Niagara Falls, large-scale hydropower is generated by diverting some water from the upper Niagara River so that it falls through turbines at generating stations rather than flowing over the falls (Figure 18-20).

Another method is *small-scale hydropower*. A low dam with no reservoir or only a small one is built across a small stream, and the stream's flow of water is used to spin turbines and produce electricity. Submerging small high-efficiency turbines in a stream without impeding stream navigation or fish movements can also produce electricity. A smaller turbine called a micro-hydrogenerator can be used to provide affordable electricity for a single home.

A third method is *pumped-storage hydropower*. Pumps use surplus electricity from a conventional power plant to pump water from a lake or a reservoir to another reservoir at a higher elevation. When more electricity is needed, water in the upper reservoir is released, flows through turbines, and generates electricity on its return to the lower reservoir.

In 2007, hydropower supplied 20% of the world's electricity, 99% in Norway, 75% in New Zealand, 59% in Canada, 21% in China, and 6% in the United States (but about 50% on that country's West Coast).

Figure 18-21 (p. 434) lists the advantages and disadvantages of using large-scale hydropower plants to produce electricity.

According to the United Nations, only about 13% of the world's technically exploitable potential for hydropower has been developed. Much of this untapped potential is in China (pp. 347–348), India, South America, Central Africa, and parts of the former Soviet Union.

Courtesy of the Ontario Power Generation Inc.

FIGURE 18-20 The hydropower generated at Niagara Falls is different from that of many large hydro projects in that there is no dam holding back a reservoir of water. Water is diverted from the Niagara River above the falls and channelled through canals and tunnels before falling through turbines at generating stations. A new development on the Canadian side of Niagara Falls involves the creation of a third tunnel, the Niagara Tunnel, which will pass under the City of Niagara Falls at a maximum depth of 140 metres and deliver water to the Sir Adam Beck Power Station Complex at a rate of 500 cubic metres per second. The photograph shows the crew celebrating after the giant boring machine, "Big Becky," broke out of the rock to finish the 10.2 k tunnel in May 2011. The Niagara Tunnel will begin adding 1.6 billion kilowatt-hours per year to Canada's hydropower generating capacity in 2013 (http://www.niagarafrontier.com/tunnel.html).

Large-Scale Hydropower

Advantages	Disadvantages

Advantages

Moderate to high net energy

High efficiency (80%)

Large untapped potential

Low-cost electricity

Long life span

No CO_2 emissions during operation in temperate areas

May provide flood control below dam

Provides water for year-round irrigation of cropland

Reservoir is useful for fishing and recreation

Disadvantages

High construction costs

High environmental impact from flooding land to form a reservoir

High CO_2 emissions from biomass decay in shallow tropical reservoirs

Floods natural areas behind dam

Converts land habitat to lake habitat

Danger of collapse

Uproots people

Decreases fish harvest below dam

Decreases flow of natural fertilizer (silt) to land below dam

FIGURE 18-21 Trade-offs: advantages and disadvantages of using large dams and reservoirs to produce electricity. Pick the single advantage and the single disadvantage that you think are the most important.

SELF CHECK

Are you wondering where the existing water power stations are, or where remaining sites with water power potential might be? What about the ones that are just on federal lands, or just within parks?

You can find out by clicking on the interactive map at http://www.lio.ontario.ca/imf-ows/imf.jsp?site=renew_en. While investigating, you can make choices about which layers of information to add to your map. Note that the MNR web page will ask you to accept the terms of use (it is safe to do so).

Because of increasing concern about the harmful environmental and social consequences of large dams, there has been growing pressure on the World Bank and other development agencies to stop funding new large-scale hydropower projects. Also, according to a 2000 study by the World Commission on Dams, hydropower in tropical countries is a major emitter of greenhouse gases. This occurs because reservoirs that power the dams can trap rotting vegetation, which can emit greenhouse gases such as carbon dioxide and methane.

Small-scale hydropower projects eliminate most of the harmful environmental effects of large-scale projects. But their electrical output can vary with seasonal changes in stream flow.

We can also produce electricity from water flows by tapping into the energy from tides and waves. Most analysts expect these sources to make little contribution to world electricity production because of high costs and lack of enough areas with the right conditions.

CONSIDER, DISCUSS, OR DEBATE

Do the advantages of using large-scale hydropower plants to produce electricity outweigh the disadvantages? How does this method compare with small-scale hydropower projects?

18-5 PRODUCING ELECTRICITY FROM WIND

What Is the Status of Wind Power? A Star Is Born

Since 1990, the use of wind turbines to produce electricity has increased almost tenfold.

The greater heating of the Earth at the equator than at the poles and the Earth's rotation (Figure 6-10, p. 117) set up flows of air called *wind*. This indirect form of solar energy can be captured by wind turbines (Figure 18-22) and converted into electricity.

FIGURE 18-22 Solutions: wind turbines can be used to produce electricity individually or in clusters, called **wind farms** or wind parks. Since 1990, wind power has frequently been the world's fastest-growing or second-fastest-growing source of energy. Our energy future may be blowing in the wind.

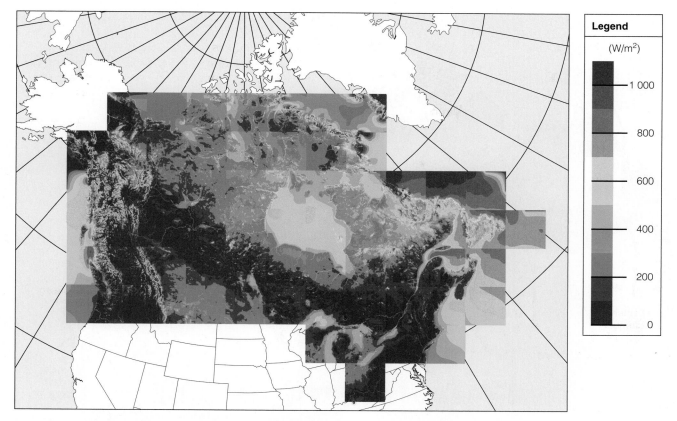

FIGURE 18-23 Distribution of wind energy across Canada. (Canadian Wind Atlas, http://www.windatlas .ca/en/EU_50m_national.pdf, Environment Canada, 2003. Reproduced with the permission of the Minister of Public Works and Government Services Canada, 2012)

Since 1990, the installed capacity of global wind power has increased more than 30-fold and is currently the second-fastest-growing source of energy, after solar energy.

As of 2011, China had 26% of the total installed capacity for wind power. Other countries with large amounts of capacity include the United States (20%), Germany (12%), Spain (9%), and India (7%). Canada comes in at number nine with 2.2% of the world's total wind capacity.

In terms of *newly installed* wind capacity, China was responsible for 43% of the wind capacity added during 2011, followed by the United Sates (17%) and India (7%). Canada is number six on that list, having installed 3.1% of the wind capacity that was added in 2011 (GWEC, 2011).

Much of the world's potential wind power remains untapped. According to a 2009 study published by the U.S. National Academy of Sciences, the world's top CO_2-emitting countries all have enough wind potential to more than meet all of their electricity needs. Canada, for example, has the potential to supply about 40 times its current electricity needs through wind power. The Canadian Wind Energy Association (2012) states that wind power currently supplies more than 2% of Canada's electricity and, with funding, could supply 20% by 2025.

In Canada, the most powerful and consistent winds are concentrated on the East and West Coasts (Figure 18-23). Forty-three windmill farms have been built in the Maritimes to take advantage of the region's wind resources, and windmills have been installed in all of the other provinces (Figure 18-24, p. 436). As of June 2012, 141 windmill farms had been installed across the country, and there is a long list of wind projects that are in various stages of construction (CanWEA, 2012a). A good deal of wind potential exists in the Great Lakes region as winds move across open expanses of water (Figure 18-25, p. 437). In recent years, Canada's wind energy capability has grown rapidly (Figure 18-26, p. 438). As windmill technology becomes less expensive and more widely available, individual homeowners are more likely to choose wind power as an energy option. To learn more

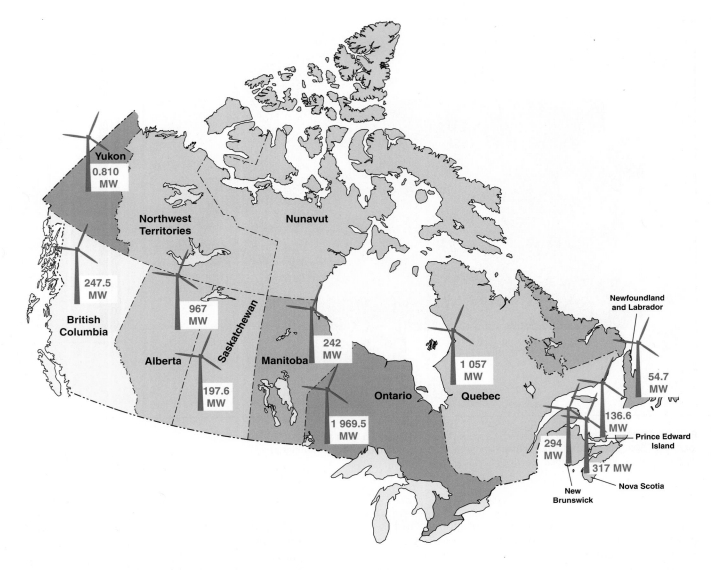

FIGURE 18-24 Distribution of installed windmill capacity across Canada in 2012. (Courtesy of Canadian Wind Energy Association (CanWEA))

about wind energy in Canada, visit the website of the Canadian Wind Energy Association (http://www .canwea.ca).

A growing number of farmers and ranchers make more money by leasing their land for wind power production than by growing crops or raising cattle. This explains why many of them are joining environmentalists and wind industry executives in urging political leaders to increase government research and development and tax breaks for wind power.

On the other hand, there has been a NIMBY effect (not in my backyard) as people who live near windmills worry about potential health effects of constantly hearing low-frequency sounds. The Ontario Ministry of the Environment (2010) reacted by commissioning a study that concluded that the regulated setback distance for windmills provides a safe buffer against human health effects.

Figure 18-27 (p. 438) lists the advantages and disadvantages of using wind to produce electricity. According to energy analysts, wind power has more advantages and fewer serious disadvantages than any other energy resource. Since 2004, the cost of wind-generated electricity dropped ninefold from 36¢ to about 4¢ per kilowatt-hour at favourable wind sites. This is about the same price as using coal, natural gas, and hydropower (at highly favourable sites) to produce electricity and three times cheaper than nuclear power. Wind power is like

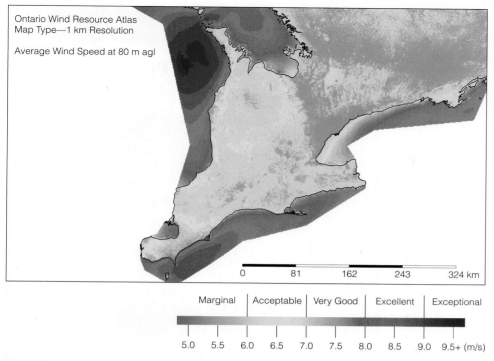

FIGURE 18-25 Average wind speed at 80 metres above ground level (agl). (Ontario Ministry of Natural Resources Wind Resource Atlas, http://www.ontariowindatlas.ca/en)

an underdog racehorse that is beginning to break out of a pack of other, more pampered (subsidized) energy racehorses.

If wind turbines are mass-produced like automobiles, the cost for a **kilowatt** of wind-generated energy could drop to 1–2 cents, making it by far the cheapest way to produce electricity. Many governments and corporations are recognizing that *there is money in wind*. Do the math. Assume an average price of electricity of 7.2¢ per kilowatt-hour. If wind companies can produce a kilowatt of electricity at about 4¢ now, and in the not-too-distant future, for 1.5–2¢, the potential profits are huge. This explains why General Electric, one of the world's largest multinational companies, recently decided to get into wind power.

Some critics allege that wind turbines suck large numbers of birds into their wind stream. However, as long as wind farms are not located along bird migration routes most birds learn to fly around them. Wind power developers now make sophisticated studies of bird migration paths to help them locate onshore and offshore wind parks and are designing new turbines to reduce this problem.

Also, studies have shown that much larger numbers of birds die when they are sucked into jet engines; killed by domesticated and feral cats; and crash into skyscrapers, plate glass windows, communications towers, and car windows.

Even larger numbers of birds, fish, and other forms of wildlife are killed by oil spills, air pollution, water pollution, and release of toxic wastes from use of fossil fuels such as coal and oil. The key questions are, "Which types of energy resources lead to the lowest loss of wildlife?" and "How can we minimize loss of wildlife from use of any energy resource?"

CONSIDER, DISCUSS, OR DEBATE

Given the potential benefits and drawbacks of wind power, should Canada greatly increase its dependence on this renewable type of energy?

18-6 PRODUCING ENERGY FROM BIOMASS

How Is Biomass Used to Provide Energy? Burning Carbon Compounds

Plant materials and animal wastes can be burned to provide heat or electricity or converted into gaseous or liquid biofuels.

Biomass consists of plant materials and animal wastes that can be burned directly as a solid fuel or converted into gaseous or liquid **biofuels** (Figure 18-28, p. 439).

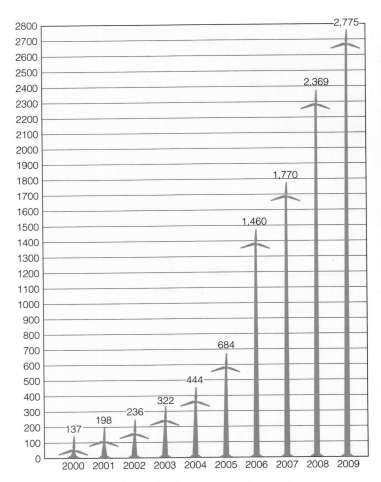

FIGURE 18-26 The installed capacity of wind energy in Canada has grown 40-fold since 2000. (Courtesy of Canadian Wind Energy Association (CanWEA))

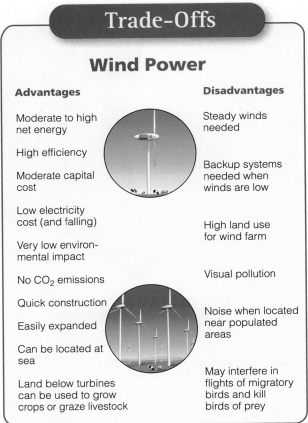

Trade-Offs

Wind Power

Advantages	Disadvantages
Moderate to high net energy	Steady winds needed
High efficiency	Backup systems needed when winds are low
Moderate capital cost	
Low electricity cost (and falling)	High land use for wind farm
Very low environmental impact	
No CO_2 emissions	Visual pollution
Quick construction	Noise when located near populated areas
Easily expanded	
Can be located at sea	
Land below turbines can be used to grow crops or graze livestock	May interfere in flights of migratory birds and kill birds of prey

FIGURE 18-27 Trade-offs: advantages and disadvantages of using wind to produce electricity. Wind power experts project that by 2025 wind power could supply more than 10% of the world's electricity and 20% of the electricity used in Canada. Pick the single advantage and the single disadvantage that you think are the most important.

Most biomass is burned *directly* for heating, cooking, and industrial processes or *indirectly* to drive turbines and produce electricity. Burning wood and manure for heating and cooking supplies about 10% of the world's energy and about 30% of the energy used in developing countries (90% in the poorest countries such as Bangladesh, Ethiopia, Burundi, and Bhutan).

One way to produce biomass fuel is to plant, harvest, and burn large numbers of fast-growing trees (especially cottonwoods, poplars, sycamores, willows, and leucaenas), shrubs, perennial grasses (such as switchgrass), and water hyacinths in *biomass plantations*.

In agricultural areas, *crop residues* (from sugarcane, rice, cotton, and coconuts) and *animal manure* can be collected and burned or converted into biofuels. In some developing countries, the poor gather animal manure or dung by hand, dry it, and burn it for heat and cooking. On the surface, this appears to be a free and logical use of wasted biomass.

But some ecologists argue that it makes more sense to use animal manure as a fertilizer and crop residues to feed livestock, retard soil erosion, and fertilize the soil. Not allowing these animal and crop wastes to return to the soil as natural fertilizer can reduce food production and food supplies in poor countries. Also, burning dried dung in open fires wastes about 90% of its heat content.

Figure 18-29 (p. 439) lists the general advantages and disadvantages of burning solid biomass as a fuel. One problem is that burning biomass produces CO_2. However, if the rate of use of biomass does not exceed the rate at which it is replenished by new plant growth (which takes up CO_2), there is no net increase in CO_2 emissions. But repeated cycles of growing and harvesting biomass plantations can deplete the soil of key nutrients.

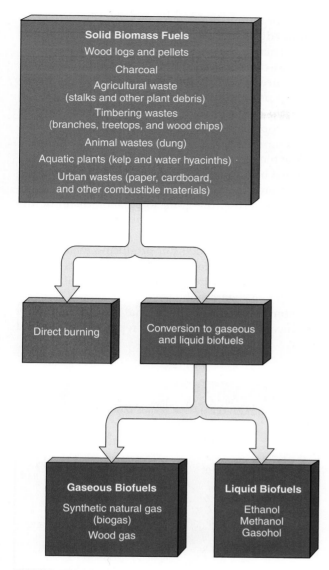

FIGURE 18-28 Principal types of biomass fuel.

Solid Biomass

Advantages

Large potential supply in some areas

Moderate costs

No net CO_2 increase if harvested and burned sustainably

Plantation can be located on semiarid land not needed for crops

Plantation can help restore degraded lands

Can make use of agricultural, timber, and urban wastes

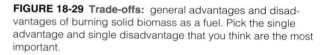

Disadvantages

Nonrenewable if harvested unsustainably

Moderate to high environmental impact

CO_2 emissions if harvested and burned unsustainably

Low photosynthetic efficiency

Soil erosion, water pollution, and loss of wildlife habitat

Plantations could compete with cropland

Often burned in inefficient and polluting open fires and stoves

FIGURE 18-29 **Trade-offs:** general advantages and disadvantages of burning solid biomass as a fuel. Pick the single advantage and single disadvantage that you think are the most important.

What Is Biodiesel? An Unusual Version of a Common Fuel

Biodiesel is a liquid fuel, made from biomass, that can be used in diesel engines.

Biodiesel is a kind of diesel fuel that is made from vegetable oil or animal fat rather than from petroleum. It has properties similar to conventional diesel fuel, and it can be used in normal or modified diesel engines, either by itself or mixed with conventional diesel fuel. It can also be used as heating oil.

Biodiesel is often made from soybeans or canola seeds, although it can be made from some surprising forms of biomass such as algae or used coffee grounds. It can also be made from waste animal materials such as chicken fat from poultry operations.

Its advantages are that it has low carbon emissions and contains no sulphur, unlike conventional diesel fuel. It has excellent lubricating properties that improve the performance of some engines. It provides a use for waste such as chicken fat and it can be a local source of fuel that allows some independence from petroleum-based fuels.

Its disadvantages are that it has lower caloric value than conventional diesel fuel, it can gel at cold temperatures, and it can damage rubber seals in engines that weren't designed for high concentrations of biodiesel.

A fish-based biodiesel is being used to run the bus system in Halifax. McDonald's UK uses a biodiesel made from their own waste cooking oil to run their fleet of vehicles. A number of trains are using biodiesel, including the Royal Train in England and the small trains at Disneyland (Have Kids Will Travel, 2009; The Prince of Wales, 2010).

How Can Gaseous Fuels Be Produced from Biomass? Bacteria and Chemistry to the Rescue

Some forms of biomass can be converted into gaseous and liquid biofuels.

Bacteria and various chemical processes can convert some forms of biomass into gaseous biofuels (Figure 18-28). One of them is *biogas*—a mixture of 60% methane and 40% CO_2.

In rural China, anaerobic bacteria in more than 500 000 *biogas digesters* on farms and in homes convert plant and animal wastes into methane gas that is used for heating and cooking. After the biogas has been removed, the almost odourless solid residue is used as fertilizer on food crops or, if it is contaminated, on trees. When they work, biogas digesters are very efficient and burning natural gas produced from dung produces much more heat than burning the dung itself. But they are slow and unpredictable, a problem that could be corrected by developing more reliable models. They also add CO_2 to the atmosphere.

In North America, biogas can be created from the livestock wastes produced by cattle, hogs, and chickens. One way to do this is to put the wastes in a long, lined, insulated pit. A flexible liner stretching across the digester pit inflates like a balloon as it collects the biogas, which can then be burned to heat the digester or nearby farm buildings or to produce electricity.

Bacteria in large digesters can also convert municipal garbage and sewage to methane gas. Wells drilled into about 300 large landfills in the United States recover methane produced by the decomposition of organic wastes and burn it to produce enough electricity to meet the needs of a million homes. BMW's automobile factory near Spartanburg, South Carolina, gets more than a fourth of its electricity and a tenth of its heat by burning methane gas piped in from a nearby landfill owned by Waste Management.

What Are the Advantages and Disadvantages of Using Liquid Ethanol and Methanol Produced from Biomass as a Fuel? Mixed Signals

Some believe we can rely much more on ethanol and methanol as a fuel, but others disagree.

Some analysts believe that liquid ethanol produced from biomass could replace gasoline and diesel fuel when oil becomes too scarce or expensive. *Ethanol* can be made from sugar and grain crops (sugarcane, sugar beets, sorghum, sunflowers, and corn) by fermentation and distillation. Gasoline mixed with 10–23% pure ethanol makes *gasohol*, which can be burned in conventional gasoline engines.

Figure 18-30 lists the advantages and disadvantages of using ethanol as a vehicle fuel compared to gasoline. Ethanol could be produced from surplus grain crops. But industrialized agriculture typically uses more energy in the form of petroleum-based vehicle fuel, fertilizers, and pesticides than the energy obtained by burning ethanol produced by such crops. Thus, there can be a *net energy loss* from growing grain crops, converting the grain to ethanol, distilling the ethanol, and distributing and burning it as a motor vehicle fuel.

Note that the process of producing ethanol from sugarcane is extremely efficient, and results in a net energy gain and many advantages for Brazil (see the Spotlight on sugarcane).

Some analysts believe that liquid methanol produced from biomass could replace gasoline and

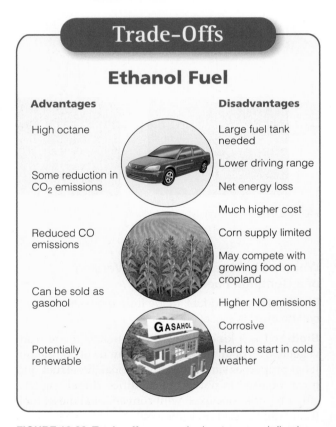

FIGURE 18-30 Trade-offs: general advantages and disadvantages of using ethanol as a vehicle fuel compared to gasoline. Pick the single advantage and single disadvantage that you think are the most important.

diesel fuel when oil becomes too scarce or expensive. *Methanol* is made mostly from natural gas but can also be produced at a higher cost from coal and biomass such as wood, wood wastes, agricultural wastes, sewage sludge, and garbage.

Figure 18-31 lists the advantages and disadvantages of using methanol as a vehicle fuel compared to gasoline. According to analysis by David Pimentel and his colleagues (see Giampietro et al., 1997, and Jallaoh, 2009), "Large-scale biofuel production is not an alternative to the current use of oil and is not even an advisable option to cover a significant fraction of it."

However, chemist George A. Olah and his colleagues (2009) claim that establishing a *methanol economy* is preferable to the highly publicized hydrogen economy. He points out that methanol can be produced chemically from carbon dioxide in the atmosphere, which could also help slow projected global warming. In addition, methanol can be converted to other hydrocarbon compounds that can be used to produce a variety of useful chemicals like those made from petroleum and natural gas.

Trade-Offs

Methanol Fuel

Advantages	Disadvantages
High octane	Large fuel tank needed
Some reduction in CO_2 emissions	Half the driving range
Lower total air pollution (30–40%)	Corrodes metal, rubber, plastic
Can be made from natural gas, agricultural wastes, sewage sludge, and garbage	High CO_2 emissions if made from coal
	Expensive to produce
Can be used to produce H_2 for fuel cells	Hard to start in cold weather

FIGURE 18-31 Trade-offs: general advantages and disadvantages of using methanol as a vehicle fuel compared to gasoline. Pick the single advantage and the single disadvantage that you think are the most important.

SPOTLIGHT

Producing Ethanol from Sugarcane in Brazil

Brazilians have been growing sugarcane since early settlement days in the 1500s. Over the past 30 years, they have been able to apply the world's most efficient sugarcane cultivation technology to the production of ethanol (mostly for fuel), sugar (a valuable product), and **bagasse** (sugarcane waste that is burned to produce heat and electricity).

The process involves growing productive fields of sugarcane, harvesting the crop, and transporting it to sugarcane-processing plants. There, the sugarcane is washed, shredded, and milled to collect a sweet juice called *garapa* and a fibrous residue called bagasse. The garapa is processed into sugar and a thick molasses that is later fermented to produce ethanol.

Initially, the ethanol is *hydrous*—meaning that it contains about 5% water. Usually, the water is removed by chemical means, and this *anhydrous* ethanol is combined 25:75 with gasoline to be burned in car engines. However, an increasing number of Brazilian "flex" vehicles are being built that can use the cheaper anhydrous ethanol and can handle other mixtures besides 25% ethanol and 75% gasoline.

Brazil has become the world's largest producer of ethanol fuel, while producing valuable sugar and harnessing the waste bagasse to power the sugarcane industry and to generate surplus electricity. The process decreases their reliance on fossil fuels, and occupies only 1.5% of their farmland. It is no wonder that Brazil is considered to have the world's most sustainable biofuels economy (Smeets et al., 2006, Goettemoeller et al., 2007).

Critical Thinking

What factors affect the success of producing ethanol from sugarcane in Brazil? Are Canadians likely to achieve the same success at producing biofuels from crop or forest biomass? Explain.

Energy Efficiency and Renewable Energy **441**

18-7 GEOTHERMAL ENERGY

What Is Geothermal Energy? Tapping the Earth's Internal Heat

We can use geothermal energy stored in the Earth's mantle to heat and cool buildings and to produce electricity.

Geothermal energy consists of heat stored in soil, underground rocks, and fluids in the Earth's mantle. Examples are volcanic rock, geysers, and hot springs. Scientists have developed several ways to tap into this stored energy to heat and cool buildings and to produce electricity.

Throughout most of the world (except tundra areas with permafrost) the temperature of the Earth at a depth of about 3 metres (10 feet) is 10–16°C (50–60°F). *Geothermal heat pumps* can tap into this difference between underground and surface temperatures in most places and use a system of pipes and ducts to heat or cool a building. These devices use the Earth as a heat source in winter and as a heat sink during summer. They are a very efficient and cost-effective way to heat or cool a space.

A related way to heat or cool a building is *geothermal exchange* or *geoexchange*. It involves using buried pipes filled with a fluid to move heat in or out of the ground depending on the season and the heating or cooling requirements. In the winter, for example, heat is removed from fluid in pipes buried in the ground and blown through house ducts. In the summer, this process is reversed. According to many energy experts, geothermal exchange is one of the most energy-efficient, cost-effective, and environmentally clean ways to heat or cool a building.

We have also learned to tap into deeper and more concentrated underground reservoirs of geothermal energy. One type of reservoir contains *dry steam* with water vapour but no water droplets. Another consists of *wet steam*, a mixture of water vapour and water droplets. The third is *hot water* trapped in fractured or porous rock at various places in the Earth's crust.

If such geothermal reservoirs are close to the surface, wells can be drilled to extract the dry steam, wet steam, or hot water (Figure 17-2, p. 384), which can be used to heat homes and buildings or to spin turbines and produce electricity.

There are three other nearly nondepletable sources of geothermal energy. One is *molten rock* (magma). Another is *hot dry-rock zones*, where molten rock that has penetrated the Earth's crust heats subsurface rock to high temperatures. A third source is low- to moderate-temperature *warm-rock reservoir deposits*. Heat from such deposits could be used to preheat water and run heat pumps for space heating and air conditioning. Hot dry-rock zones can be found almost anywhere about 8–10 kilometres (5–6 miles) below the Earth's surface. Researchers in several countries are exploring whether these zones can provide affordable geothermal energy.

Currently, about 22 countries (most of them in the developing world) are extracting energy from geothermal sites to produce about 1% of the world's electricity. Geothermal energy is used to heat about 85% of Iceland's buildings, produce electricity, and provide heat to grow most of its fruits and vegetables in greenhouses heated by geothermal energy. The world's largest operating geothermal system, called *The Geysers*, extracts energy from a dry steam reservoir north of San Francisco, California. It provides electricity for about 1.7 million homes. In 1999, Santa Monica, California, became the first city in the world to get all its electricity from geothermal energy. Geologists are assessing the potential of geothermal water found in the Western Canadian Sedimentary Basin. According to the American Association of Petroleum Geologists (http://www.aapg.org), the geothermal water in this basin would, if developed, provide substantially more energy than Alberta's oil and gas reserves.

Figure 18-32 lists the advantages and disadvantages of using geothermal energy. It generally has a much lower environmental impact than fossil fuel energy resources.

But geothermal energy has two main problems. One is that the cost of tapping large-scale reservoirs of geothermal energy is too high for all but the most concentrated and accessible sources. New technologies may bring these costs down.

The other is that some dry- or wet-steam geothermal reservoirs can be depleted if heat is removed faster than natural processes renew it. Thus geothermal resources can be nonrenewable on a human time scale, but the potential supply is so vast that it is usually classified as a renewable energy resource. Recirculating all of the hot water back into the underground reservoir can also slow heat depletion from such reservoirs.

Trade-Offs

Geothermal Energy

Advantages	Disadvantages
Very high efficiency	Scarcity of suitable sites
Moderate net energy at accessible sites	Depleted if used too rapidly
Lower CO_2 emissions than fossil fuels	CO_2 emissions
Low cost at favourable sites	Moderate to high local air pollution
Low land use	Noise and odour (H_2S)
Low land disturbance	Cost too high except at the most concentrated and accessible sources
Moderate environmental impact	

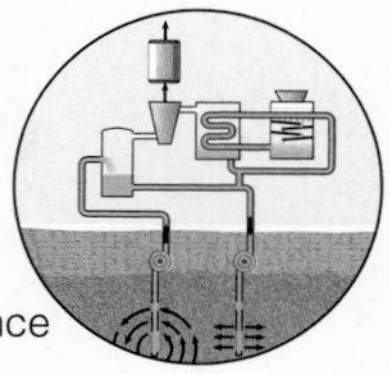

FIGURE 18-32 **Trade-offs:** advantages and disadvantages of using geothermal energy for space heating and to produce electricity or high-temperature heat for industrial processes. Pick the single advantage and the single disadvantage that you think are the most important.

18-8 HYDROGEN

Can Hydrogen Replace Oil? Goodbye Oil, Smog, and CO_2 Emissions, Hello Hydrogen

Some energy analysts view hydrogen gas as the best fuel to replace oil during the last half of this century.

When oil is gone or what is left costs too much to use, how will we fuel vehicles, industry, and buildings? Many scientists and executives of major oil companies and automobile companies say the fuel of the future is hydrogen gas (H_2)—envisioned in 1874 by science fiction writer Jules Verne in his book *The Mysterious Island.*

Figure 18-33 lists the advantages and disadvantages of using hydrogen as an energy resource. Electricity (electrolysis) or high temperatures (thermolysis) can be used to split water molecules into gaseous hydrogen and oxygen ($2\,H_2O \rightarrow 2\,H_2 + O_2$). And when the hydrogen gas is used as a fuel it combines with oxygen gas in the air and produces nonpolluting water vapour ($2\,H_2 + O_2 \rightarrow 2\,H_2O$).*

---

* Water vapour is a potent greenhouse gas. However, because there is already so much of it in the atmosphere, human additions of this gas are insignificant.

Trade-Offs

Hydrogen

Advantages	Disadvantages
Can be produced from plentiful water	Not found in nature
Low environmental impact	Energy is needed to produce fuel
Renewable if produced from renewable energy resources	Negative net energy
No CO_2 emissions if produced from water	CO_2 emissions if produced from carbon-containing compounds
Good substitute for oil	Nonrenewable if generated by fossil fuels or nuclear power
Competitive price if environmental and social costs are included in cost comparisons	High costs (but may eventually come down)
Easier to store than electricity	Will take 25 to 50 years to phase in
Safer than gasoline and natural gas	Short driving range for current fuel cell cars
Nontoxic	No fuel distribution system in place
High efficiency (45–65%) in fuel cells	Excessive H_2 leaks may deplete ozone

FIGURE 18-33 **Trade-offs:** advantages and disadvantages of using hydrogen as a fuel for vehicles and for providing heat and electricity. Pick the single advantage and the single disadvantage that you think are the most important.

Proponents envision using hydrogen in energy-efficient and nonpolluting fuel cells to provide electricity for running buses, cars (Figure 18-8), houses, and other buildings. Widespread use of hydrogen could provide most of the energy needed to run an economy (Figure 18-34, p. 444). Proponents believe that such systems can be available by 2020–30 and then be phased in during this century.

So what is the catch? There are three problems in turning the vision of widespread use of hydrogen as a fuel into reality. *First,* hydrogen is chemically locked up in water and organic compounds such as methane and gasoline. *Second,* it takes energy and money to produce hydrogen from water and

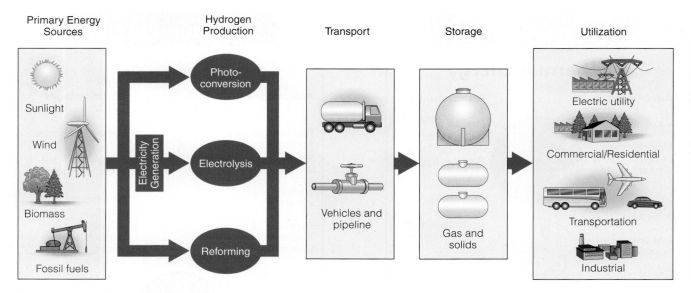

FIGURE 18-34 Solutions: hydrogen energy system used to run a sustainable hydrogen economy. (Data from U.S. Department of Energy and the Worldwatch Institute)

organic compounds. In other words, *hydrogen is not a source of energy. It is a fuel produced by using energy—lots of it. Third,* fuel cells are the best way to use hydrogen to produce electricity, but current versions are expensive.

We could use electricity from coal-burning and conventional nuclear power plants to electrolyze water. But doing this is expensive and subjects us to the harmful environmental effects associated with using these fuels (Figure 17-24, p. 402, and Figure 17-30, p. 408). We can also use a reforming process that involves using high temperatures and chemical processes to separate hydrogen from carbon atoms in organic compounds found in conventional fuels such as natural gas, methanol, ethanol, or gasoline. A problem is that getting hydrogen from organic compounds such as methane (CH_4) produces carbon dioxide ($CH_4 + 2\ H_2O \rightarrow 4\ H_2 + CO_2$). And according to a 2002 study by physicist Martin Hoffert and a team of other scientists, these reforming processes add more CO_2 to the atmosphere per unit of heat generated than does burning these carbon-containing fuels directly. Thus using this approach could accelerate projected global warming unless we can develop affordable ways to store (sequester) the CO_2 underground or in the deep ocean. We can also gasify coal or biomass to produce hydrogen, but this is more expensive than using natural gas and also releases CO_2.

Most proponents of hydrogen believe that if we are to get its very low pollution and low CO_2 emission benefits, the energy used to produce H_2 by decomposing water must come from low-polluting, renewable sources that emit little or no CO_2. The most likely sources are electricity generated by wind farms, hydropower, geothermal energy, solar cells (when their prices come down), or biological processes in bacteria and algae (Spotlight, p. 445).

In 1999, DaimlerChrysler, Royal Dutch Shell, Norsk Hydro, and Icelandic New Energy announced government-approved plans to turn the tiny country of Iceland into the world's first "hydrogen economy" by 2050—the brainchild of chemist Bragi Árnason, known as "Professor Hydrogen." The country's abundant renewable geothermal energy, hydro-power, and offshore winds will be used to produce hydrogen from seawater and the H_2 will be used to run its buses, passenger cars, fishing vessels, and factories. Iceland's first hydrogen service station opened in 2003. They have since been successful at running hydrogen-powered buses, cars, and even boats. They are gradually developing their vision of a hydrogen future.

Once hydrogen is produced we must have a way to store it for use as needed. Here are some of the ways that scientists and engineers are investigating for hydrogen storage.

Store it in compressed gas tanks either above or below the ground or aboard motor vehicles. In 2002, General Motors developed a lightweight high-pressure hydrogen storage tank that can be used on cars and can store enough hydrogen to provide a range of nearly 480 kilometres (300 miles) before refuelling.

Producing Hydrogen from Green Algae Found in Pond Scum

In a few decades, we may be able to use large-scale cultures of green algae to produce hydrogen gas. This simple organism grows almost everywhere and is commonly found in pond scum.

When living in air and sunlight, green algae carry out photosynthesis like other plants and produce carbohydrates and oxygen gas. However, in 2000, Tasios Melis, a researcher at the University of California at Berkeley, found a way to modify the photosynthesis process to make these algae produce bubbles of hydrogen rather than oxygen.

First, he grew cultures of hundreds of billions of the algae in the normal way with plenty of sunlight, nutrients, and water. Then he cut off their supply of two key nutrients: sulphur and oxygen. Within 20 hours, the plant cells underwent a metabolic change and switched from an oxygen-producing to a hydrogen-producing metabolism, allowing the researcher to collect hydrogen gas bubbling from the culture.

Melis believes he can increase the efficiency of this hydrogen-producing process tenfold. If so, sometime in the future a *biological hydrogen plant* might cycle a mixture of algae and water through a system of clear tubes exposed to sunlight to produce hydrogen. The gene responsible for producing the hydrogen might be transferred to a variety of plants to confer the ability to produce hydrogen.

Critical Thinking

What might be some ecological problems related to the widespread use of this method for producing hydrogen?

Store it as more dense liquid hydrogen. But the liquid hydrogen must be stored in tanks kept at very low temperatures. This is costly, takes almost a third of the hydrogen's original fuel energy, and requires a large amount of insulation.

Store it in solid metal hydride compounds. Certain metals can absorb and chemically bond hydrogen in their latticework of atoms. Heating such metal hydride compounds releases the hydrogen gas as needed. DaimlerChrysler has found a way to store hydrogen as *sodium borohydride* in a nontoxic and non-flammable solution that can be pumped in and out of the vehicle safely and cleanly and without leaks of hydrogen gas.

Absorb hydrogen gas on activated charcoal or graphite nanofibres. Like hydrides, this is a safe and efficient way to store hydrogen, but an input of energy is needed to release the hydrogen. *Trap and store hydrogen gas in a framework of water molecules* called *clathrate hydrates* or in tiny glass *microspheres.* Stay tuned for further developments from this research.

Hydrogen is highly flammable and burns with an invisible flame. But it may be safer than gasoline for two reasons. *First,* when this light gas is released it quickly disperses into the atmosphere instead of posing a fire hazard by puddling on the ground like gasoline. *Second,* metal hydrides, charcoal powders, graphite, nanofibres, and glass microspheres containing hydrogen will not explode or burn if a vehicle's tank is ruptured in an accident.

Will Widespread Use of Hydrogen Decrease Protective Ozone in the Stratosphere? Probably Not with Careful Use of Hydrogen

A preliminary study suggests that widespread use of hydrogen could decrease the concentration of protective ozone in the stratosphere over Antarctica for a few months each year.

In 2003, researchers Tracey Tromp and John Eiler at the California Institute of Technology published a paper that sent shivers down the spines of hydrogen proponents. On the basis of computer models, they projected that if hydrogen eventually replaces all fossil fuels, hydrogen gas leaking from such a global system could rise into the stratosphere, be oxidized to form water vapour, increase depletion of the ozone layer over Antarctica during part of the year, and allow more harmful ultraviolet radiation to reach the Earth's surface.

Most press reports failed to note that the authors and other scientists gave several reasons why this problem may not be as serious as this preliminary study suggests. *First,* the authors' model is based on still poorly understood atmospheric chemical interactions involved in the hydrogen fuel cycle. This includes the possibility that excess hydrogen in the troposphere would be absorbed by soils or removed by reactions with other chemicals in the atmosphere before most of it can reach the stratosphere. *Second,* the assumptions about leakage of hydrogen may be much too high because of improved technology and vigilance to reduce such leaks. *Third,* global efforts are in place to drastically reduce ozone depletion in the stratosphere by 2050, mostly from chlorine and bromine compounds we have been putting into the atmosphere (more on this in Chapter 21). Since widespread use of hydrogen is not expected until after 2050, this potential threat would be greatly diminished.

What Are Some Possible Potholes in the Hydrogen Highway? Getting Diverted

Because large-scale use of hydrogen is probably 25–50 years away, we should not let its potential divert us from the immediate priorities of sharply reducing greenhouse gas emissions by increasing fuel efficiency and encouraging the use of renewable energy to help us produce hydrogen and phase out fossil fuels.

Some analysts urge heavy investment over the next two decades to spur the development of a renewable-energy hydrogen revolution that would be phased in during this century. The media hype about hydrogen can divert us from the fact that it will probably not be in widespread use for 25–50 years.

While we are working to develop a renewable-energy hydrogen revolution, energy analysts call for us to focus on two more immediate and important priorities. One is to begin sharply reducing our dependence on carbon-containing fossil fuels—especially oil and coal, which emit large quantities of carbon dioxide. The other is the related challenge of sharply reducing our emissions of carbon dioxide and other greenhouse gases to help slow global warming and climate change. Analysts suggest that we do this by:

■ Greatly improving fuel-efficiency standards for motor vehicles through a combination of mandatory government standards and much higher taxes on gasoline and diesel fuels, coupled with a corresponding reduction in income and payroll taxes. This could be done within 10 years. Some energy analysts accuse car companies of misleading the public by saying that we do not need to increase fuel efficiency standards because we can depend on hydrogen.

■ Providing large tax breaks for people and businesses using fuel-efficient cars, buildings, heating systems, and household appliances and keeping such breaks in place for at least 25 years.

■ Investing much more in public transit running on less polluting natural gas as an alternative to the car and using at least half of the money collected by gasoline taxes to promote this change.

■ Greatly increasing research and development subsidies for development and phasing in of renewable-energy technologies, such as wind power, solar cells, biomass, and geothermal energy, and providing such subsidies for at least 25 years. Such noncarbon energy technologies will be needed to produce hydrogen.

■ Providing very large tax breaks for people and businesses using renewable-energy technologies and keeping such breaks in place for at least 25 years.

It will take large amounts of fossil fuel energy and money to phase in the use of hydrogen during the last two-thirds of this century. If we do not conserve fossil fuels their prices might rise to the point where we could not afford to use them to help us make the transition to a renewable-energy hydrogen economy by the end of this century. Also, failing to reduce the threat of climate change is likely to divert huge amounts of money from hydrogen to help us deal with the harmful effects of climate change.

CONSIDER, DISCUSS, OR DEBATE

Do the advantages of burning hydrogen as a source of energy outweigh the disadvantages? Why do you think Iceland has embraced the hydrogen solution while other nations hesitate?

18-9 ENTERING THE AGE OF DECENTRALIZED MICROPOWER

What Is Micropower? Think Small and Dispersed

Energy analysts expect dispersed, small-scale energy-generating units to replace centralized, large-scale power plants over the next few decades.

According to Chuck Linderman, director of energy supply policy for the Edison Electric Institute, the era of big central power plant systems is coming to a close. He and other energy analysts believe the chief feature of electricity production over the next few decades will be *decentralization* to dispersed, small-scale **micropower systems** that generate 1–10 000 kilowatts (Figure 18-35, p. 447). This shift from centralized *macropower* to dispersed *micropower* is analogous to the computer industry's shift from large centralized mainframes to increasingly smaller, widely dispersed PCs, laptops, and handheld computers.

Figure 18-36 (p. 448) lists some of the advantages of decentralized micropower systems over traditional macropower systems. The potential for financial gain by companies and investors in micropower systems is huge, with a $10 trillion (U.S.) market projected by 2018. Decentralized micropower systems could also work well for 1.7 billion people in isolated villages in developing countries and for anyone who lives at a distance from a major power source.

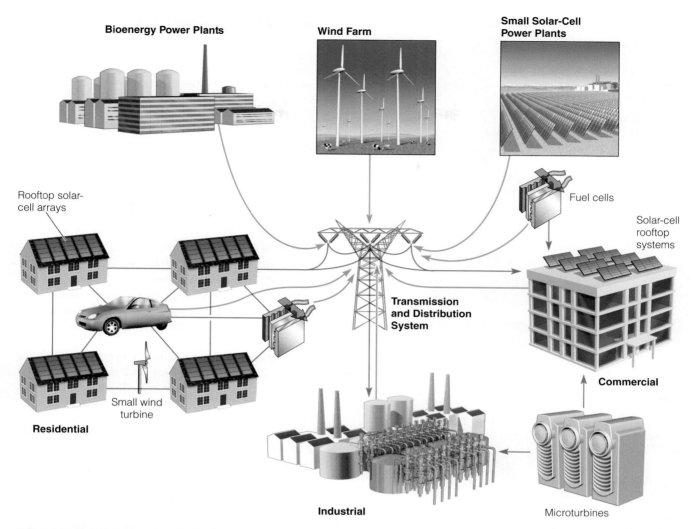

Bioenergy Power Plants

Wind Farm

Small Solar-Cell Power Plants

Rooftop solar-cell arrays

Fuel cells

Solar-cell rooftop systems

Transmission and Distribution System

Commercial

Small wind turbine

Residential

Industrial

Microturbines

FIGURE 18-35 Solutions: *decentralized power system* in which electricity is produced by a large number of dispersed, small-scale *micropower systems*. Some would produce power on site, and others would feed the power they produce into a conventional electrical distribution system. Over the next few decades, many energy and financial analysts expect a shift to this type of power system.

18-10 A SUSTAINABLE ENERGY STRATEGY

What Roles Will Economics and Politics Play in Our Energy Future? Rewards Pay Off

Governments can use a combination of subsidies, tax breaks, and taxes to promote or discourage use of various energy alternatives.

To most analysts the key to making a shift to more sustainable energy resources and societies is economics and politics. Governments can use two basic economic and political strategies to help stimulate or discourage use of a particular energy resource.

One approach is to *keep energy prices artificially low to encourage use of selected energy resources.* This is done mostly by providing research and development subsidies and tax breaks, and by enacting regulations that help stimulate the development and use of energy resources receiving such support. For decades, this approach has been used to help develop the fossil fuel and nuclear power industries in most other developed countries. This approach has created an uneven economic playing field that encourages energy waste and rapid depletion of nonrenewable energy resources and discourages the development of other energy alternatives and improvements in energy efficiency.

A second option is to *keep energy prices artificially high to discourage use of a resource.* Governments can raise the price of an energy resource by withdrawing existing tax breaks and other subsidies, enacting restrictive regulations, or adding taxes on its use. This increases government revenues, encourages

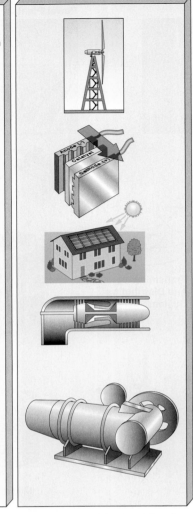

Small modular units

Fast factory production

Fast installation
(hours to days)

Can add or remove
modules as needed

High energy efficiency
(60–80%)

Low or no CO_2
emissions

Low air pollution
emissions

Reliable

Easy to repair

Much less vulnerable
to power outages

Increase national
security by dispersal
of targets

Useful anywhere

Especially useful
in rural areas in
developing countries
with no power

Can use locally
available renewable
energy resources

Easily financed
(costs included in
mortgage and
commercial loan)

FIGURE 18-36 Solutions: advantages of micropower systems.

improvements in energy efficiency, reduces dependence on imported energy, and decreases use of an energy resource that has a limited future supply.

Many economists favour *increasing taxes on fossil fuels* as a way to reduce air and water pollution, slow greenhouse gas emissions, and encourage improvements in energy efficiency and greater use of renewable energy. For example, in Germany and Great Britain, where gasoline costs more than $2.20 per litre, overall oil and gasoline consumption has fallen since the 1970s. Some economists believe the public might accept these higher taxes if income and payroll taxes were lowered as gasoline or other fossil fuel taxes were raised. And energy assistance would be provided for the poor and lower middle class who would bear the brunt of taxes on gasoline and other energy-intensive goods.

How Can We Develop a More Sustainable Energy Future? Stop the Waste, Use the Sun, and Cut Pollution

A more sustainable energy policy would improve energy efficiency, rely more on renewable energy, and reduce the harmful environmental effects of using fossil fuels and nuclear energy.

Energy analysts estimate that implementing policies such as those shown in Figure 18-37 (p. 449) over the next several decades could save money, create a net gain in jobs, reduce greenhouse gas emissions, and sharply reduce air pollution (Chapter 20) and water pollution (Chapter 22).

Canada is a huge country with great distances between many of our cities and major sources of energy such as hydroelectric dams and electric power plants. Transferring energy over vast distances is expensive, inefficient, and vulnerable to disruptions. Using a web of diverse local sources of energy (Figure 18-35) to supply our communities would solve these problems and create local jobs. Upgrading to new decentralized technologies (Figures 18-35 and 18-36) and strategies (Figure 18-37) would provide Canada with a more efficient, more renewable, more secure, less polluting, and more sustainable energy future.

We have the technology, creativity, and wealth to make the transition to a more sustainable energy future. But making this transition depends primarily on *politics,* and thus on pressure individuals and groups can put on elected officials and officials of energy resource companies by voting with their ballots and pocketbooks (by refusing to buy some products and letting company executives know why). Figure 18-38 (p. 449) lists some ways you can contribute to making this transition by reducing the amount of energy you use—and waste.

I believe that the human desire for a clean environment and a green planet will drive the Hydrogen Economy, not the argument that we are running out of oil.

GEOFFREY BALLARD

Improve Energy Efficiency

Increase fuel-efficiency standards for vehicles, buildings, and appliances

Mandate government purchases of efficient vehicles and other devices

Provide large tax credits for buying efficient cars, houses, and appliances

Offer large tax credits for investments in energy efficiency

Reward utilities for reducing demand for electricity

Encourage independent power producers

Greatly increase energy efficiency research and development

More Renewable Energy

Increase renewable energy to 20% by 2020 and 50% by 2050

Provide large subsidies and tax credits for renewable energy

Use full-cost accounting and life-cycle cost for comparing all energy alternatives

Encourage government purchase of renewable energy devices

Greatly increase renewable energy research and development

Reduce Pollution and Health Risk

Cut coal use 50% by 2020

Phase out coal subsidies

Levy taxes on coal and oil use

Phase out nuclear power or put it on hold until 2020

Phase out nuclear power subsidies

FIGURE 18-37 Solutions: suggestions of various energy analysts to help make the transition to a more sustainable and less risky energy future.

What Can You Do?

Energy Use and Waste

- Drive a car that gets at least 15 kilometres per litre (35 miles per gallon) and join a carpool.

- Use mass transit, walking, and bicycling.

- Superinsulate your house and plug all air leaks.

- Turn off lights, TV sets, computers, and other electronic equipment when they are not in use.

- Wash laundry in warm or cold water.

- Use passive solar heating.

- For cooling, open windows and use ceiling fans or whole-house attic or window fans.

- Turn thermostats down in winter and up in summer.

- Buy the most energy-efficient homes, lights, cars, and appliances available.

- Turn down the thermostat on water heaters to 43–49°C (110–120°F) and insulate hot water heaters and pipes.

FIGURE 18-38 What can you do? Ways to reduce your use and waste of energy.

CHAPTER REVIEW

1. Review the Key Questions for this chapter on p. 419. In your opinion, how realistic is David Suzuki's assertion that "we're on the cusp of a new energy revolution"? What role can tidal power technologies play for coastal cities and towns? Can the technologies used in tidal steam generators be adapted to provide power from fast-moving rivers and streams? What advantages and disadvantages are involved with generating power in this way?

2. Distinguish between *energy conservation* and *energy efficiency*. Explain why energy efficiency can be considered an important energy resource. How much of the energy used in North America is wasted? How much is wasted unnecessarily? What are the major advantages of reducing energy waste? List three reasons why efficiency is often overlooked as a source of energy.

3. What is *net energy efficiency* and why is it important? Describe three ways to save energy and money in **(a)** industry, **(b)** transportation, and **(c)** buildings. What is *cogeneration*? Describe the trends in fuel efficiency in North America since the 1970s. Distinguish among hybrid, plug-in hybrid, and fuel-cell motor vehicles. Describe five ways to save energy in an existing building.

4. List five advantages of relying more on a variety of renewable sources of energy and describe two factors holding back such a transition.

5. Distinguish between *passive solar heating* and *active solar heating* and discuss the major advantages and disadvantages of such systems. What are three ways to cool houses naturally? Discuss the major advantages and disadvantages of using solar energy to generate high-temperature heat and electricity. What is a *solar cell (photovoltaic* or *PV cell)* and what are the major advantages and disadvantages of using such cells to produce electricity?

6. What are the major advantages and disadvantages of using flowing water to produce electricity in hydropower plants? Compare the environmental impact of a single large hydro dam with that of a network of microhydro installations spread diffusely over a much larger area. What is the potential for using tides and waves to produce electricity?

7. What is a *wind turbine*? What is a *wind farm*? What are the major advantages and disadvantages of using wind to produce electricity? What are the major advantages and disadvantages of using wood to provide heat and electricity? What are *biofuels* and what are the major advantages and disadvantages of using **(a)** biodiesel and **(b)** ethanol to power motor vehicles?

Evaluate the use of corn, sugarcane, and other biomass to produce ethanol.

8. What is *geothermal energy* and what are three sources of such energy? Where in the world, and where in Canada, can large quantities of suitable energy be found? What are the major advantages and disadvantages of using geothermal energy as a source of heat and to produce electricity? What are the major advantages and disadvantages of burning hydrogen gas to provide heat, to produce electricity, and to fuel cars?

9. What conclusions have energy experts reached about possible future energy paths for the world? List five major strategies for making the transition to a more sustainable energy future. Describe two roles that governments play in determining which energy resources we use. Describe how the government of Iceland is moving toward a sustainable energy future in which hydrogen will play an important part. Why do they feel they need hydrogen?

10. To what extent do the four scientific principles of sustainability apply to Brazil's use of sugarcane?

CRITICAL THINKING

1. A home builder installs electric baseboard heat and claims, "It is the cheapest and cleanest way to go." Apply your understanding of the second law of thermodynamics and net energy efficiency chain (Figure 18-5) to evaluate this claim.

2. Someone tells you we can save energy by recycling it. How would you respond?

3. Should gas-guzzling motor vehicles be taxed heavily? Explain.

4. Congratulations! You have won $250 000 to build a house of your choice anywhere you want. With the goal of maximizing energy efficiency, what type of house would you build? Where would you locate it? What types of materials would you use? What types of materials would you *not* use? How would you heat and cool the house? How would you heat water? What type of lighting, stove, refrigerator, washer, and dryer would you use? Which of these appliances could you do without?

5. Should government subsidies and tax breaks for all energy alternatives be eliminated so all energy choices

can compete in the marketplace on an even economic footing? Explain.

6. Explain why you agree or disagree with each of the proposals suggested in Figure 18-37 (p. 449) as ways to promote a more sustainable energy future.

7. List the pros and cons of securing your electricity from local sources rather than from a grid system.

8. Congratulations! You are in charge of developing Canada's national energy policy. What proportions of your research and development budget would you devote to fossil fuel, nuclear power, renewable energy, and improving energy efficiency? How would you distribute your funds among the various types of renewable energy?

9. Congratulations! You are in charge of the world. List the five most important features of your energy policy.

10. According to the four scientific principles of sustainability, which energy choices should we favour? Why?

PROJECTS

1. Make a study of energy use in your school and use the findings to develop an energy-efficiency improvement program. Present your plan to school officials.

2. Learn how easy it is to produce hydrogen gas from water using a battery, some wire for two electrodes,

and a dish of water. Hook a wire to each of the poles of the battery, immerse the electrodes in the water, and observe bubbles of hydrogen gas being produced at the negative electrode and bubbles of oxygen at the positive electrode. Carefully add a small amount of acid to the water and notice that this increases the rate of hydrogen production.

3. Use the library or the Internet to learn about the future of wind power in Canada.

4. Use the library or the Internet to compare the characteristics of geothermal, wind, solar, biomass, and microhydro energy. What role could each of these play in providing energy for your community?

5. Design your dream home. Include details of your windows, doors, roof, lighting, insulation, hot water, energy sources, landscaping, and other decisions that would affect the energy efficiency of your home.

ECOLOGICAL FOOTPRINT ANALYSIS

Make calculations to fill in the missing data in this table. Show all calculations.

EPA Size Class/Model	Compact/Honda Civic Hybrid	Midsize/Toyota Camry Hybrid	Sport-Utility Vehicle (SUV)/ Hummer H3
Combined highway and city fuel efficiency in kilometres per litre	17.8	14.4	6.4
Litres of gasoline consumed per year, assuming an average 19 300 kilometres driven per year			
Kilograms of CO_2 produced per year, assuming combustion of gasoline releases 2.3 kilograms per litre			
Hectares of tropical rain forest needed to take up CO_2 produced per year, assuming the annual uptake of an undisturbed forest is 0.5 kilograms of CO_2 per square metre			

1. About how many times as much CO_2 per year is produced by the SUV as is produced by the compact car?

2. About how many times as much CO_2 per year is produced by the SUV as is produced by the midsize car?

3. How many hectares of tropical rain forest are needed to take up the CO_2 produced annually by 1 million SUVs?

4. How many hectares of tropical rain forest are needed to take up the CO_2 produced annually by 1 million midsize cars?

5. How many hectares of tropical rain forest are needed to take up the CO_2 produced annually by 1 million compact cars?

Energy Efficiency and Renewable Energy

19 Risk, Toxicology, and Human Health

CASE STUDY | The Big Killer

What is roughly the diameter of a 30-calibre bullet, can be bought almost anywhere, is highly addictive, and kills more than 15 000 people every day, or one every six seconds? It is a cigarette. Cigarette smoking is the world's most preventable major cause of suffering and premature death among adults.

According to the World Health Organization (WHO), tobacco helped kill more than 100 million people between 1950 and 2011. This is 3.3 times more than the 30 million people killed in battle in all wars during the 20th century!

The WHO estimates that each year tobacco contributes to the premature deaths of at least 6 million people (about half from developed countries and half from developing countries) from 34 illnesses including *heart disease, lung cancer, other cancers, bronchitis, emphysema,* and *stroke.* By 2030 the annual death toll from smoking-related diseases is projected to reach 10 million—an average of about 27 400 preventable deaths per day or one death every three seconds. About 70% of these deaths are expected to occur in developing countries.

According to the Canadian Tobacco Use Monitoring Survey (CTUMS), about 18% of the Canadian population aged 15 and over were smokers in 2009. Physicians for a Smoke-Free Canada points out that tobacco is responsible for one in every five deaths in Canada and 30% of all cancer deaths. Smoking kills about 45 000 Canadians per year prematurely, an average of 124 deaths per day (Figure 19-1). Yet, this ongoing human tragedy rarely makes the news.

The overwhelming consensus in the scientific community is that the nicotine inhaled in tobacco smoke is highly addictive. Only 1 in 10 people who try to quit smoking succeed, about the same relapse rate as for recovering alcoholics and those addicted to heroin or crack cocaine. A British government study showed that adolescents who smoke more than one cigarette have an 85% chance of becoming smokers. People can also be exposed to second-hand smoke from others, called *passive smoking.*

According to a 2002 report by the Ontario Tobacco Research Unit, smoking in Canada costs about $17.7 billion a year—a figure that includes increased insurance premiums and health-care costs, disability, lost earnings and productivity because of illness, and property damage from smoking-related fires.

Many health experts advocate the addition of further taxes to the price of a pack of cigarettes. Such a tax would mean that the users of cigarettes (and other tobacco products), not the rest of society, would pay a much greater share of the health, economic, and social costs associated with their smoking.

(continued)

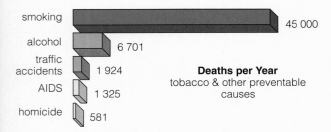

Deaths per Year
tobacco & other preventable causes

smoking	45 000
alcohol	6 701
traffic accidents	1 924
AIDS	1 325
homicide	581

FIGURE 19-1 Annual deaths in Canada from tobacco use and four other causes. (Health Canada and Physicians for a Smoke-Free Canada)

Mladen Mitrinovic/Shutterstock.com

Smoking is the nation's leading cause of preventable death.

Other suggestions for reducing the death toll and health effects of smoking include banning all cigarette advertising, prohibiting the sale of cigarettes and other tobacco products to anyone under 21 (with strict penalties for violators), and banning cigarette vending machines. Analysts also call for classifying and regulating the use of nicotine as an addictive and dangerous drug, eliminating all federal subsidies and tax breaks to tobacco farmers and tobacco companies, and using cigarette tax income to finance an aggressive antitobacco advertising and education program.

In Canada, graphic health warnings on cigarette packages, the banning or restricting of smoking in public places, and other antismoking measures have yielded positive results. Fewer Canadians are smoking (21% in 2009 compared to 35% in 1985) and smokers are lighting up 25% fewer cigarettes. On the other hand, teenage girls are now smoking more than boys, and smoking-related illnesses among females are on the rise.

The dose makes the poison.
PARACELSUS, 1540

CHAPTER PURPOSE AND QUESTIONS

Chapter 19 examines methods used to estimate toxicity levels and risks, as well as the limitations of toxicity studies. The chapter addresses the following questions:

19-1   What types of hazards do people face?

19-2   What is toxicology, and how do scientists measure toxicity?

19-3   What chemical hazards do people face, and how can they be measured?

19-4   What types of disease (biological hazards) threaten people in developing countries and developed countries?

19-5   How can risks be estimated, managed, and reduced?

19-6   How are we doing at combating HIV/ AIDS, malaria, and other diseases?

19-1   **RISK, PROBABILITY, AND HAZARDS**

What Is Risk? The Chances We Take

Risk is a measure of the likelihood that you will suffer harm from a hazard.

Risk is the *possibility* of suffering harm from a **hazard** that can cause injury, disease, death, economic loss, or environmental damage. **Risk assessment** is the scientific process of estimating how much harm a particular hazard can cause to human health. **Risk management** involves deciding whether or how to reduce a particular risk to a certain level and at what cost.

Risk is usually expressed in terms of **probability**: a mathematical statement about how likely one is to suffer harm from a hazard. Scientists often state probability in terms such as "The lifetime probability of developing lung cancer from smoking a pack of cigarettes a day is 1 in 250." This means that 1 of every 250 people who smoke a pack of cigarettes a day will develop lung cancer over a typical lifetime (usually considered 70 years).

It is important to distinguish between *possibility* and *probability*. When we say that it is *possible* that a smoker can get lung cancer we are saying that this event could happen. *Probability* gives us an estimate of the likelihood of such an event. Figure 19-2 summarizes how risks are assessed and managed.

What Are the Major Types of Hazards? They Are All Around Us, but How Risky Are They?

We can suffer harm from cultural hazards, chemical hazards, physical hazards, and biological hazards, but determining the risks involved is difficult.

We can suffer harm from four major types of hazards:

- *Cultural hazards* such as unsafe working conditions, smoking, poor diet, drugs, drinking, driving, criminal assault, unsafe sex, and poverty.

- *Chemical hazards* from harmful chemicals in the air, water, soil, and food.

- *Physical hazards* such as ionizing radiation, fire, tornado (Figure 6-4, p. 112), hurricane, flood (Figures 15-24 and 15-25, pp. 357–358), volcanic

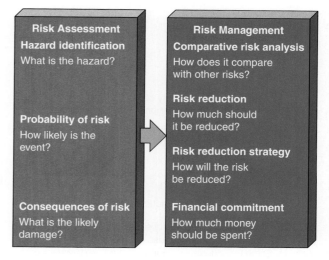

FIGURE 19-2 *Risk assessment and risk management*

eruption (Figure 16-7, p. 368), and earthquake (Figures 16-5 and 16-6, pp. 367–368).

- *Biological hazards* from pathogens (bacteria, viruses, and parasites), pollen and other allergens, and animals such as bees and venomous snakes.

CONSIDER, DISCUSS, OR DEBATE

What is the riskiest thing you do? Why do you do it? When you do it, does the concept of "probability" (perhaps a very small likelihood of a negative outcome) enter into your decision making? Can you afford to pay the consequences, or are you gambling on the probabilities?

19-2 TOXICOLOGY: ASSESSING CHEMICAL HAZARDS

What Determines Whether a Chemical Is Harmful? How Much, How Often, and Genes

The harm caused by exposure to a chemical depends on the amount of exposure (dose), frequency of exposure, who is exposed, how well the body's detoxification systems work, and one's genetic makeup.

Toxicity measures how harmful a substance is in causing injury, illness, or death to a living organism. This depends on several factors. One is **dose,** the amount of a substance a person has ingested, inhaled, or absorbed through the skin. Other factors are frequency of exposure, who is exposed (adult or child, for example), and how well the body's detoxification systems (such as the liver, lungs, and kidneys) work.

Toxicity also depends on *genetic makeup* that determines an individual's sensitivity to a particular toxin (Figure 19-3). This genetic variation in individual

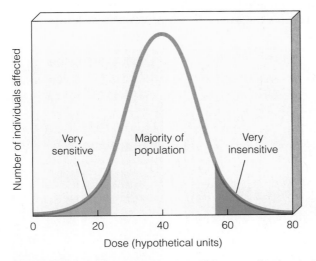

FIGURE 19-3 Typical variations in sensitivity to a toxic chemical within a population, mostly because of differences in genetic makeup. Some individuals in a population are very sensitive to small doses of a toxin (left), and others are very insensitive (right). Most people fall between these two extremes (middle).

responses to exposure to various toxins raises a difficult ethical, political, and economic question. When regulating levels of a toxic substance in the environment, should the allowed level be set to protect the most sensitive individuals (at great cost) or the average person? What is your view on this issue? Why?

Five major factors can affect the harm caused by a substance. One is its *solubility. Water-soluble toxins* (which are often inorganic compounds) can move throughout the environment and get into water supplies and the aqueous solutions that surround the cells in our bodies.

Oil- or fat-soluble toxins (which are usually organic compounds) can penetrate the membranes surrounding an organism's cells because the membranes allow similar oil-soluble chemicals to pass through them. Thus, oil- or fat-soluble toxins can accumulate in body tissues and cells.

A second factor is a substance's *persistence.* Many chemicals, such as the pesticide DDT (banned in many countries but still used in some), are often used because of their persistence or resistance to breakdown. They do their job for a long time. But this persistence also means they can have long-lasting harmful effects on the health of wildlife and people.

A third factor for some substances is **bioaccumulation,** in which some molecules are absorbed and stored in specific organs or tissues at higher than normal levels. This means that a chemical found at a fairly low concentration in the environment can build up to a harmful level in certain organs and tissues.

A related factor is **biomagnification,** in which levels of some potential toxins in the environment are magnified as they pass through food chains and webs. Organisms at low trophic levels might ingest only small amounts of a toxin, but each animal on the next level up that eats many of those organisms will take in larger amounts of that toxin. As the toxin moves through higher trophic levels, organisms at each level consume increasingly greater amounts of the toxin. Figure 19-4 (p. 455) provides an illustration of this effect. Examples of chemicals that can be biomagnified include long-lived, fat-soluble organic compounds such as DDT, PCBs (oily chemicals used in electrical transformers), and some radioactive isotopes (such as strontium-90).

A fifth factor is *chemical interactions* that can decrease or multiply the harmful effects of a toxin. An *antagonistic interaction* can reduce harmful effects. For example, vitamins E and A apparently interact to reduce the body's response to some cancer-causing chemicals.

A *synergistic interaction* multiplies effects. For instance, workers exposed to tiny fibres of asbestos increase their chances of getting lung cancer 20-fold. But asbestos workers who also smoke have a 400-fold

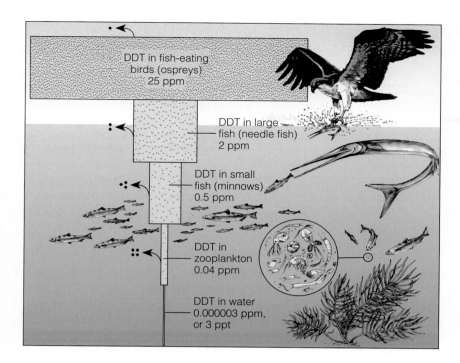

FIGURE 19-4 *Bioaccumulation* and *biomagnification*. DDT is a fat-soluble chemical that can accumulate in the fatty tissues of animals. In a food chain or web, the accumulated DDT can be biologically magnified in the bodies of animals at each higher trophic level. This diagram shows that the concentration of DDT in the fatty tissues of organisms was biomagnified about 10 million times while moving through this food chain. If each phytoplankton organism takes up from the water and retains one unit of DDT, a small fish eating thousands of zooplankton (which feed on the phytoplankton) will store thousands of units of DDT in its fatty tissue. Then each large fish that eats 10 of the smaller fish will ingest and store tens of thousands of units, and each bird (or human) that eats several large fish will ingest hundreds of thousands of units. Black dots represent DDT, and arrows show small losses of DDT through respiration and excretion.

Labels in figure:
DDT in fish-eating birds (ospreys) 25 ppm
DDT in large fish (needle fish) 2 ppm
DDT in small fish (minnows) 0.5 ppm
DDT in zooplankton 0.04 ppm
DDT in water 0.000003 ppm, or 3 ppt

increase in lung cancer rates. In such cases, one plus one can be a lot greater than two.

The effects of exposure to a chemical can be acute or chronic. The type and amount of health damage resulting from exposure to a chemical or other agent is called the **response**. An *acute effect* is an immediate or rapid harmful reaction stemming from short-term exposure to a potent chemical. A *chronic effect* is a gradual long-lasting consequence from long-term exposure to a single dose or to repeated sublethal doses of a harmful substance.

What Are Some Basic Principles of Toxicology? The Dose Makes the Poison—Or Does It?

Any substance can be harmful if ingested in a large enough quantity, but the critical question is, what is the lowest level of exposure that causes harm?

A basic concept of **toxicology** is that *any synthetic or natural chemical can be harmful if ingested in a large enough quantity.* In other words, every chemical is harmful at some level of exposure. For example, drinking 100 cups of strong coffee one after another would expose most people to a lethal dosage of caffeine. Similarly, downing 100 tablets of Aspirin or 1 litre of pure alcohol (ethanol) would kill most people.

The critical question is, *how much exposure to a particular toxic chemical causes a harmful response?* This is the meaning of the chapter-opening quote by the German scientist Paracelsus about the dose making the poison.

A basic problem is that people vary in terms of the dose of a toxin they can tolerate without significant

harm, because of differences in their genetic makeup (Figure 19-3). Because of this variation in how individuals respond to exposure to a toxic chemical, a better way to state Paracelsus's principle of toxicology is: the dose makes the poison, *but differently for different individuals.*

Your body has three major mechanisms for reducing the harmful effects of some chemicals. *First,* it can break down (usually by enzymes found in the liver), dilute, or excrete—for example, in your breath, sweat, and urine—small amounts of most toxins to keep them from reaching harmful levels. However, accumulations of high levels of toxins can overload the ability of your liver and kidneys to degrade and excrete such substances.

Second, your cells have enzymes that can sometimes repair damage to DNA and protein molecules. *Third,* cells in some parts of your body (such as your skin and the linings of your gastrointestinal tract, lungs, and blood vessels) can reproduce fast enough to replace damaged cells. However, such high rates of cell reproduction can be altered by exposure to ionizing radiation and certain chemicals so that cell growth accelerates and creates a nonmalignant or malignant (cancerous) tumour.

Should We Be Concerned about Trace Levels of Toxic Chemicals? It Depends on the Chemical

Trace amounts of chemicals in the environment or your body may or may not be harmful.

Should we be concerned about trace amounts of various chemicals in air, water, food, and our bodies?

Table 19-1 Toxicity Ratings and Average Lethal Doses for Humans

Toxicity Rating	LD50 (milligrams per kilogram of body weight)*	Average Lethal Dose†	Examples
Supertoxic	Less than 0.01	Less than 1 drop	Nerve gases, botulism toxin, mushroom toxins, dioxin (TCDD)
Extremely toxic	Less than 5	Less than 7 drops	Potassium cyanide, heroin, atropine, parathion, nicotine
Very toxic	5–50	7 drops to 1 teaspoon	Mercury salts, morphine, codeine
Toxic	50–500	1 teaspoon to 1 ounce	Lead salts, DDT, sodium hydroxide, sodium fluoride, sulphuric acid, caffeine, carbon tetrachloride
Moderately toxic	500–5 000	1 ounce to 1 pint	Methyl (wood) alcohol, ether, phenobarbital, amphetamines (speed), kerosene, Aspirin
Slightly toxic	5 000–15 000	1 pint to 1 quart	Ethyl alcohol, Lysol, soaps
Essentially nontoxic	15 000 or greater	More than 1 quart	Water, glycerin, table sugar

*Dosage that kills 50% of individuals exposed
†Amounts of substances in liquid form at room temperature that are lethal when given to a 70.4-kilogram (155-pound) human

The honest answer is that we do not know in most cases because of a lack of data and the difficulty of determining the effects of exposures to low levels of chemicals.

Some scientists think that trace levels of most chemicals are not harmful. They point to the dramatic increase in average life expectancy in many developed countries since 1950. They say we should concentrate limited research funds on much greater health risks such as smoking, obesity, and infectious diseases (especially those that affect people in developing countries).

Other scientists are not so sure and believe that much more research is needed to help us evaluate the possible long-term harm caused by exposure to low levels of thousands of new synthetic chemicals that we have put into the environment during the past few decades.

Chemists are able to detect increasingly small amounts of potentially toxic chemicals in air, water, and food. This is good news, but it can give the false impression that dangers from toxic chemicals are increasing when in some cases all we are doing is uncovering levels of chemicals that have been around for a long time.

Some people also have the mistaken idea that natural chemicals are safe and synthetic chemicals are harmful. In fact, many synthetic chemicals are quite safe if used as intended, and many natural chemicals are deadly.

The average person, for instance, is far more likely to be killed by aflatoxin, a carcinogen produced by moulds in peanut butter and corn, than to be killed by lightning or by a shark. However, the chance of dying of cancer from eating several spoonfuls of peanut butter a day is quite small.

Chemicals vary widely in their toxicity (Table 19-1). Some poisons can cause serious harm or death after a single acute exposure at very low dosages. Others cause such harm only at dosages so huge that it is nearly impossible to get enough into the body. Most chemicals fall between these two extremes. The five top toxic chemicals in terms of human and environmental health concerns are arsenic, lead, mercury, vinyl chloride (used to make polyvinylchloride or PVC plastics), and **polychlorinated biphenyls** (PCBs).

How Do Scientists Use Laboratory Experiments to Estimate Toxicity? Controversial Animal Testing

Exposing a population of live laboratory animals (especially mice and rats) to known amounts of a chemical is the most widely used method for determining its toxicity.

The most widely used method for determining toxicity is to expose a population of live laboratory animals (especially mice, rats, and fish) to measured doses of a specific substance under controlled conditions. Animal tests can take 2–5 years and cost $200 000 to $2 million per substance tested. Such tests can also kill or harm the test animals. The goal is to develop data on the response of the test animals to various doses of a chemical (called a dose-response curve).

One method of estimating the relative toxicity of a chemical is to determine its *lethal dose* (LD) in the case of injecting a dose of the chemical, or its *lethal concentration* (LC) in the case of exposing aquatic organisms to various concentrations of the chemical in water. A series of tests are done in which test animals are injected with different doses (or exposed to different concentrations) of the chemical and then observed for various responses including mortality. The results are plotted (Figure 19-5) and the amount of chemical that results in the death of 50% of the test animals is identified as the **LD50** (or the LC50). **Acute tests** are meant to establish the effect of a single large dose or exposure to the chemical and are run for a short standard period, such as 96 hours. **Chronic tests** are intended to establish the effect of lower-dose longer-term exposure to the chemical and are run for a longer standard period, such as 28 days.

Note that the same sorts of strategies can be involved in running nonlethal studies of the effects of chemicals on test animals. In this case, toxicologists would be observing animals to determine the dose or concentration of the chemical that caused the appearance of a physical abnormality (such as bent tails in tadpoles) or a change in behaviour (such as tadpoles no longer swimming at normal speeds) in 50% of the test animals.

Alternative methods for carrying out toxicity tests are available. They include computer simulations and using tissue cultures of cells and bacteria, chicken egg membranes, and measurements of changes in the electrical properties of individual animal cells. However, many scientists contend that some animal testing is needed because the alternative methods cannot adequately mimic the complex biochemical interactions of a live animal.

In Canada, research involving live animals is regulated by the Canadian Council on Animal Care (CCAC), which provides research institutions with strict guidelines pertaining to the humane treatment of animals and the design of experiments. Each institution must submit reports on all animal experimentation to the CCAC, and must have in place an animal-care committee (with representatives from the public) to ensure that CCAC rules are followed. Surprise inspections of facilities can occur at any moment.

Toxicity tests are run to develop a **dose-response curve,** which shows the effects of various dosages of a toxic agent on a group of test organisms (Figure 19-6). Such tests are *controlled experiments* in which the effects of the chemical on a test group are compared with the responses of a *control group* of organisms not exposed to the chemical. Care is taken that organisms in both groups are as identical as possible in age, health status, and genetic makeup, and that all are exposed to the same environmental conditions.

A range of dosages is used from a control of zero dosage, through environmentally relevant dosages that might be found in nature, to high dosages that represent extreme exposure. Scientists then use mathematical models, based on the dosages they used, to estimate the LD50 value for the specific chemical tested (Table 19-1).

According to the *nonthreshold dose-response model* (Figure 19-6, left), any dosage of a toxic chemical or ionizing radiation causes harm that increases with the dosage. With the *threshold dose-response model* (Figure 19-6, right), a threshold dosage must be reached

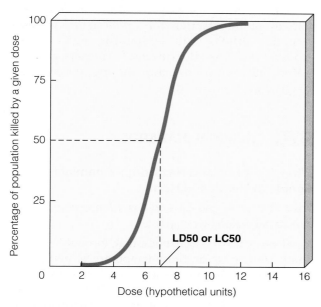

FIGURE 19-5 Hypothetical *dose-response curve* showing determination of the LD50 or LC50, the dosage of a specific chemical that kills 50% of the animals in a test group. This is one method that toxicologists use to determine and compare the toxicities of different chemicals.

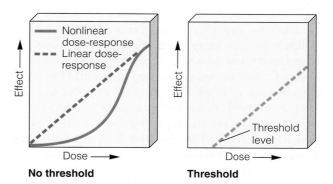

FIGURE 19-6 Two types of *dose-response curves*. The linear and nonlinear curves in the left graph apply if even the smallest dosage of a chemical or ionizing radiation has a harmful effect that increases with the dosage. The curve on the right applies if a harmful effect occurs only when the dosage exceeds a certain *threshold level*. Which model is better for a specific harmful agent is sometimes uncertain because of the difficulty in estimating the response to very low dosages. (Adapted from Chiras, *Environmental Science.* Copyright © 2004: Jones and Bartlett Publishers, Sudbury, MA. www.jbpub.com. Reprinted with permission)

before any detectable harmful effects occur, presumably because the body can repair the damage caused by low dosages of some substances. Establishing which of these models applies at low dosages is extremely difficult and controversial. To be on the safe side, scientists usually use the nonthreshold dose-response model.

Some scientists challenge the validity of extrapolating data from test animals to humans because human physiology and metabolism often differ from those of the test animals. Other scientists say that such tests and models work fairly well (especially for revealing cancer risks) when the correct experimental animal is chosen or when a chemical is toxic or harmful to several different test animal species.

The problem of estimating toxicities is difficult. One problem is that in real life each of us is exposed to a variety of chemicals, some of which can interact in ways to decrease or enhance their individual effects over short and long times. Thus we could further modify Paracelsus' original idea as follows: the dose *of a usually unknown mixture of chemicals* makes the poison, but differently for different individuals.

There are more problems. Toxicologists have great difficulty in estimating the toxicity of a single substance. Adding the problem of evaluating mixtures of potentially toxic substances, separating out which ones are the culprits, and determining how they can interact with one another is overwhelming from a scientific and economic standpoint. For example, just studying the interactions of all possible combinations of three of the 500 most widely used industrial chemicals would take 20.7 million experiments—a physical and financial impossibility.

The effects of a particular chemical can also depend upon when exposure occurs. For example, children can be much more susceptible to toxic substances than an adult for several reasons. On a per weight basis children breathe more air, drink more water, and eat more food than do adults. They are also exposed to toxins in dust or soil when they frequently put their fingers, toys, or other objects in their mouths. In addition, immune systems and processes for degrading or excreting toxins and repairing damage are usually less well developed in children than in adults. For these reasons, when risk assessments using dangerous chemicals are performed, children are often considered to be 10–100 times more vulnerable than adults.

Can a Little Bit of Arsenic or Radiation Be Good for You? Controversy over Hormesis

There is controversy over the hypothesis that very small doses of radiation and some toxins may have beneficial health effects.

There is a hypothesis that radiation and some toxic substances that can harm or kill us at high doses may have beneficial health effects at very low doses. This phenomenon is called *hormesis*. A possible explanation for this effect is that very small doses of some substances may stimulate cellular repair or other beneficial responses.

Poor Paracelsus. If this idea turns out to have validity for some substances, we must further modify his original hypothesis as follows: the dose of the mixture of chemicals usually makes the poison—differently for different individuals—but in some cases a tiny bit of a poison may be good for you. The various possible revisions of the original hypothesis proposed by Paracelsus are a good example of how scientific hypotheses are modified to account for new data.

Scientists are waiting for more evidence to come in before accepting the hormesis hypothesis. Stay tuned for more developments about this fascinating idea.

How Good Are Estimates of Toxicity? Taking Uncertainty into Account

Because all methods of estimating toxicity have serious limitations, allowed exposure levels are usually set well below the estimated harmful levels.

As we have seen, all methods for estimating toxicity levels and risks have serious limitations. But they are all we have. To take this uncertainty into account and minimize harm, scientists and regulators typically set allowed exposure levels to toxic substances and ionizing radiation at 1/100 or even 1/1 000 of the estimated harmful levels.

Despite their many limitations, carefully conducted and evaluated toxicity studies are important sources of information for understanding dose-response effects and estimating and setting exposure standards. But citizens, lawmakers, and regulatory officials must recognize the huge uncertainties involved in all such studies.

19-3 CHEMICAL HAZARDS

What Are Toxic and Hazardous Chemicals? Agents of Death and Harm

Toxic chemicals can kill, and hazardous chemicals can cause various types of harm.

A **poison** or **toxin** is a chemical that, through its action on life processes, can cause temporary or permanent harm or death to humans or animals. Its toxicity is often measured in terms of its **median lethal dose** (Figure 19-5). A **hazardous chemical** can harm humans or other animals because it is flammable or explosive or because it can irritate or damage the skin or lungs, interfere with oxygen uptake, or induce allergic reactions.

There are three major types of potentially toxic agents. One consists of **mutagens,** chemicals or ionizing radiation that cause or increase the frequency of random *mutations*, or changes, in the DNA molecules found in cells. An example is nitrous acid (HNO_2) formed by digestion of nitrite preservatives in foods. *Most mutations are harmless.* One reason is that organisms have biochemical repair mechanisms that can correct mistakes or changes in the DNA code.

But harmful mutations occurring in reproductive cells can be passed on to offspring and to future generations. It is generally accepted that there is no safe threshold for exposure to harmful mutagens.

A second type consists of **teratogens,** chemicals that cause harm or birth defects to a fetus or embryo. Ethyl alcohol is an example of a teratogen. Drinking during pregnancy can lead to offspring with a low birth weight and a number of physical, developmental, and mental problems. Thalidomide is also a potent teratogen.

The third group is **carcinogens,** chemicals or ionizing radiation that cause or promote **cancer**—the growth of a malignant (cancerous) tumour, in which certain cells multiply uncontrollably. An example is benzene, a widely used chemical solvent. Many cancerous tumours spread by **metastasis** when malignant cells break off from tumours and travel in body fluids to other parts of the body. There they start new tumours, making treatment much more difficult. Typically, 10–40 years may elapse between the initial exposure to a carcinogen and the appearance of detectable symptoms. Partly because of this time lag, many healthy teenagers and young adults have trouble believing their smoking, drinking, eating, and other lifestyle habits today could lead to some form of cancer before they reach age 50.

What Effects Can Some Chemicals Have on Immune, Nervous, and Endocrine Systems? Possible Harm from Small Doses

Long-term exposure to some chemicals at low doses may disrupt the body's immune, nervous, and endocrine systems.

Since the 1970s, a growing body of research on wildlife and laboratory animals, along with some epidemiological studies of humans, indicates that long-term exposure to low doses of some chemicals in the environment can disrupt the body's immune, nervous, and endocrine systems.

The *immune system* consists of specialized cells and tissues that protect the body against disease and harmful substances by forming antibodies that make invading agents harmless. Ionizing radiation and some chemicals can weaken the human immune system and leave the body vulnerable to attacks by allergens, infectious bacteria, viruses, and protozoans. Examples are arsenic and dioxins.

Some natural and synthetic chemicals in the environment, called *neurotoxins,* can harm the human *nervous system* (brain, spinal cord, and peripheral nerves). For example, many poisons and the venom of venomous snakes are neurotoxins, which inhibit, damage, or destroy nerve cells (neurons) that transmit electrochemical messages throughout the body. Effects can include behavioural changes, paralysis, and death. Other examples of neurotoxins are PCBs, mercury, and certain pesticides.

The *endocrine system* is a complex network of glands that release very small amounts of *hormones* in the bloodstream of humans and other vertebrate animals. Low levels of these chemical messengers turn on and off bodily systems that control sexual reproduction, growth, development, learning ability, and behaviour (Figure 19–7, page 460).

Each type of hormone has a specific molecular shape that allows it to attach only to certain cell receptors (Figure 19-7). Once bonded together, the hormone and its receptor molecule can signal cell mechanisms to execute the chemical message carried by the hormone.

Case Study: Are Hormonally Active Agents a Human Health Threat? Serious Concern but Inconclusive Evidence

Exposure to low levels of certain synthetic chemicals may disrupt the effects of natural hormones in animals, but more research is needed to determine the effects of these chemicals on humans.

There is concern that human exposure to low levels of certain synthetic chemicals can mimic and disrupt the effects of natural hormones. Over the last 25 years, experts from a number of disciplines have been piecing together field studies on wildlife, studies on laboratory animals, and epidemiological studies of human populations. These analyses suggest that a variety of human-made chemicals can act as *hormone or endocrine disrupters,* known as *hormonally active agents (HAAs).* Examples of hormone disrupters are DDT, PCBs, and certain herbicides.

Some, called *hormone mimics,* are chemicals similar to estrogens (female sex hormones). They can disrupt the endocrine system by attaching to estrogen receptor molecules (Figure 19-7, centre). Others, called *hormone blockers,* disrupt the endocrine system by preventing natural hormones such as androgens (male sex hormones) from attaching to their receptors (Figure 19-7, right). Estrogen mimics and hormone blockers are sometimes called *gender benders* because of their possible effects on sexual development and reproduction.

One way to test a chemical for potential hormonal activity is to make use of the fact that turtles exhibit temperature-dependent sex determination (TDS). In other words, the temperature at which a turtle egg is incubated determines the gender of the resulting turtle hatchling. If the eggs of red-eared slider turtles

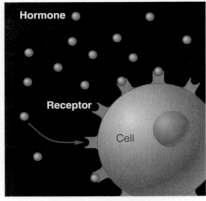
Normal Hormone Process

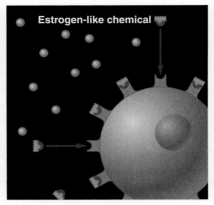
Hormone Mimic

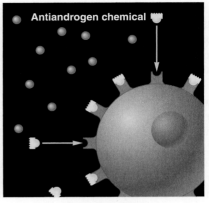
Hormone Blocker

FIGURE 19-7 Hormones are molecules that act as messengers in the endocrine system to regulate various bodily processes, including reproduction, growth, and development. Each type of hormone has a unique molecular shape that allows it to attach to specially shaped receptors on the surface of, or inside, cells and to transmit its chemical message (left). Molecules of certain pesticides and other synthetic chemicals have shapes similar to those of natural hormones and can affect the endocrine system in people and various other animals. These molecules are called *hormonally active agents* (HAAs). Some HAAs, sometimes called *hormone mimics,* disrupt the endocrine system by attaching to estrogen receptor molecules (centre) and giving too-strong, too-weak, or mistimed signals. Other HAAs, sometimes called *hormone blockers,* prevent natural hormones such as androgens from attaching to their receptors (right) so that no signal is given. Some pollutants, called *thyroid disrupters,* may disrupt hormones released by thyroid glands and cause growth and weight disorders and brain and behavioural disorders. Because of the difficulty in determining the harmful effects of long-term exposure to low levels of HAAs, there is uncertainty over their effects on human health.

(*Trachemys scripta elegans*) are incubated at 25°C (77°F), the hatchlings will all be males; if the eggs are incubated at 30°C (86°F), the hatchlings will all be females. However, the presence of a hormonally active chemical will interfere with this pattern.

The following two experiments illustrate how this knowledge can be used. In the first experiment, randomly selected eggs of red-eared slider turtles that

were incubated at 25°C and not exposed to any test chemicals all hatched as males—just as you would expect on the basis of their incubation temperature. But when randomly selected eggs were treated exactly the same way except that they were exposed to one of three different concentrations of genistein (extracted from soy products), from 30% to 70% of the turtles hatched as females (Figure 19-8). In other words, the

(a)

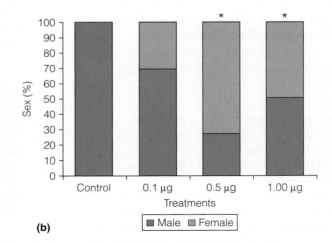
(b)

FIGURE 19-8 Gender-benders: The effects of a feminizing chemical: (a) Jacqueline Chalifoux about to incubate a tray of randomly assorted treated and untreated turtle eggs. She found that all untreated hatchlings raised at 25°C (77°F) were males, as expected on the basis of temperature; however, significant numbers of hatchlings that were raised under identical conditions but exposed to 0.5 to 1.0 μg of genistein, a chemical extracted from soy products, were females.

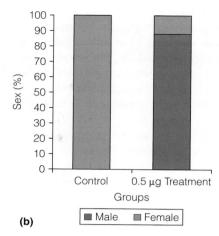

(a)   **(b)**

FIGURE 19-9 Gender-benders: The effects of a masculinizing chemical: (a) Jessica Crain holding a newly emerged turtle hatchling. She found that all untreated hatchlings raised at 30°C were females, as expected on the basis of temperature; however, 88% of the hatchlings raised under identical conditions but exposed to 0.5 μg of triclocarban, an antimicrobial chemical, were males.

genistein had estrogen-like effects that reversed the TDS effect and feminized many of the turtles.

In the second experiment, randomly selected eggs of red-eared slider turtles that were incubated at 30°C and not exposed to any test chemicals all hatched as females—as you would expect on the basis of their incubation temperature. But when randomly selected eggs were treated exactly the same way except that they were exposed to a small amount of triclocarban (an antimicrobial agent used in household products like soaps), 88% of the turtles hatched as males (Figure 19-9). In other words, the triclocarban had testosterone-like effects that reversed the TDS effect and masculinized most of the turtles.

As handy as these effects are in the lab for determining the hormonal influence of gender-bending chemicals, there is cause for alarm—for turtles and for all other animals including humans. Hormonally active chemicals are building up in our world, and they are having measurable and increasing effects. For example, various reports indicate that decreasing sperm counts, smaller genital size, genital deformities, undescended testicles, ineffectual mating behaviour, and low reproductive success have been documented in a wide variety of organisms including humans. Male fish in Britain are developing eggs in their testes. Polar bears with both penises and vaginas have been discovered. Boys born to mothers who were occupationally exposed to pesticides have undescended testicles and other forms of reproductive impairment. Our delicate hormonally balanced world appears to be under threat because of gender-bending, endocrine-disrupting chemicals we have released (Andersen et al., 2008; Lyons, 2008).

DID YOU KNOW

There are more than 23 000 chemical substances available for commercial use in Canada. Under the *Canadian Environmental Protection Act (CEPA)*, Environment Canada and Health Canada regulate these substances by applying the principles of risk assessment and risk management. To learn more about CEPA, visit http://www.ec.gc.ca/lcpe-cepa/.

CONSIDER, DISCUSS, OR DEBATE

Should chemicals be regulated on the basis of (1) their toxicity; (2) their potential to cause mutations or cancer; or (3) their effects on the nervous, immune, and endocrine systems? How would you prioritize these three choices? Explain your reasoning.

Is Pollution Prevention the Answer? Taking Precautions

Preliminary but not conclusive evidence that a chemical causes significant harm should spur preventive action, some say.

So where does this leave us? We do not know a lot about the potentially toxic chemicals around us and inside of us, and estimating their effects is very difficult, time consuming, and expensive. Is there a way out of this dilemma?

Some scientists and health officials, especially those in European Union countries, are pushing for much greater emphasis on *pollution prevention*. They say we should not release into the environment chemicals that we know or suspect can cause significant harm. This means looking for harmless or less harmful substitutes for toxic and hazardous chemicals

Risk, Toxicology, and Human Health   **461**

or recycling them within production processes so they do not reach the environment.

This prevention strategy greatly reduces the expenditures of huge amounts of money on statistically uncertain and controversial toxicity studies and exposure standards. It also lowers the risk from exposure to potentially hazardous chemicals and products and their possible but poorly understood multiple interactions.

This approach is based on the **precautionary principle:** When there is plausible but incomplete scientific evidence (frontier science evidence) of significant harm to humans or the environment from a proposed or existing chemical or technology, we should take action to prevent or reduce the risk instead of waiting for more conclusive (sound or consensus science) evidence. This principle is based on familiar axioms: "Look before you leap." "Better safe than sorry." "An ounce of prevention is worth a pound of cure."

Under this approach, those proposing to introduce a new chemical or technology would bear the burden of establishing its safety. This means two major changes in the way we evaluate risks. *First,* new chemicals and technologies would be assumed harmful until scientific studies can show otherwise. *Second,* existing chemicals and technologies that appear to have a strong chance of causing significant harm would be removed from the market until their safety can be established.

Some movement is being made in this direction, especially in Canada and in the European Union. In 2000, negotiators agreed to a global treaty that would ban or phase out use of 12 of the most notorious *persistent organic pollutants* (POPs), also called the *dirty dozen.* The list included DDT and eight other persistent pesticides, PCBs, and dioxins and furans. New chemicals would be added to the list when the harm they cause is seen as outweighing their usefulness. This treaty went into effect in 2004.

Manufacturers and businesses agree that some chemicals are too dangerous for widespread use and that some technologies such as coal-burning plants carry high health risks. But they contend that widespread application of the precautionary principle would make it too expensive and almost impossible to introduce any new chemical or technology. Strict application of the precautionary principle would stifle chemical and technological innovation and risk taking. We can never have a risk-free society. For example, if we had strictly applied the precautionary principle would we have automobiles, antibiotics, or plastics?

On the other hand, proponents of increased reliance on the precautionary principle say that it will encourage innovation in developing less harmful alternative chemicals and technologies and in finding ways to prevent as much pollution as possible instead of relying mostly on pollution control. It is true that we cannot have a risk-free society. But proponents believe we should make greater use of the precautionary principle effort to reduce many of the risks we face. As you can see, there are no easy answers for knowing when to apply the precautionary principle.

CONSIDER, DISCUSS, OR DEBATE

Should we assume that new chemicals that could end up in the enviroment are "innocent until proven guilty" or "guilty until proven innocent"? Consider the business, health, political, and ecological perspectives on this issue.

19-4 BIOLOGICAL HAZARDS: DISEASE IN DEVELOPED AND DEVELOPING COUNTRIES

What Are Nontransmissible and Transmissible Diseases? To Spread or Not to Spread

Diseases not caused by living organisms do not spread from one person to another, and those caused by living organisms such as bacteria and viruses can spread from person to person.

A **nontransmissible disease** is caused by something other than a living organism and does not spread from one person to another. Such diseases tend to develop slowly and have multiple causes. Examples are cardiovascular (heart and blood vessel) disorders, most cancers, diabetes, asthma, emphysema, and malnutrition.

A **transmissible disease** is caused by living organisms and can spread from one person to another. *Infectious agents* or **pathogens** (such as bacteria, viruses, protozoa, or parasites; Figure 19-10) cause such diseases. These agents are spread by air, water, food, and body fluids, and by some insects (such as mosquitoes; see malaria, p. 467) and other nonhuman carriers. All such pathways are called *vectors.*

Typically, a *bacterium* is a one-celled microorganism that can replicate (clone) itself by simple cell division. A *virus* is a microscopic, noncellular infectious agent. Its DNA or RNA contains instructions for making more viruses, but it has no apparatus to do this. To replicate, a virus must invade a host cell and take over the cell's DNA to create a factory for producing more viruses (Figure 19-11, p. 464). A *parasite* is an organism that feeds off another organism (p. 169). *Protists* are a diverse assortment of microscopic or near-microscopic organisms that live as single cells or in simple colonies. One example is *Giardia,* a protist that inhabits the intestines of mammals. (A person who ingests *Giardia* while drinking water contaminated by feces will contract giardiasis or *beaver fever,* which produces symptoms of severe abdominal cramping and diarrhea.) Another example is *Plasmodium,* a malaria-causing protist that is transferred from host to host by mosquitoes.

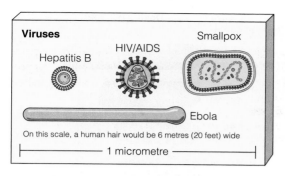
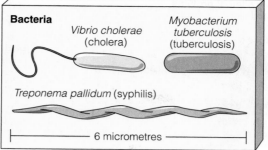
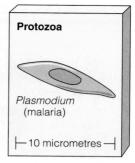

FIGURE 19-10 Examples of *pathogens* or agents that can cause transmissible diseases. A micrometre is one-millionth of a metre.

According to the World Health Organization, about 31% of all deaths per year are caused by non-transmissible cardiovascular disease, 28% by transmissible infectious disease (Figure 19-12), and 13% by nontransmissible cancers.

As a country industrializes, it usually makes an *epidemiological transition* in which deaths from the infectious diseases of childhood *decrease* and those from the chronic diseases of adulthood (heart disease and stroke, cancer, and respiratory conditions) *increase*.

Good news. Since 1900, and especially since 1950, the incidence of infectious diseases and the death rates from such diseases have been greatly reduced. This has been done mostly by a combination of better health care, using antibiotics to treat infectious disease caused by bacteria, and developing vaccines to prevent the spread of some infectious viral diseases.

Bad news. Many disease-carrying bacteria have developed genetic immunity to widely used antibiotics (Case Study). Also, many disease-transmitting species of insects such as mosquitoes have become immune to widely used pesticides that once helped control their populations.

Case Study: Are We Losing Ground in Our Struggle against Infectious Bacteria? Growing Germ Resistance to Antibiotics

Rapidly producing infectious bacteria can undergo natural selection and become genetically resistant to widely used antibiotics.

We may be falling behind in our efforts to prevent infectious bacterial diseases because of the astounding reproductive rate of bacteria, which can produce about 16 million offspring in 24 hours. Their high reproductive rate allows them to become genetically resistant to an increasing number of antibiotics through natural selection. They can also transfer such resistance to non-resistant bacteria.

Other factors play a role in the potentially serious rise in the incidence of some infectious bacterial diseases—such as tuberculosis (Case Study, below)—once controlled by antibiotics. One is that harmful bacteria are spread around the globe by human travel and the trade of goods. Another is that overuse of pesticides increases populations of pesticide-resistant insects and other carriers of bacterial diseases.

An additional factor is overuse of antibiotics. According to a 2000 study by Richard Wenzel and Michael Edward, at least half of all antibiotics used to treat humans are prescribed unnecessarily. In many countries, antibiotics are available without prescriptions, which also promotes unnecessary use.

According to a 2001 study by the Union of Concerned Scientists, nearly 75% of our antibiotics are used in feed additives to boost livestock growth production. Recent studies show that resistant strains of infectious diseases that develop in livestock animals can spread to humans through contact with infected animals or water and through food webs.

Good news. Because of public pressure, efforts are being made to phase out the use of antibiotics to boost livestock. Some fast-food chains now refuse to buy meat from livestock treated with antibiotics.

The result of these factors acting together is that every major disease-causing bacterium now has strains that resist at least one of the roughly 160 antibiotics we use to treat bacterial infections. Consequently, Canada, the United States, and other countries are reporting an increase in the number of patients who contract infectious bacterial disease while they are in a hospital or other health-care facility.

Case Study: The Global Tuberculosis Epidemic—A Potential Threat

Tuberculosis (TB) kills about 1.4 million people a year and could kill 28 million people by 2020.

Since 1990, one of the world's most underreported stories has been the spread of tuberculosis (TB). According to the World Health Organization, this highly infectious bacterial disease infects about 9 million people

A typical virus consists of a shell of proteins surrounding genetic material

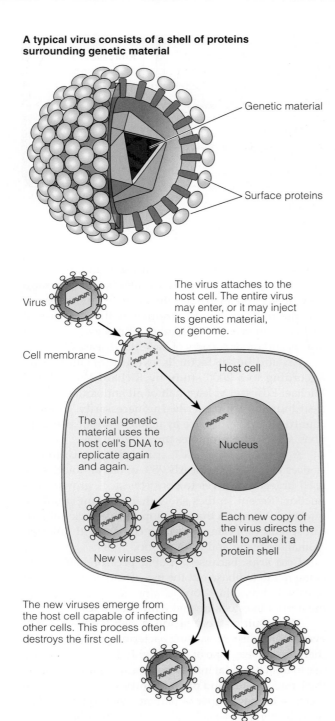

FIGURE 19-11 How a virus reproduces. (American Medical Association)

per year and kills about 1.4 million of them—mostly in developing countries (Figure 19-13). The WHO projects that between 2004 and 2020, as many as 28 million people could die of the disease, although the recent funding and efforts brought about by the UN Millennium Development Goals have provided vaccines that seem to be holding the situation in check.

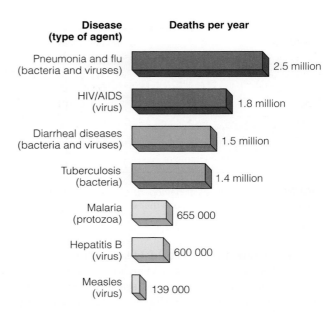

FIGURE 19-12 Each year the world's seven deadliest infectious diseases kill about 8.6 million people—most of them poor people in developing countries. This amounts to about 34 500 mostly preventable deaths every day. (Data from World Health Organization, 2010)

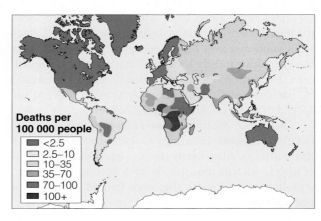

FIGURE 19-13 The current global tuberculosis epidemic. This easily transmitted disease is spreading rapidly and now kills about 1.4 million people a year—about 84% of them in developing countries. (World Health Organization)

The bacterium causing TB infection moves from person to person mainly in airborne droplets produced by coughing, sneezing, singing, or even talking. At the rate of 9 million people per year, the TB bacillus has now infected more than one of every three people in the world. To be infected means to have the organisms in your body, whether or not you are sick.

During their lifetime about 5–10% of all infected people will become sick or infectious (able to spread the disease) with active TB, especially when their immune system is weakened. Left untreated, each person with active TB typically infects 10–15 other people.

Most infected people do not appear to be sick, and about half of them do not even know they are infected. As a result, this serious health problem has been called a *silent global epidemic.*

Several factors account for the recent increase in TB. One is the lack of TB screening and control programs, especially in developing countries, where about 95% of the new cases occur. A second problem is that most strains of the TB bacterium have developed genetic resistance to almost all effective antibiotics.

Another factor is increased population growth and urbanization that have increased contacts between people and have spread TB, especially in areas where large numbers of the poor are crowded together. In addition, the spread of AIDS greatly weakens the immune system and allows TB bacteria to multiply in AIDS victims.

Slowing the spread of the disease involves early identification and treatment of people with active TB, especially those with a chronic cough. Treatment with a combination of four inexpensive drugs can cure 90% of those with active TB. However, to be effective, the drugs must be taken every day for 6–8 months. Because the symptoms disappear after a few weeks, many patients think they are cured and stop taking the drugs. This allows the disease to recur in a hard-to-treat form. It then spreads to other people, and drug-resistant strains of TB bacteria develop.

How Serious Is the Threat from Viral Diseases? Watch Out for HIV, Flu, and Hepatitis B

HIV, flu, and hepatitis B viruses infect and kill many more people each year than the highly publicized Ebola, West Nile, and SARS viruses.

What are some of the world's most widespread and dangerous viruses?

The *influenza* or *flu* virus is transmitted by the body fluids or airborne emissions of an infected person and kills about 500 000 people per year. In 1919, a highly virulent global strain of the influenza virus infected up to 500 million people around the world. At least 20 million people (some say 50 million) died within six months. Many health scientists believe that sooner or later such a mass infection from a new and very potent flu virus will sweep the world again and perhaps kill several hundred million people.

The *human immuno deficiency virus (HIV)* is transmitted by unsafe sex, sharing of needles by drug users, infected mothers to offspring before or during birth, and exposure to infected blood. On a global scale, HIV infects about 5 million people a year (about 4 000 in Canada), and the resulting complications from AIDS kill about 1.8 million people a year.

Another major killer is the *hepatitis B virus (HBV)* that damages the liver and kills about 600 000 a year.

Like HIV, it is transmitted by unsafe sex, sharing of needles by drug users, infected mothers to offspring before or during birth, and exposure to infected blood.

In recent years, three other viruses have received widespread coverage in the media. *West Nile virus* is transmitted by the bite of a common mosquito that has become infected by feeding on birds carrying the virus. West Nile virus first emerged in 1937 in the West Nile district of Uganda, but did not reach North America until 1999. Since its initial appearance in New York City, the virus has been detected in seven provinces and more than 40 states. Victims of West Nile virus may exhibit flu-like symptoms or be asymptomatic. Fatalities are rare.

Severe acute respiratory syndrome (SARS) originated in China in 2002. Within weeks, this highly contagious disease had spread to 30 countries around the world, including Canada. Before the outbreak was brought under control, SARS had infected more than 8 000 people and killed nearly 800 worldwide. Health Canada reported more than 400 cases and 43 deaths primarily in the Greater Toronto Area, where health-care workers were infected and hospitals quarantined. The intensive media coverage of the outbreak devastated Toronto's tourism industry. On June 30, 2003, in an effort to demonstrate to the world that the city was back on its feet, the Rolling Stones and other performers entertained a crowd of 450 000 at "SARS-stock" (Figure 19-14). In the aftermath of the outbreak, new health guidelines and emergency measures were put in place to ensure that Canadians were better prepared to face future threats.

Avian influenza, or **bird flu** as it is popularly known, is a viral infection that normally affects only birds. Since 2003, a strain of avian influenza virus called *H5N1* has been decimating commercial poultry flocks in Europe and Asia. In February 2009, a milder strain of avian influenza (H7N3) infected poultry on 16 farms in the Fraser Valley of British Columbia. The situation was controlled with a mass cull of 17 million turkeys, chickens, and ducks on farms in the area. Only two poultry workers became ill, and both recovered from the illness.

As of July 2012, 358 of the 607 people with the more virulent strain of avian influenza (H5N1) have died (WHO, 2012). At present, avian flu is passed from infected birds to humans who have come into direct contact with them. Health officials fear that the virus could mutate into a form that is easily transmitted from human to human, resulting in a worldwide flu **pandemic**.

Influenza A (H1N1), also known as "swine flu," is caused by a virus that is thought to have arisen from four strains of influenza—two endemic in pigs, one endemic in birds, and one endemic in humans. The new strain is highly contagious among people and is

FIGURE 19-14 The 2003 SARS Benefit Concert in Toronto, which featured the Rolling Stones and a host of other performers, signalled to the world that Canada's SARS crisis was over.

Christine Chew/UPI/Landov

spreading rapidly throughout the world. The World Health Organization is calling it "Pandemic H1N1" because the virus has global distribution despite attempts to stop it.

Milder forms of the disease result in flu-like symptoms; more aggressive strains can be lethal. As of July 2010, worldwide there were 18 500 lab-confirmed deaths attributable to H1N1 (428 in Canada). The WHO (2010) pointed out that this number was probably a considerable underestimate of the number of H1N1-related deaths around the world because many areas lacked access to laboratory testing facilities. A recent study (CDC, 2012; Dawood et al., 2012) places the number of deaths between 151 700 and 575 400— 8 to 31 times the number of lab-confirmed deaths. Fortunately, the number of deaths was in steep decline after May 2010, and the pandemic was declared over in August 2010 because the number of H1N1 cases had tapered off to a low level.

The concern of health officials is that the virus will become more virulent, causing massive numbers of deaths instead of mostly causing sickness. They are also concerned that poor countries with inadequate health systems, and with populations already weakened by hunger and by other diseases, will be overwhelmed by H1N1 even in its milder form.

You can greatly reduce your chances of getting infectious diseases such as flu, the common cold, and SARS that spread from person to person by practising good old-fashioned hygiene. Wash your hands thoroughly and often, and avoid touching your mouth, nose, and eyes.

It is much harder to fight viral infections than infections caused by bacteria and protozoa. One problem is that most drugs that can kill a virus also harm the cells of its host. Treating viral infections such as colds, flu, and most mild coughs and sore throats with antibiotics is useless and increases genetic resistance in disease-causing bacteria.

The best weapons against viruses are *vaccines* that stimulate the body's immune system to produce antibodies to ward off viral infections. Immunization with vaccines has helped reduce the spread of viral diseases such as smallpox, polio, rabies, influenza, measles, and hepatitis B. But vaccines are not available for many viral diseases.

Case Study: How Serious Is the Global Threat from HIV and AIDS? A Rapidly Growing Health Threat

The spread of acquired immune deficiency syndrome (AIDS), caused by HIV, is one of the world's most serious and rapidly growing health threats.

Sex can be hazardous to your health. Worldwide, more than 448 million people are infected with a *sexually transmitted disease (STD)* each year. STDs are rampant in high schools, colleges, and universities, where many students think, "It won't happen to me." Polls indicate that 50–66% of sexually active students do not use condoms and more than 40% have two or more sex partners. Some STDs can cause infertility in men and women. Others can cause genital warts and genital cancers or, in the case of HIV, eventually death.

The global spread of *acquired immune deficiency syndrome (AIDS)*, caused by HIV, is a serious and rapidly growing health threat. The virus itself is not deadly, but it kills immune cells and leaves the body defence-less against infectious bacteria and other viruses. According to the WHO, by the beginning of 2010 some 34 million people worldwide (96% of them in developing countries, especially African countries south of the Sahara Desert) were infected with HIV. Every day about 7 500 more people—most of them between the ages of 15 and 24—get infected with HIV. According to then U.S. Secretary of State Colin Powell, "AIDS is … now more destructive than any army, any conflict, and any weapon of mass destruction."

Within 7–10 years, at least half of those with HIV develop AIDS. This long incubation period means that infected people often spread the virus for several years without knowing they are infected. So far, *there is no vaccine to prevent HIV and no cure for AIDS.* Once you get AIDS, you will die from its effects, although drugs may help some infected people live longer. However, only a tiny fraction of those suffering from AIDS can afford to use these costly drugs.

AIDS has caused the life expectancy of 700 million people living in sub-Saharan Africa to drop from 62 to 47 years. The premature deaths of teachers, health-care workers, and other young, productive adults in such countries leads to diminished education and health care, decreased food production and economic development, and disintegrating families. Such deaths drastically alter a country's age structure diagram (Figure 19-15). AIDS has left 15 million orphans—roughly equal to half the population of Canada.

Between 2004 and 2020, the WHO estimates 60 million more deaths from AIDS and a death toll reaching as high as 5 million a year by 2020.

According to the WHO, a global strategy to slow the spread of AIDS should have five major priorities. *First,* shrink the number of people capable of infecting others by quickly reducing the number of new infections below the number of deaths. *Second,* concentrate on the groups in a society that are most likely to spread the disease, such as truck drivers, sex workers, and soldiers. *Third,* provide free HIV testing and pressure people to get tested.

Fourth, use a mass advertising and education program for adults and schoolchildren to help prevent the disease with emphasis on abstinence and condom use.

Fifth, provide free or low-cost drugs to slow the progress of the disease.

Senegal acted early to check the spread of the virus and has kept the proportion of its young adults infected with HIV below 1%. Within a decade, Botswana cut its HIV infection rates in half with good leadership from its government, health-care facilities that are better than average, and vast wealth from diamonds. It provided free testing for HIV and pressured people to get tested. Those with HIV or AIDS were provided with free or low-cost drugs to slow the disease's progress.

CONSIDER, DISCUSS, OR DEBATE

Should developed nations mount a global campaign to reduce the spread of AIDS and to help countries affected by this disease? What will happen if no action is taken?

Case Study: Malaria—A Deadly Parasitic Disease That Is Making a Comeback

Malaria kills about 1 million people a year and has probably killed more people than all of the wars ever fought.

About one of every five people in the world—most of them living in poor African countries—is at risk of malaria. Worldwide, an estimated 216 million people are infected with the protozoan parasites that cause malaria, and there are 250 million new cases each year. Malaria is not just a concern for the people living in the areas where it occurs, but also for anyone travelling to these areas—including many unsuspecting tourists—because there is no vaccine for this disease.

Malaria is caused by a parasite that is spread by the bites of certain mosquito species. It infects and destroys red blood cells, causing fever, chills, drenching sweats, anemia, severe abdominal pain and headaches, vomiting, extreme weakness, and greater susceptibility to other diseases. The disease kills about 655 000 people each year (mostly children under age 5)—an average of 1 800 deaths per day. Many children who survive severe malaria have brain damage or impaired learning ability.

Malaria is caused by four species of protozoan parasites in the genus *Plasmodium*. Most cases of the disease are transmitted when an uninfected female mosquito from any one of about 60 *Anopheles* mosquito species bites an infected person, ingests blood that contains the parasite, and later bites an uninfected person (Figure 19-16, p. 468). When this happens, *Plasmodium* parasites move out of the mosquito and into the human's bloodstream, multiply in the liver, and enter blood cells to continue multiplying. Malaria can also be transmitted by blood transfusions or by sharing needles.

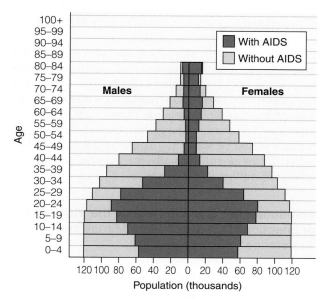

FIGURE 19-15 How AIDS can affect the age structure of a population. This figure shows the projected age structure of Botswana's population in 2020 with and without AIDS. (U.S. Census Bureau)

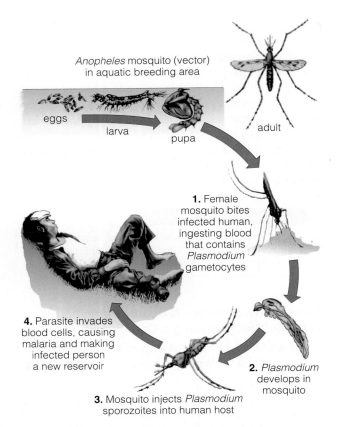

Anopheles mosquito (vector) in aquatic breeding area

eggs
larva
pupa
adult

1. Female mosquito bites infected human, ingesting blood that contains *Plasmodium* gametocytes

4. Parasite invades blood cells, causing malaria and making infected person a new reservoir

3. Mosquito injects *Plasmodium* sporozoites into human host

2. *Plasmodium* develops in mosquito

FIGURE 19-16 The life cycle of malaria. *Plasmodium* circulates from mosquito to human and back to mosquito.

The malaria cycle repeats itself until immunity develops, treatment is given, or the victim dies. *Over the course of human history, malarial protozoa probably have killed more people than all the wars ever fought.*

The mosquitoes that transmit malaria breed in shallow pools and puddles—often in tire ruts and hoof prints—near human dwellings and apparently are attracted to smelly feet. During the 1950s and 1960s, the spread of malaria was sharply curtailed by draining swamplands and marshes, spraying breeding areas with insecticides, and using drugs to kill the parasites in the bloodstream. Since 1970, malaria has come roaring back. Most species of the malaria-carrying *Anopheles* mosquito have become genetically resistant to widely used insecticides. Worse, the *Plasmodium* parasites have become genetically resistant to common antimalarial drugs.

Researchers are working to develop new antimalarial drugs (such as artemisinins derived from the Chinese herbal remedy qinghaosu), vaccines, and biological controls for *Anopheles* mosquitoes. But such approaches receive too little funding and have proved more difficult than originally thought.

In 2002, scientists announced they had broken the genetic codes for both the mosquito and the parasite

responsible for most malaria cases. Eventually, this important information could uncover genetic vulnerabilities in these organisms. This could allow scientists to alter the genetic makeup of mosquitoes so they cannot carry and transmit the parasite to humans. It could also lead to more effective drugs, vaccines, insecticides, and insect repellents to counter the disease.

Meanwhile, health experts say prevention is the best approach to slowing the spread of malaria. Methods include increasing water flow in irrigation systems to prevent mosquito larvae from developing (an expensive solution that uses much more water than required for irrigation) and fixing leaking water pipes.

A problem is that poor villagers in malarial regions cannot afford screens on their homes and mosquito nets for their beds. The WHO calls for countries to do away with all taxes and tariffs on insecticide-treated bed nets, and to give such bed nets to the poor.

Other approaches include cultivating fish that feed on mosquito larvae (biological control), clearing vegetation around houses, planting trees that soak up water in low-lying marsh areas where mosquitoes thrive (a method that can degrade or destroy ecologically important wetlands), and using zinc and vitamin A supplements to boost resistance to malaria in children.

Spraying the inside of homes with low concentrations of DDT about twice a year greatly reduces the number of malaria cases. But under an international treaty enacted in 2002, DDT and five of its chlorinated-hydrocarbon cousins are being phased out in developing countries. However, the treaty allows 25 countries to continue using DDT for malaria control until other alternatives are available.

Health officials in developing countries call for much greater funding for research on finding ways to prevent and treat malaria. Each year more than $70 billion (U.S.) is spent on research on disease. If you look at the number of people dying each year from malaria, a fair share of the global research funding for malaria would be about $1.75 billion (U.S.) a year. The actual figure spent annually for malaria research is about $85 million (U.S.) a year.

Solutions: How Can We Reduce the Incidence of Infectious Diseases? More Money and Assistance

We can sharply reduce the incidence of infectious diseases if the world is willing to provide the necessary funds and assistance.

Bad news. First, death rates from infectious diseases in developing countries are unacceptably high. *Second*, only about 10% of global medical research and development money is spent on infectious diseases in developing countries, even though more people worldwide suffer and die from these diseases than from all other diseases combined. *Third*, major drug companies have greatly decreased research on developing antibiotics and vaccines because they are difficult and costly to develop. They also produce lower profits because patients take them for only a short time compared to medicines for treating chronic diseases such as diabetes and hypertension that must be taken every day for years.

Fourth, about one-third of the world's people, mostly in developing countries, lack adequate access to clean drinking water and sanitation facilities.

Fifth, the WHO estimates that children under five make up only 10% of the world's population but account for 40% of global illness. Eleven million children a year die before their fifth birthday from causes that are mostly preventable and treatable.

Good news. According to the WHO, the global death rate from infectious diseases dropped by about two-thirds between 1970 and 2006 and is projected to continue dropping. Also, between 1971 and 2006, the percentage of children in developing countries immunized with vaccines to prevent tetanus, measles, diphtheria, typhoid fever, and polio increased from 10% to 90%—saving about 10 million lives a year.

Figure 19-17 lists measures that health scientists and public health officials suggest to help prevent or reduce the incidence of infectious diseases that affect humanity (especially in developing countries). An important breakthrough has been the development of simple *oral rehydration therapy* to help prevent death from dehydration for victims of diarrheal diseases, which cause about one-fourth of all deaths of children under age 5. It involves administering a simple solution of boiled water, salt, and sugar or rice, at a cost of only a few cents per person. It has been the major factor in reducing the annual number of deaths from diarrhea from 4.6 million in 1980 to 1.5 million in 2010. Few investments have saved so many lives at such a low cost.

In 2001, the WHO began promoting a do-it-yourself technique that uses sunlight to disinfect water. The process is simple: fill a transparent plastic bottle with contaminated water and lay it horizontally on a flat black surface (which absorbs more heat and kills more pathogens than a lighter surface can) in the sunlight. After several hours, the heat and ultraviolet rays of the sun kill most illness-causing microorganisms in polluted water. This simple method is especially useful in tropical countries where there is intense sunlight.

Solutions

Infectious Diseases

Increase research on tropical diseases and vaccines

Reduce poverty

Decrease malnutrition

Improve drinking water quality

Reduce unnecessary use of antibiotics

Educate people to take all of an antibiotic prescription

Reduce antibiotic use to promote livestock growth

Careful hand washing by all medical personnel

Immunize children against major viral diseases

Oral rehydration for diarrhea victims

Global campaign to reduce HIV/AIDS

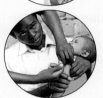

FIGURE 19-17 Solutions: ways to prevent or reduce the incidence of infectious diseases, especially in developing countries. Which two of these solutions do you believe are the most important?

19-5 RISK ANALYSIS

How Can We Estimate Risks? Evaluate, Compare, Decide

Scientists have developed ways to evaluate and compare risks, decide how much risk is acceptable, and find affordable ways to reduce them.

Risk analysis involves identifying hazards and evaluating their associated risks (*risk assessment*, Figure 19-2, left), ranking risks (*comparative risk analysis*), determining options and making decisions about reducing or eliminating risks (*risk management*, Figure 19-2, right), and informing decision makers and the public about risks (*risk communication*).

Statistical probabilities based on past experience, animal testing and other tests, and epidemiological studies are used to estimate risks from older technologies and chemicals. To evaluate new

Risk, Toxicology, and Human Health **469**

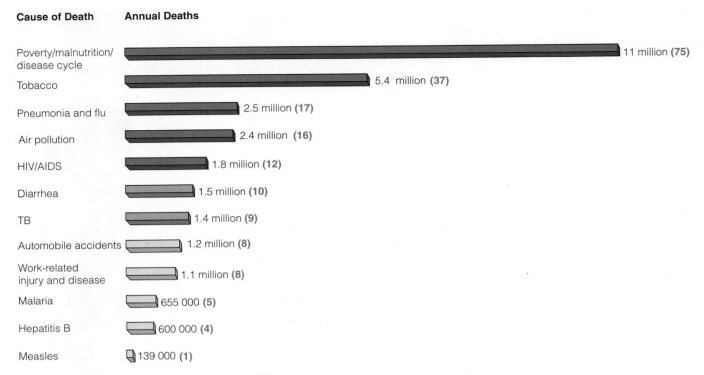

Cause of Death   **Annual Deaths**

Poverty/malnutrition/disease cycle — 11 million **(75)**

Tobacco — 5.4 million **(37)**

Pneumonia and flu — 2.5 million **(17)**

Air pollution — 2.4 million **(16)**

HIV/AIDS — 1.8 million **(12)**

Diarrhea — 1.5 million **(10)**

TB — 1.4 million **(9)**

Automobile accidents — 1.2 million **(8)**

Work-related injury and disease — 1.1 million **(8)**

Malaria — 655 000 **(5)**

Hepatitis B — 600 000 **(4)**

Measles — 139 000 **(1)**

FIGURE 19-18 Number of deaths per year in the world from various causes. Numbers in parentheses give these deaths in terms of the number of fully loaded 400-passenger jumbo jets crashing *every day of the year* with no survivors. Because of sensational media coverage, most people have a distorted view of the largest annual causes of death. (World Health Organization and U.S. Centers for Disease Control and Prevention)

technologies and products, risk evaluators use more uncertain statistical probabilities, based on models rather than actual experience and testing.

The greatest risks many people face today are rarely dramatic enough to make the daily news. In terms of the number of premature deaths per year (Figure 19-18), *the greatest risk by far is poverty*. Its high death toll is a result of malnutrition, increased susceptibility to normally nonfatal infectious diseases, and often fatal infectious diseases from lack of access to a safe water supply.

Thus *the sharp reduction or elimination of poverty would do far more to improve longevity and human health than any other measure*. It would also greatly improve human rights, provide more people with income to stimulate economic development, and reduce environmental degradation and the threat of terrorism. Sharply reducing poverty is a win-win situation for people, economies, and the environment.

Aside from the health risks associated with poverty, reducing the chance of premature death is a matter of managing risks by trying to avoid or recover from diseases while making prudent decisions about health-related lifestyle choices within our control.

The best ways to reduce one's risk of premature death and serious health problems are to avoid smoking and exposure to smoke, lose excess weight, reduce consumption of foods containing cholesterol and saturated fats, eat a variety of fruits and vegetables, exercise regularly, avoid alcohol or drink no more than two drinks a day, avoid excess sunlight (which ages skin and may cause skin cancer), and have only safe sex.

> **DID YOU KNOW**
>
> Dr. William Leiss, professor emeritus at the School of Social Policy Studies, Queen's University, is an internationally recognized risk communications author and researcher. He has worked extensively with industry and the federal and provincial governments, and is the author of many books and articles about environmental and health risks, including climate change, West Nile virus, mad cow disease, and genetically modified crops. More information about Dr. Leiss's contributions to the field is available at http://www.leiss.ca.

How Can We Estimate Risks of Using Increasingly Complex Technology in Our Lives? A Difficult Task

Estimating risks from using certain technologies is difficult because of the unpredictability of human behaviour, human error, and sabotage.

The more complex a technological system and the more people needed to design and run it, the more difficult it is to estimate the risks. The overall reliability of a technological system (expressed as a percentage) or the probability expressed as a percentage that a device will complete a task without failing is the product of two factors:

$$\text{System reliability (\%)} = \frac{\text{Technology}}{\text{reliability}} \times \frac{\text{Human}}{\text{reliability}}$$

With careful design, quality control, maintenance, and monitoring, a highly complex system such as a nuclear power plant or space shuttle can achieve a high degree of technology reliability. But human reliability usually is much lower than technology reliability and is almost impossible to predict: To err is human.

Suppose the technology reliability of a nuclear power plant is 95% (0.95) and human reliability is 75% (0.75). Then the overall system reliability is 71% (0.95 $\times$ 0.75 $\times$ 100 = 0.71 = 71%). Even if we could make the technology 100% reliable (1.0), the overall system reliability would still be only 75% (1.0 $\times$ 0.75 $\times$ 100 = 75%). The crucial dependence of even the most carefully designed systems on unpredictable human reliability helps explain essentially "impossible" tragedies such as the Chernobyl nuclear power plant accident and the *Challenger* and *Columbia* space shuttle accidents.

One way to make a system more foolproof or fail-safe is to move more of the potentially fallible elements from the human side to the technical side. However, chance events such as a lightning bolt can knock out an automatic control system, and no machine or computer program can completely replace human judgment. Also, the parts in any automated control system are manufactured, assembled, tested, certified, and maintained by fallible human beings. In addition, computer software programs used to monitor and control complex systems can also contain human error or can be deliberately modified by computer viruses to malfunction.

How Useful Is Risk Analysis? Uncertain Results

The results of risk analysis are usually very uncertain.

Here are some of the key questions involved in evaluating the reliability of risk analysis:

- How reliable are risk assessment data and models? (Sections 19-2 and 19-3)

- Who profits from a risk analysis that allows certain levels of harmful chemicals into the environment, and who suffers?

- Should estimates emphasize short-term risks, or should more weight be put on long-term risks? Who should make this decision?

- Who should do a particular risk analysis, and who should review the results? A government agency? Independent scientists? The public?

- Should cumulative effects of various risks be considered, or should risks be considered separately, as is usually done? Suppose a pesticide is found to have an annual risk of killing 1 out of 1 million people through cancer. Cumulatively, however, effects from 40 such pesticides might kill 40 people, or 400 of every million people because of synergistic reactions with other chemicals.

- How widespread is each risk? About how many people are likely to be affected?

- Should risk levels be higher for workers (as is almost always the case) than for the general public? What say should workers and their families have in this decision?

- How much risk is acceptable, and to whom is it acceptable?

Proponents point to the numerous advantages of risk analysis. It is a useful way to organize and analyze available scientific information, identify significant hazards, and focus on areas that need more research. It can also help regulators to decide how money for reducing risks should be allocated and to stimulate people to make more informed decisions about health and environmental goals and priorities.

However, critics point out that results of risk analysis are very uncertain. For example, a recent study documented the significant uncertainties involved in even simple risk analysis. Eleven European governments established 11 different teams of their best scientists and engineers (including those from private companies) to assess the hazards and risks from a small plant storing only one hazardous chemical (ammonia). The 11 teams, consisting of world-class experts analyzing this very simple system, disagreed with one another on fundamental points and varied in their assessments of the hazards by a factor of 25 000. Such inherent uncertainty explains why regulators setting human exposure levels for toxic substances usually divide the best results by 100 to 1 000 to provide the public with a margin of safety.

How Should Risks Be Managed? A Complex and Controversial Process

Risk management involves trying to answer a number of difficult and controversial questions about whether and how to reduce a particular societal risk to a certain level and at what cost.

Risk management includes the administrative, political, and economic actions taken to decide whether and how to reduce a particular societal risk to a certain level and at what cost.

Risk management involves answering the following questions:

- How reliable is the risk analysis for each risk?

- Which risks to human health should be given the highest priority?

- How much risk is acceptable and to whom?

- How much is a life worth, and how much money should we spend per life saved? Most government risk analyses set the value of a life at about $3.7 million (U.S.) for people under 70 and about $1.4 million (U.S.) for people over 70. How much do you believe your life is worth?

- How much will it cost to reduce each risk to an acceptable level?

- How should limited funds be spent to provide the greatest benefit?

- How will the risk management plan be monitored, enforced, and communicated to the public?

Each step in this process involves making value judgments and weighing trade-offs to find some reasonable compromise among often conflicting political, economic, health, and environmental interests.

How Well Do We Perceive Risks? Most of Us Flunk

Most individuals are poor at evaluating the relative risks they face, mostly because of misleading information and irrational fears.

Most of us are not good at assessing the relative risks from the hazards that can affect us. Also, many people deny or shrug off the high-risk chances of death (or injury) from voluntary activities they enjoy, such as *motorcycling* (1 death in 50 participants), *smoking* (1 in 300 participants by age 65 for a pack-a-day smoker), *hang gliding* (1 in 1 250), and *driving* (1 in 3 300 without a seatbelt and 1 in 6 070 with a seatbelt). Indeed, the most dangerous thing most people in many countries do each day is drive or ride in a car.

Yet some of these same people may be terrified about the possibility of being killed by a *nuclear power plant accident* (1 in 200 000), *West Nile virus* (1 in 1 million), *lightning* (1 in 3 million), *commercial airplane crash* (1 in 9 million), *snakebite* (1 in 36 million), or *shark attack* (1 in 281 million).

CONSIDER, DISCUSS, OR DEBATE

What hazards in your daily life do you worry about the most? The least? Do your perceptions of risk make sense or are they irrational?

How Can You Become Better at Risk Analysis? Analyze, Compare, and Evaluate Your Lifestyle

To become better at risk analysis you can carefully evaluate the barrage of good and bad news, compare risks, and concentrate on reducing risks over which you have some control.

You can do three things to become better at estimating risks. *First*, carefully evaluate what the media presents. Recognize that the media often give an exaggerated view of risks to capture our interest and thus sell newspapers or gain TV viewers.

Second, compare risks. Do you risk getting cancer by eating a charcoal-broiled steak once or twice a week? Yes, because in theory anything can harm you. The question is whether this danger is great enough for you to worry about. In evaluating a risk the question is not, "Is it safe?" but rather, "How risky is it compared to other risks?"

Third, concentrate on the most serious risks to your life and health over which you have some control and stop worrying about smaller risks and those over which you have little or no control. When you worry about something, the most important question to ask is, "Do I have any control over this?"

For example, the top four killers of Canadians (and people in many countries) are heart attacks, strokes, cancer, and accidents (many of them involving motor vehicles). You have control over major ways to reduce these risks because you decide whether to smoke, what to eat, how much exercise you get, how much alcohol you consume, your exposure to the sun's ultraviolet rays, how safely you drive, and whether or not you practise safe sex. Concentrate on making good choices, and you will have a much greater chance of living a healthy, longer, happier, and less fearful life.

19-6 CHECKING OUR PROGRESS AT COMBATING HIV/AIDS, MALARIA, AND OTHER DISEASES

How Well Are We Proceeding with Millennium Goal 6? Mixed Progress

Our progress at meeting the health-related targets of Goal 6 has involved some hope for portions of Targets 6A and 6C. However, it seems unlikely that Target 6B will be met.

The eight Millennium Development Goals were introduced in Chapter 1 and have been addressed in Chapters 9, 10, 13, 14, and 15 so far. Goal 6—aimed at ensuring protection from diseases—has three targets (Figure 19-19).

Millennium Development Goal 6

Combat HIV/AIDS, Malaria, and Other Diseases

Target 6A: Have halted by 2015 and begun to reverse the spread of HIV/AIDS.

Target 6B: Achieve, by 2010, universal access to treatment of HIV/AIDS for all those who need it.

Target 6C: Have halted by 2015 and begun to reverse the incidence of malaria and other major diseases.

FIGURE 19-19 Ensuring protection from diseases: Millennium Development Goal 6 aims to prevent and treat HIV/AIDS, malaria, and other diseases. (Courtesy of the UNDP)

Target 6A is *to have halted by 2015 and begun to reverse the spread of HIV/AIDS.* There are four indicators, focusing on monitoring HIV prevalence in youths aged 15 to 24, on increasing condom use, on increasing education about AIDS, and on providing education for orphans of AIDS.

- As mentioned on p. 466, there were 34 million cases of people living with HIV/AIDS worldwide in 2010. The World Health Organization has released information to show that about 80% of HIV-positive adults were infected through unprotected sex; about 70% of these cases involved heterosexual intercourse.

- Efforts to focus on youths, to increase use of condoms, and to promote education about HIV/AIDS have been effective in the countries where these tools of prevention have been applied.

- The number of people newly infected with HIV has declined 21% since 1997, and the number of AIDS-related deaths has declined 19% since 2004. Therefore, it appears that Target 6A is being accomplished.

Target 6B was *to achieve, by 2010, universal access to treatment of HIV/AIDS for all those who need it.* There is one indicator focused on increasing the proportion of HIV-infected people with access to antiretroviral drugs.

- The number of people receiving antiretroviral treatment for HIV or AIDS has increased 13-fold since 2004. However, only about half the people requiring the treatment were able to receive it, largely because it is expensive. Clearly, Target 6B was not achieved by 2010 and may not be reached by 2015. Universal treatment of HIV/AIDS appears to be many years—and dollars—in the future.

Target 6C is *to have halted by 2015 and begun to reverse the incidence of malaria and other major diseases.* It has five indicators focused on decreasing the incidence of disease, decreasing the death rates, and increasing opportunities for treatment of major diseases such as malaria and tuberculosis.

- Malaria continues to kill about 655 000 people per year, mostly children, but this is a reduction from 1 million deaths per year in 2008. Much of the success achieved can be credited to a program that gave people access to increasing numbers of insecticide-treated mosquito bednets, but many poor people are still in need. Improvements have been made in the prevention and treatment of tuberculosis and polio; in fact, death, attributable to tuberculosis have fallen by more than a third since 1990. However, relatively little attention and funding has gone to other tropical diseases, which continue to affect a billion people (http://www.undp.org/mdg/).

You can continue to monitor progress toward these goals at websites such as http://www.mdgmonitor.org/.

The burden of proof imposed on individuals, companies, and institutions should be to show that pollution prevention options have been thoroughly examined, evaluated, and used before lesser options are chosen.

JOEL HIRSCHORN

CHAPTER REVIEW

1. Review the Key Questions for this chapter on p. 453. Describe each of the following smoking-related illnesses: heart disease, lung cancer, bronchitis, emphysema, and stroke. Exactly how are these diseases caused by smoking? Consider all the things that have been done to discourage smoking; what further steps would you take if it was your job to greatly reduce smoking in Canada?

2. Distinguish among *risk, risk assessment,* and *risk management.* Distinguish between *possibility* and *probability.*

   What is a *pathogen*? Give an example of a risk from each of the following: *biological hazards, chemical hazards, physical hazards, cultural hazards,* and *lifestyle choices.*

3. Distinguish between a *nontransmissible disease* and a *transmissible disease* and give an example of each. In terms of death rates, what are the world's seven most serious infectious diseases? Distinguish between an *epidemic* and a *pandemic.* Describe the causes and possible solutions for the increasing genetic resistance in microbes to commonly used antibiotics.

4. Describe the global threat from tuberculosis. Describe the threat from flu and the effects of a global flu pandemic. Describe the health threats from the global HIV/AIDS pandemic and list six ways to reduce this threat. Describe the threats from the hepatitis B, West Nile, and SARS viruses. Describe the threat from malaria for many of the world's people and how we can reduce this threat.

5. Why would we be concerned about *hormonally active agents* (HAAs) affecting wild ecosystems? How would these chemicals affect us? How should we react to this threat?

6. What is a *toxic chemical*? Discuss the threat from PCBs. Distinguish among *mutagens, teratogens,* and *carcinogens,* and give an example of each. Describe the toxic legacy from PCBs. Describe the human immune, nervous, and endocrine systems and give an example of a chemical that can threaten each of these systems. Describe the toxic effects of the various forms of mercury and ways to reduce these threats. What are hormonally active agents, what risks do they pose, and how can we reduce these risks?

7. Define *toxicology, toxicity, dose,* and *response*. Give three reasons why children are more vulnerable to harm from toxic chemicals. Describe how the toxicity of a substance can be estimated by using laboratory animals, and discuss the limitations of this approach. What is a *dose-response curve*? Describe how toxicities are estimated by case reports and epidemiological studies and discuss the limitations of these approaches. Why do we know so little about the harmful effects of chemicals? Discuss the use of pollution prevention and the precautionary principle in dealing with health threats from chemicals.

8. What is *risk analysis*? In terms of deaths per year, what are the five greatest threats that humans face? Describe the health threats from smoking in terms of risk.

9. How can we reduce the threats from the use of various technologies? List five principles that can help us realistically evaluate and reduce risk.

10. Describe how an HIV/AIDS epidemic in a country can affect the age structure of its population. How exactly does HIV/AIDS work to compromise human health? Who is at the highest risk of contracting HIV/AIDS? What five steps could be taken to reduce the threat of AIDS?

CRITICAL THINKING

1. Explain why you agree or disagree with the proposals for reducing the death toll and other harmful effects of smoking listed on p. 452. Do you believe that there should be a ban on smoking indoors in all public places? Explain.

2. Do you believe the precautionary approach should be used to deal with the *potential* harm from hormonally active agents (HAAs) while more definitive research is carried out over the next two decades? Explain. What harmful effects could using this approach have on the economy and on your lifestyle?

3. Should we have zero pollution levels for all toxic and hazardous chemicals? Explain. What are the alternatives?

4. Evaluate the following statements:

   a. We should not get worked up about exposure to toxic chemicals because almost any chemical in a large enough dosage can cause some harm.

   b. We should not worry so much about exposure to toxic chemicals because through genetic adaptation we can develop immunity to such chemicals.

   c. We should not worry so much about exposure to toxic chemicals because we can use genetic engineering to reduce or eliminate such problems.

5. Should pollution levels be set to protect the most sensitive people in a population (Figure 19-3, left, p. 454) or the average person (Figure 19-3, middle)? Explain.

6. What are the five major risks you face from (a) your lifestyle, (b) where you live, and (c) what you do for a living? Which of these risks are voluntary and which are involuntary? List the five most important things you can do to reduce these risks. Which of these things do you actually plan to do?

7. Congratulations! You are in charge of a global risk–benefit analysis board to evaluate whether certain chemicals or technologies should be approved for widespread use. Explain why you would approve or disapprove each of the following: (a) drugs to slow the aging process; (b) drugs that would cause people to have unconditional love for everyone and thus have the potential to do away with hate, violence, and war; (c) genetic engineering advances that would allow parents to have genes inserted into lab-produced fetuses to produce designer babies with their desired checklist of enhanced genetic traits; (d) allowing people to have a genetic clone that they can use for spare parts to help them live longer; and (e) putting everyone in the world under constant electronic surveillance to help prevent bioterrorism.

PROJECTS

1. Use the library or the Internet to find recent articles that support or refute the hormesis hypothesis.

2. Use the library or the Internet to find recent articles describing the increasing genetic resistance in disease-causing bacteria to commonly used antibiotics. Evaluate the evidence and claims in these articles.

3. Pick a specific viral disease and use the library or Internet to find out (a) how it spreads, (b) its effects, (c) strategies for controlling its spread, and (d) possible treatments.

4. Use the library or the Internet to learn about endocrine disruptors. Which organisms are being most affected and which chemicals seem to be causing the problems? How do these chemicals function? What can we do to help solve the problem?

5. Use the Internet to learn more about Environment Canada's National Pollution Release Inventory (NPRI). Evaluate the NPRI's effectiveness as a mechanism for identifying and monitoring sources of pollution in Canada.

CASE STUDY   When Is a Lichen Like a Canary?

Nineteenth-century coal miners took canaries with them into the mines—not for their songs but for the moment when they stopped singing. Then the miners knew it was time to get out of the mine because the air contained methane, which could ignite and explode.

Today we use sophisticated equipment to monitor air quality, but living things such as lichens (Figure 20-1) can also warn us of polluted air. Lichens, which are not plants, consist of a fungus and an alga living together, usually in a mutually beneficial (mutualistic) partnership.

You have probably seen lichens growing as crusts or leafy growths on rocks (Figure 20-1, right), walls, tombstones, and tree trunks or as beards hanging down from twigs and branches (Figure 20-1, left).

These hardy pioneer species are good biological indicators of air pollution because they are always absorbing air as a source of nourishment. A highly polluted area around an industrial plant may have no lichens or only grey-green crusty lichen. An area with moderate air pollution may have orange crusty lichens on walls. Walls and trees in areas with fairly clean air may have leafy lichens.

Some lichen species are sensitive to specific air-polluting chemicals. Old man's beard *(Usnea trichodea)* and yellow Evernia lichens, for example, sicken or die in the presence of too much sulphur dioxide.

Because lichens are widespread, long lived, and anchored in place, they can also help track pollution to its source. The scientist who discovered sulphur dioxide pollution on Isle Royale in Lake Superior, where no car or smokestack had ever intruded, used Evernia lichens to point the finger northward to coal-burning facilities at Thunder Bay, Ontario.

In 1986, the Chernobyl nuclear power plant in Ukraine (Figure 17-1, p. 382) exploded and spewed radioactive particles into the atmosphere. Some of these particles fell to the ground over northern Scandinavia and were

(continued)

FIGURE 20-1 *Usnea trichodea* lichen growing on a branch of a larch tree (left), and red and yellow crustose lichens growing on rock (right). The vulnerability of various lichen species to specific air pollutants can help researchers detect levels of these pollutants and track down their sources.

absorbed by lichens that carpet much of Lapland. The area's Saami people depend on reindeer meat for food, and the reindeer feed on lichens. After Chernobyl, more than 70 000 reindeer had to be killed and the meat discarded because it was too radioactive to eat. Scientists helped the Saami identify where to find the remaining uncontaminated reindeer by analyzing lichens to pinpoint the most contaminated areas.

We all must breathe air from a global atmospheric commons in which air currents and winds can transport some pollutants long distances. Lichens can alert us to the danger, but as with all forms of pollution, the best solution is prevention.

I thought I saw a blue jay this morning. But the smog was so bad that it turned out to be a cardinal holding its breath.

MICHAEL J. COHEN

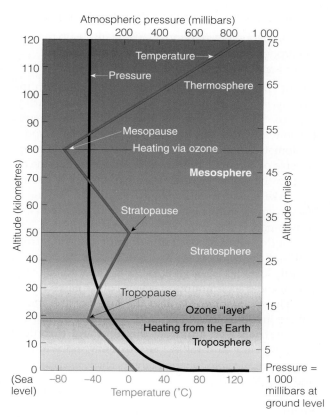

FIGURE 20-2 Natural capital: the Earth's atmosphere consists of several layers. The average temperature of the atmosphere varies with altitude (red line). The average temperature of the atmosphere at the Earth's surface is determined by a combination of two factors. One is *natural heating* by incoming sunlight and certain greenhouse gases that release absorbed energy as heat into the lower troposphere (the natural *greenhouse effect*; Figure 6-16, p. 120). The other is *natural cooling* by surface evaporation of water and convection processes that transfer heat to higher altitudes and latitudes (Figure 6-11, p. 117). Most UV radiation from the sun is absorbed by ozone (O_3), found primarily in the stratosphere in the ozone layer 17–26 kilometres (10–16 miles) above sea level.

CHAPTER PURPOSE AND QUESTIONS

Chapter 20 discusses outdoor and indoor pollutants, and how they can be reduced. The chapter addresses the following questions:

20-1 What are the key characteristics of the atmosphere?

20-2 What are the major types and sources of air pollution?

20-3 What is photochemical smog?

20-4 What is acid deposition and where does it occur?

20-5 How serious is indoor air pollution?

20-6 How does your respiratory system help protect you from air pollution?

20-1 STRUCTURE AND SCIENCE OF THE ATMOSPHERE

What Are Key Characteristics of the Atmosphere? Several Layers with Different Properties

The atmosphere consists of several layers with different temperatures, pressures, and composition.

We live at the bottom of a thin layer of gases surrounding the Earth, called the *atmosphere*. It is divided into several spherical sublayers (Figure 20-2), each characterized by abrupt changes in temperature as a result of differences in the absorption of incoming solar energy.

Density and atmospheric pressure also vary throughout the atmosphere. Gravitational forces pull the gas molecules in the atmosphere toward the Earth's surface. This means that the air we breathe at sea level has a higher *density* (more molecules per litre) than the air we inhale on top of the world's highest mountain.

Atmospheric pressure is a measure of the mass per unit area of air. It is caused by the bombardment of a surface by the molecules in air. The pressure of the atmosphere increases as the density of air increases because a volume of air with a high density has more gas molecules than a volume with a lower density. Thus, *atmospheric pressure decreases with altitude.* This explains why the pressure exerted on each square centimetre of your body by the bombardment of hordes of gas molecules is greater at sea level than at the top of a tall mountain.

What Is the Troposphere? Weather Breeder

The atmosphere's innermost layer is made up mostly of nitrogen and oxygen, with smaller amounts of water vapour and carbon dioxide.

About 75–80% of the Earth's air mass is found in the *troposphere*, the atmospheric layer closest to the Earth's surface. This layer extends only about 17 kilometres (11 miles) above sea level at the equator and about 8 kilometres (5 miles) over the poles. If the Earth were the size of an apple, this lower layer containing the air we breathe would be no thicker than the apple's skin.

Take a deep breath. About 99% of the volume of the air you just inhaled from the troposphere consists of two gases: nitrogen (78%) and oxygen (21%). The remainder consists of water vapour (varying from 0.01% at the frigid poles to 4% in the humid tropics), slightly less than 1% argon (Ar), 0.038% carbon dioxide (CO_2), and trace amounts of several other gases.

The troposphere is also the layer of the atmosphere involved in the chemical cycling of the Earth's vital nutrients. In addition, this thin and turbulent layer of rising and falling air currents and winds is largely responsible for the planet's short-term *weather* and long-term *climate*.

To biologist and environmental scientist David Suzuki, "Air is a matrix or universal glue that joins all life together…. Every breath is an affirmation of our connection with other living things, a renewal of our link with our ancestors, and a contribution to generations yet to come."

What Is the Stratosphere? Earth's Global Sunscreen

Ozone in the atmosphere's second layer filters out most of the sun's UV radiation that is harmful to us and most other species.

The atmosphere's second layer is the *stratosphere*, which extends from about 17 to 48 kilometres (11–30 miles) above the Earth's surface (Figure 20-2). Although the stratosphere contains less matter than the troposphere, its composition is similar, with two notable exceptions: its volume of water vapour is about 1/1 000 as much and its concentration of ozone (O_3) is much higher (Figure 20-3).

Stratospheric ozone is produced when some of the oxygen molecules there interact with ultraviolet (UV) radiation emitted by the sun ($3 O_2 + UV \rightarrow 2 O_3$). This "global sunscreen" of ozone in the stratosphere keeps about 95% of the sun's harmful UV radiation from reaching the Earth's surface.

This UV filter of "good" ozone in the lower stratosphere allows us and other forms of life to exist on land and helps protect us from sunburn, skin and eye cancer, cataracts, and damage to our immune systems.

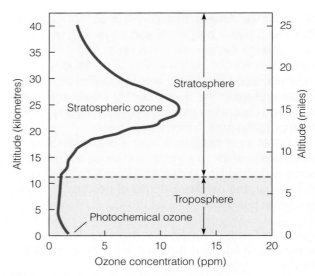

FIGURE 20-3 **Natural capital:** average distribution and concentrations of ozone in the troposphere and stratosphere. Beneficial ozone that forms in the stratosphere protects life on Earth by filtering out most of the incoming harmful UV radiation emitted by the sun. Harmful or photochemical ozone forms in the troposphere when various air pollutants undergo chemical reactions under the influence of sunlight. Ozone in this atmosphere near the Earth's surface damages plants, lung tissues, and some materials such as rubber.

It also prevents much of the oxygen in the troposphere from being converted to photochemical ozone, a harmful air pollutant.

Much evidence indicates that some human activities are *decreasing* the amount of beneficial or "good" ozone in the stratosphere and *increasing* the amount of harmful or "bad" ozone in the troposphere—especially in some urban areas.

20-2 OUTDOOR AIR POLLUTION

What Are the Major Types and Sources of Air Pollution? Burning Fossil Fuels Is the Major Culprit

Outdoor air pollutants come mostly from natural sources and burning fossil fuels in motor vehicles and power and industrial plants.

Air pollution is the presence of chemicals in the atmosphere in concentrations high enough to affect climate and harm organisms and materials. The effects of airborne pollutants range from annoying to lethal.

Table 20-1 (p. 479) lists the major classes of pollutants commonly found in outdoor (ambient) air. The majority come from natural sources. They include dust particles blowing off the Earth's surface (Figure 6-1, p. 109), volatile organic chemicals released by some plants, the decay of plants, forest fires, volcanic

Table 20-1 Major Classes of Air Pollutants

Class	Examples
Carbon oxides	Carbon monoxide (CO) and carbon dioxide (CO_2)
Sulphur oxides	Sulphur dioxide (SO_2) and sulphur trioxide (SO_3)
Nitrogen oxides	Nitric oxide (NO), nitrogen dioxide (NO_2), nitrous oxide (N_2O) (NO and NO_2 often are lumped together and labelled NO_x)
Volatile organic compounds (VOCs)	Methane (CH_4), propane (C_3H_8), chlorofluorocarbons (CFCs)
Suspended particulate matter (SPM)	Solid particles (dust, soot, asbestos, lead, nitrate, and sulphate salts), liquid droplets (sulphuric acid, PCBs, dioxins, and pesticides)
Photochemical oxidants	Ozone (O_3), peroxyacyl nitrates (PANs), hydrogen peroxide (H_2O_2), aldehydes
Radioactive substances	Radon-222, iodine-131, strontium-90, plutonium-239 (Table 3-1, p. 51)
Hazardous air pollutants (HAPs), which cause health effects such as cancer, birth defects, and nervous system problems	Carbon tetrachloride (CCl_4), methyl chloride (CH_3Cl), chloroform ($CHCl_3$), benzene (C_6H_6), ethylene dibromide ($C_2H_2Br_2$), formaldehyde (CH_2O_2)

eruptions, and sea spray. Most natural sources of air pollution are spread out and, except for those from volcanic eruptions and some forest fires, rarely reach harmful levels.

Air pollution is not new (Spotlight, p. 481). Throughout human history, beginning with the discovery of fire, we have added various types of pollutants to the troposphere. Our inputs increased when we began extracting and burning coal, first for heat and later for generating electricity and producing materials such as steel.

Burning oil, gasoline, and natural gas also adds pollutants to the atmosphere. Pollutants from our activities can reach harmful levels in the troposphere, especially in urban areas where people, cars, and industrial activities are concentrated.

Most outdoor pollutants in today's urban areas enter the atmosphere from the burning of fossil fuels in power plants and factories (*stationary sources*) and in motor vehicles (*mobile sources*). Scientists classify outdoor air pollutants into two categories. **Primary pollutants** are those emitted directly into the troposphere in a potentially harmful form. Examples are soot and carbon monoxide. While in the troposphere, some of these primary pollutants may react with one another or with the basic components of air to form new pollutants, called **secondary pollutants** (Figure 20-4).

With their concentration of cars and factories, cities normally have higher outdoor air pollution levels than rural areas. However, prevailing winds can spread long-lived primary and secondary air pollutants from urban and industrial areas to the countryside and to other urban areas.

Indoor air pollutants come from infiltration of polluted outside air and various chemicals used or produced inside buildings, as discussed in Section 20-5. Experts in risk analysis rate indoor and outdoor air pollution as high-risk human health problems.

According to the World Health Organization (WHO), one of every six people on the Earth, or more than 1.1 billion people, live in urban areas where outdoor air is unhealthy to breathe. Most of them live in densely populated cities in developing countries where air pollution control laws do not exist or are poorly enforced. In other words, poverty can mean poor air for the poor.

In Canada and most other developed countries, government-mandated standards set maximum allowable atmospheric concentrations, or criteria, for six *criteria* or *conventional air pollutants* commonly found in outdoor air (Table 20-2, p. 482). Most scientists would also add volatile organic compounds (VOCs, Table 20-1) to this list because of their role in the formation of photochemical smog that plagues many cities. Most air pollutants are gases. But some are *aerosols,* which consist of tiny particles of solids or droplets of liquids suspended in the air.

Good news. Regulating these six criteria pollutants has helped sharply reduce their levels in most developed countries.

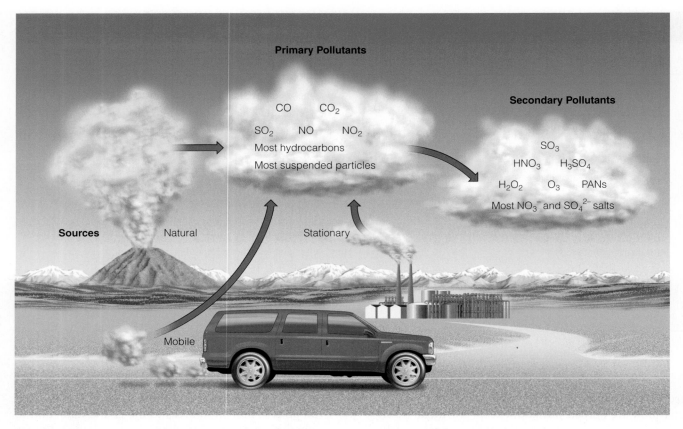

FIGURE 20-4 Natural capital degradation: sources and types of air pollutants. Human inputs of air pollutants may come from *mobile sources* (such as cars) and *stationary sources* (such as industrial and power plants). Some *primary air pollutants* may react with one another or with other chemicals in the air to form *secondary air pollutants.*

Should Carbon Dioxide Be Classified as an Air Pollutant? Most Scientists Say Yes

Carbon dioxide can be classified as an air pollutant because it can warm the atmosphere and contribute to global climate change.

Most scientists would add CO_2 to the gang of six criteria air pollutants (Table 20-2) despite the fact that most industries, and some regulatory agencies, do not agree with this classification.

These scientists give three reasons for classifying CO_2 as an air pollutant. *First,* in high enough concentrations any chemical in the air can become a pollutant. *Second,* we have been increasing the concentration of CO_2 in the troposphere by burning fossil fuels and clearing CO_2-absorbing trees faster than they are growing back in many areas. *Third,* the troposphere is warming and there is considerable evidence that the additional CO_2 (a greenhouse gas) added to the troposphere by human activities plays a role in this change.

So who cares if it gets a little warmer? Warmer winters would be nice. The problem is that enhancement of the Earth's natural greenhouse effect (Figure 6-16,

p. 120)—called *global warming*—can change where and how much precipitation falls, affect where we can grow food, and flood some areas of the world because of rising sea levels. Thus because higher atmospheric levels of CO_2 can harm some people, economies, and ecosystems, most scientists say that it meets the criteria for being classified as an air pollutant.

CONSIDER, DISCUSS, OR DEBATE

Consider this issue from a variety of perspectives (scientist, industry leader, politician, etc.).

Case Study: Air Quality in Ontario

The Ministry of the Environment monitors and reports changes in air quality across the province.

In Ontario, the Ministry of the Environment (MOE) monitors air quality in the province through a network of 40 monitoring stations across the province. This air monitoring network tracks six major pollutants: carbon monoxide, nitrogen oxides, volatile organic compounds, sulphur dioxide, fine particulate matter,

Air Pollution in the Past: The Bad Old Days

Modern civilization did not invent air pollution. It probably began when humans discovered fire and used it to burn wood in poorly ventilated caves for warmth and cooking and inhaled unhealthy smoke and soot.

During the Middle Ages, a haze of wood smoke hung over densely packed urban areas. The industrial revolution brought even worse air pollution as coal was burned to power factories and heat homes.

By the 1850s, London had become well known for its "pea soup" fog, a mixture of coal smoke and fog that blanketed the city. In 1880, a prolonged coal fog killed an estimated 2 200 people. Another in 1911 killed more than 1 100 Londoners. The authors of a report on this disaster coined the word **smog** for the deadly mixture of smoke and fog that enveloped the city.

In 1952, an even worse yellow fog lasted for five days and killed an estimated 4 000–12 000 Londoners, prompting Parliament to pass the Clean Air Act of 1956. Additional air pollution disasters

in 1956, 1957, and 1962 killed 2 500 more people. Because of strong air pollution laws, London's air today is much cleaner, and "pea soup" fogs are a thing of the past. Now the major threat is from air pollutants emitted by motor vehicles.

The industrial revolution, powered by coal-burning factories and homes, brought air pollution to North America. Large industrial cities such as Pittsburgh, Pennsylvania, and St. Louis, Missouri, were known for their smoky air. By the 1940s, the air over some cities was so polluted that people had to use their automobile headlights during the day.

The first documented air pollution disaster in the United States occurred on October 29, 1948, at the small industrial town of Donora in Pennsylvania's Monongahela River Valley south of Pittsburgh. Pollutants from the area's coal-burning industries became trapped in a dense fog that stagnated over the valley for five days. About 6 000 of the town's 14 000 inhabitants became sick, and 22 of them died. This killer fog resulted from a com-

bination of mountainous terrain surrounding the valley and weather conditions that trapped and concentrated deadly pollutants emitted by the community's steel mill, zinc smelter, and sulphuric acid plant.

In 1963, high concentrations of air pollutants accumulated in the air over New York City, killing about 300 people and injuring thousands. Other episodes in New York, Los Angeles, and other large cities in the 1960s led to much stronger air pollution control programs in the 1970s.

In Canada, formerly polluted industrial centres such as the Ontario cities of Hamilton (the country's largest steel producer) and Sudbury (Case Study, p. 491) are being transformed through the application of pollution controls, beautification programs, and green technologies.

Critical Thinking

Explain why you think the air pollution outlook in your province is improving or getting worse.

---

and total reduced sulphur compounds. The ministry uses real-time air quality data gathered by the network to calculate the *air quality index (AQI)*, which informs Ontarians and the news media about local air quality conditions at predetermined intervals each day.

The colour-coded AQI readings are based on the concentration of each pollutant for a given hour and indicate the following air quality conditions:

0–15 (very good)
16–31 (good)
32–49 (moderate)
50–99 (poor)
100+ (very poor)

Thus if the AQI reading were 23, as shown in Figure 20-5, the air quality would be considered good. An AQI value of more than 100 (very poor category) indicates an air quality that may have adverse effects on a large proportion of the human or animal popu-

lations exposed. The public can access the daily AQI values at http://www.airqualityontario.com.

Figure 20-6 (p. 483) shows the sources of five common pollutants tracked by Ontario's air monitoring network. (The health effects of each of these pollutants are described in Table 20-2.) About 85% of the province's *carbon monoxide* is generated by various forms of transportation, whereas 7% comes from residential sources and 5% comes from industrial sources. Transportation accounts for 68% of Ontario's *nitrogen oxides*, including *nitrogen dioxide*, which plays a role in the formation of ground-level ozone. About 50% of Ontario's sulphur dioxide comes from smelting metals, whereas 19% is produced by burning coal to generate electricity. Sulphur dioxide is a major contributor to acid deposition.

Fine particulate matter (or suspended particulate matter) smaller than 2.5 micrometres is designated

Table 20-2 Major Outdoor Air Pollutants*

CARBON MONOXIDE (CO)

Description: Colourless, odourless gas that is poisonous to air-breathing animals; forms during the incomplete combustion of carbon-containing fuels ($2 C + O_2 \rightarrow 2 CO$).

Major human sources: Cigarette smoking (p. 452), incomplete burning of fossil fuels. About 77% (95% in cities) comes from motor vehicle exhaust.

Health effects: Reacts with hemoglobin in red blood cells and reduces the ability of blood to bring oxygen to body cells and tissues. This impairs perception and thinking; slows reflexes; causes headaches, drowsiness, dizziness, and nausea; can trigger heart attacks and angina; damages the development of fetuses and young children; and aggravates chronic bronchitis, emphysema, and anemia. At high levels it causes collapse, coma, irreversible brain cell damage, and death.

NITROGEN DIOXIDE (NO₂)

Description: Reddish-brown irritating gas that gives photochemical smog its brownish colour; in the atmosphere can be converted to nitric acid (HNO_3), a major component of acid deposition.

Major human sources: Fossil fuel burning in motor vehicles (49%) and power and industrial plants (49%).

Health effects: Lung irritation and damage; aggravates asthma and chronic bronchitis; increases susceptibility to respiratory infections such as the flu and common colds (especially in young children and older adults).

Environmental effects: Reduces visibility; acid deposition of HNO_3 can damage trees, soils, and aquatic life in lakes.

Property damage: HNO_3 can corrode metals and eat away stone on buildings, statues, and monuments; NO_2 can damage fabrics.

SULPHUR DIOXIDE (SO₂)

Description: Colourless, irritating; forms mostly from the combustion of sulphur-containing fossil fuels such as coal and oil ($S + O_2 \rightarrow SO_2$); in the atmosphere can be converted to sulphuric acid (H_2SO_4), a major component of acid deposition.

Major human sources: Coal burning in power plants (88%) and industrial processes (10%).

Health effects: Breathing problems for healthy people; restriction of airways in people with asthma; chronic exposure can cause a permanent condition similar to bronchitis. According to the WHO, at least 625 million people are exposed to unsafe levels of sulphur dioxide from fossil fuel burning.

Environmental effects: Reduces visibility; acid deposition of H_2SO_4 can damage trees, soils, and aquatic life in lakes.

Property damage: SO_2 and H_2SO_4 can corrode metals and eat away stone on buildings, statues, and monuments; SO_2 can damage paint, paper, and leather.

SUSPENDED PARTICULATE MATTER (SPM)

Description: Variety of particles and droplets (aerosols) small and light enough to remain suspended in atmosphere for short periods (large particles) to long periods (small particles; Figure 20-8, p. 486); cause smoke, dust, and haze.

Major human sources: Burning coal in power and industrial plants (40%), burning diesel and other fuels in vehicles (17%), agriculture (ploughing, burning off fields), unpaved roads, construction.

Health effects: Nose and throat irritation, lung damage, and bronchitis; aggravates bronchitis and asthma; shortens life; toxic particulates (such as lead, cadmium, PCBs, and dioxins) can cause mutations, reproductive problems, cancer.

Environmental effects: Reduces visibility; acid deposition of H_2SO_4 droplets can damage trees, soils, and aquatic life in lakes.

Property damage: Corrodes metal; soils and discolours buildings, clothes, fabrics, and paints.

OZONE (O₃)

Description: Highly reactive, irritating gas with an unpleasant odour that forms in the troposphere as a major component of photochemical smog (Figures 20-4 and 20-7).

Major human sources: Chemical reaction with volatile organic compounds (VOCs, emitted mostly by cars and industries) and nitrogen oxides to form photochemical smog (Figure 20-7, p. 484).

Health effects: Breathing problems; coughing; eye, nose, and throat irritation; aggravates chronic diseases such as asthma, bronchitis, emphysema, and heart disease; reduces resistance to colds and pneumonia; may speed up lung tissue aging.

Environmental effects: Ozone can damage plants and trees; smog can reduce visibility.

Property damage: Damages rubber, fabrics, and paints.

LEAD

Description: Solid toxic metal and its compounds, emitted into the atmosphere as particulate matter.

Major human sources: Paint (old houses), smelters (metal refineries), lead manufacture, storage batteries, leaded gasoline (being phased out in developed countries).

Health effects: Accumulates in the body; brain and other nervous system damage and mental retardation (especially in children); digestive and other health problems; some lead-containing chemicals cause cancer in test animals.

Environmental effects: Can harm wildlife.

*Data from U.S. Environmental Protection Agency.

FIGURE 20-5 The air quality index (AQI) developed by Ontario's Ministry of the Environment. The AQI reading of 23 shown here indicates air quality that is considered good. (Ministry of the Environment, Monitoring Air Quality, http://www.airqualityontario.com/science/background.cfm. © Queen's Printer for Ontario. Reproduced with permission)

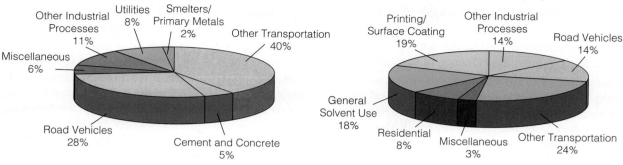

Ontario Nitrogen Oxides Emissions by Sector (Emissions from Point/Area/Transportation Sources, 2006 Estimates)

- Other Industrial Processes 11%
- Utilities 8%
- Smelters/Primary Metals 2%
- Other Transportation 40%
- Miscellaneous 6%
- Road Vehicles 28%
- Cement and Concrete 5%

Ontario Volatile Organic Compounds Emissions by Sector (Emissions from Point/Area/Transportation Sources, 2006 Estimates)

- Printing/Surface Coating 19%
- Other Industrial Processes 14%
- Road Vehicles 14%
- General Solvent Use 18%
- Residential 8%
- Miscellaneous 3%
- Other Transportation 24%

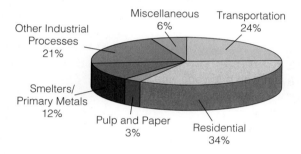

Ontario PM$_{2.5}$ Emissions by Sector (Emissions from Point/Area/Transportation Sources, 2006 Estimates)

- Miscellaneous 6%
- Transportation 24%
- Other Industrial Processes 21%
- Smelters/Primary Metals 12%
- Pulp and Paper 3%
- Residential 34%

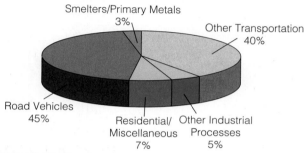

Ontario Carbon Monoxide Emissions by Sector (Emissions from Point/Area/Transportation Sources, 2006 Estimates)

- Smelters/Primary Metals 3%
- Other Transportation 40%
- Road Vehicles 45%
- Residential/Miscellaneous 7%
- Other Industrial Processes 5%

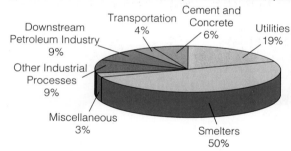

Ontario Sulphur Dioxide Emissions by Sector (Emissions from Point/Area/Transportation Sources, 2006 Estimates)

- Downstream Petroleum Industry 9%
- Transportation 4%
- Cement and Concrete 6%
- Utilities 19%
- Other Industrial Processes 9%
- Miscellaneous 3%
- Smelters 50%

FIGURE 20-6 Source of emissions for five air pollutants in Ontario. (Ministry of the Environment, *Air Quality in Ontario, 2007 Report (PIBS 6390e)*. © Queen's Printer for Ontario, 2008. Reproduced with permission)

as PM$_{2.5}$ in Ontario. Small solid or liquid particles of this size are light enough to remain suspended in the air for great lengths of time. The primary source of PM$_{2.5}$ is elemental and organic carbon associated with residual burning of fuels and with transportation. The second-largest source of this pollutant is sulphates from industrial processes and smelting metals. More than 50% of Ontario's PM$_{2.5}$ is from the United States.

Ground-level ozone (O$_3$) is not directly emitted into the atmosphere. It is produced through photochemical reactions between oxides of nitrogen (NO$_x$) and volatile organic compounds (VOCs) in the presence of sunlight (p. 484). Consequently, this aspect of ozone has a season (May to September), a time of the day (noon through afternoon), and even a weather pattern (sunny and hot). The use of solvents is the second-largest source of ozone. Forested areas such as northern Ontario receive significant contributions of VOCs from trees (see Section 20-3). More than 50% of Ontario's ground-level ozone comes from the United States.

PHOTOCHEMICAL AND INDUSTRIAL SMOG

What Is Photochemical Smog? Brown-Air Smog

Photochemical smog is a mixture of air pollutants formed by the reaction of nitrogen oxides and volatile organic hydrocarbons under the influence of sunlight.

A *photochemical reaction* is any chemical reaction activated by light. Air pollution known as **photochemical smog** is formed when a mix of nitrogen oxides (NO and NO_2, both called NO_x) and volatile organic hydrocarbon compounds from natural and human sources react chemically under the influence of UV radiation from the sun to produce a mixture of more than 100 primary and secondary pollutants (Figure 20-7). In greatly simplified terms,

$$VOCs + NO_x + heat + sunlight \rightarrow \begin{array}{l} \text{ground level ozone } (O_3) \\ + \text{ other photochemical} \\ \quad \text{oxidants} \\ + \text{ aldehydes} \\ + \text{ other secondary air} \\ \quad \text{pollutants} \end{array}$$

The formation of photochemical smog involves a complex series of chemical reactions. It begins inside automobile engines and in the boilers of coal-burning power and industrial plants. At the high temperatures found there, nitrogen and oxygen in air react to produce colourless nitric oxide ($N_2 + O_2 \rightarrow 2\ NO$). In the atmosphere, some of the NO is converted to nitrogen dioxide (NO_2), a yellowish-brown gas with a choking odour (Table 20-2). NO_2 is the cause of the brownish haze that hangs over many cities during the afternoons

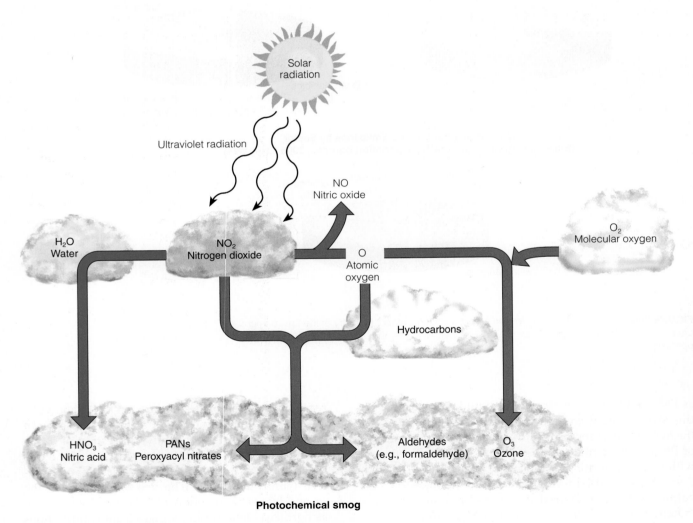

FIGURE 20-7 Natural capital degradation: simplified scheme of the formation of photochemical smog. The severity of smog generally is associated with atmospheric concentrations of ozone at ground level.

of sunny days, explaining why photochemical smog sometimes is called *brown-air smog*.

When exposed to ultraviolet radiation from the sun, some of the NO_2 engages in a complex series of reactions with hydrocarbons (mostly released by vegetation, motor vehicles, and other human activities) that produce photochemical smog—a mixture of ozone, nitric acid, aldehydes, peroxyacyl nitrates (PANs), and other secondary pollutants.

Collectively, NO_2, O_3, and PANs are called *photochemical oxidants* because they can react with and oxidize certain compounds in the atmosphere or inside your lungs that normally are not oxidized. Mere traces of these oxidants (especially ozone, Table 20-2) and aldehydes in photochemical smog can irritate the respiratory tract and damage crops and trees.

Hotter days lead to higher levels of ozone and other components of smog. As traffic increases on a sunny day, smog builds up to peak levels by early afternoon, irritating people's eyes and respiratory tracts.

All modern cities have some photochemical smog, but it is much more common in cities with sunny, warm, dry climates and lots of motor vehicles. Examples are Los Angeles, Denver, and Salt Lake City in the United States; Sydney, Australia; Mexico City; São Paulo, Brazil; and Buenos Aires, Argentina.

Smog is likely to become more widespread and more serious globally as more people in developing countries begin to drive gasoline-powered vehicles. This will contribute to urban air pollution, as well as adding to massive pollution phenomena such as the Asiatic brown cloud (p. 487) that is covering large portions of Asia and occasionally extending as far as North America.

How Can Trees Contribute to Photochemical Smog? Hydrocarbon Emitters

Some hydrocarbon-emitting tree species can contribute to the formation of photochemical smog.

Trees have many environmental benefits. They emit oxygen, absorb CO_2, provide shade (which reduces energy needed for air conditioning), and help absorb and remove various pollutants from the air.

Recently scientists have found that some species of trees and plants (such as some oak species, sweet gums, poplars, and kudzu) in and around urban areas play a larger role in smog formation than was once thought. They do so by emitting volatile organic compounds (VOCs, especially hydrocarbons such as isoprene) that are ingredients in the development of photochemical smog.

Unless forests of such trees are close to urban areas, most of their VOC emissions occur in nonurban areas and disperse into the atmosphere. Thus they do not make a significant contribution to the formation of photochemical smog except in forested areas near urban areas with large sources of NO_x and plenty of sunlight. This is in contrast to cars, which along with refineries and other sources emit most of their VOCs, NO_x, and other pollutants into urban air.

Because of trees' ecological and aesthetic benefits, environmentalists support their widespread planting in urban areas. But they say the emphasis should be on tree species that emit low levels of VOCs.

How Does Industrial Smog Form, and How Big a Problem Is It? Grey-Air Smog Is a Danger in Some Developing Countries

Industrial smog is a mixture of sulphur dioxide, droplets of sulphuric acid, and a variety of suspended solid particles emitted by burning coal and oil.

Fifty years ago, cities such as London, England, and Chicago and Pittsburgh in the United States burned large amounts of coal and heavy oil (which contain sulphur impurities) in power plants and factories and for heating homes and cooking food. During winter, people in such cities were exposed to **industrial smog** consisting mostly of sulphur dioxide, aerosols containing suspended droplets of sulphuric acid formed from sulphur dioxide, and a variety of suspended solid particles (Figure 20-8).

The chemistry of industrial smog is fairly simple. When burned, the carbon in coal and oil is converted to carbon dioxide ($C + O_2 \rightarrow CO_2$) and carbon monoxide ($2\,C + O_2 \rightarrow 2\,CO$). Some of the unburned carbon also ends up in the atmosphere as suspended particulate matter (soot), another ingredient of industrial smog.

The sulphur compounds in coal and oil also react with oxygen to produce sulphur dioxide (SO_2), a colourless, suffocating gas. Sulphur dioxide also is emitted into the troposphere when metal sulphide ores are roasted or smelted to convert a metal ore (such as lead sulphide, PbS) to a free metal (such as Pb).

In the troposphere, some of the sulphur dioxide reacts with oxygen to form sulphur trioxide (SO_3), which then reacts with water vapour in the air to produce tiny suspended droplets of sulphuric acid (H_2SO_4). Some of these droplets react with ammonia in the atmosphere to form solid particles of ammonium sulphate [$(NH_4)_2SO_4$]. The tiny suspended particles of such salts and carbon (soot) give the resulting industrial smog a grey colour, explaining why it is sometimes called *grey-air smog*.

Today urban industrial smog is rarely a problem in most developed countries. This has happened because coal and heavy oil are burned only in large

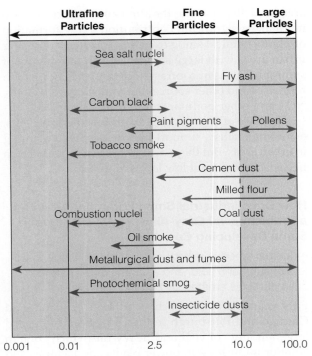

Ultrafine Particles | Fine Particles | Large Particles

Sea salt nuclei

Fly ash

Carbon black

Paint pigments | Pollens

Tobacco smoke

Cement dust

Milled flour

Combustion nuclei | Coal dust

Oil smoke

Metallurgical dust and fumes

Photochemical smog

Insecticide dusts

0.001   0.01   2.5   10.0   100.0

Average particle diameter (micrometres, or microns)

FIGURE 20-8 Suspended particulate matter consists of particles of solid matter and droplets of liquid that are small and light enough to remain suspended in the atmosphere for some period (the larger the particle, the sooner it usually falls to Earth). Suspended particles are found in a wide variety of types and sizes, ranging in diameter from 0.001 micrometre to 100 micrometres (a micrometre, or micron, is one-millionth of a metre, or about 0.00004 inch). Since 1987, the U.S. Environmental Protection Agency (EPA) has focused on *fine particles* smaller than 10 microns (known as PM-10). In 1997, the agency began focusing on reducing emissions of *ultrafine particles* with diameters less than 2.5 microns (known as PM-2.5) because these particles are small enough to reach the lower part of human lungs and contribute to respiratory diseases.

boilers with reasonably good pollution control or with tall smokestacks that transfer the pollutants to downwind rural areas.

However, industrial smog is a problem in industrialized urban areas of China, India, Ukraine, and some eastern European countries (especially the "black triangle" region of Slovakia, Poland, Hungary, and the Czech Republic), where large quantities of coal are burned with inadequate pollution controls.

In addition to providing electricity and running industries, coal is burned for heating homes and cooking by millions of poor families. As a result, China has some of the world's most polluted indoor and outdoor air. This explains why many residents of Chinese cities develop serious respiratory problems and some die prematurely from the coal-generated air pollution. After only a few days

in this region visitors often suffer from coughs and bronchial irritation.

Some Chinese cities have so many smokestacks and home chimneys belching coal smoke that residents see the sun for only a few weeks a year. This is similar to conditions that prevailed in many industrial cities in the United States and Europe a hundred or more years ago (Spotlight, p. 481).

What Factors Influence the Formation of Photochemical and Industrial Smog? Rain, Wind, Buildings, Mountains, and Temperature

Outdoor air pollution can be reduced by precipitation, sea spray, and winds and increased by urban buildings, mountains, and high temperatures.

The frequency and severity of smog in an area depend on local climate and topography, population density, the amount of industry, and the fuels used in industry, heating, and transportation.

Three natural factors help *reduce* outdoor air pollution. One is *rain and snow,* which help cleanse the air of pollutants. This helps explain why cities with dry climates are more prone to photochemical smog than cities with wet climates. A second factor is *salty sea spray from the oceans,* which can wash out particulates and other water-soluble pollutants from air that flows from land onto the oceans.

A third factor is *winds,* which can help sweep pollutants away, dilute them by mixing them with cleaner air, and bring in fresh air. However, these pollutants are blown somewhere else or are deposited from the sky onto surface waters, soil, and buildings. There is no away.

Four other factors can *increase* outdoor air pollution. One is *urban buildings,* which can slow wind speed and reduce dilution and removal of pollutants. Another is *hills and mountains.* They can reduce the flow of air in valleys below them, allowing pollutant levels to build up at ground level. In addition, *high temperatures* found in most urban areas promote the chemical reactions leading to photochemical smog formation.

A fourth factor is called the *grasshopper effect* based on atmospheric distillation, which transfers volatile air pollutants from tropical and temperate areas to the Earth's poles. It occurs when volatile compounds evaporate from warm terrestrial areas at low latitudes and rise high into the atmosphere. Then they are deposited in the oceans or carried to higher latitudes at or near the Earth's poles by atmospheric currents and oceanic currents of water.

This explains why for decades pilots have reported dense layers of reddish-brown haze over the Arctic. It also explains why polar bears, whales, sharks, and other top carnivores and Native peoples in the Arctic have high levels of DDT and other long-lived pesticides, toxic metals (such as lead and mercury), and polychlorinated biphenyls (PCBs) in their bodies even though there are no concentrations of industrial facilities and cars in these remote areas.

How Can Temperature Inversions Increase Outdoor Air Pollution? Trapping Pollutants Near the Ground

A layer of warm air sitting on top of a layer of cool air near the ground can prevent outdoor pollutants from rising and dispersing.

During daylight, the sun warms the air near the Earth's surface. Normally, this warm air and most of the pollutants it contains rise to mix with the cooler air above it. This mixing of warm and cold air creates turbulence, which disperses the pollutants.

Under certain atmospheric conditions, however, a layer of warm air can lie atop a layer of cooler air nearer the ground, a situation known as a **temperature inversion.** Because the cooler air is denser than the warmer air above it, the air near the surface does not rise and mix with the air above it. Pollutants can concentrate in this stagnant layer of cool air near the ground.

Areas with two types of topography and weather conditions are especially susceptible to prolonged temperature inversions (Figure 20-9, p. 488). One such area is a town or city located in a valley surrounded by mountains that experiences cloudy and cold weather during part of the year (Figure 20-9, top). In such cases, the surrounding mountains along with the clouds block much of the winter sun that causes air to heat and rise, and the mountains block air from being blown away. As long as these stagnant conditions persist, concentrations of pollutants in the valley below will build up to harmful and even lethal concentrations.

The second type of area typically is a city with several million people and motor vehicles in an area with a sunny climate, light winds, mountains on three sides, and the ocean on the other. Here, the conditions are ideal for photochemical smog worsened by frequent **thermal inversions** (Figure 20-9, bottom).

This describes California's heavily populated Los Angeles basin, which has prolonged subsidence temperature inversions at least half of the year, mostly during the warm summer and fall. When a thermal inversion persists throughout the day, the surrounding mountains prevent the polluted surface air from being blown away by sea breezes.

Case Study: South Asia's Massive Brown Cloud—Choking in China and India

A huge dark brown cloud of industrial smog, caused by coal burning in countries such as China and India, stretches over much of southeastern Asia.

A number of studies (IPCC, 2007; Ramanathan et al., 2008) have warned of the harmful effects of a huge blanket of industrial smog plus smoke from sources such cooking fires and burning crop waste—called the *Asian brown cloud* or the *atmospheric brown cloud*.

Satellite images show a dark brown cloud, 3 kilometres (2 miles) thick, stretching nearly continuously across much of India, Bangladesh, and the industrial heart of China and parts of the open sea in this area.

This cloud is caused by huge emissions of ash, smoke, dust, and acidic compounds produced by people burning coal in industries and homes and clearing and burning forests for planting crops, along with dust blowing off deserts in western Asia. As the cloud travels, it picks up many toxic pollutants.

In a way, the rapid industrialization of parts of southeastern Asia, especially China and India, is repeating on a much larger scale the smoky, unhealthy coal-burning past of the industrial revolution in Europe and North America during the 19th and early 20th centuries (Spotlight, p. 481).

Here are some of the possible harmful effects of the Asian pollution. One is that the cloud reduces the amount of solar energy hitting the Earth's surface underneath it by 2% to as much as 15% in some areas. This may be reducing India's winter rice harvests by 3–10%. And acids in the haze falling to the surface can damage crops, trees, and life in lakes.

The cloud may also be an important contributor to illnesses and premature deaths from respiratory diseases for people who live under it. In Beijing, China, atmospheric concentrations of airborne particulates are routinely five times higher than those in the Los Angeles basin. Not one of India's 22 cities with more than 1 million people meets WHO air pollution standards. Instead of blue skies, many of the inhabitants living under the Asian brown cloud see grey skies much of the year.

Another problem is that the aerosols of fine particles and droplets in this huge cloud appear to be causing changes in regional climate, warming some areas, cooling other areas, and shifting patterns of rainfall including India's vital winter monsoon season. It may even play a role in the intensity and frequency of the El Niño–Southern Oscillation (ENSO) climate cycle (Figure 6-14, p. 119) and may thus affect North and South America and other parts of the world (Figure 6-15, p. 119).

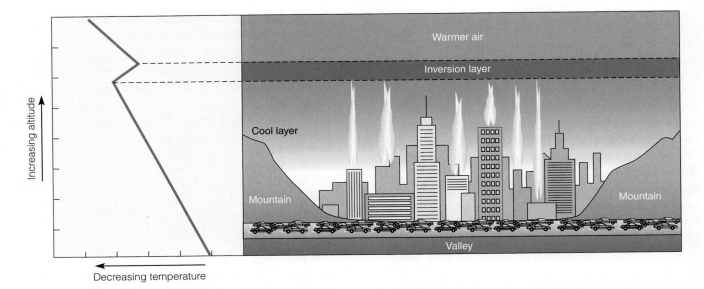

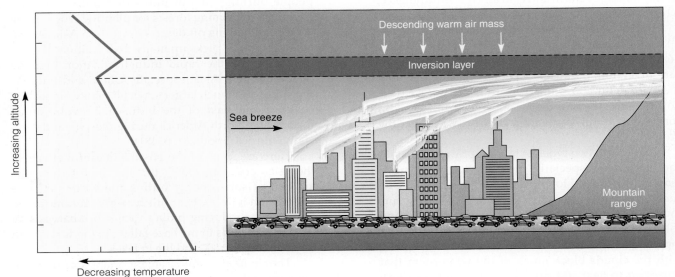

FIGURE 20-9 Two sets of topography and weather conditions that lead to prolonged *temperature inversions,* in which a warm air layer sits atop a cooler air layer. Air pollutants can build to harmful levels during an inversion. A temperature inversion can occur during cold, cloudy weather in a valley surrounded by mountains (top). Frequent and prolonged temperature inversions can also occur in an area with a sunny climate, light winds, mountains on three sides, and the ocean on the other (bottom). A layer of descending warm air from a high-pressure system prevents ocean-cooled air near the ground from ascending enough to disperse and dilute pollutants. Because of their topography, Los Angeles and Mexico City have frequent temperature inversions, many of them prolonged during the summer.

There are reports that black carbon (soot) from the Asian brown cloud and other sources is contributing to the melting of snow and ice in the Arctic; the dark particles of soot have a warming effect on the atmosphere and darken sea ice, reducing its ability to reflect sunlight (IPCC, 2007; Ramanathan et al., 2008).

The history of air pollution control shows that atmospheric hazes can be cleared up fairly quickly. This is done by setting standards for coal-burning industries and utilities, shifting from coal to cleaner-burning natural gas in industries and dwellings in urban areas, relying more on renewable energy resources such as wind and hydropower to produce electricity, and requiring catalytic converters on cars. China made strides at improving the air pollution around Beijing in time for the 2008 Olympics, and progress has been continuing. India's capital city of Delhi has also made progress in reducing air pollution under orders from India's Supreme Court.

What Is Acid Deposition, and Where Does It Occur? Acids Falling on Your Head

Sulphur dioxide, nitrogen oxides, and particulates can react in the atmosphere to produce acidic chemicals that can travel long distances before returning to the Earth's surface.

Most coal-burning power plants, ore smelters, and other industrial plants in developed countries use tall smokestacks to emit sulphur dioxide, suspended particles, and nitrogen oxides high into the troposphere where wind can mix, dilute, and disperse them.

These tall smokestacks reduce *local* air pollution, but they can increase *regional* air pollution downwind. This occurs because the primary pollutants, sulphur dioxide and nitrogen oxides, emitted into the atmosphere above the inversion layer are transported as much as 1 000 kilometres (600 miles) by prevailing winds. During their trip, they form secondary pollutants such as nitric acid vapour, droplets of sulphuric acid, and particles of acid-forming sulphate and nitrate salts.

These acidic substances remain in the atmosphere for 2–14 days, depending mostly on prevailing winds, precipitation, and other weather patterns. During this period, they descend to the Earth's surface in two forms. One is *wet deposition* as acidic rain, snow, fog, and cloud vapour with a pH less than 5.6 (Figure 3-6, p. 43). The other is *dry deposition* as acidic particles. The resulting mixture is called **acid deposition** (Figure 20-10), sometimes termed **acid rain.** Most dry deposition occurs within about 2–3 days fairly near the emission sources, whereas most wet deposition takes place within 4–14 days in more distant downwind areas.

Acid deposition is a regional air pollution problem in most parts of the world that are downwind from coal-burning facilities and from urban areas with large numbers of cars. Such areas include Canada, the eastern United States, and other parts of the world (Figure 20-11, p. 490). Look at the maps to see if you live in a major acid deposition area.

In the United States, coal-burning power and industrial plants in the Ohio Valley emit the largest quantities of sulphur dioxide and other pollutants that can cause acid deposition. Mostly as a result of these emissions along with those by other industries and motor vehicles in urban areas, typical precipitation in eastern Canada and the eastern United States can be in the range of pH 4.4–4.8. This is about 10 or more times the acidity of natural precipitation, which has a pH of 5.6. Some mountaintop forests in the eastern United States and east of Los Angeles, California, are

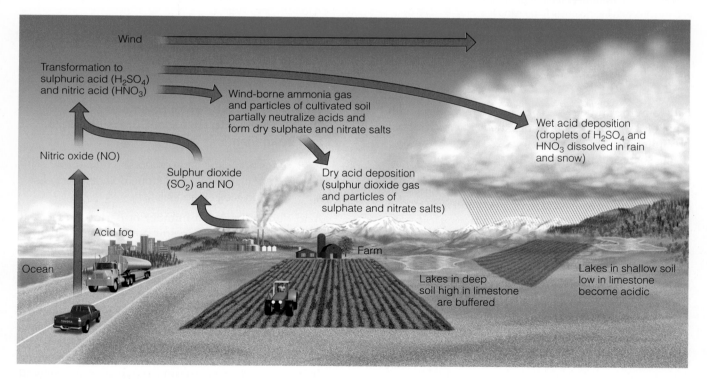

CENGAGENOW™ **ACTIVE FIGURE 20-10 Natural capital degradation:** *acid deposition,* which consists of rain, snow, fog, or dust with a pH lower than 5.6, is commonly called acid rain. Soils and lakes vary in their ability to buffer or remove excess acidity. Further details of chemistry can be found in Appendix 3 and on the book's website. *See an animation based on this figure at* CengageNow.

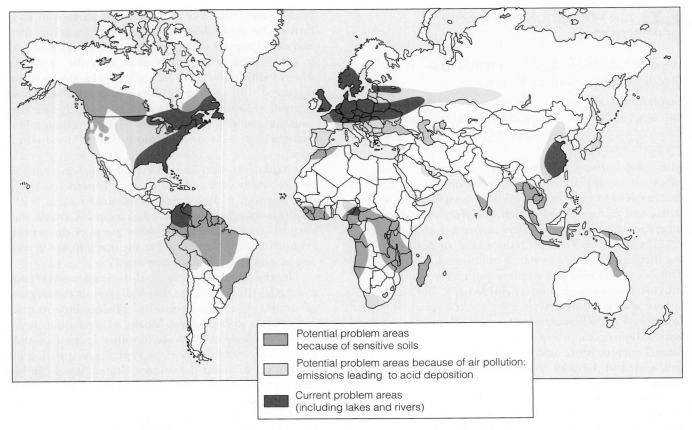

	Potential problem areas because of sensitive soils
	Potential problem areas because of air pollution: emissions leading to acid deposition
	Current problem areas (including lakes and rivers)

FIGURE 20-11 Natural capital degradation: regions where acid deposition is now a problem (red) and regions with the potential to develop this problem (yellow and green). Such regions have large inputs of air pollution (mostly from power plants, industrial plants, and ore smelters) or are sensitive areas with soils and bedrock that cannot neutralize (buffer) inputs of acidic compounds (green areas and most red areas). (World Resources Institute and U.S. Environmental Protection Agency)

bathed in fog and dews as acidic as lemon juice, with a pH of 2.3—about 1 000 times the acidity of normal precipitation.

In some areas, soils contain basic compounds such as calcium carbonate ($CaCO_3$) or limestone that can react with and neutralize, or **buffer,** some inputs of acids. Two types of *sensitive areas* are vulnerable to acid deposition because they lack the buffering capacity needed to neutralize the acidic compounds falling from the sky. One has areas with thin acidic soils derived mostly from granite rock without such natural buffering (Figure 20-11, green and most red areas). The other is areas where the buffering capacity of soils has been depleted by decades of acid deposition (some red areas in Figure 20-11).

The worst acid deposition is in Asia, especially China, which gets about 66% of its energy from burning coal. China is now the world's largest emitter of sulphur dioxide and faces all of the environmental problems that come with serious acid deposition.

What Are Some Harmful Effects of Acid Deposition? Lung Disease, Corrosion, Haze, and Dead Fish

Acid deposition can cause or worsen respiratory disease, attack metallic and stone objects, decrease atmospheric visibility, and kill fish.

Acid deposition has a number of harmful effects. It contributes to human respiratory diseases such as bronchitis and asthma, and can leach toxic metals (such as lead and copper) from water pipes into drinking water. It also damages statues, national monuments, buildings, metals, and car finishes. Limestone, marble (which is a form of limestone), and sandstone, which are used in statues and as building materials, are especially susceptible because they dissolve even in weak acid solutions. Large amounts of money are spent each year to clean and repair monuments and buildings that have been attacked by acid deposition. Acid deposition also decreases atmospheric visibility, mostly because of the sulphate particles it contains.

For most aquatic systems, acid deposition has harmful effects when the pH falls below 6 and especially below 4.5, which kills most fish. Another effect is the release into lakes of aluminum ions (Al^{3+}) attached to minerals in nearby soil. These ions asphyxiate many kinds of fish by stimulating excessive mucus formation, which clogs their gills.

Lakes vary in their sensitivity to inputs of acids. Those on sand or igneous rocks, such as granite, generally have little buffering capacity to neutralize acids and thus are more susceptible to acidification. Much of the damage to aquatic life in such sensitive areas is a result of *acid shock.* This is caused by the sudden runoff of large amounts of highly acidic water and aluminum ions into lakes and streams when snow melts in the spring or after unusually heavy rains.

Because of excess acidity, several thousand lakes in Norway and Sweden contain no fish, and many more lakes there have lost most of their acid-neutralizing capacity. In the United States, several hundred lakes (mostly in the northeast) are threatened with excess acidity. In Canada, at least 7 000 lakes on the Canadian Shield were acidified by SO_2 pollution and resulting acid precipitation; following improvements in air quality, particularly since the 1990s, some lakes have recovered chemically although they may not yet have recovered all their biodiversity. Other lakes have exhausted almost all calcium and other ions that could neutralize acids, and these lakes remain vulnerable to even minor inputs of acid.

What Are the Effects of Acid Deposition on Plants and Soils? Depleting Nutrients and Damaging and Weakening Plants

Acid deposition can deplete some soil nutrients, release toxic ions into the soil, and weaken plants so they become more susceptible to other stresses.

Acid deposition (often along with other air pollutants such as ozone) can harm forests and crops, especially when the soil pH falls below 5.1. Effects of acid deposition on trees and other plants are caused partly by chemical interactions in forest and cropland soils (Figure 20-12, p. 492).

At first, sustained acid precipitation adds nitrogen and sulphur to the soils, which stimulates plant growth. But continued acid inputs can cause several problems. One is that the acids leach essential plant nutrients and calcium and magnesium salts (which can reduce acidity) from soils. This reduces plant productivity and the ability of the soils to buffer or neutralize acidic inputs.

Another problem is that calcium deficiencies in plants produced in such nutrient-depleted soils can be passed on to herbivores. For example, birds eating calcium-deficient plant material could have less calcium

for egg production, mammals could have weaker bones, and insects could have weaker exoskeletons—another example of connections and unintended consequences.

In addition, some air pollutants can harm some types of trees through *synergistic effects.* For example, studies show that no visible injury occurs to white pine seedlings when they are exposed individually to low concentrations of sulphur dioxide or ozone. However, if the seedlings are exposed to the same concentrations of both pollutants simultaneously, visible damage occurs, apparently because the two pollutants interacted synergistically.

Acid inputs can also dissolve insoluble soil compounds and release ions of metals such as aluminum, lead, cadmium, and mercury. When absorbed from soil, these ions are highly toxic to plants and animals. In addition, acid deposition can promote growth of acid-loving mosses that can kill trees. These mosses hold enough water to drown tree roots and can kill mycorrhizae fungi that help the roots absorb nutrients (Figure 8-12c, p. 170).

A major problem is that acid deposition weakens trees and other plants so they become more susceptible to other types of damage such as severe cold, diseases, insect attacks, drought, and harmful mosses. Thus acid deposition rarely kills trees directly but can weaken them and make them more susceptible to other stresses.

Mountaintop forests are the terrestrial areas hardest hit by acid deposition. These areas tend to have thin soils without much buffering capacity, and trees on mountain tops (especially conifers such as red spruce and balsam fir that keep their leaves year-round) are bathed almost continuously in very acidic fog and clouds.

Case Study: Transforming Sudbury from Black to Green

Initiated in the 1960s, the greening of the Sudbury area has been an ecological success story.

At one time, Sudbury resembled other forested areas in the Great Lakes–St. Lawrence Forest. The rolling hills were covered in a mixed forest of maples, yellow birch, red oak, trembling aspen, spruces, red pines, and hemlocks, topped by the occasional towering white pine. However, railway surveyors discovered nickel and copper deposits when the CPR line went through the area in 1883, and over time the rich mineral wealth of the Sudbury basin was exploited for commercial use.

In the early days, ore-processing methods were simple. Huge piles of wood and ore were layered on the ground in open-air roast beds. The resulting heat drove off the sulphur. Meanwhile local pockets of acidic barren ground, laden with heavy metals, were formed in areas around these roast beds (Figure 20-13).

Later, mining companies such as the International Nickel Company (Inco) and Falconbridge mined and processed the ore using large-scale industrial methods. Greater volumes of metal were smelted. Despite the use

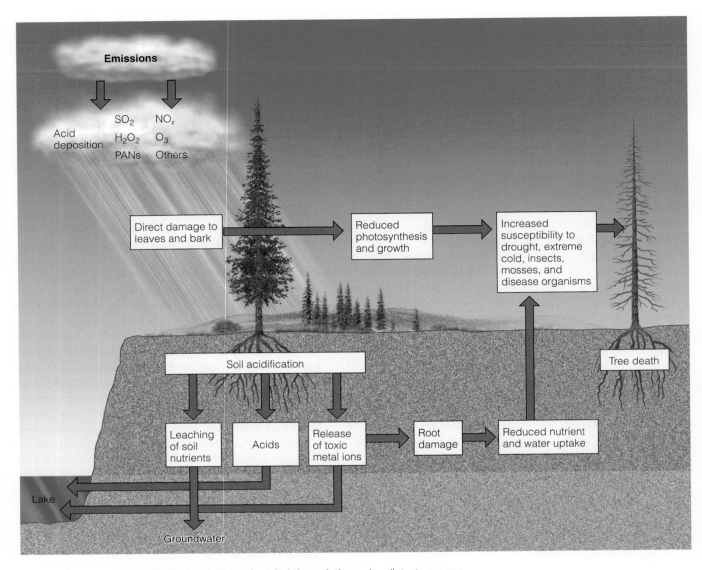

Emissions

Acid
deposition

SO_2 NO_x
H_2O_2 O_3
PANs   Others

Direct damage to
leaves and bark

Reduced
photosynthesis
and growth

Increased
susceptibility to
drought, extreme
cold, insects,
mosses, and
disease organisms

Tree death

Soil acidification

Leaching
of soil
nutrients

Acids

Release
of toxic
metal ions

Root
damage

Reduced nutrient
and water uptake

Lake

Groundwater

CENGAGENOW ACTIVE FIGURE 20-12 Natural capital degradation: air pollutants are one
of several interacting stresses that can damage, weaken, or kill trees and pollute surface and
groundwater. Further details of chemistry can be found in Appendix 3 and at http://www.nelson.com/
livingintheevironment3e.com. *See an animation based on this figure at* CengageNow.

FIGURE 20-13A The O'Donnell roast bed (1915–29) in Sudbury,
Ontario, was the world's largest open ore roasting bed.

FIGURE 20-13B Young forest encroaches on the roast bed
today, but the acidic, metal-laden soil is inhospitable to all but a
dozen vascular plants, a dozen lichens, and several mosses.

FIGURE 20-14 The chimneys of Inco and Falconbridge distributed sulphur dioxide and heavy metals to a wider area around Sudbury following the closure of the roast beds.

of chimneys, the pollution settled on the surrounding terrain (Figure 20-14). Eventually, there was an area of about 850 square kilometres (321 square miles) in which trees were reduced to stunted and scattered red maples and white birches. At the heart of this area were 150 square kilometres (85 square miles) of barren land that surrounded and extended downwind from the three smelters. On the bare hills of these lands—now industrial barrens—stumps of the former forest rested on acid-blackened rocks.

Sudbury's air quality was affected by two main factors: SO_2 and metals from local smelters (Figure 20-14), and long-distance transport of SO_2 from the United States. In terms of local influences, the construction of the 381-metre (1 250-foot) Inco superstack in 1972 immediately dispersed pollutants over a wider area and decreased the concentration near Sudbury. At the same time, Inco (now Vale Inco) was investing in technology to reduce pollution, and SO_2 emissions decreased steadily from about 1970 (Figure 20-15). This

was accomplished by means of better filters, higher-quality ore, improvements in flash smelting, and recapturing and fixing fluid bed gases. The end result was that local emissions were reduced by 90%.

Sudbury was also receiving transboundary SO_2 from the United States, as were many other parts of eastern Canada. In 1985, transboundary SO_2 accounted for about half of the SO_2 and associated acid precipitation in Canada. Wet sulphate deposition (the amount of sulphate deposited by rain and snow) at the time was as high as 40 kilograms per hectare (36 pounds per acre) in southern Ontario. The Eastern Canadian Acid Rain Program was initiated in 1985, and by 1994 Canadian sulphur dioxide emissions had been reduced by 43%. Alterations to the U.S. Clean Air Act in 1990, followed by the commencement of the 1991 Canada–U.S. Air Quality Agreement, reduced levels of SO_2 in the United States; these levels have now declined by about 50%. Wet sulphate deposition in southern Ontario is now 15 to 20 kilograms per hectare.

Sudbury's air quality, in terms of SO_2, ozone, and particulates, is now better than industrial cities like Hamilton and is comparable to other small cities in northern Ontario. Air quality is closely monitored, and Vale Inco adjusts its operations to allow for weather conditions that might prevent the rapid dispersal of pollutants (Clean Air Sudbury, 2009).

Beginning in the 1960s, scientists from Laurentian University and local government agencies began to study the acid- and metal-impacted ecosystems. Along with citizens, they tried to aid the recovery of the local industrial barrens. Initially, the combination of acidic-metallic soils with acid precipitation thwarted their progress. As air quality improved, the greening of Sudbury began to succeed. Academics, citizens' groups, government, and industry joined the cause. Some of the techniques they used included liming soils to reduce acidity, planting metal-tolerant grasses to begin succession on the black rocks, and planting millions of trees over time.

There has also been much natural succession now that conditions are less challenging to plants (Figure 20-16). Studies have shown that

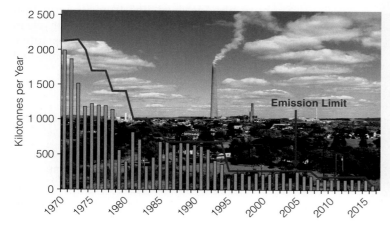

FIGURE 20-15 SO_2 emissions at Vale Inco in Sudbury have declined since 1970 and are projected to decline further. The blue line represents government-mandated emission limits. (Courtesy of Vale)

FIGURE 20-16 The young forest of red maples and white birch shows early autumn syndrome (premature colouring of the leaves) in places, an indication that the trees are still experiencing some stress.

Air Pollution **493**

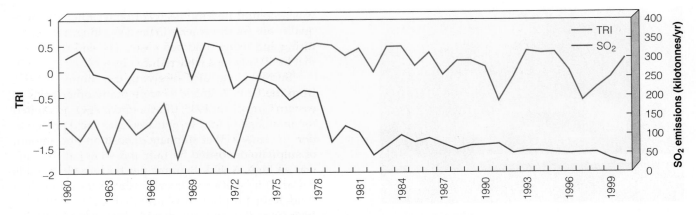

FIGURE 20-17 The relationship between SO_2 emissions and standardized tree ring indices (TRI) for white birch trees located within 1.5 kilometres of a nickel copper smelter. The decline in SO_2 around 1972 coincided with the construction of the Inco superstack, the closure of the Falconbridge scintering plant, and improved smelting technology. (Reprinted by permission of Dave Marshall and Peter Nosko)

herbaceous plants are returning, trees are more productive as reflected by tree ring growth (Figure 20-17), acid-sensitive lichens are re-invading rocky openings, and animal communities are responding to the recovering habitat (Gunn et al., 1995; Robitaille and Linley, 2005).

The water chemistry of Sudbury lakes has also been recovering, reflecting the reductions in industrial emissions of SO_2 and metals. However, there has been a delay in the re-establishment of typical aquatic biological communities; this has been influenced not only by the acid sensitivities of organisms, but also by their dispersal abilities. For example, it has been necessary to re-stock fish in certain lakes that are not connected to other water bodies, but pollution-sensitive mayflies were able to return on their own when the water chemistry became suitable. In some cases Sudbury lakes were limed, but in other cases they recovered without liming, or with indirect aid that resulted from liming nearby soil to promote the recovery of terrestrial plant communities (Pearson et al., 2002; Keller et al., 2004).

Good news: the aurora trout (*Salvelinus fontinalis timagamiensis*), a subspecies of brook trout, was saved from extinction by the actions of MNR personnel (Figure 20-18). Aurora trout existed in only two lakes north of Sudbury: Whitepine Lake and Whirligig Lake. When those lakes were threatened by declining acidity in the late 1950s, some aurora trout were collected and sheltered at the Hills Lake Fish Culture Station near Englehart. In the 1990s, after some precautionary liming, the fish were returned to their original lakes and to 10 other lakes. Aurora trout are still considered endangered but there is a recovery plan and the fish are reproducing in the wild at several lakes (http://www.sararegistry.gc.ca/).

Sudbury has "greened up" from its industrial past to become a city that enjoys fresh air, clean water, recovering successional forest, and cooperative people with experience at overcoming environmental problems.

What Can Be Done to Reduce Acid Deposition? Plenty, but There Can Be Complications

A number of prevention and control methods can reduce acid deposition, but implementing these solutions can be difficult.

Figure 20-19 summarizes ways to reduce acid deposition. According to most scientists studying the problem, the best solutions are *prevention approaches* that reduce or eliminate emissions of SO_2, NO_x, and particulates, as discussed in Section 20-6.

Photo by Ed Snucins.

FIGURE 20-18 Aurora trout were nearly driven to extinction by SO_2 pollution and acid precipitation. MNR personnel sheltered some of these trout at a fish hatchery until the acidity of their lakes recovered through natural processes and liming. Aurora trout have now been restored to a dozen lakes in the wild.

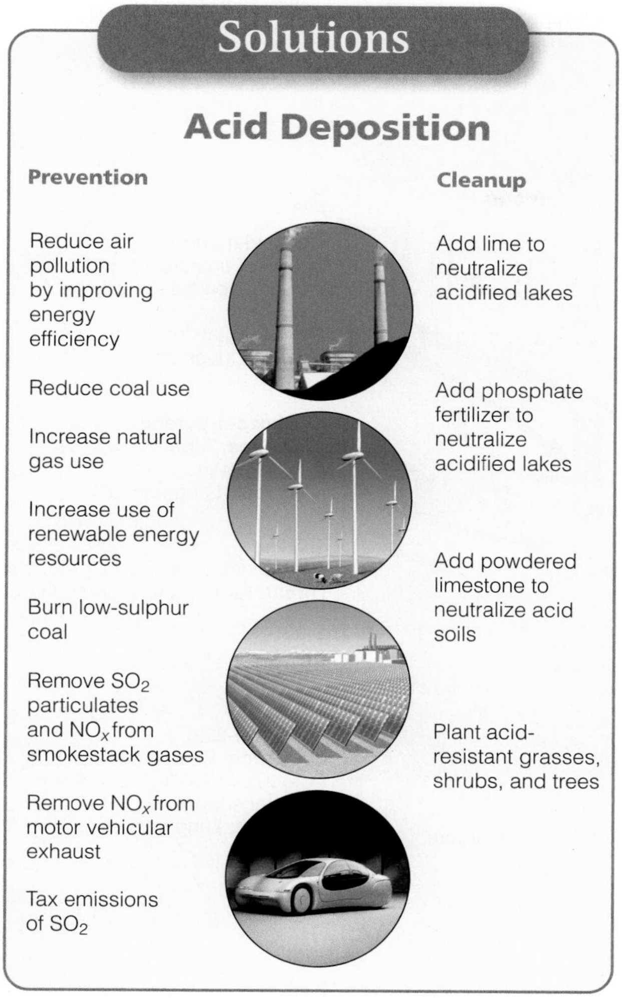

Solutions

Acid Deposition

Prevention		Cleanup
Reduce air pollution by improving energy efficiency		Add lime to neutralize acidified lakes
Reduce coal use		Add phosphate fertilizer to neutralize acidified lakes
Increase natural gas use		
Increase use of renewable energy resources		
Burn low-sulphur coal		Add powdered limestone to neutralize acid soils
Remove SO_2 particulates and NO_x from smokestack gases		
Remove NO_x from motor vehicular exhaust		Plant acid-resistant grasses, shrubs, and trees
Tax emissions of SO_2		

FIGURE 20-19 Solutions: methods for reducing acid deposition and its damage.

To help reduce SO_2 emissions and thus acid deposition, some coal-burning power plants increased their use of low-sulphur lignite coal (Figure 17-23, p. 401). However, because low-sulphur lignite coal has a low heating value, more coal must be burned to generate the same amount of electricity. This increases air pollution by emitting more CO_2, toxic mercury, and radioactive particles into the troposphere—connections again.

Controlling acid deposition can be a political hot potato. One problem is that the people and ecosystems it affects often are quite distant from those that cause the problem. Also, countries with large supplies of coal (such as China, India, Russia, and the United States) have a strong incentive to use it as a major energy resource. And owners of coal-burning power plants say the costs of adding pollution control equipment, using low-sulphur coal, or removing sulphur from coal are too high and would increase the cost of electricity for consumers.

Environmentalists respond that affordable and much cleaner ways are available to produce electricity—including wind turbines and burning natural gas in turbines. They also point out that the largely hidden health and environmental costs of burning coal are roughly twice its market cost. They urge inclusion of these costs in the price of producing electricity from coal. Then consumers would have more realistic knowledge about the harmful effects of burning coal.

Large amounts of limestone or lime can be used to neutralize acidified lakes or surrounding soil. But there are several problems with liming. One is that it is an expensive and temporary remedy that usually must be repeated annually. Also, it can kill some types of plankton and aquatic plants and can harm wetland plants that need acidic water. Finally, it is difficult to know how much lime to put where (in the water or at selected places on the ground).

Researchers in England have discovered that adding a small amount of phosphate fertilizer can neutralize excess acidity in a lake. The effectiveness of this approach is being evaluated.

20-5 INDOOR AIR POLLUTION

How Serious Is Indoor Air Pollution? Being Indoors Can Be Hazardous to Your Health

Indoor air pollution usually is a much greater threat to human health than outdoor air pollution.

If you are reading this book indoors, you may be inhaling more air pollutants with each breath than if you were outside. Figure 20-20 shows some typical sources of indoor air pollution. Which are you exposed to?

Studies have revealed some alarming facts about indoor air pollution. *First,* levels of 11 common pollutants generally are 2–5 times higher inside homes and commercial buildings than outdoors and as much as 100 times higher in some cases. *Second,* pollution levels inside cars in traffic-clogged urban areas can be up to 18 times higher than outside. *Third,* the health risks from exposure to such chemicals are magnified because people typically spend 70–98% of their time indoors or inside vehicles.

As a result of these studies, indoor air pollution is near the top of the list of sources of cancer risks—causing as many as 6 000 premature cancer deaths per year in North America. At greatest risk are smokers, infants and children under age 5, the old, the sick, pregnant women, people with respiratory or heart problems, and factory workers.

Studies have linked various air pollutants found in buildings to dizziness, headaches, coughing, sneezing, shortness of breath, nausea, burning eyes,

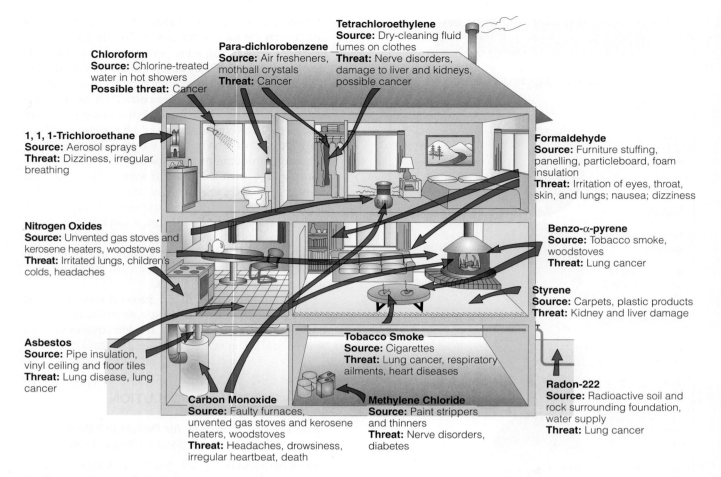

Chloroform
Source: Chlorine-treated water in hot showers
Possible threat: Cancer

Para-dichlorobenzene
Source: Air fresheners, mothball crystals
Threat: Cancer

Tetrachloroethylene
Source: Dry-cleaning fluid fumes on clothes
Threat: Nerve disorders, damage to liver and kidneys, possible cancer

1, 1, 1-Trichloroethane
Source: Aerosol sprays
Threat: Dizziness, irregular breathing

Formaldehyde
Source: Furniture stuffing, panelling, particleboard, foam insulation
Threat: Irritation of eyes, throat, skin, and lungs; nausea; dizziness

Nitrogen Oxides
Source: Unvented gas stoves and kerosene heaters, woodstoves
Threat: Irritated lungs, children's colds, headaches

Benzo-α-pyrene
Source: Tobacco smoke, woodstoves
Threat: Lung cancer

Styrene
Source: Carpets, plastic products
Threat: Kidney and liver damage

Asbestos
Source: Pipe insulation, vinyl ceiling and floor tiles
Threat: Lung disease, lung cancer

Tobacco Smoke
Source: Cigarettes
Threat: Lung cancer, respiratory ailments, heart diseases

Radon-222
Source: Radioactive soil and rock surrounding foundation, water supply
Threat: Lung cancer

Carbon Monoxide
Source: Faulty furnaces, unvented gas stoves and kerosene heaters, woodstoves
Threat: Headaches, drowsiness, irregular heartbeat, death

Methylene Chloride
Source: Paint strippers and thinners
Threat: Nerve disorders, diabetes

FIGURE 20-20 Some important indoor air pollutants. (Data from U.S. Environmental Protection Agency)

chronic fatigue, irritability, skin dryness and irritation, and flu-like symptoms, known as the *sick-building syndrome*. New buildings are more commonly "sick" than old ones because of reduced air exchange (to save energy) and chemicals released from new carpeting and furniture. EPA studies indicate that almost one in five of the 4 million commercial buildings in the United States are considered "sick" (including EPA headquarters).

According to public health officials, the four most dangerous indoor air pollutants in developed countries are *cigarette smoke, formaldehyde, radioactive radon-222 gas,* and *very small fine and ultrafine particles. Good news.* In recent years, a growing number of cities in Canada and other developed nations have elected to ban indoor smoking in facilities used by the public.

In developing countries, the indoor burning of wood, charcoal, dung, crop residues, and coal in open fires or in unvented or poorly vented stoves for cooking and heating exposes inhabitants to high levels of particulate air pollution. According to the World Bank, as many as 2.8 million people (most of them

women and children) in developing countries die prematurely each year from breathing elevated levels of such indoor smoke. *Thus indoor air pollution for the poor is by far the world's most serious air pollution problem—a glaring example of the relationship between poverty and environmental quality.*

Are You Exposed to Formaldehyde? A Serious Problem

Formaldehyde, found in a variety of common materials and household products, can cause a number of health problems.

The chemical that causes most people in developed countries difficulty is *formaldehyde,* a colourless, extremely irritating gas widely used to manufacture common household materials. About 40 million North Americans suffer from chronic breathing problems, dizziness, rash, headaches, sore throat, sinus and eye irritation, wheezing, and nausea caused by daily exposure to low levels of formaldehyde emitted from common household materials. Are you one of these people?

There are many sources of formaldehyde. They include building materials (such as plywood, particleboard, panelling, and high-gloss wood used in floors and cabinets), furniture, drapes, upholstery, adhesives in carpeting and wallpaper, urethane-formaldehyde insulation, fingernail hardener, and wrinkle-free coating on permanent-press clothing (Figure 20-20). The EPA estimates that as many as 1 of every 5 000 people who live in manufactured homes for more than 10 years will develop cancer from formaldehyde exposure.

Case Study: Are You Being Exposed to Radioactive Radon Gas? Test the Air in Your House

Radon-222, a radioactive gas found in some soil and rocks, can seep into some houses and increase the risk of lung cancer.

Radon-222—a naturally occurring radioactive gas that you cannot see, taste, or smell—is produced by the radioactive decay of uranium-238. Most soil and rock contain small amounts of uranium-238. But this isotope is much more concentrated in underground deposits of minerals such as uranium, phosphate, granite, and shale.

When radon gas from such deposits seeps upward through the soil and is released outdoors, it disperses quickly in the atmosphere and decays to harmless levels. However, in buildings above such deposits radon gas can enter through cracks in foundations and walls, openings around sump pumps and drains, and hollow concrete blocks (Figure 20-21). It tends to be pulled into a house because of the slightly lower atmospheric pressure inside most homes. Once inside it can build up to high levels, especially in unventilated lower levels of homes and buildings.

Radon-222 gas quickly decays into solid particles of other radioactive elements such as polonium-210 that if inhaled expose lung tissue to a large amount of ionizing radiation from alpha particles. According to the National Academy of Sciences and the EPA, prolonged exposure for a lifetime of 70 years to low levels of radon or radon acting together with smoking is responsible about 10% (14 000) of the approximately 140 000 lung cancer deaths each year in North

America. This makes radon the second leading cause of lung cancer after smoking. Most of the deaths are among smokers or former smokers. Each year non-smokers account for about 2 100–2 900 deaths from lung cancer.

Scientists make two assumptions in estimating risks from radon. One is that there is no safe threshold dose for radon exposure. The other is that the incidence of lung cancer in uranium miners exposed to high levels of radon in mines can be extrapolated to estimate lung cancer deaths for people in homes exposed to much lower levels of radon. Some scientists question the validity of these assumptions.

Because radon hot spots can occur almost anywhere, we do not know which buildings have unsafe levels of radon without conducting tests. Ideally, radon levels should be monitored continuously in the main living areas (not basements or crawl spaces) for 2 months to a year. Have you tested your home for radon? Remedies include sealing cracks in the foundation and walls, increasing ventilation by opening a window or installing vents, and using a fan to create cross ventilation.

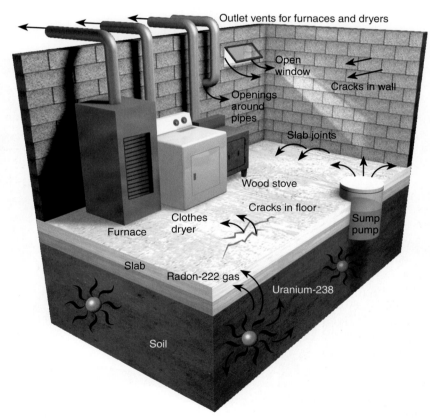

FIGURE 20-21 Sources and paths of entry for indoor radon-222 gas. (Data from U.S. Environmental Protection Agency)

20-6 EFFECTS OF AIR POLLUTION ON LIVING ORGANISMS AND MATERIALS

How Does Your Respiratory System Help Protect You from Air Pollution? Your Air Pollution Security System

Your respiratory system has several ways to help protect you from air pollution, but some air pollutants can overcome these defences.

Your respiratory system (Figure 20-22) has a number of mechanisms that help protect you from much air pollution. Hairs in your nose filter out large particles. Sticky mucus in the lining of your upper respiratory tract captures smaller (but not the smallest) particles and dissolves some gaseous pollutants. Sneezing and coughing expel contaminated air and mucus when pollutants irritate your respiratory system.

In addition, hundreds of thousands of tiny mucus-coated hairlike structures called *cilia* line your upper respiratory tract. They continually wave back and forth and transport mucus and the pollutants they trap to your throat (where they are swallowed or expelled).

But prolonged or acute exposure to air pollutants including tobacco smoke can overload or break down these natural defences. This can cause or contribute to various respiratory diseases. One that can start early in life is *asthma*, typically an allergic reaction causing muscle spasms in the bronchial walls and acute shortness of breath. According to the director-general of the World Health Organization, asthma is on the rise everywhere in the world. In rapidly developing China, the prevalence of asthma among urban children increased 64% between 1990 and 2000, and another 40% between 2001 and 2006. Prevalence of childhood asthma was more than twice as high in heavily polluted cities compared to less polluted cities (Watts, 2006; WHO 2008).

Years of smoking and breathing air pollutants can lead to other respiratory disorders including *lung cancer* and *chronic bronchitis*, which involves persistent inflammation and damage to the cells lining the bronchi and bronchioles. The results are mucus buildup; loud, painful coughing; and shortness of breath. Damage deeper in the lung can cause *emphysema*, which is irreversible damage to air sacs or alveoli leading to loss of lung elasticity and acute shortness of breath (Figure 20-23, p. 499).

People with respiratory diseases are especially vulnerable to air pollution, as are older adults, infants, pregnant women, and people with heart disease.

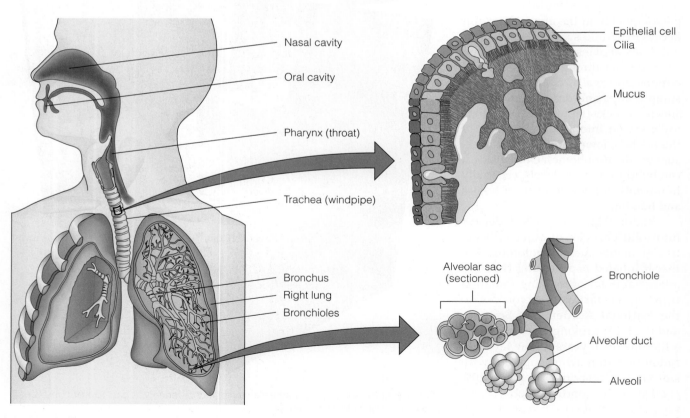

FIGURE 20-22 Major components of the human respiratory system.

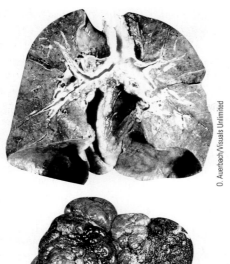

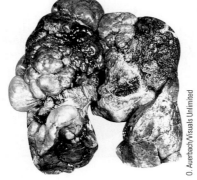

O. Auerbach/Visuals Unlimited

O. Auerbach/Visuals Unlimited

FIGURE 20-23 Normal human lungs (top) and the lungs of a person who died of emphysema (bottom).

How Many People Die Prematurely from Air Pollution? A Major Killer

Each year air pollution prematurely kills about 2.4 million people, mostly from indoor air pollution in developing countries.

Refer to Table 20-2 for some of the harmful health effects of prolonged or chronic exposure to six major air pollutants. According to the World Health Organization, worldwide at least 2.4 million people (most of them in Asia) die prematurely each year from the effects of air pollution—an average of 6 580 deaths per day. About 1.6 million of these deaths (66%) are from *indoor* air pollution, mostly from burning wood or coal inside dwellings in developing countries. *This explains why the World Health Organization and the World Bank consider indoor air pollution one of the world's most serious environmental problems.*

Case Study: Should We Use the Marketplace to Reduce Pollution? Emissions Trading

Allowing producers of air pollutants to buy and sell government air pollution allotments in the marketplace is a controversial emissions-reduction strategy.

To help reduce SO_2 emissions, the U.S. Clean Air Act of 1990 allows an *emissions trading policy*, which enables the 110 most polluting power plants in 21 states (primarily in the Midwest and East) to buy and sell SO_2 pollution rights.

This process begins with each of the coal-burning plants measuring the sulphur dioxide emitted from their smokestacks. Each year, a coal-burning power plant is given a certain number of pollution credits, or rights to emit a certain amount of SO_2. A utility that emits less SO_2 than its limit has a surplus of pollution credits. It can use these credits to avoid reductions in SO_2 emissions at another of its plants, keep them for future plant expansions, or sell them to other utilities, private citizens, or environmental groups.

Proponents argue that this system allows the marketplace to determine the cheapest, most efficient way to get the job done instead of having the government dictate how to control air pollution. Some environmentalists see this *cap-and-trade* market approach as an improvement over the regulatory *command-and-control* approach, as long as it achieves a net reduction in SO_2 pollution. This would be accomplished by limiting the total number of credits and gradually lowering the *emissions cap* or annual number of credits, as has been done since 2000.

One of the interesting things about the SO_2 emissions market is that anyone can participate. Environmental groups can buy up such rights to pollute and not use them. You could personally reduce air pollution by buying a certificate allowing you to add 0.9 metric ton of SO_2 to the atmosphere and hanging it on the wall. You can purchase these certificates and give them away as birthday or holiday gifts. See http://www.epa.gov/airmarkets/ for a list of brokers and other sellers of SO_2 permits.

Some environmentalists criticize the cap-and-trade program. They contend that it allows utilities with older, dirtier power plants to buy their way out and keep on emitting unacceptable levels of SO_2. This could lead (as it has) to continuing high levels of air pollution in certain areas or "hot spots."

This approach also creates incentives to cheat because air quality regulation is based largely on self-reporting of emissions. To help keep the system honest, the environmentalists call for unannounced spot monitoring by the government and high fines for cheaters.

In addition, the success of any emissions trading approach depends on how low the initial cap is set and then on how much it is reduced annually to promote continuing innovation in air pollution prevention and control. Without these elements, these critics say that emissions trading programs mostly move air pollutants from one area to another without achieving an overall reduction in air quality.

Good news. Between 1990 and 2006, the emissions trading system helped reduce SO_2 emissions from electric power plants in the United States by 53%. And the cost of doing this was less than one-tenth the cost projected by industry because this market-based system motivated companies to reduce emissions in more efficient ways.

The EPA has also created an emissions trading program for smog-forming nitrogen oxides (NO_x) in a number of states in the East and Midwest. Emissions trading may also be implemented for particulate emissions and volatile organic compounds (VOCs) and for the combined emissions of SO_2, NO_x, and mercury from coal-burning power plants.

Bad news. In 2002, the EPA reported results from evaluation of the country's oldest and largest emissions trading program, in effect since 1993 in southern California. The **EPA** study found that this cap-and-trade model "produced far less emissions reductions than were either projected for the program or could have been expected from" the command-and-control system it replaced. The study also found accounting abuses, including emissions caps set 60% higher than current emissions levels. Cap-and-trade programs need to be carefully monitored.

CONSIDER, DISCUSS, OR DEBATE

Do you agree with the idea of emissions trading programs? What do you consider to be the strengths and weaknesses of this approach?

How Can We Reduce Outdoor Air Pollution from Coal-Burning Facilities? Prevention Is Best

There are a number of ways to prevent and control air pollution from coal-burning facilities.

Figure 20-24 summarizes ways to reduce emissions of sulphur oxides, nitrogen oxides, and particulate matter from stationary sources such as electric power plants and industrial plants that burn coal.

Good news. Between 1980 and 2008, emissions of SO_2 from electric power plants decreased by 59%, emissions of NO_x emissions by 35%, and soot emissions by 31%. Emphasis has been on output approaches that add equipment to remove some of the particulate, NO_x, and SO_2 pollutants after they are produced (Figure 20-25). Pollution can also be reduced at the input stage by using cleaner coal technologies. One is *fluidized-bed combustion,* which reduces pollutant emissions and burns coal more efficiently by blowing a stream of hot air into a boiler to burn a mixture of powdered coal and crushed limestone. Another is *coal gasification,* which has a mixture of advantages and disadvantages (Figure 17-25, p. 402). Environmentalists argue for much greater emphasis on prevention approaches to decrease the levels of these pollutants reaching the troposphere.

How Can We Reduce Outdoor Air Pollution from Motor Vehicles? Emphasize Prevention

There are a number of ways to prevent and control air pollution from motor vehicles.

Figure 20-26 (p. 502) lists ways to reduce emissions from motor vehicles, the primary culprits in producing

Solutions

Stationary Source Air Pollution

Prevention	Dispersion or Cleanup
Burn low-sulphur coal	Disperse emissions above thermal inversion layer with tall smokestacks
Remove sulphur from coal	
Convert coal to a liquid or gaseous fuel	Remove pollutants after combustion
Shift to less polluting fuels	Tax each unit of pollution produced

FIGURE 20-24 Solutions: methods for reducing emissions of sulphur oxides, nitrogen oxides, and particulate matter from stationary sources such as coal-burning electric power plants and industrial plants.

photochemical smog. One way to make significant reductions is to get older, high-polluting vehicles off the road. According to EPA estimates, 10% of the vehicles on the road in the United States emit 50–70% of vehicular air pollutants. But people who cannot afford to buy a newer car often own old cars. One suggestion is to pay people to take their old cars off the road, which would result in huge savings in health and air pollution control costs.

In 2003, a team of research engineers working with grants from the National Science Foundation and an oil company found a way for oil refineries, power plants, and vehicles to use a class of chemicals called *zeolites* to do a better job than other alternatives in removing sulphur impurities from diesel fuel, jet fuel, and gasoline. This *adsorption process,* which is carried out at room temperature and pressure, should be cheaper, easier, and more effective than using expensive catalytic converters that operate at high temperatures and pressures to remove sulphur. Stay tuned to see if this technology works as projected and is implemented.

Good news. Over the next 10–20 years, North American air pollution stemming from motor vehicles should decrease because of improved engine and emission systems, *hybrid-electric vehicles,* and vehicles powered by fuel cells running on hydrogen (Figures 18-7, p. 423, and 18-8, p. 424).

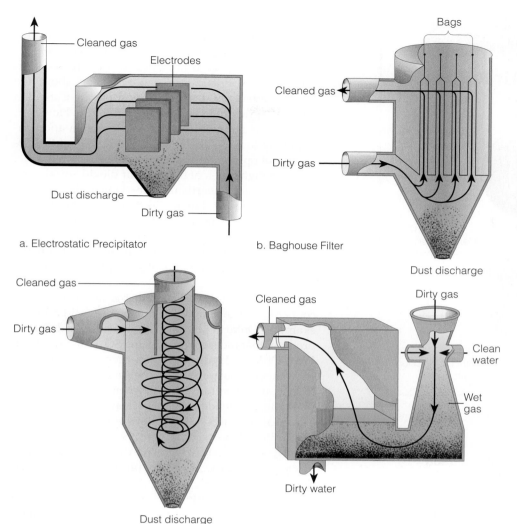

a. Electrostatic Precipitator

b. Baghouse Filter

c. Cyclone Separator

d. Wet Scrubber

FIGURE 20-25 Solutions: four commonly used output or control methods for removing particulates (a, b, c, d) and SO_2 (d) from the exhaust gases of electric power and industrial plants. Of these, only baghouse filters remove many of the more hazardous fine particles. All these methods produce hazardous materials that must be disposed of safely, and except for cyclone separators, all of them are expensive. Modern wet scrubbers remove 98% of the SO_2 and 98% of the particulate matter in smokestack emissions, but they are expensive to install and maintain.

Bad news. The growing numbers of motor vehicles in urban areas of many developing countries are contributing to the already poor air quality there. Many of these vehicles are 10 or more years old, have no pollution control devices, and continue to burn leaded gasoline.

What Should We Do About Ultrafine Particles? Another Controversy

There is controversy over reducing emissions of ultrafine particles that pose a serious threat to human health.

Research indicates that invisible particles—especially *fine particles* with diameters less than 10 microns (PM-10) and *ultrafine particles* with diameters less than 2.5 microns (PM-2.5)—pose a significant health hazard. Such particles come from a variety of sources (Figure 20-8, p. 486).

They are not effectively captured by most air pollution control equipment and are small enough to penetrate the respiratory system's natural defences against air pollution. They can also bring with them droplets or other particles of toxic or cancer-causing pollutants that become attached to their surfaces.

Once they are lodged deep within the lungs, these fine particles can cause chronic irritation that can trigger asthma attacks, aggravate other lung diseases, and cause lung cancer. These lung problems interfere with the blood's uptake of oxygen and release of CO_2, which strains the heart and increases the risk of death from heart disease. According to several recent studies of air pollution in cities, fine and ultrafine particles prematurely kill at least 70 000 North Americans each year.

Exposure to particulate air pollution is much worse in most developing countries, where urban air quality has generally deteriorated. The World Bank estimates that reducing particulate levels globally to WHO guidelines would prevent 300 000–700 000 premature deaths per year!

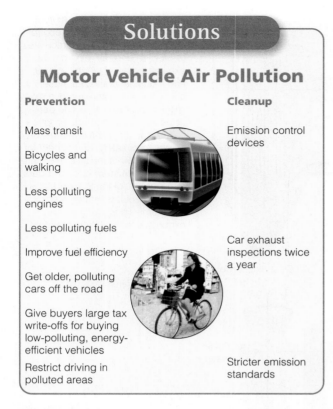

Solutions

Motor Vehicle Air Pollution

Prevention	Cleanup

Prevention

Mass transit

Bicycles and walking

Less polluting engines

Less polluting fuels

Improve fuel efficiency

Get older, polluting cars off the road

Give buyers large tax write-offs for buying low-polluting, energy-efficient vehicles

Restrict driving in polluted areas

Cleanup

Emission control devices

Car exhaust inspections twice a year

Stricter emission standards

FIGURE 20-26 Solutions: methods for reducing emissions from motor vehicles.

Case Study: Transboundary Air Pollution

Acid deposition in the 1980s.

In the mid- to late 1980s, acid deposition was a serious problem in Canada. Recently acidified lakes and dying forests numbered in the thousands, and it was clear that 50% of the sulphur dioxide responsible for the acid deposition originated in the United States.

Prime Minister Brain Mulroney expressed concerns to U.S. President Ronald Reagan about the adverse effects of acid deposition on the Canadian forestry, agriculture, and fishing industries. However, Reagan did not see acid rain as a problem and consequently took no action to reduce it. Part of the difference of opinion might have stemmed from the fact that although much of the sulphur dioxide originated in the industrial heartland of the United States, there were few signs of damage in that region because its well-developed soils and eutrophic lakes were better able to buffer the effects of acidity. A much greater effect was seen when acid deposition fell on the thin unbuffered soils and oligotrophic lakes of the Canadian Shield.

Beginning in 1985, and in the absence of U.S. cooperation, Canada took action against acid rain. For example, Ontario launched *Countdown Acid Rain*, a program that focused on reducing SO_2 emissions from Inco, Ontario Hydro, Algoma Steel, Falconbridge, and other primary emitters. The Americans joined the fight against acid rain in 1990, when President George H. W. Bush amended the U.S. Clean Air Act to lower U.S. emissions of SO_2. The following year, Canada and the United States signed the 1991 Canada–U.S. Air Quality Agreement, which coordinated the attempts of the two countries to deal with transboundary acid deposition.

Although considerable progress has been made (Figure 20-27), researchers such as Shaun Watmough

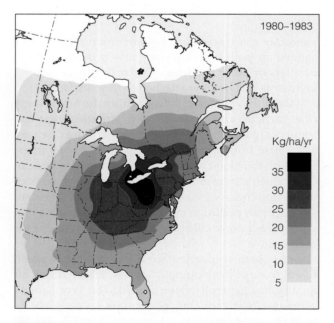

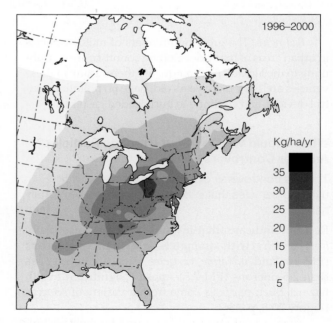

FIGURE 20-27 Wet sulphate deposition (kilograms/hectare/year) declined considerably from the early 1980s (left) to the late 1990s (right). (Canadian National Atmospheric Chemistry Database, Meteorological Service of Canada, and Environment Canada)

of Trent University have warned that we must do more to avoid future problems when northern soils exhaust their limited abilities to buffer acid deposition.

Back to the Future

Today, as in the past, Canada receives a significant portion of its air pollutants from the United States. Studies by Ontario's Ministry of the Environment (MOE) found that the U.S. contribution to ozone during widespread smog episodes can be as high as 90% in Canadian cities and towns close to the U.S. border (Figure 20-28). Nearby U.S. states release approximately 28 times as much particulate matter as Ontario does. The United States is still producing about 90% of the SO_2 and the NO_x emissions involved in transboundary air pollution.

Air pollution has a high cost in terms of health and environmental damages. According to the MOE studies, Ontario incurs about $9.6 billion in damages each year (70% health and 39% environmental damages). Approximately $5.3 billion (55%) of this amount is attributable to the effects of U.S. transboundary pollution. Furthermore, smog and other pollutants result in premature mortality. In Ontario, about 56% of the premature deaths resulting from pollution—or 2 750 deaths—are related to transboundary pollution from the United States.

Governments on both sides of the border are establishing pollution reduction programs based on increased regulations, emission control programs, clean energy incentives, and public education. Discussions between Canada and the United States on the subject of transboundary air pollutants are ongoing. As they continue to find and implement solutions, both countries recognize that much remains to be done.

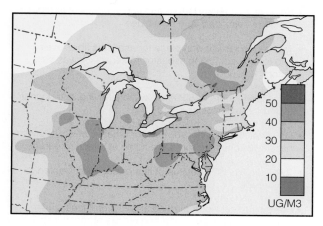

FIGURE 20-28 The concentration of fine particulate matter during the smog event of June 22–26, 2003. Hot sunny conditions with light southerly winds brought hot muggy polluted air into Canada. This air expanded across Ontario and Quebec and persisted until a cold front and rain cooled and cleaned the air. (Ministry of the Environment 2005, http://www.ene.gov.on.ca/envision/techdocs/5158e.pdf)

How Can We Reduce Indoor Air Pollution? Emphasize Prevention

Little effort has been spent on reducing indoor air pollution even though it is a much greater threat to human health than outdoor air pollution.

Reducing indoor air pollution does not require setting indoor air quality standards and monitoring millions of homes and buildings. Instead, air pollution experts suggest several ways to prevent or reduce indoor air pollution (Figure 20-29). Another possibility for cleaner indoor air in some high-rise buildings is rooftop greenhouses through which building air can be circulated.

In developing countries, indoor air pollution from open fires and leaky and inefficient stoves that burn wood, charcoal, or coal could be reduced if governments gave people inexpensive clay or metal stoves, which burn biofuels more efficiently while venting their exhaust to the outside, or stoves that

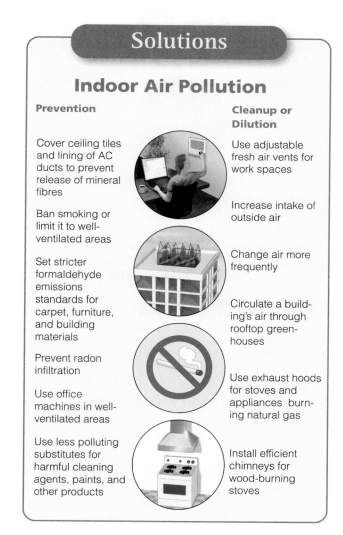

FIGURE 20-29 Solutions: ways to prevent and reduce indoor air pollution.

Air Pollution **503**

Outdoor

Improve energy efficiency to reduce fossil fuel use

Indoor

Reduce poverty

Rely more on lower-polluting natural gas

Distribute cheap and efficient cookstoves to poor families in developing countries

Rely more on renewable energy (especially solar cells, wind, and solar-produced hydrogen)

Reduce or ban indoor smoking

Transfer technologies for latest energy efficiency, renewable energy, and pollution prevention to developing countries

Develop simple and cheap tests for indoor pollutants such as particulates, radon, and formaldehyde

FIGURE 20-30 Solutions: ways to prevent outdoor and indoor air pollution over the next 30–40 years.

use solar energy to cook food (solar cookers) in sunny areas. Doing this would also reduce deforestation by using less fuelwood and charcoal (Figure 20–30).

CONSIDER, DISCUSS, OR DEBATE

What specific actions should the federal and provincial governments take to deal with the problem of transboundary air pollutants? How do you think U.S. officials would respond to your proposals?

What Is the Next Step? Individuals Matter

We need to focus on preventing air pollution, with emphasis on sharply reducing indoor air pollution in developing countries.

It is encouraging that since 1970 most of the world's developed countries have enacted laws and regulations that have significantly reduced outdoor air pollution. But without individuals and organized groups putting strong political pressure on elected officials in the 1970s and 1980s these laws and regulations would not have been enacted,

funded, and implemented. In turn, these legal requirements spurred companies, scientists, and engineers to come up with better ways to control outdoor pollution.

The current laws are a useful *output approach* to controlling pollution. To environmentalists, however, the next step is to shift to *preventing air pollution*. With this approach, the question is not "What can we do about the air pollutants we produce?" but "How can we avoid producing such pollutants in the first place?"

Figure 20-30 shows ways to prevent outdoor and indoor air pollution over the next 30–40 years. Like the shift to controlling outdoor air pollution between 1970 and 2000, this new shift to preventing outdoor and indoor air pollution will not take place without political pressure on elected officials by individual citizens and groups. Figure 20-31 lists some ways that you can reduce your exposure to indoor air pollution.

Turning the corner on air pollution requires moving beyond patchwork, end-of-pipe approaches to confront pollution at its sources. This will mean reorienting energy, transportation, and industrial structures toward prevention.

HILARY F. FRENCH

What Can You Do?

Indoor Air Pollution

- Test for radon and formaldehyde inside your home and take corrective measures as needed.

- Do not buy furniture and other products containing formaldehyde.

- Remove your shoes before entering your house to reduce inputs of dust, lead, and pesticides.

- Test your house or workplace for asbestos fibre levels and for any crumbling asbestos materials if it was built before 1980.

- Don't live in a pre-1980 house without having its indoor air tested for asbestos and lead.

- Do not store gasoline, solvents, or other volatile hazardous chemicals inside a home or attached garage.

- If you smoke, do it outside or in a closed room vented to the outside.

- Make sure that wood-burning stoves, fireplaces, and kerosene- and gas-burning heaters are properly installed, vented, and maintained.

- Install carbon monoxide detectors in all sleeping areas.

FIGURE 20-31 What can you do? Ways to reduce your exposure to air pollution.

CHAPTER REVIEW

1. Review the Key Questions for this chapter on p. 477. What are lichens? Why are they useful as indicators of pollution? Under what circumstances might a living indicator be a better means of assessing air pollution than taking a measurement of an air sample?

2. Define *density, atmospheric pressure, troposphere, stratosphere,* and *ozone layer*. Describe how the troposphere and stratosphere differ.

3. What is *air pollution*? Summarize the history of air pollution. Distinguish between *primary pollutants* and *secondary pollutants* and give an example of each. List the major outdoor air pollutants and their harmful effects.

4. Describe a chemical method and a biological method for detecting air pollutants. Describe the effects of ultrafine particles as pollutants, and how we can reduce our exposure to them.

5. Distinguish between *industrial smog* and *photochemical smog* in terms of their chemical composition and formation. List and briefly describe five factors that can reduce outdoor air pollution and six factors that can worsen it. What is a *temperature inversion* and how can it affect air pollution levels?

6. What is *acid deposition* and how does it form? Briefly describe its major environmental impacts on vegetation, lakes, human-built structures, and human health. List three major ways to reduce acid deposition.

7. What are the top four indoor air pollutants in countries like Canada and the United States? What is the major indoor air pollutant in many developing countries? Describe indoor air pollution associated with radon-222; how can radon-222 be detected and dealt with?

8. Briefly describe the human body's defences against air pollution, how they can be overwhelmed, and illnesses that can result. How many people die prematurely from air pollution each year?

9. Describe the issue of transboundary air pollution between Canada and the United States. Is this a serious problem? Does the international aspect of this problem make it harder or easier to solve?

10. Describe the difficulties you can foresee in terms of solving future international and global air pollution problems. Draw upon your knowledge of Canada–U.S. transboundary air pollution (p. 502) and the expanding Asiatic brown cloud (p. 487) in forming your conclusions.

CRITICAL THINKING

1. Explain why you agree or disagree with the following statement: "Because we have not proved absolutely that anyone has died or suffered serious disease from nitrogen oxides, current federal emission standards for this pollutant should be relaxed."

2. Identify climate and topographic factors in your local community that **(a)** intensify air pollution and **(b)** help reduce air pollution.

3. Should all tall smokestacks be banned? Explain.

4. Explain how sulphur in coal can increase the acidity of rainwater.

5. Explain why you agree or disagree with each of the proposals listed in Figure 20-30, p. 504 for shifting the emphasis to preventing air pollution over the next several decades. Which two of these proposals do you believe are the most important?

6. Congratulations! You are in charge of reducing air pollution in Canada. List the three most important features of your policy for **(a)** outdoor air pollution and **(b)** indoor air pollution.

PROJECTS

1. Evaluate your exposure to some or all of the indoor air pollutants in Figure 20-20 (p. 496) in your school, workplace, and home. Come up with a plan for reducing your exposure to these pollutants.

2. Have buildings at your school been tested for radon? If so, what were the results? What has been done about areas with unacceptable levels? If this testing has not been done, talk with school officials about having it done.

3. Use the library or the Internet to find bibliographic information about *Michael J. Cohen* and *Hilary F. French,* whose quotes appear at the beginning and end of this chapter.

21 Climate Change and Ozone Loss

Climate
Control

CASE STUDY — Heating Up the Arctic

The Arctic was historically a remote and pristine ecosystem where snow and ice set the stage for a fantastically adapted flora and fauna, and for the hardy Inuit people who used snow and ice for their homes, transportation, and sustenance. In recent decades, chemicals from the industrial world reached the Arctic and were biomagnified through the fatty food chains there (Chapters 20 and 22). Now the Arctic is warming, with potentially massive consequences for this polar ecosystem and for the rest of the world.

In 2003, the Study of Environmental Arctic Change (SEARCH) brought together 400 Arctic scientists to compare their findings. Since then, ArcticNet, a Canadian group comprising more than 100 researchers, has been studying all aspects of change in the Arctic. So far, the scientists have agreed on the following points. The Arctic has already warmed by 2–3°C over the past century. The sea ice is measurably thinner and has decreased in extent. Scientists are predicting a rise in mean temperature of as much as 5–7°C over the next 100 years.

The traditional ecological knowledge (TEK) of the Inuit people supports these findings. They report that the sea ice has become much less predictable. This is crucial to their way of life since the thickness of ice and the timing of ice cover are key factors in terms of safe transportation and successful hunting. Unusual things are happening more often: people are falling through thin ice and having trouble crossing streams of fast-moving meltwater.

Other negatives lie ahead. If the permafrost melts underfoot, it will cause landslides and erosion, and create problems for transportation and infrastructure. If the wildlife has trouble adapting to changes, it will impact Arctic ecosystems and

directly affect those Inuit who depend on hunting. Studies show that polar bears are losing weight and having to swim greater distances to hunt seals on pack ice (Figure 21-1A). Herbivores such as caribou and musk oxen are being subjected to unusual weather conditions such as freezing rain, which can form a layer of ice over their food.

A potentially positive consequence for Arctic people is that the Northwest Passage could be open for ships. The continental shelf would be ice-free more often for extraction of fossil fuels. This would create jobs and generate money, but would also bring new sources of impact. All of this northern activity might help to settle Canada's claim of sovereignty over northern waters, or it might attract new competitors to challenge for access to northern resources.

A warmer Arctic would affect the rest of the world. Snow and ice would melt. The ground would heat. Huge quantities of methane and carbon dioxide, now frozen in the permafrost, would be released to add to global warming. Bacterial composition of vast amounts of organic matter would begin, releasing further greenhouse gases. Extensive melting of glaciers, which is being documented by researchers such as Dr. Eric Mattson (Figure 21-1B),

(continued)

FIGURE 21-1A A starving polar bear on Bathurst Island is unable to climb onto pack ice in order to hunt for seals.

FIGURE 21-1B Dr. Eric Mattson, a glaciologist, studies ice in the Arctic, the Antarctic, and alpine environments.

could raise sea levels an estimated 7 metres and lead to coastal flooding. The great volumes of fresh water could change ocean currents with unknown impacts on various regions and world climate.

However uncertain some of the impacts of a warmer Arctic may be, this much is crystal clear: *a little extra warmth would convert solid to liquid over a vast area of the Arctic at crucial times of the year—just a few degrees could make a world of difference.*

Climate change is considered by many scientists to be the most serious threat facing the world today.
DAVID SUZUKI

CHAPTER PURPOSE AND QUESTIONS

Chapter 21 discusses how our activities are changing the world's climate and depleting ozone in the stratosphere, and what we can do about these threats. The chapter addresses the following questions:

21-1 How have the Earth's temperature and climate changed in the past?

21-2 What role does the natural greenhouse effect play in the Earth's temperature and climate?

21-3 How have human activities affected concentrations of greenhouse gases?

21-4 How do scientists model changes in the Earth's temperature?

21-5 What factors affect the Earth's temperature?

21-6 What are some possible effects of a warmer troposphere?

21-7 What are our options for dealing with the threat of climate change?

21-8 What is being done to reduce greenhouse gas emissions?

21-9 What is the threat from ozone depletion?

21-10 How can we protect the ozone layer?

21-11 How well are we controlling CO_2 emissions and ozone-depleting substances?

21-1 PAST CLIMATE CHANGE

How Have the Earth's Temperature and Climate Changed in the Past? Climate Change Is Not New

Temperature and climate have been changing throughout the Earth's history.

The Earth's climate—determined mostly by its average temperature and average precipitation—is not fixed.

Therefore, climate change is neither new nor unusual. Over the past 4.7 billion years it has shifted due to volcanic emissions, changes in solar input, continents moving as a result of shifting tectonic plates, strikes by large meteorites, and other factors.

At some times (over hundreds to millions of years), the troposphere's average temperature has changed gradually and at other times fairly quickly (over a few decades to 100 years) as shown in the Figure 21-2 (p. 508) graphs. Over the past 900 000 years, the average temperature of the troposphere has undergone prolonged periods of *global cooling* and *global warming* (Figure 21-2, top left). These alternating cycles of freezing and thawing are known as *glacial and inter-glacial* (between ice ages) *periods.*

During each cold period, thick glacial ice covered much of the Earth's surface for about 100 000 years. Most of it melted during a *warmer interglacial period* lasting 10 000–12 500 years that followed each glacial period.

For roughly 10 000 years, we have had the good fortune to live in an interglacial period with a fairly stable climate based on a moderate and steady global average surface temperature (Figure 21-2, top right). Those favourable conditions allowed the human population to grow as agriculture developed and as civilization flourished. For the past 1 000 years, the average temperature of the atmosphere has remained fairly stable but began to rise during the last century (Figure 21-2, bottom left) when more people began clearing more forests and burning more fossil fuels. Most of the increase in temperature over the past 100 years has taken place since 1975 (Figure 21-2, bottom right).

How Do Scientists Study Climate Change? Drill Holes and Make Measurements

Geologic records and atmospheric measurements provide a wealth of information about past atmospheric temperatures and climate.

Scientific clues about the Earth's past temperatures and climate are found deep within its glaciers and ice caps, such as those in Greenland and Antarctica. Scientists drill into these museums of atmospheric history and extract long cores of ice (Figure 21-3, p. 509). In 2004, data from cores drilled in Antarctic ice indicated that the current interglacial period could last for another 15 000 years before a new ice age occurs—unless our activities seriously alter the Earth's climate.

Scientists analyze air bubbles trapped in different segments of these *ice cores* to uncover information about past tropospheric composition, temperature trends such as those in Figure 21-2, greenhouse gas concentrations, solar activity, snowfall, and forest fire frequency (from trapped layers of soot particles).

Climate Change and Ozone Loss: Two Global Problems

In Chapter 20, we dealt with a number of air pollution topics that were local, national, or even international in terms of affecting larger or smaller areas and crossing political borders. In this chapter, we focus on two topics that are *global* in nature. Climate change and ozone loss both affect *the entire planet*; the solutions to both require *the cooperation of many nations*.

We will tackle climate change first, since that is the more formidable of the two issues at present. Yet students should realize that at one point, ozone loss was a shocking, mysterious, and new challenge for the world. We had no immediate answers, but through careful study, effective planning, and cooperation, we managed to turn the tide to such an extent that 98%

of all ozone-depleting substances controlled under the Montreal Protocol have been phased out, and the ozone layer is projected to return to its pre-1980 levels by about 2050 (p. 536). It is hoped that we can apply the lessons we learned from dealing with the ozone problem to the problem of global climate change.

One final point—climate change and ozone thinning are two different problems, but there are connections between the two. For example, a thinning ozone layer allows more UV light to penetrate to the Earth's surface, potentially burning our skin and scalding phytoplankton, but this new abundance of UV light also degrades to a new source of heat energy, potentially affecting the global warming equation. Reducing

the ozone-depleting gases that we release to the atmosphere helps to restore the ozone layer, but since these gases also function as greenhouse gases, we are having an impact on climate change at the same time.

Get ready to think big and complex thoughts as you read about the global problems of climate change and ozone loss.

Comstock/Thinkstock

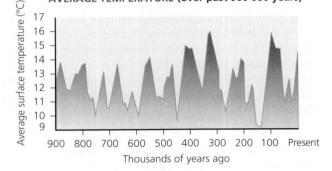

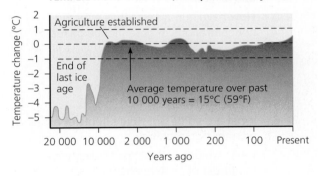

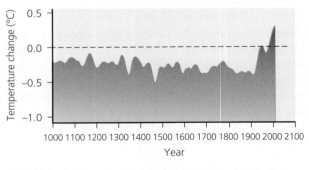

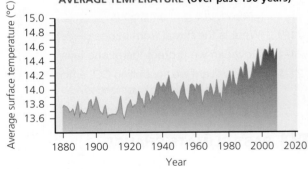

FIGURE 21-2 Estimated changes in the average global temperature of the atmosphere near the Earth's surface over different periods of time. Past temperature changes are estimated by analysis of radioisotopes in rocks and fossils, plankton and radioisotopes in ocean sediments, ice cores from ancient glaciers, temperature measurements at different depths in boreholes drilled deep into the Earth's surface, pollen from lake bottoms and bogs, tree rings, historical records, and temperature measurements (since 1861). (Data from Goddard Institute for Space Studies, Intergovernmental Panel on Climate Change, National Academy of Sciences, National Aeronautics and Space Agency, National Center for Atmospheric Research, and National Oceanic and Atmospheric Administration)

FIGURE 21-3 Ice cores such as this one extracted by drilling deep holes in ancient glaciers at various sites in Antarctica and Greenland can be analyzed to obtain information about past climates.

By kind permission of the British Antarctic Survey

Scientists also study past climates by drilling cores into the bottoms of lakes, ponds, and swamps. Then they analyze different zones of the sediment for pollen, fossils, and other clues about what types of plants lived in the past and trends in plant life over time. For those who like detective work, finding out about the Earth's climate history is a fascinating activity.

Scientists also make direct measurements to get current information about tropospheric temperature, composition, and trends. They measure temperatures using thermometers on land and at sea and on weather balloons at various altitudes. Direct temperature records go back to 1861. Scientists have also been using infrared sensors on satellites to get temperature information about the troposphere.

Finally, scientists collect air samples at different locations and altitudes and analyze them to detect changes in the chemical composition of the troposphere. For example, since 1958 environmental chemist Charles Keeling has analyzed CO_2 levels in the troposphere at the Mauna Loa observatory in Hawaii.

Once they have accumulated a certain amount of data, scientists get together to try to reach a consensus. In 1988, the United Nations and the World Meteorological Organization established the *Intergovernmental Panel on Climate Change (IPCC)* to document past climate change and project future climate change. The IPCC is a network of over 2 000 leading climate experts from 70 nations.

Recall that science can never give us absolute certainty or proof. Instead, it establishes levels of certainty or probability that a scientific model or theory is true. The IPCC expresses its conclusions and projections in probabilities using several levels of certainty: *virtually certain* (more than 99% probability), *very likely*

(90–99% probability), and *likely* (66–90% probability). Throughout this chapter, these categories are used to describe IPCC conclusions and projections about atmospheric temperature changes and their possible effects on climate.

21-2 THE EARTH'S NATURAL GREENHOUSE EFFECT

What Role Does the Natural Greenhouse Effect Play in the Earth's Temperature and Climate? A Giver of Life

Certain gases in the atmosphere absorb heat and warm the lower atmosphere.

In addition to incoming sunlight, a natural process called the *greenhouse effect* (Figure 6-16, p. 120) warms the Earth's lower troposphere and surface. Some of the energy from the sun warms the Earth's surface, causing it to radiate infrared energy back toward space. Clouds, water vapour, carbon dioxide, and other gases in the lower troposphere are heated when they absorb some of this outgoing infrared energy. These clouds and gases (called *greenhouse gases*) then radiate heat as longer-wavelength infrared radiation in all directions. Some of the released energy is radiated into space and some warms the troposphere and the Earth's surface.

Swedish chemist Svante Arrhenius first recognized this natural tropospheric heating effect in 1896. Since then, numerous laboratory experiments and measurements of atmospheric temperatures at different altitudes have confirmed this relationship. As a result, it is one of the most widely accepted theories in the atmospheric sciences.

A *natural cooling process* also takes place at the Earth's surface. Large quantities of heat are absorbed by the evaporation of liquid surface water, and the water vapour molecules rise, condense to form droplets in clouds, and release their stored heat higher in the troposphere (Figure 6-11, p. 117). Because of the impact of this natural heating and cooling, the Earth's average surface temperature is about 15°C (59°F).

SELF CHECK

Do you remember how climate results from a host of interacting factors including differential heating of the planet, air circulation, ocean circulation, topography, and greenhouse gases?

Briefly review Figures 6-2 to 6-17 for a quick reminder of the basics of climate.

What Are the Major Greenhouse Gases? Two Important Molecules

The two major greenhouse gases are water vapour and carbon dioxide.

Table 21-1 shows the major sources, average time in the troposphere, and relative warming potential of various greenhouse gases in the troposphere. The two greenhouse gases with the largest concentrations are *water vapour,* controlled by the hydrologic cycle, and *carbon dioxide* (CO_2), controlled by the carbon cycle. Carbon dioxide is a greenhouse gas we have added to the troposphere in huge quantities.

The coal, oil, and natural gas that support the world's economy all contain carbon that plants and sunshine converted to organic compounds hundreds of millions of years ago. Under high pressures and temperatures these buried organic compounds were converted to fossil fuels. Extracting and burning these storehouses of carbon releases carbon dioxide into the atmosphere.

According to the measurements of CO_2 concentrations in glacial ice, estimated changes in tropospheric CO_2 levels correlate fairly closely with estimated variations in the average global temperature near the Earth's surface during the past 160 000 years (Figure 21-4). Trace the curves in this figure.

21-3 CLIMATE CHANGE AND HUMAN ACTIVITIES

How Have Human Activities Affected Tropospheric Concentrations of Greenhouse Gases? Messing with the Carbon Cycle

Humans have increased concentrations of greenhouse gases in the troposphere by burning fossil fuels, clearing and burning forests and grasslands, raising large numbers of livestock such as cattle, planting rice, and using inorganic fertilizers.

Figure 21-5 shows that since 1861, the concentrations of the greenhouse gases CO_2, CH_4, and N_2O in the

Table 21-1 Major Greenhouse Gases from Human Activities

Greenhouse Gas	Human Sources	Average Time in the Troposphere	Relative Warming Potential (compared to CO_2)
Carbon dioxide (CO_2)	Fossil fuel burning, especially coal (70–75%), deforestation, and plant burning	100–120 years	1
Methane (CH_4)	Rice paddies, guts of cattle and termites, landfills, coal production, coal seams, and natural gas leaks from oil and gas production and pipelines	12–18 years	23
Nitrous oxide (N_2O)	Fossil fuel burning, fertilizers, livestock wastes, and nylon production	114–120 years	296
Chlorofluorocarbons (CFCs)*	Air conditioners, refrigerators, plastic foams	11–20 years (65–110 years in the stratosphere)	900–8 300
Hydrochloro-fluorocarbons (HCFCs)	Air conditioners, refrigerators, plastic foams	9–390 years	470–2 000
Hydrofluorocarbons (HFCs)	Air conditioners, refrigerators, plastic foams	15–390 years	130–12 700
Halons	Fire extinguishers	65 years	5 500
Carbon tetrachloride	Cleaning solvent	42 years	1 400

*CFC use is being phased out, but CFCs remain in the troposphere for 1–2 decades.

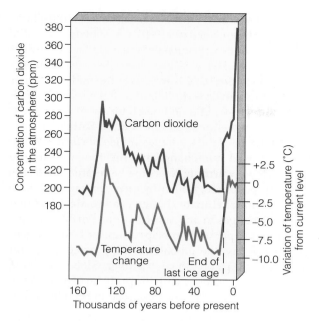

FIGURE 21-4 Atmospheric carbon dioxide levels and global temperature. Estimated long-term variations in average global temperature of the atmosphere near the Earth's surface are graphed along with average tropospheric CO_2 levels over the past 160 000 years. The rough correlation between CO_2 levels in the troposphere and temperature shown in these estimates based on ice core data suggests a connection between these two variables, although no definitive causal link has been established. In 1999, the world's deepest ice core sample revealed a similar correlation between air temperatures and the greenhouse gases CO_2 and CH_4 going back 460 000 years. (Data from Intergovernmental Panel on Climate Change and National Center for Atmospheric Research)

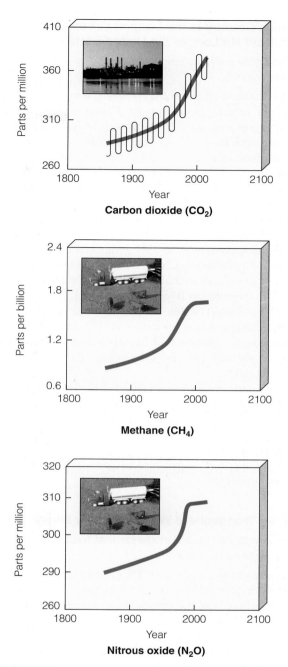

FIGURE 21-5 Increases in average concentrations of the greenhouse gases carbon dioxide, methane, and nitrous oxide in the troposphere between 1861 and 2003. The fluctuations in the CO_2 curve represent seasonal changes in photosynthetic activity that cause small differences between summer and winter concentrations of CO_2. (Data from Intergovernmental Panel on Climate Change, National Center for Atmospheric Research, and World Resources Institute)

troposphere have risen sharply, especially since 1950. Current CO_2 levels in the troposphere (Figure 21-5, top) appear to be higher than they have been in at least 160 000 years (Figure 21-4, blue curve). According to the 2007 IPCC report, three human activities have emitted large amounts of greenhouse gases into the troposphere at a faster rate than natural processes can remove them.

One has been the sharp rise in the use of fossil fuels, which release large amounts of CO_2 and CH_4 into the troposphere. Electricity generated by coal is responsible for about 42% of this input, transportation 24%, industrial processes 20%, and residential and commercial uses 14%. Exhale, start a car, turn up the thermostat, turn on a light, burn leaves or a fireplace log, or do just about anything, and you add carbon dioxide to the troposphere. Burning a gallon of gasoline (which weighs about 2.7 kilograms, or 6 pounds) produces about 9 kilograms (20 pounds) of CO_2.

A second process is deforestation and clearing and burning of grasslands to raise crops and build cities, which release CO_2 and N_2O. Third is the raising of an increasing number of cattle and other livestock that release methane as a result of their digestive processes. A fourth process is cultivation of rice in paddies and use of inorganic fertilizers that release N_2O into the troposphere.

Which Country Is the Largest Greenhouse Gas Emitter? No Longer the United States

China now emits more greenhouse gases than any other country.

Until 2006, the United States was the world's largest emitter of CO_2, followed by China, the European Union (consisting of 27 countries), Indonesia, Russia, Japan, and India. However, according to a number of studies (Gregg et al., 2008; NEAA, 2008), China's fast-growing coal-intensive economy began to produce CO_2 in greater quantities than the U.S. economy in 2006. China has been producing large amounts of CO_2 for a relatively short time and is estimated to have contributed about 5% of the world's cumulative CO_2 emissions, compared to 25% generated by the United States. Furthermore, China's CO_2 emissions represent that of a population that is about four times the size of the U.S. population (Figure 10-4, p. 197).

The United States also emits large quantities of CH_4. Most comes from landfills (35% of all U.S. CH_4 emissions), domesticated livestock and their manure (26%), natural gas and oil systems (20%), and coal mining (10%).

Canadians produce about 700 megatonnes of greenhouse gases every year, largely due to wasteful energy use. This is only 2% of global emissions, but we are only 0.5% of the world's population. In other words, at a rate of 23.6 tonnes per person per year, Canadians produce greenhouse gases at four times the global average.

Is the Troposphere Warming? Very Likely

There is considerable evidence that the Earth's troposphere is warming.

Here are five of many 2007 IPCC findings that support the scientific consensus that it is *very likely* (90–99% probability) that the troposphere is getting warmer. *First,* the 20th century was the hottest century in the past 1 000 years (Figure 21-2, bottom left). *Second,* since 1861 the average global temperature of the troposphere near the Earth's surface has risen 0.7°C (1.3°F) over the entire globe and about 0.8°C (1.4°F) over the continents. Most of this increase has taken place since 1980.

Third, 11 of the 12 years from 1995–2006 rank among the 12 warmest years in the instrumental record of global surface temperature (since 1850), and the temperature increase has been greatest at high northern latitudes. *Fourth,* glaciers and floating sea ice in many parts of the world are melting and shrinking (Case Study, below). *Fifth,* during the last century the world's average sea level rose by 0.1–0.2 metre (4–8 inches), partly from runoff from melting ice and partly because the volume of ocean water expands when its temperature increases.

A few scientists have been skeptical of atmospheric warming. They pointed to a 1990 study showing that since 1979 temperature measurements near the Earth's surface have been rising while satellite and other measurements showed no appreciable warming of the mid and upper troposphere. However, in 2002 and 2004 researchers analyzed these data and found much the same warming in these areas as thermometers show at the Earth's surface.

The terms *global warming* and *global climate change* are often used interchangeably but they are not the same. **Global warming** refers to temperature increases in the troposphere, which in turn can cause climate change. **Global climate change** is a broader term that refers to changes in any aspects of the Earth's climate, including temperature, precipitation, and storm intensity. It can involve global warming or cooling, but our focus will be on global warming. Global warming should not be confused with the problem of *ozone depletion* (Table 21-2, p. 513), as discussed in Section 21-9.

Case Study: Warning Signals from the Earth's Ice and Snow: Meltdowns Are Underway

Some of the world's floating ice and land-based glaciers are slowly melting, reflecting less incoming sunlight back into space, and helping warm the troposphere further.

The average temperature of the troposphere is strongly affected by the vast amounts of frozen water found as ice and snow near the Earth's poles and in most of the world's mountain glaciers. In the Arctic region, this water is locked up in ice caps that cover Greenland and floating sea ice in the Arctic Ocean. The South Pole is covered by Antarctica, which contains about 70% of the Earth's ice.

As the atmosphere warms, it causes more convection that transfers surplus heat from equatorial to polar areas (Figure 6-12, p. 117). *Thus, temperature increases tend to be greater in polar regions.* This explains why scientists regard the ice- and snow-covered areas at or near the Earth's poles as *early warning sentinels* of changes in the average temperature of Earth's troposphere. Measurements from the Arctic Sea, Greenland, and the northwestern shores of Alaska show that floating sea ice around the North Pole (Arctic) and Greenland is melting and thinning faster than it is being formed. For example, in 1979 when the satellite image on the left side of Figure 21-6 was taken, the minimum extent of Arctic sea ice was about 6.8 million square kilometres (2.6 million square miles). Sea ice varies from year to year, but in general the minimum extent of sea ice has been declining at a rate of about 13% per decade. The September 2012 minimum extent of 3.4 million square kilometres (1.3 million square miles) smashed the previous record of 4.2 million square kilometres (1.6 million square miles) set in

Table 21-2 Major Characteristics of Global Warming and Ozone Depletion

Characteristic	Global Warming	Ozone Depletion
Region of atmosphere involved	Troposphere.	Stratosphere.
Major substances involved	CO_2, CH_4, N_2O (greenhouse gases).	O_3, O_2, chlorofluorocarbons (CFCs).
Interaction with radiation	Molecules of greenhouse gases absorb infrared (IR) radiation from the Earth's surface, vibrate, and release longer-wavelength IR radiation (heat) into the lower troposphere. This natural greenhouse effect helps warm the lower troposphere.	About 95% of incoming ultraviolet (UV) radiation from the sun is absorbed by O_3 molecules in the stratosphere and does not reach the Earth's surface.
Nature of problem	There is a high (90–99%) probability that increasing concentrations of greenhouse gases in the troposphere from burning fossil fuels, deforestation, and agriculture are enhancing the natural greenhouse effect and raising the Earth's average surface temperature (Figures 21-2, bottom right, and 21-11, p. 517).	CFCs and other ozone-depleting chemicals released into the troposphere by human activities have made their way to the stratosphere, where they decrease O_3 concentration. This can allow more harmful UV radiation to reach the Earth's surface.
Possible consequences	Changes in climate, agricultural productivity, water supplies, and sea level.	Increased incidence of skin cancer, eye cataracts, and immune system suppression and damage to crops and phytoplankton.
Possible responses	Decrease fossil fuel use and deforestation; prepare for climate change.	Eliminate or find acceptable substitutes for CFCs and other ozone-depleting chemicals.

September 2007. According to the World Wildlife Fund, the diminishing levels of sea ice force polar bears to swim up to 100 kilometres (62 miles) in search of sea ice from which to hunt seals.

Why should we care if there is less ice in the Arctic? The answers lies in the **albedo**, or reflectivity, of different parts of the Earth's surface (Figure 21-7). Light-coloured surfaces of ice and snow help cool the Earth by reflecting 80–90% of incoming sunlight back into space. Much less sunlight is reflected by darker surfaces such as forests, grass, cities, and oceans.

Thus the world's coldest regions are part of the Earth's air-conditioning system.

A rise in the Earth's temperature can cause gradual melting of some of the Earth's ice caps, floating ice, and mountain glaciers. This would expose darker and less reflective surfaces of water and land and result in a warmer troposphere. As more ice melts, the troposphere can become warmer, which melts more ice and increases the tropospheric temperature even more.

Many scientists believe that the biggest long-term climate danger comes from Greenland. They are

U.S. Goddard Space Flight Center, and NASA, and National Snow and Ice Data Center

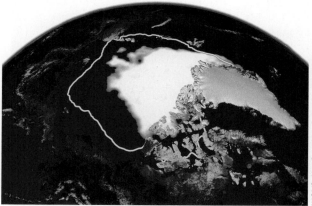

NASA/Goddard Space Flight Center Scientific Visualization Studio. The Blue Marble data is courtesy of Reto Stockli (NASA/GSFC).

FIGURE 21-6 Satellite imagery showing the minimum extent of Arctic sea ice (measured in September each year) in 1979 (left) and in 2012 (right). According to NASA, the minimum extent of sea ice cover has declined by about 50% since satellite measurements began in 1979. The yellow line represents the average of the minimum extents from 1979 to 2010. (NASA, 2012a)

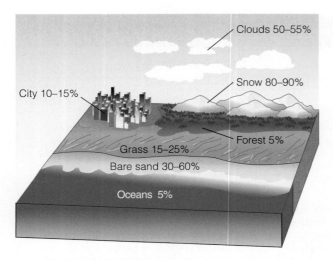

FIGURE 21-7 The *albedo*, or reflectivity of incoming solar energy, of different parts of the Earth's surface varies greatly. (Data from NOAA)

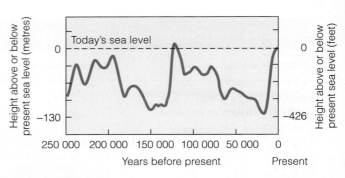

FIGURE 21-8 Changes in *average sea level* over the past 250 000 years based on data from cores removed from the ocean. The coming and going of glacial periods (ice ages) largely determine the rise and fall of sea level. As glaciers melted and retreated since the peak of the last glacial period about 18 000 years ago, the Earth's average sea level has risen about 125 metres (410 feet). (Adapted from Tom Garrison, *Oceanography: An Invitation to Marine Science*, 3/E, © 1998. Brooks/Cole.)

especially concerned about partial or eventually complete melting of the land-based glaciers or ice sheets that cover Greenland.

If this occurred, as it did in a previous interglacial warm period 110 000–130 000 years ago (Figure 21-8), average sea levels would rise by 7 metres (23 feet). In 2002, glaciologist Konrad Steffen reported that ice covering about a third of Greenland's total area was melting at a much faster rate than at any time since records have been kept. Researchers have calculated that a 3°C (5°F) rise in the Earth's average atmospheric temperature—within the range projected during this century—would be enough eventually to melt the entire Greenland ice sheet. They estimate this would take about 1 000 years but partial melting could accelerate an increase in average sea level during this century.

During the last 25 years, glaciers have also been melting and shrinking at accelerating rates on many of the world's mountaintops (Figure 21-9). Only 27 of the

FIGURE 21-9 Melting of the Athabasca Glacier. The left view shows the glacier as it was in 1919. The right view was photographed in 2000.

150 glaciers found during the middle of the last century in Montana's Glacier National Park remain. Tanzania's Mount Kilimanjaro—Africa's tallest peak—may be ice-free within 15 years. Other evidence indicates that 80% of South American glaciers could disappear within 15 years.

The disappearance of mountain glaciers means a loss of frozen water reservoirs that partially thaw out during warm months and release water for use by farms and city dwellers in the valleys below. This is *bad news* for countries like Peru, Ecuador, and Bolivia, which rely on annual water release by mountain glaciers for irrigation and household use.

21-4 PROJECTING FUTURE CHANGES IN THE EARTH'S TEMPERATURE

How Do Scientists Model Changes in the Earth's Temperature and Climate? Computer Models as Crystal Balls

Scientists have developed complex mathematical models of the Earth's climate systems, and they use them to project future changes in the Earth's average temperature.

To project the effects of increases in greenhouse gases on average global temperature, scientists develop models of how interactions among solar energy and the Earth's land, oceans, ice, and greenhouse gases determine the average temperature of the troposphere. Figure 21-10 (p. 516) gives a greatly simplified summary of some of these interactions. Trace the flows and connections in this figure.

Scientists use this information to develop global climate models (also known as *coupled global circulation models*) that are applied to the atmosphere to project the effects of increases in greenhouse gases on average global temperature. Currently 14 research laboratories are operating, evaluating, and improving coupled global circulation models.

These modellers develop a three-dimensional representation of how energy, air masses, and moisture flow through the atmosphere, based on the laws of physics and the major factors affecting the Earth's temperature and climate shown in Figure 21-10 (p. 516).

Computer simulations begin by covering the Earth's surface with a grid of several hundred huge squares (Figure 21-11, p. 517). Each square provides the base for a stack of gigantic imaginary cells, each several hundred kilometres on a side and about 3 kilometres (2 miles) high. These layers of cells extend down into the ocean and up into the atmosphere. Data on variables such as solar energy, sunlight, air pressure, temperature, water vapour, and winds or currents that affect climate in each cell are fed into

the model. Then a complex set of mathematical equations simulates flows of matter and energy among the cells and the entire climate model is fed into a supercomputer. New climate data can be added to the model to improve its accuracy.

Such models provide scenarios of what is *very likely* or *likely* to happen based on various assumptions and data fed into the model. How well the results correspond to the real world depends on the assumptions of the model (based on current knowledge about the systems making up the Earth, oceans, and atmosphere) and the accuracy of the data used.

What Is the Scientific Consensus About Future Changes in the Earth's Temperature? Hotter Times Ahead

Most climate scientists agree that human activities have influenced recent temperature increases and will lead to further significant temperature increases during this century.

In 1990, 1995, 2001, and 2007, the IPCC published reports that evaluate how global temperatures changed in the past (Figure 21-2) and are likely to change during this century. (The next IPCC report is due in 2014.) The IPCC reached its conclusions on the basis of scientific principles governing climate, data from past events, human emissions of CO_2 and other greenhouse gases, current temperature measurements, and global climate models.

Here are three major findings of the 2007 report.

■ Despite many uncertainties, the latest climate models match the records of global temperature changes since 1850 very closely.

■ "There is new and stronger evidence that most of the warming observed over the last 50 years is attributable to human activities."

■ It is very likely (90–99% probability) that the Earth's mean surface temperature will increase by 1.4–5.8°C (2.5–10.4°F) between 2000 and 2100 (Figure 21-12, p. 517).

IPCC and other climate scientists holding the consensus view agree that current climate models need to be improved. This is why the *very likely* projected range of average atmospheric temperature during this century is quite broad (Figure 21-11, p. 517). Scientists are hard at work trying to develop better models and narrow down such uncertainties.

A few climate scientists disagree with the consensus view about future temperature changes in the Earth's atmosphere. They say we know too little about how the Earth's climate works to make reliable projections about such changes. They also point out that some of the projected climate changes can be

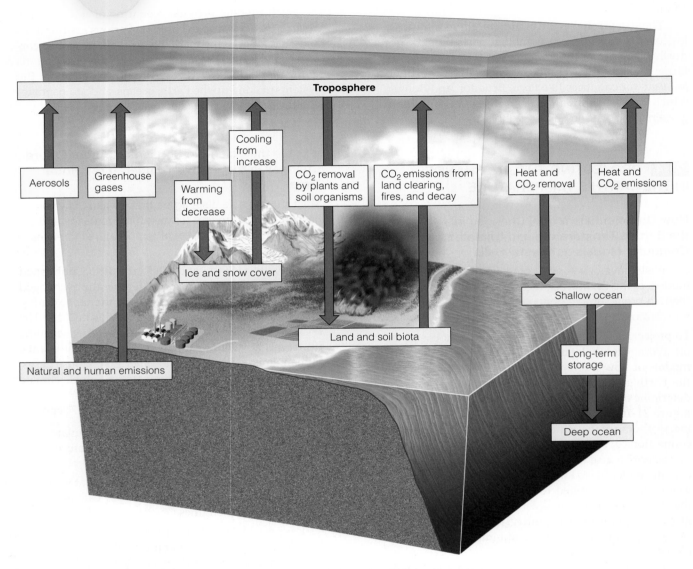

Sun

Troposphere

Aerosols

Greenhouse gases

Cooling from increase

Warming from decrease

CO_2 removal by plants and soil organisms

CO_2 emissions from land clearing, fires, and decay

Heat and CO_2 removal

Heat and CO_2 emissions

Ice and snow cover

Natural and human emissions

Land and soil biota

Shallow ocean

Long-term storage

Deep ocean

FIGURE 21-10 Natural capital: simplified model of some of the major processes that interact to determine the average temperature and greenhouse gas content of the troposphere and thus the Earth's climate.

beneficial to some regions. And they believe we can use our ingenuity to offset most of the undesirable effects of climate change.

CONSIDER, DISCUSS, OR DEBATE

Should we take action against global warming immediately, or should we wait until scientists have had more opportunity to gather and analyze data about its possible effects? Give reasons for your answer.

Why Should We Be Concerned About a Warmer Earth? The Speed of Change Is What Counts

A rapid increase in the temperature of the troposphere would give humans and other species little time to deal with its effects.

Climate scientists warn that the concern is not just a temperature change but how rapidly it occurs, regardless of cause. Past temperature changes often took place over thousands to a hundred thousand years

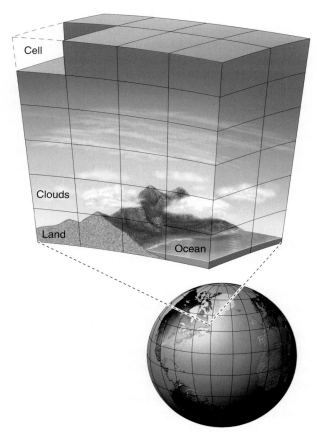

FIGURE 21-11 Global circulation model (GCM) of climate divides the Earth's atmosphere into large numbers of gigantic boxes, or cells, stacked many layers high. The laws of physics and our understanding of global air circulation patterns and other factors that can affect climate are used to describe numerically what happens to major variables affecting climate in each cell and how they change from one cell to another.

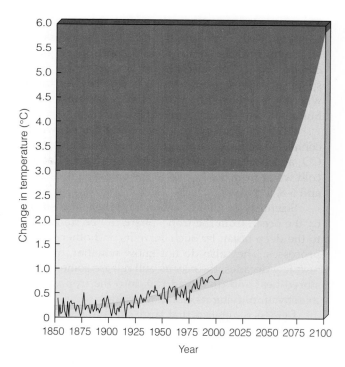

FIGURE 21-12 Comparison of measured changes in the average temperature of the atmosphere at the Earth's surface between 1860 and 2008 and the projected range of temperature increase during the rest of this century. (Data from U.S. National Academy of Sciences, National Center for Atmospheric Research, and Intergovernmental Panel on Climate Change)

> **CONSIDER, DISCUSS, OR DEBATE**
>
> Do you believe that we will experience significant global warming during this century? Support your answer by referring to unusual weather events in recent years that have been attributed to global warming.

21-5 FACTORS AFFECTING THE EARTH'S TEMPERATURE

Scientists have identified a number of natural and human-influenced factors that might *amplify* (positive feedback) or *dampen* (negative feedback) projected changes in the average temperature of the troposphere. The fairly wide range of projected future temperature changes shown in Figure 21-12 results from including what is known about these factors in climate models. Let us examine some possible wild cards that could help or make matters worse or better during this century.

Can the Oceans Store More CO$_2$ and Heat? We Do Not Know

There is uncertainty about how much CO$_2$ and heat the oceans can remove from the troposphere and how long they might remain in the oceans.

(Figure 21-2, top left). The problem we face is a fairly sharp projected increase in the temperature of the troposphere during this century (Figure 21-12).

According to the IPCC, it is *very likely* that this will be the fastest temperature change of the past 1 000 years. Such rapid temperature change can affect the availability of water resources by altering rates of evaporation and precipitation. It can also change wind patterns and weather, dry some areas, add moisture to others, alter some ocean currents, shift areas where crops can be grown, increase average sea levels and flood some coastal wetlands and cities and low-lying islands, and alter the structure and location of some of the world's biomes. These are major changes in the Earth's atmospheric conditions. An increase in the Earth's average temperature within a few decades or a century gives us little time to deal with its effects.

The oceans help moderate the Earth's average surface temperature by removing about 29% of the excess CO_2 we pump into the atmosphere as part of the global carbon cycle. They also absorb heat from the atmosphere and slowly transfer some of it to the deep ocean, where it is removed from the climate system for long but unknown periods of time (Figure 21-10).

Ocean currents on the surface and deep down are connected and act like a gigantic conveyor belt to store CO_2 and heat in the deep sea and to transfer hot and cold water from the tropics to the poles (Figures 21-13 and 6-8, p. 116).

Scientists do not know how rapidly heat absorbed by the ocean from the troposphere can be transferred to the deep ocean by such currents and other mixing processes. They also do not know whether, over the next few decades, the oceans will release some of their stored heat and dissolved CO_2 into the troposphere, thereby amplifying its global warming.

Evidence suggests that large changes in the speed of the ocean currents in this conveyor belt, and its stopping and starting, contributed to wild swings in northern hemisphere temperatures during past ice ages. Scientists are trying to learn more about how these currents operate to evaluate the likelihood of the loop slowing down or stalling during this century and the effects this might have on regional and global atmospheric temperatures.

In 2003, a group of physical oceanographers, including Sydney Levitus of the National Oceanic and Atmospheric Administration (NOAA) and Ruth Curry of the Woods Hole Oceanographic Institute, announced the results of a compilation of millions of observations and measurements of the Atlantic Ocean from pole to pole. Their analysis indicated that tropical oceans are now much saltier and oceans closer to the poles are less salty than they were 40 years ago. In other words, during this period fresh water has been lost from the low latitudes and added at high latitudes.

They suggest that this indicates that global warming may be playing a key role in accelerating the global water cycle. If this hypothesis is correct, global warming may affect global precipitation patterns and alter the distribution, severity, and frequency of droughts, floods, and storms. Such an accelerated hydrologic cycle could also intensify global warming by increasing the rate of evaporation of water—a potent greenhouse gas—into the troposphere.

It could also slow down the conveyor belt (Figure 21-13) that helps draw warm Gulf Stream waters northward in the Atlantic, pumping heat into northern regions and moderating wintertime air temperatures, especially in western Europe.

The large loop of shallow and deep ocean currents shown in Figure 21-13 helps keep much of the northern hemisphere (especially Europe) fairly warm by pulling

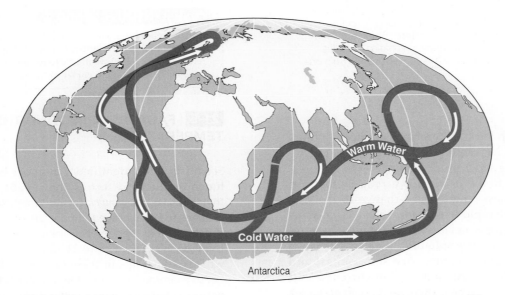

FIGURE 21-13 Natural capital: a connected loop of shallow and deep ocean currents stores CO_2 in the deep sea and transmits warm and cool water to various parts of the Earth. It occurs when ocean water in the North Atlantic near Iceland is dense enough (because of its salt content and cold temperature) to sink to the ocean bottom, flow southward, and then flow eastward to well up in the warmer Pacific. Then a shallower return current aided by winds brings warmer and less salty—and thus less dense—water to the Atlantic, which can then cool and sink to begin the cycle again. A warmer planet would be a rainier one, which, coupled with melting glaciers, would increase the amount of fresh water flowing into the North Atlantic. This could slow or even jam the loop by diluting the salt water and making it more buoyant (less dense) and less prone to sinking.

warm tropical water north, pushing cold water south, and releasing much of the heat stored in the water into the troposphere.

If this loop of currents should slow sharply or shut down, northern Europe and the northeast coast of North America would experience severe regional cooling. In other words, *global warming can lead to significant global cooling in some parts of the world,* with the climate of western Europe possibly resembling that of Siberia. Disruption or significant slowing of the loop would also disrupt other parts of the world with floods, droughts, severe storms, and searing heat.

How Might Stored CO_2 Affect Water Chemistry? Ocean Acidification

When oceans absorb CO_2 they become more acidic, with potential consequences for marine life.

The uptake of CO_2 in water leads to the formation of weak carbonic acid. Studies have shown that the ocean has become more acidic by 0.1 pH units (pp. 42–43) since the industrial revolution, and scientists project that pH levels could drop by 0.5 pH units before the end of this century (IPCC, 2007).

In an acidic ocean, calcium carbonate would be less available to be precipitated into the shells and skeletons of marine organisms. This would directly affect a wide range of shell-forming organisms including molluscs, corals, and protists, as well as all the organisms that rely upon them. It could affect the larval development of marine organisms. It could affect the respiration of fish. Scientists are particularly concerned that corals would be negatively impacted since these animals have large requirements for calcium carbonate to build their exoskeletons, and since corals are already stressed by warming seas.

This is a relatively new area of study, but the topic is being actively researched by groups such as the UK Ocean Acidification Research Programme (http://www.oceanacidification.org.uk/), Biological Impacts of Ocean ACIDification (http://www.bioacid.de/), European Project on Ocean Acidification (http://www.epoca-project.eu/), and U.S. Ocean Carbon and Biochemistry (http://www.us-ocb.org/). Paleoceanographic evidence has been discovered that shows there was a massive disappearance of carbonate 55 million years ago, as determined by examination of sediment cores. Scientists speculate that an abundant release of methane at the time contributed to global warming, and as the methane was oxidized to CO_2, ocean acidification resulted in the disappearance of calcium carbonate from ocean sediment (http://co2.cms.udel.edu/).

There are many unknowns at this point, but two things are clear: (1) higher concentrations of atmospheric CO_2 will lead to increased ocean acidification,

and (2) schemes that involve disposal of CO_2 into the ocean (p. 525) now seem inadvisable in view of our awareness of ocean acidification.

How Might Changes in Cloud Cover Affect the Troposphere's Temperature? Another Uncertainty

Warmer temperatures create more clouds that could warm or cool the troposphere, but we do not know which effect might dominate.

One of the largest unknowns in global climate models is the effect of changes in the global distribution of clouds on the temperature of the troposphere. Warmer temperatures increase evaporation of surface water and create more clouds. These additional clouds can have a *warming effect* (positive feedback), by absorbing and releasing heat into the troposphere, or a *cooling effect* (negative feedback) by reflecting more sunlight back into space.

The net result of these two opposing effects depends on several factors. One is how much water vapour will enter the troposphere as the Earth's surface warms. In 2004, measurements by researchers Andrew Dessler and Ken Minschwaner verified that water vapour is increasing in the troposphere as the Earth warms. However, they found that increases in water vapour in the upper troposphere were not as high as many global circulation climate models have assumed.

The effects of clouds on atmospheric temperatures also depend on whether it is day or night. Other factors include the type (thin or thick), coverage (continuous or discontinuous), and altitude of the cloud, and the size and number of water droplets or ice crystals formed in clouds.

For example, an increase in thick and continuous clouds at low altitudes can decrease surface warming by reflecting and blocking more sunlight. However, an increase in thin and discontinuous cirrus clouds at high altitudes can warm the lower troposphere and increase surface warming. What climate scientists know about the effects of clouds has been included in the latest climate models, but much uncertainty remains.

How Might Outdoor Air Pollution Affect the Troposphere's Temperature? A Temporary Effect

Aerosol pollutants and soot produced by human activities can warm or cool the troposphere, but such effects will decrease with any decline in such outdoor air pollution.

Aerosols (microscopic droplets and solid particles) of various air pollutants are released or formed in the troposphere by volcanic eruptions and human activities (see Figure 20-4, p. 480). They can warm or cool the atmosphere as well as hinder or enhance cloud formation, depending on factors such as their size and reflectivity.

Most aerosols, such as light-coloured sulphate particles produced by fossil fuel combustion, tend to reflect incoming sunlight and cool the lower atmosphere. Sulphate particles also cool the lower atmosphere by serving as condensation nuclei that form clouds. Scientists estimate that sulphate particles have played a role in slowing atmospheric warming since 1880. However, a study by Ramanathan et al. (2008) demonstrated the importance of soot—the black carbon particulate matter produced by coal burning, cooking fires, forest fires, and diesel exhaust—as a factor that warms the atmosphere.

Climate scientists do not expect aerosol and soot pollutants to counteract or enhance projected global warming very much in the next 50 years for two reasons. One is that aerosols and soot fall back to the Earth or are washed out of the lower atmosphere within weeks or months, whereas CO_2 and other greenhouse gases remain in the troposphere for decades to several hundred years. The other is that aerosol inputs into the troposphere are being reduced—especially in developed countries.

Can Increased CO_2 Levels Stimulate Photosynthesis and Remove More CO_2 from the Air? A Temporary and Limited Effect

Increased CO_2 in the troposphere could increase plant photosynthesis, but several factors can limit or offset this effect.

Some studies suggest that more CO_2 in the troposphere could increase the rate of plant photosynthesis in areas where there are no other limiting factors such as lack of water or soil nutrients. This would remove more CO_2 from the troposphere and help slow atmospheric warming.

However, recent studies indicate that this CO_2 removal would be temporary for two reasons. One is that it would slow as the plants reach maturity and take up less CO_2 from the troposphere. The other is that carbon stored by the plants as organic compounds would be returned to the troposphere as CO_2 when the plants die and decompose or burn.

A 2004 study showed that undisturbed old-growth Amazon rain forests are experiencing rapid changes in species composition apparently because of rising atmospheric levels of carbon dioxide. Higher CO_2 levels are fertilizing many species of trees and fast-growing larger trees are out-competing smaller younger trees. This is changing the mix of tree and wildlife species or biodiversity makeup of these rain forests. Initially, this can increase the uptake of CO_2 from the atmosphere. But as these larger trees mature and die out sooner the reduction in denser wood and foliage could eventually lead to a drop in the amount of carbon dioxide these rain forests remove from the atmosphere. In addition, plant-eating insects that breed more rapidly and year-round in warmer temperatures could offset much of the increased plant growth.

How Might a Warmer Troposphere Affect Methane Emissions? Accelerated Warming

Warmer air can release methane gas stored in bogs, wetlands, and tundra soils, causing a feedback loop that makes the air warmer.

Global warming could be accelerated by an increased release of methane (a potent greenhouse gas) from two major sources. One is bogs and other wetlands and the other is ice-like compounds called *methane hydrates* trapped beneath the Arctic permafrost. Significant amounts of methane would be released into the troposphere if the permafrost in tundra and boreal forest soils partially or completely melts, as is occurring in parts of Canada, Alaska, China, and Mongolia. The resulting tropospheric warming could lead to more methane release and still more warming.

21-6 POSSIBLE EFFECTS OF A WARMER WORLD

What Are Some Possible Effects of a Warmer Troposphere? Winners and Losers

A warmer troposphere would have beneficial and harmful effects, but poor nations in the tropics will suffer the most.

A warmer troposphere could have a number of beneficial and harmful effects, listed in Figures 21-14 (p. 521) and 21-15 (p. 521), for humans, other species, and ecosystems, depending mostly on their locations and on how rapidly the temperature changes. Study these figures carefully. However, betting on living in an area with favourable climate change in the future is like playing a game of Russian roulette. Global climate models are improving, but so far we cannot make reliable projections about how the climates of particular regions are likely to change.

According to the IPCC, the largest burden of the harmful effects of moderate global warming will fall on people and economies in poorer tropical and subtropical nations without the economic and technological resources needed to adapt to its harmful impacts.

The World Health Organization estimates that each year about 150 000 people—mostly children in

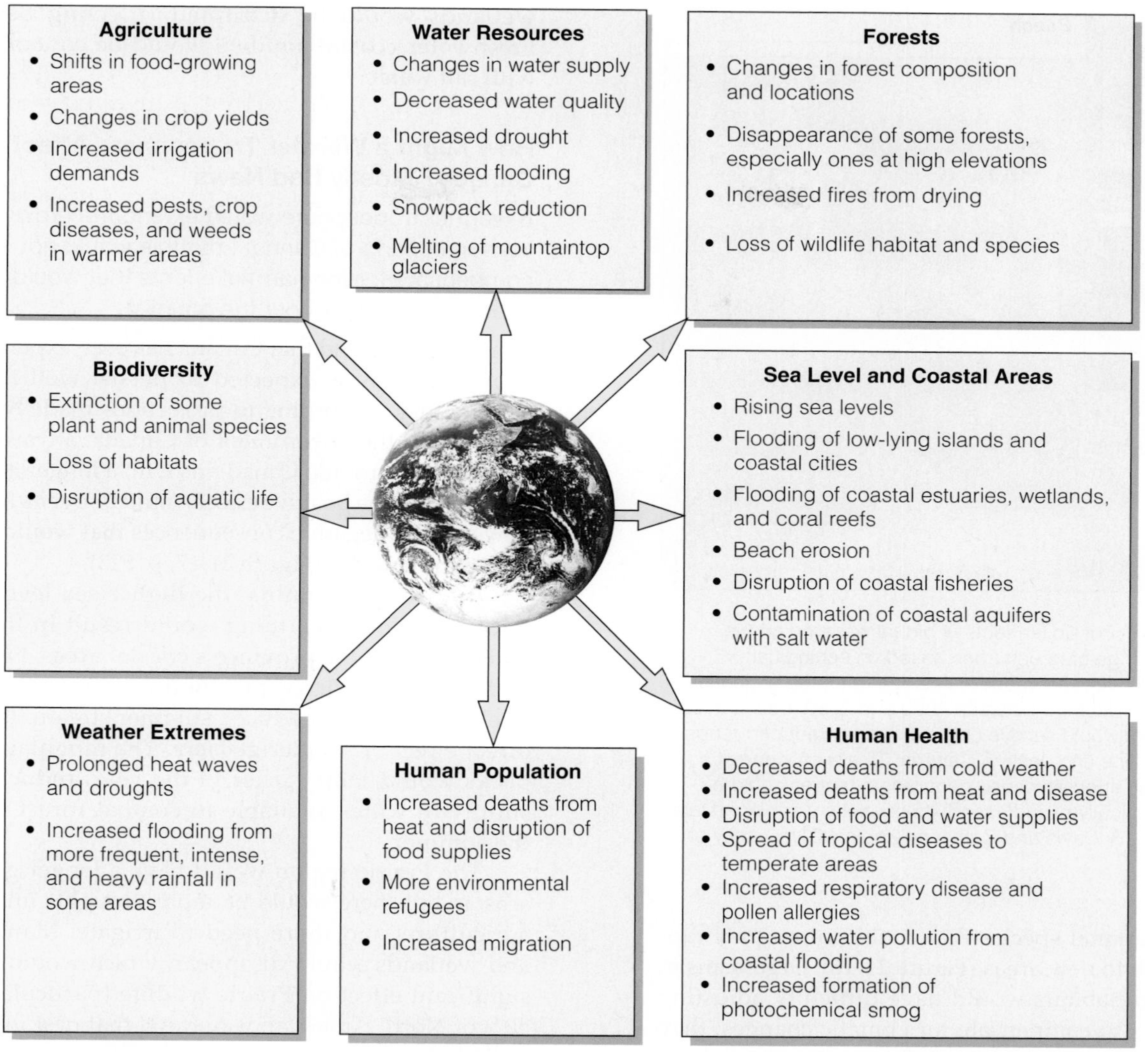

Agriculture
- Shifts in food-growing areas
- Changes in crop yields
- Increased irrigation demands
- Increased pests, crop diseases, and weeds in warmer areas

Water Resources
- Changes in water supply
- Decreased water quality
- Increased drought
- Increased flooding
- Snowpack reduction
- Melting of mountaintop glaciers

Forests
- Changes in forest composition and locations
- Disappearance of some forests, especially ones at high elevations
- Increased fires from drying
- Loss of wildlife habitat and species

Biodiversity
- Extinction of some plant and animal species
- Loss of habitats
- Disruption of aquatic life

Sea Level and Coastal Areas
- Rising sea levels
- Flooding of low-lying islands and coastal cities
- Flooding of coastal estuaries, wetlands, and coral reefs
- Beach erosion
- Disruption of coastal fisheries
- Contamination of coastal aquifers with salt water

Weather Extremes
- Prolonged heat waves and droughts
- Increased flooding from more frequent, intense, and heavy rainfall in some areas

Human Population
- Increased deaths from heat and disruption of food supplies
- More environmental refugees
- Increased migration

Human Health
- Decreased deaths from cold weather
- Increased deaths from heat and disease
- Disruption of food and water supplies
- Spread of tropical diseases to temperate areas
- Increased respiratory disease and pollen allergies
- Increased water pollution from coastal flooding
- Increased formation of photochemical smog

FIGURE 21-14 *Winners and losers.* Projected effects of a warmer atmosphere for the world. Most of these effects could be harmful or beneficial depending on where one lives. Current models of the Earth's climate cannot make reliable projections about where such effects might take place at a regional level and how long they might last. (Data from Intergovernmental Panel on Climate Change, U.S. Global Climate Change Research Program, U.S. National Academy of Sciences)

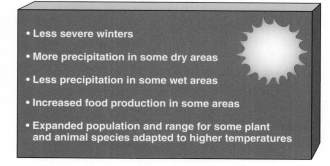

- **Less severe winters**
- **More precipitation in some dry areas**
- **Less precipitation in some wet areas**
- **Increased food production in some areas**
- **Expanded population and range for some plant and animal species adapted to higher temperatures**

FIGURE 21-15 *Winners:* Possible *beneficial effects* of a warmer atmosphere for some countries and people.

developing countries in Asia and Africa—die prematurely from side effects of global warming ranging from increases in malaria to malnutrition. They estimated that this death toll could double by 2020. Some researchers estimate that by the end of this century the annual death toll from global warming could reach 6 million or more. Some analysts say these estimates are exaggerated. But even with a lower toll this is a serious and largely preventable human tragedy.

According to the IPCC, a warmer troposphere could seriously disrupt coral reefs, polar seas, coastal wetlands, arctic and alpine tundra, and high-elevation ecosystems. A warmer climate would also threaten

Climate Change and Ozone Loss

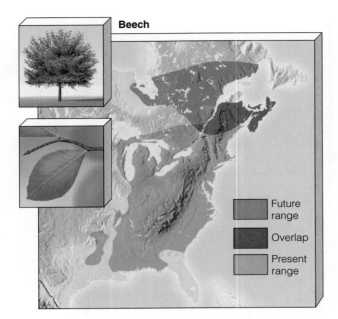

Beech

Future range

Overlap

Present range

FIGURE 21-16 Possible effects of global warming on the geographic range of beech trees based on ecological evidence and computer models. According to one projection, if CO_2 emissions doubled between 1990 and 2050, beech trees (now common) would survive only in a greatly reduced range in northern Maine and eastern Canada. This is only one of a number of tree species whose geographic ranges could be changed drastically by increased atmospheric warming. (Data from Margaret B. Davis and Catherine Zabinski, University of Minnesota)

plant and animal species that could not migrate rapidly enough to new areas (Figure 21-16). Organisms in fragmented habitats would have difficulty adjusting their ranges to compensate for climatic changes; they might find themselves stranded in patches of habitat that would become less suitable with passing time. Conservation efforts would be hampered because parks cannot be shifted to track changes in climate and are often discrete units unfavourable to natural dispersal.

A decrease in high-elevation snow packs throughout the world would have negative consequences for agriculture that depends on meltwater. For example, agriculture in central and southern California depends largely on water from snow melting in the Sierra Nevada and Rocky Mountains. The world's two largest wheat harvests in China and in India rely on irrigation from the Yellow, Indus, and Ganges Rivers, which receive water from snow melting in the Himalayas each summer.

Sea levels may rise as much as 7 metres (23 feet) if most of the ice on Greenland and in the Canadian Arctic melts. This would cause flooding problems for coastal cities and for many islands. Low-lying agricultural lands and productive deltas would be lost. Most of the world's productive coastal estuaries and wetlands would be disrupted, affecting fisheries. Freshwater coastal aquifers would be contaminated with salt water.

How Might a Warmer Troposphere Affect Canada? Mostly Bad News

A warmer troposphere would extend the growing season in parts of Canada, but this would not compensate for the harmful effects that would be experienced throughout the country.

The warming trend that Canada has been experiencing in recent years is expected to persist well into the 21st century. According to projections made by IPCC reports and the government of Canada, a warmer climate would provide Canadians with a longer growing season. This one positive effect would be overwhelmed, however, by negative consequences that would be felt across the country (Figure 21-17, p. 523).

In British Columbia, the higher sea levels produced by global warming would result in flooding and erosion of the province's coastal areas. Fisheries and hydroelectricity production would be negatively impacted by reduced summer stream flows—a direct effect of smaller glaciers. The mountain snow packs would melt earlier in the year, reducing the supply of water available to combat forest fires in the summer.

The Prairie region would have a longer growing season, but there would be more droughts impacting agriculture, and more need to irrigate. Many lakes and wetlands would disappear, which would have a significant effect on Prairie wildlife (particularly the 50% of North American waterfowl that nest in Prairie potholes).

Harmful effects experienced in other regions of Canada include the following:

- The Arctic and Subarctic regions would experience widespread changes in ice-cover and permafrost characteristics that would greatly disrupt the people and wildlife of the region (Case Study, p. 506).

- The boreal forest region would have a longer growing season and shift about 500 kilometres (310 miles) northward over time. At the same time, it would experience more fires, more damage from insect pests, and more threats to wildlife such as woodland caribou.

- The Great Lakes region would experience a greater number of heat waves, resulting in more high-smog days with their attendant health problems. Lower lake levels would have adverse effects on shipping and hydroelectricity generation. Severe weather events such as ice storms would be on the rise, and there would be a greater need to irrigate in summer.

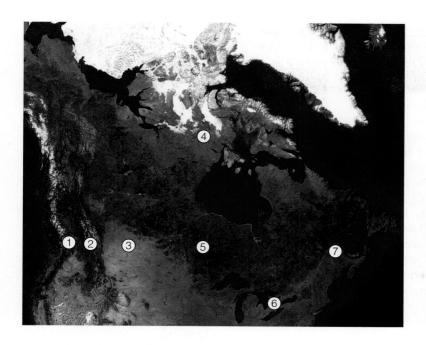

FIGURE 21-17 How will climate change affect Canada? (1) West Coast: flooding, stress on fish; (2) Rocky Mountains: more precipitation, earlier melt; (3) Prairies: more droughts, impacts on farming and wildlife; (4) Arctic and Subarctic: melting ice and permafrost, problems for people and wildlife; (5) Boreal Forest: more forest fires and pests, wildlife extinctions; (6) Great Lakes: hydroelectricity problems, changes in flora and fauna; (7) Eastern Canada: decreased snow, loss of bogs, coastal erosion, threatened fisheries. (Government of Canada, 2005; IPCC, 2001; IPCC, 2007; and NASA)

- In eastern Canada, higher sea levels would lead to flooding of coastal cities, erosion of beaches and coastlines, a loss of wetlands, increased damage to forests from insect pests, and regional fisheries under threat due to changes in fish migrations.

21-7 DEALING WITH THE THREAT OF GLOBAL WARMING

What Are Our Options? The Great Climate Debate

There is disagreement over what we should do about the threat of global warming.

As we have seen, nearly all climate scientists agree that the Earth's temperature is very likely to increase during this century and that human activities play a part in this change. Despite this scientific consensus, there is debate among scientists over the causes of these changes (natural or human), how rapidly they might occur, the effects on humans and ecosystems, and how we should respond to this potentially serious long-term global threat.

Economists and policymakers also disagree over how we should respond to the threat of climate change. They disagree on whether

- the economic costs of reducing greenhouse gas emissions are higher than the economic benefits;

- developed countries, developing countries, or both should take responsibility for reducing greenhouse gas emissions; and

- actions to reduce greenhouse gas emissions should be voluntary or required as a result of national laws and an international treaty.

As a result of these scientific, economic, and political disagreements, there are three schools of thought concerning what we should do about projected global warming. One is to *do more research before acting.* With this *wait-and-see-strategy,* many scientists and economists call for more research and a better understanding of the Earth's climate system before making far-reaching and controversial economic and political decisions such as phasing out fossil fuels. This has been the pre-Obama position of the U.S. government.

A second and rapidly growing group of scientists, economists, business leaders, and political leaders especially in the European Union believe that we should *act now to reduce the risks from climate change brought about by global warming.* They argue that the potential for harmful economic, ecological, and social consequences is so great that action should not be delayed. They believe that current evidence indicates that global warming is occurring and that if we delay by waiting for even more conclusive evidence, it will be too late to slow down the degree and rate of such warming. In other words, global warming is a good candidate for applying the *precautionary principle.*

In 1997, more than 2 500 scientists from a variety of disciplines signed a Scientists' Statement on Global Climate Disruption and concluded, "We endorse those [IPCC] reports and observe that the further accumulation of greenhouse gases commits the Earth irreversibly to further global climatic change and consequent ecological, economic, and social disruption. The risks associated with such changes justify preventive action through reductions in emissions of greenhouse gases." Also in 1997, 2 700 economists led by eight Nobel laureates declared, "As economists, we believe that global climate change carries with it significant environmental, economic, social, and geopolitical risks and that preventive steps are justified."

A third strategy is to *act now as part of a no-regrets strategy*. Scientists and economists supporting this approach say we should take the key actions needed to slow global warming—even if the threat does not materialize—because such actions lead to other important environmental, health, and economic benefits. For example, we should be seizing the chance to advance alternative energy sources, for many reasons aside from global warming. Reduced burning of fossil fuels, especially coal, will lead to sharp reductions in air pollution that lowers food and timber productivity, decreases biodiversity, and prematurely kills large numbers of people. Reducing oil use would also decrease dependence on imported oil, which threatens economic and military security. As well, we should be improving energy efficiency, which has numerous economic and environmental advantages (Figure 18-2, p. 419). We should also be practising sustainable forestry for economic, biodiversity, and health reasons—aside from global warming issues.

> **CONSIDER, DISCUSS, OR DEBATE**
>
> Which of the three schools of thought concerning what should be done about global warming do you favour? Why?

What Can We Do to Reduce the Threat? Conserve Energy, Use Renewable Energy, and Intercept Greenhouse Gas Emissions

We can improve energy efficiency, rely more on carbon-free renewable energy resources, and find ways to keep much of the CO_2 we produce out of the troposphere.

Figure 21-18 presents a variety of prevention and cleanup solutions that climate analysts have suggested for slowing the rate and degree of global warming. The solutions come down to three major strategies: *improve energy efficiency to reduce fossil fuel use; shift from carbon-based fossil fuels to a mix of carbon-free renewable energy resources;* and *sequester or store as much CO_2 as possible in soil, in vegetation, underground, and in the deep ocean.* The effectiveness of these three strategies would be enhanced by *reducing population growth* to decrease the number of fossil fuel consumers and CO_2 emitters and by *reducing poverty* to decrease the need of the poor to clear more land for crops and wood.

Solutions

Global Warming

Prevention

Cut fossil fuel use (especially coal)

Shift from coal to natural gas

Improve energy efficiency

Shift to renewable energy resources

Transfer energy efficiency and renewable energy technologies to developing countries

Reduce deforestation

Use more sustainable agriculture

Limit urban sprawl

Reduce poverty

Slow population growth

Cleanup

Remove CO_2 from smokestack and vehicle emissions

Store (sequester) CO_2 by planting trees

Sequester CO_2 deep underground

Sequester CO_2 in soil by using no-till cultivation and taking crop land out of production

Sequester CO_2 in the deep ocean

Repair leaky natural gas pipelines and facilities

Use feeds that reduce CH_4 emissions by belching cows

FIGURE 21-18 Solutions: methods for slowing atmospheric warming during this century.

Scientists are also developing new power plant designs that would eliminate smokestack emissions of CO_2 and other pollutants. One approach is to develop modified forms of coal gasification to increase the energy efficiency of coal-fired power plants from 35% to 70%. There is also research on using metal-ceramic membranes in coal gasification plants to trap CO_2 for sequestering. However, if such plants can be developed, they are likely to be quite costly and it would take many decades for them to replace existing power plants.

Can We Remove and Store (Sequester) Enough CO_2 to Slow Global Warming? Are Output Approaches the Answer?

We can prevent some of the CO_2 we produce from circulating in the troposphere, but the costs may be high and the effectiveness of various approaches is unknown.

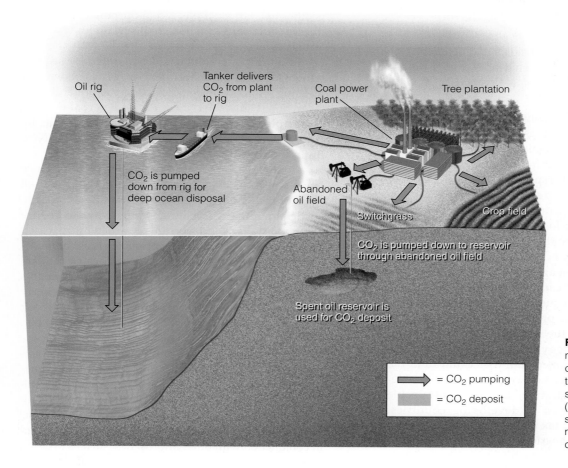

Oil rig

Tanker delivers CO_2 from plant to rig

Coal power plant

Tree plantation

CO_2 is pumped down from rig for deep ocean disposal

Abandoned oil field

Switchgrass

Crop field

CO_2 is pumped down to reservoir through abandoned oil field

Spent oil reservoir is used for CO_2 deposit

⟶ = CO_2 pumping

▬ = CO_2 deposit

FIGURE 21-19 Solutions: methods for removing carbon dioxide from the atmosphere or from smokestacks and storing (sequestering) it in plants, soil, deep underground reservoirs, and the deep ocean.

Figure 21-19 shows several potential techniques to remove CO_2 from the troposphere or from smokestacks and store (sequester) it in other parts of the environment.

One possible way to remove CO_2 from the atmosphere is to plant trees that store (sequester) it in biomass. While it is true that trees release their stored CO_2 once they die and decompose, or burn, the idea is to increase the total area of forested land in the world. Preventing deforestation, and increasing reforestation, would sequester CO_2 and add ecological benefits. Furthermore, wood that goes into construction of buildings or into other long-lasting products represents stored CO_2.

A second approach is *soil sequestration* in which plants such as switchgrass are used to remove CO_2 from the air and store it in the soil. But warmer temperatures can increase decomposition in soils and return some of the stored CO_2 to the atmosphere.

A third strategy is to *reduce the release of carbon dioxide and nitrous oxide from soil*. Ways to do this include *conservation cultivation* (Figure 14-12, p. 312) and retiring depleted crop fields, leaving them untouched as conservation reserves.

A fourth approach is to remove CO_2 from smokestacks and *pump it deep underground* into unminable coal seams and abandoned oil fields or *inject it into the deep ocean,* as shown in Figure 21-19.

There are several problems with this strategy. One is that current methods can remove only about 30% of the CO_2 from smokestack emissions and would double or triple the cost of producing electricity by burning coal. The U.S. Department of Energy estimates that the cost of sequestering carbon dioxide in various underground and deep ocean repositories will have to be reduced at least ten-fold to make this approach economically feasible. In addition, injecting large quantities of CO_2 into the ocean could upset the global carbon cycle, seawater acidity, and some forms of deep-sea life in unpredictable ways (recall ocean acidification, p. 519).

CONSIDER, DISCUSS, OR DEBATE

Which of the solutions presented in Figure 21-18 do you think would be the most difficult to carry out? Why?

How Can Governments Reduce the Threat of Global Warming? Use Sticks and Carrots

Governments can tax greenhouse gas emissions and energy use, increase subsidies and tax breaks for saving energy and using renewable energy, and decrease subsidies and tax breaks for fossil fuels.

Governments could use three major methods to promote the solutions to slowing global warming listed in Figure 21-18. One is to phase in output-based *carbon taxes* on each unit of CO_2 emitted by fossil fuels (especially coal and gasoline) or input-based *energy taxes* on each unit of fossil fuel (especially coal and gasoline) that is burned. Decreasing taxes on income, labour, and profits to offset increases in consumption taxes on carbon emissions or fossil fuel use could help make such a strategy more politically acceptable.

A second strategy is to *level the economic playing field* by greatly increasing government subsidies for energy-efficiency and carbon-free renewable-energy technologies, carbon sequestration, and more sustainable agriculture, and by phasing out subsidies and tax breaks for using fossil fuels.

The third strategy is *technology transfer*. Governments of developed countries could fund the transfer of energy-efficiency, carbon-free renewable-energy, carbon-sequestration, and more sustainable agriculture technologies to developing countries. Increasing the current tax on each international currency transaction by a quarter of a penny could finance this technology transfer, which would then generate wealth for developing countries.

How Can We Use the Marketplace to Reduce or Prevent Greenhouse Gas Emissions? Emissions Trading

Establishing a global emissions trading program could help reduce greenhouse gas emissions.

An economic approach to slow global warming is to agree to global and national limits on greenhouse gas emissions and encourage industries and countries to meet these limits by selling and trading greenhouse gas emission permits in the marketplace. This approach stimulates companies to develop new technologies to reduce greenhouse gas emissions and increase profits. In the United States, this market approach has been used to reduce SO_2 emissions.

In a greenhouse gas emissions trading program, industries and countries could earn greenhouse gas emission credits by improving energy efficiency, switching from coal to natural gas, and adopting certain farming, ranching, and soil-building and conservation practices. Credits could also be earned by switching from coal and other fossil fuels to forms of carbon-free renewable energy such as solar, wind, hydrogen, and geothermal. For example, a coal-burning company in Illinois could earn emission credits by building a wind farm in Oregon.

In addition, credits could be earned by sequestering CO_2 from the atmosphere by reforestation or by injecting it into the deep ocean or secure underground reservoirs (Figure 21-19). For example, a coal-burning power plant in Saskatchewan might earn credits by financing a CO_2-removing reforestation project in New Brunswick or Costa Rica.

Companies or countries that manage to produce fewer emissions than their permits allowed could sell some of their credits to other participants. As a result, participants that devise innovative ways to reduce greenhouse gas production are rewarded by increased profit. And participants that produce excess amounts of greenhouse gas face increased costs because they are fined or have to buy extra permits from participants who have earned credits by reducing their emissions.

Some analysts believe this market-based approach is more politically and economically feasible than relying primarily on government regulation to impose taxes on carbon emissions or fuel used. Other analysts point to some problems with emissions trading. One is that carbon fuels are burned in so many homes, vehicles, factories, and crop fields that it would be difficult to monitor compliance. For that reason, many analysts think that emissions trading programs should be used in conjunction with other approaches, such as taxes on fossil fuel use, significant government subsidies for energy efficiency and renewable energy, and removal of subsidies for fossil fuels.

Another problem is that it is politically difficult for the world's countries to agree on what should count as credits or how any such credits should be divided among nations.

Can We Afford to Reduce the Threat of Global Warming? Not Acting Will Probably Cost More

It will very likely cost us less to help slow and adapt to global warming now than to deal with its harmful effects later.

Some economists project that the costs of reducing CO_2 emissions will greatly exceed the projected benefits. Other economists criticize these models as being unrealistic and too gloomy for two reasons. *First,* they do not include the huge cost savings from implementing many of the strategies listed in Figure 21-18 such as improving energy efficiency. *Second,* they underestimate the ability of the marketplace to act rapidly when money is to be made from reducing greenhouse gas emissions.

According to a 2001 study by the UN Environment Programme, *projected global warming will cost the world* *economy more than $300 billion (U.S.) annually by 2050* unless nations make strong efforts to curb greenhouse gas emissions.

According to a number of economic studies, implementing the strategies listed in Figure 21-18 would boost global and national economies, provide much-needed jobs (especially in developing countries with large numbers of unemployed and underemployed people), and *cost much less than trying to deal with the harmful effects of these problems.*

21-8   WHAT IS BEING DONE TO REDUCE GREENHOUSE GAS EMISSIONS?

What Is the Kyoto Protocol? A Controversial International Agreement

Getting countries to agree on reducing their greenhouse gas emissions is difficult.

In December 1997, more than 2 200 delegates from 161 nations met in Kyoto, Japan, to negotiate a treaty to help slow global warming. The resulting *Kyoto Protocol* required 39 developed countries to cut emissions of CO_2, CH_4, and N_2O to an average of about 5.2% below 1990 levels by 2012. The initial steps of the protocol were directed at these 39 countries because they were responsible for a majority of the world's CO_2 emissions (58% in 1999) and thus should take the lead in reducing their emissions.

The protocol did not require poorer developing countries to make cuts in their greenhouse gas emissions until a later version of the treaty. It did allow greenhouse gas emissions trading among participating countries. By mid-2004, the Kyoto Protocol had been ratified by more than 120 countries.

The Kyoto Protocol, the world's first binding agreement that set targets to reduce greenhouse gas emissions, has been praised by many climate analysts as a small but important step in attempting to slow global warming. Opponents of the agreement claim that it would be expensive to implement, result in loss of jobs, and make participating countries less able to compete economically. Groups such as the Suzuki Foundation, the Pembina Institute, and the Sierra Club of Canada argue that Kyoto-linked energy efficiencies will save money in the long run, reduce pollution, improve health, and create new kinds of jobs.

In 2001, President George W. Bush withdrew U.S. participation from the Kyoto Protocol because he argued that it was too expensive and did not require reductions in emissions by developing countries such as China and India that have large and increasing emissions of greenhouse gases. He also stated that the plan would hurt the U.S. economy and cost American

workers their jobs. As an alternative to Kyoto, the Bush administration pursued a "made-in-the-U.S.A." solution that involved reducing power plant emissions and offering incentives to businesses to voluntarily curb production of greenhouse gases by an estimated 4.5% over 10 years. Critics argued that by proposing a plan that was considerably weaker than the 33% reduction sought by the Kyoto Protocol, the Bush administration was essentially protecting the fossil fuel industry.

What Is Canada's Position on the Kyoto Protocol? Inconsistent

While past Liberal governments supported the Kyoto Protocol, the Conservative government elected in 2006 sought a "made-in-Canada" alternative.

Canada's involvement with global warming issues began in 1988, almost 10 years before Kyoto, when Canadian Prime Minister Brian Mulroney and Norwegian Prime Minister Gro Harlem Bruntland co-hosted the Toronto Conference on the Changing Atmosphere. This meeting identified global warming as a major threat and called for a 20% reduction of greenhouse gas emissions by 2005.

In 1992, the Earth Summit (or Rio Convention) was held in Rio de Janeiro, Brazil. At this meeting—which was chaired by Canadian environmentalist and diplomat Maurice Strong—Canada, the United States, and other countries ratified an agreement to stabilize 1990 greenhouse gas emissions by 2000.

At the 1997 Kyoto Convention in Japan, participating counties decided that the original targets of the Earth Summit were too weak. It was agreed that 1990 greenhouse gas emissions should be reduced by 5% between 2008 and 2012. Canada and the United States both signed the protocol and set targets of 6% and 7%, respectively.

In 2002, a year after President W. George Bush withdrew U.S. support, Prime Minister Jean Chrétien ratified the Kyoto Protocol in the House of Commons, thereby committing Canada to a 6% reduction in greenhouse gas emissions. In 2003, the Canadian government allotted $2 billion to Kyoto initiatives over the next five years. The government also compiled a list of the major emitting industries and began negotiating greenhouse gas reductions.

In December 2005, Canada hosted the United Nations Climate Change Conference in Montreal. At this meeting, which was chaired by Environment Minister Stéphane Dion, Kyoto's 159 members agreed to begin negotiating for greenhouse gas emissions beyond 2012, after the Kyoto agreement expires. Although this meeting was heralded as a great success, environmental groups pointed out that the host country had made little progress in reducing its own greenhouse gas emissions: Canada's 2004 emissions were 758 million tonnes—34% higher than the Kyoto target.

In 2006, Canadian Prime Minister Stephen Harper followed the example set by George W. Bush and proposed what he called a "made-in-Canada" solution to the problem of greenhouse gas emissions. In October of that year, Harper's minority Conservative government unveiled its Clean Air Act, which sought to cut greenhouse gas emissions by 45% to 65% by 2050. The opposition parties and environmental activists attacked the proposed legislation for not imposing fixed caps on greenhouse gas emissions until 2050. Moreover, the Clean Air Act made no reference to the Kyoto Protocol.

It is too soon to judge the effectiveness of the Clean Air Act. The act (introduced to Parliament as Bill C-30) provided the government with the authority to regulate air pollutants and greenhouse gases, but it didn't impose immediate deadlines or targets. Some programs are now in effect (aimed at improving transportation efficiency, for example), and more will be developed over time (Blakes, 2006; Parliament of Canada, 2007; http://www.canadaglobalwarming.com).

Meanwhile, Canada's greenhouse gas emissions reached an all-time high in 2007 (751 Mt). Levels have since declined in 2008 (731 Mt), 2009 (690 Mt), and 2010 (692 Mt) (Environment Canada, 2012b). One could argue that some of this has to do with the sluggish economy of the last few years; however, time will begin to tell as trends in greenhouse gases and the economy play out further.

Figure 21-20 shows trends in Canada's greenhouse gas emissions from 1990 to 2020, as well as some emission targets. Canada signed the Copenhagen Accord in 2009; this is a nonbinding agreement by which our government agreed to lower greenhouse gas emissions 17% below our 2005 emissions (i.e., 607 Mt) by 2020. This is considerably less ambitious than the original Kyoto commitment (16% below our 1990 baseline, i.e., 558 Mt).

Canada formally withdrew from the Kyoto Protocol in December 2011 amid strong criticism from the international community. Environment Minister Peter Kent said that Canada would not be able to meet its Kyoto commitments and would face enormous financial penalties under the treaty unless it withdrew. As well, he suggested that the Kyoto Protocol would not work because it didn't include the two largest emitters of greenhouse gases, China and the United States ("Canada Pulls Out," 2011; Vaughn, 2011).

We will follow developments with Canada's Clean Air Act, the Kyoto Protocol, and post–Kyoto Protocol negotiations at the book's website (http://www.nelson.com/livingintheenvironment3e.com).

SELF CHECK

Given that CO_2 makes up 79% of Canada's greenhouse gases (CH_4 13%, N_2O 7%, and other greenhouse gases 1%) and that 81% of our greenhouse gases are emitted through our use of energy (45% stationary combustion, 28% transportation, and 8% "fugitive" greenhouse gases that escape though incidents such fuel spills and leaks), how would *you* proceed to lower greenhouse gas emissions in time to meet the Copenhagen target?

For further ideas, see Environment Canada's *National Inventory Report 1990–2010* at http://ec.gc.ca/.

What Are Some Countries, Businesses, and Cities Doing to Help Delay Global Warming? Good News

Many countries, companies, and cities are reducing their greenhouse gas emissions, improving energy efficiency, and increasing their use of carbon-free renewable energy.

Many countries are reducing their greenhouse gas emissions. For example, by 2000 Great Britain had reduced its CO_2 emissions to its 1990 level, well ahead of its Kyoto target goal. It did this mostly by relying more on natural gas than on coal, improving energy efficiency in industry and homes, and reducing gasoline use by raising its tax on gasoline. Between 2000 and 2050, Great Britain aims to cut its CO_2 emissions by 60%, mostly by improving energy efficiency and by relying on renewable resources for 20% of its energy by 2030. To help accomplish this goal, the government has greatly increased research and development spending for renewable energy and tax breaks for renewable energy.

China is taking steps to reduce its dependence on coal by increasing the energy efficiency of its industries, and by pursing the development of

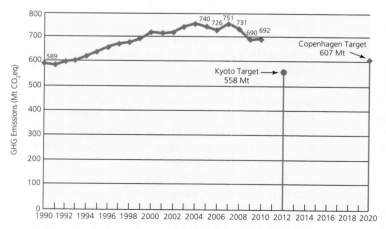

FIGURE 21-20 Canadian greenhouse gas emissions from 1990 to 2010. The Canadian government has withdrawn from its commitment to meet the Kyoto target but has agreed to meet the Copenhagen target by 2020. (National Inventory Report, http://ec.gc.ca/publications/A91164E0-7CEB-4D61-841C-EA8BAA223F9/Executive-Summary-2012_WEB-v3.pdf, Environment Canada, 2012. Reproduced with the permission of the Minister of Public Works and Government Services Canada, 2012.)

other energy sources such as hydro (for example, the Three Gorges Dam, p. 347) and fusion (for example, the ITER Project, p. 414). As well, China is becoming a world leader at developing solar cells, wind turbines, high-tech batteries, and electric cars.

A growing number of major global companies, such as Alcoa, DuPont, IBM, Toyota, BP Amoco, and Shell, have established targets to reduce their greenhouse gas emissions by 10–65% from 1990 levels. For example, BP Amoco has already met goals that exceed those in the Kyoto Protocol at no net cost to the company. Wal-Mart has become the world's largest retailer of energy-efficient light bulbs. It also saves money by using such devices; for example, Wal-Mart has reduced its energy costs by $12 million (U.S.) per year by using energy-efficient LED lights in its refrigeration units. Canada Post has commissioned a fleet of fuel-efficient delivery vehicles that will reduce greenhouse gas emissions by 90%.

Since 1990, governments in more than 500 cities around the world have established programs to reduce their greenhouse gas emissions. See Calgary's ecological footprint on p. 11.

CONSIDER, DISCUSS, OR DEBATE

What is your community doing? Figure 21-21 lists some things you can do to cut your CO_2 emissions. How many of these things are you doing?

What Can You Do?

Reducing CO_2 Emissions

- Drive a fuel-efficient car, walk, bike, carpool, and use mass transit
- Use energy-efficient windows
- Use energy-efficient appliances and lights
- Heavily insulate your house and seal all drafts
- Reduce garbage by recycling and reuse
- Insulate your hot water heater
- Use compact fluorescent bulbs
- Plant trees to shade your house during summer
- Set water heater no higher than 49°C (120°F)
- Wash laundry in warm or cold water
- Use low-flow shower head

FIGURE 21-21 **What can you do?** Ways to reduce your annual emissions of CO_2.

How Can We Prepare for Global Warming? Get Ready for Change

A growing number of countries and cities are looking for ways to cope with the harmful effects of climate change.

According to global climate models, the world needs to cut current emissions of greenhouse gases (not just CO_2) 50–85% by 2050 to stabilize concentrations of such gases in the atmosphere. That large reduction in emissions is extremely unlikely for political and economic reasons because it would require rapid, widespread changes in industrial processes, energy sources, transportation options, and individual lifestyles.

As a result, a growing number of climate analysts and economists suggest that we should also begin preparing for the possible effects of long-term atmospheric warming and climate change. Figure 21-22 (p. 530) shows some ways to implement this *adaptation* strategy.

CONSIDER, DISCUSS, OR DEBATE

Which of the solutions presented in Figure 21-22 do you favour? What other solution(s) would you add to the ones presented here?

Why Are Global Warming and Climate Change Such Difficult Problems to Deal With? A Complex, Long-Term, and Controversial Challenge

Global warming and climate change are hard to deal with because they have many causes (some poorly understood); their effects are long-term and uneven; and there is controversy over how they should be addressed.

Several characteristics of global warming and climate change pose difficult and often controversial scientific, economic, political, and ethical questions about how to address these threats.

First, these problems have many complex and still poorly understood causes and effects. *Second*, they are long-term problems. Elected officials who have to make tough decisions about dealing with these issues will be long gone when the beneficial or harmful effects of their actions occur. The long-term effects of climate change also raise an important ethical question. How much are we willing to change or sacrifice *now* for benefits that may not be realized in our lifetimes but could greatly benefit our children, grandchildren, and the plants and animals that we share the planet with?

Third the harmful and beneficial effects of climate change are uneven. There will be winners and losers. Winning nations are less likely to bring about controversial changes or spend large sums of money to slow down something that will benefit them. The catch: we do not know which countries and parts of countries

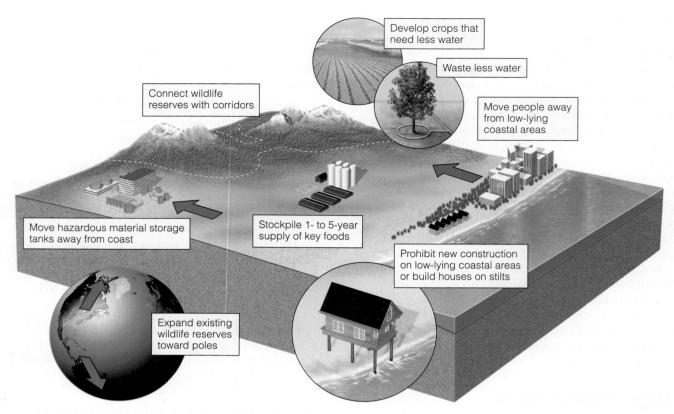

FIGURE 21-22 Solutions: ways to prepare for the possible long-term effects of global warming.

will be winners and losers until it is too late to avoid harmful effects.

Fourth, reducing greenhouse gas emissions will take unprecedented international response to a global problem that is of uncertain magnitude. And this must be done using political and economic systems not designed to deal with long-term threats.

Because of these characteristics, you can see why so many analysts believe that responding to this threat is one of the most important and challenging dilemmas we face.

CONSIDER, DISCUSS, OR DEBATE

Some countries have refused to sign the Kyoto Protocol because of the perceived economic costs of implementing targets on greenhouse gas emissions. How do these costs compare to the potential costs (flooded cities, damaged crops, etc.) of doing nothing to reduce greenhouse gas emissions?

21-9 OZONE DEPLETION IN THE STRATOSPHERE

What Is the Threat from Ozone Depletion? A Clear Danger

Less ozone in the stratosphere will allow more harmful UV radiation to reach the Earth's surface.

The **ozone layer** in the lower stratosphere (Figures 20-2, p. 477, and 20-3, p. 478) keeps about 95% of the sun's harmful ultraviolet (UV) radiation from reaching the Earth's surface. Measuring instruments on balloons, aircraft, and satellites show considerable seasonal depletion (thinning) of ozone concentrations in the stratosphere above Antarctica and the Arctic. Similar measurements reveal a lower overall loss of stratospheric ozone everywhere except over the tropics.

Based on these measurements and on mathematical and chemical models, the overwhelming consensus of researchers in this field is that **ozone depletion** (thinning) in the stratosphere is a serious threat to humans, other animals, and some of the sunlight-driven primary producers (mostly plants) that support the Earth's food.

What Causes Ozone Depletion? From Dream Chemicals to Nightmare Chemicals

Widespread use of a number of useful and long-lived chemicals has reduced ozone levels in the stratosphere.

Thomas Midgley, Jr., a General Motors chemist, discovered the first *chlorofluorocarbon (CFC)* in 1930, and chemists developed similar compounds to create a family of highly useful CFCs. The two most widely used are CFC-11 (trichlorofluoromethane, CCl_3F) and CFC-12 (dichlorodifluoromethane, CCl_2F_2), known by their trade name, **Freon**s.

These chemically stable (nonreactive), odourless, nonflammable, nontoxic, and noncorrosive compounds seemed to be dream chemicals. Inexpensive to manufacture, they became popular as coolants in air conditioners and refrigerators (replacing toxic sulphur dioxide and ammonia), propellants in aerosol spray cans, cleaners for electronic parts such as computer chips, fumigants for granaries and ship cargo holds, and bubbles in plastic foam used for insulation and packaging. Between 1960 and the early 1990s, CFC production rose sharply.

But it turned out that CFCs were too good to be true. In 1974, calculations by chemists Sherwood Rowland and Mario Molina at the University of California–Irvine indicated that CFCs were lowering the average concentration of ozone in the stratosphere. They shocked both the scientific community and the $28-billion-per-year CFC industry by calling for an immediate ban of CFCs in spray cans (for which substitutes were available).

Rowland and Molina's research led them to four major conclusions. *First,* CFCs remain in the troposphere because they are insoluble in water and chemically unreactive. *Second,* over 11–20 years these heavier-than-air chemicals are lifted into the stratosphere mostly through convection, random drift, and the turbulent mixing of air in the troposphere.

Third, once they reach the stratosphere, the CFC molecules break down under the influence of high-energy UV radiation. This releases highly reactive chlorine atoms (Cl), as well as atoms of fluorine (F), bromine (Br), and iodine (I), which accelerate the breakdown of ozone (O_3) into O_2 and O in a cyclic chain of chemical reactions, one of which is shown in Figure 21-23. This causes ozone in various parts of the stratosphere to be destroyed faster than it is formed.

Finally, each CFC molecule can last in the stratosphere for 65–385 years, depending on its type. During that time, each chlorine atom released from these molecules can convert hundreds of molecules of O_3 to O_2.

Overall, according to Rowland and Molina's calculations and later models and atmospheric measurements of CFCs in the stratosphere, these dream molecules had turned into global ozone destroyers.

The CFC industry (led by DuPont), a powerful, well-funded adversary with a lot of profits and jobs at stake, attacked Rowland and Molina's calculations and conclusions. The researchers held their ground, expanded their research, and explained the meaning of their calculations to other scientists, elected officials, and the media. After 14 years of delaying tactics, DuPont officials acknowledged in 1988 that CFCs were depleting the ozone layer and agreed to stop producing them once they found substitutes.

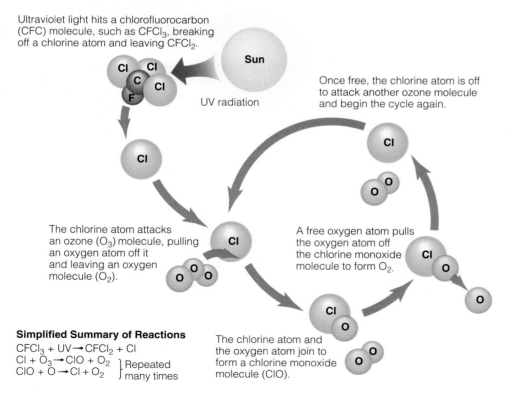

Ultraviolet light hits a chlorofluorocarbon (CFC) molecule, such as $CFCl_3$, breaking off a chlorine atom and leaving $CFCl_2$.

Sun

UV radiation

Once free, the chlorine atom is off to attack another ozone molecule and begin the cycle again.

The chlorine atom attacks an ozone (O_3) molecule, pulling an oxygen atom off it and leaving an oxygen molecule (O_2).

A free oxygen atom pulls the oxygen atom off the chlorine monoxide molecule to form O_2.

The chlorine atom and the oxygen atom join to form a chlorine monoxide molecule (ClO).

Simplified Summary of Reactions

$CFCl_3 + UV \rightarrow CFCl_2 + Cl$
$Cl + O_3 \rightarrow ClO + O_2$ }
$ClO + O \rightarrow Cl + O_2$ } Repeated many times

FIGURE 21-23 Natural capital degradation: simplified summary of how chlorofluorocarbons (CFCs) and other chlorine-containing compounds can destroy ozone in the stratosphere faster than it is formed. Note that chlorine atoms are continuously regenerated as they react with ozone. Thus they act as catalysts, chemicals that speed up chemical reactions without being used up by the reaction. Bromine atoms released from bromine-containing compounds that reach the stratosphere also destroy ozone by a similar mechanism.

In 1995, Rowland and Molina received the Nobel Prize in Chemistry for their work. In awarding the prize, the Royal Swedish Academy of Sciences said that they contributed to "our salvation from a global environmental problem that could have catastrophic consequences."

What Other Chemicals Deplete Stratospheric Ozone? More Culprits

A number of chemicals can end up in the stratosphere and deplete ozone there for up to several hundred years.

CFCs are not the only ozone-depleting compounds (ODCs). Others are *halons* and *hydrobromofluorocarbons* (*HBFCs*) (used in fire extinguishers); *methyl bromide* (a widely used fumigant); *hydrogen chloride* (emitted into the stratosphere by space shuttles); and cleaning solvents such as *carbon tetrachloride, methyl chloroform,* n-*propyl bromide,* and *hexachlorobutadiene.*

The oceans and occasional volcanic eruptions also release chlorine compounds into the troposphere. But most of these do not make it to the stratosphere because they dissolve easily in water and wash out of the troposphere in rain. Bromine compounds may be less likely to wash out of the troposphere, but further study is needed to confirm this possibility. Measurements and models indicate that 75–85% of the observed ozone losses in the stratosphere since 1976 are the result of ozone-depleting chemicals released into the atmosphere by human activities beginning in the 1950s.

What Happens to Ozone Levels Over the Earth's Poles Each Year? Levels Drop Each Winter and Spring

During four months of each year up to half of the ozone in the stratosphere over Antarctica is depleted.

In 1984, researchers analyzing satellite data discovered that 40–50% of the ozone in the upper stratosphere over Antarctica disappeared during the Antarctic late winter and spring (August–November), especially since 1976.

Figure 21-24 shows the seasonal variation of ozone with altitude over Antarctica during 2003. The observed loss of ozone above Antarctica often is called an *ozone hole.* A more accurate term is *ozone thinning* because the ozone depletion varies with altitude and location.

The total area of the stratosphere above Antarctica that suffers from ozone thinning during the peak season varies from year to year and in some recent years has covered an area greater than that of North

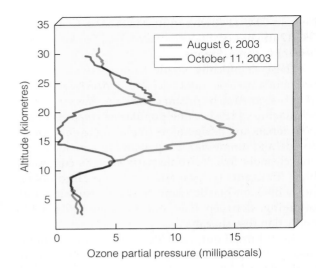

FIGURE 21-24 Seasonal variation of ozone level with altitude over Antarctica during 2003. Note the severe depletion of ozone during October (during the Antarctic spring, red line) and its return to more normal levels in August (during the Antarctic winter, green line). (Data from National Oceanic and Atmospheric Administration)

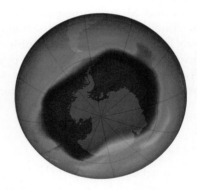

FIGURE 21-25 From September 21–30, 2006, the average area of the thin part of the ozone layer (the so-called ozone hole) was the largest ever observed, at 27.5 million square kilometres (10.6 million square miles). This image, captured by satellite instruments on September 24, 2006, uses the colours blue and purple to show where the ozone layer was thinnest. Note the outline of the Antarctic continent, which was experiencing high levels of incoming UV radiation. (NASA, 2006)

America. In 2006, the area of thinning was the largest size ever (Figure 21-25).

Measurements indicate that CFCs and other ODCs are the primary culprits. Each winter, steady winds blow in a circular pattern over the Earth's poles. This creates a *polar vortex:* a huge swirling mass of very cold air that is isolated from the rest of the atmosphere until the sun returns a few months later.

When water droplets in clouds enter this circling stream of extremely frigid air, they form tiny ice crystals. The surfaces of these ice crystals collect CFCs and other ozone-depleting chemicals in the stratosphere, setting up conditions for the formation of ClO, the molecule most responsible for the seasonal loss of ozone over the Antarctic.

When partial sunlight returns in October, the light stimulates ClO molecules, which reduce ozone (Figure 21-23). Within weeks, this cyclic reaction typically destroys 40–50% of the ozone above Antarctica (100% in some places).

As summer approaches and temperatures warm, the polar vortex begins to break up and mix again with the rest of the atmosphere. Then new ozone forms over Antarctica until the next dark winter.

When the vortex breaks up, huge masses of ozone-depleted air above Antarctica flow northward and linger for a few weeks over parts of Australia, New Zealand, South America, and South Africa. This raises biologically damaging UV-B levels in these areas by 3–10%, and in some years as much as 20%.

In 1988, scientists discovered that similar but usually less severe ozone thinning occurs in the stratosphere over the Arctic during the spring and early summer (February–May), with a seasonal ozone loss of 11–38% (compared to a typical 50% loss above Antarctica). When this mass of air above the Arctic breaks up each spring, large masses of ozone-depleted air flow south to linger over parts of Europe, North America, and Asia. Scientists think that the Arctic is unlikely to develop the large-scale ozone thinning found over the Antarctic. However, according to a model developed by scientists at NASA's Goddard Institute for Space Studies, ozone depletion over the Antarctic and Arctic will peak between 2012 and 2019. This will put further stress on delicate Arctic ecosystems that are already being pressured by the effects of global warming and by high concentrations of fat-soluble chemicals in food chains.

Why Should We Be Worried About Ozone Depletion? Life in the Ultraviolet Zone

Increased UV radiation reaching the Earth's surface from ozone depletion in the stratosphere is harmful to human health, crops, forests, animals, and materials.

Why should we care about ozone loss? Figure 21-26 lists some of the expected effects of decreased levels of ozone in the stratosphere. From a human standpoint the answer is that with less ozone in the stratosphere, more biologically damaging UV-A and UV-B radiation will reach the Earth's surface. This will give humans worse sunburns, more eye cataracts (a clouding of the eye's lens that reduces vision and can cause blindness if not corrected), and more skin cancers (Figure 21-27 and Connections, p. 534).

Humans can make cultural adaptations to increased UV radiation by staying out of the sun,

Natural Capital Degradation

Effects of Ozone Depletion

Human Health

- Worse sunburn
- More eye cataracts
- More skin cancers
- Immune system suppression

Food and Forests

- Reduced yields for some crops
- Reduced seafood supplies from reduced phytoplankton
- Decreased forest productivity for UV-sensitive tree species

Wildlife

- Increased eye cataracts in some species
- Decreased populations of aquatic species sensitive to UV radiation
- Reduced populations of surface phytoplankton
- Disrupted aquatic food webs from reduced phytoplankton

Air Pollution and Materials

- Increased acid deposition
- Increased photochemical smog
- Degradation of outdoor paints and plastics

Global Warming

- Accelerated warming because of decreased ocean uptake of CO_2 from atmosphere by phytoplankton and CFCs acting as greenhouse gases

FIGURE 21-26 **Natural capital degradation:** expected effects of decreased levels of ozone in the stratosphere.

protecting their skin with clothing, and applying sunscreens. However, plants and animals that help support us and other forms of life cannot make such changes except through biological evolution, a process that can take a long time.

DID YOU KNOW

The Brewer Ozone Spectrophotometer is the world's most accurate ozone-measuring instrument. Developed by Environment Canada scientists, it provides data used to produce the UV Index (see p. 535).

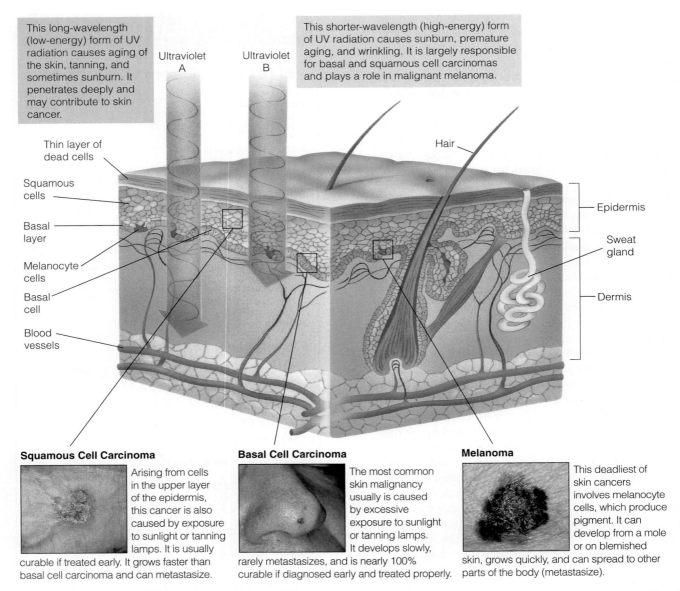

This long-wavelength (low-energy) form of UV radiation causes aging of the skin, tanning, and sometimes sunburn. It penetrates deeply and may contribute to skin cancer.

This shorter-wavelength (high-energy) form of UV radiation causes sunburn, premature aging, and wrinkling. It is largely responsible for basal and squamous cell carcinomas and plays a role in malignant melanoma.

Ultraviolet A

Ultraviolet B

Hair

Thin layer of dead cells

Squamous cells

Basal layer

Melanocyte cells

Basal cell

Blood vessels

Epidermis

Sweat gland

Dermis

Squamous Cell Carcinoma Arising from cells in the upper layer of the epidermis, this cancer is also caused by exposure to sunlight or tanning lamps. It is usually curable if treated early. It grows faster than basal cell carcinoma and can metastasize.

Basal Cell Carcinoma The most common skin malignancy usually is caused by excessive exposure to sunlight or tanning lamps. It develops slowly, rarely metastasizes, and is nearly 100% curable if diagnosed early and treated properly.

Melanoma This deadliest of skin cancers involves melanocyte cells, which produce pigment. It can develop from a mole or on blemished skin, grows quickly, and can spread to other parts of the body (metastasize).

FIGURE 21-27 Structure of the human skin and the relationships between ultraviolet (UV-A and UV-B) radiation and the three types of skin cancer. (The Skin Cancer Foundation)

Connections: What Cancer Are You Most Likely to Get? Look in the Mirror

Exposure to UV radiation is a major cause of skin cancers.

Research indicates that years of exposure to UV-B ionizing radiation in sunlight is the primary cause of *squamous cell* (Figure 21-27, left) and *basal cell* (Figure 21-27, centre) *skin cancers*. Together these two types make up 95% of all skin cancers. Typically, there is a 15- to 40-year lag between excessive exposure to UV-B and development of these cancers.

Caucasian children and adolescents who experience only one severe sunburn double their chances of getting these two types of cancers. Some 90–95%

of these types of skin cancer can be cured if detected early enough, although their removal may leave disfiguring scars.

A third type of skin cancer, *malignant melanoma* (Figure 21-27, right) occurs in pigmented areas such as moles anywhere on the body. Within a few months, this type of cancer can spread to other organs.

It kills about one-fourth of its victims (most under age 40) within five years, despite surgery, chemotherapy, and radiation treatments. Each year it kills about 100 000 people, mostly Caucasians. It can be cured if detected early enough, but recent studies show that some melanoma survivors have a recurrence more than 15 years later.

A 2003 study found that women who used tanning parlours once a month or more increased their chance of developing malignant melanoma by 55%. And a 2004 study at Dartmouth College found that people using tanning beds were 2.5 times more likely to develop basal cell carcinoma and 1.5 times more susceptible to squamous cell carcinoma.

Recent evidence suggests that about 90% of sunlight's melanoma-causing effect may come from exposure to UV-A (which is not blocked by window glass) and 10% from UV-B. Tanning booth lights and sunlamps emit mostly UV-A. Some sunscreens provide little or no protection from UV-A unless they contain chemicals such as zinc oxide or avobenzone. Read the fine print on the tube to see if such chemicals are present.

Evidence indicates that people (especially Caucasians) who experience three or more blistering sunburns before age 20 are five times more likely to develop malignant melanoma than those who have never had severe sunburns. About 10% of those who get malignant melanoma have an inherited gene that makes them especially susceptible to the disease. Figure 21-28 lists ways for you to protect yourself from harmful UV radiation.

21-10 PROTECTING THE OZONE LAYER

How Can We Protect the Ozone Layer? Say No

To reduce ozone depletion we must stop producing ozone-depleting chemicals.

The consensus of researchers in this field is that we should immediately stop producing all ozone-depleting chemicals. However, even with immediate and

What Can You Do?

Reducing Exposure to UV Radiation

- Stay out of the sun, especially between 10 a.m. and 3 p.m.

- Do not use tanning parlours or sunlamps.

- When in the sun, wear protective clothing and sunglasses that protect against UV-A and UV-B radiation.

- Be aware that overcast skies do not protect you.

- Do not expose yourself to the sun if you are taking antibiotics or birth control pills.

- Use a sunscreen with a protection factor of 15 or 25 if you have light skin.

- Examine your skin and scalp at least once a month for moles or warts that change in size, shape, or colour or sores that keep oozing, bleeding, and crusting over. If you observe any of these signs, consult a doctor immediately.

FIGURE 21-28 What can you do? Ways to reduce your exposure to harmful UV radiation.

consistent action, models indicate it will take about 50 years for the ozone layer to return to 1980 levels and about 100 years for recovery to pre-1950 levels. *Good news.* Substitutes are available for most uses of CFCs, and others are being developed.

In 1987, representatives of 36 nations meeting in Montreal developed a treaty commonly known as the *Montreal Protocol.* Its goal was to cut emissions of CFCs

CONNECTIONS

UV Light in Your Life

Environment Canada developed the UV Index to inform Canadians about the strength of the sun's UV radiation. The UV Index has been part of our weather reports since 1992.

UV Index	Category	Burn Times
8–10	Very High	10–20 minutes
6–7	High	20–30 minutes
3–5	Moderate	30–60 minutes
0–2	Low	>60 minutes

In general, the UV Index is highest in summer, and highest farther south.

Environment Canada recommends the use of hats, sunglasses, light protective clothing, and a sunscreen with a sun protection factor (SPF) rating of at least 15 that provides protection from both UV-A and UV-B (Environment Canada).

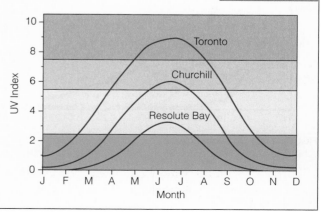

(but not other ozone depleters) into the atmosphere by about 35% between 1989 and 2000. After hearing more bad news about seasonal ozone thinning above Antarctica in 1989, representatives of 93 countries met in London in 1990 and in Copenhagen, Denmark (1992), and adopted the *Copenhagen Protocol,* an amendment that accelerated the phasing out of key ozone-depleting chemicals. Now 187 countries have signed these international agreements.

The Montreal Protocol is credited with being an unprecedented success that illustrates what can be accomplished through international coopera-tion. By the end of 2010, the consumption of 98% of all ozone-depleting substances controlled under the Montreal Protocol had been phased out (Figure 21-29). Atmospheric concentrations of these chemicals are declining and the ozone layer is expected to return to its pre-1980 condition by mid-century (UN, 2011, 2012).

Since ozone-depleting chemicals also function as greenhouse gases, the success of the Montreal Protocol has yielded a net reduction of planet-warming gases equivalent to eliminating 25 billion tonnes of CO_2 (UN, 2011).

SELF CHECK

World avoided: What would have happened if we had never detected and dealt with the problem of ozone thin-ning? What kind of world have we avoided by taking action to solve this problem?

Visit http://www.nasa.gov/topics/earth/features/world_avoided.html to see NASA's feature about the world we avoided by tackling this problem. Visit http://www.atmos-chem-phys.net/9/2113/2009/acp-9-2113-2009.html to see a scientific paper that delves into this topic.

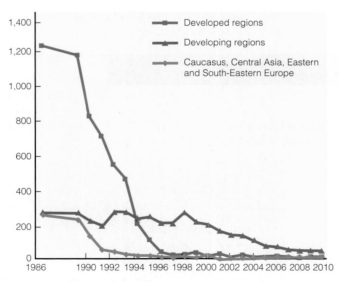

FIGURE 21-29 Solutions: Consumption of ozone-depleting substances (ODSs) between 1986 and 2010. Note that the Montreal Protocol, launched in 1987, led to dramatic reductions of ozone-depleting substances being released to the atmosphere. (United Nations. The Millennium Development Goals Report 2012, p. 48. Courtesy of the UNDP.)

The ozone protocols set an important precedent for global cooperation and action to avert potential global disaster by using *prevention* to solve a serious environmental problem. Nations and companies agreed to work together to solve this problem for three reasons. *First*, there was convincing and dramatic scientific evidence of a serious problem. *Second*, CFCs were produced by an easily identifiable group of man-ufacturers. *Third*, the certainty that CFC sales would decline over a period of years unleashed the economic and creative resources of the private sector to find even more profitable substitute chemicals.

CONSIDER, DISCUSS, OR DEBATE

How can we apply the lessons learned from dealing with global ozone depletion to solving the problems posed by global climate change?

21-11 CHECKING OUR PROGRESS AT ENSURING ENVIRONMENTAL SUSTAINABILITY

How Well Are We Proceeding Toward Millennium Goal 7? Problems with CO_2, but Success with Ozone-Depleting Substances

We have not been effective at decreasing CO_2 levels, but we have been very successful at controlling ozone-depleting substances by means of interna-tional conventions.

The eight Millennium Development Goals were introduced in Chapter 1 and have been addressed in Chapters 9, 10, 13, 14, 15, and 19 so far. Goal 7—aimed at ensuring environmental sustainability—has two indicators that relate specifically to CO_2, the major greenhouse gas emitted by human activity, and to the consumption of ozone-depleting substances (Figure 21-30). Other Goal 7 targets and indicators are discussed in Chapters 9, 13, and 15.

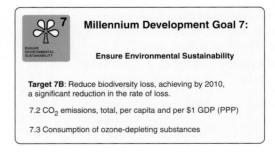

FIGURE 21-30 Millennium Development Goal 7, Target 7B, has two indicators that take aim at environmental sustainability through CO_2, the major greenhouse gas emitted by human activities, and through the consumption of substances that can damage the Earth's ozone layer. (Courtesy of the UNDP)

Both of the following indicators are part of Target 7B, aimed at *reducing biodiversity loss significantly by 2015*. The UN recognizes that global warming and thinning of the ozone layer would both impose pressures on biodiversity.

■ Indicator 7.3 monitors CO_2 emissions, total, per capita, and per \$1 GDP. Unfortunately, total CO_2 emissions have continued to rise by about 39% since 1990. There was a reduction in 2009 but this was temporary and related to the global economic crisis that was occurring. Per capita CO_2 emissions have been highest in developed countries (about 10 metric tons per person per year, compared to 25% of that amount in developing countries and 1% of that amount in sub-Saharan Africa). Emissions per unit of economic output decreased by 20% in developed countries, reflecting new technologies and efficiencies, but the opposite trend was true in developing countries. In short, CO_2 levels are not being effectively slowed.

As mentioned at the end of Chapter 13, biodiversity continues to decline.

■ Indicator 7.3 monitors *the consumption of ozone-depleting substances*. As mentioned on p. 536, the 1987 Montreal Protocol and the 1992 Copenhagen Protocol have effectively reduced ozone-depleting substances by 98%. The Earth's ozone layer is expected to return to 1980s levels by 2050. The lessons learned in controlling ozone-depleting gases give encouragement toward controlling greenhouse gases.

You can continue to monitor progress toward the Millennium Development Goals at websites such as http://www.mdgmonitor.org/.

The balance of scientific evidence demands effective steps now to avert damaging changes to the Earth's climate.

Royal Society of Canada

CHAPTER REVIEW

1. Review the Key Questions for this chapter on p. 507. Describe evidence that indicates the Arctic is warming. Why do the poles of the Earth have greater potential for temperature change than the equator? Why might a few degrees of temperature change have a huge impact on the Arctic?

2. What are five IPCC findings that support the scientific consensus that it is very likely (90–99%) the Earth's troposphere is warming? Why do scientists state their consensus in terms of probability?

3. Describe global warming and cooling over the past 900 000 years and during the last century. How do scientists learn about past temperatures and climates? What is the greenhouse effect and why is it so important to life on the Earth? How are organisms likely to react to sudden changes in the Earth's temperature? Given that the Earth's temperature has changed in the past, why do some scientists think that global warming could cause extra difficulties for organisms of our modern world?

4. How can positive feedback loops affect future temperature changes and thus global climate? Give two examples of such loops. Describe the role played by oceans in the regulation of atmospheric temperatures. What are three factors that could decrease its effect in moderating temperature increases?

5. Describe how each of the following might affect global warming and its resulting influences on global climate: **(a)** cloud cover and **(b)** air pollution. Briefly describe the projections of scientists on how global warming is likely to affect drought; ice cover; flooding; sea levels; permafrost; ocean currents; extreme weather; biodiversity; crop yields; and human health during this century.

6. What are three schools of thought about how to react to the threat of global warming? What are five reasons why it is difficult to deal with the problem of climate change due to global warming caused mostly by human activities? What are three major strategies for slowing projected climate change? What is *carbon capture and storage*? Describe three problems associated with capturing and storing carbon dioxide emissions.

7. List three things that governments could do to help slow projected climate change. What are the pros and cons of the Kyoto Protocol? How should governments of the world be reacting to climate change?

8. Give two examples of what some major corporations have done to reduce their carbon footprints. List five ways in which you can reduce your carbon footprint. List five ways in which we can prepare for the possible long-term effects of climate change.

9. Describe how human activities have depleted ozone in the stratosphere, and list five harmful effects of such depletion. Describe the relationships between higher UV levels and three types of skin cancer. What has the world done to help reduce the threat from ozone depletion in the stratosphere? Describe any relationships there may be between depletion of the ozone layer and global warming.

10. Describe how the four *scientific principles of sustainability* can be applied to seeking solutions for the problems of climate change (**Core Case Study**) and ozone depletion.

CRITICAL THINKING

1. What changes might occur in **(a)** the global hydrologic cycle (Figure 4-27, p. 80) and **(b)** the global carbon cycle (Figure 4-28, p. 82) if the troposphere experiences significant warming? Explain.

2. What will be the likely effect of clearing forests and converting them to grasslands and crops on **(a)** the Earth's reflectivity (albedo) and **(b)** the Earth's average surface temperature? Explain.

3. One way to help slow the rate of CO_2 emissions is to reduce the clearing of forests—especially in developing countries where intense deforestation is taking place. Should Canada and other developed countries pay poorer countries to stop cutting their forests? Explain.

4. What consumption patterns and other features of your lifestyle directly add greenhouse gases to the atmosphere? Which, if any, of these things would you be willing to give up to slow global warming and reduce other forms of air pollution?

5. Congratulations! You are in charge of the world. List your three most important actions for dealing with the problems of **(a)** global warming and **(b)** depletion of ozone in the stratosphere.

PROJECTS

1. Use the Internet to learn about arguments both for and against the Kyoto Protocol. List some of the strengths and weaknesses of each position. Where do you stand on this issue? Give reasons for your answer.

2. As a class, conduct a poll of students at your school to determine whether they believe stratospheric ozone depletion is a very serious problem, a moderately serious problem, or of little concern. Tally the results to see whether there are differences related to each poll participant's year in school, major, political party, religion, or gender.

3. Use the library or the Internet to determine how the current government policy on global warming compares with the policy suggestions made by various analysts and listed in Figures 21-18 (p. 524) and 21-22 (p. 530).

4. Write a one- to two-page scenario of what your life could be like by 2060 if nations, companies, and individuals do not take steps to reduce projected global warming caused at least partly by human activities. Contrast your scenario with the future you would expect if global warming is controlled by effective counter-measures. Compare and critique scenarios written by other members of your class.

5. If you drive a car, calculate how much CO_2 it emits per day. Multiply the kilometres driven by the number of litres of gasoline it takes to drive your car 100 kilometres and divide the result by 42 to get your daily CO_2 emissions in kilograms. In either case, add another 20% to include the CO_2 emitted in manufacturing the gasoline you used. Compare your results with other members of your class.

6. Use the library or the Internet to learn more about the following organizations: Climate Change (Government of Canada), David Suzuki Foundation, Environment Canada, Intergovernmental Panel on Climate Change, NASA, Pembina Institute, Royal Society of Canada, Sierra Club of Canada, World Meteorological Organization, and World Wildlife Fund.

7. List the most important steps that should be taken to slow global warming. Use the Internet to learn more about the merits of each of these steps. Would implementing them be advantageous even if the threat of global warming did not exist?

8. Use the Internet or visit your local drug store to determine which of the sunscreens available in Canada provides the greatest protection from both UV-A and UV-B.

ECOLOGICAL FOOTPRINT ANALYSIS

Per capita CO_2 emissions for North America are nearly five times the world average. According to a recent report from the International Energy Agency, the average North American is responsible for adding 19.6 tonnes of CO_2 per year to the atmosphere, compared with a world average of 4.23 tonnes. The table below is designed to help you understand the sources of your personal inputs of CO_2 into the atmosphere and how you can reduce your inputs.

Some typical data are provided in the "Typical Quantity per Year" column of the table. However, the calculations will be more accurate if you can substitute for these typical values information based on your own personal lifestyle, which you can enter in the blank "Personal Quantity per Year" column. For example, you could add up your monthly utility bills for a year and divide the total by the number of persons in your household to determine your utility use, and you could analyze your driving habits to determine how much fuel you use in automobile transportation.

After you complete the table, compare your emissions against the per capita North American average.

Your answer should be considerably less—roughly half the per capita value—because this computation accounts only for direct emissions. For instance, CO_2 resulting from driving a car is included, but the CO_2 emitted in manufacturing or disposing of the car is not.

Finally, you can check your result against an online greenhouse gas calculator such as http://www.livesmartbc.ca/homes/h_calc.html. Search for several online calculators and compare the results.

	Units of Measurement	Personal Quantity per Year	Typical Quantity per Year	Multiplier	Emissions per Year (kg CO_2)
Residential Utilities					
Electricity	kwh		4 500	0.7	
Heating oil	litres		168	2.2	
Natural gas	hundreds of cubic metres		11.3	193	
Propane	litres		36	1.3	
Coal	tonnes		–	4 118	
Transportation					
Automobiles	litres		2 730	1.9	
Air travel	kilometres		3 220	0.17	
Bus, urban	kilometres		19	0.02	
Bus, intercity	kilometres		0	0.06	
Rail or subway	kilometres		45	0.17	
Taxi or limousine	kilometres		3.2	0.28	
Other motor fuel	litres		41	2.2	
Household Waste					
Garbage	kilograms		355	0.75	
Recycled Items	kilograms		153	−2	
				Total (kilograms)	
				Total (metric tons)	

Source: This CO_2 calculator was developed by Thomas B. Cobb, Bowling Green State University, Bowling Green, Ohio (USA).

1. Calculate your carbon footprint. To calculate your emissions, first complete the blank "Personal Quantity per Year" column using your personal information (for a more accurate outcome) or using data from a typical utility bill and from other personally known information. If your information is not available, use the data listed in the "Typical Quantity per Year" column. Then, for each activity, calculate your annual consumption (using the units specified in the "Units of Measurement" column), and multiply your annual consumption by the associated number in the "Multiplier" column to obtain an estimate of the kilograms of CO_2 resulting from that activity. Finally, add the numbers in the "Emissions" column to find your carbon footprint, and express the final CO_2 result in kilograms and tonnes.

2. Compare your emissions with the per capita North American average of 19.6 tonnes of CO_2 per person per year and with those of your classmates.

3. Consider what actions you might take to reduce your carbon footprint by 20%.

22 Water Pollution

CASE STUDY

The Effects of Pollution on Biological Signals

In studying the effects of water pollution, scientists have traditionally measured the concentration of a pollutant that would kill or cause significant physiological damage to 50% of a test group of organisms in controlled laboratory tests (the LD50 or LC50; p. 456). Although this is useful in identifying the extreme effects of high levels of pollution, a more ecological level of analysis would require that effects be documented either in natural circumstances in the wild, or in the lab but using levels of pollutants that actually occur. Moreover, traditional testing usually involves exposure to one or two contaminants at a time, which does not replicate the mixtures of contaminants that aquatic organisms face in polluted bodies of water.

Dr. Reehan Mirza of Nipissing University is a leading expert in how aquatic organisms use chemical information to guide their activities; he believes that examining the responses of animals collected from contaminated water bodies gives a more stringent measure of how animals have actually been impacted by pollution. Chemical information is fundamentally important in water because most compounds dissolve well enough to be detected by aquatic organisms, and these cues tend to have greater persistence than other sensory information (such as visual or mechanical/auditory). Disruption of the ability to use chemical information could have a large impact on how effectively aquatic organisms interact with their environments.

Here are some findings of studies that Mirza has done with his students and colleagues:

- Juvenile yellow perch (*Perca flavescens*) and fathead minnows (*Pimephales promelas*) from metal-contaminated lakes do not recognize and respond to chemical alarm cues from wounded fish (Figure 22-1A). This puts them at a distinct disadvantage at surviving when a predator is in the vicinity.

- Normally, prey fish can learn to recognize novel fish as predators if the scent of that fish coincides with chemical alarm cues released by wounded fish. However, fathead minnows from contaminated lakes are unable to use chemical alarm cues to learn that smallmouth bass (*Micropterus dolomieu*) are predators (Figure 22-1B). Without this knowledge, the fathead minnows have a lower probability of avoiding predation.

The above examples illustrate how the abilities of organisms can be impacted by low levels of pollutants that exist in the environment. Studies such as these are causing us to rethink how water pollutants can cause tremendous harm to aquatic ecosystems, not strictly through toxicity but by disrupting the way aquatic animals gain information from their environments (Figure 22-1C). To learn more about this phenomenon and its implications, visit http://www.nipissingu.ca/about-us/people/pages/Pages/Reehan-Mirza.aspx.

(continued)

FIGURE 22-1A Fathead minnows (shown above) can normally rely on their ability to detect chemical alarm cues from wounded fish to warn them of impending danger.

FIGURE 22-1B Normal fathead minnows can quickly identify and remember this bass as a predator if its odour is associated with the odour of chemical alarm cues from other fish.

FIGURE 22-1C Reehan Mirza and his students study the abilities and disabilities of fish collected from polluted lakes to gain new insights about the impacts of pollution.

Today everybody is downwind or downstream from somebody else.

WILLIAM RUCKELSHAUS

22-1 TYPES, EFFECTS, AND SOURCES OF WATER POLLUTION

What Are the Major Types and Effects of Water Pollutants? Unseen Threats

Infectious bacteria, inorganic and organic chemicals, and excess heat pollute water.

Water pollution is any chemical, biological, or physical change in water quality that has a harmful effect on living organisms or that makes water unsuitable for desired uses. Table 22-1 (p. 542) lists the major classes of water pollutants along with their major human sources and harmful effects. Study this table carefully. Note that excessive heat is considered a water pollutant.

Table 22-2 (p. 542) lists some common diseases that can be transmitted to humans through drinking water contaminated with infectious agents. The World Health Organization (WHO) estimates that 5 million people die prematurely each year from waterborne diseases. This means that during your lunch hour about 570 people died from such diseases. Each year, diarrhea alone kills about 1.5 million people—about 90% of them children under 5 in developing countries. The number of children killed by largely preventable diarrhea in the past 10 years is greater than the number of people killed in all armed conflicts since World War II.

In North America, more than 1.6 million people a year become ill from infectious agents found in water and food. For example, in April 2001, 6 000 people in North Battleford, Saskatchewan, became ill after a protozoan parasite called *Cryptosporidium* contaminated the public drinking water supply. In 1993, a much larger outbreak involving the same parasite occurred in Milwaukee, Wisconsin; about 370 000 people became ill and at least 100 people with weakened immune systems died.

How Do We Measure Water Quality? Biology and Chemistry in Action

Scientists monitor water quality by using bacterial counts, chemical analysis, and indicator organisms.

Scientists use a number of biological and chemical methods to measure water quality. One involves measuring the number of colonies of *fecal coliform bacteria* (such as various strains of *Escherichia coli*) present in a water sample (Figure 22-2, p. 543). Various strains of these bacteria live in the colon or intestines of humans and other animals and thus are present in their fecal wastes. Although most strains of coliform bacteria do not cause disease, their presence indicates that water has been exposed to human or animal wastes that are likely to contain disease-causing agents.

To be considered safe for drinking, water should contain no colonies of coliform bacteria in a sample of 100 millilitres (about 1/2 cup). To be considered safe for swimming, it should have no more than 100 (200 in the United States) colonies per 100 millilitres. By contrast, raw sewage may contain several million coliform bacterial colonies in 100 millilitres of water.

When dangerous levels of fecal coliform bacteria are detected, scientists try to determine whether the source is from humans, various types of livestock, or wild animals such as birds or raccoons. A new field of science, called *bacterial source tracking (BST)*, uses molecular biology techniques to determine subtle differences in strains of *E. coli* based on their animal hosts.

Another important indicator of water quality is the level of *dissolved oxygen (DO)* found in water at 20°C (68°F). It can be determined using a variety of electronic probes or chemical tests, and is measured in parts per million (ppm) or milligrams of oxygen per litre (mg O/L). Some fish, such as trout, require high levels of dissolved oxygen (9 ppm) to thrive; other species, such as carp, can continue to thrive at lower levels (5 ppm). Fish and other aquatic species can occur only where the dissolved oxygen content of the water suits their needs. Various species of trout occur in

Table 22-1 Major Categories of Water Pollutants

INFECTIOUS AGENTS

Examples: Bacteria, viruses, protozoa, and parasitic worms
Major human sources: Human and animal wastes
Harmful effect: Disease

OXYGEN-DEMANDING WASTES

Examples: Organic waste such as animal manure and plant debris that can be decomposed by aerobic (oxygen-requiring) bacteria
Major human sources: Sewage, animal feedlots, paper mills, and food-processing facilities
Harmful effects: Large populations of bacteria decomposing these wastes can degrade water quality by depleting water of dissolved oxygen. This causes fish and other forms of oxygen-consuming aquatic life to die.

INORGANIC CHEMICALS

Examples: Water-soluble (1) acids; (2) compounds of toxic metals such as lead (Pb), arsenic (As), and selenium (Se); and (3) salts such as sodium chloride (NaCl) in ocean water and fluorides (F^-) found in some soils.

Major human sources: Surface runoff, industrial effluents, and household cleansers
Harmful effects: Can (1) make fresh water unusable for drinking or irrigation; (2) cause skin cancers and crippling spinal and neck damage (F^-); (3) damage the nervous system, liver, and kidneys (Pb and As); (4) harm fish and other aquatic life; (5) lower crop yields; and (6) accelerate corrosion of metals exposed to such water.

ORGANIC CHEMICALS

Examples: Oil, gasoline, plastics, pesticides, cleaning solvents, detergents, and medications
Major human sources: Industrial effluents, household cleansers, and surface runoff from farms and yards
Harmful effects: Can (1) threaten human health by causing nervous system damage (some pesticides), reproductive disorders (some solvents), and some cancers (gasoline, oil, and some solvents) and (2) harm fish and wildlife.

PLANT NUTRIENTS

Examples: Water-soluble compounds containing nitrate (NO_3^-), phosphate (PO_4^{3-}), and ammonium (NH_4^+) ions
Major human sources: Sewage, manure, and runoff of agricultural and urban fertilizers
Harmful effects: Can cause excessive growth of algae and other aquatic plants, which die, decay, deplete water of dissolved oxygen, and kill fish. Drinking water with excessive levels of nitrates lowers the oxygen-carrying capacity of the blood and can kill unborn children and infants ("blue-baby syndrome").

SEDIMENT

Examples: Soil, silt
Major human source: Land erosion
Harmful effects: Can (1) cloud water and reduce photosynthesis; (2) disrupt aquatic food webs; (3) carry pesticides, bacteria, and other harmful substances; (4) settle out and destroy feeding and spawning grounds of fish; and (5) clog and fill lakes, artificial reservoirs, stream channels, and harbours.

RADIOACTIVE MATERIALS

Examples: Radioactive isotopes of iodine, radon, uranium, cesium, and thorium
Major human sources: Nuclear and coal-burning power plants, mining and processing of uranium and other ores, nuclear weapons production, and natural sources
Harmful effects: Genetic mutations, miscarriages, birth defects, and certain cancers.

HEAT (THERMAL POLLUTION)

Examples: Excessive heat
Major human sources: Water cooling of electric power plants and some types of industrial plants
Harmful effects: Lowers dissolved oxygen levels and makes aquatic organisms more vulnerable to disease, parasites, and toxic chemicals. When a power plant first opens or shuts down for repair, fish and other organisms adapted to a particular temperature range can be killed by the abrupt change in water temperature—known as *thermal shock*.

Table 22-2 Common Diseases Transmitted to Humans Through Contaminated Drinking Water

Type of Organism	Disease	Effects
Bacteria	Typhoid fever	Diarrhea, severe vomiting, enlarged spleen, inflamed intestine; often fatal if untreated
	Cholera	Diarrhea, severe vomiting, dehydration; often fatal if untreated
	Bacterial dysentery	Diarrhea; rarely fatal except in infants without proper treatment
	Enteritis	Severe stomach pain, nausea, vomiting; rarely fatal
Viruses	Infectious hepatitis	Fever, severe headache, loss of appetite, abdominal pain, jaundice, enlarged liver; rarely fatal but may cause permanent liver damage
Parasitic protozoa	Amoebic dysentery	Severe diarrhea, headache, abdominal pain, chills, fever; if not treated can cause liver abscess, bowel perforation, and death
	Giardiasis	Diarrhea, abdominal cramps, flatulence, belching, fatigue
Parasitic worms	Schistosomiasis	Abdominal pain, skin rash, anemia, chronic fatigue, and chronic general ill health

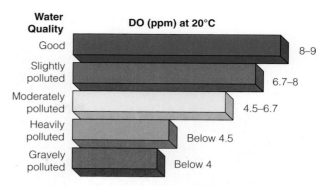

FIGURE 22-3 Water quality and dissolved oxygen (DO) content in parts per million (ppm) at 20°C (68°F). Only a few fish species can survive in water with less than 4 ppm of dissolved oxygen at this temperature.

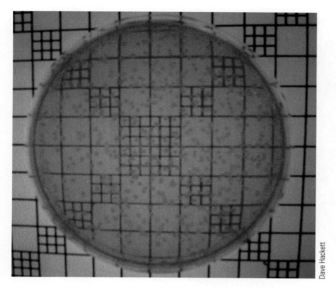

FIGURE 22-2 Fecal coliform bacteria tests are used to indicate the likely presence of disease-causing bacteria in water. A sample of water is passed through a filter to collect bacteria. These are placed on a plate of suitable medium (the orange circular shape) that supports coliform bacteria, such as *E. coli*, and allowed to grow for 24 hours. At that point the colonies (small spots throughout the plate) can be counted using the naked eye, assisted by the rectangular counting grids behind the plate.

fast-flowing cold streams or cold lakes where oxygen content is high; carp can be found in slow-flowing rivers and still ponds because they can tolerate much lower levels of dissolved oxygen than trout.

Scientists also determine the **biological oxygen demand (BOD)** of a sample taken from a body of water. This is the amount of oxygen consumed by aquatic decomposers such as bacteria over five days at 20°C. It reflects the amount of organic waste that is polluting the water, and which, by allowing "oxygen-demanding" decomposers to flourish lowers the dissolved oxygen that is available for other aquatic life forms.

Figure 22-3 shows the relationship between water quality and dissolved oxygen content at 20°C. A standard water temperature of 20°C is used so that the results of DO and BOD tests can be compared.

Scientists use *chemical analysis* to determine the presence and concentrations of inorganic and organic chemicals that pollute water. They measure sediment content by evaporating the water in a sample and weighing the resulting sediment. Suspended sediment clouds water. Scientists use an instrument called a colorimeter, or turbidity meter, to measure the turbidity (transparency) of a water sample.

Scientists can also monitor water pollution by using living organisms as *indicator species*. For example, the presence of trout, mayflies, and dragonflies—all of which require water with high oxygen content—is an indication of good water quality; carp, midge larvae,

and leeches, on the other hand, can tolerate more pollution and lower levels of oxygen. Scientists can also determine water quality by collecting and analyzing species such as cattails and mussels, which are known to concentrate toxins.

Genetic engineers are working to develop bacteria and yeasts (single-celled fungi) that fluoresce or glow in the presence of specific pollutants such as toxic heavy metals in the ocean, toxins in the air from chemical weapons, and carcinogens in food. This development of *biomonitors* or *biosensors* is a rapidly growing field that might interest you as a career choice.

What Are Point and Nonpoint Sources of Water Pollution? Concentrated and Diffuse Sources

Water pollution can come from single sources or a variety of dispersed sources.

Point sources discharge pollutants at specific locations through drain pipes, ditches, or sewer lines into bodies of surface water (Figure 22-4). Examples include factories, sewage treatment plants (which remove some but not all pollutants), underground mines, and oil tankers.

Because point sources are at specific places, they are easy to identify, monitor, and regulate. Most developed countries control point-source discharges of many harmful chemicals into aquatic systems. But there is little control of such discharges in most developing countries.

Nonpoint sources are scattered and diffuse and cannot be traced to any single site of discharge (Figure 22-4). Examples include acid deposition and runoff of chemicals into surface water from croplands, livestock feedlots, logged forests, urban streets, lawns, golf courses, and parking lots. There has been little progress in controlling water pollution from nonpoint sources because of the difficulty and expense of identifying and controlling discharges from so many diffuse sources.

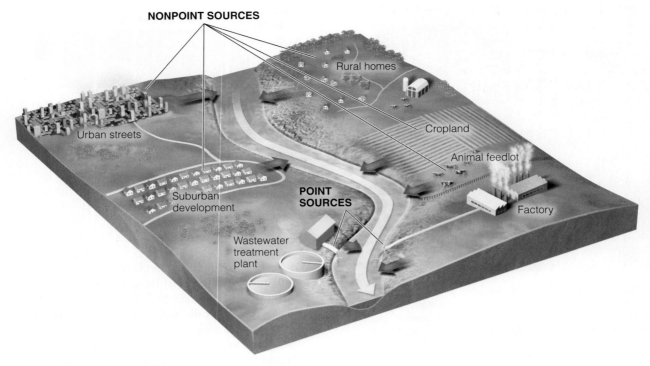

NONPOINT SOURCES

Rural homes

Cropland

Urban streets

Animal feedlot

Suburban
development

**POINT
SOURCES**

Factory

Wastewater
treatment
plant

FIGURE 22-4 Natural capital degradation: point and nonpoint sources of water pollution.
It is much easier to identify and control point sources than more dispersed, nonpoint sources.

What Are the Major Sources of Water Pollution? Supplying Food and Goods

The leading sources of water pollution are agriculture, industries, and mining.

Agricultural activities, such as ploughing fields to grow crops or raising large numbers of livestock, are by far the leading cause of water pollution. Sediment eroded from agricultural lands and overgrazed rangeland is the largest source. Other major agricultural pollutants include fertilizers and pesticides, bacteria from livestock and food-processing wastes, and excess salt from soils of irrigated cropland.

Industrial facilities are another large source of water pollution. *Mining* is a third source. Surface mining disturbs the Earth's surface, creating a major source of eroded sediments and runoff of toxic chemicals. Acidic compounds draining from active and abandoned subsurface and surface mines into streams can kill fish and other aquatic life (Figure 16-13, p. 374).

Is the Water Safe to Drink? For Most but Not All

One of every five people in the world lacks access to safe drinking water.

Good news. About 99% of the people in developed countries and 84% of those in developing countries have access to clean drinking water.

Bad news. According to the WHO, about 800 million people in developing countries do not have access to clean drinking water. As a result, each day about 10 000 people die prematurely from infectious diseases spread by contaminated water or the lack of water for adequate hygiene.

The United Nations estimates it would cost about $23 billion (U.S.) a year over 8–10 years to bring low-cost safe water and sanitation to the people in the world who do not have it. If developed countries paid half of that cost, it would amount to an average of about $20 a year for each person in such countries.

Connections: How Might Projected Climate Change Affect Water Quality? More Pollution

In a warmer world, too much rain and too little rain can increase water pollution.

Global warming projections include changes in precipitation: Some areas will get much more precipitation and other areas will get less. A moisture-laden atmosphere generates more intense downpours, which can flush more harmful chemicals, plant nutrients, and microorganisms into waterways. Massive flooding can spread disease-carrying pathogens by contaminating water treatment facilities and wells. It can also cause lagoons that store animal wastes, as well as sewer lines that carry both sewage and storm runoff, to overflow and release raw sewage into rivers and streams.

Prolonged drought can reduce river flows that dilute wastes. It can also spread infectious diseases more rapidly among people who lack enough water to stay clean. Warmer water temperatures can threaten aquatic life by reducing dissolved oxygen levels, and can increase the growth rates of populations of harmful bacteria.

22-2 POLLUTION OF FRESHWATER STREAMS

What Are the Water Pollution Problems of Streams? Pollution Overload and Low Flow

Flowing streams can recover from a moderate level of degradable water pollutants if their flows are not reduced.

Rivers and other flowing streams can recover rapidly from moderate levels of degradable, oxygen-demanding wastes and excess heat through a combination of dilution and biodegradation of such wastes by bacteria. But this natural recovery process does not work when streams are overloaded with pollutants or when drought, damming, or water diversion for agriculture and industry reduce their flows. Also, these natural dilution and biodegradation processes do not eliminate slowly degradable and nondegradable pollutants.

In a flowing stream, the breakdown of degradable wastes by bacteria depletes dissolved oxygen and creates an *oxygen sag curve* (Figure 22-5). This reduces or eliminates populations of organisms with high oxygen requirements until the stream is cleansed of wastes.

The depth and width of the oxygen sag curve and thus the time and distance needed for a stream to recover depend on several factors. They include the volume of incoming degradable wastes and the stream's volume, flow rate, temperature, and pH level. Similar oxygen sag curves can be plotted when heated water from industrial and power plants is discharged into streams.

What Have Developed Countries Done to Reduce Stream Pollution? Good and Bad News

Most developed countries have sharply reduced point-source pollution, but toxic chemicals and pollution from nonpoint sources are still problems.

Water pollution control laws enacted in the 1970s have greatly increased the number and quality of

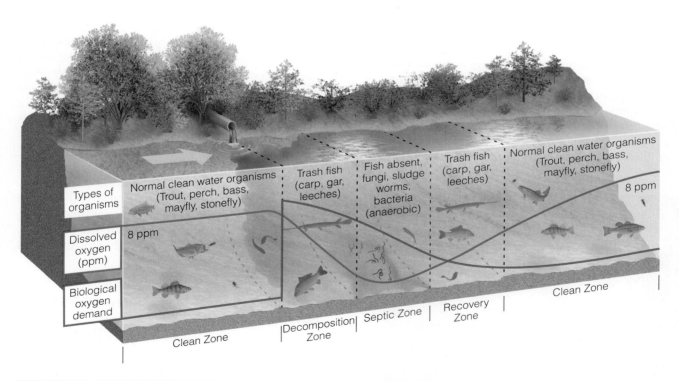

CENGAGENOW **ACTIVE FIGURE 22-5 Natural capital:** dilution and decay of degradable, oxygen-demanding wastes and heat in a stream, showing the oxygen sag curve (blue) and the curve of oxygen demand (red). Depending on flow rates and the amount of pollutants, streams recover from oxygen-demanding wastes and heat if they are given enough time and are not overloaded. *See an animation based on this figure at* CengageNow.

wastewater treatment plants in Canada and most other developed countries. Such laws also require industries to reduce or eliminate point-source discharges into surface waters.

These efforts have enabled Canada to hold the line against increased pollution by disease-causing agents and oxygen-demanding wastes in most of its streams. This is an impressive accomplishment given the rise in the country's industrial activity, resource consumption, and population since passage of these laws.

Before its rehabilitation, the Credit River in Mississauga, Ontario, was heavily polluted. Olympian Silken Laumann, who learned to row on the river, recalls the floating garbage. Then, in the late 1980s, volunteers from the West Credit Appreciation, Rehabilitation and Enhancement Project (WeCARE), the Credit River Anglers Association (CRAA), and the Credit River Alliance, among other groups, took on the task of cleaning up the river. They picked up garbage, planted trees, fenced livestock, reduced soil erosion, and worked to prevent stormwater runoff. Today the Credit River is a place for nature walks, wildlife, and water sports. It has also become a famous fishing river that supports salmon, steelhead, and trout—all of which require good water quality with high oxygen content (Figure 22-6).

One dramatic success story in the United States is the cleanup of Ohio's Cuyahoga River. It was so polluted that in 1959 and again in 1969 it caught fire and burned for several days as it flowed through Cleveland. The highly publicized image of this burning river prompted elected officials to enact laws limiting the discharge of industrial wastes into the river and sewage systems and provide funds to upgrade sewage treatment facilities. Today the river is cleaner and is widely used by boaters and anglers. This accomplishment illustrates the power of bottom-up pressure by citizens to spur elected officials to change a severely polluted river into an economically and ecologically valuable public resource. Individuals matter!

Another spectacular cleanup occurred in Great Britain. In the 1950s, the Thames River was little more than a flowing anaerobic sewer. Now, after more than 45 years of effort and hundreds of millions of dollars spent by British taxpayers and private industry, the Thames has made a remarkable recovery. Commercial fishing is thriving and the number of fish species has increased 20-fold since 1960. In addition, many species of waterfowl and wading birds have returned to their former feeding grounds.

There is also some *bad news*. Large fish kills and drinking water contamination still occur in parts of developed countries. Two causes of these problems are accidental or deliberate releases of toxic inorganic and organic chemicals by industries or mines and malfunctioning sewage treatment plants. A third cause is nonpoint runoff of pesticides and excess plant nutrients from cropland and animal feedlots (see Walkerton, p. 553).

What Have Developing Countries Done to Reduce Stream Pollution? Little Progress

Stream pollution in most developing countries is a serious and growing problem.

Available data indicate that stream pollution from discharges of untreated sewage and industrial wastes is a serious and growing problem in most developing countries. According to a report by the World Commission on Water in the 21st Century, half of the world's 500 major rivers are heavily polluted, most of them running through developing countries. Most of these countries cannot afford to build waste treatment plants and do not have or do not enforce laws for controlling water pollution.

Industrial wastes and sewage pollute more than two-thirds of India's water resources (Case Study, below) and more than 70% of the lakes and rivers in China. Only about 20% of the sewage produced in Chinese cities is treated. In Latin America and Africa, most streams passing through urban or industrial areas suffer from severe pollution.

Case Study: India's Ganges River—Religion, Poverty, and Health

Religious beliefs, cultural traditions, poverty, little economic development, and a large population interact to cause severe pollution of the Ganges River in India.

To India's Hindu people, the Ganges is a holy river. Each day more than 1 million Hindus bathe or take a "holy dip" in the river. Many people also drink its water and use it to wash their clothes.

FIGURE 22-6 Once a badly polluted river, the Credit River near Mississauga, Ontario, has been rehabilitated to provide top-notch fishing and recreational opportunities.

Bad news. The Ganges is highly polluted. About 400 million people—one-third of the country's population—live in the Ganges River basin. Very little of the sewage produced by these people and by the industries and 29 large cities in the basin is treated.

This situation is complicated by the Hindu belief in cremating the dead to free the soul and throwing the ashes in the holy Ganges to increase the chances of the soul getting into heaven. Traditionally, wood fires burn most bodies in the open air. This creates air pollution and helps deplete India's forests.

It also causes water pollution because many people cannot afford enough wood for cremation. As a result, many bodies are dumped into the river without cremation or are only partially burned. Decomposition of these bodies depletes dissolved oxygen and adds disease-carrying bacteria and viruses to the water. This problem is expected to get worse because about 19 million people are added to India's population each year—about a third of them to the Ganges River basin.

Good news. The Indian government has launched a plan to help clean up the river. It involves building waste treatment plants in the basin's 29 large cities and constructing 32 electric crematoriums along the banks of the river that can burn bodies more efficiently and at a lower cost than wood cremation. The government also introduced 25 000 snapping turtles to devour corpses.

Bad news. Most of the sewage treatment plants are not completed or do not work very well and only a few of the crematoriums have been completed. There is also concern that many Hindus will not abandon the traditional ritual of wood cremation or will not be able to afford any type of cremation.

This situation shows how religious and cultural conditions and poverty can affect environmental problems and solutions to such problems.

22-3 POLLUTION OF FRESHWATER LAKES

Why Are Lakes and Reservoirs More Vulnerable to Pollution Than Most Streams? Too Little Flow and Mixing

Dilution of pollutants in lakes is less effective than in most streams because most lake water is not mixed well and has little flow.

In lakes and reservoirs, dilution of pollutants often is less effective than in streams for two reasons. One is that lakes and reservoirs often contain stratified layers that undergo little vertical mixing (pp. 150–151). The other is that they have little flow. The flushing and changing of water in lakes and large artificial reservoirs can take from 1 to 100 years, compared with several days to several weeks for streams.

This means that lakes and reservoirs are more vulnerable than streams to contamination by runoff or discharge of plant nutrients, oil, pesticides, and toxic substances such as lead, mercury, and selenium. These contaminants can kill bottom life and fish and birds that feed on contaminated aquatic organisms. Many toxic chemicals and acids also enter lakes and reservoirs from the atmosphere (pp. 489 and 608).

As they pass through food webs in lakes, the concentrations of some chemicals can be biologically magnified. Examples include DDT (Figure 19-4, p. 455), PCBs (Figure 22-7, p. 548), some radioactive isotopes, and some mercury compounds.

What Is Cultural Eutrophication and How Can It Be Reduced? Too Much of a Good Thing

Various human activities can overload lakes with plant nutrients, which decrease dissolved oxygen and kill some aquatic species.

Eutrophication is the name given to the natural nutrient enrichment of lakes, mostly from runoff of plant nutrients such as nitrates and phosphates from surrounding land. Over time, some lakes become more eutrophic (Figure 7-16, right, p. 152) than others because of differences in the surrounding drainage basins.

An increase in plant nutrients can be beneficial to populations of floating phytoplankton that feed aquatic organisms. In turn, this can increase the growth rate and abundance of some fish and other desirable species.

But excessive inputs of nutrients can upset aquatic ecosystems. Near urban or agricultural areas, human activities can greatly accelerate the input of plant nutrients to a lake. This process is called **cultural eutrophication.** It is mostly nitrate- and phosphate-containing effluents from various sources that cause such a change (Figure 22-8, p. 549).

During hot weather or drought, this nutrient overload produces dense growths or "blooms" of organisms such as algae and cyanobacteria and thick growths of water hyacinths, duckweed, and other aquatic plants. These dense colonies of plant life can reduce lake productivity and fish growth by decreasing the input of solar energy needed for photosynthesis of other lake-dwelling organisms.

In addition, when the algae die, their decomposition by swelling populations of aerobic bacteria depletes dissolved oxygen in the surface layer of water near the shore and in the bottom layer. This oxygen depletion can kill fish and other aerobic aquatic animals. If excess nutrients continue to flow into a lake, anaerobic bacteria take over and produce gaseous decomposition products such as smelly, highly toxic hydrogen sulphide and flammable methane.

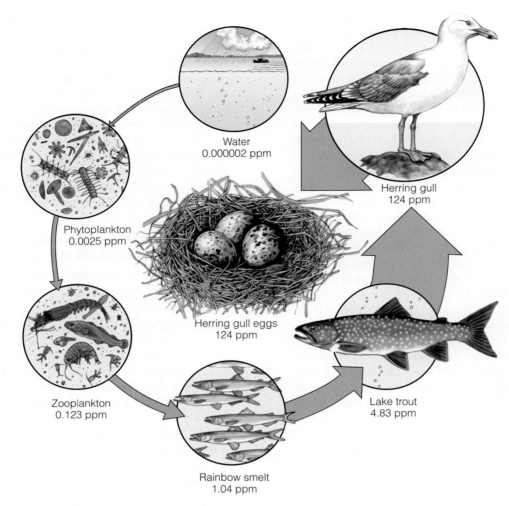

Water
0.000002 ppm

Phytoplankton
0.0025 ppm

Herring gull
124 ppm

Herring gull eggs
124 ppm

Zooplankton
0.123 ppm

Lake trout
4.83 ppm

Rainbow smelt
1.04 ppm

FIGURE 22-7 *Biological magnification* of PCBs (polychlorinated biphenyls) in an aquatic food chain in the Great Lakes. Most of the 209 different PCBs are insoluble in water, soluble in fats, and resistant to biological and chemical degradation—properties that result in their accumulation in the tissues of organisms and their biological amplification in food chains and webs. Although the long-term health effects on people exposed to low levels of PCBs are unknown, high doses of PCBs, when given to laboratory animals, produce liver and kidney damage, gastric disorders, birth defects, skin lesions, hormonal changes, smaller penis size, and tumours. Boys in Taiwan exposed to PCBs while in their mothers' wombs developed abnormally small penises. In North America, manufacture and use of PCBs have been banned since 1977. Before then, millions of metric tons of these long-lived chemicals were released into the environment. Many of them still exist in bottom sediments of lakes, streams, and oceans.

About 75% of Canada's lakes are still oligotrophic, but 70% of U.S. lakes show a high degree of cultural eutrophication. One-fourth of the lakes in China also suffer from cultural eutrophication.

Cultural eutrophication also occurs in marine ecosystems, especially in coastal waters and partially enclosed estuaries and bays. It also affects enclosed seas, such as the Mediterranean, Baltic, and Black Seas.

There are several ways to *prevent* or *reduce* cultural eutrophication. They include using advanced (but expensive) waste treatment systems to remove nitrates and phosphates before wastewater enters lakes, banning or limiting the use of phosphates in household detergents and other cleaning agents, and using soil conservation and land-use control to reduce nutrient runoff.

There are also several ways to *clean up* lakes suffering from cultural eutrophication. Examples are mechanically removing excess weeds, controlling undesirable plant growth with herbicides and algicides, and pumping air through lakes and reservoirs to avoid oxygen depletion (an expensive and energy-intensive method).

As usual, pollution prevention is more effective and usually is cheaper in the long run than cleanup.

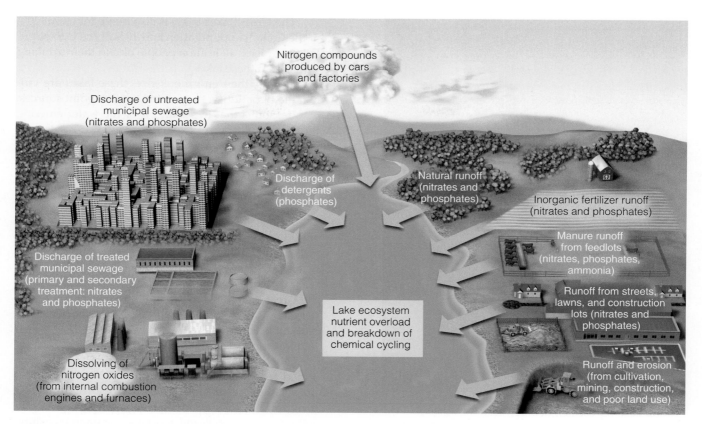

FIGURE 22-8 Natural capital degradation: principal sources of nutrient overload causing *cultural eutrophication* in lakes and coastal areas. The amount of nutrients from each source varies according to the types and amounts of human activities occurring in each airshed and watershed. The enlarged populations of algae and plants (stimulated by increased nutrient input) die. Then their decomposition by aerobic bacteria lowers levels of dissolved oxygen. This can kill fish and other aquatic life and reduce biodiversity and the aesthetic and recreational value of the lake.

Good news. If excessive inputs of plant nutrients are stopped, a lake can usually return to its previous state (Case Study, below).

Case Study: Canada's Experimental Lakes Area—A Famous Outdoor Laboratory

Researchers at Canada's Experimental Lakes Area (ELA) have produced world-class science aimed at solving major environmental problems.

Forty-five years ago there were many unknowns in water chemistry, but it was clear that major environmental impacts were being felt in the Great Lakes. Lake Erie, for instance, was so choked with algae and dead fish that many considered it a dying lake. Yet there was little agreement about the causes of this problem.

In 1967, the federal government established the Experimental Lakes Area (ELA) near Kenora, Ontario (Fisheries and Oceans Canada, 2010). It was here that David Schindler and other scientists performed "whole lake" experiments on bodies of water

much smaller than the Great Lakes. In one famous experiment, Lake #226 was divided by a sea wall. Nitrogen and carbon were added to the lake on one side of the wall, while nitrogen, carbon, and phosphate were added to the other side. The result was the prolific algal bloom illustrated in Figure 22-9. Reforms swiftly followed as governments in North America and Europe rushed to tighten controls over phosphorus in water, soap manufacturers began to produce phosphate-free products, and consumers altered their buying habits.

Researchers at Canada's ELA also shed light on the acid rain problem. At the height of the crisis in the mid-1980s, they deliberately acidified lakes and studied the effects on organisms; then they rebalanced the pH of the lakes with calcium carbonate and studied the lakes' recovery. In other experiments, ELA researchers demonstrated that mercury would be released by large hydroelectric projects that flooded out forests, and that greenhouse gases would be released by large projects that flooded peat bogs.

FIGURE 22-9 The experiment at ELA Lake #226 clearly showed that phosphate was the pollutant that caused algae to grow prolifically.

Research performed at Canada's Experimental Lakes Area has led to the publication of more than a thousand scientific papers. Since 1999, a number of ELA lakes have been used to study climate change. Since some of these lakes had served as controls in previous Experimental Lakes studies, scientists involved in this research have had access to 20 years of data showing warming and drying trends in the area.

Recently, the federal government has announced plans to stop funding the ELA in order to save money; this has caused a strong reaction from people concerned about science and the environment (McCarthy, 2012).

Case Study: Pollution in the Great Lakes—Hopeful Progress

Pollution of the Great Lakes has dropped significantly, but there is a long way to go.

The five interconnected Great Lakes of North America (Figure 22-10, p. 551) formed about 10 500 years ago when retreating glaciers melted and poured water into the land basins carved out by the slowly moving glaciers. These lakes contain at least 90% of the volume of fresh surface water in Canada and 20% of the volume of the world's fresh surface water.

The Great Lakes basin is also home for about 30% of the Canadian population and 10% of the U.S. population. At least 40 million people obtain their drinking water from these lakes.

Despite their enormous size, these lakes are vulnerable to pollution from point and nonpoint sources. One reason is that less than 1% of the water entering these lakes flows out to the St. Lawrence River each year. Another reason is that in addition to land runoff these lakes get atmospheric deposition of large quantities of acids, pesticides, and other toxic chemicals, often blown in from hundreds or thousands of kilometres away.

By the 1960s, many areas of the Great Lakes were suffering from severe cultural eutrophication, huge fish kills, and contamination from bacteria and a variety of toxic industrial wastes. The impact on Lake Erie was particularly intense because it is the shallowest of the Great Lakes and has the highest concentrations of people and industrial activity along its shores. Many bathing beaches had to be closed, and by 1970 the lake had lost most of its native fish.

Since 1972, Canada and the United States have joined forces and spent more than $20 billion (U.S.) on a Great Lakes pollution control program. This program has decreased algal blooms, increased dissolved oxygen levels and sport and commercial fishing catches in Lake Erie, and allowed most swimming beaches to reopen.

These improvements occurred mainly because of new or upgraded sewage treatment plants, better treatment of industrial wastes, and bans on use of detergents, household cleaners, and water conditioners that contained phosphates.

Despite this important progress many problems remain. Each August a large zone severely depleted of dissolved oxygen is likely to stretch across the bottom of the shallow Central Basin of Lake Erie. The oxygen-poor water in this zone kills fish and microorganisms that support the lake's food web. During the last 10 years, the time that the zone lasts has increased from two weeks to a month and scientists do not know why. Possible causes include oxygen depletion by zebra mussels (Case Study, p. 294), undetected inputs of phosphates from fertilizers through storm runoff sewers, an unknown naturally occurring cycle, or climate change.

Bad news. About three-quarters of the shoreline of the Great Lakes is not clean enough for swimming or for supplying drinking water. Much of the problem has to do with nonpoint land runoff of pesticides, fertilizers, and other chemicals emanating from agriculture and industry in the surrounding area. In addition, in the mid-1980s Environment Canada and the United States Environmental Protection Agency (EPA) identified 43 *Areas of Concern* (AOCs) where the water and sediment was

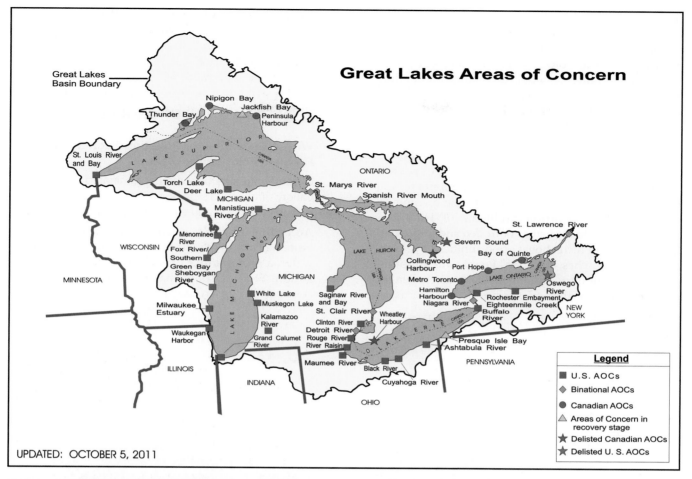

FIGURE 22-10 **Natural capital degradation:** In the mid-1980s, 43 *Areas of Concern* in the Great Lakes were identified as *hot spots* of toxic concentrations in water and sediments. By 2011, three Canadian AOCs (Collingwood Harbour, Severn Sound, and Wheatley Harbour) and one U.S. AOC (Oswego River) had been cleaned up and delisted. Of the 39 remaining AOCs, 9 are in Canada, 25 are in the United States, and 5 are shared by both countries. (United States Environmental Protection Agency, http://www.epa.gov/glnpo/aoc/index.html)

contaminated by toxins. The two countries were to develop and implement *Remedial Action Plans (RAPs)* for the recovery of each AOC.

So far, three Canadian sites have been cleaned up and delisted as AOCs: Collingwood Harbour in 1994, Severn Sound in 2003, and Wheatley Harbour in 2010. One U.S. AOC, Aswego River, was delisted in 2006. The remaining 39 AOCs are in various stages of recovery (see Environment Canada, 2012, and EPA, 2012, for more information).

Good news. Hamilton Harbour is an example of an AOC on the mend. Hamilton Harbour is the largest naturally protected harbour on the western shore of Lake Ontario. The 5 400-hectare (13 344-acre) area, also known as Burlington Bay, is protected by a natural sand bar. Other notable features are Cootes Paradise (a 250-hectare/618-acre marsh that provides crucial habitat for wildlife) and three streams—Grindstone, Red Hill, and

Spencer Creeks—that drain a 500-square-kilometre (193-square-mile) area into Hamilton Harbour.

Historically, the watershed was forested, and water entering the bay was clear. Abundant wildlife thrived, including a diverse fish population that supported a commercial fishery. Over time the watershed was settled, decreasing the quality of water arriving in the three streams. Local industry, urbanization, and agriculture further impacted Hamilton Harbour. By the early 1900s, there were serious problems with degraded water quality, sewer discharges, sediment accumulation, toxic spills, and impacts of heavy industry such as the nearby Stelco (recently renamed U.S. Steel Canada) and Dofasco steel mills. "Randle Reef," an area near the steel mills, was contaminated with coal tar and other chemicals and considered to be one of the most challenging remediation sites in Canada.

In 1987, the International Joint Commission (IJC) designated Hamilton Harbour as one of 43 AOCs in the Great Lakes. By 1992, a Remedial Action Plan (RAP) had been developed by a group of stakeholders that included public groups, government, and industry. The stakeholders were able to inspire action from a broad range of supporters. Money and effort was invested in restoring Cootes Paradise. Many of the toxic sediments throughout the bay were cleaned up or contained. Waterfront parks were established. Stelco changed its production methods in order to have less impact on the area. The City of Hamilton, and other nearby cities, agreed to improve their sewage systems.

The winning result is that diverse groups of people have learned to work together to tackle a common challenge. The pollution problems of Hamilton Harbour are gradually being controlled and improved. Educational and recreational opportunities have been flourishing. Beaches are open. People are adopting their waterfront once again. Some serious challenges remain, but more than 65 species of fish are using

Hamilton Harbour, and Cootes Paradise can now rival Point Pelee as an outstanding place to observe migrating birds. Hamilton Harbour is on the path to recovery. (For further information, visit http://www.hamiltonharbour.ca/.)

22-4 POLLUTION OF GROUNDWATER

Why Is Groundwater Pollution Such a Serious Problem? Not Easily Cleaned

Groundwater can become contaminated with a variety of chemicals because it cannot effectively cleanse itself and dilute and disperse pollutants.

According to many scientists, a serious threat to human health is the out-of-sight pollution of groundwater, a prime source of water for drinking and irrigation. Studies show that groundwater pollution comes from numerous sources (Figure 22-11). People

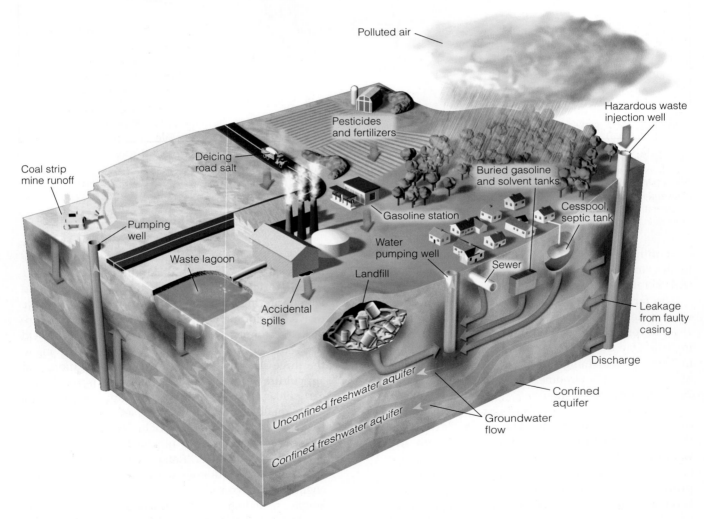

FIGURE 22-11 Natural capital degradation: principal sources of groundwater contamination in North America. Another source is **saltwater intrusion** from excessive groundwater withdrawal (Figure 15-18, p. 352).

who dump or spill gasoline, oil, and paint thinners and other organic solvents onto the ground also contaminate groundwater.

Although experts rate groundwater pollution as a low-risk ecological problem, they consider pollutants in drinking water (much of it from groundwater) a high-risk health problem. Once a pollutant from a leaking underground tank or other source contaminates groundwater it permeates the nearby porous layers of sand, gravel, or bedrock in the aquifer like water saturating a sponge. This makes removal of the contaminant difficult and costly.

Then the contaminated water slowly flows through the aquifer and creates a widening *plume* of contaminated water. If this plume reaches a well used to extract groundwater, the polluted water can get into drinking water and into water used to irrigate crops.

When groundwater becomes contaminated, it cannot cleanse itself of *degradable wastes* as flowing surface water does (Figure 22-5). One reason is that groundwater flows so slowly—usually less than 0.3 metre or 1 foot per day—that contaminants are not diluted and dispersed effectively. Another problem is that groundwater usually has much lower concentrations of dissolved oxygen (which helps decompose many contaminants) and smaller populations of decomposing bacteria. Also, the usually cold temperatures of groundwater slow down chemical reactions that decompose wastes.

Thus it can take hundreds to thousands of years for contaminated groundwater to cleanse itself of *degradable* wastes. On a human time scale, *nondegradable wastes* (such as toxic lead, arsenic, and fluoride) are there permanently.

What Is the Extent of Groundwater Pollution? Uncertain Overall, but Serious in Some Areas

Leaks from chemical storage ponds, underground storage tanks, and piping as well as seepage of agricultural fertilizers can contaminate groundwater.

On a global scale we do not know much about groundwater pollution because few countries go to the great expense of locating, tracking, and testing aquifers. But scientific studies in scattered parts of the world provide us with some *bad news*.

Organic chemicals are contaminating an increasing number of private wells and municipal groundwater supplies. Underground tanks storing gasoline, diesel fuel, home heating oil, and toxic solvents are leaking their contents into groundwater in North America (Figure 22-11). High concentrations of nitrates from fertilizers have been discovered in wells located in southern Ontario and the Prairie provinces. Other harmful sources of groundwater contamination include on-site septic systems, industrial chemical

spills, municipal landfills, road salts, and air contaminants captured within precipitating rain and snow.

Canada's water treatment system came under intense public scrutiny in May 2000, when contaminated drinking water left seven people dead and sickened over 2 300 in Walkerton, Ontario. The source of the contamination was *E. coli* bacteria in fertilizer manure that had leached into one of the town's wells during that spring's unusually heavy rainfall. Water officials detected the bacteria but failed to take immediate action. Beyond the human tragedy, the people of Walkerton suffered a variety of economic repercussions, including medical costs, legal fees, infrastructure repairs, and decreased property values. The Ontario government responded to the recommendations of a public inquiry into the tragedy by introducing the *Safe Drinking Water Act* (2002) and other new legislation and regulations. Municipalities across Canada upgraded their water facilities, training, and procedures. Governments at all levels made drinking water safety a much higher priority.

During this century, scientists expect many of the millions of underground tanks installed around the world in recent decades to corrode, leak, contaminate groundwater, and become a major global health problem. Determining the extent of a leak from a single underground tank can cost \$30 000–\$300 000, and cleanup costs range from \$12 000 to more than \$300 000. If the chemical reaches an aquifer, effective cleanup is often not possible or is too costly. *Bottom line:* wastes we think we have thrown away or stored safely can escape and come back to haunt us.

According to the WHO, an estimated 26 million people in China and 66 million in India drink groundwater contaminated with high levels of naturally occurring *fluoride* (F^-). This can cause crippling damage to the vertebrae of the neck and back and a variety of dental problems.

Groundwater used as a source of drinking water can also be contaminated with *nitrate ions* (NO_3^-), especially in agricultural areas where nitrates in fertilizer can be leached into groundwater. Nitrite ions (NO_2^-) in the stomach, colon, and bladder can convert some of the nitrate ions in drinking water to organic compounds, which can cause cancer in various organs in more than 40 test animal species. The conversion of nitrates in tap water to nitrites in infants under 6 months old can cause a potentially fatal condition known as "blue-baby syndrome," in which blood lacks the ability to carry sufficient oxygen to body cells.

Toxic *arsenic* (As) contaminates drinking water when a well is drilled into aquifers where soils and rock are naturally rich in arsenic. According to the WHO, more than 112 million people are drinking water with arsenic levels 5–100 times the WHO standard of 10 parts per billion (ppb). They include an estimated 30 million people in Bangladesh, 6 million in India's state of West Bengal, and 6 million in China. According to estimates by the WHO, long-term exposure to arsenic in drinking water is likely to cause 200 000–270 000 premature deaths from cancer of the skin, bladder, and lung in Bangladesh alone.

Good news. The United Nations Children's Fund (UNICEF) and several nongovernmental organizations in Bangladesh have started a program to evaluate wells serving several million people to identify those contaminated with arsenic and mark them with red paint.

Arsenic can also be released into the air and water by coal burning, copper and lead smelting, municipal trash incinerators, landfills containing arsenic-laden ash produced by coal-burning power plants, and use of certain arsenic-containing pesticides.

The international standard for arsenic in drinking water of 10 ppb was adopted in 1993 by the WHO and in 1998 by the European Union, and became the standard in Canada and the United States in 2006. But according to the WHO and other scientists, even the 10-ppb standard is not safe. Canada is considering lowering the standard to 5 ppb.

Solutions: How Can We Protect Groundwater? Monitor and Say No

Prevention is the most effective and affordable way to protect groundwater from pollutants.

Key factors in preventing bacterial contamination of groundwater include proper construction and maintenance of wells and infrastructure, and a well-trained staff that continuously monitors the water and stands poised to alert the public at the first sign of a problem.

Figure 22-12 lists ways to prevent and clean up chemical groundwater contamination. Treating a contaminated aquifer involves eliminating the source of pollution and drilling monitoring wells to determine how far, in what direction, and how fast the contaminated plume is moving. Then a computer model is used to project future dispersion of the contaminant in the aquifer. The final step is to develop and implement a strategy to clean up the contamination (Figure 22-12). This time-consuming and expensive process is somewhat like a blind surgeon trying to find and remove a cancer in your body before it grows too large.

Because of the difficulty and expense of cleaning up a contaminated aquifer, *preventing contamination is the most effective and cheapest way to protect groundwater resources* (Figure 22-12).

Underground tanks in Canada and a number of other developed countries are now strictly regulated. Throughout North America, thousands of

Solutions

Groundwater Pollution

Prevention	Cleanup
Find substitutes for toxic chemicals	Pump to surface, clean, and return to aquifer (very expensive)
Keep toxic chemicals out of the environment	
Install monitoring wells near landfills and underground tanks	Inject microorganisms to clean up contamination (less expensive but still costly)
Require leak detectors on underground tanks	
Ban hazardous waste disposal in landfills and injection wells	Pump nanoparticles of inorganic compounds to remove pollutants (may be the cheapest, easiest, and most effective method but is still being developed)
Store harmful liquids in aboveground tanks with leak detection and collection systems	

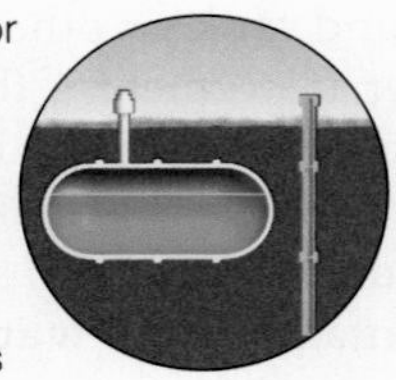

FIGURE 22-12 Solutions: methods for preventing and cleaning up contamination of groundwater. Which two of these solutions do you believe are the most important?

old leaking tanks from gasoline stations and other facilities have been removed and the surrounding soil and groundwater have been treated to remove gasoline. This is expensive but there is little choice because of the urgent need to prevent groundwater contamination.

22-5 OCEAN POLLUTION

How Much Pollution Can the Oceans Tolerate? We Do Not Know

Oceans can disperse and break down large quantities of degradable pollutants if they are not overloaded.

The oceans can dilute, disperse, and degrade large amounts of raw sewage, sewage sludge, oil, and some types of degradable industrial waste, especially in deep-water areas. Also, some forms of marine life have been affected less by some pollutants than expected.

This has led some scientists to suggest it is safer to dump sewage sludge and most other harmful wastes into the deep ocean than to bury them on land or burn them in incinerators. Other scientists disagree, pointing out we know less about the deep ocean than we do about the moon. They add that dumping harmful wastes in the ocean would delay urgently needed pollution prevention and promote further degradation of this vital part of the Earth's life-support system. (See Ocean Acidification on p. 519).

How Do Pollutants Affect Coastal Areas? More People and Development Cause More Pollution

Pollution of coastal waters near heavily populated areas is a serious problem.

Coastal areas—especially wetlands and estuaries, coral reefs, and mangrove swamps—bear the brunt of our enormous inputs of pollutants and wastes into the ocean (Figure 22-13). This is not surprising

because about 40% of the world's population lives on or within 100 kilometres (62 miles) of the coast and 14 of the world's 15 largest **metropolitan areas** (each with 10 million people or more) are near coastal waters.

In most coastal developing countries and in some coastal developed countries, municipal sewage and industrial wastes are dumped into the sea without treatment. Victoria, B.C., is an example of a Canadian city that still discharges raw sewage into the sea. About 75% of the sewage from large cities along the Mediterranean Sea (with a coastal population of 200 million people during tourist season) is discharged into the sea untreated. This causes widespread beach pollution and shellfish contamination.

Recent studies of some U.S. coastal waters have found vast colonies of human viruses from raw

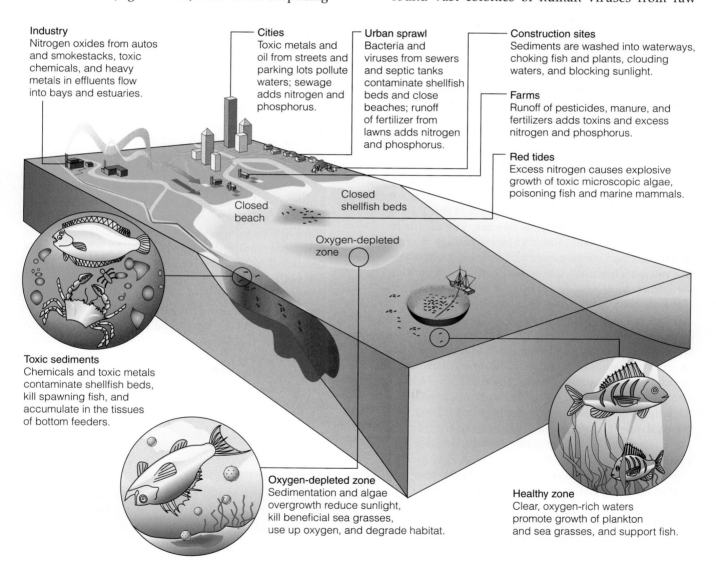

Industry
Nitrogen oxides from autos and smokestacks, toxic chemicals, and heavy metals in effluents flow into bays and estuaries.

Cities
Toxic metals and oil from streets and parking lots pollute waters; sewage adds nitrogen and phosphorus.

Urban sprawl
Bacteria and viruses from sewers and septic tanks contaminate shellfish beds and close beaches; runoff of fertilizer from lawns adds nitrogen and phosphorus.

Construction sites
Sediments are washed into waterways, choking fish and plants, clouding waters, and blocking sunlight.

Farms
Runoff of pesticides, manure, and fertilizers adds toxins and excess nitrogen and phosphorus.

Red tides
Excess nitrogen causes explosive growth of toxic microscopic algae, poisoning fish and marine mammals.

Closed beach

Closed shellfish beds

Oxygen-depleted zone

Toxic sediments
Chemicals and toxic metals contaminate shellfish beds, kill spawning fish, and accumulate in the tissues of bottom feeders.

Oxygen-depleted zone
Sedimentation and algae overgrowth reduce sunlight, kill beneficial sea grasses, use up oxygen, and degrade habitat.

Healthy zone
Clear, oxygen-rich waters promote growth of plankton and sea grasses, and support fish.

FIGURE 22-13 Natural capital degradation: how residential areas, factories, and farms contribute to the pollution of coastal waters and bays. According to the U.N. Environment Programme, coastal water pollution costs the world $16 billion (U.S.) annually—$731 000 a minute—due to ill health and premature death.

sewage, effluents from sewage treatment plants (which do not remove viruses), and leaking septic tanks. According to one study, about one-fourth of the people using coastal beaches in the United States develop ear infections, sore throats, eye irritations, respiratory disease, or gastrointestinal disease.

Runoffs of sewage and agricultural wastes into coastal waters introduce large quantities of nitrate (NO_3^-) and phosphate (PO_4^{3-}) plant nutrients, which can cause explosive growth of harmful algae. These *harmful algal blooms* (*HABs*) are called red, brown, or green toxic tides, depending on their colour. They can release waterborne and airborne toxins that damage fisheries, kill some fish-eating birds, reduce tourism, and poison seafood.

According to a 2008 report by the U.N. Environment Programme, each year some 200 large *oxygen-depleted zones* (sometimes inaccurately called "dead zones") form mostly in temperate coastal waters and in land-locked seas such as the Baltic and Black Seas. These zones result from excessive nonpoint inputs of fertilizers and animal wastes from land runoff and deposition of nitrogen compounds from the atmosphere. This cultural eutrophication depletes dissolved oxygen. Without oxygen most of the aquatic life (except bacteria) dies or moves elsewhere. The largest such zone in North America forms every summer in a narrow stretch of the Gulf of Mexico off the mouth of the Mississippi River.

Promising news. Scientists in Asia and elsewhere are experimenting with adding certain types of fine clay to the water to help control algal blooms. The idea is to find clay with particles fine and heavy enough to stick to the algae and remove them by weighing them down like microanchors. More tests are needed to determine the effectiveness of the method and to be sure that the clay particles do not harm other aquatic organisms.

The enclosed Baltic Sea is highly polluted because it receives runoff and air pollutants from a huge area with more than 80 million people and 15% of the world's industrial production. *Good news.* In 1980, the countries surrounding the Baltic Sea signed the *Helsinki Convention*—the world's first international agreement to reduce marine pollution. Despite some limitations, this agreement serves as an example of how countries can work together to help reduce common water pollution problems.

Preventive measures for reducing the number and size of such oxygen-depleted zones include reducing nitrogen inputs from various sources (Figure 22-8), planting forest and grasslands to soak up excess nitrogen and keep it out of waterways, restoring coastal wetlands, improving sewage treatment to reduce discharge of nitrates into waterways, requiring further reduction of NO_x emissions from motor vehicles, and phasing in forms of renewable energy to replace the burning of fossil fuels.

What Is Being Done to Control the Dumping of Pollutants into the Ocean? There Is No Away

Parts of the world's oceans are dump sites for a variety of toxic materials and sewage and garbage from ships.

Dumping industrial waste off Canadian and U.S. coasts has stopped, although it still occurs in a number of other developed countries and some developing countries. But barges and ships still legally dump large quantities of **dredge spoils** (materials, often laden with toxic metals, scraped from the bottoms of harbours and rivers to maintain shipping channels) in the ocean.

Many countries also dump large quantities of **sewage sludge** into the ocean. It is a gooey mixture of toxic chemicals, infectious agents, and settled solids removed from wastewater at sewage treatment plants.

Good news. Since 1997, Canada has banned the disposal of industrial and radioactive waste at sea. If it is satisfied that no practical alternative exists, Environment Canada still issues (for a fee) permits for certain types of waste such as fish-processing waste and old ships that will be sunk at sea. And 50 countries with at least 80% of the world's merchant fleet have agreed not to dump sewage and garbage at sea.

Bad news. It is difficult to enforce the ban on dumping at sea and violations are common. Most ship owners save money by dumping wastes at sea and, if caught, get only small fines. Each year as many as 2 million seabirds and more than 100 000 marine mammals (including whales, seals, dolphins, and sea lions) die when they ingest or become entangled in fishing nets, ropes, and other debris dumped into the sea or discarded on beaches (see photo on p. x.).

Under the London Dumping Convention of 1972, 100 countries agreed not to dump highly toxic pollutants and high-level radioactive wastes in the open sea beyond the boundaries of their national jurisdictions. Since 1983, these same nations have observed a moratorium on the dumping of low-level radioactive wastes at sea, which in 1994 became a permanent ban.

But these agreements are hard to monitor and enforce. In 1992, it was learned that for decades, the former Soviet Union had been dumping large quantities of high- and low-level radioactive wastes into the Arctic Ocean and its tributaries.

What Are the Major Sources of Ocean Oil Pollution? Land-Based Activities, Not Tankers, Are the Major Culprits

Most ocean oil pollution comes from human activities on the land.

Crude petroleum (oil as it comes out of the ground) and *refined petroleum* (fuel oil, gasoline, and other processed petroleum products) reach the ocean from a number of sources. In 1989, the *Exxon Valdez* oil tanker went off course, hit rocks, and released large amounts of oil into Alaska's Prince William Sound in an accident that ended up costing about $7 billion (U.S.) (including cleanup costs and fines for damage against ExxonMobil). In 2002, the oil tanker *Prestige* sank off the coast of Spain and over two years leaked about twice as much oil as the *Exxon Valdez.* Such tanker accidents and blowouts at offshore drilling rigs (when oil escapes under high pressure from a borehole in the ocean floor) get most of the publicity because of their high visibility. See the Spotlight on the Deepwater Horizon blowout.

But much more oil is released from other smaller, day-to-day, and less visible activities. They include the normal operation of offshore wells, washing oil tankers and releasing the oily water, loading and unloading of oil tankers at ports, and leaks from oil

---

SPOTLIGHT

The Deepwater Horizon Blowout

On April 20, 2010, a fire and explosion occurred on the Deepwater Horizon, a drilling platform operating for the British Petroleum Company (BP) about 65 kilometres (40 miles) offshore in the Gulf of Mexico (Figure 22-14a).

The cause of the disaster was a blowout of methane gas and oil that escaped from the well and rose to the surface. The gas exploded when it reached a source of open flame on the rig, and the oil fueled the fire. The Deepwater Horizon burned and sank. Eleven men died in the accident.

It was soon clear that oil was escaping from the well below. The original reports were that 1 000 barrels of oil were escaping per day; at the peak of the disaster, some estimates were as high as 60 000 barrels per day.

While experts attempted to shut down the well using various techniques, a massive oil slick formed that was at least 6 500 square kilometres (2 510 square miles) in area (Figure 22-14b). The well was capped on July 12, although oil still leaked at a slower rate until the well was sealed on September 17. By then, at least 5 million barrels of oil had escaped (some estimates were as high as 18 to 28 million barrels). Even the lower estimate of 5 million barrels is considerably larger than the 260 000 to 750 000 barrels of oil thought to have leaked from the *Exxon Valdez*, making the Deepwater Horizon blowout the worst marine oil disaster in history (ScienceDaily, 2010).

The cleanup operation involved a variety of techniques such as using absorbent booms to soak up the oil, corralling and burning it, using barriers to try to contain it, and spraying chemical dispersants to try to break it down. An added dimension to this case is that, for the first time ever, chemical dispersants were added to the oil as it escaped the well. The idea was to begin breaking down the oil sooner; however, huge plumes of semi-dispersed oil hung in the water column rather than rising to the surface in the normal way. There are various opinions about whether or not this was a good thing (Associated Press, 2010).

Despite efforts to clean up the problem, oil was widely distributed through the Gulf of Mexico, beaches and coastal wetlands were impacted, marine animals of many kinds died, and fishing and tourism were devastated. There are reports of strange mutations among the fish and shellfish, which some scientists suspect may be linked to the chemical dispersants that were used (Gerkin, 2012). It will be years before all the information is gathered and the court cases are settled.

What did we learn from this? We are reminded that drilling at sea is a risky business, that there are many consequences if anything goes wrong, and that we are ill-prepared to handle disasters of this magnitude.

Critical Thinking

Will countries continue to allow ocean drilling? If so, what changes can be made to prevent such disasters from taking place? When disasters happen, who should pay and how much? (Take note of how the courts handle this as specific cases play out over the next few years.) How would this disaster have been different if it had taken place in the Arctic?

(a) U.S. Coast Guard photo
(b) NASA image by Jeff Schmaltz, MODIS Rapid Response Team

FIGURE 22-14 The Deepwater Horizon drilling rig suffered an explosion and then burned for 36 hours, despite the efforts of fireboats, before sinking. The oil slick and smoke spreading from the disaster were documented from space by NASA's Terra satellite.

pipelines, refineries, and storage tanks. Natural oil seeps also release large amounts of oil into the ocean at some sites.

Studies show that most ocean oil pollution comes from activities on land. According to a study by the Pew Oceans Commission, every eight months an amount of oil equal to that spilled by the *Exxon Valdez* tanker drains from the land into the oceans. Almost half (some experts estimate 90%) of the oil reaching the oceans is waste oil dumped on the ground, poured down the drain, spilled, or leaked onto the land or into sewers by cities, industries, and people changing their own motor oil.

What Are the Effects of Oil Pollution on Ocean Ecosystems and Coastal Communities? Serious, but Not Long-Lasting

Oil pollution can have a number of harmful ecological and economic effects, but most disappear within 3–15 years.

The effects of oil on ocean ecosystems depend on a number of factors: type of oil (crude or refined), type of aquatic system, amount released, distance of release from shore, time of year, weather conditions, average water temperature, and ocean currents.

Volatile organic hydrocarbons in oil immediately kill a number of aquatic organisms, especially in their vulnerable larval forms. Some other chemicals form tarlike globs that float on the surface and coat the feathers of birds (especially diving birds) and the fur of marine mammals. This oil coating destroys their natural insulation and buoyancy, causing many of them to drown or die of exposure from loss of body heat.

Heavy oil components that sink to the ocean floor or wash into estuaries can smother bottom-dwelling organisms such as crabs, oysters, mussels, and clams or make them unfit for human consumption. Some oil spills have killed reef corals.

Research shows that most (but not all) forms of marine life recover from exposure to large amounts of *crude oil* within about three years. But recovery from exposure to *refined oil,* especially in estuaries and salt marshes, can take 10–15 years. The effects of spills in cold waters and in shallow enclosed gulfs and bays generally last longer.

Oil slicks that wash onto beaches can have a serious economic impact on coastal residents, who lose income normally gained from fishing and tourist activities. Oil-polluted beaches washed by strong waves or currents become clean after about a year, but beaches in sheltered areas remain contaminated for several years. Despite the localized harmful effects, oil spills are often considered low-risk ecological problems.

How Well Can We Clean Up Oil Spills? Not Very Well

Current methods can recover no more than about 15% of the oil from a major spill, explaining why prevention is the best strategy.

If they are not too large, oil spills can be partially cleaned up by mechanical, chemical, fire, and natural methods. *Mechanical methods* include using *floating booms* to contain the oil spill or keep it from reaching sensitive areas, *skimmer boats* to vacuum up some of the oil into collection barges, and *absorbent devices* such as large mesh pillows filled with feathers or hair to soak up oil on beaches or in waters too shallow for skimmer boats.

Chemical methods include using *coagulating agents* to cause floating oil to clump together for easier pickup or to sink to the bottom (where it usually does less harm) and *dispersing agents* to break up oil slicks. But these agents can damage some types of organisms. *Fire* can burn off floating oil, but crude oil is hard to ignite and burning it produces air pollution.

In time, the natural action of wind and waves mixes or emulsifies oil with water (like emulsified salad dressing), and bacteria biodegrade some of the oil. Scientists are developing *biological methods* in which "cocktails" of bacteria are sprayed on the oil to break it down into chemicals that the bacteria consume or that disperse harmlessly into the sea. Adding special nutrients required by the bacteria usually speeds up the decomposition process. This bioremediation cleanup by naturally occurring bacteria is cheaper and may be much more effective than other cleanup methods.

Scientists estimate that current methods can recover no more than 15% of the oil from a major spill. This explains why preventing oil pollution is the most effective and in the long run the least costly approach.

Good news. The 1989 *Exxon Valdez* oil spill focused attention on the issue of liability. In Canada, the responsible party is liable for both the cleanup costs and any economic losses resulting from the spill. In the United States, the Oil Protection Act of 1990 set up a trust fund to provide up to $1 million (U.S.) per spill for cleanup. It also required that by 2015, all oil tankers operating in U.S. waters must be constructed with two hulls—one inside the other—to help protect against spills. Similar international laws have been established, and in 2002 the European Union voted to ban single-hull oil tankers from their waters by 2010 and by 2005 for the largest tankers.

Bad news. In 2010, at least 300 single-hulled oil tankers were still in operation despite their greater vulnerability to oil spills. Cruise ships can also pollute coastal waters with oil and other waste—most of which is dumped at sea or in fragile coastal areas when the ships visit various ports. Scuba diving, anyone?

Solutions: How Can We Protect Coastal Waters? Think Prevention

Preventing or reducing the flow of pollution from the land and from streams emptying into the ocean is the key to protecting the oceans.

Figure 22-15 lists ways analysts have suggested to prevent and reduce excessive pollution of coastal waters. Study this figure carefully.

The key to protecting oceans is to reduce the flow of pollution from the land and from rivers emptying into the ocean. Thus ocean pollution control must be linked with land-use and air pollution policies because about one-third of all pollutants entering the ocean worldwide come from air emissions from land-based sources.

Solutions

Coastal Water Pollution

Prevention	Cleanup
Reduce input of toxic pollutants	Improve oil-spill cleanup capabilities
Separate sewage and storm lines	
Ban dumping of wastes and sewage by maritime and cruise ships in coastal waters	Sprinkle nanoparticles over an oil or sewage spill to dissolve the oil or sewage without creating harmful by-products (still under development)
Ban ocean dumping of sludge and hazardous dredged material	
Protect sensitive areas from development, oil drilling, and oil shipping	Require at least secondary treatment of coastal sewage
Regulate coastal development	
Recycle used oil	Use wetlands, solar-aquatic, or other methods to treat sewage
Require double hulls for oil tankers	

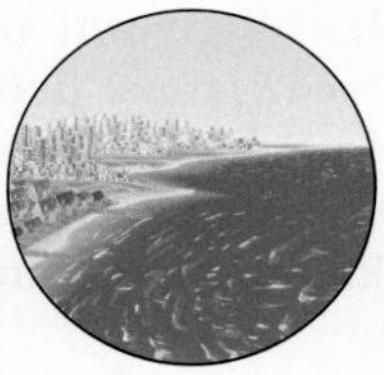

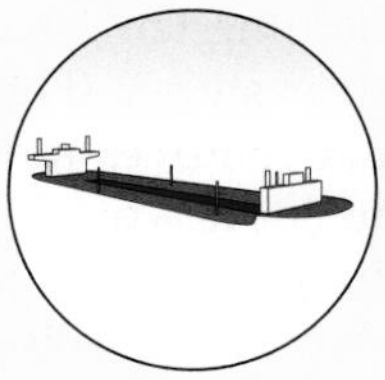

FIGURE 22-15 Solutions: methods for preventing and cleaning up excessive pollution of coastal waters. Which two of these solutions do you believe are the most important?

22-6 PREVENTING AND REDUCING SURFACE WATER POLLUTION

How Can We Reduce Surface Water Pollution from Nonpoint Sources? Emphasize Prevention

The key to reducing nonpoint pollution, most of it from agriculture, is to prevent it from reaching bodies of surface water.

There are a number of ways to reduce nonpoint water pollution, most of it from agriculture. Farmers can reduce soil erosion, especially by keeping cropland covered with vegetation and by reforesting critical watersheds. They can also reduce the amount of fertilizer running off into surface waters and leaching into aquifers by using slow-release fertilizer, using none on steeply sloped land, and planting buffer zones of vegetation between cultivated fields and nearby surface water.

Applying pesticides only when needed and relying more on biological control of pests can reduce pesticide runoff. Farmers can control runoff and infiltration of manure from animal feedlots by planting buffers and locating feedlots and animal waste sites away from steeply sloped land, surface water, and flood zones.

Good news. Researchers are developing methods to make renewable biodiesel fuel for vehicles. They are also experimenting with planting poplar trees to suck up waste from contaminated hog waste lagoons.

Scientists are seeking better ways to deal with animal waste. They are exploring ways to burn it, convert it to natural gas, recycle undigested nutrients in manure back into animal feed, and extract valuable chemicals from manure to make plastics or even cosmetics.

Other scientists are looking at ways to rinse away many of the soluble and smelly ingredients in manure to leave tough, strawlike particles of fibre that can be pressed into fibreboard for making cabinets and furniture. The resulting fibre is called animal processed fibre, a formal name for processed cow and hog poop.

CONSIDER, DISCUSS, OR DEBATE

Should we greatly increase efforts to reduce water pollution from nonpoint sources? What personal contributions could you make to this effort?

How Can We Reduce Water Pollution from Point Sources? Legal and Market Approaches

Most developed countries use laws to set water pollution standards, but in most developing countries such laws do not exist or are poorly enforced.

Federal legislation aimed at controlling water pollution includes the Fisheries Act (1985), the Canadian Environmental Protection Act (1988), and the

Canadian Water Act (1970). The Great Lakes Water Quality Agreement (first signed in 1972 and renewed in 1978) establishes common water-quality objectives for Canada and the United States in the Great Lakes; it also coordinates Great Lakes research, monitoring, and management programs initiated by either or both of the two countries.

In the United States, the Clean Water Act (1977) and the Water Quality Act (1987) form the basis of U.S. efforts to control pollution of the country's surface waters. The Clean Water Act sets standards for allowed levels of key water pollutants and requires polluters to get permits specifying how much of various pollutants they can discharge into aquatic systems.

Some water experts suggest that industrialized nations such as Canada and the United States should adopt a *discharge trading policy* that uses market forces to reduce water pollution (as has been done with sulphur dioxide for air pollution control in the United States, p. 499). Under this program a water pollution source is allowed to pollute at a higher level than allowed in its permit by buying credits from permit holders with pollution levels below their allowed levels.

Some environmentalists support discharge trading. But they warn that such a system is no better than the caps set for total pollution levels in various areas, and call for careful scrutiny of the cap levels. They also warn that discharge trading could allow pollutants to build up to dangerous levels in areas where credits are bought. In addition, they call for gradually lowering the caps to encourage prevention of water pollution and development of better technology for controlling water pollution.

Bad news. According to Sandra Postel, director of the Global Water Policy Project, most cities in developing countries discharge 80–90% of their untreated sewage directly into rivers, streams, and lakes, which are used for drinking water, bathing, and washing clothes.

How Can We Reduce Water Pollution from Point Sources? The Technological Approach

Septic tanks and various levels of sewage treatment can reduce point-source water pollution.

In rural and suburban areas with suitable soils, sewage from each house can be discharged into a **septic tank** (Figure 22-16). About one-fourth of all homes in North America are served by septic tanks.

In Canadian and U.S. urban areas, most water-borne wastes from homes, businesses, factories, and storm runoff flow through a network of sewer pipes to *wastewater* or *sewage treatment plants*. Some cities have a separate network of pipes for carrying runoff of storm water from streets and parking lots. But many cities have combined the sewer lines for these two systems because it is cheaper.

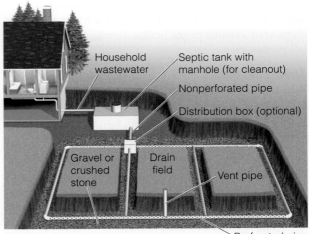

FIGURE 22-16 Solutions: *septic tank system* used for disposal of domestic sewage and wastewater in rural and suburban areas. This system separates solids from liquids, digests organic matter and large solids, and discharges the liquid wastes in a network of buried pipes with holes over a large drainage or absorption field. As these wastes drain from the pipes and percolate downward, the soil filters out some potential pollutants, and soil bacteria decompose biodegradable materials. To be effective, septic tank systems must be properly installed in soils with adequate drainage, not placed too close together or too near well sites, and pumped out when the settling tank becomes full.

Bad news. Heavy rains or too many users hooked up to the system can cause combined sewer lines to overflow and discharge untreated (raw) sewage directly into surface waters. Every year, millions of people get sick from swimming in waters contaminated by sewage overflows. Symptoms include vomiting; diarrhea; skin infections; and ear, eye, or throat infections.

Raw sewage reaching a treatment plant typically undergoes one or both of two levels of wastewater treatment. One is **primary sewage treatment.** It is a *physical* process that uses screens and a grit tank to remove large floating objects and solids such as sand and rock, and a settling tank that allows suspended solids to settle out as sludge (Figure 22-17). By itself, primary treatment removes about 60% of the suspended solids and 30–40% of the oxygen-demanding organic wastes from sewage but removes no phosphates, nitrates, salts, radioisotopes, or pesticides.

A second level is called **secondary sewage treatment**. It is a *biological* process in which aerobic bacteria remove up to 90% of dissolved and biodegradable, oxygen-demanding organic wastes. This is done by trickling wastewater through beds of gravel covered with films of aerobic bacteria or by passing it through an *aeration tank* where air is pumped through a slurry of aerobic bacteria before the wastewater is sent to a second settling tank.

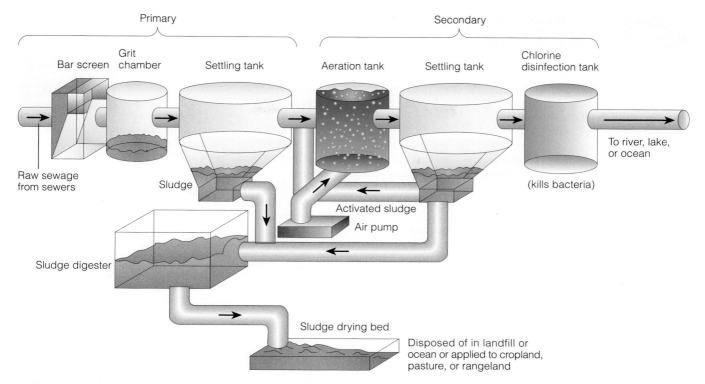

FIGURE 22-17 Solutions: primary and secondary sewage treatment.

A combination of primary and secondary treatment (Figure 22-17) removes 95–97% of the suspended solids and oxygen-demanding organic wastes, 70% of most toxic metal compounds and nonpersistent synthetic organic chemicals, 70% of the phosphorus (mostly as phosphates), 50% of the nitrogen (mostly as nitrates), and 5% of dissolved salts. But this process removes only a tiny fraction of long-lived radioactive isotopes and persistent organic substances such as some pesticides.

A third level of cleanup is **advanced** or **tertiary sewage treatment.** It is a series of specialized chemical and physical processes that remove specific pollutants left in the water after primary and secondary treatment. Its most widespread use is to remove phosphates and nitrates from wastewater before it is discharged into surface waters to help reduce nutrient overload. Advanced treatment is expensive and is used to treat only 5% of the wastewater in North America.

Before discharge, water from primary, secondary, or advanced treatment undergoes *bleaching* to remove water colouration and *disinfection* to kill disease-carrying bacteria and some but not all viruses. The usual method for doing this is *chlorination*. But chlorine can react with organic materials in water to form small amounts of chlorinated hydrocarbons. Some of these chemicals can cause cancers in test animals and may damage the human nervous, immune, and endocrine systems (Case Study, p. 459).

Use of other disinfectants, such as *ozone* and *ultraviolet light,* is increasing. But they cost more and their effects do not last as long as chlorination.

What Should We Do with Sewage Sludge? An Unsettled Problem

Sewage sludge can be used as a soil conditioner, but this can cause health problems if it contains infectious bacteria and toxic chemicals.

Sewage treatment produces a gooey *sludge* containing a slimy mixture of bacteria-laden solids and often-toxic chemicals and metals when sewer systems mix industrial and household waste. In North America, about 9% by weight of this sludge is placed in large circular digesters and kept warm for several weeks to allow anaerobic bacteria to decompose organic materials and produce compost for use as a soil conditioner. About 36% of the sludge, also known as *biosolids*, is used to fertilize farmland, forests, golf courses, cemeteries, parkland, highway medians, and degraded land. The remaining 55% is dumped in conventional landfills where it can contaminate groundwater, or is incinerated. Such burning of waste can pollute the air with toxic chemicals, and it produces a toxic ash usually buried in landfills that will eventually leak.

From an ecological standpoint, it is desirable to recycle plant nutrients in sewage sludge to the soil on land. But there are problems with using sewage sludge

National Sewage Report Card

Ecojustice Canada (formerly the Sierra Legal Defence Fund) wrote a report card about the state of sewage treatment in 22 cities across Canada (Ecojustice, 2009). The report ranks each city on level of sewage treatment provided, volume of raw sewage discharged, compliance with regulations, method of disinfecting effluent before releasing it back into natural waters, method of sludge disposal, and frequency of sewer overflows. Here are some of the report's findings.

- Calgary received an A+ for achieving 100% tertiary treatment, for having separate sewage and stormwater drainage systems, for avoiding sewage overflows, and for adding UV disinfection equipment, among other positive features.
- Halifax received a D for its practice of discharging raw sewage into Halifax Harbour. Halifax subsequently installed a sewage treatment system, but there have been recurring problems with releases of raw sewage (CBC News, 2011).

- Toronto (B–) is among those cities that have successfully applied sewer-use bylaws to prevent harmful substances from entering the sewage system.

Critical Thinking

Do you think that "report cards" serve a useful purpose in situations like this? How can cities be convinced to upgrade their sewage standards?

to fertilize crops (Figure 22-18, p. 563). As long as harmful bacteria and other pathogens and toxic chemicals are not present, sludge can fertilize land used for food crops or livestock. But removing bacteria (usually by heating), toxic metals, and organic chemicals is expensive and rarely done.

A growing number of alleged health problems and lawsuits have resulted from use of sludge to fertilize crops. To protect consumers and avoid lawsuits, some food packers such as Del Monte and Heinz have banned produce grown on farms using sludge as a fertilizer.

How Can We Improve Sewage Treatment? Eliminate Toxics

Preventing toxic chemicals from reaching sewage treatment plants would eliminate such chemicals from the sludge and water discharged from such plants.

Environmental scientist Peter Montague calls for redesigning sewage treatment systems to prevent toxic and hazardous chemicals from reaching sewage treatment plants and thus from getting into sludge and the water discharged from such plants.

He suggests several ways to do this. One is to require industries and businesses to remove toxic and hazardous wastes from water sent to municipal sewage treatment plants. Another is to encourage industries to reduce or eliminate toxic chemical use and waste.

Another suggestion is to have more households, apartment buildings, and offices eliminate sewage outputs by switching to waterless *composting toilet systems* (Figure 22-19, p. 563). Such systems would be cheaper

to install and maintain than current sewage systems because they do not require vast systems of underground pipes connected to centralized sewage treatment plants. They also save large amounts of water and they work very well.

> **DID YOU KNOW**
>
> In addition to human waste, sewage can contain heavy metals, PCBs, cyanide, pesticides, oil, grease, dioxins, radioactive substances, and anything else that people dump into toilets or sewers.

Solutions: How Can We Treat Sewage by Working with Nature? Ecological Purification

Natural and artificial wetlands and other ecological systems can be used to treat sewage.

More than 150 cities and towns in North America use natural and artificial wetlands to treat sewage as a low-tech, low-cost alternative to expensive waste treatment plants.

For example, the coastal town of Arcata, California, created some 65 hectares (160 acres) of wetlands between the town and the adjacent Humboldt Bay. The marshes and ponds developed on this land that was once a garbage dump act as an inexpensive natural waste treatment plant. The project cost less than half the estimated cost of a conventional treatment plant.

Here is how it works. First, sewage goes to sedimentation tanks, where the solids settle out as sludge that is removed and processed for use as fertilizer. Next, the liquid is pumped into oxidation ponds, where bacteria break down remaining wastes. After a month or so, the water is released into the artificial

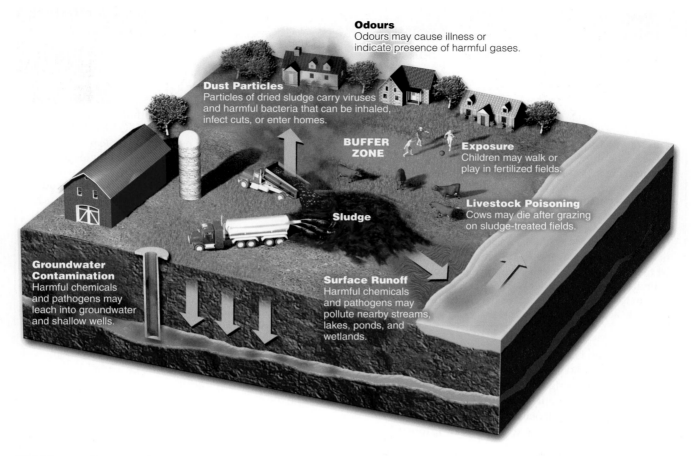

Odours
Odours may cause illness or indicate presence of harmful gases.

Dust Particles
Particles of dried sludge carry viruses and harmful bacteria that can be inhaled, infect cuts, or enter homes.

BUFFER ZONE

Exposure
Children may walk or play in fertilized fields.

Livestock Poisoning
Cows may die after grazing on sludge-treated fields.

Sludge

Groundwater Contamination
Harmful chemicals and pathogens may leach into groundwater and shallow wells.

Surface Runoff
Harmful chemicals and pathogens may pollute nearby streams, lakes, ponds, and wetlands.

FIGURE 22-18 Natural capital degradation: potential problems with using sludge from sewage treatment plants as a fertilizer on croplands. Some experts say that sludge is safe to use if applied following guidelines. Scientists and people who have gotten sick from exposure to sludge fertilizer claim the guidelines are insufficient and not adequately enforced.

Courtesy of Sancor Industries Ltd.

FIGURE 22-19 Composting toilets are proving to be increasingly popular in camps, cottages, and homes. They require no plumbing, save on water, and produce compost. (http://www.compostingtoilet.org)

marshes, where plants and bacteria carry out further filtration and cleansing. Then the purified water flows into the Humboldt Bay with its abundant marine life.

The marshes and ponds also serve as a bird sanctuary and provide habitats for thousands of otters, seabirds, and marine animals. The town celebrates its natural sewage treatment system with an annual "Flush with Pride" festival. However, large cities do not have the land available for this approach.

Mark Nelson has developed a small, low-tech, and inexpensive artificial wetland system to treat raw sewage from hotels, restaurants, and homes in developing countries (Figure 22-20, p. 564). This *wastewater garden* system removes 99.9% of fecal coliform bacteria and more than 80% of the nitrates and phosphates from incoming sewage that in most developing countries is often dumped untreated into the ocean or into shallow holes in the ground. The water flowing out of

Dr. John Todd and Nancy Jack Todd

Canadian Dr. John Todd and his wife Nancy Jack Todd are pioneers in the use of "Living Machines" for treating wastewater while producing a range of products including fish, flowers, and fruit. Living Machines are an example of **ecological engineering** in which human needs are met not by mechanical or electrical means, but by harnessing the properties of natural ecosystems.

A Living Machine designed to treat wastewater is a contained set of ecosystems in which the water to be treated flows through a series of cylinders. In each cylinder is an ecosystem that has been chosen for its ability to accomplish a certain task.

As water flows through the series of cylinders, bacteria consume organic wastes, algae absorb nitrates, and cattails and water hyacinths take up heavy metals and toxins. In the end, the purified water flows through ecosystems of fish and flowers that can be sold for profit!

In 1980, John and Nancy co-founded Ocean Arks International, a company aimed at developing Living Machines and other forms of ecological engineering. According to John and Nancy, such systems have the advantages of being effective, inexpensive, easy to operate, low in energy consumption, low in impact, mechanically simple but ecologically complex, and suitable for both the developing world and the developed world. They believe that by learning to harness living technologies that work with and not against nature humans will be able to reduce our footprint on the planet by as much as 90%. Living machines are being used to treat wastes and provide products in a growing number of countries including Canada, the United States, the U.K., and Australia. For more information, visit Ocean Arks International at http://oceanarks.org.

such systems can be used to irrigate gardens or fields or to flush toilets and thus help save water.

Genetic engineering may also get into the act. The internal organs of some insects are resistant to pesticides. Researchers have isolated the gene that provides this resistance, and they have transferred it to easily cultured bacterial species. They envision passing contaminated water through a large vessel or *bioreactor* containing the genetically modified bacteria that consume the pesticides. Stay tuned about developments in this promising area of frontier science. This might be an interesting career choice.

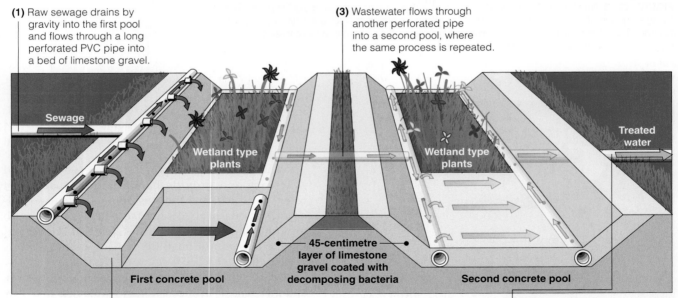

(1) Raw sewage drains by gravity into the first pool and flows through a long perforated PVC pipe into a bed of limestone gravel.

(3) Wastewater flows through another perforated pipe into a second pool, where the same process is repeated.

Sewage

Treated water

Wetland type plants

Wetland type plants

45-centimetre layer of limestone gravel coated with decomposing bacteria

First concrete pool

Second concrete pool

(2) Microbes in the limestone gravel break down the sewage into chemicals that can be absorbed by the plant roots, and the gravel absorbs phosphorus.

(4) Treated water flowing from the second pool is nearly free of bacteria and plant nutrients. Treated water can be recycled for irrigation and flushing toilets.

FIGURE 22-20 Solutions: *wastewater garden.* Hotels, restaurants, and homes in developing countries can use this small gravity-fed artificial wetland system to treat sewage. It uses only 1.9–3.8 square metres (20–30 square feet) of space per person.

How Is Urban Drinking Water Purified? The High-Tech Centralized Approach

Centralized water treatment plants that operate much like wastewater treatment plants can provide safe drinking water for city dwellers.

Areas that depend on surface water for drinking usually store it in a reservoir for several days. This improves taste and clarity by increasing dissolved oxygen content and allowing suspended matter to settle. Next, the water is pumped to a purification plant where it is filtered as needed and chlorinated to meet government drinking water standards. In areas with very pure groundwater sources, little treatment except disinfection is necessary.

How Can We Purify Rural Drinking Water in Developing Countries? The Low-Tech, Decentralized Approach

Researchers have developed several simple and inexpensive ways for individuals and villages in developing countries to purify drinking water.

Ways to purify drinking water can be simple. In tropical countries without centralized water treatment systems, the WHO is urging people to purify drinking water by exposing a clear plastic bottle filled with contaminated water to intense sunlight. In the strong sunlight found in most tropical countries, heat and the sun's UV rays can kill infectious microbes in as little as three hours. Painting one side of the bottle black can improve heat absorption in this simple solar disinfection method. Where it has been used, incidences of dangerous childhood diarrhea have decreased by 30–40%.

In Bangladesh, households receive strips of cloth for filtering cholera-producing bacteria from drinking water. Villages where women use such strips to strain water have cut cholera cases in half.

Another simple method involves adding a small amount of a chlorine-disinfectant solution to plastic or clay water-storage vessels with a narrow mouth and cap and a spigot—similar to what campers frequently use. The storage vessel design helps protect the disinfected water from additional bacterial contamination. Trials in Zambia, Kenya, and India show that this approach can cut the rate of diarrheal disease in half. This highly publicized method is now in use in 15 developing countries.

How Well Is Drinking Water Quality Protected by Law?

Most developed countries have laws or guidelines establishing drinking water standards, but most developing countries do not.

About 54 countries, most of them in North America and Europe, have standards for safe drinking water. In Canada, drinking water is regulated by all three levels of government. The federal and provincial governments establish guidelines and monitor research concerning water safety. Municipal governments run the day-to-day operations of publicly owned water utilities. The federal and provincial guidelines set forth acceptable limits for a wide range of chemicals that might be found in drinking water. The guidelines are not legally binding, but most water utilities in Canada abide by them.

Privately owned wells often do not meet drinking water standards for two reasons. One is that it costs at least $1 000 to test each well and owners would need to retest their water every few years. The other is that some homeowners oppose mandatory testing and compliance.

Health scientists call for protecting drinking water systems in several ways. One is to combine many of the drinking water treatment systems that serve fewer than 3 300 people with nearby larger systems. Another is to strengthen and enforce public notification requirements about violations of drinking water standards. They also propose that all traces of lead, including lead-based solder, be removed from plumbing pipes, faucets, and fixtures.

How good is Canada's drinking water? See the Spotlight about Canada's drinking water report card.

Is Bottled Water the Answer? Solution or Expensive Rip-off?

Some bottled water is not as pure as tap water and costs much more.

Despite some problems, experts say North America has some of the world's cleanest drinking water. Yet many of us worry about getting sick from tap water contaminants, and many drink bottled water or install expensive water purification systems.

Studies reveal that in North America bottled water is 240 to 10 000 times more expensive than tap water. In addition, about one-fourth of it is tap water, bacteria contaminate about one-third of it, and various potentially harmful organic chemicals contaminate about one-fifth of it. On the other hand, some countries must rely on bottled water because some of their tap water is too polluted to drink.

Use of bottled water can also cause some environmental problems. For example, 1.4 million tonnes of plastic bottles are thrown away globally each year, and toxic gases and liquids are released during the manufacture of plastic water bottles. In addition, greenhouse gases and other air pollutants are emitted by the fossil fuels burned to make plastic bottles and to deliver bottled water to suppliers.

Before drinking expensive bottled water and buying costly home water purifiers, health officials suggest

Drinking Water Report Card

Ecojustice Canada has created a report card that assesses Canada's drinking water. The grades assigned are as follows:

A Ontario and Nova Scotia received A's for positive actions such as high-quality water treatment and *source water protection* (SWP)—in other words, making sure that the sources of drinking water (lakes, rivers, wells, and so on) are safe and secure.

B The grade of B was awarded to New Brunswick, Newfoundland and Labrador, Prince Edward Island, Quebec, and Saskatchewan. All of these provinces had good practices but in each case there was a flaw. For example, water treatment is not mandatory in Prince Edward Island.

C C's were given to British Columbia, Northwest Territories, Alberta, and Yukon. Each of these places had more serious problems. For example, British Columbia has some of Canada's lowest water treatment standards and has not protected its water sources well.

D The grade of D was assigned to Nunavut because it has no official protection for its water sources and its treatment standards are low.

F An F was reserved for the federal government. The government has been failing to create legislation to protect drinking water and has not improved the water quality of First Nations communities. As well, the government has made drastic budget cuts to Environment Canada, which will make it very difficult for the department to monitor water properly.

The report can be read as a full report, a short executive summary, or a poster at http://www.ecojustice.ca/publications/files/waterproof-3. Read one of these versions and see if you agree with the above assessments. Report cards such as this are often useful because they promote discussion and comparison that can lead to action.

---

that consumers have their water tested by local health authorities or private labs (not companies trying to sell water purification equipment). The goals are to identify what contaminants (if any) must be removed and to determine the type of purification needed to remove such contaminants. Independent experts contend that unless tests show otherwise, for most Canadian and American households served by large municipal drinking water systems, home water treatment systems are not worth the expense and maintenance hassles.

One option available to Canadians is the jug filter (http://www.livestrong.com/article/291489-comparison-of-water-filtration-pitchers/?htm_source=undefined_R1&LS-2659). This inexpensive device removes some of the impurities found in tap water, and can improve the taste and clarity of water. The system's filters must be changed regularly to avoid bacteria buildup.

CONSIDER, DISCUSS, OR DEBATE

Should quality standards for bottled water be established and policed?

How Can We Reduce Water Pollution? Individuals Matter

Shifting our priorities from controlling to preventing and reducing water pollution will require bottom-up political action by individuals and groups.

It is encouraging that since 1970 most of the world's developed countries have enacted laws and regulations that have significantly reduced point-source water pollution. Most of these improvements were the result of *bottom-up* political pressure on elected officials by individuals and organized groups. However, little has been done to reduce water pollution in most developing countries.

To health scientists and environmentalists the next step is to increase efforts to reduce and prevent water pollution in developed and developing countries by asking the question: *How can we avoid producing water pollutants in the first place?* Figure 22-21 lists ways to do this over the next several decades.

This shift to *preventing water pollution* will not take place in developed countries without *bottom-up* political pressure on elected officials. It will not occur in developing countries without similar pressure from citizens as well financial and technical aid from developed countries. Figure 22-22 lists some actions you can take to help reduce water pollution.

It is a hard truth to swallow, but nature does not care if we live or die. We cannot survive without the oceans, for example, but they can do just fine without us.

ROGER ROSENBLATT

Solutions

Water Pollution

- Prevent groundwater contamination.
- Greatly reduce nonpoint runoff.
- Reuse treated wastewater for irrigation.
- Find substitutes for toxic pollutants.
- Work with nature to treat sewage.
- Practise five R's of resource use (refuse, reduce, recycle, reuse, and rethink).
- Reduce resource waste.
- Reduce air pollution.
- Reduce poverty.

FIGURE 22-21 Solutions: methods for preventing and cleaning up excessive pollution of coastal waters. Which two of these solutions do you believe are the most important?

What Can You Do?

Water Pollution

- Fertilize your garden and yard plants with manure or compost instead of commercial inorganic fertilizer.
- Minimize your use of pesticides.
- Never apply fertilizer or pesticides near a body of water.
- Grow or buy organic foods.
- Compost your food wastes.
- Do not use water fresheners in toilets.
- Do not flush unwanted medicines down the toilet.
- Do not pour pesticides, paints, solvents, oil, antifreeze, or other products containing harmful chemicals down the drain or onto the ground.

FIGURE 22-22 What can you do? Ways to help reduce water pollution.

CHAPTER REVIEW

1. Review the Key Questions for this chapter on p. 541. Describe the consequences to individual organisms, to specific species, and to aquatic ecosystems in general if biological signals used for communication, coordination, defence, and food location are blocked by fairly low levels of chemicals in water.

2. What is *water pollution*? Distinguish between *point sources* and *nonpoint sources* of water pollution and give an example of each. List nine major types of water pollutants and give an example of each. List three diseases transmitted to humans by polluted water. Describe chemical and biological methods that scientists use to measure water quality.

3. Describe how streams can cleanse themselves and how these cleansing processes can be overwhelmed. Describe the state of stream pollution in developed and developing countries. Describe the pollution problems of the Ganges River, which runs through part of India.

4. Give two reasons why lakes cannot cleanse themselves as readily as streams can. Distinguish between *eutrophication* and *cultural eutrophication*. List three ways to prevent or reduce cultural eutrophication. Describe pollution of the Great Lakes and the progress made in reducing this pollution.

5. Explain why groundwater cannot cleanse itself very well. What are the major sources of groundwater

contamination in Canada? Describe the threat from arsenic in groundwater. List ways to prevent or clean up groundwater contamination.

6. How can drinking water be better protected from pollution? What are the pros and cons of people drinking bottled water instead of tap water?

7. How are coastal waters and deeper ocean waters polluted? What causes harmful algal blooms and what are their harmful effects? How does a "dead zone" form in a body of water? How can the water pollution problems of Hamilton Harbour and Lake Erie be solved? How serious is oil pollution of the oceans, what are its effects, and what can be done to reduce such pollution?

8. List two ways to reduce water pollution from **(a)** nonpoint sources and **(b)** point sources. What is a *septic tank* and how does it work? Describe how *primary sewage treatment* and *secondary sewage treatment* are used to help purify water.

9. What is a *composting toilet*? How does it work, and what are its advantages and disadvantages? Describe how wetlands can be used to treat sewage. List six ways to reduce or prevent water pollution. List five steps you can take to reduce water pollution.

10. Describe connections between *Living Machines* and the four *principles of sustainability*.

CRITICAL THINKING

1. Explain why dilution is not always the solution to water pollution.

2. For each of the eight categories of pollutants listed in Table 22-1, is it most likely to originate from (a) point sources or (b) nonpoint sources?

3. A large number of fish are found floating dead on a lake during the summer. You are asked to determine the cause of the fish kill. What reason would you suggest for the kill? What measurements would you make to verify your hypothesis?

4. Are you for or against banning injection of liquid hazardous wastes into deep wells below drinking water aquifers (Figure 22-11, p. 552)? Explain. What are the alternatives?

5. When you flush a toilet, where does the wastewater go? Trace the actual flow of this wastewater in your community from your toilet through sewers to a wastewater treatment plant and from there to the environment. Try to visit a local sewage treatment plant to see what it does with your wastewater. Compare the processes it uses with those shown in Figure 22-17 (p. 561). What happens to the sludge produced by this plant? What improvements, if any, would you suggest for this plant?

6. Congratulations! You are in charge of sharply reducing water pollution from nonpoint sources throughout the world. What are the three most important things you would do?

7. Congratulations! You are in charge of sharply reducing groundwater pollution throughout the world. What are the three most important things you would do?

8. Congratulations! You are in charge of providing safe drinking water for the poor and other people in developing countries. What are the three most important things you would do?

PROJECTS

1. In your community,

   a. What are the principal nonpoint sources of contamination of surface water and groundwater?

   b. What is the source of drinking water?

   c. How is drinking water treated?

   d. Has pollution led to swimming bans in any of the beaches in your region? If so, what action (if any) has your local government taken to deal with the problem?

   e. Has pollution led to fishing bans or warnings not to eat fish from any lakes or rivers in your region?

   f. Is groundwater contamination a problem? If so, where, and what has been done about the problem?

   g. Is there a vulnerable aquifer or critical recharge zone that needs protection to ensure the quality of groundwater? Is your local government aware of this? What action (if any) has it taken?

2. Are storm drains and sanitary sewers combined or separate in your area? Are there plans to reduce pollution from runoff of storm water? If not, make an economic evaluation of the costs and benefits of developing separate storm drains and sanitary sewers, and present your findings to local officials.

3. Use library research, the Internet, and user interviews to evaluate the relative effectiveness and costs of home water purification devices. Determine the type or types of water pollutants each device removes and the effectiveness of this process.

4. Find out the price of tap water where you live. Then go to a grocery or other store and get prices per litre (or other volume unit) on all the available types of bottled water. Use these data to compare the price per litre of various brands of bottled water with the price of tap water.

Pest Management

Along Came a Spider: Biological Pest Control

Since agriculture began about 10 000 years ago, we have been competing with insect pests for the food we grow. Today we are not much closer to winning this competition than we were then, mostly because of the astounding abilities of insect pests to multiply and, through natural selection, rapidly develop genetic resistance to poisons we throw at them.

Some Chinese farmers use a biological strategy to help control insect pests. Instead of spraying their rice and cotton fields with poisons, they build little straw huts around the fields in the fall.

These farmers are encouraging insects' worst enemy, one that has hunted them for millions of years: *spiders* (Figure 23-1). The little huts are for hibernating spiders. Protected from the winter cold by the huts, far more of the hibernating spiders become active in the spring. Ravenous after their winter fast, they scuttle off into the fields to stalk their insect prey.

Even without human help, the world's 40 000 known species of spiders kill far more insects every year than insecticides do. A typical acre of meadow or woods contains an estimated 50 000–2 million spiders, each devouring hundreds of insects per year.

Entomologist Willard H. Whitcomb found that leaving strips of weeds around cotton and soybean fields provides the kind of undergrowth favoured by insect-eating wolf spiders (Figure 23-1, left). He also sings the praises of a type of banana spider, which lives in warm climates and can keep a house clear of cockroaches.

In Maine, Daniel Jennings of the U.S. Forest Service uses spiders to help control the spruce budworm, which devastates spruce and fir forests in the Northeast. Spiders also attack the much-feared gypsy moth, which destroys tree foliage.

The idea of encouraging populations of spiders in fields, forests, and even houses scares some people because spiders have bad reputations. A few spider species, such as the black widow, the brown recluse, and eastern Australia's Sydney funnel web, are dangerous to people. But most spider species, including the ferocious-looking wolf spider, do not harm humans. Even the giant tarantula rarely bites people, and its venom is too weak to harm us or other large mammals unless we are allergic to it. As we seek new ways to coexist with the insect rulers of the planet, we would do well to be sure that spiders are on our side.

(continued)

FIGURE 23-1 Natural capital: *working with nature.* Spiders are insects' worst enemies. Most spiders, such as the wolf spider (left) and the crab spider (right), found in many parts of the world, are harmless to humans.

This chapter looks first at the advantages and disadvantages of the conventional chemical approach to pest control based on using synthetic chemical pesticides. Then it discusses the advantages and disadvantages of a variety of biological and ecological alternatives for controlling pest populations.

A weed is a plant whose virtues have not yet been discovered.

RALPH WALDO EMERSON

CHAPTER PURPOSE AND QUESTIONS

Chapter 23 discusses the advantages and disadvantages of chemical, biological, and ecological approaches to pest control. The chapter addresses the following questions:

23-1   What are the types and uses of pesticides?

23-2   What are the advantages of using modern pesticides?

23-3   What are the disadvantages of using modern pesticides?

23-4   How well is pesticide use regulated?

23-5   What are the alternatives to using conventional pesticides, and what are the advantages and disadvantages of each alternative?

23-1 PESTICIDES: TYPES AND USES

How Does Nature Keep Pest Populations Under Control? Natural Enemies

Predators, parasites, and disease organisms found in nature control populations of most pest species as part of the Earth's free ecological services.

A **pest** is any species that competes with us for food, invades lawns and gardens, destroys wood in houses, spreads disease, invades ecosystems, or is simply a nuisance. Worldwide, only about 100 species of plants (which we call weeds), animals (mostly insects), fungi, and microbes (which can infect crop plants and livestock animals) cause about 90% of the damage to the crops we grow.

In natural ecosystems and polyculture agroecosystems, *natural enemies* (predators, parasites, and disease organisms) control the populations of about 98% of the potential pest species as part of the Earth's free ecological services and thus help keep any one species from taking over for very long. As we saw in the Case Study (p. 569), spiders kill more far more insects every year than insecticides do. Since the second law of thermodynamics has an *ecological efficiency* of only about 10% (p. 74), each insect predator needs to

consume large quantities of insects throughout its life just to meet its energy requirements. A healthy community of insect predators can thus exert a powerful controlling influence over insect populations.

When we clear forests and grasslands, plant monoculture crops, and douse fields with pesticides, we upset many of these natural population checks and balances. Then we must devise ways to protect our monoculture crops, tree plantations, and lawns from insects and other pests that nature once controlled at no charge.

CONSIDER, DISCUSS, OR DEBATE

Whether or not an organism is considered a pest is largely subjective. One homeowner's weed-infested lawn is another homeowner's wildflower-meadow oasis. Although they are widely considered to be pests, insects produce honey, silk, shellac, and royal jelly, among other products. They also perform invaluable ecological services, from pollinating the majority of the world's plants to speeding decomposition and returning nutrients to the soil. Assume that a mad scientist discovered a way to rid the world of insects. What effects would the eradication have on the world's ecosystems in general and human beings in particular?

What Are Pesticides? Ways to Repel or Kill Pests

Pesticides are chemicals designed to repel or kill pest organisms as plants have done for millions of years to defend themselves against hungry herbivores.

To help control pest organisms, we have developed a variety of **pesticides** or **biocides**—chemicals to kill or control populations of organisms we consider undesirable. Common types of pesticides include **insecticides** (chemicals that kill insects by blocking reproduction, clogging their airways, or disrupting their nervous system), **herbicides** (chemicals that kill weeds by disrupting their metabolism and growth), **fungicides** (fungus killers), and *rodenticides* (rat and mouse killers). *Biocide* is a more accurate name for these chemicals because most pesticides kill other organisms as well as their pest targets.

We did not invent the use of chemicals to repel or kill other species; plants have been producing chemicals to ward off, deceive, or poison herbivores that feed on them for about 225 million years. This is a never-ending, ever-changing coevolutionary process: herbivores overcome various plant defences through natural selection; then new plant defences are favoured by natural selection in this ongoing cycle of evolutionary punch and counterpunch.

As the human population grew and agriculture spread, people began looking for ways to protect their crops, mostly by using chemicals to kill or repel insect pests. Sulphur was used as an insecticide well before 500 B.C.; by the 1400s, people were applying toxic compounds of arsenic, lead, and mercury to crops as insecticides. Farmers abandoned this approach in the late 1920s when the increasing number of human poisonings and fatalities prompted a search for less toxic substitutes. *Bad news*. Traces of these nondegradable toxic metal compounds are still found in soils dosed with them long ago.

In the 1600s, farmers used nicotine sulphate, extracted from tobacco leaves, as an insecticide. In the mid-1800s, two more natural pesticides were introduced: *pyrethrum* (obtained from the heads of chrysanthemum flowers) and *rotenone* (extracted from the roots of various tropical forest legumes). These *first-generation pesticides* were mainly natural chemicals or botanicals borrowed from plants that had been defending themselves against insects eating them and herbivores grazing on them. In other words, we learned to copy nature.

> **DID YOU KNOW**
>
> Only about 1% of the 1 million catalogued insects might be considered pests. Of these, about 1% (100 species) cause 90% of the damage. And human beings created or facilitated some of these pests by introducing them as *invasive species* in places where they had no natural enemies, or by removing ecological checks and balances that kept their populations under control.

What Is the Second Generation of Pesticides? Chemistry and Natural Plants to the Rescue

Chemists have developed hundreds of chemicals that can kill or repel pests, and they have improved natural pesticides produced by plants.

A major pest control revolution began in 1939, when entomologist Paul Müller discovered that **DDT** (dichlorodiphenyltrichloroethane), a chemical known since 1874, was a potent but problematic insecticide (Spotlight, p. 572). DDT was the first of the so-called *second-generation pesticides*. It soon became the world's most-used pesticide, and Müller received the Nobel Prize in 1948 for his discovery. Since then, chemists have created hundreds of other pesticides by making slight modifications in the molecules in various classes of chemicals (Table 23-1).

Other second-generation pesticides are listed in Table 23-1. *Chlorinated hydrocarbons* are persistent, fat soluble, able to biomagnify, and toxic to many organisms, including humans. *Organophosphates* such as malathion are less persistent than DDT and water

Table 23-1 Major Types of Pesticides

Type	Examples	Persistence	Biologically Magnified?
Insecticides			
Chlorinated hydrocarbons	DDT, aldrin, dieldrin, toxaphene, lindane, chlordane, methoxychlor, mirex	High (2–15 years)	Yes
Organophosphates	Malathion, parathion, diazinon, TEPP, DDVP, mevinphos	Low to moderate (1–2 weeks), but some can last several years	No
Carbamates	Aldicarb, carbaryl (Sevin), propoxur, maneb, zineb	Low (days to weeks)	No
Botanicals	Rotenone, pyrethrum, and camphor extracted from plants, synthetic pyrethroids (variations of pyrethrum), rotenoids (variations of rotenone), and neonicotinoids (variations of nicotine)	Low (days to weeks)	No
Microbotanicals	Various bacteria, fungi, protozoa	Low (days to weeks)	No
Herbicides			
Contact chemicals	Atrazine, simazine, paraquat	Low (days to weeks)	No
Systemic chemicals	2,4-D, 2,4,5-T, Silvex, diuron, daminozide (Alar), alachlor (Lasso), glyphosate (Roundup)	Mostly low (days to weeks)	No
Soil sterilants	Tribulan, diphenamid, dalapon, butylate	Low (days)	No
Fungicides			
Various chemicals	Captan, pentachlorophenol, zeneb, methyl bromide, carbon bisulphide	Most low (days)	No
Fumigants			
Various chemicals	Carbon tetrachloride, ethylene dibromide, methyl bromide	Mostly high	Yes (for most)

Unintended Consequences of DDT

DDT was an immediate success. It was cheap and easy to produce. It was *persistent* (not readily broken down). It was not soluble in water, so it stayed on the crop. And it was a *broad spectrum* pesticide, so it killed a wide range of pests.

On the negative side, DDT was soluble in fat. This meant that organisms could not excrete this chemical; it would *bioaccumulate* in body tissues and *biomagnify* up food chains to top predators. At one point, high concentrations of DDT and its by-products were being found in human breast milk causing concern about babies, and the eggs of peregrine falcons were collapsing under them because of DDT-related eggshell thinning. Also, DDT tended to kill off insect predators as it biomagnified up food chains; this left farmers with greater pest control problems than ever, which often caused them to use even more pesticides.

Furthermore, insects have the ability to develop genetic resistance to DDT. Since insects are so numerous, and lay large numbers of eggs, if the same pesticide is sprayed over and over any individuals with resistant tendencies that survive pass their traits on to their numerous progeny, which in turn mate with other resistant progeny. Over time, at least 50 species of malaria-carrying mosquitoes developed genetic resistance to DDT.

The negative aspects of DDT gradually became known through the efforts of Rachel Carson. DDT was banned in North America in 1972. Yet DDT has not gone away. It is manufactured legally in several countries, and is still used to treat crops and to kill disease-carrying insects in a number of developing countries.

In 2001, delegates from 122 countries agreed on a global pollution prevention treaty called the Stockholm Convention to control,

reduce, phase out, and destroy stockpiles of 12 persistent organic pollutants (POPs). This list of chemicals, called the *dirty dozen*, includes DDT and eight other chlorine-containing persistent pesticides.

The treaty, which went into effect in 2004, allows 18 developing countries to continue using DDT to combat malaria until safer, affordable alternatives are available. This was permitted because the health benefits of using DDT to decrease deaths related to malaria—655 000 per year—were thought to outweigh the potential harm of using DDT. Opponents argue that a complete ban on DDT will spur research efforts to find other cost-effective means of combating malaria.

Note that there are now 176 parties to the convention, and 10 additional POPs have been added to the list (UNEP, 2012).

---

soluble so we can wash them off our food; however, these insecticides are highly toxic to humans and other vertebrates, and they are beginning to show up in well water. *Carbamates* have low persistence but are highly toxic to vertebrates and are associated with the catastrophic industrial accident that occurred in Bhopal, India (p. 602). *Botanicals* can now be extracted from plants more efficiently, as well as created synthetically; they have low persistence, can be washed off food, and are effective against pests when properly applied.

Herbicides based on *glyphosate* (the active ingredient in Roundup and Vision) appear to be effective against target plants without harming most animals. However, the herbicides also contain chemicals called surfactants, designed to increase the absorption of glyphosate into plants, which can be damaging to larval amphibians.

Researchers have discovered that an invasive plant called *knapweed* may hold the key to developing effective natural herbicides. This plant secretes a toxic chemical compound (*catechin*) into the soil that can kill all other surrounding plants. This new natural

herbicide, discovered by learning from nature, should soon be on the market.

23-2 THE CASE FOR PESTICIDES

What Are the Advantages of Modern Synthetic Pesticides? Many Benefits

Modern pesticides save lives, increase food supplies, increase profits for farmers, work fast, and are safe if used properly.

Proponents of conventional chemical pesticides contend that their benefits outweigh their harmful effects. Conventional pesticides have a number of important benefits.

They save human lives. Since 1945, DDT and other chlorinated hydrocarbon and organophosphate insecticides probably have prevented the premature deaths of at least 7 million people (some say as many as 500 million) from insect-transmitted diseases such as malaria (carried by the *Anopheles* mosquito), bubonic plague (carried by rat fleas), and typhus (carried by body lice and fleas).

They increase food supplies. According to the UN Food and Agriculture Organization, more than 40% of the world's potential human food supply is lost to pests—about two-thirds of that before harvest and the rest after.

They increase profits for farmers. Pesticide companies estimate that every $1 spent on pesticides leads to an increase in North American crop yields worth approximately $4 (but studies have shown this benefit drops to about $2 if the harmful effects of pesticides are included).

They work faster and better than alternatives. Pesticides control most pests quickly at a reasonable cost, have a long shelf life, are easily shipped and applied, and are safe when handled properly by farm workers. When genetic resistance occurs, farmers can use stronger doses or switch to other pesticides.

When used properly, their health risks are very low compared with their benefits. According to the U.S. Environmental Protection Agency (EPA), the worst-case scenario is that synthetic pesticides in food cause 0.5–1% of all cancer-related deaths in the United States, or 3 000–6 000 premature deaths per year, far less than the estimated number of lives saved each year by pesticides.

Newer pesticides are safer and more effective than many older pesticides. Greater use is being made of botanicals and microbotanicals (Table 23-1). Derived originally from plants, they are safer to users and less damaging to the environment than many older pesticides. Genetic engineering is also being used to develop pest-resistant crop strains and genetically altered crops that produce pesticides.

Many new pesticides are used at much lower rates per unit area than older products. For example, application amounts per hectare for many new herbicides are 1/100 the rates for older ones, and genetically engineered crops could reduce the use of toxic insecticides.

What Is the Ideal Pesticide? An Ongoing Search

Scientists work to develop more effective and safer pesticides, but through coevolution pests find ways to combat the pesticides we throw at them.

Scientists continue to search for the ideal pest-killing chemical, which would have these qualities:

- Affect only the target organism
- Not cause genetic resistance in the target organism
- Disappear or break down into harmless chemicals after doing its job
- Be more cost effective than doing nothing

The search continues, but so far no known natural or synthetic pesticide chemical meets all or even most of these criteria.

What Is the Major Problem with Using Pesticides? Insects Have an Evolutionary Advantage

Insects can rapidly become genetically resistant to widely used pesticides.

Opponents of widespread pesticide use believe their harmful effects outweigh their benefits. They cite several serious problems with the use of conventional pesticides.

The major problem is that the widespread use of synthetic pesticides *accelerates the development of genetic resistance to these chemicals by pest organisms.* Insects breed rapidly (Figure 23-2), and within 5–10 years (much sooner in tropical areas) they can develop immunity to pesticides through natural selection and come back stronger than before. Weeds and plant disease organisms also develop genetic resistance, but more slowly. Since 1945, about 1 000 species of insects, 300 plant disease organisms, and 200 weed species have developed genetic resistance to one or more pesticides.

Because of genetic resistance, many insecticides (such as DDT) no longer do a good job of protecting people from insect-transmitted diseases in some parts of the world. This has led to the resurgence of tropical-diseases such as malaria. Genetic resistance can also put farmers on a *pesticide treadmill,* whereby they pay more and more for a pest control program that often becomes less and less effective.

U.S. Department of Agriculture

FIGURE 23-2 A boll weevil, just one example of an insect capable of rapid breeding. Each female lays thousands of eggs, producing a new generation every 21 days and as many as six generations in a single growing season. Attempts to control the cotton boll weevil account for at least one-fourth of insecticide use in the United States. For example, it typically takes about 114 grams (one-quarter pound) of pesticides to make one cotton T-shirt. Some farmers are increasing their use of natural predators and other biological methods to control this major pest.

What Are Other Problems with Using Pesticides? Some Serious Concerns

Pesticides can wipe out natural enemies of pest species, create new pest species, and end up in the environment, and some can harm wildlife and people.

Another problem is that *most pesticides kill beneficial species as well as the target pest species.* For example, most insecticides kill natural predators and parasites that help control the populations of insect pest species. Wiping out natural predators can unleash new pests, whose populations their predators had previously held in check, and can cause other unexpected effects (Connections, pp. 192 and 575). Of the 300 most destructive insect pests in North America, 100 were once minor pests that became major pests after widespread use of insecticides. With wolf spiders (Figure 23-1, left), wasps, predatory beetles, and other natural enemies out of the way, the population of a rapidly reproducing insect pest species can rebound and even get larger within days or weeks after initially being controlled.

Also, *pesticides do not stay put.* Only about 1% of the insecticide applied to crops by aerial (Figure 23-3) or ground spraying reaches the target pests. Also, less than 5% of herbicide applied to crops reaches the target weeds. In other words, 99% of the insecticides and more than 95% of the herbicides we apply end up in the air, surface water, groundwater, bottom sediments, food, and nontarget organisms, including humans and wildlife (Figure 19-4, p. 455). Crops that have been genetically altered to release small amounts of pesticides directly to pests can help overcome this problem. But this can promote genetic resistance to such pesticides.

Some pesticides harm wildlife. Each year pesticides applied to cropland in North America wipe out about 20% of the honeybee colonies and damage another 15%. This costs farmers at least $200 million per year from reduced pollination of vital crops. Pesticides also kill more than 67 million birds and 6–14 million fish, and contribute to the pressures faced by endangered and threatened species.

Some pesticides can threaten human health. The World Health Organization (WHO) and the UN Environment Programme (UNEP) estimate that each year pesticides seriously poison at least 3 million agricultural workers

FIGURE 23-3 A crop duster spraying an insecticide. Aircraft apply about 25% of the pesticides used on North American cropland, but only about 1% of these insecticides actually reach the target pests. To compensate for the drift of pesticides from target to nontarget areas, aircraft apply up to 30% more pesticide than ground-based application does.

in developing countries and at least 300 000 in North America. This causes 20 000–40 000 deaths per year. Health officials believe the actual number of pesticide-related illnesses and deaths among the world's farm workers is greatly underestimated because of poor record-keeping, lack of doctors, inadequate reporting of illnesses, and faulty diagnoses.

Each year more than 110 000 North Americans, mostly children, get sick from misuse or unsafe storage of pesticides in the home, and about 20 die.

Studies have linked exposure to some pesticides to childhood leukemia, Parkinson's disease, immune system disorders, and prostate and breast cancer.

Some scientists are becoming increasingly concerned about possible **genetic mutations,** birth defects, nervous system disorders (especially behavioural disorders), and effects on the immune and endocrine systems from long-term exposure to low levels of various pesticides (Case Study, p. 459). The pesticide industry disputes such claims.

What Goes Around Can Come Around

People in developing nations are being exposed to pesticides that have been banned in North America and other industrialized regions of the world. In some cases, the choice in developing nations is between contracting malaria or risking the effects of a banned pesticide.

In other cases, however, pesticides banned in North America are being used in agriculture simply because they are cheap and available. Sweaty, half-naked workers are breathing dangerous chemicals and absorbing them through their skin as they pump pesticides onto crops from backpacks. Even when the banned pesticides are sprayed from airplanes, only about 1% of the chemical hits the target crop. The remainder drifts on the wind to be delivered to other parts of the environment.

In what environmentalists call the *pesticide boomerang*, banned chemicals are being returned in the form of produce to the industrialized nations that manufactured and exported them. About 50% of the produce imported by industrialized nations is contaminated with pesticides.

Critical Thinking

Should companies in industrialized nations be allowed to export banned chemicals to developing nations? Do you think that most people in industrialized nations know about the *pesticide boomerang*? How do you think they would react if they were made aware of this situation?

Case Study: How Successful Have Pesticides Been in Reducing Crop Losses? Barely Holding the Line

A slightly higher percentage of food supply is lost to pests today than in the 1940s.

Studies indicate that pesticides have not been as effective in reducing crop losses to pests as agricultural experts had hoped, mostly because of genetic resistance and reductions in natural predators.

David Pimentel, an expert in insect ecology, has evaluated data from more than 300 agricultural scientists and economists and come to three major conclusions.

First, although the use of various kinds of synthetic pesticides has increased 33-fold since 1942, about 37% of the U.S. food supply is lost to pests today compared to 31% in the 1940s. Since 1942, losses attributed to insects alone almost doubled from 7% to 13% despite a tenfold increase in the use of synthetic insecticides.

Second, the estimated environmental, health, and social costs of pesticide use in the United States range from $4 billion to $10 billion (U.S.) per year. The International Food Policy Research Institute puts the estimate much higher, at $100– $200 billion (U.S.) per year, or $5–$10 in damages for every dollar spent on pesticides.

Third, numerous studies and experience show that pesticide use can be reduced significantly without reducing yields, and in some cases, yields increase. Sweden has cut pesticide use in half with almost no decrease in crop yields. Campbell Soup uses no pesticides on tomatoes it grows in Mexico, and yields have not dropped. After a two-thirds cut in pesticide use on rice in Indonesia, yields increased by 15%.

CONSIDER, DISCUSS, OR DEBATE

Reflect on the fact that since 1942, food losses attributed to insects have almost doubled despite a tenfold increase in the use of synthetic pesticides. If we fail to step off this pesticide treadmill, what do you think the consequences will be?

23-4 PESTICIDE REGULATION

How Are Pesticides Regulated in Canada?

Pesticide use in Canada is regulated to varying degrees at the federal, provincial, and municipal levels.

There are about 6 000 pesticide products registered in Canada. According to the World Wildlife Fund, at least 50 million kilograms of pesticides, valued at $1 billion, are released into the Canadian environment each year.

At the *federal level*, all pesticides manufactured, imported, sold, or used in Canada are regulated by the Pest Management Regulatory Agency (PMRA), a branch of Health Canada. The major piece of legislation is the Pest Control Products Act (2002). This act governs all pesticides, including insecticides, herbicides, and fungicides. It also regulates a host of related chemicals such as insect repellents, wood preservatives, and swimming pool algicides. Manufacturers of these products must satisfy the PMRA that the benefits of a given product far outweigh any potential risks. The PMRA stands ready to take action if problems arise.

In June 2006, a revised version of the Pest Control Products Act came into force. The new PCPA increases public protection from pest control products. The David Suzuki Foundation has praised the updated act and asked the federal government to use the new legislation to address the fact that *more than 60 pesticide ingredients that have been banned in other industrialized nations continue to be used in Canada.*

At the *provincial level*, pesticide use is controlled by a variety of acts and regulations designed to ensure proper use, storage, and disposal of pesticides. All pesticides used within the provinces must be among those registered with and approved by the federal government.

At the *municipal level*, public concern over the use of pesticides for strictly aesthetic reasons has led to a variety of initiatives. In 1991, the Montreal suburb of Hudson became the first Canadian municipality to ban the use of pesticides for cosmetic purposes on lawns. The ban did not apply to farmland, and the owners of golf courses were given a five-year grace period in which to find alternative means of pest control. Landscapers and lawn-care companies opposed the ban and took the matter to court.

In 2001, the Supreme Court of Canada ruled that municipalities have the right to ban the residential use of pesticides. The judges said that "our common future, that of every Canadian community, depends on a healthy environment." A number of Canadian cities had already gone ahead with pesticide bans; the Supreme Court ruling encouraged others to follow suit. In 2000, shortly before the ruling, Halifax imposed a pesticide ban that initially applied only to municipal properties but became more inclusive over the first three years; a "notwithstanding clause" allowed pesticide use for genuine needs (as opposed to cosmetic purposes).

In 2002, Cobalt became the first municipality in Ontario to ban nonessential uses of pesticides. Two years later, Toronto introduced a pesticide ban whose application was gradually widened over a three-year "education period." In Waterloo, Ontario, pesticide restrictions were imposed as far back as 1983, when the park services department put an end to the practice of blanket spraying with pesticides; the city's Plant Health Care Program, which focuses on turf management through horticultural techniques, has virtually eliminated the need to use pesticides and has reduced the cost of maintaining a hectare of green space by 42%.

At least 75 Canadian municipalities had adopted cosmetic pesticide restrictions by 2006. In that year, Brandon—the first city in Manitoba to do so—restricted the cosmetic use of pesticides near schools, medical facilities, senior citizens' complexes, day-care centres, parks, and homes where people have applied for a 30-metre buffer zone around their properties for health reasons. As of April 2009, there were 154 municipal pesticide bylaws protecting their communities from the potential effects of cosmetic pesticide use.

In response to this groundswell of public support, an increasing number of provinces have developed provincewide legislation banning or severely restricting the use of pesticides for cosmetic purposes; this overrides municipal bylaws and provides a consistent level of protection for all citizens throughout a given province. Quebec enacted the first provincewide legislation in 2006. By 2009, provincewide legislation banning or restricting the cosmetic use of pesticides was in effect in Ontario, New Brunswick, Alberta, Prince Edward Island, and Newfoundland and Labrador. Some of the other provinces are still considering whether or not to follow suit.

23-5 ALTERNATIVES TO CONVENTIONAL CHEMICAL PESTICIDES

What Should Be the Primary Goal of Pest Control? Pest Reduction, Not Eradication

Reducing crop damage to an economically tolerable level should be the primary goal of pest control efforts.

In most cases, the primary goal of spraying with conventional pesticides is to eradicate pests in the area affected. However, critics say the primary goal of any pest control strategy should be to reduce crop damage to an economically tolerable level. The point at which the economic losses caused by pest damage outweigh the cost of applying a pesticide is called the *economic threshold*. Because of the risk of increased genetic resistance and other problems, continuing to spray beyond the economic threshold can make matters worse and can cost more than it is worth.

The problem is determining when the economic threshold has been reached. This involves careful monitoring of crop fields to assess crop damage and determine pest populations.

Many farmers do not want to bother doing this and instead are likely to use additional *insurance spraying* to be on the safe side. One method used to reduce unnecessary insurance spraying is the purchase of *pest-loss insurance*. It pays farmers for losses caused by pests and is usually cheaper than using excess pesticides.

> **CONSIDER, DISCUSS, OR DEBATE**
>
> Which do you prefer: aesthetically pleasing fruits and vegetables that have been subjected to cosmetic spraying, or produce that is blemished but pesticide-free? Do you routinely wash whatever fruits and vegetables you do buy? Explain.

Another source of increased pesticide use is *cosmetic spraying*. Extra pesticides are used because most consumers often buy only the best-looking fruits and vegetables even though there is nothing wrong with blemished ones. The only solution to this problem is consumer education.

What Are Other Ways to Control Pests? Copy Nature

A mix of cultivation practices and biological and ecological alternatives to conventional chemical pesticides can help control pests.

Many scientists believe we should greatly increase the use of biological, ecological, and other alternative methods for controlling pests and diseases that affect crops and human health. A number of methods are available.

One is to bring back various *cultivation practices* that make life difficult for pest species (Spotlight). Examples are rotating the types of crops planted in a field each year, adjusting planting times so major insect pests either starve or get eaten by their natural predators, and growing crops in areas where their major pests do not exist. Also, farmers can increase the use of polyculture, which uses plant diversity to reduce losses to pests.

Instead of using pesticides, homeowners can manually remove weeds from their gardens and lawns. They can reduce weed invasions by cutting grass no lower than 8 centimetres (3 inches) high. This provides a dense enough cover to keep out crabgrass and many other undesirable weeds. As an alternative to the conventional grass lawn, some homeowners cover their yards with weed-suppressing pebbles or bark mulch.

Homeowners can also avoid growing plants that attract large numbers of pests (such as roses) in favour of plants that are hardy and repel insect pests (such as

chrysanthemums and marigolds). A gardening technique called *companion planting* can be effective in repelling insect pests. Onions and garlic are considered to be good companion plants to tomatoes and carrots because the former repel pests of the latter. Various wild and decorative forms of goldenrod are considered to be good companion plants to many species because goldenrod attracts a long list of predatory insects. Other companion plants such as celery and cabbage are simply thought to grow well together. To learn more about companion planting, visit http://www.organicgardening.com.

DID YOU KNOW

When buying produce, some people take into account the "dirty dozen" of fruits and vegetables that have the highest levels of pesticide residues. They are, in order from highest to lowest pesticide use, apples, celery, sweet bell peppers, peaches, strawberries, nectarines, grapes, spinach, lettuce, cucumbers, blueberries, and potatoes. Your options? You can carefully wash your produce in soap and water; you can peel and discard the outside layers as much as is practical, depending on the type of produce; or you can purchase these fruits and vegetables from an organic supplier who avoids the use of pesticides. Read more about pesticides in produce at http://www.ewg.org/foodnews/summary/.

Those with vegetable gardens that are laid out in conventional patches or rows of monocultures can minimize garden pests by restructuring their gardens into squares of about 1.5 square metres (16 square feet), allowing for walking areas between the squares. A variety of different plants can be placed in each of these squares, including companion plants, plants that are already well started, and plants that

SPOTLIGHT

Ecological Cultivation Practices

The cultivation technique known as crop rotation takes advantage of the fact that larval insects are often not very mobile. The highly mobile (perhaps flying) adult insects may have laid their eggs in a field where a perfect target crop was growing, but if that crop is sown into a different field next season, then the insect pests may hatch into an inappropriate crop or perhaps in a field that is not being used for crops that year.

Farmers who vary planting times are taking advantage of the

fact that insect hatches are often highly synchronized with huge numbers of larvae appearing all at once. If this hatch could be mistimed relative to the sprouting of the crop, then insect pests might hatch into an empty field with no food or cover yet, or into a more mature crop with greater plant defences and more insect predators already in place.

The use of polyculture, which creates plant diversity as opposed to planting huge monocultures of

the same plant, makes it harder for larval insects to find their food plants and at the same time produces a greater habitat diversity to support a thriving community of insect predators.

Instead of using pesticides, some farmers hire workers to go through the fields or orchards and remove pests by hand. Other farmers use special machinery that goes up and down the rows vacuuming pests from the crops.

will repel insects. Since the ground is not bare, weeds are forced to compete with well-established plants, and the diverse arrangement of plants in each square provides a habitat for insect predators as they wait for potential pests to hatch.

Genetic engineering can be used to speed up the development of pest- and disease-resistant crop strains. But there is controversy over whether the projected advantages of the increasing use of genetically modified plants and foods outweigh their projected disadvantages (Figure 14-19, p. 320).

We can increase the use of **biological pest control**. It involves importing natural predators, parasites, and disease-causing bacteria and viruses to help regulate pest populations. More than 1 000 species have been introduced to help control pest species in North America, with generally favourable results. For example, several species of European beetles are being used to help reduce the purple loosestrife plant that has invaded many North American wetlands.

Biological control often focuses on selected target species, is nontoxic to other species, and minimizes genetic resistance. Also, it can save large amounts of money—about $25 for every $1 invested in controlling pests. However, biological agents cannot always be mass produced, are often slower acting and more difficult to apply than conventional pesticides, can sometimes multiply and become pests themselves, and must be protected from pesticides sprayed in nearby fields.

Homeowners can take advantage of the fact that spiders, birds, bats, amphibians, predatory insects, and other species eat many times their weight in insects (Figure 23-4). A little water, shelter, and plant diversity is beneficial to many insect predators. Bat houses can be hung. Nesting material can be left out for birds. The cat can become an inside pet instead of a backyard danger to small animals. Farmers and residential gardeners can even purchase from specialized supply houses

FIGURE 23-5 Predatory insects can be bought by the thousands and released to control pests. Adult convergent ladybugs are consuming aphids.

predatory insects such as lady bugs, (Figure 23-5) lacewings, *Trichogramma* (parasitic wasps), and praying mantis (Figure 4-1); often, they are sold as eggs that can be hatched as needed.

A particularly promising form of biological control involves the use of *Bacillus thuringiensis* (Bt). Bt is a bacterium that occurs naturally in soil, on plants, and in caterpillars of some moths and butterflies. Spores of Bt and protein toxins created by Bt can be concentrated into a fluid and sprayed on plants. When caterpillars ingest this material, their digestive systems are damaged and the caterpillars soon die. Bt can also be used for mosquito control by spraying larval mosquitoes in water. When inserted into genetically modified crops, Bt genes appear to confer an even distribution of toxin throughout the plant, and it is present constantly rather than only after a plant has been sprayed. Bt is generally considered to be environmentally friendly because it is not particularly harmful to humans; however, Bt can have a substantial impact on an ecosystem if it wipes out large numbers of moths and butterflies that would normally be food for other organisms.

FIGURE 23-4 Backyard guardians such as this toad can defend gardens against a host of potential pests.

FIGURE 23-6 Infestation of a steer by screwworm fly larvae. An adult steer can be killed in 10 days by thousands of maggots feeding on a single wound.

U.S. Department of Agriculture

Another strategy is *insect birth control*. This involves raising males of insect pest species in the laboratory and sterilizing them by exposure to radiation or chemicals. The sterile males are released into an infested area to mate with fertile wild females who then lay eggs that never hatch. This method was used to completely eradicate the screwworm fly, a major livestock pest from the southern United States (Figure 23-6). Clearly, the method worked well; however, it is only appropriate for some species of insects. Challenges included knowing the exact mating time and behaviour of the target insects and having large numbers of sterile males to release year after year until the wild population of screwworm flies had collapsed.

Sex attractants can also help control pests. Plants and animals have evolved a variety of natural attractants called *pheromones*. Scientists have identified many of these natural chemicals and use them to lure pests such as Japanese beetles into traps or to attract their natural predators into crop fields (usually the more effective approach). Pheromones can also be released into the air to confuse insects and make it difficult for them to find mates. More than 50 companies worldwide sell about 250 pheromones to control pests.

> **DID YOU KNOW**
>
> Leafy spurge (*Euphorbia esula*) is an invasive, noxious weed that has spread through prairie rangelands since it was introduced in the 1800s. It causes mouth blistering and death in cattle, and contact dermatitis in humans. Enter the black dot surge beetle (*Aphthona nigriscutis*)—introduced as a means of biocontrol—and now leafy spurge density has been reduced by as much as 99% in some areas!

These chemicals attract only one species, work in trace amounts, have little chance of causing genetic resistance, and are not harmful to nontarget species.

However, it is costly and time consuming to identify, isolate, and produce the specific sex attractant for each pest or predator.

Another approach is to use *hormones that disrupt an insect's normal life cycle* (Figure 23-7) and prevent it from reaching maturity and reproducing (Figure 23-8).

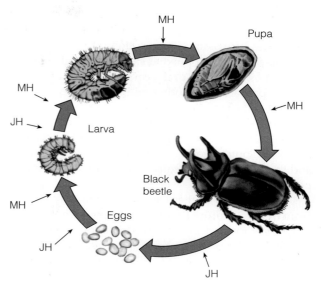

FIGURE 23-7 For normal insect growth, development, and reproduction to occur, certain juvenile hormones (JH) and moulting hormones (MH) must be present at genetically determined stages in the insect's life cycle. If applied at the proper time, synthetic hormones disrupt the life cycles of insect pests and help control their populations.

Agricultural Research Service/USDA

FIGURE 23-8 A use of hormones to prevent insects from maturing completely, making it impossible for them to reproduce. The stunted tobacco hornworm (left) was fed a hormone that prevents production of moulting hormones. They eat but die when they cannot shed the skin off their bulging bodies—somewhat like being trapped in a tight wetsuit while you put on lots of weight. A normal hornworm is shown on the right.

Pest Management **579**

Insect hormones are natural chemicals produced by insects to regulate their growth at various stages of their natural life cycle. By learning what hormones an insect needs at various stages in its life, scientists can use these chemicals to disrupt and kill the insect—another example of learning from nature.

Insect hormones have the same advantages as sex attractants. But they take weeks to kill an insect, often are ineffective with large infestations of insects, and sometimes break down before they can act. In addition, they must be applied at exactly the right time in the target insect's life cycle, can sometimes affect the target's predators and other nonpest species, and are difficult and costly to produce.

Some farmers have controlled some insect pests by *spraying them with hot water*. This has worked well on alfalfa and potato fields and in citrus groves in Florida, and the cost is roughly equal to that of using chemical pesticides.

Farmers and homeowners can hang insect traps from trees to capture flying insect pests (Figure 23-9). Barriers wrapped around tree trunks can prevent tent caterpillars and other crawling insect pests from gaining access to the foliage. Simply removing tree branches, bark, fallen fruit, and other organic litter from under trees helps to reduce attacks from codling moths. Homeowners can control insect grubs in their lawns by using spiked rollers, or reduce garden slugs with products like the slug bar, which uses beer to attract and drown slugs. Insecticidal soap, which homeowners can safely spray, is an effective control against soft-bodied insects like aphids.

FIGURE 23-9 Insect traps come in styles ranging from the decorative to the purely functional. They can be baited with something sweet like sugary water, with meat to trap carnivorous insects, or with pheromones (available through commercial suppliers) to lure insects through sexual attraction. This decorative wasp trap is defending a backyard barbecue.

Is Integrated Pest Management the Answer? A Combined Ecological Approach

An ecological approach to pest control uses an integrated mix of cultivation and biological methods, and small amounts of selected chemical pesticides as a last resort.

An increasing number of pest control experts and farmers believe the best way to control crop pests is a carefully designed **integrated pest management (IPM)** program. In this approach, each crop and its pests are evaluated as parts of an ecological system. Then farmers develop a control program that includes cultivation, biological, and chemical methods applied in proper sequence and with the proper timing.

The overall aim of IPM is not to eradicate pest populations but to reduce crop damage to an economically tolerable level. Fields are monitored carefully to determine when an economically damaging level of pests has been reached. When this happens farmers first use biological methods (natural predators, parasites, and disease organisms) and cultivation controls, including vacuuming up harmful bugs. Small amounts of insecticides—mostly based on natural insecticides produced by plants—are applied only as a last resort. Also, different chemicals are used in order to slow the development of genetic resistance and to avoid killing predators of pest species.

In 1986, the Indonesian government banned 57 of the 66 pesticides used on rice and phased out pesticide subsidies over a two-year period. It also launched a nationwide education program to help farmers switch to IPM. The results were dramatic. Between 1987 and 1992, pesticide use dropped by 65%, rice production rose by 15%, and more than 250 000 farmers were trained in IPM techniques. In Sri Lanka IPM increased rice yields 11–44% and increased farmer incomes 38–178%. Sweden and Denmark have used IPM to cut their pesticide use in half.

The experiences of these and other countries show that a well-designed IPM program can reduce pesticide use and pest control costs by at least half, cut pre-harvest losses from pests by half, and improve crop yields. It can also reduce inputs of fertilizer and irrigation water and slow the development of genetic resistance because pests are assaulted less often and with lower doses of pesticides.

Thus *IPM is an important form of pollution prevention* that reduces risks to wildlife and human health. Consumers Union estimates that if all North American farmers practised IPM by 2020, public health risks from pesticides would drop by 75%.

In Canada, IPM programs are used by a number of forest agencies. The Nova Scotia Forestry Division, for example, closely monitors populations of the spruce budworm (*Choristoneura fumiferana*)—typically the

FIGURE 23-10 Spruce budworms, which cause serious damage to coniferous trees, can be controlled by means of natural predators, biological agents, and selective spraying.

most destructive forest insect pest in North America east of the Rocky Mountains (Figure 23-10). Before an epidemic can occur, stands of trees that are harbouring the pests may be selectively harvested. At an appropriate time, the Nova Scotia Forestry Division may use contact insecticides or a biological agent such as Bt—all the while taking care not to interfere with naturally occurring predators and parasites that can help to control the outbreak.

Another population closely tracked by the Nova Scotia Forestry Division is the gypsy moth (*Lymantria dispar*), an invasive species that is among the most notorious defoliators of broad-leaf trees in Canada (Figure 23-11). Natural predators such as chickadees, blue jays, and parasitic insects keep small populations of the gypsy moth in check. When major infestations occur, the Nova Scotia Forestry Division may employ a synthetic version of the pheromone that females use to attract males. This pheromone can be used to lure males into traps, or it can be sprayed in the forest to make it difficult for males and females to find each

FIGURE 23-11 Gypsy moths, which attack deciduous trees, can be controlled by means of natural predators, pheromone strategies, biological agents, and chemical insecticides.

other. Biological controls or chemical insecticides may also be used, depending on the circumstances.

Why Have More Farmers Not Switched to Integrated Pest Management? Politics in Action

Government subsidies for conventional pesticides, opposition by pesticide manufacturers, and a lack of experts to advise farmers hinder a widespread shift to integrated pest management.

Despite its promise, IPM, like any other form of pest control, has some challenges. It requires expert knowledge about each pest situation including a pest's life cycles, feeding habits, movements, and nesting habits. Farmers are unfamiliar with IPM and may lack confidence in the outcome. IPM is also slower acting than conventional pesticides, and methods developed for a crop in one area might not apply to areas with even slightly different growing conditions. Also, initial costs may be higher, although long-term costs typically are lower than those of using conventional pesticides.

Widespread use of IPM is hindered by government subsidies of conventional chemical pesticides and opposition from agricultural chemical companies, whose pesticide sales would drop sharply. There is also a lack of experts to help farmers shift to IPM.

Here are some strategies that might encourage the growth of IPM:

- Add a 2% sales tax on pesticides and use the revenue to fund IPM research and education.

- Set up government-funded demonstration projects on a number of farms in every province.

- Send agricultural experts to farms to talk directly with farmers about the advantages of IPM.

- Create special crop insurance for farmers willing to switch to IPM.

- Allow farms that switch to IPM to be recognized by the EcoLogo labelling system.

- Remove subsidies that currently favour pesticides.

Good news. Several UN agencies and the World Bank have joined together to establish an IPM facility. Its goal is to promote use of IPM by disseminating information and establishing networks among researchers, farmers, and agricultural extension agents involved in IPM.

We need to recognize that pest control is basically an ecological, not a chemical, problem.
ROBERT L. RUDD

CONSIDER, DISCUSS, OR DEBATE

Should governments heavily subsidize a switch to integrated pest management?

SPOTLIGHT

Mountain Pine Beetles

Mountain pine beetles (*Dendroctonus ponderosae*) are small (5-millimetre-long), dark-coloured bark beetles native to forests of western North America (Figure 23-12). They inhabit various species of pine trees such as ponderosa, lodgepole, Scotch, and limber. Normally these insects play a role in forest succession by attacking old or weak trees, thereby making room for younger trees to grow.

However, since 2000, populations of mountain pine beetles have been rapidly expanding in numbers and distribution. This outbreak is ten times larger than previous outbreaks and is affecting huge

swaths of pine forests in British Columbia, Alberta, Colorado, and Wyoming. Researchers think that several factors may be at work. Mild winters and climate change may have favoured the survival of beetles; at the same time, these conditions may have weakened the trees, making them more susceptible to the beetles.

Foresters are using IPM to combat the infestation. Some techniques they are using, in various combinations, are (1) removing infested trees; (2) luring male beetles into traps using chemicals that mimic the pheromones of female beetles; (3) fooling beetles into ignoring trees by means of a compound similar to

a pheromone that the beetles use to signal when a tree is no longer worth invading; (4) carrying out controlled burning of badly infested patches; (5) pre-arming the trees to defend themselves more effectively by watering the ground with a solution of chitosan, an eco-friendly biopesticide that the trees quickly absorb; and (6) undertaking limited spraying with an assortment of insecticides.

Meanwhile, foresters are hoping for cold winters and rainy summers that will favour the trees and disadvantage the beetles. For more information, visit websites such as http://www.gov.bc.ca/pinebeetle.

FIGURE 23-12 Adult beetles lay their eggs in pine trees. They and their larvae (left) tunnel in the wood and inadvertently introduce fungi that kill the trees within 2–6 years. Adults disperse by flying from tree to tree (centre). Large areas of pine trees (right) have been damaged or killed in this unprecedented outbreak of mountain pine beetles.

CHAPTER REVIEW

1. Review the Key Questions for this chapter on p. 570. Describe the amazing ability of insects to multiply and adapt. Approximately what percentage of insects are serious *pests* on our farms and in our forests? What services are provided by insects? What would the world be like without them? On the other hand, describe some serious insect-related threats to our health and food supply that require our careful attention. Describe four general types of *pesticides* and the organisms they are intended to kill.

2. Why are a relatively small number of spiders and other insect-predators able to have a large impact on insect populations? Can energy- and trophic-level arguments

be used to explain this effect? List the many organisms, and groups of organisms, that depend on insects for food.

3. Why do some people say that plants and insects have been in an "arms race" for millions of years? What chemicals have plants evolved to deter predation from plants? How well do those chemicals work in nature, and have we been able to make use of these chemicals?

4. Why does the practice of spraying insecticides and raising crops in monocultures (our conventional agriculture) actually favour insect pests and disadvantage their predators? Why would their predators gain advantages if we didn't spray insecticides (or used

them very sparingly), and raised our crops among a diversity of other plants?

5. What were some of the early chemicals that humans used to try to control insect pests? How well did these chemicals work? Describe some of the first-generation pesticides that were plant extracts.

6. What is *DDT*? Why was it received so favourably at first? What properties of DDT led to problems over the years that followed? Why is DDT banned in many countries? Why do some countries continue to use DDT despite the well-known dangers associated with using this insecticide?

7. Name four major types of second-generation pesticides. What are the properties of each type? Name five pros and five cons of spraying crops with modern pesticides. What is meant by the *pesticide treadmill*? Should we continue to depend on chemicals

for most of our pest control? Describe alternative strategies that involve cultivation procedures, biological control, pheromones, hormones, and traps.

8. Describe how pesticides are regulated in Canada. Why are many communities against the spraying of pesticides for cosmetic purposes? What are these communities doing to control the spraying of pesticides, and what will the effect be?

9. Define *integrated pest management (IPM)*. What are its advantages and disadvantages? Does it work as well as conventional pest control? Why haven't more farmers and foresters switched to IPM? What future trends do you anticipate for pest management in Canada?

10. Describe a farmer's field (an agro-ecosystem) that is being managed using IPM in terms of the four *scientific principles of sustainability*.

CRITICAL THINKING

1. What are the advantages and disadvantages of banning the use of pesticides on city lawns?

2. If increased mosquito populations threatened you with malaria or West Nile virus, would you spray DDT in your yard and inside your home to reduce the risk? Explain. What are the alternatives?

3. Explain how widespread use of a pesticide can (a) increase the damage done by a particular pest and (b) create new pest organisms.

4. Explain why biological pest control often is more successful on a small island than on a continent.

5. Should farmers be given government subsidies for switching to integrated pest management (IPM)? Explain your position.

6. Congratulations! You are in charge of pest control for the entire world. What are the three most important components of your global pest management strategy?

PROJECTS

1. How are insects and weeds controlled in (a) your yard and garden; (b) the grounds of your school; and (c) public school grounds, parks, and playgrounds in your community?

2. List all pesticides used in or around your home. Compare the results for your entire class. Which ones should be eliminated?

3. Some research shows that although many people agree we need to make greater use of alternatives to conventional pesticides for controlling pests, when they are faced with an actual infestation from insects or rodents

the first thing they do is spray with pesticides. Survey members of your class and other groups to help determine the validity of these research findings.

4. Use the library or the Internet to learn about the life cycle of a particular pest. What kind of damage does this pest cause? Use your understanding of the pest's characteristics to suggest strategies for controlling it.

5. Some people are slaves to their high-maintenance, perfectly manicured lawns. Research and make a case for an ecologically friendly alternative (wildflower lawns, rock gardens, ponds, retaining walls, patios, etc.).

Solid and Hazardous Waste

The Sydney Tar Ponds: A Toxic Legacy

Sydney, the third largest city in Nova Scotia (Figure 24-1A), was once the heart of a thriving steel industry based on local coal and iron resources, as well as iron ore that could be shipped from mines in Wabana, Newfoundland, and Labrador. When the Dominion Iron and Steel Company (DISCO) in Sydney began its operations in 1901, it was the largest steel mill in North America. By 1912, DISCO produced nearly half the steel that was made in Canada (Figure 24-1B).

The coal was high in sulphur, and coke ovens had to be constructed to bake vast quantities of coal to produce a higher grade of fuel for the steel mill's open-hearth blast furnaces. The iron ore from Wabana contained impurities that had to be removed by a process that used large quantities of limestone. The result was an inefficient process that resulted in higher costs and larger amounts of wastes than many other steel operations. In 1967, the current owner announced that the steel mill was losing money and would soon be closing. The Sydney Steel Corporation (SYSCO), a provincial Crown corporation,

was created to extend the operation in the hopes that a private investor could be found. The steel plant finally ceased operations in 2001.

Throughout the century of steel production, air pollutants had been released to the area. A tarry sludge from the coking process was dumped into nearby Muggah Creek. Over time, a huge pile of limestone slag accumulated and filled in Muggah Creek from the east. As well, the area received raw sewage from the city, leachate from the garbage dump, and contaminated water from other industrial processes. All these activities combined to form the Sydney Tar Ponds, a 31-hectare (76-acre) body of polluted water and sediment (Figure 24-1C). Analysis showed that the sludge in the Tar Ponds contained 700 000 tonnes of sediment contaminated with heavy metals (such as arsenic, copper, lead, thallium, and zinc), polyaromatic hydrocarbons (PAHs), and polychlorinated biphenyls (PCBs). It was described as the largest chemical waste site in Canada.

(continued)

FIGURE 24-1A The location of Sydney, Nova Scotia, at the north end of Cape Breton Island. (Norman Einstein)

FIGURE 24-1B Historical view of the Sydney Steel Plant. (From the Sydney Steel Museum, http://www.sydneysteelmuseum .com/gallery/historical_section1.htm)

FIGURE 24-1C An aerial view of the tar ponds at the edge of Sydney, Nova Scotia. A causeway and bridge divide the North Tar Pond (right) from the South Tar Pond (left). The realigned coke oven brook flows past the left side of a round cooling pond formerly used by the Sydney Steel Plant. The plant was situated at the right side of this picture. (http://www .sydneytarponds.com/default.asp?T=4&M=27)

Many individuals and groups have wrestled with the issues posed by the Sydney Tar Ponds. A Joint Action Group (JAG) was formed in 1996 to seek consensus on cleanup methods to be used. The Sydney Tar Ponds Agency was formed by the province in 2001 to manage the cleanup; however, progress was slow. Elizabeth May, at the time executive director of the Sierra Club of Canada, co-authored a book about the Tar Ponds with Maude Barlow (pp. 351 and 666), and staged a hunger strike on Parliament Hill to bring attention to the issue. Some other recognizable names involved with the Tar Ponds include David Suzuki and Lois Gibbs (associated with the contaminated Love Canal site in the United States).

In 2005, Environment Minister Stéphane Dion ordered a full environmental assessment (http://www.tarpondscleanup.ca/). In 2007, the federal and provincial governments announced plans to stabilize and fully remediate the Tar Ponds and coke ovens. The project will cost $400 million and is slated to be complete within 7 to 10 years. Plans are being considered to use the area as a park, a golf course, or a light industrial park.

Solid wastes are only raw materials we're too stupid to use.

ARTHUR C. CLARKE

CHAPTER PURPOSE AND QUESTIONS

Chapter 24 encourages readers to rethink conventional approaches to the treatment of solid and hazardous wastes. The chapter addresses the following questions:

24-1 Why should we care about solid waste?

24-2 What options do we have for reducing solid waste?

24-3 What is industrial ecology?

24-4 What are the advantages and disadvantages of reuse?

24-5 What are the advantages and disadvantages of recycling?

24-6 What are the advantages and disadvantages of burning or burying solid waste?

24-7 What is hazardous waste?

24-8 What is the threat from lead, mercury, and dioxins?

24-9 What is the role of grassroots action in achieving a low-waste society?

24-1 WASTING RESOURCES

Why Should We Care About Solid Waste? Resource Waste and Pollution

Solid waste is a symptom of an unnecessary waste of resources whose production causes pollution and environmental degradation.

Solid waste is any unwanted or discarded material that is not a liquid or a gas. So what is the big deal? For most people, garbage trucks arrive and whisk away the solid waste they produce—out of sight, out of mind.

In nature there is essentially no solid waste because the wastes of one organism become nutrients for other organisms. But humans will always produce some solid waste. Indeed, we produce such wastes directly and indirectly in almost everything we do. The solid waste we produce directly is called *garbage*. But most people do not realize that mines, factories, food growers, and businesses supplying the goods and services they use are responsible for about 98% of the world's solid waste.

We need to be concerned about such waste production for two reasons. One is that much of it represents an unnecessary waste of the Earth's precious resources. The other is that producing the solid products we use and often discard is responsible for huge amounts of air pollution (including greenhouse gases), water pollution, soil erosion, and land degradation (Figure 16-12, p. 374).

Some *good news* is that we could reduce our direct and indirect production of solid waste by 75–90%, as you will learn in this chapter.

Case Study: Waste Production in North America

North America produces about one-third of the world's solid waste.

North America, with less than 5% of the world's population, produces about one-third of the world's solid waste—a glaring symptom of affluenza (p. 13). About 98.5% of the solid waste in North America (and in most developed countries) comes from mining, oil and natural gas production, agriculture, sewage sludge, and industrial activities (Figure 24-2). This solid waste is produced *indirectly* to provide goods and services to meet the needs and growing wants of consumers.

Suppose you buy a desktop computer. You probably do not know that making it used 700 or more different materials obtained from mines, oil wells, and chemical factories all over the world. You may also be unaware that for every 0.5 kilogram (1 pound) of electronics it contains, approximately 3 600 kilograms (8 000 pounds) of solid and liquid waste was created somewhere in the world. Extracting these resources and converting them into your computer also required large amounts of energy produced

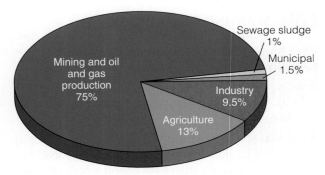

FIGURE 24-2 Natural capital degradation: sources of the estimated 11 billion metric tonnes of solid waste produced each year in North America. Mining, oil and gas production, agricultural, and industrial activities produce 65 times as much solid waste as household activities. (Data from U.S. Environmental Protection Agency, U.S. Bureau of Mines, and Statistics Canada)

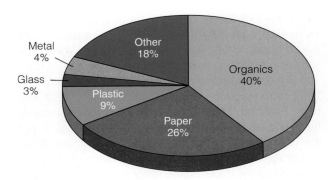

FIGURE 24-3 Composition of municipal solid waste in Canada. The "Other" category represents miscellaneous materials and mixtures of materials that would be much harder to work with than the categories identified. (Statistics Canada)

mostly by burning fossil fuels, which emits pollutants and CO_2 into the air.

The remaining 1.5% of solid waste is **municipal solid waste (MSW)**—often called *garbage* (in Canada) or *trash* (in the United States)—generated mostly by homes and workplaces. This small part of the overall solid waste problem is still huge. *Bad news.* Between 1960 and 2005, the total amount of MSW in North America each year increased threefold and is still rising. Each year North America generates enough MSW to fill a bumper-to-bumper convoy of garbage trucks encircling the globe almost eight times! Between 1960 and 1990, the amount of MSW produced per person in North America increased by 70%.

Japan and most developed countries in Europe produce about half as much MSW per person as North America, and most developing countries produce about one-fourth to one-tenth as much.

What Is in Garbage? Paper and Organics Rule

Paper products and organic matter make up the largest percentage of municipal solid waste in Canada and the United States.

Organics make up about 40% of municipal solid waste in Canada, followed by paper (26%), miscellaneous

materials (18%), plastic (9%), metal (4%), and glass (3%) (Figure 24-3). Some key points about Canadian garbage:

- Amount of municipal solid waste produced annually per Canadian: 383 kilograms or 30 green garbage bags

- Amount of MSW diverted by recycling and other programs: 21%

- Cost of waste management to municipalities: $1.5 billion

- Percentage of paper that is recycled: 40%

- Amount of e-waste (computers, televisions, and cell phones) discarded annually: 140 000 tonnes (Statistics Canada)

Electronic waste, or *e-waste,* consisting of discarded TV sets, cell phones, computers, and other electronic devices is the fastest-growing solid waste problem in Canada, the United States, and many other developed countries. It is also a source of toxic and hazardous wastes such as polyvinyl chloride (PVC) and compounds containing lead and mercury that can contaminate the air, surface water, groundwater, and soil. In North America, only about 2% of such e-waste is recycled.

How do we know the composition of garbage in landfills? Much of it comes from research by *garbologists* such as William Rathje who pioneered this field. These scientists are modern versions of archaeologists who examine people's garbage and dig holes in garbage dumps and analyze what they find.

Many people think of landfills as huge compost piles where biodegradable wastes are decomposed within a few months. But garbologists looking at the contents of landfills found 50-year-old newspapers that were still readable and hot dogs and pork chops buried for decades that still looked edible. In landfills (as opposed to open dumps), garbage can resist decomposition for perhaps centuries because it is tightly packed and protected from sunlight, water, and air.

The specific problems and solutions related to e-waste, and the study of garbology, are explored further at http://www.nelson.com/livingintheenvironment3e.com.

What Does It Mean to Live in a High-Waste Society? A Throwaway Mentality

Most solid waste is a highly visible sign of how a society infected with affluenza wastes valuable resources.

According to architect and environmental designer William McDonough, the industrial revolution that has been taking place for about 275 years has a number of harmful consequences. It has put huge amounts of toxic material into the air, water, and soil. It has put hard-to-separate mixtures of potentially valuable resources in landfills or other holes all over the planet, where they are too difficult or expensive to retrieve and separate into resources. It has spurred government regulations that are mainly designed to keep people from being poisoned or harmed by the immediate effects of dangerous wastes and give little thought to keeping people and natural systems safe for the long term.

It has depleted and degraded the Earth's natural capital and eroded biodiversity and human cultural diversity. Finally, it has counted these harmful consequences as economic progress because they raise the gross domestic product.

Here are a few of the solid wastes that consumers throw away in the high-waste economy found in Canada and the United States:

- Enough aluminum to rebuild the entire commercial airline fleets of both countries every three months
- Enough tires each year to encircle the planet almost three times
- Enough disposable diapers each year that if they were linked end to end they would reach to the moon and back seven times
- About 2 billion disposable razors, 130 million cell phones, 50 million computers, and 8 million television sets each year
- Discarded carpet each year that could cover Prince Edward Island
- About 2.5 million nonreturnable plastic bottles every hour
- About 670 000 metric tons (1.5 billion pounds) of edible food per year
- Enough office paper each year to build a wall 3.5 metres (11 feet) high across the country from the Atlantic to the Pacific
- Some 186 billion pieces of junk mail (an average of 660 per person) each year, about half of which are thrown in the garbage unopened

Strange things happen in a society infected with affluenza. For example, according to the United Nations Environment Programme, North Americans spend more on trash bags each year than 90 other countries spend for everything. Comedian Lily Tomlin has observed, "We buy a wastebasket and take it home in a plastic bag. Then we take the wastebasket out of the bag, and put the bag in the wastebasket." In your own life, you may have noticed that much of the content of a typical bag of groceries is in fact packaging.

24-2 PRODUCING LESS WASTE

What Are Our Options? Management or Prevention

We can try to manage the solid wastes we produce, or we can try to reduce or prevent their production.

We can deal with the solid wastes we create in two ways. One is *waste management*. This is a *high-waste approach* (Figure 3-18, p. 56) that views waste production as a largely unavoidable product of economic growth. It attempts to manage the resulting wastes in ways that reduce environmental harm, mostly by mixing and often crushing them together and then burying them, burning them, or shipping them off to another province or country. In effect, it mixes the wastes we produce together and then transfers them from one part of the environment to another.

The second approach is *waste reduction*, a *low-waste approach* that recognizes there is no "away." It views most solid waste as potential resources that we should be reusing, recycling, or composting. With this approach we should be taught to think of garbage cans and trucks as *resource containers*. Figure 24-4 lists ways to reduce waste. Study this figure carefully.

Waste reduction can be classified according to five R's for dealing with the wastes we produce:

- *Refuse* to manufacture or purchase harmful products.
- *Reduce* packaging and other wasteful materials in products.
- *Reuse* products and buy reusable products like returnable bottles.
- *Recycle* products (including composting).
- *Rethink* traditional strategies for dealing with wastes.

Another R, *recover*, is used by industries to retain materials that might otherwise be wasted; for example, a mining company might add electrostatic precipitators to its smokestacks in order to recover gold and silver that would otherwise be lost up the chimney.

Waste reduction is the preferred solution because it tackles the problem of waste production at the front end—before it occurs—rather than at

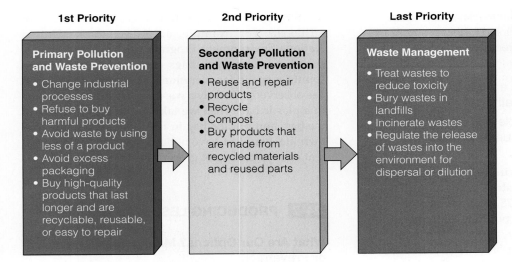

Primary Pollution and Waste Prevention

- Change industrial processes
- Refuse to buy harmful products
- Avoid waste by using less of a product
- Avoid excess packaging
- Buy high-quality products that last longer and are recyclable, reusable, or easy to repair

Secondary Pollution and Waste Prevention

- Reuse and repair products
- Recycle
- Compost
- Buy products that are made from recycled materials and reused parts

Waste Management

- Treat wastes to reduce toxicity
- Bury wastes in landfills
- Incinerate wastes
- Regulate the release of wastes into the environment for dispersal or dilution

FIGURE 24-4 Solutions: priorities suggested by prominent scientists for dealing with material use and solid waste. To date, the first two columns of waste-reduction priorities have not been followed in most countries. Instead, most efforts are devoted to waste management (bury it or burn it).

the back end after wastes have already been produced. It also saves matter and energy resources, reduces pollutants (including emissions of greenhouse gases), helps protect biodiversity, and saves money.

The fifth R—*Rethink*—merits special consideration. In the past, products were developed with little thought that we might one day run short of needed materials, or experience negative environmental impacts resulting from our wastes, or run out of disposal space. What would happen if we now focused the type of ingenuity that went into making these products on finding production methods that minimize their environmental impact?

> **CONSIDER, DISCUSS, OR DEBATE**
>
> Rank the five R's in order of importance. Explain the reasoning behind your choice for the most important R.

Solutions: How Can We Reduce Solid Waste? The Sustainability Six

Reducing consumption and redesigning the products we manufacture are the best ways to cut wastes and promote sustainability.

Here are six ways to reduce resource use, waste, and pollution—what we might call the *sustainability six*. First, *consume less*. Before buying anything, ask questions such as: Do I really *need* this or do I just *want* it? Can I buy it secondhand (reuse)? Can I borrow or rent it (reuse)?

Second, *redesign manufacturing processes and products to use less material and energy*. A skyscraper built today includes about a third less steel than one the same size built in the 1960s because of the use of lighter-weight but higher-strength steel. The

weight of cars has been reduced by about one-fourth by using such steel along with lightweight plastics and composite materials. Plastic milk jugs weigh 40% less than they did in the 1970s, and aluminum drink cans contain one-third less aluminum. All of these changes involve savings in energy use as well as materials.

Third, *redesign manufacturing processes to produce less waste and pollution*. Most toxic organic solvents can be recycled within factories or replaced with more benign water-based or citrus-based solvents. Hydrogen peroxide can be used instead of toxic chlorine to bleach paper and other materials. Nontoxic ways to clean clothes are now available. One way cleans clothes with water in computer-controlled machines and another uses a nontoxic silicone solvent in conventional dry-cleaning machines. A third method submerses clothes in liquid carbon dioxide. Check your local phone directory to locate dry cleaners that use these alternative methods.

Fourth, *develop products that are easy to repair, reuse, remanufacture, compost, or recycle*. A Xerox photocopier with every part reusable or recyclable for easy remanufacturing should eventually save the company $1 billion in manufacturing costs.

Fifth, *design products to last longer*. Today's tires have an average life of 97 000 kilometres (60 000 miles). Researchers believe this use could be extended to at least 160 000 kilometres (100 000 miles).

Sixth, *eliminate or reduce unnecessary packaging*. From an environmental standpoint, the preferred hierarchy for packaging is *no packaging* (nude products), *minimal packaging, reusable packaging,* and *recyclable packaging*. Canada has a set goal of using the first three of these packaging priorities to cut excess packaging in half. Here are some key questions for designers, manufacturers, and consumers to ask about packaging:

Is it necessary? Can it use fewer materials? Can it be reused? Are the resources that went into it renewable? Does it contain the highest feasible amount of recycled material? Can it be biodegraded into harmless nutrients that are recycled in the Earth's natural chemical cycles? Is it designed to be recycled easily? Can it be incinerated without producing harmful air pollutants or a toxic ash? Can it be buried and decomposed in a landfill without producing chemicals that can contaminate groundwater?

Figure 24-5 lists some ways you can reduce your output of solid waste.

Improvements in resource productivity and environmental design are very important. But we can do much better through a new *resource productivity revolution*. In their 1999 book *Natural Capitalism*, Paul Hawken, Amory Lovins, and Hunter Lovins contend that we have the knowledge and technology to greatly increase resource productivity by getting 75–90% more work or service from each unit of material resources we use. To these analysts, the only major obstacles to such an economic and ecological revolution are laws, policies, taxes, and subsidies that continue to reward inefficient resource use and fail to reward efficient resource use. There are many fulfilling career choices

What Can You Do?

Solid Waste

- Follow the five R's of resource use: Refuse, Reduce, Reuse, Recycle, and Rethink.

- Rethink your way through a lifestyle makeover.

- Question each potential purchase. Do you really need this product?

- Rent, borrow, or barter goods and services when you can.

- Buy things that are reusable, recyclable, or compostable, and be sure to reuse, recycle, and compost them.

- Do not use throwaway paper and plastic plates, cups, eating utensils, and other disposable items when reusable or refillable versions are available.

- Use e-mail in place of conventional paper mail.

- Read newspapers and magazines online.

- Buy products in concentrated form whenever possible.

- Choose nude products or those with minimal packaging.

FIGURE 24-5 What can you do? Ways to reduce your output of solid waste.

for people wanting to become part of the resource productivity revolution.

What Is Industrial Ecology? Reducing Waste Production by Copying Nature

We can make industrial manufacturing processes more sustainable by redesigning them to mimic how nature deals with wastes.

There are growing signs that a revolution in *industrial ecology* will take place over the next 50 years. *Industrial ecology* is a shift in processes whereby systems that convert resources to wastes are altered to become recycling systems. The goal is to redesign industrial manufacturing processes to mimic how nature deals with wastes. *Recall that in nature the waste outputs of one organism become nutrient inputs for another organism, so all of the Earth's matter is endlessly recycled.*

One way we can mimic nature is to recycle and reuse most chemicals used in industries instead of dumping them into the environment. Another is to have industries interact in complex *resource exchange webs* where the wastes of one manufacturer become raw materials for another—similar to food webs in natural ecosystems (Figure 4-19, p. 73). Waste exchanges and chemical clearinghouses operating in Canada and the United States include the Waste Exchange of Canada (http://www.recyclexchange.net), and the Waste Exchange Network (http://www.wastechange.com). In Kalundborg, Denmark, an electric power plant and a number of nearby industries, farms, and homes are functioning as an *ecoindustrial park* to save money and reduce their outputs of waste and pollution. They do this by exchanging waste outputs and thus converting them into resources, as shown in Figure 24-6 (p. 590). Trace the connections in this diagram.

Today there are about 40 ecoindustrial parks similar to the one in Kalundborg in various parts of the world and more are being built or planned. Some are being developed on abandoned industrial sites, called *brownfields,* which are cleaned up and redeveloped.

In Europe at least one-third of all industrial wastes are sent to waste-material exchanges or clearinghouses where they are sold or given away as raw materials for other industries. About a tenth of the industrial waste in North America is sent to such clearinghouses, a figure that could be greatly increased.

In addition to eliminating most waste and pollution, these industrial forms of *biomimicry* provide many economic benefits for businesses. They reduce the costs of controlling pollution and complying with pollution regulations. If a company does not add pollutants to

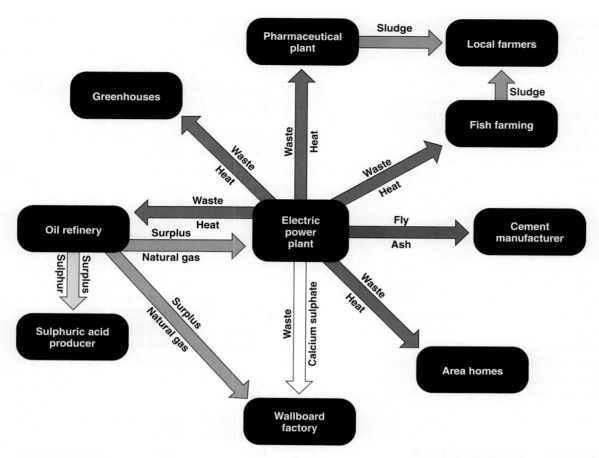

FIGURE 24-6 Solutions: *industrial ecosystem* in Kalundborg, Denmark, reduces waste production by mimicking a natural food web. The wastes of one business become the raw materials for another. Waste heat in the form of hot air or water can be piped from the power plant to several of the other sites.

the environment, it does not have to worry about government regulations or being sued because the wastes harm someone. The company also improves the health and safety of its workers by reducing their exposure to toxic and hazardous material and thus reduces company health-care insurance costs.

Biomimicry also stimulates companies to come up with new, environmentally beneficial chemicals, processes, and products that can be sold worldwide. Such companies have a better image among consumers based on results rather than public relations campaigns.

In 1975, the American company 3M, which makes 60 000 different products in 100 manufacturing plants, began a Pollution Prevention Pays (3P) program. It redesigned equipment and processes, used fewer hazardous raw materials, identified hazardous chemical outputs (and recycled or sold them as raw materials to other companies), and began making more nonpolluting products.

Now 3M has become more efficient, reduced its solid waste by 68%, decreased its energy consumption by 82%, lowered its volatile air emissions by 96%, and cut back on its greenhouse gas emissions by 72%. 3M has also saved itself $1.5 billion (U.S.) and become a very profitable company that is famous for its innovative products and services.

What Is a Service-Flow Economy? Selling Services Instead of Things

Businesses can greatly decrease their pollution and waste by shifting from selling goods to selling services that the goods provide.

In the mid-1980s, German chemist Michael Braungart and Swiss industry analyst Walter Stahel independently proposed a new economic model that would provide profits while greatly reducing resource use and waste. Their idea for more sustainable economies involves shifting from our current *material-flow economy* (Figure 3-18, p. 56) to a *service-flow economy* over the next few decades. Instead of buying most goods outright, customers would use eco-leasing, renting the *services* that such goods provide.

In a service-flow economy, a manufacturer makes more money on a product if it uses the minimum amount of materials, lasts as long as possible, and is easy to maintain, repair, remanufacture, reuse, or recycle.

There is evidence that such an economic shift based on *eco-leasing* is underway. Since 1992, the Xerox Corporation has been leasing most of its copy machines as part of its mission to provide *document services* instead of selling photocopiers. When the service contract expires, Xerox takes the machine back for reuse or remanufacture and has a goal of sending no material to landfills or incinerators. To save money, machines are designed to use recycled paper; have few parts; be energy efficient; and emit as little noise, heat, ozone, and copier chemical waste as possible. Canon in Japan and Fiat in Italy are taking similar measures.

Another example is Carrier, the world's leading maker of air conditioning equipment, which now leases *cooling services*. Carrier teams up with other service providers to install superefficient windows and more efficient lighting and to make other energy-efficiency upgrades that reduce the cooling needs of its customers. Carrier makes money by providing such services rather than installing equipment.

Dow and several other chemical companies are doing a booming business in leasing organic solvents (used mostly to remove grease from surfaces), photographic developing chemicals, and dyes and pigments. In this *chemical service business*, the company delivers the chemicals, helps the client set up a recovery system, takes away the recovered chemicals, and delivers new chemicals as needed.

Finally, the late Ray Anderson, CEO of a large carpet tile company, has been an outstanding example of revolutionizing business and providing services (see Individuals Matter). There are many entrepreneurial and career opportunities in the emerging service-flow economy.

CONSIDER, DISCUSS, OR DEBATE

Taking into consideration the experiences of Xerox and other companies discussed in this section, identify three local businesses that could be redesigned as service-flow companies. How would each of them make money?

INDIVIDUALS MATTER

Ray Anderson

The late Ray Anderson was CEO of Interface, a company based in Atlanta, Georgia, that makes carpet tiles. The company is the world's largest commercial carpet manufacturer, with 26 factories in six countries, customers in 110 countries, and more than $1 billion in annual sales.

Anderson changed the way he viewed the world and his business after reading Paul Hawken's book *The Ecology of Commerce*. In 1994, he announced plans to develop the nation's first totally sustainable green corporation.

He implemented hundreds of projects with the goals of zero waste, greatly reduced energy use, and eventually zero use of fossil fuels by relying on renewable solar energy. So far the company has reduced solid waste by 63% and decreased water usage by 74%. It has become more efficient, lowered energy use by 44%, and gained 88% of its electricity by means of renewable energy sources. As a result of

these changes, the company has lowered its greenhouse gas emissions by 94% and saved more than $433 million. One of Interface's factories in California runs mostly on solar cells to produce the world's first solar-made carpet.

To achieve the goal of zero waste, Interface has been shifting its emphasis from selling carpet to leasing it as a way to encourage recycling. For a monthly fee, the company will install, clean, and inspect the carpet on a monthly basis; repair worn carpet tiles overnight; and recycle worn-out tiles into new carpeting. As Anderson puts it, "We want to harvest yesterday's carpets and recycle them with zero scrap going to the landfill and zero emissions into the ecosystem—and run the whole thing on sunlight."

Anderson was one of a growing number of business leaders committed to finding a more economically and ecologically sustainable way to do business while still

making a profit for shareholders. Ray Anderson's innovative and efficient company has more than doubled its revenues and more than tripled its profits by reinventing itself. Ray, who served on the board of the David Suzuki Foundation, made a very positive contribution to the world through his business and through his environmental activities.

© Aurora Photos/Alamy

REUSE

What Are the Advantages and Disadvantages of Reuse? Improves Environmental Quality for Some, Can Create Hazards for Others

Reusing products is an important way to reduce resource use, waste, and pollution in developed countries but can create hazards for the poor in developing countries.

Reuse involves cleaning and using materials over and over and thus increasing the typical life span of a product. This form of waste reduction reduces use of matter and energy resources, cuts pollution and waste, creates local jobs, and saves money. Traditional forms of reuse include salvaging automobile parts from older cars in junkyards and salvaging bricks, doors, fine woodwork, and other items from old houses and buildings.

However, in today's high-throughput societies we have increasingly substituted throwaway tissues for reusable handkerchiefs; disposable paper towels and napkins for reusable cloth ones; throwaway paper plates and cups and plastic utensils for reusable plates, cups, and silverware; and throwaway beverage containers for refillable ones. We even have disposable cameras.

Reuse is alive and well in most developing countries but can be a health hazard for the poor. About 80% of the e-waste in North America, including discarded TV sets, computers, and cell phones, is shipped to China, India, Pakistan, and other (mostly Asian) countries where labour is cheap and environmental regulations are weak or poorly enforced. Workers there, many of them children, dismantle the products to recover reusable parts and are thus exposed to toxic metals such as lead, mercury, and cadmium. The scrap left over is dumped in waterways and fields, or burned in open fires, which exposes the workers to toxic dioxins.

In cities such as Manila, Mexico City, and Cairo, large numbers of people—many of them children—eke out a living by scavenging, sorting, and selling materials they get from open city dumps. This exposes them to toxins and infectious diseases.

> **DID YOU KNOW**
>
> Because it accepts refillable beer bottles from many available sources, Ontario Brewer's Retail Organization—the Beer Store—can boast an astonishing bottle-recovery rate of 107%. This is reuse par excellence.

Should We Use Refillable Containers? Reviving Reuse

Refilling and reusing containers uses less resources and energy, produces less waste, saves money, and creates local jobs.

Two examples of reuse are refillable glass beverage bottles and refillable soft drink bottles made of

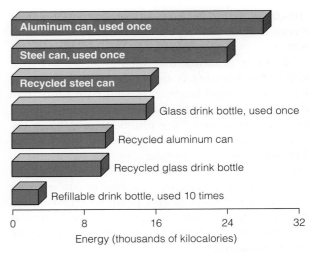

FIGURE 24-7 Energy consumption for different types of 350-millilitre (12-fluid-ounce) beverage containers. (Data from Argonne National Laboratory)

polyethylene terephthalate (PET) plastic. Typically such bottles make 15 round-trips before they become too damaged for reuse and then are recycled. Reusing these containers saves energy (Figure 24-7) and reduces the pollution and wastes associated with using energy resources. Refilling beverage bottles also stimulates local economies by creating local jobs related to their collection and refilling. Moreover, studies by Coca-Cola and PepsiCo of Canada show that their soft drinks in 0.5-litre (16-ounce) bottles cost one-third less in refillable bottles than in throwaway bottles.

But big companies make more money by producing and shipping throwaway beverage and food containers at centralized facilities. This shift has put many small local bottling companies, breweries, and canneries out of business.

Denmark and Prince Edward Island have led the way by banning all beverage containers that cannot be reused. To encourage use of refillable glass bottles, Ecuador has a refundable beverage container deposit fee that is half of the cost of the drink. In Finland, 95% of the soft drink, beer, wine, and spirits containers are refillable, and in Germany, about three-fourths are refillable.

> **CONSIDER, DISCUSS, OR DEBATE**
>
> Do you support banning all beverage containers that cannot be reused, as Denmark has done? What are the advantages and disadvantages of adopting a system that is based entirely on reuse?

What Are Other Ways to Reuse Things? Reducing Throwaway Items

We can use reusable shopping bags, food containers, and shipping pallets, and borrow tools from tool libraries.

Reusable shopping bags are becoming increasingly available and increasingly appreciated. They are typically large, attractive, and durable bags that we can use for future shopping trips and to carry numerous other items. Not only are these superior bags, but their use is often further encouraged by merchants who charge money for their flimsy plastic bags. Every year, 500 billion to 1 trillion plastic bags are manufactured, potentially to be used once and then thrown away. Choosing reusable shopping bags instead saves oil, cuts litter, and helps to keep nondegradable bags out of our landfills.

Many other items can easily be reused, including batteries, coffee cups, and water bottles. With a little effort, almost any item has the potential for reuse. We have yard sales, flea markets, and classified sections in newspapers to aid the redistribution of such items to new owners. We also have online agencies such as eBay (http://www.eBay.ca) and Kijiji (http://www.kijiji.ca) where people gladly exchange and reuse all manner of merchandise and equipment. Reuse is a *win-win* for everyone.

Other examples of reusable items are metal or plastic lunchboxes and plastic containers for storing lunchbox items and refrigerator leftovers, instead of using throwaway plastic wrap and aluminum foil.

Manufacturers can use shipping pallets made of recycled plastic waste instead of throwaway wood pallets. In 1991, Toyota shifted entirely to reusable shipping containers. A similar move by the Xerox Corporation saves the company more than $3 million per year.

Another example of reuse involves leasing rather than buying tools and equipment that are rarely used. Sharing these items among neighbours can produce social as well as ecological benefits.

Figure 24-8 lists several ways for you to reuse some of the items you buy.

24-5 RECYCLING

What Is Recycling? An Environmental Success Story

Recycling is an important way to collect waste materials and turn them into useful products that can be sold in the marketplace.

Recycling involves reprocessing discarded solid materials into new, useful products. Recycling has a number of important benefits to people and the environment. Recycling creates useful products, encourages new

What Can You Do?

Reuse

- Buy beverages in refillable glass containers instead of cans or throwaway bottles.

- Use reusable plastic or metal lunchboxes.

- Carry sandwiches and store food in the refrigerator in reusable containers instead of wrapping them in aluminum foil or plastic wrap.

- Use rechargeable batteries and recycle them when their useful life is over.

- Carry groceries and other items in a reusable basket, a canvas or string bag, or a small cart.

- Use reusable sponges and washable cloth napkins, dishtowels, and handkerchiefs instead of throwaway paper ones.

FIGURE 24-8 **What can you do?** Ways to reuse some of the items you buy.

kinds of jobs, and saves us money and energy while reducing waste, decreasing air pollution, extending our resources, and reducing our impact on the environment. Recycling also reduces unsightly litter, which costs time and money to pick up. Households and workplaces produce five major types of materials that can be recycled: *paper products* (including newspaper, magazines, office paper, and cardboard), *glass, aluminum, steel,* and some types of *plastics.*

Materials collected for recycling can be reprocessed in two ways. *Primary* or *closed-loop* recycling occurs when waste is recycled into new products of the same type—turning used newspapers into new newspaper and used aluminum cans into new aluminum cans, for example.

Secondary recycling, also called *downcycling,* involves converting waste materials into different products. For example, used tires can be shredded and converted into rubberized road surfacing and newspapers can be converted to cellulose insulation.

Environmentalists distinguish between two types of wastes that can be recycled. One is *pre-consumer* or *internal waste.* It consists of waste generated in a manufacturing process and recycled instead of being discarded. The other is *post-consumer* or *external waste* generated by consumer use of products. There is about 25 times more pre-consumer than post-consumer waste. It is important to recycle both types.

In theory, just about anything is recyclable, but only two things count. *First,* will the item actually be recycled? Sometimes separated wastes collected for recycling are mixed with other wastes and sent to landfills or incinerated, mostly when prices for recycled raw materials fall sharply.

Second, will businesses and individuals complete the recycling loop by buying products that are made from recycled materials? If we do not buy those products, recycling does not work.

But we cannot close the loop and do our bit in creating a market for recycled materials unless we can easily identify whether a product is made entirely or partly from recycled material. This would be clear if governments required that all products made from recycled materials have an easily recognizable logo and a label clearly showing the percentage of recycled material they contain, perhaps with a highly visible strip with a green bar extending from 0% to 100%.

Switzerland and Japan recycle about half of their MSW. North America recycles about 30% of its MSW—up from 6.4% in 1960. This roughly fivefold increase in recycling is an impressive achievement. But the total amount of solid waste has continued to increase although the MSW per person has levelled off since 1990. Studies indicate that with economic incentives and better design of waste management systems, Canada and other developed countries could easily recycle 60–80% of their MSW.

How Useful Is Composting? Recycling by Copying Nature

Composting biodegradable organic waste mimics nature by recycling plant nutrients to the soil.

Composting is a simple process in which we copy nature by recycling some of the biodegradable organic wastes we produce. The organic material produced by composting can be added to soil to supply plant nutrients, slow soil erosion, retain water, and improve crop yields.

Some cities in Austria, Belgium, Denmark, Germany, Luxembourg, and Switzerland recover and compost more than 85% of their biodegradable wastes. *Bad news.* Only about 5% of the paper, yard, and vegetable food waste produced in North America is composted, but studies show that it could be raised to 35%.

Such wastes can be collected and composted in centralized community facilities, as is done in many European Union countries. The resulting compost can be used as an organic soil fertilizer, topsoil, or landfill cover. It can also be used to help restore eroded soil on hillsides and along highways, strip-mined land, overgrazed areas, and eroded cropland.

To be successful, a large-scale composting program must be located carefully and control odours, because people do not want to live near a giant compost pile or plant. Composting programs must also exclude toxic materials that can contaminate the compost and make it unsafe for fertilizing crops and lawns.

You can easily make your own compost by collecting organic wastes in a backyard bin. You should use vegetable matter (not meat) and aerate the compost by turning it over periodically. The resulting compost will serve as an excellent soil conditioner, providing your lawn, garden, or house plants with essential nutrients and organic material. For details on composting, visit http://www.compost.org. For people living in apartments or residence dorms, a practical alternative is vermicomposting. Red wriggler worms (which can be purchased online) housed in a modified plastic container will produce a rich vermicompost for your houseplants and gardens. To learn more about vermicomposting, visit http://www.greenventure.ca and http://www.allthingsorganic.com/How_To/01.asp.

How Should We Recycle Solid Waste? To Separate or Not to Separate

There is disagreement over whether to send mixed urban wastes to centralized resource recovery plants or have individuals sort recyclables for collection and sale to manufacturers as raw materials.

One way to recycle is to send mixed urban wastes to a centralized *materials-recovery facility (MRF)* shown in Figure 24-9. There, machines or workers separate the mixed waste to recover valuable materials for sale to manufacturers as raw materials. The remaining paper, plastics, and other combustible wastes are recycled or burned to produce steam or electricity to run the recovery plant or to sell to nearby industries or homes. Ash from the incinerator is buried in a landfill. Trace the flow of materials through an MRF as diagrammed in Figure 24-9.

Such plants are expensive to build, operate, and maintain. They can emit toxic air pollutants if not operated properly, and they produce a toxic ash that must be disposed of safely.

MRFs are hungry beasts that must have a large input of garbage to make them financially successful. Thus their owners have a vested interest in increasing *throughput* of matter and energy resources to produce more garbage—the reverse of what prominent scientists believe we should be doing (Figure 24-4).

To many experts, it makes more sense economically and environmentally for households and businesses to separate their trash into recyclable categories such as glass, paper, metals, certain types of plastics, and compostable materials. Then these segregated wastes are collected and sold to scrap dealers, compost plants, and manufacturers. This approach is well established in Canada. Ontario, for example, has a Blue Box program that involves curbside pickup of cans, glass and plastic bottles, corrugated cardboard, tin foil, and other recyclable materials. Other provinces offer similar curbside recycling programs or various cash-for-recyclables programs. In some jurisdictions, people can deposit their sorted materials into recycling bins located in public places.

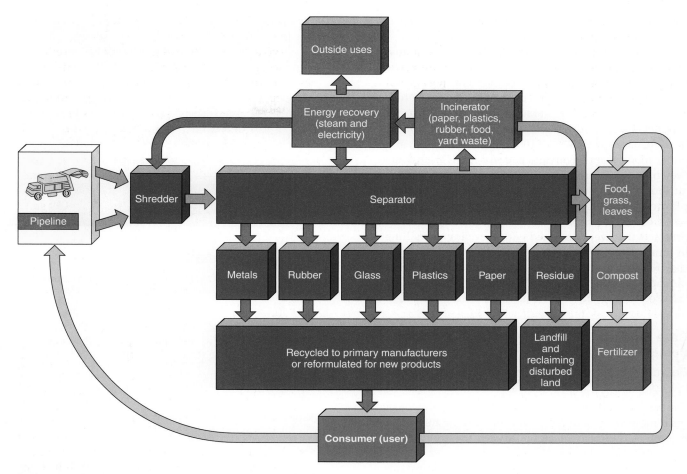

FIGURE 24-9 Solutions: a generalized *materials-recovery facility (MRF)* sorts mixed wastes for recycling and burning to produce energy. Because such plants need high volumes of trash to be economical, they discourage reuse and waste reduction.

The *source separation* approach has several advantages over the centralized approach. It produces much less air and water pollution and has lower start-up costs and operating costs than an MRF. It also saves more energy, provides more jobs per unit of material, and yields cleaner and usually more valuable recyclables. In addition, it educates people about the need for waste reduction, reuse, and recycling.

To promote separation of wastes for recycling, many communities use a *pay-as-you-throw (PAUT)* waste collection system. It charges households and businesses for the amount of mixed waste picked up but does not charge for pickup of materials separated for recycling.

Case Study: How Much Wastepaper Is Being Recycled? Encouraging News

Recycling paper has a number of environmental and economic benefits and is easy to do.

Paper (especially newspaper and cardboard) is easy to recycle. Recycling newspaper involves removing its ink, glue, and coating and then reconverting it to pulp

that is pressed into new paper. A variety of affordable high-quality recycled papers are available to meet most printing demands (including this book).

> **CONSIDER, DISCUSS, OR DEBATE**
>
> Should households and businesses be charged for the amount of mixed waste picked up but not charged for pickup of materials separated for recycling? What are the advantages and disadvantages of such an arrangement?

One problem associated with making paper is the chlorine (Cl_2) and chlorine compounds (such as chlorine dioxide, ClO_2), used to bleach about 40% of the world's pulp for making paper. These compounds are corrosive to processing equipment, hazardous for workers, hard to recover and reuse, and harmful when released to the environment. However, a growing number of paper mills (mostly in the European Union) are replacing chlorine-based bleaching chemicals with chemicals such as hydrogen peroxide (H_2O_2) or oxygen (O_2).

Environmentalists propose that governments require paper companies to use labels that list the recycled content of paper products and whether the paper was bleached with chlorine or a chlorine-free process.

In 2002, Staples, a major office supply company, pledged to phase out purchases of paper products from endangered forests and achieve an average of 30% post-consumer recycled content in all paper products it sells. Now the company sells a range of paper products that includes paper from FSC-certified forests (p. 226), paper with 30% to 100% recycled content, and paper made from sugarcane bagasse (p. 441). In total, they have 2 700 products with positive environmental attributes. Wherever possible, they have switched from plastic packing to materials made of crop wastes or wood fibres from FSC-certified forests. They sell many products that were designed with recycling or refilling in mind. They have services in the stores that make it easy for customers to recycle their cell phones or other personal electronics. Even the cleaning supplies that are used throughout the chain are all eco-logo certified!

Case Study: Is It Feasible to Recycle Plastics? Some Problems

Recycling many plastics is chemically and economically difficult.

Plastics are made of various types of large polymer or resin molecules made by chemically linking monomer molecules (petrochemicals) produced mostly from oil and natural gas (Figure 24-10).

Currently, only about 10% of all plastic wastes in North America are recycled, for three reasons. *First,* many plastics are difficult to isolate from other wastes because the many different resins used to make them are often difficult to identify and some plastics are composites of different resins. Most plastics also contain stabilizers and other chemicals that must be removed before recycling.

Second, recovering individual plastic resins does not yield much material because only small amounts of any given resin are used per product. *Third,* the price of oil used to produce petrochemicals for making plastic resins is so low that the cost of virgin plastic resins is much lower than that of recycled resins. An exception is PET (polyethylene terephthalate), used mostly in plastic drink bottles. It can be melted and remanufactured into products such as fleece, clothing, carpet, and nonfood packaging. However, the PET collected for recycling must not have other plastics mixed with it. For example, a single PVC (polyvinyl chloride) bottle in a truckload of PET can render it useless for recycling.

Thus, mandating that plastic products contain a certain amount of recycled plastic resins is unlikely to work. It could also hinder the use of recycled plastics in reducing the resource content and weight of many widely used items such as plastic bags and bottles.

Cargill Dow, a joint venture by a giant agricultural company (Cargill) and a chemical company

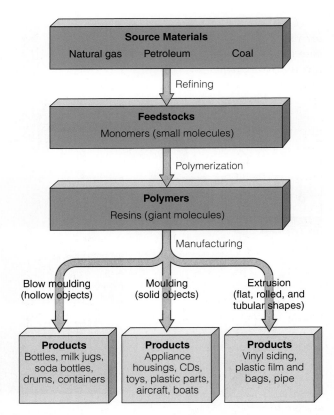

FIGURE 24-10 How plastics are made. (Adapted from Society of the Plastics Industry)

(Dow), is manufacturing biodegradable and recyclable plastic containers made from a polymer called polyactide (ACT) made from the sugar in corn syrup. Instead of being sent to landfills, containers made from this *bioplastic* could be composted to produce a soil conditioner.

Toyota, the world's No. 1 automaker, is investing $38 billion (U.S.) in a process that makes plastics from plants. By 2020, it expects to control two-thirds of the world's supply of such bioplastics.

Does Recycling Make Economic Sense? Yes, for Many Materials

Recycling materials such as paper and metals has important economic and environmental benefits.

Whether recycling makes monetary sense depends on how you look at the economic and environmental benefits and costs of recycling. Critics say recycling does not make sense if it costs more to recycle materials than to send them to a landfill or incinerator. They also point out that recycling is often not needed to save landfill space because many areas are not running out of space.

Critics concede that recycling may make economic sense for valuable and easy-to-recycle materials (such as aluminum, paper, and steel), but not for cheap or plentiful resources such as glass from silica and most plastics that are expensive to recycle.

Critics of recycling also argue that it should pay for itself. But proponents of recycling point out that conventional garbage disposal systems are paid for mostly by charges to households and businesses. So why should recycling be held to a different standard and forced to compete on an uneven playing field?

Proponents also point out that recycling provides important benefits for people and the environment. They point to studies showing that the net economic, health, and environmental benefits of recycling far outweigh the costs. Also, they remind us that the recycling industry is an important part of the economy. It employs more than a million people in North America and its annual income is much larger than both the mining and the waste management industries together.

Cities that make money by recycling and have higher recycling rates tend to use a *single-pickup system* for both garbage and materials to be recycled instead of a more expensive dual-pickup system. In single-pickup systems, dealing with recyclables costs about half as much per metric ton as disposing of the same amount of waste in a typical modern landfill.

Successful systems also tend to charge people for the garbage that they discard but not for the recyclables they sort. San Francisco, California, uses such a system to recycle almost half of its MSW.

CONSIDER, DISCUSS, OR DEBATE

Do the advantages of recycling materials such as paper, plastics, and metals outweigh the disadvantages?

Why Do We Not Have More Reuse and Recycling? Faulty Accounting and an Uneven Economic Playing Field

Prices of goods that do not tell the ecological truth, too few government subsidies and tax breaks, low landfill dumping costs, and price fluctuations hinder reuse and recycling.

Four factors hinder reuse and recycling. *First* is a faulty accounting system in which the market price of a product does not include the harmful environmental health costs associated with the product during its *life cycle* (Figure 24-11). Many scientists and economists believe that a life-cycle analysis should be made and published for products.

Second, there is an uneven economic playing field because in most countries resource-extracting industries receive more government tax breaks and subsidies than recycling and reuse industries. We get more of what we reward.

Third, charges for depositing wastes in landfills (called *tipping fees*) in North America are lower than those in most of Europe. *Fourth,* the demand and thus the price paid for recycled materials fluctuates mostly because

LIFE-CYCLE ANALYSIS OF A SHIRT

FIGURE 24-11 *Life-cycle analysis* of the resources used and pollutants produced over the lifetime of a product. Including all of these costs in the market prices of the products we buy would allow us to compare the harmful environmental costs of different products and thus make more informed choices about the products we buy.

buying goods made with recycled materials is not a priority for most governments, businesses, and individuals.

How can we encourage reuse and recycling? Proponents say that levelling the economic playing field is the best way to start. Governments can *increase* subsidies and tax breaks for reusing and recycling materials (the carrot) and *decrease* subsidies and tax breaks for making items from virgin resources (the stick).

Another way to encourage recycling is to greatly increase use of the *pay-as-you-throw (PAUT)* system and encourage or require government purchases of recycled products to help increase demand and lower prices. Governments can also pass laws requiring companies to take back and recycle or reuse packaging discarded by consumers. Globally, at least 29 countries (most in the European Union) have such "take-back" laws. In the Netherlands, all packaging waste is banned from landfills. In 2002, the European Union adopted a ruling requiring its member countries to recycle 55–80% of all packaging waste.

Governments can also require manufacturers to take back and recycle or reuse appliances, computers and other electronic equipment, and motor vehicles at the end of their useful lives. Such *product stewardship* is required for car manufacturers and appliance makers in European Union (EU) countries and for major appliances in Japan.

The EU also requires companies to take back electronic products from consumers without charge and bans e-waste in municipal solid waste. In 2006, manufacturers were required to phase out use of toxic and hazardous materials in electronic products. These *product stewardship policies* create a strong economic incentive for companies to redesign products for safer and easier recycling, reuse, and remanufacturing.

North America lags far behind the European Union in dealing with the problem of e-waste. However, as mentioned on page 596, office supplier Staples has a service that allows store visitors to drop off their cell phones, PDAs, pagers, and rechargeable batteries for recycling. A portion of the proceeds from this recycling program will be donated to the Sierra Club to help support environmental education and conservation programs.

> **CONSIDER, DISCUSS, OR DEBATE**
>
> Should governments pass laws requiring manufacturers to take back and reuse or recycle all packaging waste, appliances, electronic equipment, and motor vehicles at the end of their useful lives? Explain.

Finally, we can require detailed labels on all products listing recycled content and the types and amounts of any hazardous materials they contain—similar to labels on food products that list ingredients and provide nutritional information. This can help consumers make more informed choices about the environmental consequences of buying certain products.

24-6 BURNING AND BURYING SOLID WASTE

What Are the Advantages and Disadvantages of Burning Solid Waste? A Faded Rose in Some Countries

Japan and a few European countries incinerate most of their municipal waste, but this is done less in North America and in most European countries.

Globally, municipal solid waste is burned in over 1 000 large *waste-to-energy incinerators,* which boil water to make steam for heating water or space or for producing electricity. Trace the flow of materials through the process as diagrammed in Figure 24-12. Japan and Switzerland burn more than half of their MSW in incinerators, compared to 4% in Canada and 13% in the United States (Figure 24-13, p. 599).

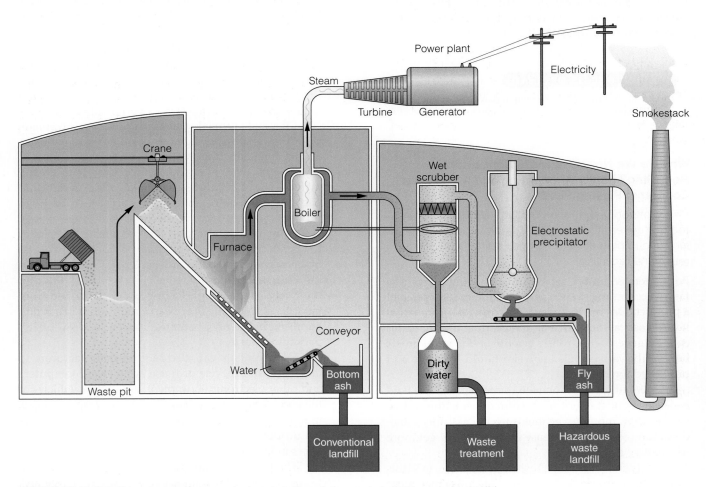

FIGURE 24-12 Solutions: *waste-to-energy incinerator* with pollution controls that burns mixed solid waste and recovers some of the energy to produce steam used for heating or producing electricity. (Adapted from EPA, *Let's Reduce and Recycle*)

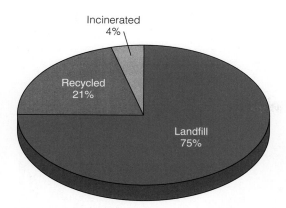

FIGURE 24-13 Treatment of municipal solid waste in Canada. Most MSW goes to landfills, a small amount is incinerated, and an ever-increasing component is being diverted to recycling, reusing, and composting programs. (Statistics Canada)

Trade-Offs

Incineration

Advantages

Reduced trash volume

Less need for landfills

Low water pollution

Quick and easy

Disadvantages

High cost

Air pollution (especially toxic dioxins)

Produces a highly toxic ash

Encourages waste production

Discourages recycling and waste reduction

FIGURE 24-14 Trade-offs: advantages and disadvantages of incinerating solid waste. These trade-offs also apply to the incineration of hazardous waste. Pick the single advantage and disadvantage that you think are the most important.

In some plants, called *mass-burn incinerators,* mixed trash is dumped into a huge furnace. This saves the expense and hazards of removing nonburnable material. But often there are air pollution and corrosion problems because of the difficulty of having to constantly adjust combustion conditions for different mixes of garbage.

In *refuse-derived fuel incinerators,* burnable waste is separated from unburnable and recyclable materials. Burning only combustible waste produces more energy and also leads to less air pollution.

Figure 24-14 lists the advantages and disadvantages of using incinerators to burn solid and hazardous waste. Study this figure carefully.

What Are the Advantages and Disadvantages of Burying Solid Waste? A Widely Used Last Resort

Most of the world's municipal solid waste is buried in landfills that will eventually leak toxic liquids into the soil and underlying aquifers.

About 75% of the MSW in Canada is buried in sanitary landfills, compared to 90% in the United Kingdom, 54% in the United States, 15% in Japan, and 12% in Switzerland. There are two types of landfills. **Open dumps** are essentially fields or holes in the ground where garbage is deposited and sometimes covered with soil. These are illegal in Canada and rare in developed countries but widely used in many developing countries.

In newer landfills, called **sanitary landfills,** solid wastes are spread out in thin layers, compacted, and covered daily with a fresh layer of clay or plastic foam. Modern state-of-the-art landfills on geologically suitable sites and away from lakes, rivers, floodplains, and aquifer recharge zones are lined with clay and plastic before being filled with garbage, as seen in Figure 24-15 (p. 600). Note in the figure that the landfill bottom is covered with a second impermeable liner, usually made of several layers of clay, thick plastic, and sand. This liner collects *leachate* (rainwater contaminated as it percolates through the solid waste) and is intended to prevent its leakage into groundwater. Wells are drilled around the landfill to monitor any leakage.

Collected leachate is pumped from the bottom of the landfill, stored in tanks, and sent to a regular sewage treatment plant or an on-site treatment plant. When full, the landfill is covered with clay, sand, gravel, and topsoil to prevent water from seeping in.

These new landfills are equipped with a connected network of vent pipes to collect landfill gas (consisting mostly of two greenhouse gases, methane and carbon dioxide) released by the underground decomposition of wastes. The methane is filtered out and burned in small gas turbines to produce steam or electricity for nearby facilities or sold to utilities for use as a fuel. Figure 24-16 (p. 601) lists the advantages and disadvantages of using sanitary landfills to dispose of solid waste.

Thousands of older and abandoned landfills throughout the world do not have gas collection systems and will emit methane and carbon dioxide, both potent greenhouse gases, for decades.

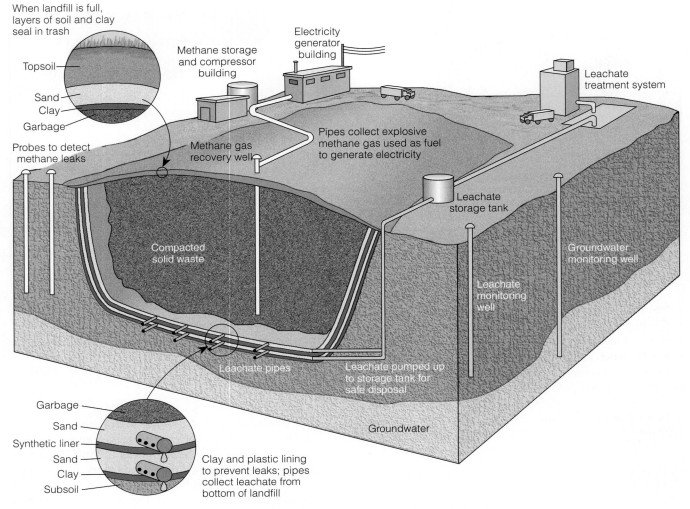

When landfill is full, layers of soil and clay seal in trash

Topsoil

Sand

Clay

Garbage

Probes to detect methane leaks

Methane storage and compressor building

Methane gas recovery well

Electricity generator building

Pipes collect explosive methane gas used as fuel to generate electricity

Leachate treatment system

Leachate storage tank

Compacted solid waste

Leachate monitoring well

Groundwater monitoring well

Leachate pipes

Leachate pumped up to storage tank for safe disposal

Groundwater

Garbage

Sand

Synthetic liner

Sand

Clay

Subsoil

Clay and plastic lining to prevent leaks; pipes collect leachate from bottom of landfill

FIGURE 24-15 Solutions: state-of-the-art *sanitary landfill*, which is designed to eliminate or minimize environmental problems that plague older landfills. Even such state-of-the-art landfills are expected to leak eventually, passing both the effects of contamination and cleanup costs on to future generations.

Contamination of groundwater and nearby surface water by leachate from unlined and lined older landfills is also a serious (and inevitable) problem. Most older landfills throughout the world are chemical time bombs that release greenhouse gases and will eventually leak hazardous chemicals.

As landfill sites have filled up and local opposition to the presence of landfills in their communities has intensified, many cities in Canada and other countries have been hard-pressed to find landfills to dispose of their garbage. To prepare for the 2002 closure of its local Keele Valley landfill, Toronto announced plans to ship its garbage to an abandoned open-pit mine near Kirkland Lake, 600 kilometres (373 miles) north of the city. After community opposition stymied the proposal, Toronto was forced to implement its backup plan of hauling garbage by truck to landfills in Michigan.

This option not only came with a hefty price tag but also enraged U.S. residents and lawmakers who accused Toronto of using Michigan as a dumping ground.

In 2007, city officials acquired the right to use the Green Lane Landfill, southwest of London, 200 kilometres (124 miles) from Toronto. This landfill will last for 17 years if Toronto continues to divert 42% of its wastes from landfill (through recycling, reuse, composting, and other "green" programs); the landfill could be used for 28 years if Toronto's diversion rate were improved to 70%. Toronto's Waste Diversion Task Force made adjustments accordingly and reached a diversion rate of about 70% by 2010.

Some other Canadian cities have already achieved impressive diversion rates. Markham, in southern Ontario, diverts 70% of its municipal solid waste from landfill; city officials believe they owe their success

Trade-Offs

Sanitary Landfills

Advantages	Disadvantages
No open burning	Noise and traffic
Little odour	Dust
Low groundwater pollution if sited properly	Air pollution from toxic gases and volatile organic compounds
Can be built quickly	Releases greenhouse gases (methane and CO_2) unless they are collected
Low operating costs	Groundwater contamination
Can handle large amounts of waste	Slow decomposition of wastes
Filled land can be used for other purposes	Discourages recycling and waste reduction
No shortage of landfill space in many areas	Eventually leaks and can contaminate groundwater

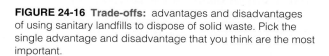

FIGURE 24-16 **Trade-offs:** advantages and disadvantages of using sanitary landfills to dispose of solid waste. Pick the single advantage and disadvantage that you think are the most important.

to the strategy of sending trucks to pick up recycling every week, but garbage only once every two weeks. Edmonton diverts nearly 70% of its municipal solid waste by using the strategy of convenience; citizens place their recyclables into blue bags that the city then sorts for them, ensuring widespread participation as well as properly sorted recyclables. Other Canadian cities—such as Whitby, Halifax, and Vancouver—are in the range of 60% diversion, with plans to reach 70% and higher rates soon.

According to Statistics Canada, Canada as a whole diverted 25% of its municipal solid waste from landfill in 2008. The top provinces were Nova Scotia (41%), Prince Edward Island (38%), New Brunswick (36%), and British Columbia (32%).

CONSIDER, DISCUSS, OR DEBATE

Do the advantages of burying solid waste in sanitary landfills outweigh the disadvantages?

24-7 HAZARDOUS WASTE

What Is Hazardous Waste? Harmful Material Requiring Careful Disposal

Developed countries produce about 80–90% of the world's solid and liquid wastes that can harm people.

Hazardous waste is any discarded solid or liquid material that has the potential to harm people. Hazardous wastes can be toxic, explosive, flammable, combustible, dangerously reactive, infectious, corrosive, or radioactive. These properties are shared by *hazardous chemicals*, which become hazardous wastes as soon as they are used. Figure 24-17 lists hazardous and toxic chemicals that are discarded by households.

In Canada, the *Workplace Hazardous Materials Information System (WHMIS)* is widely used to inform workers about the potential dangers of hazardous wastes and hazardous chemicals. WHMIS classifies these materials according to the symbols and classes shown in Figure 24-18 (p. 602). The eight

What Harmful Chemicals Are in Your Home?

Cleaning
- Disinfectants
- Drain, toilet, and window cleaners
- Spot removers
- Septic tank cleaners

Paint
- Latex and oil-based paints
- Paint thinners, solvents, and strippers
- Stains, varnishes, and lacquers
- Wood preservatives
- Artist paints and inks

General
- Dry-cell batteries (mercury and cadmium)
- Glues and cements

Gardening
- Pesticides
- Weed killers
- Ant and rodent killers
- Flea powders

Automotive
- Gasoline
- Used motor oil
- Antifreeze
- Battery acid
- Solvents
- Brake and transmission fluid
- Rust inhibitor and rust remover

FIGURE 24-17 Harmful chemicals found in many homes. Make a survey to see which of these chemicals are in your home.

A—Compressed Gas

D2—Other Toxic Effects

B—Flammable or Combustible

D3—Biohazardous Infectious Materials

C—Oxidizing Materials

E—Corrosive

D1—Immediate and Serious Toxic Effect

F—Dangerously Reactive

FIGURE 24-18 Symbols developed by WHMIS to designate different classes of hazardous chemicals. (Health Canada)

classes identified by WHMIS have the following characteristics:

- *Class A* includes compressed gases that could leak or explode.

- *Class B* includes flammable materials that could ignite at room temperature and combustible materials that could ignite when heated (e.g., varnish and propane).

- *Class C* includes oxidizing materials that could aid a fire or cause spontaneous combustion when combined with another material (e.g., oxygen and nitric acid).

- *Class D1* materials cause immediate and serious toxic effects such as death through carbon monoxide poisoning.

- *Class D2* materials cause less immediate problems such as cancer or less serious problems like allergies.

- *Class D3* consists of biohazardous infectious materials that can spread diseases (e.g., hospital wastes that harbour dangerous microbes).

- *Class E* materials are corrosive (e.g., sulphuric acid).

- *Class F* materials are dangerously reactive in that they could combine vigorously with water to produce a toxic gas or explode when bumped (e.g., vinyl chloride and picric acid).

WHMIS issues detailed material safety data sheets and offers programs that train employees in the proper handling, documentation, and disposal of hazardous wastes. More information on WHMIS is available on the Canadian Centre for Occupational Health and Safety website at http://www.ccohs.ca.

About 72% of these hazardous wastes are produced by chemical and petroleum industries and another 22% are generated by mining and metal processing industries. According to the United Nations Environment Programme, developed countries produce 80–90% of these wastes.

The amount of hazardous and toxic waste in the world is likely to increase because of the projected 80% global increase in chemical production (including many hazardous and toxic chemicals) between 1995 and 2020.

Case Study: A Black Day in Bhopal, India

The world's worst industrial accident occurred in 1984 at a pesticide plant in Bhopal, India.

December 2, 1984, will long be a black day for India. On that date the world's worst industrial accident occurred at a Union Carbide pesticide plant in Bhopal, India.

An explosion in an underground storage tank released a large quantity of highly toxic methyl isocyanate (MIC) gas, used to produce carbamate pesticides. Investigation found that water leaking into the tank through faulty valves and corroded pipes caused an explosive chemical reaction.

Once in the atmosphere, some of the toxic MIC was converted to more deadly hydrogen cyanide gas. The toxic cloud of gas settled over about 78 square kilometres (30 square miles), exposing up to 600 000 people. Many were illegal squatters living near the plant because they had no other place to go. The deadly cloud spread through Bhopal without warning because the plant's warning sirens had been turned off to save money.

According to Indian officials, at least 8 000 people died within a few days after the accident. The International Campaign for Justice in Bhopal estimates that by 2003 the accident had killed

23 000 and the death toll is still climbing. It also puts the number of people suffering from chronic illnesses from the accident at 120 000–150 000. An international team of medical specialists estimated in 1996 that 50 000–60 000 people sustained permanent injuries such as blindness, lung damage, and neurological problems. With any of these estimates, this was the world's largest industrial tragedy.

Indian officials claim that Union Carbide probably could have prevented the tragedy by spending about $1 million to upgrade plant equipment and improve safety. According to an investigation by India's Central Bureau of Investigation (CBI), corporate managers of Union Carbide in the United States made a decision to save money by cutting back on maintenance and safety because the plant had proven to be a financial disappointment for the company. The CBI found that on the night of the disaster, six safety measures designed to prevent a leak of toxic materials were inadequate, shut down, or malfunctioning.

After the accident, Union Carbide reduced the corporation's liability risks for compensating victims by selling off a portion of its assets and giving much of the profits to its shareholders in the form of special dividends. In 1994, Union Carbide sold its holdings in India and later was taken over by Dow Chemical.

In 1989, Union Carbide agreed to pay an out-of-court settlement of $470 million (U.S.) to compensate the victims (low estimate of 3 000 deaths) without admitting any guilt or negligence concerning the accident. In 1992, the Court of the Chief Judicial Magistrate for Bhopal charged Warren Anderson, CEO of Union Carbide at the time of the accident, with "culpable homicide" (the equivalent of manslaughter) and issued a warrant for his arrest. Since then he has refused to appear in court and the U.S. government has not responded to India's request to extradite him to India to stand trial. Every December since 1984, marchers in Bhopal have paraded an effigy of Warren Anderson through town and burned it. Dow, which bought Union Carbide in 1999, refused to accept any of the company's alleged Bhopal liabilities.

What Can We Do with Hazardous Waste? Manage It or Produce Less

We can burn, bury, detoxify, reuse, recycle, or not produce hazardous wastes.

We can *manage* hazardous waste mostly by burning or burying it. This is an *output* approach that tries to figure out what to do with such wastes after we have produced them. The output approach is expensive and creates health and environmental problems.

We can also use a *pollution prevention* or *waste reduction* approach. This is an *input* approach that tries to reduce the production of such wastes and their release into the air, water, and soil. With this approach, scientists look for substitutes for toxic or hazardous materials, reuse or recycle them within industrial cycles, or use them as raw materials for new products (Figure 24-6, p. 590) instead of burning or burying them.

Figure 24-19 lists the priorities that prominent scientists believe we should follow in dealing with hazardous waste. Study this figure carefully. Denmark is following these priorities but most countries are not.

FIGURE 24-19 Solutions: priorities suggested by prominent scientists for dealing with hazardous waste. To date, these priorities have not been followed in most countries. (Data from U.S. National Academy of Sciences)

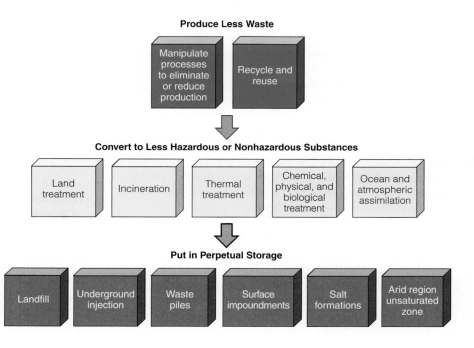

How Can We Remove or Detoxify Hazardous Waste? Science to the Rescue

Chemical and biological methods can be used to remove hazardous wastes or to reduce their toxicity.

In Denmark, all hazardous and toxic waste from industries and households is delivered to 21 transfer stations throughout the country. The waste is then transferred to a large treatment facility. There, about three-fourths of the waste is detoxified by physical, chemical, and biological methods and the rest is buried in a carefully designed and monitored landfill.

Physical methods used to detoxify hazardous wastes include filtering out solids, distilling liquid mixtures to separate out harmful chemicals, and precipitating such chemicals from solution. Especially deadly wastes can be encapsulated in glass, cement, or ceramics and then isolated in storage sites.

Chemical reactions can also be used to convert hazardous chemicals to less harmful or harmless chemicals. Scientists are testing the use of *cyclodextrin*—a type of sugar made from corn starch—to remove toxic materials such as solvents and pesticides from contaminated soil and groundwater. To clean up a site, a solution of cyclodextrin is injected. After this molecular-sponge material moves through the soil or groundwater and attracts various toxic chemicals, it is pumped out of the ground, stripped of its contaminants, and reused.

Some scientists and engineers consider biological treatment the wave of the future for cleaning up some types of toxic and hazardous waste. One approach is *bioremediation,* in which bacteria and enzymes are used to help destroy toxic or hazardous substances or convert them to harmless compounds.

Another biological way to treat hazardous wastes is *phytoremediation*. It involves using natural or genetically engineered plants to absorb, filter, and remove contaminants from polluted soil and water. For example, researchers at the University of Georgia used genetic engineering to add extra detoxifying power to a cottonwood tree. They inserted a mercury-detoxifying gene of *E. coli* into the genome of a common soil bacterium, which was incorporated into day-old cottonwood trees. After reaching maturity such trees can extract more mercury ions (Hg^{2+}) from contaminated soil than can conventional cottonwoods. Various plants, including many wetland species, have been identified as potential "pollution sponges" to help clean up soil and water contaminated with chemicals such as pesticides, organic solvents, radioactive metals, and toxic metals such as lead, mercury, and arsenic. Figure 24-20 lists advantages and disadvantages of phytoremediation. Study this figure carefully.

Another way to detoxify hazardous waste is with a plasma torch. **Plasma**—a fourth state of matter—is an ionized gas made up of electrically conductive ions

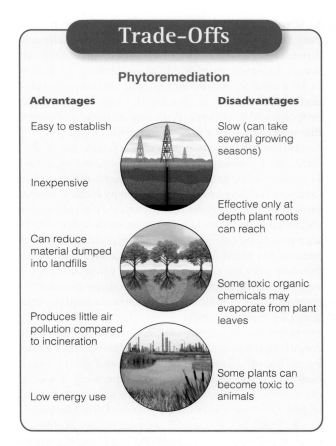

Trade-Offs

Phytoremediation

Advantages	Disadvantages
Easy to establish	Slow (can take several growing seasons)
Inexpensive	
	Effective only at depth plant roots can reach
Can reduce material dumped into landfills	
	Some toxic organic chemicals may evaporate from plant leaves
Produces little air pollution compared to incineration	
	Some plants can become toxic to animals
Low energy use	

FIGURE 24-20 Trade-offs: advantages and disadvantages of using *phytoremediation* to remove or detoxify hazardous waste. Pick the single advantage and disadvantage that you think are the most important.

and electrons. Passing electrical current through a gas to generate an electric arc and very high temperatures can create a plasma. This process can be carried out continuously in a *plasma torch* somewhat similar to a welding torch.

High temperatures from the torch can decompose liquid or solid hazardous organic material into ions and atoms that can be converted into simple molecules, cleaned up, and released as a gas. They can also convert hazardous inorganic matter into a molten glassy material that encapsulates toxic metals and keeps them from leaching into groundwater.

What Are the Advantages and Disadvantages of Burning and Burying Hazardous Waste? Last Resorts

Hazardous waste can be incinerated or disposed of on or underneath the Earth's surface, but this can pollute the air and water.

Hazardous waste can be incinerated. This has the same mixture of advantages and disadvantages as burning solid wastes (Figure 24-14, p. 599). Two major disadvantages of incinerating hazardous waste are that it releases air pollutants such as toxic dioxins and it produces a highly toxic ash that must be safely and permanently stored.

Canada's largest hazardous waste incineration facility, Alberta's Swan Hills Treatment Centre (http://www.shtc.ca), is intended to be a state-of-the-art solution to the problem of hazardous waste. However, the Sierra Club of Canada, Mining Watch Canada, and other critics have linked the Swan Hills facility to such problems as leaks, explosions, failure to report emissions, and high levels of contaminants in local wildlife.

In *deep-well disposal*, liquid hazardous wastes are pumped under pressure through a pipe into dry, porous geologic formations or zones of rock far beneath aquifers tapped for drinking and irrigation water. Theoretically, these liquids soak into the porous rock material and are isolated from overlying groundwater by essentially impermeable layers of rock. This method is not widely used in Canada; 90% of the country's deep-well disposal takes place in Alberta. Figure 24-21 lists the advantages and disadvantages of deep-well disposal of liquid hazardous wastes.

> **CONSIDER, DISCUSS, OR DEBATE**
>
> Do the advantages of deep-well disposal of liquid hazardous waste outweigh their disadvantages?

Surface impoundments are excavated depressions such as ponds, pits, or lagoons into which liquid hazardous wastes are drained and stored (Figure 22-11, p. 552). As water evaporates, the waste settles and becomes more concentrated. Figure 24-22 lists the advantages and advantages of this method. Study this figure carefully.

Sometimes liquid and solid hazardous wastes are put into drums or other containers and buried in carefully designed and monitored *secure hazardous waste landfills* (Figure 24-23, p. 606). Many large companies have secure landfills for their own hazardous waste and there are commercial hazardous waste landfills that will deal with wastes for a hefty price.

Sweden goes further and buries its concentrated hazardous wastes in underground vaults made of reinforced concrete. By contrast, in the United Kingdom most hazardous wastes are mixed with household garbage and stored in hundreds of conventional landfills throughout the country.

Hazardous wastes can also be stored in carefully designed *aboveground buildings*. This is especially useful in areas where the water table is close to the surface or areas that are above aquifers used for drinking water. These structures are built to withstand storms and to prevent the release of toxic gases. Leaks are monitored and any leakage is collected and treated.

Each year there are more than 500 000 shipments of hazardous chemicals throughout North America.

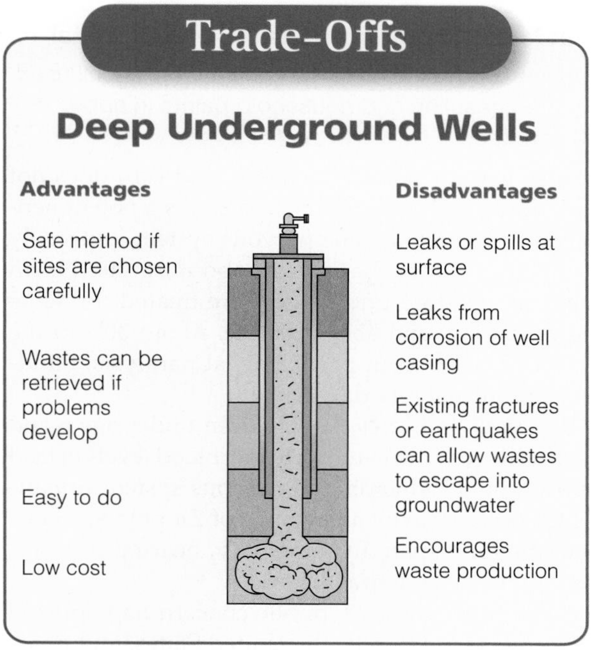

Trade-Offs

Deep Underground Wells

Advantages	Disadvantages
Safe method if sites are chosen carefully	Leaks or spills at surface
Wastes can be retrieved if problems develop	Leaks from corrosion of well casing
Easy to do	Existing fractures or earthquakes can allow wastes to escape into groundwater
Low cost	Encourages waste production

FIGURE 24-21 Trade-offs: advantages and disadvantages of injecting liquid hazardous wastes into deep underground wells. Pick the single advantage and disadvantage that you think are the most important.

Trade-Offs

Surface Impoundments

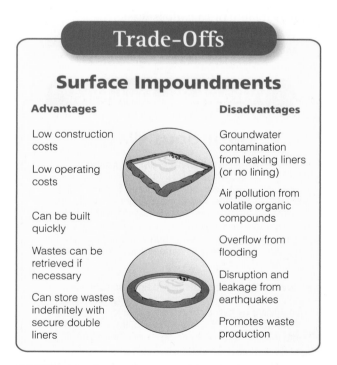

Advantages	Disadvantages
Low construction costs	Groundwater contamination from leaking liners (or no lining)
Low operating costs	Air pollution from volatile organic compounds
Can be built quickly	Overflow from flooding
Wastes can be retrieved if necessary	Disruption and leakage from earthquakes
Can store wastes indefinitely with secure double liners	Promotes waste production

FIGURE 24-22 Trade-offs: advantages and disadvantages of storing liquid hazardous wastes in surface impoundments. Pick the single advantage and disadvantage that you think are the most important.

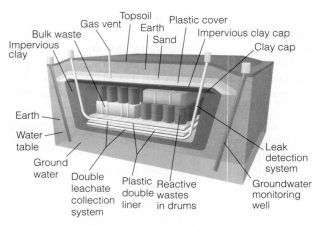

FIGURE 24-23 **Solutions:** secure hazardous waste landfill.

These materials move between manufacturing plants, incinerators, and landfills. On average, these shipments result in about 13 000 accidents per year in North America, involving about 100 deaths, more than 10 000 injuries, and evacuations of more than 500 000 people. Most communities do not have the equipment and trained personnel needed to deal with hazardous waste spills. How well is your community prepared to deal with such spills? In the future, some of the risks might be reduced by using solid nanoparticle materials to absorb the hazardous liquids.

Figure 24-24 lists ways you can reduce your environmental input of hazardous waste.

What Can You Do?

Hazardous Waste

• Use pesticides in the smallest amount possible.

• Use less harmful substances instead of commercial chemicals for most household cleaners. For example, use liquid ammonia to clean appliances and windows; vinegar to polish metals, clean surfaces, and remove stains and mildew; baking soda to clean household utensils, deodorize, and remove stains; borax to remove stains and mildew.

• Do not dispose of pesticides, paints, solvents, oil, antifreeze, or other products containing hazardous chemicals by flushing them down the toilet, pouring them down the drain, burying them, throwing them into the garbage, or dumping them down storm drains.

FIGURE 24-24 **What can you do?** Ways to reduce your input of hazardous waste into the environment.

What Are Brownfields? Recycling Dangerous Sites

Many abandoned industrial and other hazardous waste sites are being cleaned up and put to use.

Brownfields are abandoned industrial and commercial sites usually contaminated with hazardous wastes. Examples include factories, junkyards, older landfills, and gas stations.

Brownfields can be cleaned up and reborn as parks, nature reserves, athletic fields, and ecoindustrial parks (p. 589). But first old oil and grease, industrial solvents, toxic metals, and other contaminants must be removed from their soil and groundwater.

Brownfield redevelopment is now seen as a way to rebuild parts of cities, create jobs, and increase the tax base. In Canada, the Canadian Brownfields Network (http://www.aboutremediation.com) and the National Round Table on the Environment and the Economy (http://www.nrtee-trnee.ca) are spearheading efforts to clean up and redevelop many of Canada's 30 000 urban brownfields.

CONSIDER, DISCUSS, OR DEBATE

Would you be willing to buy produce from a farmers' market located on a former hazardous waste site? Would you purchase a house or condominium located there? Explain.

24-8 CASE STUDIES: LEAD, MERCURY, AND DIOXINS

What Is the Threat from Lead? A Toxic Metal

Lead is especially harmful to children and is still used in leaded gasoline and household paints in about 100 countries.

Because it is a chemical element, lead (Pb) does not break down in the environment. Lead is a potent neurotoxin that can harm the nervous system, especially in young children. Each year, about 16 000 North American children under age 9 are treated for acute lead poisoning, and about 200 die. About 30% of the survivors suffer from palsy, partial paralysis, blindness, and mental retardation.

Research indicates that children under age 6 and unborn fetuses with even fairly low blood levels of lead are especially vulnerable to nervous system impairment, lowered IQ (by an average of 7.4 points), shortened attention span, hyperactivity, hearing damage, and various behavioural disorders.

Good news. By 1990, public concern had spurred governments in Canada, the United States, and much of Europe to ban leaded gasoline. In doing so, they demonstrated the benefits of *preventing* a problem—in this case, lead poisoning—as opposed to *reacting* to it after the damage is done.

Bad news. A number of sources of lead remain. A major source of exposure is inhalation or ingestion of lead particles from peeling lead-based paint found in houses built before 1960. Lead can also leach from water lines and pipes and faucets containing lead. In addition, a 1993 study by the U.S. National Academy of Sciences and numerous other studies indicate *there is no safe level of lead in children's blood.*

Health scientists have proposed a number of ways to help protect children from lead poisoning, as listed in Figure 24-25. Phasing out lead will be a costly and time-consuming endeavour, but the alternative is to keep poisoning and mentally handicapping millions of children.

Although the threat from lead has been reduced in North America, this is not the case in many developing countries. About 80% of the gasoline sold in the world today is unleaded, but about 100 countries still use leaded gasoline. The World Health Organization (WHO) estimates that 130–200 million children around the world are at risk from lead poisoning, and 15–18 million

children in developing countries have permanent brain damage because of lead poisoning—mostly from effects of leaded gasoline. *Good news.* China recently phased out leaded gasoline in less than three years.

> **DID YOU KNOW**
>
> The threat from lead has not been eliminated. It has been linked to learning disabilities and violence, among other problems. Check out http://www.healthyenvironmentforkids.ca/english/special_collections/fulltext.shtml?x=2375.

What Is the Threat from Mercury? Some Fish May Come with a Side of Toxic Mercury

Mercury is released into the environment mostly by burning coal and incinerating wastes and can build to high levels in some types of fish consumed by humans.

Mercury—the only metal that is liquid at room temperature—is used in thermometers, dental fillings, fluorescent lights, mercury light switches, and other

Solutions

Lead Poisoning

Prevention		Control
Phase out leaded gasoline worldwide	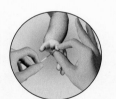	Sharply reduce lead emissions from old and new incinerators
Phase out waste incineration		Replace lead pipes and plumbing fixtures containing lead solder
Test blood for lead by age 1		Remove leaded paint and lead dust from older houses and apartments
Ban lead solder in plumbing pipes, fixtures, and food cans		Remove lead from TV sets and computer monitors before incineration or land disposal
Ban lead glazing for ceramicware used to serve food		Test for lead in existing ceramicware used to serve food
		Test existing candles for lead
Ban candles with lead cores		Wash fresh fruits and vegetables

FIGURE 24-25 Solutions: ways to help protect children from lead poisoning. Which two of the solutions do you believe are the most important?

electrical equipment and is released into the atmosphere from burning coal and incinerating municipal and industrial wastes. Mercury compounds are also used as paint pigments, fungicides, insecticides, and in dry-cell batteries.

Once released into the atmosphere from natural or human sources, elemental mercury often is converted to more toxic inorganic and organic mercury compounds, as shown in Figure 24-26. Trace the paths in this diagram.

Humans are exposed to mercury in two ways. One is by inhaling vaporized elemental mercury (Hg) or particulates of inorganic mercury (Hg^{2+}) salts (such as HgS and $HgCl_2$). The other is by eating fish contaminated with methylmercury (CH_3Hg^+), which is toxic and can be biologically magnified in food chains and webs. The greatest risk is brain damage from exposure to even low levels of methylmercury (CH_3Hg^+)

in fetuses and young children whose nervous systems are still developing.

Mercury is released naturally from rocks, soil, and volcanoes and by vaporization from the ocean. However, 50–75% of mercury emissions are believed to come from human activities, mostly coal burning and to a lesser degree waste incineration. Mercury is also released into the air when it is used to help extract gold and silver from ores, in some chlorine manufacturing processes, and when a fluorescent light bulb breaks.

These human-related sources emit elemental mercury (Hg) vapour and particles of inorganic mercury (Hg^{2+}) salts into the atmosphere. Within hours to days, these forms of mercury fall back to the Earth's land and aquatic systems in rain, snow, or as dry particles. Some falls out locally and some in downwind areas.

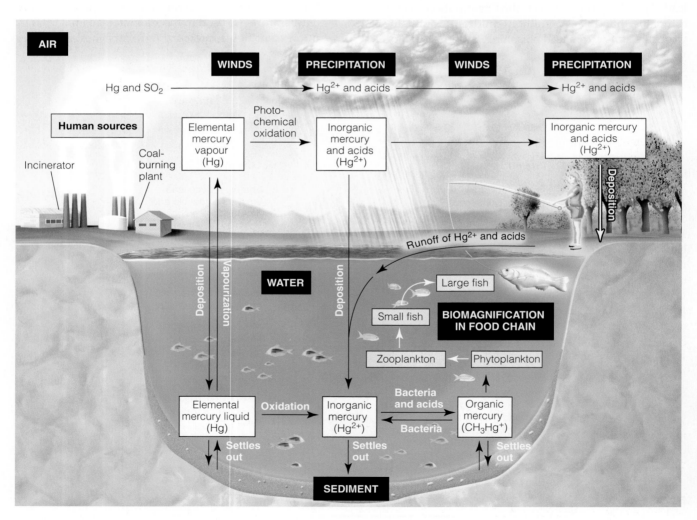

FIGURE 24-26 Cycling of mercury in aquatic environments, in which mercury is converted from one form to another. The most toxic form to humans is methylmercury (CH_3Hg^+), which can be biologically magnified in aquatic food chains. Some mercury is also released back into the atmosphere as mercury vapour.

Once moderately harmful inorganic mercury ions (Hg^{2+}) enter an aquatic system, bacteria can convert them to highly toxic methylmercury that can be biologically magnified in food chains and webs (Figure 24-26). This explains why high levels of methylmercury are often found in the tissues of sharks, swordfish, king mackerel, tilefish, and albacore (white) tuna feeding at high trophic levels in food chains and webs. In 2004, the Food and Drug Administration (FDA) and the U.S. EPA advised women who may become pregnant, pregnant women, and nursing mothers not to eat shark, swordfish, king mackerel, or tilefish and to limit their consumption of albacore tuna to no more than 170 grams (6 ounces) per week. They also advised such individuals to check local advisories about the safety of fish caught in local lakes, rivers, and coastal areas.

Levels of methylmercury in lakes and lake organisms appear to be connected to acid deposition, because the conversion rate of inorganic mercury to methylmercury is higher in acidified lakes.

According to a study by the Centers for Disease Control and Prevention, about 8% of North American women of childbearing age risk having a baby born with irreversible neurological problems because of exposure of the fetus to mercury, mostly from the mother eating fish and other seafood contaminated with methylmercury. Problems include brain and nerve system damage that can result in cerebral palsy, delayed onset of walking and talking, learning disabilities, tremors, irritability, impaired coordination, and memory loss.

Figure 24-27 lists ways to prevent or control human exposure to mercury. In its 2003 report on global mercury pollution, the U.N. Environment Programme recommended phasing out coal burning and waste incineration as rapidly as possible.

How Dangerous Are Dioxins? Controversy Over Unintended Culprits

Dioxins are potentially harmful chlorinated hydrocarbons produced as by-products of various industrial processes such as waste incineration and paper bleaching.

Dioxins (or polychlorinated dibenzodioxins) are a family of more than 75 different chlorinated hydrocarbon compounds. They form as by-products in high-temperature chemical reactions involving chlorine and hydrocarbons.

For example, dioxins are an unintended by-product of manufacturing herbicides at high temperature, and are linked to health effects of using herbicides. Natural processes such as forest fires and volcanic eruptions also produce them.

Worldwide, incineration of municipal and medical wastes accounts for about 70% of dioxin and furan

FIGURE 24-27 Solutions: ways to prevent or control inputs of mercury into the environment from human activities—mostly through coal-burning plants and incinerators. Which two of these solutions do you believe are the most important?

Solutions

Mercury Pollution

Prevention

Phase out waste incineration

Remove mercury from coal before it is burned

Convert coal to liquid or gaseous fuel

Switch from coal to natural gas and renewable energy resources such as wind, solar cells, and hydrogen

Phase out use of mercury in all products unless they are recycled

Control

Sharply reduce mercury emissions from coal-burning plants and incinerators

Tax each unit of mercury emitted by coal-burning plants and incinerators

Collect and recycle mercury-containing electric switches, relays, and dry-cell batteries

Require labels on all products containing mercury

releases to the atmosphere. Other sources include wood-burning fireplaces, coal-fired power plants, metal smelting and refining facilities, wood-pulp and paper mills, and sludge from municipal wastewater treatment plants.

Toxicology studies indicate that about 30 dioxin compounds have significant toxicity. One dioxin compound, TCDD, is the most toxic (Table 19-1, p. 456) and the most widely studied. Dioxins are persistent chemicals that linger in the environment for decades, especially in soil and human fat tissue. About 90% of the human exposure to trace levels of dioxins occurs through eating contaminated food.

There is concern about possible harmful health effects on humans and wildlife from exposure to even low levels of dioxins. A 2001 draft report of an EPA-sponsored comprehensive review of the scientific literature by more than 100 scientists around the world came to three major conclusions.

First, TCDD is a human carcinogen, and other dioxin compounds are likely human carcinogens, especially for people who eat large amounts of fatty meats and dairy products. *Second,* the most powerful possible effects of exposure to low levels of dioxin on humans are disruption of the reproductive, endocrine, and immune systems (Case Study, p. 459) and harmful effects on developing fetuses. *Third,* very low levels of dioxin in the environment can cause serious damage to certain wildlife species. But industries producing dioxins say the dangers of long-term exposure of humans to low levels of dioxins are over-estimated.

Because it will take decades to resolve these issues, some environmental and health scientists call for using a *precautionary strategy* to sharply reduce emissions of dioxins now. This would be done mostly by banning the use of chlorine for bleaching paper (as several European countries have done) and eliminating chlorinated hydrocarbon compounds that produce dioxins from hazardous wastes burned in incinerators, iron ore sintering plants, and cement kilns. As well, people should be encouraged to eat less fat and meat, which tend to have higher levels of dioxins.

24-9 ACHIEVING A LOW-WASTE SOCIETY

What Is the Role of Grassroots Action? Making a Difference

In Canada and the United States, citizens have kept large numbers of incinerators, landfills, and hazardous waste treatment plants from being built in their local areas.

In Canada and the United States, individuals have worked together to prevent hundreds of incinerators, landfills, or treatment plants for hazardous and radioactive wastes from being built in or near their communities. Opposition has grown as numerous studies have shown that such facilities have traditionally been located in low-income communities. This practice has been cited as an example of *environmental injustice.*

Health risks from incinerators and landfills, when averaged over the entire country, are quite low, but the risks for people living near these facilities are much higher. They, not the rest of the population, are the ones whose health, lives, and property values are being threatened.

Manufacturers and waste industry officials point out that something must be done with the toxic and hazardous wastes produced to provide people with certain goods and services. They contend that if local citizens adopt a "not in my back yard" (NIMBY) approach, the waste still ends up in someone's back yard.

Many citizens do not accept this argument. To them, the best way to deal with most toxic or hazardous wastes is to produce much less of them as illustrated by Figure 24-19. For such materials, their goal is "not in anyone's back yard" (NIABY) or "not on planet Earth" (NOPE) by emphasizing pollution prevention and use of the precautionary principle.

How Can We Make the Transition to a Low-Waste Society? A New Vision

A number of the principles and programs discussed in this chapter can be used to make the transition to a low-waste society during this century.

According to physicist Albert Einstein, "A clever person solves a problem, a wise person avoids it." To prevent pollution and reduce waste production, many environmental scientists urge us to understand and live by four key principles:

- Everything is connected.

- There is no "away" for the wastes we produce.

- Dilution is not always the solution to pollution.

- The best and cheapest way to deal with waste and pollution is to produce less pollutants and to reuse and recycle most of the materials we use.

Currently, the order of priorities for dealing with solid waste in most countries is the reverse of the order suggested by prominent scientists in Figure 24-4.

It does not have to be that way. Some scientists and economists estimate that 60–80% of the solid waste we produce can be eliminated by a combination of *reducing waste production, reusing and recycling materials* (including composting), and *redesigning* manufacturing processes and buildings to produce less waste. Much of this boils down to *rethinking* the choices we made before waste management became the problem that it is today.

The governments of Norway, Austria, and the Netherlands have committed themselves to reduce their resource waste by 75%. Other countries are following their lead.

Likewise, there is growing interest in and use of increased *resource productivity, pollution prevention, industrial ecology,* and *service-flow* businesses.

In addition, at least 24 countries have *eco-labelling programs* that certify a product or service as having met specified environmental standards. The first was Germany's *Blue Angel* program, begun in 1978. It now awards its seal of approval to more than 10 000 products and services. Other examples are Canada's *EcoLogo,* India's *Ecomark,* Singapore's *Green Label,* and the *Green Seal* program in the United States (Figure 26-13, p. 653).

Such revolutions start off slowly but can accelerate rapidly as their economic, ecological, and health advantages become more apparent to investors, business leaders, elected officials, and citizens.

The key to addressing the challenge of toxics use and wastes rests on a fairly straightforward principle: harness the innovation and technical ingenuity that has characterized the chemicals industry from its beginning and channel these qualities in a new direction that seeks to detoxify our economy.

ANNE PLATT MCGINN

CHAPTER REVIEW

1. Review the Key Questions for this chapter on p. 585. Describe the hazardous waste problems at the Sydney Tar Ponds and how they came to be (**Core Case Study**). Could these problems have been avoided? If so, how?

2. Distinguish among *solid waste, industrial solid waste, municipal solid waste (MSW),* and *hazardous (toxic) waste* and give an example of each. Give two reasons for sharply reducing the amount of solid and hazardous waste we produce. Describe the production of solid waste in Canada and what happens to such waste.

3. Distinguish between *waste management* and *waste reduction.* Describe the priorities that prominent scientists believe we should use for dealing with solid waste. What is garbology? Distinguish among *refusing, reducing, reusing,* and *recycling* as strategies for waste

reduction. What priority should *rethinking* have in our efforts to manage wastes? Describe six ways in which industries and communities can reduce resource use, waste, and pollution.

4. Explain why reusing and recycling materials are so important and give two examples of each. Describe the importance of using refillable containers and list five other ways to reuse various items. Distinguish between *primary (closed-loop)* and *secondary recycling* and give an example of each. Describe two approaches to recycling household solid wastes and evaluate each approach. What is a materials recovery facility? What is composting?

5. Describe the recycling of paper and the problems involved. Describe the recycling of plastics and the

problems involved. Describe progress in recycling plastics. What are bioplastics? What are the major advantages and disadvantages of recycling? What are three factors that discourage recycling? Describe three ways to encourage recycling and reuse.

6. What are the major advantages and disadvantages of using incinerators to burn solid and hazardous waste? Distinguish between *open dumps* and *sanitary landfills.* What are the major advantages and disadvantages of burying solid waste in sanitary landfills?

7. Explain how each of the following help to encourage sustainable waste management: considering the full cost of a product during its life cycle; creatively using tax breaks and subsidies; altering tipping fees; using pay-as-you-throw systems; requiring companies to take back and reuse their packaging, requiring product stewardship so manufacturers are responsible for taking back old appliances and equipment once those items can no longer be used.

8. Describe all the different ways that hazardous wastes are destroyed or stored or discarded in order to minimize their negative impact on the environment.

9. Explain how composting and vermicomposting could result in a huge reduction of wastes in a wide variety of scales and circumstances including municipal, industrial, business, and personal. Explain how the idea of industrial ecosystems could result in decreased production of industrial waste, at considerable savings for industry and society.

10. Describe the environmental and health concerns associated with each of the pollutants listed on p. 584. Who should be responsible for the costs of this cleanup? What factors were involved in the move to at last transform the Sydney Tar Ponds from a chemical waste site to an area of potential benefit such as a park? (Be sure to visit http://www.nelson.com/livingintheenvironment3e.com for a more detailed account of the history and issues of the Sydney Tar Ponds.)

CRITICAL THINKING

1. Use the second law of thermodynamics (p. 54) to explain why a *properly designed* source-separation recycling program takes less energy and produces less pollution than a centralized program that collects mixed waste over a large area and hauls it to a centralized facility where workers or machinery separate the wastes for recycling.

2. Are you for or against implementing the goals of *industrial ecology* in the region and community where you live? Explain. Do you believe it will be possible to phase in these goals over the next two to three decades? Explain.

3. Explain why some businesses participating in an exchange and chemical-cycling network (Figure 24-6, p. 590) might produce large amounts of waste for use as resources within the network rather than redesigning their manufacturing processes to reduce waste production. Is this acceptable? Explain.

4. Are you for or against shifting to a *service-flow economy* in the region and community where you live? Explain. Do you believe it will be possible to shift to such an economy over the next two to three decades? Explain.

5. Would you oppose having a hazardous waste landfill, waste treatment plant, deep-injection well, or

incinerator in your community? Explain. If you oppose these disposal facilities, how do you believe the hazardous waste generated in your community and your area should be managed?

6. Give your reasons for agreeing or disagreeing with each of the following proposals for dealing with hazardous waste:

   a. Reduce the production of hazardous waste and encourage recycling and reuse of hazardous materials by charging producers a tax or fee for each unit of waste generated.
   b. Ban all land disposal and incineration of hazardous waste to encourage recycling, reuse, and waste treatment and to protect air, water, and soil from contamination.
   c. Provide low-interest loans, tax breaks, and other financial incentives to encourage industries producing hazardous waste to reduce, recycle, reuse, treat, and decompose such waste.

7. Congratulations! You are in charge of the world. List the three most important components of your strategy for dealing with (a) solid waste and (b) hazardous waste.

PROJECTS

1. Collect all of the garbage (excluding food waste) that you generate in a typical week. Measure its total weight and volume. Sort it into major categories such as paper, plastic, metal, and glass. Then weigh each category and calculate the percentage in each category. What percentage of this waste consists of

materials that could be recycled or reused? What percentage of the items could you have done without? Tally and compare the results for your entire class.

2. What percentage of the municipal solid waste in your community is (a) placed in a landfill, (b) incinerated, (c) composted, and (d) recycled? What technology is

used in local landfills and incinerators? What leakage and pollution problems have local landfills or incinerators had? Does your community have a recycling program? Is it voluntary or mandatory? Does it have curbside collection? Drop-off centres? Buyback centres? A hazardous waste collection system? Devise a plan for improving the MSW system in your community and submit it to local officials.

3. Make a survey of the hazardous materials (Figure 24-17, p. 601) found in your house or apartment, or in your family home if you live in a dorm. What threats do they pose? Which of these materials are actually used? Call city officials to find out how you can dispose of hazardous chemicals you do not need.

4. What wastes and hazardous wastes are produced at your school? What happens to these wastes?

5. If possible, visit a local recycling centre or materials-recovery facility to find out how it works, where the materials separated out for recycling go, how the prices of these separated materials have fluctuated in the last three years, and the major problems faced by the facility.

6. Go to a large office supply store and compare prices for comparable grades of copy paper made from virgin paper with those containing some recycled content. Make the same price comparison at a stationery store.

ECOLOGICAL FOOTPRINT ANALYSIS

This pie chart shows the composition of North American municipal solid waste (MSW).

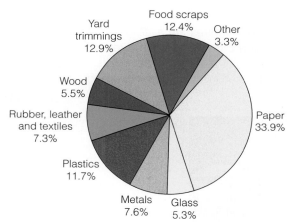

Food scraps 12.4%
Other 3.3%
Yard trimmings 12.9%
Wood 5.5%
Rubber, leather and textiles 7.3%
Plastics 11.7%
Metals 7.6%
Glass 5.3%
Paper 33.9%

Source: U.S. Environmental Protection Agency.

1. The average daily municipal solid waste production in North America is about 2 kilograms per person. Use the information in the pie chart to understand what makes up the annual MSW ecological footprint for a typical North American. For each category in the pie chart, calculate the total weight in kilograms generated by an average person.

2. Pull on some rubber gloves and conduct your own MSW audit at home. How do your results compare with the MSW ecological footprint of an average North American?

Biodiversity

Energy

Air

Water

CASE STUDY

The Ecocity Concept in Curitiba, Brazil

Environmental and urban designers envision the development of more sustainable cities, called *ecocities* or *green cities*. The ecocity is not a futuristic dream. One of the world's most livable and sustainable major cities is Curitiba, Brazil, with more than 3.2 million people.

This city decided in 1969 to focus on mass transit. Curitiba probably has the world's best bus system, which each day carries more than three-fourths of its people throughout the city along express lanes dedicated to buses (Figure 25-1).

Bike paths run throughout most of the city. Cars are banned from 49 blocks of the city's downtown area, which has a network of pedestrian walkways connected to bus stations, parks, and bike paths. Because Curitiba relies less on automobiles, it uses less energy per person and has less air pollution, greenhouse gas emissions, and traffic congestion than most comparable cities.

To reduce flood damage and add green space, the city transformed flood-prone areas along its rivers into a series of interconnected parks that are criss-crossed by bike paths. Volunteers have planted more than 1.5 million trees throughout the city. No tree in the city can be cut down without a permit, and two trees must be planted for each one cut.

The city recycles roughly 70% of its paper and 60% of its metal, glass, and plastic, which is sorted by households for collection three times a week. Recovered materials are sold mostly to the city's more than 500 major industries that must meet strict pollution standards. Most industries are in an industrial park outside the city limits. A major bus line runs to the park, but many of the workers live nearby and can walk or bike to work.

FIGURE 25-1 Solutions: Bus system in Curitiba, Brazil. This system moves large numbers of passengers around rapidly because each of the five major spokes has two express lanes used only by buses. Double- and triple-length bus sections are hooked together as needed, and boarding is speeded up by the use of extra-wide doors and raised tubes that allow passengers to pay before getting on the bus (top left).

The city uses old buses as roving classrooms to give the poor basic skills needed for jobs. Other retired buses have become health clinics, soup kitchens, and some of the city's 200 day-care centres, which are open 11 hours a day and are free for low-income parents.

The poor receive free medical, dental, and childcare, and 40 feeding centres are available for street children. The city has a *build-it-yourself* system that gives each poor family a plot of land, building materials, two trees, and an hour's consultation with an architect.

(continued)

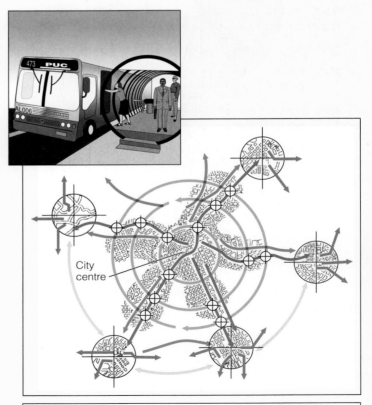

City centre

Route				
— Express	— Interdistrict	— Direct	— Feeder	— Workers

In Curitiba, virtually all households have electricity, drinking water, and garbage collection. About 95% of its citizens can read and write, and 83% of the adults have at least a high-school education. All schoolchildren study ecology. Polls show that 99% of the city's inhabitants would not want to live anywhere else.

This ecocity design is the brainchild of architect and former college teacher Jaime Lerner, who has served as the city's mayor three times since 1969. Under his leadership, the municipal government dedicated itself to two goals. *First*, find simple, innovative, fast, cheap, and fun solutions to problems. *Second*, establish a government that is honest, accountable, and open to public scrutiny.

An exciting challenge during this century will be to reshape existing cities and design new ones like Curitiba that are more livable and sustainable and that have a lower environmental impact.

The city is not an ecological monstrosity. It is rather the place where both the problems and the opportunities of modern technological civilization are most potent and visible.

Peter Self

CHAPTER PURPOSE AND QUESTIONS

Chapter 25 discusses urban problems and ways to create sustainable urban landscapes. The chapter addresses the following questions:

25-1   What causes urban growth?

25-2   What are the major resource and environmental problems of urban areas?

25-3   How do transportation systems shape urban areas and growth?

25-4   What methods are used for planning and controlling urban growth?

25-5   How can cities be made more sustainable and more desirable places to live?

25-6   How are we doing at ensuring environmental sustainability?

25-1 URBANIZATION AND URBAN GROWTH

What Causes Urban Growth? Magnets for Business and Hope for the Poor

Many people move to cities because "push" factors force them out of rural areas and "pull" factors give them the hope of finding jobs and a better life in the city.

At the beginning of the industrial revolution about 275 years ago, most people lived in **rural areas** and small villages and towns. Today almost half of the world's people live in densely populated **urban areas**, as rural people have migrated to cities with the hope of finding jobs and a better life.

Urban areas grow in two ways—by *natural increase* (more births than deaths) and by *immigration*, mostly from rural areas. This urban immigration is influenced by *push factors* such as poverty, lack of land to grow food, declining agricultural jobs, and **famine**, and war that force people out of rural areas. Rural people are also *pulled* to urban areas in search of jobs, food, housing, a better life, entertainment, and freedom from religious, racial, and political conflicts.

People are also pushed and pulled to cities by government policies that favour urban over rural areas. For example, developing countries spend most of their budgets on economic development and job creation in urban areas, especially in capital cities where their leaders live. Some governments establish lower food prices in urban areas, which pleases city dwellers, helps keep leaders in power, and attracts the rural poor.

What Are the Worldwide Patterns of Urbanization and Urban Growth? More People and More Poverty

Urban populations are growing rapidly throughout the world, and many cities in developing countries have become centres of poverty.

A country's **degree of urbanization** is the percentage of its population living in an urban area. **Urban growth** is the rate of increase of urban populations.

Five major trends are important in understanding the problems and challenges of urbanization and urban growth. First, *the proportion of the global population living in urban areas is increasing.* Between 1850 and 2011, the percentage of people living in urban areas increased from 2% to 50% (Figure 25-2, p. 616). According to UN projections, by 2050 about 68% of the world's people will live in urban areas. Between 2011 and 2050 the world's urban population is projected to increase from 3.6 billion to 6.3 billion. Almost all of this growth will occur in already overcrowded cities in developing countries such as India, Brazil, China, and Mexico (Figure 25-2).

Second, *the number of large cities is mushrooming.* In 2004, there were about 400 cities with a million or more people; by 2012, there were about 500 cities of this size. By 2012 there were 27 **megacities** (up from 8 in 1985) with 10 million or more people—most of them in developing countries (Figure 25-2).

A third trend is that *urbanization and urban populations are increasing rapidly in developing countries.* Between 2011 and 2050, the degree of urbanization in developing countries is expected to increase from 47% to 64%. In Latin American and Caribbean

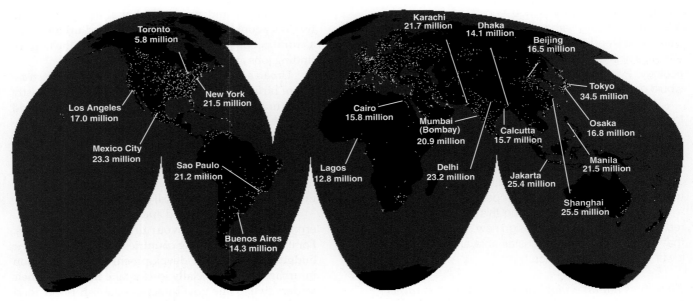

FIGURE 25-2 Major urban areas throughout the world based on satellite images of the Earth at night that show city lights. Currently, the 50% of the world's people living in urban areas occupy about 2% of the Earth's land area. Note that most of the world's urban areas are found along the coasts, and most of Africa and much of the interior of South America, Asia, and Australia are dark at night. This figure also shows the populations of Toronto and 18 *megacities* with 10 or more million people in 2012. Note that Canada's largest urban area, Toronto, is small compared to many throughout the world. Use this figure to list in order the world's five most populous urban areas in 2012. (National Geophysical Data Center/National Oceanic and Atmospheric Administration, and United Nations)

developing countries, 79% of the people are urban dwellers compared to only 40% in Africa and 45% in Asia.

Fourth, *urban growth is much slower in already heavily urbanized developed countries (with 78% urbanization) than in developing countries.* North America's urbanization is 83%, the highest in the world. By 2050, urbanization in developed countries is projected to increase to 86%.

Fifth, *poverty is becoming increasingly urbanized as more poor people migrate from rural to urban areas, mostly in developing countries.* The United Nations estimates that at least 1 billion poor people live in the urban areas of developing countries. This number is expected to triple by 2050. If you visit poor areas of such a city your senses may be overwhelmed with a chaotic but vibrant crush of people, vehicles of all sorts, street vendors, traffic jams, noise, smells, smoke from wood and coal fires, and people sleeping on streets or living in crowed, unsanitary, and rickety and unsafe slums and shantytowns.

How Urbanized Are Canada and the United States? City-Dwellers Dominate

Almost eight of every ten North Americans live in urban areas, about half of them in sprawling suburbs.

Between 1870 and 2011, the percentage of the Canadian population living in urban areas increased from 20% to

81% (Figure 10-10, p. 201). The population has shifted in four phases. First, *people migrated from rural areas to large central cities.*

Second, many people *migrated from the centre of large cities to suburbs and smaller cities.* Currently, about 50% live in the suburbs.

Third, many people *migrated from the East to the West.* Over time, the proportions of Canadians living in Quebec and the Maritimes declined, whereas proportions living in the Prairie provinces (led by Alberta) and British Columbia increased. Similar east-to-west trends occurred in the United States.

Fourth, *some people have migrated from urban areas back to rural areas* since the 1970s, and especially since 1990.

How Has the Quality of Urban Life in North America Changed? Progress and Challenges

The quality of urban life improved significantly for most North Americans during the last century, but there is still a long way to go.

Since 1920, many of the worst urban environmental problems in Canada and the United States have been reduced significantly. Most people have better working and housing conditions, and air and water quality have improved. Better sanitation, public water supplies, and medical care have slashed death rates and the prevalence of sickness from malnutrition and infectious diseases. And concentrating most of the population in urban areas may have helped to protect the country's biodiversity by reducing the destruction and degradation of wildlife habitat.

However, a number of cities, especially older ones in the United States, have *deteriorating services* and *aging infrastructures* (streets, schools, bridges, housing, and sewers). Many also face *budget crunches* from rising costs as some businesses and people move to the suburbs or rural areas and reduce revenues from property taxes. And there is *rising poverty* in the centres of many older U.S. cities.

What Is Urban Sprawl, and What Are Its Effects? Paving Paradise and Driving to Get Anywhere

When there is ample and affordable land, urban areas tend to sprawl outward, swallowing up surrounding countryside.

Another major problem in Canada and other countries with lots of room for expansion is **urban sprawl**. Growth of low-density development on the edges of cities and towns gobbles up surrounding countryside—frequently prime farmland or forests—and increases dependence on cars. The result is a far-flung hodgepodge of housing developments, shopping malls, parking lots, and office complexes—loosely connected by multilane highways (Figure 25-3).

Before sprawl, people in cities and small towns lived, shopped, and worked close to their homes and could meet most of their daily needs by walking. Every few blocks had a small grocery store, a pharmacy, professional offices, and other stores. Often shop owners lived above their stores or rented out such spaces. Most people could walk, bike, or take mass transit to neighbourhood schools and parks without the need for a car.

Starting in 1945, most Canadian and U.S. cities began spreading out as more people pursued the idea of living in their own house on their own piece of land away from the central city.

Six major factors promoted urban sprawl. *First,* ample land was available for most cities to spread outward. *Second,* governments facilitated the acquisition of new single-family homes for World War II veterans. *Third,* low-cost gasoline and government funding of highways encouraged automobile use and the development of outlying tracts of land that were now affordable and accessible.

Fourth, tax laws encouraged home ownership. *Fifth,* most zoning laws required large residential lots and separation of residential and commercial use of land in new communities.

Sixth, most urban areas consist of numerous political jurisdictions, which rarely work together to develop an overall plan for managing and controlling urban growth and sprawl. *In a nutshell, urban sprawl is the product of affordable land, automobiles, cheap gasoline, and poor urban planning.*

Figure 25-4 (p. 618) shows some of the undesirable consequences of urban sprawl. Look carefully at this figure. Urban sprawl has increased travel time in automobiles; decreased energy efficiency; increased urban flooding problems; and destroyed prime cropland, forests, open space, and wetlands. It has also led to the economic decline of many central cities.

To pay for heavily mortgaged houses and cars, adults in a typical suburban family work long hours, and have to spend many of their nonworking hours driving to and from work, or running errands over a vast suburban landscape. This leaves many of them with little energy and time for their children and themselves, or getting to know their neighbours.

In 2003, Reid Ewing and other researchers discovered a connection between sprawling suburbs and

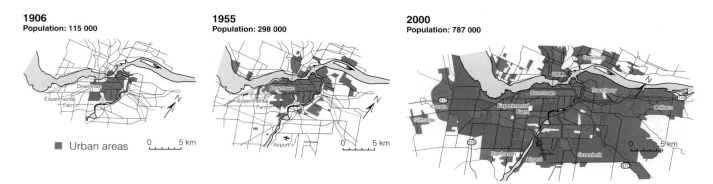

1906
Population: 115 000

1955
Population: 298 000

2000
Population: 787 000

■ Urban areas

FIGURE 25-3 The growth of urban sprawl in and around Ottawa. The formerly compact, pedestrian-friendly city has become increasingly dependent on cars and highways. (From "2020 VISION" by Steven Fick and Elizabeth Shilts, *Canadian Geographic*, May/June 2006, pp. 42–43. Reproduced with permission from *Canadian Geographic*, http://www.canadiangeographic.ca)

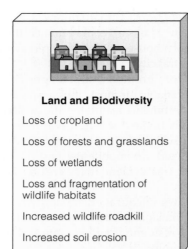

Land and Biodiversity

Loss of cropland

Loss of forests and grasslands

Loss of wetlands

Loss and fragmentation of wildlife habitats

Increased wildlife roadkill

Increased soil erosion

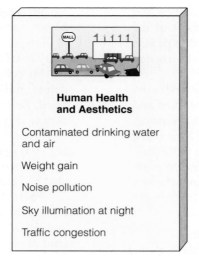

Human Health and Aesthetics

Contaminated drinking water and air

Weight gain

Noise pollution

Sky illumination at night

Traffic congestion

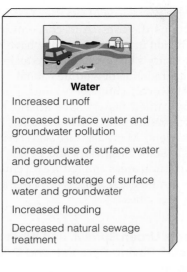

Water

Increased runoff

Increased surface water and groundwater pollution

Increased use of surface water and groundwater

Decreased storage of surface water and groundwater

Increased flooding

Decreased natural sewage treatment

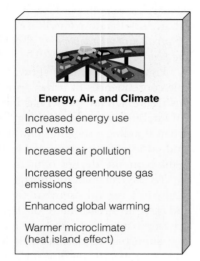

Energy, Air, and Climate

Increased energy use and waste

Increased air pollution

Increased greenhouse gas emissions

Enhanced global warming

Warmer microclimate (heat island effect)

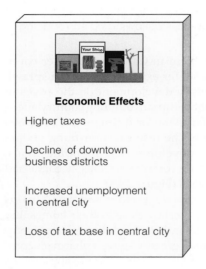

Economic Effects

Higher taxes

Decline of downtown business districts

Increased unemployment in central city

Loss of tax base in central city

FIGURE 25-4 Some undesirable impacts of *urban sprawl* or car-dependent development. Do you live in an area suffering from urban sprawl?

spreading waistlines. They found that people living in suburbs, where it is hard to get anywhere on foot or by bicycle, are heavier than those in central cities and in pedestrian-friendly towns.

As cities grow and sprawl outward, separate urban areas may merge to form a **megalopolis**. For example, the remaining open space that extends from Hamilton through the Greater Toronto Area to Oshawa is rapidly urbanizing and coalescing. In this area, known as the Golden Horseshoe, much of Ontario's prime farmland is being paved over.

Megalopolises developing all over the world include the area between Amsterdam and Paris in Europe; Japan's Tokyo–Yokohama–Osaka–Kobe corridor known as Tokohama; and the Brazilian industrial triangle made up of São Paulo, Rio de Janeiro, and Belo Horizonte.

25-2 URBAN RESOURCE AND ENVIRONMENTAL PROBLEMS

Case Study: What Are the Advantages of Urbanization? Concentrating People Helps

Urban areas can offer more job opportunities and better education and health, and can help protect biodiversity by concentrating people.

For more than 6 000 years, cities have been centres of economic development, education, jobs, technological developments, culture, social change, and political power. The high density of urban populations provides governments and businesses with significant cost advantages in delivering goods and services.

Urban residents in many parts of the world live longer than rural residents, and urban populations tend to have lower infant mortality and fertility rates. In addition, urban dwellers generally have better access to medical care, family planning, education, and social services than people in rural areas.

Urban areas also have some environmental advantages. For example, recycling is more economically feasible because of the large concentrations of recyclable materials, and per capita expenditures on environmental protection are higher in urban areas. Also, concentrating people in urban areas helps preserve biodiversity by reducing the stress on wildlife habitats.

Case Study: What Are the Disadvantages of Urbanization? Concentrating People Has Some Harmful Effects

Cities are rarely self-sustaining, and they threaten biodiversity; lack trees; grow little of their food; concentrate pollutants and noise; spread infectious diseases; and are centres of poverty, crime, and terrorism.

Although urban dwellers occupy only about 2% of the Earth's land area, they consume about three-fourths of all resources. Because of this and their high waste output (Figure 25-5), most of the world's cities are not self-sustaining systems.

Large areas of land must be disturbed and degraded to provide urban dwellers with food, water, energy, minerals, and other resources. This decreases the Earth's biodiversity. Also, as cities expand they destroy rural cropland, fertile soil, forests, wetlands, and wildlife habitats. At the same time, they provide little of the food they use. From an environmental standpoint, urban areas are somewhat like gigantic vacuum cleaners, sucking up much of the world's matter, energy, and living resources and spewing out pollution, wastes, and heat. Thus, urban areas have large *ecological footprints* (Figure 1-7, p. 8) that extend far beyond their boundaries.

In urban areas, most trees, shrubs, and other plants are destroyed to make way for buildings, roads, and parking lots. Most cities thus largely lose the benefits provided by vegetation that would help absorb air pollutants, give off oxygen, help cool the air through transpiration, provide shade, reduce soil erosion, muffle noise, provide wildlife habitats, and give aesthetic pleasure. As one observer remarked, "Most cities are places where they cut down all or most of the trees and then name the streets after them."

As cities grow and water demands increase, expensive reservoirs and canals must be built and deeper wells drilled. This can deprive rural and wild

Inputs

Energy

Food

Water

Raw materials

Manufactured goods

Money

Information

Outputs

Solid wastes

Waste heat

Air pollutants

Water pollutants

Greenhouse gases

Manufactured goods

Noise

Wealth

Ideas

FIGURE 25-5 Natural capital degradation: urban areas rarely are sustainable systems. The typical city depends on large nonurban areas of land and water for huge inputs of matter and energy resources and for large outputs of waste matter and heat. For example, according to an analysis by Mathis Wackernagel and William Rees, an area 58 times as large as that of London is needed to supply its residents with resources. They estimate that meeting the needs of all the world's people at the same rate of resource use as that of London would take at least three more Earths.

areas of surface water and deplete groundwater faster than it is replenished.

Flooding also tends to be greater in cities, in some cases because they are built on floodplains or in low-lying coastal areas subject to natural flooding. Another reason is that covering land with buildings, asphalt, and concrete causes precipitation to run off quickly and overload storm drains. In addition, urban development often destroys or degrades wetlands that act as natural sponges to help absorb excess water.

Another threat is that many of the world's largest cities are in coastal areas (Figure 25-2) that could be flooded sometime in this century if sea levels rise due to projected global warming.

Because of their high population and resource consumption, urban dwellers produce most of the world's air pollution, water pollution, and solid and hazardous wastes. Also, pollutant levels are generally higher in urban areas because they are produced in a smaller area and cannot be as readily dispersed and diluted as are those produced in most rural areas.

Most urban dwellers are subjected to **noise pollution:** any unwanted, disturbing, or harmful sound that impairs or interferes with hearing, causes stress, hampers concentration and work efficiency, or causes accidents. Noise levels (Figure 25-6) above 65 dBA are considered unacceptable, and prolonged exposure to levels above 85 dBA can cause permanent hearing damage.

In addition, high population densities in urban areas can increase the spread of infectious diseases, especially if adequate drinking water and sewage systems are not available.

Cities generally are warmer, rainier, foggier, and cloudier than suburbs and nearby rural areas mostly because of their buildings, pavement, and lack of green space. The enormous amounts of heat generated by cars, factories, furnaces, lights, air conditioners, and heat-absorbing dark roofs and roads in cities create an *urban heat island* surrounded by cooler suburban and rural areas.

Higher CO_2 and soot concentrations from fossil fuel–burning, cars, factories, and buildings intensify this heat-island effect. The higher CO_2 levels can increase plant growth, especially opportunistic species such as ragweed, that can worsen asthma. Also, tiny soot and other particles help deliver pollen, mould, and other allergens deep into the lungs. This may help explain why childhood asthma rates have climbed steadily in recent years in many Canadian and U.S. urban areas. As cities grow and merge, their heat islands also merge and can keep polluted air from being diluted and cleansed.

There are also problems with the artificial light created by urban areas (Figure 25-2). Lighting up the sky prevents people from seeing the glories of a starry night and hinders astronomers from conducting their research. There is also growing evidence that artificial light is affecting plants and animals in a variety of ecosystems. Species affected by such *light pollution* include turtles that lay their eggs on beaches at night and migrating birds that are lured off course by lights on high-rise office buildings and fatally collide with such structures. In 1996, Toronto established a lights-out program to encourage major city-centre buildings to turn off their lights between 11 p.m. and dawn.

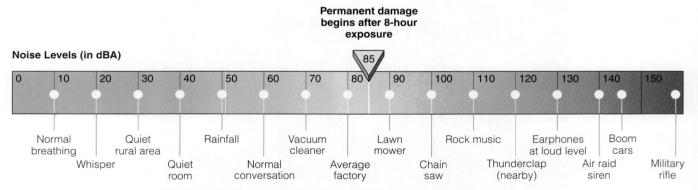

FIGURE 25-6 *Noise levels* (in decibel-A [dBA] sound pressure units) of some common sounds. Sound pressure becomes damaging at about 75 dBA and painful at around 120 dBA. At 180 dBA it can kill. Because the dB and dBA scales are logarithmic, sound pressure is multiplied 10-fold with each 10-decibel rise. Thus a rise from 30 dBA (quiet rural area) to 60 dBA (normal restaurant conversation) represents a 1 000-fold increase in sound pressure on the ear. You are being exposed to a sound level high enough to cause permanent hearing damage if you need to raise your voice to be heard above the racket, if a noise causes your ears to ring, or if nearby speech seems muffled. Ways to control noise include modifying noisy activities and devices, shielding noisy devices or processes, shielding workers from noise, moving noisy operations or machinery away from people, and using anti-noise (a new technology that cancels out one noise with another).

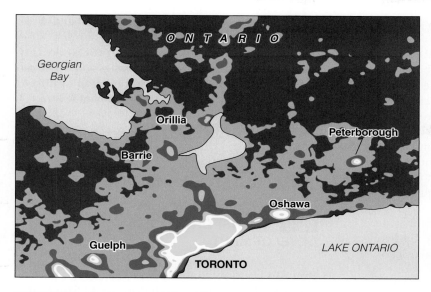

FIGURE 25-7 For some people, the ability to see the night sky without light pollution is a precious and threatened resource. (Muskoka Heritage Foundation)

At the *Ecology of the Night International Symposium* in 2003, Monte Hummel, president of the World Wildlife Fund Canada, spoke of the need to protect pockets of dark sky for the benefit of stargazers, just as we protect parks for the benefit of pedestrians. In 1999, the world's first permanent *Dark Sky Reserve* was established northeast of Orillia, Ontario (Figure 25-7). To learn about the Dark Sky Reserve, visit http://www.muskokaheritage .org/programs/dark-skies/torrance-barrens/.

Researchers have found evidence that artificial illumination can alter aquatic ecosystems and could ultimately decrease water quality. Minute zooplankton avoid predators by remaining well below the surface during the day and then rising to graze on algae at night. But artificial light from urban glows can discourage their nightly surface feeding. If their grazing is inhibited, algae populations could explode and these blooms would deplete dissolved oxygen needed by fish and decrease water quality.

Urban areas can intensify poverty and social problems. Crime rates also tend be higher in urban areas than in rural areas (Connections, p. 622). And urban areas are more likely and desirable targets for terrorist acts.

Case Study: How Do the Urban Poor in Developing Countries Live? Living on the Edge with Ingenuity and Hope

Most of the urban poor in developing countries live in crowded, unhealthy, and dangerous conditions, but many are better off than the rural poor.

Many of the world's poor live in crowded central city *slums*—multifamily tenements and rooming houses where three to six people live in a single room. Most of these dwellings have inadequate sanitation and ventilation and many are in unsafe structures. Others live in *squatter settlements* and *shantytowns* on the outskirts of most cities in developing countries, some perched precariously on steep hillsides subject to landslides. In these illegal settlements, people take over unoccupied land and build shacks from corrugated metal, plastic sheets, scrap wood, and other scavenged building materials. Still others live or sleep on the streets, having nowhere else to go.

Squatters living near the edge of survival in these areas usually lack clean water, sewers, electricity, and roads, and often are subject to severe air and water pollution and hazardous wastes from nearby factories (Case Study, p. 602). Their locations may be especially prone to landslides, flooding, earthquakes, or volcanic eruptions.

Most cities cannot afford to provide squatters with basic protections and services, and their officials fear that doing so will attract even more of the rural poor. Many city governments regularly bulldoze squatter shacks and send police to drive the illegal settlers out. The people later move back in or develop another shantytown somewhere else.

Despite joblessness, squalor, overcrowding, and environmental and health hazards, most squatters and slum residents are better off than the rural poor. With better access to family planning programs, they tend to have fewer children and better access to schools. They work, raise families, educate their children, and often have to care for their parents. Some work together to establish water supplies, sewer and health-care facilities, and schools. Many squatter settlements provide a sense of community and a vital safety net of neighbours, friends, and relatives.

Mexico City is an example of an urban area in crisis. About 23.3 million people—roughly one of every six Mexicans—live there (Figure 25-2). It is already densely crowded, and each year about 400 000 new residents arrive.

Mexico City suffers from severe air pollution, close to 50% unemployment, deafening noise, overcrowding, traffic congestion, inadequate public transportation, and a soaring crime rate. More than one-third of its residents live in slums called *barrios* or in squatter settlements without running water or electricity.

At least 3 million people have no sewer facilities. This means huge amounts of human waste are deposited in gutters, vacant lots, and open sewers every day, attracting armies of rats and swarms of flies. When the winds pick up dried excrement, a *fecal snow* often falls on parts of the city. Open garbage dumps also contribute dust and bacteria to the atmosphere. This bacteria-laden fallout leads to widespread salmonella and hepatitis infections, especially among children.

Mexico City has one of the world's worst photochemical smog problems because of a combination of too many cars and polluting industries, a sunny climate, and topographical bad luck. The city lies in a high-elevation bowl-shaped valley surrounded on three sides by mountains—ideal conditions for thermal inversions that trap pollutants at ground level (Figure 20-9, top, p. 488). Since 1982, the amount of contamination in the city's air has more than tripled, and breathing that air is said to be roughly equivalent to smoking three packs of cigarettes a day.

The city's air and water pollution cause an estimated 100 000 premature deaths per year. Writer Carlos Fuentes has nicknamed this megacity "Makesicko City."

Water demands are pushing the city's aquifer beyond its limits. Energy costs to extract water have soared as wells have become much deeper. Withdrawal from aquifers caused parts of the city to subside by 9 metres (30 feet) during the 20th century. Some areas now subside as much as 30 centimetres (1 foot) a year.

The city government has banned cars from a 50-block central zone; required catalytic converters on all cars made after 1991; phased out use of leaded gasoline; and replaced old buses, taxis, and delivery vehicles with cleaner vehicles running mostly on liquefied petroleum gas. The city also planted more than 25 million trees to help absorb pollutants and bought some land for use as green space.

Some progress has been made. The percentage of days each year in which air pollution standards are violated has fallen from 50% to 20%. But the city still has an inadequate mass transportation system and weak, poorly enforced air pollution standards for industries and motor vehicles. If you were in charge of Mexico City, what are the three most important things you would do?

Further details of slums can be found at http://www.nelson.com/livingintheenvironment3e.com.

CONSIDER, DISCUSS, OR DEBATE

Should squatters around cities of developing countries be given title to land they live on?

25-3 TRANSPORTATION AND URBAN DEVELOPMENT

How Do Land Availability and Transportation Systems Affect Urban Development? Stack or Sprawl

Land availability determines whether a city grows vertically or spreads out horizontally and whether it relies mostly on mass transportation or the automobile.

The two main types of ground transportation are *individual* (such as cars, motor scooters, bicycles, and walking) and **mass transit** (mostly buses and rail systems). About 90% of all travel in the world is by foot, bicycle, motor scooter, or bus—mostly because only about 10% of the world's people can afford a car.

Land availability is a key factor determining the types of transportation people use. If a city cannot spread outward, it must grow vertically—upward and downward (below ground)—so it occupies a small land area with a high population density. Most people

---

CONNECTIONS

How Can Reducing Crime Help the Environment?

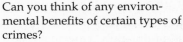

Most people do not realize that reducing crime can help improve environmental quality. Crimes such as robbery, assault, and shootings can have several harmful environmental effects.

Crime can drive people out of cities, which are our most energy-efficient living arrangements. Every brick in an abandoned urban building represents an energy waste equivalent to burning a 100-watt light bulb for 12 hours. Each new suburb means replacing farmland or reservoirs of natural biodiversity such as forests with dispersed, energy- and resource-wasting roads, houses, and shopping centres.

Crime can make people less willing to walk, bicycle, and use energy-efficient public transit systems. It also forces many people to use more energy to deter burglars. For example, trees and bushes near a house help save energy by reducing solar heat gain in the summer and providing windbreaks in the winter. But to help reduce break-ins many homeowners clear away trees and bushes near their houses, as well as installing yard lights and leaving indoor lights, TVs, and radios on to deter burglars.

The threat of crime also causes overpackaging of many items to deter shoplifting or poisoning of food or drug items.

Critical Thinking

Can you think of any environmental benefits of certain types of crimes?

living in such *compact cities* like Hong Kong and Tokyo walk, ride bicycles, or use energy-efficient mass transit.

A combination of cheap gasoline, plentiful land, and a network of highways produces *dispersed cities*. They are found in countries such as Canada, the United States, and Australia, where ample land often is available for outward expansion. Sprawling cities depend on the automobile; motor vehicles are increasing in both compact and dispersed cities. Today there are about 700 million cars, trucks, and buses in the world. By 2050, the number of motor vehicles is projected to increase sevenfold to 3.5 billion—2.5 billion of them in today's developing countries.

Is this sustainable? No one knows. Some analysts believe that phasing in motor vehicles with clean-burning hybrid and fuel-cell engines would allow the world's motor vehicle fleet to double while emitting less air pollution than today's fleet.

Vehicle emissions are not the only problem. Producing motor vehicles and building roads, parking lots, and garages uses huge amounts of energy and matter resources that produce pollution and environmental degradation. Also, motor vehicles take up space and thus cause congestion as their numbers multiply. More and more people could end up stuck in traffic jams in fuel-efficient and low-polluting cars going nowhere.

What Is the Role of Motor Vehicles in Canada and the United States? Cars Rule

Passenger vehicles account for almost all North American urban transportation and travel to work, and each year North Americans drive as far as everyone else in the world combined.

North America showcases the advantages and disadvantages of living in a society dominated by motor vehicles. With about 5% of the world's people, North America has about a third of the world's motor vehicles. Approximately two-thirds of the 250 million motor vehicles (excluding big trucks and buses) in North America are cars and the remainder are sport utility vehicles (SUVs), pickup trucks, and vans.

Mostly because of urban sprawl and convenience, passenger vehicles are used for about 98% of all urban transportation and 90% of travel to work in Canada and the United States. About three-fourths of all trips are less than 1.6 kilometres (1 mile) from home. About 75% of North Americans drive alone to work, 5% commute on public transit, and 0.5% bicycle to work. Mostly because of urban sprawl and a network of highways, North Americans drive about 4 trillion kilometres (2.5 trillion miles) each year, about the same distance driven by all other drivers in the world. Each year North American vehicles consume about 43% of the world's gasoline.

Many governments in rapidly industrializing countries such as China want to develop an automobile-centred transportation system. Suppose China succeeds in having one or two cars in every garage and consumes oil at the North American rate. According to environmental leader Lester R. Brown, China would then need slightly more oil each year than the world now produces and would have to pave an area equal to half of the land it now uses to produce food.

What Are the Advantages and Disadvantages of Motor Vehicles? A Troubled Love Affair

Motor vehicles provide personal benefits and help run economies, but they also kill lots of people, pollute the air, promote urban sprawl, and lead to time- and gas-wasting traffic jams.

Motor vehicles have a number of important benefits. On a personal level, they provide mobility and are a convenient and comfortable way to get from one place to another. They also are symbols of power, sex, social status, and success for many people. For some they also provide escape from an increasingly hectic world.

From an economic standpoint, much of the world's economy is built on producing motor vehicles and supplying roads, services, and repairs for them. In Canada and the United States, for example, about $1 of every $4 spent and one of every six nonfarm jobs is connected to the automobile. And five of the seven largest North American industrial firms produce motor vehicles or their fuel.

Despite their important benefits, motor vehicles have many harmful effects on people and the environment. They have killed almost 18 million people since 1885, when Karl Benz built the first automobile. Throughout the world they kill an estimated 1.2 million people each year—an average of 3 300 deaths per day—and injure another 15 million. Each year they also kill about 50 million wild animals and family pets.

In Canada and the United States, motor vehicle accidents kill more than 40 000 people a year and injure another 5 million, at least 300 000 of them severely. *Car accidents have killed more North Americans than have all wars in the history of North America.*

Motor vehicles are the world's largest source of air pollution. They emit six of the eight major air pollutants (Table 20-2, p. 482), which prematurely kill 30 000–60 000 people per year in Canada and the United States. Motor vehicles are also the fastest-growing source of carbon dioxide emissions—now producing almost one-fourth of them. In addition, they account for two-thirds of the oil used in Canada and the United States and one-third of the world's oil consumption.

Motor vehicles have helped create urban sprawl. At least a third of urban land worldwide and half in Canada and the United States is devoted to roads, parking lots, gasoline stations, and other automobile-related uses.

Another problem is congestion. If current trends continue, North American motorists will spend an average of two years of their lives in traffic jams, wasting about $60 billion (U.S.) a year in gasoline and lost time.

Building more roads may not be the answer. Many analysts agree with the idea, stated by economist Robert Samuelson, that "cars expand to fill available concrete."

Motor vehicles have harmful economic costs, mostly because of deaths and injuries, higher insurance rates, pollution, work time wasted in traffic jams, and decreased property values near noisy, congested roads. According to the International Center for Technology Assessment, such costs amount to $1 970–$5 990 (U.S.) per North American each year. Because these costs are not included in the prices of motor vehicles and gasoline, most people do not associate them with the motor vehicles they buy and use.

How Can We Reduce Automobile Use? Use Honest Accounting

We can reduce automobile use by having users pay for its harmful effects, but this is politically unpopular.

Environmentalists and a number of economists suggest that one way to reduce the harmful effects of automobile use is to make drivers pay directly for most of the harmful costs of automobile use—a *user-pays* approach based on honest environmental accounting. One option is to include the estimated harmful costs of driving as a tax on gasoline. Such taxes would amount to about $1.30–$2.10 per litre ($5–$8 per gallon) of gasoline in North America and would spur the use of more energy-efficient motor vehicles.

Proponents urge governments to use gasoline tax revenues to help finance mass transit systems, bike paths, and sidewalks. The government could reduce taxes on income and wages to offset the increased taxes on gasoline and thus make such a *tax shift* more politically acceptable.

Another way to reduce automobile use and congestion is to raise parking fees and charge tolls on roads, tunnels, and bridges—especially during peak traffic times. For example, densely populated Singapore is rarely congested because it taxes cars heavily and auctions the rights to buy a car. Also, anyone driving downtown pays a daily user fee of $3–$6 that rises during rush hours. The government uses the revenue from taxes and fees to fund an excellent mass transit system. This approach is also being used in Oslo, Norway; Melbourne, Australia; and London, England. In London, charging $8 for any vehicle entering the central city during the workday has cut traffic congestion by a fourth and increased use of mass transit.

Scores of cities including Rome, Italy; Stockholm, Sweden; Copenhagen, Denmark; Prague, Czech Republic; Geneva, Switzerland; and Curitiba, Brazil (p. 614) have established *car-free areas* (Figure 25-8). On *International Car Free Day*, which has been celebrated in over 1 500 cities since its inauguration on September 22, 1999, certain streets are closed to traffic to accommodate events promoting a car-free lifestyle (http://www.carfreeday.ca).

More than 300 cities in Germany, Austria, Italy, Switzerland, and the Netherlands have a *car-sharing* network. Each member pays for a card that opens lockers containing keys to cars parked at designated spots around a city. Members reserve a car in advance or call the network and are directed to the closest locker and car. They are billed monthly for the time they use a car and the distance they travel. In Berlin, Germany, car sharing has cut car ownership by 75% and car commuting by nearly 90%.

Another way to reduce car use and accidents and save gasoline is the *electronic commute* in which people use computers and other telecommunication devices to do all or much of their work at home. Shopping online also reduces the need to travel to shopping malls and other stores, although this is offset partially by increased delivery truck trips.

Is It Feasible to Reduce Automobile Use in Canada and the United States? Kicking Auto Addiction Is Hard

Reducing car use in Canada and the United States is difficult because of political opposition from the public and powerful car-related industries; too little emphasis on establishing modern, efficient mass transit options; and addiction to cars.

Most analysts doubt that the approaches just discussed are feasible in North America, for three reasons. *First*, it faces strong political opposition from two groups, one being the public, largely unaware of the huge hidden costs they are already paying. The other group is the politically powerful transportation-related industries such as oil and tire companies, road builders, carmakers, and many real-estate developers. However, taxpayers might accept sharp increases in gasoline taxes if the extra costs were offset by decreases in taxes on wages and income.

Second, fast, efficient, reliable, and affordable mass transit options and bike paths are not widely available in most of North America. In addition, the dispersed nature of most urban areas makes people dependent on cars.

FIGURE 25-8 Take back the streets. Residents of Canadian cities are discovering the benefits of banning cars from some streets and allowing a pedestrian lifestyle to re-emerge.

Third, most North Americans who can afford cars are virtually addicted to them, seeing them as much more than a mode of transportation.

What Are Alternatives to the Car? Use Your Muscles, and Travel with Others

Alternatives include walking, bicycling, driving scooters, and taking subways, trolleys, trains, and buses.

There are a number of alternatives to cars, each with advantages and disadvantages. One widely used alternative is the *bicycle.* Because of their advantages (Figure 25-9), bicycles outsell cars by more than two to one.

Bicycles are widely used for urban trips in countries such as the Netherlands, China, and Japan. Bicycling and walking account for about 28% of the trips in the Netherlands, compared to only 6% in North America. In Copenhagen, Denmark, 2 300 bicycles are available for public use at no charge. The system is financed by ads attached to the bicycle frames and wheels, and is so popular that each bicycle is used on average once every eight minutes.

Only one of every 200 North Americans bicycles to work. But one out of five say they would do so if safe bike lanes were available and if their employers provided secure bike storage and showers at work.

About 2 million *electric bicycles* are on the road worldwide, and about 400 000 more are added each year. Existing bikes can easily be converted to electric bikes, and new ones can be bought for $500–$1 200. Bicycles powered by small fuel cells should be available within a few years.

Motor scooters have advantages and disadvantages (Figure 25-10, p. 626) and are especially useful for people in developing countries who cannot afford a car. Electric scooters can reduce air pollution and noise.

Heavy-rail systems (subways, elevated railways, and metro trains) and *light-rail* systems (streetcars, trolley cars, and tramways) have their advantages and disadvantages (Figure 25-11). To be cost effective, rail systems must travel along densely populated corridors in urban areas. At one time the United States had an effective light-rail system, but it was dismantled to promote car and bus use (Case Study, p. 627).

Trade-Offs

Bicycles

Advantages	Disadvantages
Affordable	Little protection in an accident
Produce no pollution	Do not protect riders from bad weather
Quiet	
Require little parking space	Not practical for trips longer than 8 kilometres (5 miles)
Easy to manoeuvre in traffic	
Take few resources to make	Can be tiring (except for electric bicycles)
Very energy efficient	
Provide exercise	Lack of secure bike parking

FIGURE 25-9 Trade-offs: advantages and disadvantages of *bicycles*. Pick the single advantage and disadvantage that you think are the most important.

Trade-Offs

Motor Scooters

Advantages	Disadvantages
Affordable	Little protection in an accident
Produce less air pollution than cars	Does not protect drivers from bad weather
Require little parking space	
Easy to manoeuvre in traffic	Gasoline engines are noisy
Electric scooters are quiet and produce little pollution	Gasoline engines emit large quantities of air pollutants

FIGURE 25-10 Trade-offs: advantages and disadvantages of *motor scooters*. Pick the single advantage and disadvantage that you think are the most important.

Trade-Offs

Mass Transit Rail

Advantages	Disadvantages
More energy efficient than cars	Expensive to build and maintain
Produces less air pollution than cars	Cost effective only along a densely populated narrow corridor
Requires less land than roads and parking areas for cars	
Causes fewer injuries and deaths than cars	Commits riders to transportation schedules
Reduces car congestion in cities	Can cause noise and vibration for nearby residents

FIGURE 25-11 Trade-offs: advantages and disadvantages of *mass transit rail systems in urban areas*. Pick the single advantage and disadvantage that you think are the most important.

Toronto has managed to retain an efficient—if chronically underfunded—system of subways and streetcars. Montreal's subway system is adorned with art and links a number of underground shopping centres, an especially welcome feature during the winter months.

The rail system in Hong Kong is one of the world's most successful for three reasons. *First,* the city is densely populated, making it ideal for a rapid-rail system running through its corridor. *Second,* half the population can walk to a subway station in five minutes. *Third,* a car is an economic liability in this crowded city even for those who can afford one.

Buses are the most widely used form of mass transit within urban areas, mainly because they have more advantages than disadvantages (Figure 25-12). Curitiba, Brazil, has one of the world's best bus systems (Figure 25-1).

A *rapid-rail system between urban areas* is another option. In western Europe and Japan, high-speed bullet trains travel between cities at up to 330 kilometres (200 miles) per hour. Figure 25-13 lists the major advantages and disadvantages of such rapid-rail systems. In 2004, Shanghai, China, began operating the world's first commercial high-speed magnetic levitation train between its airport and downtown.

Trade-Offs

Buses

Advantages

- More flexible than rail system
- Can be rerouted as needed
- Cost less to develop and maintain than heavy-rail system
- Can greatly reduce car use and pollution

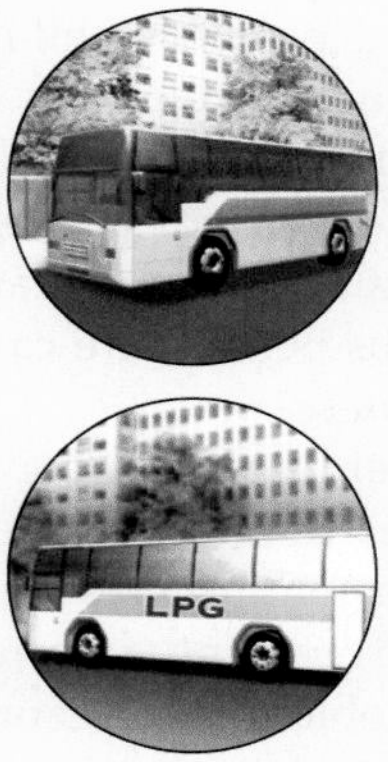

Disadvantages

- Can lose money because they need low fares to attract riders
- Often get caught in traffic unless operating in express lanes
- Commits riders to transportation schedules
- Noisy

FIGURE 25-12 Trade-offs: advantages and disadvantages of *bus systems in urban areas.* Pick the single advantage and disadvantage that you think are the most important.

The train, suspended in air slightly above the track and propelled forward by strong repulsive and attractive magnetic forces, travels much faster than bullet trains.

In Canada and the United States, a high-speed bullet train network could replace airplanes, buses, and private cars for most medium-distance travel between major cities. Critics say such a system would cost too much in government subsidies. But this ignores the fact that motor vehicle transportation receives massive subsidies every year.

Case Study: Mass Transit in the United States—Destroying a Great System

In the early 1900s the United States had one of the world's best streetcar systems, but it was bought up and destroyed by several companies in order to sell cars and buses.

In 1917, all major U.S. cities had efficient electric trolley or streetcar (light-rail) systems. Many people think of Los Angeles as the original car-dominated city. But in the early 20th century, Los Angeles had the largest electric-rail mass transit system in the United States.

That changed when General Motors, Firestone Tire, Standard Oil of California, Phillips Petroleum, and Mack Truck (which also made buses) formed a holding company called National City Lines. By 1950, the holding company had purchased privately owned streetcar systems in 83 major cities. It then dismantled these systems to increase sales of cars and buses.

The courts found the companies guilty of conspiracy to eliminate the country's light-rail system, but the damage had already been done. The executives responsible were fined $1 each, and each company paid a fine of $5 000, less than the profit returned by replacing a single streetcar with a bus.

During this same period, National City Lines worked to convert electric-powered commuter locomotives to much more expensive and less reliable diesel-powered locomotives. The resulting increase in costs contributed significantly to the sharp decline of the nation's railroad system.

In both Canada and the United States, far more government revenue is used to build and maintain roads, highways, and parking lots than is used for mass transit, bike paths, and walkways. Car owners are further rewarded by a tax system that includes deductions for various driving-related expenses.

Trade-Offs

Rapid Rail

Advantages

- Can reduce travel by car or plane
- Ideal for trips of 200–1 000 kilometres (120–620 miles)
- Much more energy efficient per rider over the same distance than a car or plane

Disadvantages

- Expensive to run and maintain
- Must operate along heavily used routes to be profitable
- Causes noise and vibration for nearby residents

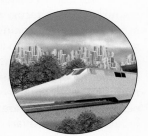

FIGURE 25-13 Trade-offs: advantages and disadvantages of *rapid-rail systems between urban areas.* Pick the single advantage and disadvantage that you think are the most important.

25-4 URBAN LAND-USE PLANNING AND CONTROL

What Is Conventional Land-Use Planning? Focusing on Growth

Most land-use planning in Canada and the United States leads to poorly controlled urban sprawl and environmental degradation and funds this often-destructive process with property taxes.

Most urban and some rural areas use some form of **land-use planning** to determine the best present and future use of each parcel of land.

Much land-use planning is based on the assumption that considerable future population growth and economic development should be encouraged, regardless of environmental and other consequences. Typically this leads to uncontrolled or poorly controlled urban growth and sprawl.

A major reason for this often destructive process is that 90% of the revenue that local governments use to provide public services such as schools, police and fire protection, and water and sewer systems comes from *property taxes* levied on all buildings and property based on their economic value. Thus local governments often try to raise money by promoting economic growth because they usually cannot raise property tax rates enough to meet expanding needs. Typically the long-term result is poorly managed economic growth, leading to more environmental degradation.

Land-use planning can be aided by the use of geographic information system (GIS) technology (Figure 4-34, p. 89). Many cities have used this technology to convert their planning maps into digital form.

What Are the Advantages and Disadvantages of Using Zoning to Control Land Use? Useful but Improvable

Zoning is useful but can favour high-priced development over environmental protection and can discourage innovative solutions to urban problems.

Once a land-use plan is developed, governments control the uses of various parcels of land by legal and economic methods. The most widely used approach is **zoning**, in which various parcels of land are designated for certain uses.

Zoning can be used to control growth and protect areas from certain types of development. For example, many cities use zoning to encourage high-density development along major mass transit corridors to reduce automobile use and air pollution. David Caplan, Ontario's Minister of Public Infrastructure and Renewal (2003–8), established that planning new developments in the province will incorporate the following assumptions: (1) densities of 400 people and jobs per hectare can support subway transit; (2) densities of 200 people and jobs per hectare can support frequent bus or light-rail transit; and (3) densities of 150 people and jobs per hectare can support bus service every 15 minutes.

Despite its usefulness, zoning has several drawbacks, one being that some developers can influence or modify zoning decisions in ways that cause destruction of wetlands, prime cropland, forested areas, and open space. Another problem is that zoning often favours high-priced housing, factories, hotels, and other businesses over protecting environmentally sensitive areas and providing low-cost housing. The reason is, again, that most local governments depend on property taxes for their revenue.

In addition, overly strict zoning can discourage innovative approaches to solving urban problems. For example, the pattern in many countries has been to prohibit businesses in residential areas, which increases suburban sprawl. Some urban planners want to return to *mixed-use zoning* to help reduce sprawl. For example, in an effort to reduce driving and gasoline consumption, a city might permit the development of retail space in a residential neighbourhood.

How Is Smart Growth Used to Control Growth and Sprawl? Channelling Growth and Reining in the Car

Smart growth can control growth patterns, discourage urban sprawl, reduce car dependence, and protect ecologically sensitive areas.

There is growing use of the concept of **smart growth** or *new urbanism* to encourage more environmentally sustainable development that requires less dependence on cars, controls and directs sprawl, and reduces wasteful resource use. It recognizes that urban growth will occur. But it uses zoning laws and an array of other tools to channel growth to areas where it can cause less harm, discourage sprawl, protect ecologically sensitive and important lands and waterways, and develop more environmentally sustainable urban areas and neighbourhoods that are more enjoyable places to live. Figure 25-14 lists smart growth tools used to prevent and control urban growth and sprawl. Which, if any, of these tools are being used in your community?

Solutions

Smart Growth Tools

Limits and Regulations

Limit building permits

Urban growth boundaries

Greenbelts around cities

Public review of new development

Zoning

Encourage mixed use

Concentrate development along mass transportation routes

Promote high-density cluster housing developments

Planning

Ecological land-use planning

Environmental impact analysis

Integrated regional planning

Provincial and national planning

Protection

Preserve existing open space

Buy new open space

Buy development rights that prohibit certain types of development on land parcels

Taxes

Tax land, not buildings

Tax land on value of actual use (such as forest and agriculture) instead of highest value as developed land

Tax Breaks

For owners agreeing legally to not allow certain types of development (conservation easements)

For cleaning up and developing abandoned urban sites (brownfields)

Revitalization and New Growth

Revitalize existing towns and cities

Build well-planned new towns and villages within cities

FIGURE 25-14 Solutions: *smart growth* or *new urbanism tools* used to prevent and control urban growth and sprawl.

The most widely used ways to slow and control urban sprawl are to set growth boundaries around cities, preserve open space outside of urban areas, develop spaces within urban areas that have been left behind from urban sprawl, create new towns and villages within existing cities, and revitalize neighbourhoods and downtown areas.

Portland, Oregon, used some of these strategies to control sprawl and reduce dependence on the car, and it worked. Since 1975 Portland's population has grown by about 50% but its urban area has increased by only 2%. And abundant green space and natural beauty is just 20 minutes from downtown.

The city encourages clustered, mixed-use neighbourhood development consisting of stores, light industries, professional offices, high-density housing, and access to mass transit that allows most people to meet their daily needs without a car. Portland has further reduced car use by developing an excellent light-rail line and an extensive network of bus lines, bike lanes, and walkways. Employers are encouraged to give their employees bus passes instead of providing parking spaces. Curitiba, Brazil (Case Study, p. 614) has also used a variety of such strategies to control sprawl and reduce dependence on the car. And car-free villages have been created in cities such as Vancouver, Canada; Munich, Germany; and Zurich, Switzerland. Several studies have shown that most forms of smart growth provide more jobs and spur more economic renewal than conventional economic growth.

China has taken the strongest stand of any country against sprawl. The government has designated 80% of the country's **arable land** as *fundamental land*. Building on such land requires approval from local and provincial governments and the State Council— somewhat like having to get federal permission for a new subdivision in Canada. Developers violating these rules face the death penalty. National land-use planning also is used in Japan and much of western Europe.

Most European countries have been successful in discouraging urban sprawl and encouraging compact cities. They have controlled development at the national level and imposed high gasoline taxes to discourage car use and encourage people to live closer to workplaces and shops. High taxes on heating fuel also encourage people to live in apartments and small houses. Governments have used most of the resulting gasoline and heating fuel tax revenues to develop efficient train and other mass transit systems within and between cities.

The Ontario government has assumed a leadership role in controlling urban sprawl. The province's Greater Golden Horseshoe (GGH), which stretches from Niagara to Peterborough and north to Collingwood, is the fastest-growing urban area in Canada, with projected growth of more than 4 million people and 2 million jobs by 2031. The Ontario government recently unveiled a plan designed to mitigate traffic gridlock, loss of farmland, and other potential adverse effects of population growth in the area. The *Growth Plan for the Greater Golden Horseshoe, 2006* calls for higher-density, mixed-use neighbourhoods; more public transit; and the development of communities in which people can work, shop, and pursue leisure activities without being dependent on cars. To learn more about the plan, visit https://www.placestogrow.ca/ and read the 5-year progress update.

How Can Urban Open Space Be Preserved and Used? Be Protective and Creative

Small and large parks, greenbelts, urban growth boundaries, cluster development, and greenways can be used to preserve open space.

One way to preserve open space outside a city is to employ an *urban growth boundary* model, which involves drawing an urban growth line around a given area (with no development allowed outside the boundary), and zoning outlying areas as green space and agricultural land. A more traditional way is to preserve significant blocks of open space in the form of municipal parks. Stanley Park in Vancouver and Central Park in New York City are examples of large urban parks. Many European cities also have large- and medium-size parks.

Some cities provide open space and control urban growth by surrounding a large city with a *greenbelt* (Figure 25-15): an open area used for recreation, sustainable forestry, or other nondestructive uses. Satellite towns can be built outside the belt. Ideally, the outlying towns and the central city are linked by

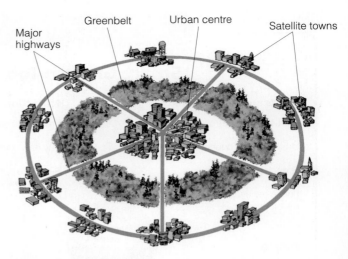

FIGURE 25-15 Establishing a *greenbelt* around a large city can control urban growth and provide open space for recreation and other nondestructive uses. Satellite towns sometimes are built outside the belt. Highways or rail systems can be used to transport people around the periphery or into the central city.

an extensive public transport system. Canadian cities such as Toronto and Vancouver, and many cities in western Europe, have used this approach. To limit urban sprawl, Ottawa has announced a plan that incorporates elements of the urban growth boundary model (Figure 25-16).

We can also let nature reclaim spaces we have developed as examples of *reconciliation ecology* (pp. 271–272). On the west side of Manhattan, New York, an abandoned elevated rail line now supports abundant plant and animal life—an example of nature creating a self-seeding, self-sustaining urban landscape without human input. In Canada, many abandoned railways have been allowed to become linear wild spaces, or have been developed as trails.

Case Study: How Is New Urbanism Creating More Livable Spaces? Returning to Traditional Neighbourhood Development

There is a growing movement to create mixed-use villages and neighbourhoods within urban areas where people can live, work, and shop close to their homes.

Since World War II, the typical approach to suburban housing development in North America has been to bulldoze a tract of woods or farmland and build rows of houses on standard-size lots. (Figure 25-17, middle, p. 632). Many of these developments and their streets are named after the trees and wildlife they displaced, such as Oak Lane, Cedar Drive, Pheasant Run, and Fox Fields.

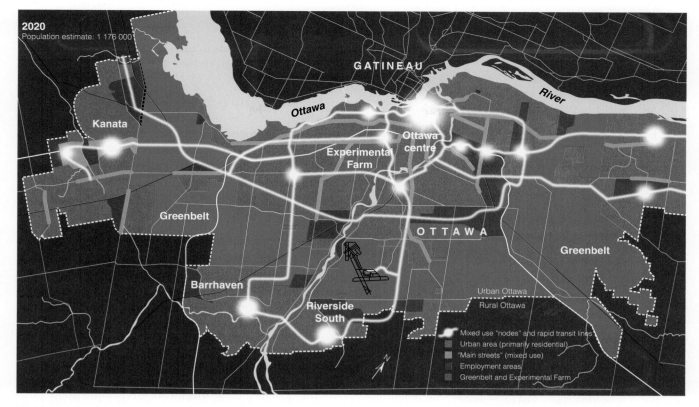

FIGURE 25-16 Ottawa's plan for the year 2020 imposes a strict boundary (dashed line) within which all city development will occur. The plan calls for more mass transit and rapid transit lines; the creation of high-density, mixed-use neighbourhoods; and the preservation of green space throughout the city. (From "2020 VISION" by Steven Fick and Elizabeth Shilts, *Canadian Geographic*, May/June 2006, pp. 42–43. Reproduced with permission from *Canadian Geographic*, http://www. canadiangeographic.ca)

In recent years, builders have increasingly used a pattern, known as *cluster development*, in which high-density housing units are concentrated on one portion of a parcel, with the rest of the land (often 30–50%) used for commonly shared open space (Figure 25-17, bottom. When done properly, high-density cluster developments are a win-win solution for residents, developers, and the environment. Residents get more open and recreational space, aesthetically pleasing surroundings, and lower heating and cooling costs because some walls are shared. Developers can cut their costs for site preparation, roads, utilities, and other forms of infrastructure.

Some communities are going further and using principles of new urbanism to develop entire villages and re-create mixed-use neighbourhoods within existing cities. These principles include *walkability* with most things within a 10-minute walk of home and work by recognizing that our bodies are biologically designed for walking; *mixed-use and diversity* where there is a mix of pedestrian-friendly shops, offices, apartments, and homes and people of different ages, classes, cultures, and races; *quality urban design* emphasizing beauty, aesthetics, and architectural

diversity; *environmental sustainability* based on development with minimal environmental impact; and *smart transportation* with high-quality trains connecting neighbourhoods, towns, and cities. The goal is to create places that uplift, enrich, and inspire the human spirit, and that are incubators of friendship, cooperation, and civic engagement.

25-5 MAKING URBAN AREAS MORE LIVABLE AND SUSTAINABLE

How Can We Make Cities More Sustainable, Desirable Places to Live? The Ecocity Concept

An ecocity allows people to walk, bike, or take mass transit for most of their travel, and recycles and reuses most of its wastes, grows much of its own food, and protects biodiversity by preserving surrounding land.

According to most environmentalists and urban planners, the primary problem is not urbanization but our failure to make cities more sustainable and livable. They call for us to make new and existing urban areas

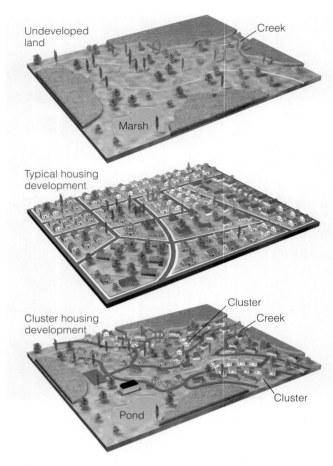

FIGURE 25-17 *Conventional and cluster housing developments* as they might appear if constructed on the same land area. With cluster development, houses, townhouses, condominiums, and two- to six-story apartments are built on part of the tract. The rest, typically 30–50% of the area, is left as open space, parks, and cycling and walking paths.

more self-reliant, sustainable, and enjoyable places to live through good ecological design. For an example of how this can be accomplished, see the spotlight about Vancouver on p. 633.

A more environmentally sustainable city, called an *ecocity* or *green city*, emphasizes:

- Preventing pollution and reducing waste

- Using energy and matter resources efficiently

- Recycling and reusing at least 60% of all municipal solid waste

- Using solar and other locally available renewable energy resources

- Protecting and encouraging biodiversity by preserving surrounding land and protecting and restoring natural systems and wetlands within urban areas

- Promoting urban gardens and farm markets

- Promoting green design of buildings, including green roofs

- Using wetlands to treat sewage while retaining their ecological and educational values (Solutions, p. 562)

An ecocity is a people-oriented city, not a car-oriented city. Its residents are able to walk, bike, or use low-polluting mass transit for most of their travel. An ecocity requires that all buildings, vehicles, and appliances meet high energy-efficiency standards. Trees and plants adapted to the local climate and soils are planted throughout to provide shade and beauty; supply wildlife habitats; and reduce pollution, noise, and soil erosion. Small organic gardens and a variety of plants adapted to local climate conditions often replace monoculture grass lawns.

Abandoned lots and industrial sites and polluted creeks and rivers are cleaned up and restored. Nearby forests, grasslands, wetlands, and farms are preserved. Much of an ecocity's food comes from nearby organic farms, solar greenhouses, and community gardens. There are also gardens on rooftops (Figure 25-18) and in yards, on abandoned lots, and in window boxes. People designing and living in ecocities take seriously the advice Lewis Mumford gave more than three decades ago: "Forget the damned motor car and build cities for lovers and friends."

China is planning to develop 10 model ecocities. Green initiatives include relocating polluting industries outside of the city, requiring local taxis to run on natural gas, and building light rail and subway lines. China also plans to promote the use of solar water heaters, to phase out gasoline-powered motorcycles, and to provide a network of battery exchange and disposal centres to serve the rapidly increasing use of electric-powered bicycles and mopeds.

FIGURE 25-18 Urban rooftop gardens offer many benefits: they cool buildings, reduce air and noise pollution, provide habitat for wildlife, and beautify the urban landscape. (Photo courtesy of Weston Solutions Inc., http://216.27.8.42/%7Eeconewsl/eco_june06/eco-home.html)

Vancouver: A Showcase for Urban Renewal

Whereas many city centres have stagnated, Vancouver has the fastest-growing downtown core in North America. Vancouver frequently tops the charts as the best North American city in which to live. Urban planners from around the world use terms like *Vancouverism* to describe the planning they see there.

Vancouver has succeeded at creating *vertical neighbourhoods*. Abandoned shipyards and industrial lands were reclaimed and rezoned to allow for the development of retail space, condominiums, trendy restaurants, parks, and family-oriented centres—in other words, mixed-use

neighbourhoods in which everything is within walking distance. The city enhanced the visual appeal of its tall buildings by requiring that the first three floors be dedicated to retail or residential space. At night, Vancouver's downtown remains vital, in stark contrast to the many North American downtowns that empty as commuters return home to the suburbs. For an increasing number of Vancouverites, home is downtown.

Vancouver is also home to Canada's first model *sustainable community*, a 32-hectare site that was reclaimed from sawmills and shipyards along False Creek. More

than a mixed-use neighbourhood, this community aims to be self-sufficient: it produces energy from sewage, and promotes energy-efficient buildings, rooftop gardens, and other elements of sustainable living. Further descriptions and photographs of False Creek appear at this book's website.

Critical Thinking

Why have urban planners from around the world expressed so much interest in Vancouver? What aspects of life in downtown Vancouver appeal to you—or don't appeal to you?

China has a long way to go in converting its urban sustainability goals into reality. But if successful, China could become a model for the world in ecocity design.

Case Study: North Bay, Ontario—Reclaiming the Rail Yards

In North Bay, Ontario, volunteerism and cooperative planning are transforming contaminated rail lands on the city's waterfront into a vital recreational space for the enjoyment of tourists and local residents alike.

The North Bay waterfront was once dominated by a rugged industrial rail yard, which crowded the edge of Lake Nipissing. In the early 1980s, the city decided to develop the area. Over time, it was transformed into a narrow, winding lakeside park replete with trails, gardens, beaches, and a marina (Figure 25-19). By the 1990s, the park boasted extensive flower beds that were maintained by the Heritage Gardeners, a group of more than 300 volunteers.

In 1993, the Heritage Railway Co., a group of model-train enthusiasts and retired railway workers, added a landscaped track and a mini-train that provided a profit-making 35 000 rides a year. This attraction was followed by a carousel ride (the product of the combined talents of 425 volunteers), which provided 138 000 rides a year and profits that were used for further park enhancements.

In 1999, North Bay purchased the majority of Canadian Pacific Railway (CPR) lands between the city and the lakefront. Unfortunately, much of the soil was contaminated and would cost $11 million to be remediated for conventional types of development. In 2000, the Community Waterfront Friends (CWF), a local group with 14 000 supporters, came to the rescue by offering to remediate the park for one-tenth of the estimated cost. The CWF envisioned a park that would connect the city to the existing waterfront facilities, and that would be environmentally, socially, and economically sustainable.

In April 2006, after years of consultation and planning, North Bay and the CWF unveiled a final plan for the Community Waterfront Park (Figure 25-20, p. 635). This year-round park is in the process of being developed. When finished, it will include a learning centre and museum in the renovated CPR building, extensive gardens and paths, an operational mini-train, two old-fashioned carousels, fountains, concessions, a greenhouse, and picnic grounds, among many other features. There will be skating and snowmobile access in winter. The area will connect to the downtown via pedestrian-friendly streets and patio restaurants. Many of these features are in place now and North Bay's revitalized waterfront is helping to rejuvenate the city's downtown core.

FIGURE 25-19 An eyesore before its initial redevelopment in the early 1980s, North Bay's lakefront has been evolving into a tourist attraction and vital recreational space.

25-6 CHECKING OUR PROGRESS AT ENSURING ENVIRONMENTAL SUSTAINABILITY

How Well Are We Proceeding with Millennium Goal 7? We Are Losing Ground

Our progress at meeting the portion of Target 7 that deals with slums is not encouraging; the growing number of people living in slum conditions is outpacing our efforts to provide aid.

The eight Millennium Development Goals were introduced in Chapter 1 and have been addressed so far in Chapters 9, 10, 13, 14, 15, 19, and 21. Goal 7—aimed at ensuring environmental sustainability—has one target that relates specifically to poor people living in slums (Figure 25-21). Other Goal 7 targets and indicators are discussed in Chapters 9, 13, and 15.

Target 7D is to have achieved a significant improvement in the lives of at least a hundred million slum dwellers by 2020.

There is one indicator for assessing progress toward this target:

- Indicator 7.10 is *the proportion of urban population living in slums*. More than one-third of the growing urban populations in developing countries now live in slums. The number varies regionally; more than 60% of urban dwellers in sub-Saharan Africa live in slum conditions. And the number is projected to vary temporally; slum dwellers in developing countries are expected to triple by 2050.

The UN points out that while providing housing is expensive, there are aspects of *improving the lives* of slum dwellers, such as providing access to clean water, that are not so expensive. Note that Target D is a modest target that seeks *improvement* for only *one-tenth* of the billon people now living in slums. While it is encouraging that the *percentage* of urban residents living in slums has declined from 39% to 33%, urbanization is happening so rapidly in some countries that the *number* of people living in slums continues

Unearthing A Dream...

1. CONSERVATORY WITH MEETING ROOM & WASHROOM	11. TRANQUILITY GARDEN	22. RAILWAY TRACK PAVING PATTERN	32. SCREEN / SIGNAGE	43. CHILDREN'S GARDEN	54. PROPOSED CONCRETE PLATFORM	65. LAKE OVERLOOK
2. PATIO	12. ENGINE 503 DISPLAY & RAILWAY TRACK	23. POND / SKATING RINK	33. SCULPTURE GARDEN	44. SHED	55. TAXIS AND TOUR BUSSES	66. EXISTING MINI-TRAIN
3. ORNAMENTAL GARDEN	13. SKATING TRACK	24. UPPER POOL	34. TOBOGGAN HILL	45. TOWER SCULPTURE	56. VENDOR & SHORT TERM PARKING	67. SYMBOLIC WAVE PAVING PATTERN
4. ROSE GARDEN	14. FOUNTAIN	25. MIDDLE POOL	35. THE COMMON	46. MAZE	57. CIVIC PLAZA	68. RETAINING WALL EMERGES AS SEAT WALL
5. PICNIC AREA	15. MINI-TRAIN	26. LOWER POOL	36. OBSERVATORY	47. CHILDREN'S THEATER	58. MUSEUM	69. BIKE-PATH
6. SEAT WALL	16. NATIVE BOTANICAL GARDENS	27. SCREE GARDEN	37. CHILDREN'S GARDEN ENTRANCE	48. SPIRAL MOUND	59. WALKWAY TO MAIN STREET	
7. SIGN	17. PICNIC SHELTER	28. PAVING PATTERN	38. DONOR RECOGNITION SCULPTURE	49. SEAT ROCK	60. NEW MINI-TRAIN UNDERPASS	
8. CAROUSEL	18. CHILDREN'S PLAYGROUND	29. ACCESS DOOR TO STORAGE / DRESSING ROOM	39. WATER PLAY AREA	50. MAINTENANCE AREA	61. CABOOSE	
9. TICKET BOOTH	19. SEATING AREA	30. SIDE STAGE	40. CHILDREN'S PLAYGROUND	51. UTILITY BUILDING	62. GRAVEL PARKING LOT	
10. MINI-TRAIN STATION	20. RAILWAY STOP	31. MAIN STAGE	41. FLOWER FENCE	52. PARKING	63. UNDERPASS	
	21. TRAIN THEME METAL FENCE		42. WASHROOM / CHANGE ROOM PAVILION	53. BUS TERMINAL	64. BUSKER STAGE	

FIGURE 25-20 The Community Waterfront Park will replace the unsightly rail yard that once stood as a barrier between North Bay and its recently enhanced lakefront (Figure 25-19). (Plan courtesy of the Community Waterfront Friends, http://www.waterfrontfriends.org)

Millennium Development Goal 7:

Ensure Environmental Sustainability

Target 7D: By 2020, to have achieved a significant improvement in the lives of at least 100 million slum dwellers.

7.10 Proportion of urban population living in slums.

FIGURE 25-21 Ensuring Environmental Sustainability: Millennium Development Goal 7, aimed at ensuring environmental sustainability, has a target and an indicator that are specific to slum dwellers, in addition to other targets and indicators that we encountered at the end of Chapters 13 and 15. (Courtesy of the UNDP)

to grow and outpace the gains that have been made. UN officials feel that an influx of extra funding will be required to meet Target 7D.

You can continue to monitor progress toward these goals at websites such as http://www.mdg monitor.org/. This book's website at http://www .nelson.com/livingintheenvironment3e.com has further information about issues surrounding poverty.

A sustainable world will be powered by the sun; constructed from materials that circulate repeatedly; made mobile by trains, buses, and bicycles; populated at sustainable levels; and centered around just, equitable, and tight-knit communities.

GARY GARDNER

CHAPTER REVIEW

1. Review the Key Questions for this chapter on p. 615. Describe how Curitiba, Brazil, has attempted to become a more sustainable city.

2. Distinguish between *urbanization* and *urban growth*. Describe two factors that increase the population of a city.

3. List five trends in global urban growth. Describe four phases of urban growth in Canada and the United States.

4. What is *urban sprawl*? List six factors that have promoted urban sprawl in Canada and other countries. List five undesirable effects of urban sprawl.

5. What are four advantages of urbanization? What are six disadvantages of urbanization? What is *noise pollution* and how can it be reduced? Explain why most cities and urban areas are not sustainable.

6. What are squatter settlements and shantytowns? Describe some of the problems faced by the poor who live in urban areas. How can governments help to reduce these problems? Describe the urban problems of Mexico City, Mexico.

7. Distinguish between compact and dispersed cities and give an example of each. What are the major advantages and disadvantages of motor vehicles? List four ways to reduce dependence on motor vehicles. Describe the major advantages and disadvantages of relying more on **a)** bicycles, **b)** mass transit rail systems, and **c)** bus rapid transit systems within urban areas, and **d)** rapid-rail systems between urban areas.

8. What is *land-use planning*? What is *zoning* and what are its limitations? What is *smart growth*? List five tools used to promote smart growth. Describe strategies used by Portland, Oregon; Curitiba, Brazil; and China to help control urban sprawl.

9. What are the five guiding principles of new urbanization? What is cluster development? List eight goals of ecocity design. Describe China's plan to build ecocities that will have less environmental impact than conventional cities. What other features could their ecocities incorporate in addition to the features that are already planned?

10. Explain how people in Curitiba, Brazil, have applied each of the four *scientific principles of sustainability* to improve their city.

CRITICAL THINKING

1. Do you prefer living in a rural, suburban, small-town, or urban environment? Describe the ideal environment in which you would like to live, and list the environmental advantages and disadvantages of living in such a place. Compare your answers with those of other members of your class.

2. Do you believe that Canada should develop a comprehensive and integrated mass transit system over the next 20 years, including building an efficient rapid-rail network for travel within and between its major cities? How would you propose to pay for such a system?

3. If you own a car or hope to own one, what conditions, if any, would encourage you to rely less on the automobile and to travel to school or work by bicycle, on foot, by mass transit, or by carpool or vanpool?

4. Do you believe that Vancouver's approach to land-use planning (Spotlight, p. 633) should be used in the city or area where you live? Explain your position.

5. In June 1996, representatives from many countries met in Istanbul, Turkey, at the Second UN Conference on Human Settlements (nicknamed the City Summit). One issue was the question of whether housing is a universal *right* (a position supported by most developing countries) or just a *need* (supported by many developed countries). What is your position on this issue? Defend your choice.

6. Some analysts suggest phasing out government subsidies that encourage sprawl by funding roads, single-family housing, and large malls and superstores. These would be replaced with subsidies that encourage sidewalks and bicycle paths; multifamily housing; high-density residential development; and a mix of housing, shops, and offices (mixed-use development). Do you support this approach? Explain.

7. Congratulations! You are in charge of the world. List the five most important features of your urban policy.

PROJECTS

1. Consult local officials to determine how land use is decided in your community. What roles do citizens play in this process?

2. For a class or group project, borrow one or more decibel meters from your school's physics or engineering department or from a local electronics repair

shop. Make a survey of sound pressure levels at various times of day and at several locations. Plot the results on a map. Also, measure sound levels in a room with a sound system and from earphones at several different volume settings. If possible, measure sound levels at an indoor concert, a club, and inside and outside a boom car at various distances from the speakers. Correlate your findings with those in Figure 25-6, p. 620.

3. As a class project, **(a)** evaluate land use and land-use planning by your school, **(b)** draw up an improved plan based on ecological principles and the principles of sustainability listed in Figure 9-14, p. 191, and **(c)** submit the plan to school officials.

4. As a class project, use the following criteria to rate the community where you live or go to school on a green index from 0 to 10. Rate the community for each of the following questions and average the results to get an overall score. Are existing trees protected and new ones planted throughout the city? Do you have parks to enjoy? Can you swim in any nearby lakes and rivers? What is the quality of your water and air? Is there an effective noise pollution reduction program? Does your city have a recycling program, a composting program, and a hazardous waste collection program, with the goal of reducing the current solid waste output by at least 60%? Is there an effective mass transit system? Are there bicycle paths? Are all buildings required to meet high energy-efficiency standards? How much of the energy is obtained from locally available renewable resources? Are environmental regulations for existing industry tough enough and enforced well enough to protect citizens? Do local officials look carefully at an industry's environmental record and plans before encouraging it to locate in your city or county? Is ecological planning used to make land-use decisions? Are city officials actively planning to improve the quality of life for all of its citizens? If so, what is the plan? Compare your answers with those of your classmates.

5. Calculate the ecological footprint of the city where you live by going to the website http://www.redefining-progress.org.

ECOLOGICAL FOOTPRINT ANALYSIS

Under normal driving conditions, an internal combustion engine produces approximately 0.2 kilograms of CO_2 per kilometre driven. Given that in a hypothetical large city there are 7 million cars, and each car is driven an average of 20 000 kilometres per year:

1. Calculate the carbon footprint per car (the number of metric tons of CO_2 produced by a typical car in one year). Calculate the total carbon footprint for all cars in the city (the number of metric tons of CO_2 produced by all the cars in one year).

2. If 20% of the people were to use a carpool or to take mass transit in the city instead of driving their cars, how many metric tons of CO_2 emissions would be eliminated?

3. Imagine you are the city planner whose job it is to reduce by half the carbon footprint calculated for all the cars in the city (the second part of Question 1). Describe various scenarios to achieve this that would involve a proportion of the citizens not driving at all, and other proportions of the citizens driving their cars less than they do now. Which of these scenarios do you consider most realistic and why? Describe how you would convince the citizens to cooperate with your carbon-footprint-reduction plan.

CASE STUDY

How Important Are Natural Resources?

Economics is the study of how individuals and societies choose to use limited or scarce resources to satisfy their unlimited wants. Recall that *economic growth* is an increase in a nation's capacity to provide people with goods and services, and *economic development* is the improvement of human living standards by economic growth. For more than 200 years, there has been a debate on whether there are limits to economic growth.

Neoclassical economists such as Milton Friedman and Robert Samuelson view economic growth as both necessary and desirable. Neoclassical economists also view economic growth as unlimited because if we deplete a particular resource we should be able to use our ingenuity and technology to find a substitute. For example, if we run out of oil we should be able to find a substitute such as hydrogen or solar power. Thus natural capital is viewed as an important but not indispensable economic resource.

Ecological economists such as Herman Daly and Robert Costanza disagree. They point out that there are no substitutes for many natural resources, such as air, water, fertile soil, and biodiversity. They conclude that ultimately economic

growth is limited because some forms of economic growth can deplete and degrade the quantity and quality of these irreplaceable forms of natural capital. They call for us to redesign our economic systems to encourage environmentally sustainable forms of economic development and to discourage environmentally harmful forms of economic growth.

In the middle of this debate are *environmental economists*. They generally agree with ecological economists that some forms of economic growth are not sustainable. But they believe we can modify the principles of neoclassical economics and reform current economic systems, rather than totally redesigning them. Figure 26-1

(continued)

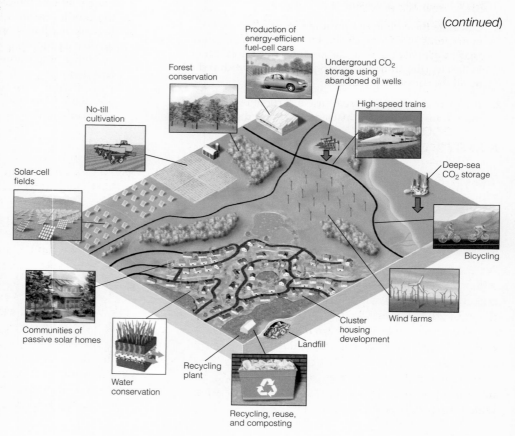

FIGURE 26-1 Solutions: these are some components of more environmentally sustainable economic development favoured by ecological and environmental economists. The goal is to have economic systems put more emphasis on conserving and sustaining the air, water, soil, biodiversity, and other natural resources that sustain all life and all economies.

No-till cultivation

Forest conservation

Production of energy-efficient fuel-cell cars

Underground CO_2 storage using abandoned oil wells

High-speed trains

Solar-cell fields

Deep-sea CO_2 storage

Bicycling

Wind farms

Cluster housing development

Landfill

Recycling plant

Recycling, reuse, and composting

Water conservation

Communities of passive solar homes

shows some of the forms of economic growth and development that most ecological and environmental economists want to encourage.

When it is asked how much it will cost to protect the environment, one more question should be asked: How much will it cost our civilization if we do not?

GAYLORD NELSON

CHAPTER PURPOSE AND QUESTIONS

Chapter 26 discusses how we can use economics to promote environmental quality and sustainability. The chapter addresses the following questions:

26-1 What are economic systems and how do they impact the environment?

26-2 How do economists differ in their views of economic systems, pollution control, and resource management?

26-3 How can we monitor environmental progress?

26-4 What are external and internal costs?

26-5 Should we rethink our use of subsidies and tax breaks?

26-6 How does poverty reduce environmental quality, and how can we reduce poverty?

26-7 How can economic tools and choices help us to become a more environmentally sustainable society?

26-8 How are we progressing at reducing poverty in the world?

26-1 ECONOMIC RESOURCES AND SYSTEMS

What Supports and Drives Economies? Three Types of Capital

An economic system produces and distributes goods and services by using natural, human, and physical resources.

An **economic system** is the social institution through which goods and services are produced, distributed, and consumed to satisfy people's unlimited wants in the most efficient possible way.

Recall that *capital* is any form of wealth used to sustain a business or produce more wealth. Three types of resources or capital are used to produce goods and services. One is **natural resources,** or **natural capital,** the materials produced by the Earth's natural processes, which support all economies and all life.

A second resource type is **human resources** or **human capital,** people's physical and mental talents that provide skills and abilities, innovation, culture, and organization. A third type is **physical** or **manufactured resources,** items made from natural resources with the help of human resources, such as tools, machinery, equipment, factories, and shipping facilities.

> **DID YOU KNOW**
>
> The words *economy* and *ecology* both come from the same Greek word *oikos,* meaning "home." Ecology is the study of our Earthly home. Economics is the study of how we run the financial affairs of our homes, companies, or nations.

What Is a Pure Free Market? A Theoretical Model of Supply, Demand, and Marginal Costs and Benefits

A purely free market is an ideal that does not match real-world markets.

A **pure free-market economic system** is a theoretical ideal or model in which buyers (demanders) and sellers (suppliers) freely interact in *markets* without any government or other interference to make all economic decisions. No one can influence the price at which a good or service sells. All parties have full access to the market and enough information about the beneficial and harmful aspects of economic goods and services to make decisions.

According to these ideals, all economic decisions are governed solely by the competitive interactions of *demand* (the amount of a good or service that people want), *supply* (the amount of a good or service that is available), and *price* (the market cost of a good or service). *Supply* is represented on the graph in Figure 26-2 by the blue curve showing how much a producer of any good or service is willing to supply (measured on the horizontal *quantity* axis) for different prices (measured on the vertical *price* axis). *Demand* is shown on the orange curve showing how much consumers will pay for different quantities of the good or service.

The point at which the curves intersect is called the *market price equilibrium point*, where the supplier's price matches what buyers are willing to pay for the same quantity and a sale is made. In Figure 26-2 it is the point at which the supply and demand curves intersect. In a pure free-market economy, such competition between willing sellers and buyers is said to bring about the greatest efficiency of resource use. *Profit* or *loss* is the difference between the cost of producing something and the price buyers are willing to pay.

Changes in supply and demand can shift one or both curves back and forth, and thus change the equilibrium price. For example, when supply is increased (shifting the blue curve to the right) and demand remains the same the equilibrium price will go down.

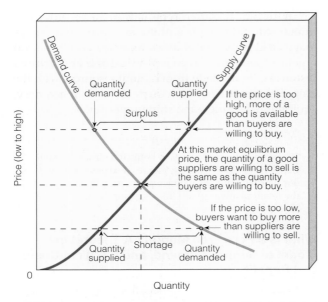

FIGURE 26-2 Supply, demand, and market equilibrium for a good or service in a pure market system. If all factors except price, supply, and demand are held fixed, market equilibrium occurs at the point at which the demand and supply curves intersect. This is the price at which sellers are willing to sell and buyers are willing to pay for the good or service provided.

Similarly, when demand is increased (shifting the orange curve to the right) and supply remains the same, the equilibrium price will increase. Try moving the curves in Figure 26-2 in different ways that represent changes in supply and demand, and notice how the equilibrium price changes.

Two related economic concepts are those of *marginal costs* and *marginal benefits*. In economics, anything described as *marginal* usually refers to an increase in some measurement involving a certain number of units of a good or service and that number of units plus one. **Marginal cost** is the increase in total cost resulting from producing one more unit of a good or service. For example, a supplier (seller) might ask, "How much would it cost and how much profit might I make if I produce one more unit of my product?" Look at Figure 26-2 again, and note that if you start at any point on the quantity axis and move to the right, the supply curve takes you up on the price axis. The difference between a seller's starting price and the new price represents the seller's *marginal cost*—the cost of producing that one more unit. The seller's *marginal benefit* is the profit made by producing and selling one more unit.

Similarly, when a seller produces one more unit of a product or service, the increase in the benefit that it provides to a buyer is the **marginal benefit**. For example, as a buyer you might ask, "How much would I benefit if I buy one more shirt?" You can think of marginal benefit of buying a new shirt as the *difference* between the benefit you gain from having ten shirts and the benefit you enjoyed from having nine. In this case, the shirtmaker's marginal cost is the *difference* between the cost of producing 1 000 shirts and the cost of producing 1 001. And your marginal cost is what it costs you to buy one more shirt. A sale occurs if both the seller and buyer find the marginal costs and benefits advantageous. In real-world **economics,** marginal costs and benefits are what actually determine prices and benefits to consumers and costs and profits to producers.

In fact, the market economic systems found in the real world do not meet the theoretical conditions described above. *In practice truly free markets do not exist.*

Businesses strive to drive their competitors out of business and exert as much control as possible over the prices of the goods and services they provide. Companies lobby for government subsidies, tax breaks, or regulations that give their products a market advantage over their competitors. Some companies also try to withhold information from consumers about dangers posed by products unless the government requires them to provide such information.

Also, there are exceptions to the free market theory of supply and demand. Some consumers may buy a good or service regardless of its price. For example, raising the price of gasoline or cigarettes may not significantly reduce consumer demand because some buyers feel they have to have these products. Economists call this *price inelasticity.*

Why Have Governments Intervened in Market Economic Systems? Making Up for Market Deficiencies

Governments intervene in market systems to help provide economic stability; national security; and public services such as education, crime protection, and environmental protection.

Markets often work well in guiding the production of *private goods*, but experience shows that they cannot be relied upon to provide adequate levels of *public services* such as national security and environmental protection. Thus governments intervene in market systems to help correct *market failures*. For example, a single seller or buyer (monopoly) or a single group of sellers or buyers (oligopoly) might come to dominate the market and thus control supply or demand and price for a good or service. Governments can prevent this and other market failures through laws and regulations. Governments can also promote economic stability by trying to control boom-and-bust cycles that occur in market systems.

Other reasons for government interventions are to:

- Provide public services such as national security and education

- Provide an economic safety net for people who because of health, age, and other factors cannot meet their basic needs

- Protect people from fraud, trespass, theft, and bodily harm

- Establish and enforce civil rights and property rights

- Protect the health and safety of workers and consumers

- Prevent or reduce pollution and depletion of natural resources

- Manage public land resources such as national and provincial parks, Crown lands, and wildlife reserves

26-2 ECONOMISTS' VIEWS OF POLLUTION CONTROL AND RESOURCE MANAGEMENT

How Do Economists Differ in Their View of Market-Based Economic Systems? The Importance of Natural Capital

Neoclassical economists see natural resources as a component of an economic system, and ecological economists see economic systems as a component of nature's economy.

Neoclassical economists view the Earth's natural capital as a subset or part of a human economic system (Figure 26-3). Natural resources are seen as important but not vital because of our ability to find substitutes for scarce resources and ecosystem services.

To neoclassical economists, economic growth is necessary, desirable, and essentially unlimited. It is seen as the best way to provide jobs and distribute wealth. If the economy is growing, there is money available to provide jobs; develop new resources;

and supply public services such as environmental protection, education, national security, and crime protection. In this prevailing view, the global economy is, and should be, hard-wired to accelerating growth based mostly on increasing throughputs of matter and energy resources (Figure 3-18, p. 56).

Ecological and *environmental economists* disagree with this model. They view economic systems as subsystems of the environment that depend heavily on the Earth's irreplaceable natural resources (Figure 26-4). According to ecological economist Herman Daly, the neoclassical model of an economy "ignores the origin of natural resources flowing into the system and the fate of wastes flowing out of the system. It is as if a biologist had a model of an animal that contained a circulatory system but had no digestive system that tied it firmly to the environment at both ends." Ecological economists also believe that conventional economic growth eventually is unsustainable because it can deplete or degrade the natural resources on which economic systems depend.

Ecological and environmental economists distinguish between unsustainable economic growth and environmentally sustainable economic development (Figure 26-5, p. 643). They call for making a shift from our current economy based on unlimited economic growth to a more *environmentally sustainable economy,* or *eco-economy.*

Various ecological and environmental economists have suggested eight strategies to help make the shift to an eco-economy over the next several decades.

1. Use resources more efficiently.

2. Use indicators that monitor economic and environmental health.

3. Have the market prices of goods and services include their harmful effects on the environment and human health (full-cost pricing).

4. Phase out environmentally harmful government subsidies and tax breaks.

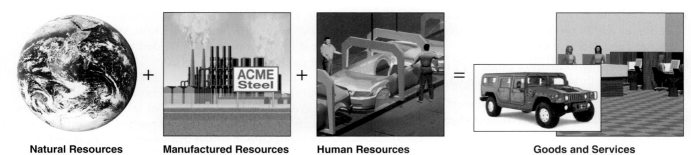

Natural Resources   **Manufactured Resources**   **Human Resources**   **Goods and Services**

FIGURE 26-3 *Neoclassical economists* view the Earth's natural capital, or natural resources, as a subset, or part of, a human economic system. They contend that economic growth is not limited by the Earth's natural resources because we should be able to find substitutes for scarce resources and ecosystem services. Economic growth is seen as good and essentially unlimited.

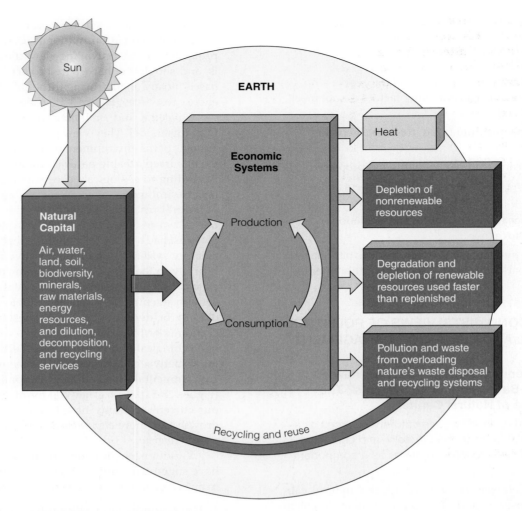

ACTIVE FIGURE 26-4 *Ecological economists* see all economies as human subsystems that depend on resources and services provided by the sun and the Earth's natural resources. *See an animation based on this figure at* CengageNow.

5. Shift taxes by lowering taxes on income and wealth and increasing taxes on pollution and resource waste.

6. Pass laws and regulations to prevent pollution and resource depletion in certain areas.

7. Use tradable permits or rights to pollute or use resources within programs that limit overall pollution and resource use in given areas.

8. Use *eco-labelling* to identify products produced by environmentally sound methods and thus help consumers make informed choices.

We will look at these solutions in more detail.

CONSIDER, DISCUSS, OR DEBATE

Which of the eight strategies listed above do you think holds the most promise? After reading this chapter, decide whether or not you would change your answer.

How Can Technological Developments Improve Market Efficiency? Producing More with Less

Better technology and more efficient production systems can produce goods and services with fewer resources.

All economists agree that technological developments and more efficient production systems can mean that fewer resources are needed to produce the same amount of a good or service.

For example, between 1975 and 1995 the food output of Canada and most countries per unit of land increased while the inputs of labour and resources such as water and fertilizer needed to produce each unit of that output fell. However, ecological and environmental economists warn that such increases in the efficiency of food production might not be sustainable because of the degradation of soil, water, and other natural resources needed to produce food. These economists believe that this may be a factor in the levelling

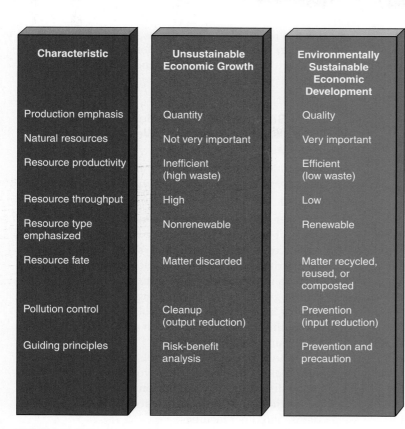

Characteristic	Unsustainable Economic Growth	Environmentally Sustainable Economic Development
Production emphasis	Quantity	Quality
Natural resources	Not very important	Very important
Resource productivity	Inefficient (high waste)	Efficient (low waste)
Resource throughput	High	Low
Resource type emphasized	Nonrenewable	Renewable
Resource fate	Matter discarded	Matter recycled, reused, or composted
Pollution control	Cleanup (output reduction)	Prevention (input reduction)
Guiding principles	Risk-benefit analysis	Prevention and precaution

FIGURE 26-5 Comparison of unsustainable economic growth and environmentally sustainable economic development according to ecological economists and many environmental economists.

off of global grain production since 1985 (Figure 14-16, p. 315).

Economists agree that increases in technological and production efficiencies can cause significant changes to supply, demand, and prices for a good or service. For example, technological improvements can make it cheaper to produce a good or service and increase its supply at a particular price. This can cause its market equilibrium point (Figure 26-2) to shift to a lower price and thus benefit buyers. Trace such a shift in Figure 26-2.

Scarcity of a resource can stimulate research and development for new and more efficient technologies and production systems and a search for new reserves (Figure 16-9, p. 371) and for substitutes for such resources. It can also lead to increased recycling and reuse of a resource (Figure 16-18, p. 378).

For example, scarcity of a metal such as copper has led to improved technology for extracting and processing lower-grade ores, use of microorganisms to remove copper (and other metals) from its ore, increased recycling of copper, and use of aluminum as a substitute for copper in wiring. This can lead to lower prices and a rise in demand, which can eventually deplete reserves, raise prices, and stimulate a new search for improved technology and substitutes.

However, ecological and environmental economists warn that as demand keeps rising at some point the harmful environmental effects of extracting, processing, and using increasing amounts of various nonrenewable mineral and energy resources can limit their availability and that in some cases substitutes may not be available.

How Do Economists Value Pollution Control and Resource Management? Some Advocate Using Market Prices, While Others Disagree

Economists think about optimum levels of pollution control and resource use, but there is considerable disagreement on how to arrive at those levels.

An important concept in environmental economics is that of *optimum levels* for pollution control and resource use. In the early days of a new coal mining operation, for example, the cost of removing coal is easy for developers to recover in sales of their product. However, after most of the more readily accessible coal has been removed, taking what is left can become too costly. In this case, the marginal cost of removal goes up with each unit of coal taken. Figure 26-6 shows this in terms of supply, demand, and equilibrium. Where the demand curve crosses the supply curve is the point at which it no longer pays to remove the coal. The optimum level of coal mining is at or below that equilibrium point.

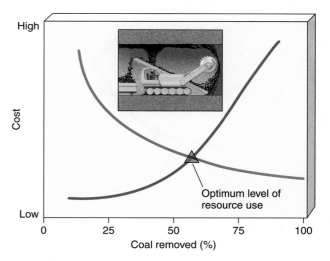

FIGURE 26-6 The cost of mining coal (blue line) rises with each additional unit removed. Mining a certain amount of coal is profitable, but at some point the cost of mining exceeds the monetary benefits (red line). That is, the marginal cost of mining increases while the marginal benefits decrease as more coal is removed. Where the two curves meet is theoretically the optimum level of resource use.

You might think that pollution control is an all-or-nothing proposition—that the best solution is to clean up every last bit of any pollutant. In fact, there are optimum levels for various kinds of pollution, because the marginal cost of pollution control also goes up for each unit of a pollutant removed from the environment. Figure 26-7 shows various possible optimal levels of pollution control. In this case, cleanup costs are shown on the blue curve. This is the supply curve, because the service supplied is removal of pollutants. Note that it slopes up more sharply (costing more) as we get closer to removing 100% of the pollutant in question.

The red line in Figure 26-7 represents the *demand* for cleanup by users of water or air. With their air or drinking water polluted, consumers are initially up in arms, but as the pollutant is removed, their concern is relieved and demand approaches zero. In other words, the marginal benefits of pollution control decrease with each unit of pollution removed.

At some point, the cost of removing the pollutant gets higher than what people are willing to pay, as their demand for cleanup lessens. That point is the equilibrium point, or the *optimum level* for cleanup.

Another factor determining the shape and placement of the demand curve is how much people value their resources. If no one cares whether or not the water in a lake is clear or groundwater is pure, the optimum level of cleanup will be close to zero. But if they demand a clean lake and groundwater, the optimum

level will rise. In other words, pollution control (or resource use) that is optimum for some will be high or low for others. The levels depend on human values as much as anything else.

Case Study: What Is Cost-Benefit Analysis, and How Can It Be Improved? Weighing Costs and Benefits to Make Choices

Comparing likely costs and benefits of an environmental action can help with decision making, but it is a limited tool.

Another widely used tool for making economic decisions about how to control pollution and manage resources is **cost-benefit analysis (CBA)**. It involves comparing estimated costs and benefits for actions such as implementing a pollution control regulation, building a dam on a river, filling in a wetland, or preserving an area of forest. It involves trying to estimate the optimum level of pollution cleanup (Figure 26-7) or resource use (Figure 26-6).

CBA is one of the main tools economists and decision makers throughout the world use to help them make decisions about pollution control; biodiversity protection; and the construction of roads, airports, dams, and other facilities.

Making a CBA involves determining who or what might be affected by a particular regulation or project, projecting potential outcomes, evaluating alternative actions, and determining who benefits and who is harmed. Then an attempt is made to assign monetary costs and benefits to each of the factors and components involved.

Direct costs involving land, labour, materials, and pollution-control technologies are often fairly easy to estimate. But indirect costs of things we value such as clean air and water that are not traded in the marketplace are difficult to estimate and are controversial. We can put estimated price tags on human life, good health, clean air and water, and various forms of natural capital such as an endangered species, a forest, a wetland, and other forms of natural capital. However, the monetary values that different people assign to such things vary widely because of different assumptions and value judgments. This can lead to a wide range of projected costs and benefits.

CBA is controversial because making accurate estimates of costs and benefits is difficult. They are also easy to manipulate by parties supporting or opposing a particular regulation or project.

Because of these drawbacks, CBA can lead to wide ranges of benefits and costs with a lot of room for error. For example, one U.S. industry-sponsored CBA estimated that compliance with a standard to

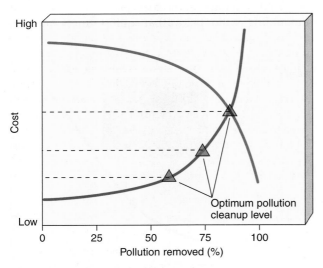

FIGURE 26-7 The cost of cleaning up pollution (blue line) rises with each additional unit removed. Cleaning up a certain amount of pollution is affordable, but at some point the cost of pollution control is greater than the harmful costs of the pollution to society. That is, the marginal cost of pollution cleanup increases (blue line) and the marginal benefits decrease (red line) as more pollution is removed. Where the blue curve intersects with any other curve is a point of optimum pollution control for the pollutant represented.

protect U.S. workers from vinyl chloride would cost $65–$90 billion (U.S.). In the end, meeting the standard cost the industry less than $1 billion. A study by the Washington-based Economic Policy Institute found that the estimated costs made by industries for complying with proposed environmental regulations are almost always more (and often much more) than the actual costs of implementing the regulations.

Some environmental groups use CBA to help evaluate proposed environmental projects and regulations. But some environmentalists oppose putting too much emphasis on using this approach as a primary factor in decision making because the large uncertainties involved allow manipulation of the data and estimates to come up with a desired result.

If conducted fairly and accurately, CBA is a useful tool for helping to make economic decisions. To minimize possible abuses and errors, environmentalists and economists advocate using the following guidelines for a CBA:

- Use uniform standards.

- Clearly state all assumptions used.

- Rate the reliability of data used.

- Estimate short- and long-term benefits and costs for all affected population groups.

- Compare the costs and benefits of alternative courses of action.

- Summarize the range of estimated costs and benefits.

Various economists make use of tools such as optimum levels and CBA in different ways. The neoclassical approach would tend to value resources strictly according to market information. They would look at the going prices for timber or coal, for example, or estimate the amount of money that tourists are likely to spend visiting a lake after it is cleaned up. They would calculate marginal costs and benefits of developing a resource or of cleaning up pollution somewhere, and then determine optimum levels of resource use or pollution control.

Environmental and ecological economists would tend to be less bound by market prices. They might assign higher-than-market values to resources to account for their importance to ecosystem health, biodiversity, and future generations. They would thus determine higher optimum levels of pollution control and lower optimum levels of resource use than would some neoclassical economists.

CONSIDER, DISCUSS, OR DEBATE

Economic activities are responsible for many environmental problems. Does it follow, then, that economic solutions must be used to address those problems?

26-3 MONITORING ENVIRONMENTAL PROGRESS

How Can We Evaluate Environmental Quality and Human Well-Being? Develop and Use New Indicators

We need new indicators to accurately reflect changing levels of environmental quality and human health.

Economists and environmental scientists use the *gross domestic product* (GDP) indicator to measure and compare the economic outputs of nations. In doing so, they make no attempt to draw any distinction between goods and services that are environmentally or socially beneficial and those that are harmful. Most governments and business leaders, on the other hand, incorrectly use the GDP to measure environmental quality or human well-being.

Environmental and ecological economists and environmental scientists call for the development of new indicators to help guide sustainable development. One approach is to create indicators that *add* to the GDP things not counted in the marketplace that enhance environmental quality and human well-being. They would also *subtract* from the GDP the costs of things that lead to a lower quality of life and depletion of natural resources.

One such indicator is the *genuine progress indicator* (GPI), introduced in 1995 by Redefining Progress, a nonprofit organization that develops economics and policy tools to help evaluate and promote sustainability. (This group also developed the concept of ecological footprints, Figures 1-7, p. 8, and 9-12, p. 189). Within the GPI, the estimated value of beneficial transactions that meet basic needs, but in which no money changes hands, are added to the GDP. Examples are unpaid volunteer work, health care for family members, child care, and housework. Then the estimated harmful environmental costs (such as pollution and resource depletion and degradation) and social costs (such as crime) are subtracted from the GDP.

Genuine progress indicator	= GDP	+ benefits not included in market transactions	− harmful environmental and social costs

Figure 26-8 compares GDP and GPI for Alberta between 1961 and 2001. Note that whereas the GDP increased by 483%, the GPI decreased by 20%. The decline in GPI reflects growing household debt, a widening income gap between rich and poor, higher divorce and crime rates, and a host of other problems that the GDP does not calculate. Similar studies have been performed to analyze the progress of countries and to guide thinking about sustainable development (Talberth et al., 2006).

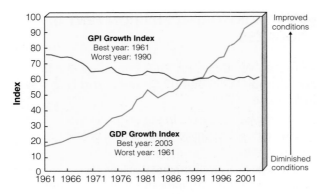

FIGURE 26-8 Comparison of the gross domestic product (GDP) and the genuine progress indicator (GPI) for Alberta between 1961 and 2001. (Data from the Pembina Institute, http://www.pembina.org)

The United Nations has developed a *Human Development Index* (HDI) based on measurements of a country's standard of living, education, and life expectancy. According to this indicator, Canada has been the top-ranked country in the world nine times since 1990. Yet strictly in terms of economic activity, Canada would typically be number 10 or 11 in a list of countries ranked according to GDP values.

A national steering committee developed the *Canadian Index of Well-being* (CIW) that measures living standards, how time is allocated, the health of the population, the health of ecosystems, education of the populace, the vitality of communities, and the engagement of Canadians in civic activities (Coyle, 2011).

These and other indicators are far from perfect. But without such indicators, we do not know much about what is happening to people, the environment, and the planet's natural resource base, and we have no effective way to measure which policies work. In effect, according to ecological and environmental economists, we are trying to guide national and global economies through treacherous economic and environmental waters at ever-increasing speeds without a good radar system.

The *good news* is that several of these indicators are available. The *bad news* is that they are not widely used and reported. Proponents call for us to get to the point that every time a change in GDP is reported we also get information on a change in one or more environmental and social indicators.

How Can We Assign Monetary Values to Resources Not Traded in the Marketplace? Ways to Represent Nature

Economists have developed several ways to estimate the nonmarket values of the Earth's ecological services.

Environmental and ecological economists have developed various tools for estimating the values of the Earth's ecological services.

This involves estimating *nonuse values* not represented in market transactions. One is an *existence value* based on knowing that an old-growth forest or endangered species exists, even though we may never see them or use them. Another is *aesthetic value* based on putting a monetary value on a forest, species, or part of nature because of its beauty. A third type, called a *bequest* or *option value*, is based on the willingness of people to pay to protect some forms of natural capital for use by future generations.

Economists have developed several ways to estimate the monetary value of resources that cannot be priced by conventional means. One approach is to estimate a *mitigation cost* of how much it would take to offset an environmental damage. For example, how much would it cost to protect a forest from cutting, move an endangered species to a new habitat, or restore a statue damaged by air pollution?

Another method is to estimate a *willingness to pay* by using a survey to determine how much people would be willing to pay to keep a particular species from becoming extinct, a particular forest from being cut down, or a specific river or beach from being polluted. This approach is controversial because people may inflate their estimates and not indicate the prices they would really pay to preserve various nonuse values.

How Can We Estimate the Future Value of a Resource? Assigning Discount Rates

Economists use discount rates to estimate the future value of a resource.

The **discount rate** is an estimate of a resource's future economic value compared to its present value. It is based on the idea that having something today may be worth more than it will be in the future. The size of the discount rate (usually given as a percentage) is a primary factor affecting how a resource such as a forest or fishery is used or managed.

At a zero discount rate, for example, a stand of trees worth $1 million today will still be worth $1 million 50 years from now. However, most businesses and the World Bank typically use a 10% annual discount rate to evaluate how resources should be used. At this rate, the stand of redwood trees will be worth only $10 000 in 50 years. With this discount rate, it makes sense from an economic standpoint for an owner to cut these trees down as quickly as possible and invest the money in something else.

The value of discount rates are controversial. Proponents cite several reasons for using high (5–10%) discount rates. One is that inflation may reduce the value of their future earnings on a resource. Another is innovation or changes in consumer preferences could make a product or resource obsolete. For example, natural-looking composites of wood made from plastics may reduce the future use and market value of renewable redwood, and wind and hydrogen may greatly reduce the economic value of nonrenewable oil in the future. Also, resource owners argue that without a high discount rate they can make more money by investing their capital in some other venture.

Critics point out that high discount rates encourage such rapid exploitation of resources for immediate payoffs and that sustainable use of most renewable natural resources is virtually impossible. These critics believe that a 0% or even a negative discount rate should be used to protect unique and scarce resources. They also point out that moderate discount rates of 1–3% would make it profitable to use nonrenewable and renewable resources more sustainably or slowly. In addition, suppose that an acceptable substitute for a resource such as oil does not become available. Then these resources could become priceless. As you can see, there are no easy ways to make such decisions.

Economic return is not always the determining factor in how resources are used or managed. In some cases, farmers and owners of forests, wetlands, and other resources use *ethical concerns* in determining how they use and manage such resources. Their respect for the land and nature or what they believe to be their responsibility to future generations can override their desire for short-term profit at the expense of long-term resource and environmental sustainability.

26-4 HARMFUL EXTERNAL COSTS AND FULL-COST PRICING

What Are External or Indirect Costs? Hidden Costs

The direct price you pay for something does not include indirect environmental, health, and other harmful costs associated with its production and use.

All economic goods and services have *internal* or *direct costs* associated with producing them. For example, if you buy a car the direct price you pay includes the costs of raw materials, labour, and shipping, as well as a markup to allow the car company and its dealers some profits. Once you buy the car you must pay additional direct costs for gasoline, maintenance, and repair.

Making, distributing, and using any economic good or service also involve *indirect* or **external costs** or **benefits** not included in the market price and affecting people other than the buyer and seller. Economists call such costs and benefits **externalities**. A *positive externality* benefits someone not involved in an economic transaction. For example, if a car dealer volunteers to remove litter and debris from a stretch of highway you will benefit even if you have never bought a car from the dealer.

A *negative externality* is a harmful cost borne by someone not involved in an economic transaction. For example, extracting and processing raw materials to make a car uses nonrenewable energy and mineral resources, produces solid and hazardous wastes, disturbs land, and pollutes the air and water (Figure 16-12, p. 374). These external costs not included in the price of the car can have short- and long-term harmful effects on other people and on the Earth's life-support systems. Since these harmful external costs are not included in the market price of a car, most people do not connect them with car ownership. Still, the car buyer and other people in a society pay these hidden costs sooner or later, in the form of poorer health, higher costs of health care and insurance, higher taxes for pollution control, increased traffic congestion, and loss of land used for highway and parking.

In Canada, more than one-third of every dollar of consumer spending is directed at cars and their related expenses such as gasoline and repairs. The cost of building and maintaining roads accounts for three-quarters of government spending on transportation. Car accidents cause about half of all severe injuries in Canada, and smog caused in part by CO_2 emissions from motor vehicles kills at least 5 000 people per year. Therefore, many of our health-care costs are directly or indirectly linked to cars.

> **CONSIDER, DISCUSS, OR DEBATE**
>
> Can you think of any further costs of using cars that are not mentioned above? What harmful external costs are associated with using incandescent light bulbs, rather than more energy-efficient lighting, in homes and workplaces?

What Is Full-Cost Pricing? Creating An Environmentally Honest Market

Including external costs in market prices informs consumers about the cost of their purchases on the Earth's life-support systems and to human health.

For many economists, creating an *environmentally transparent or honest market system* is a way to deal with the harmful costs of goods and services. It requires including costs, as much as possible, in the market price of any good or service, such that its price would come as close as possible to its **full cost**—its actual **internal costs** plus its actual external costs.

This system would allow consumers to make more informed choices, because they would be aware of most or all of the costs involved, which is one of the major goals of a truly free-market economy. It would likely cause consumers to give more thought to choosing fuel-efficient cars over much more expensive gas-guzzlers. Many people would probably conserve more water because its price would be much higher. They might also produce less garbage, because the cost of collecting and disposing of nonrecyclable garbage would go way up.

With full-cost pricing, some eco-friendly (or green) goods and services that now cost more would eventually cost less because internalizing external costs encourages producers to invent more resource-efficient and less polluting methods of production, thereby cutting their production costs. Jobs would be lost in environmentally harmful businesses as consumers more often chose green products, but more jobs would be created in environmentally beneficial businesses. If a shift to full-cost pricing took place over several decades, most environmentally harmful businesses would have time to transform themselves into environmentally beneficial businesses. And consumers would have time to adjust their purchases and buying habits to more environmentally friendly products and services.

CONSIDER, DISCUSS, OR DEBATE

Should full-cost pricing be used in setting the market prices of goods and services? If you were Canada's finance minister, how would you go about implementing full-cost pricing?

Full-cost pricing seems to make a lot of sense. So why is it not used more widely? There are various reasons. One is that many producers of harmful and wasteful goods would have to charge more and some would go out of business. Naturally, they oppose such pricing.

Also, it is difficult to put a price tag on many environmental and health costs. But to ecological and environmental economists, making the best possible estimates is far better than not including such costs in what we pay for most goods and services.

Phasing in such a system requires government action. Few if any companies will volunteer to reduce short-term profits by becoming more environmentally responsible. For example, assume you own an electronics company and you believe that we should all pay for the pollution resulting from production of electronics products. Assume also that your competitors do not believe this. Will you raise your prices to include the estimated costs of that pollution, while they do not? If you do, your customers will probably buy their electronics from your competitors. Most consumers are looking for the best price, and by doing the right thing, you may eventually go bankrupt. So full-cost pricing has to be initiated across the market by an outside force, namely, the government.

Governments can use several strategies to encourage or force producers to work toward full-cost pricing including phasing out environmentally harmful subsidies, levying taxes on environmentally harmful goods and services, passing laws to regulate pollution and resource depletion, and using tradable permits for pollution or resource use. Let us look at these and other strategies in more detail.

26-5 WAYS TO IMPROVE ENVIRONMENTAL QUALITY AND SHIFT TO FULL-COST PRICING

How Can Ending Certain Subsidies and Tax Breaks Improve Environmental Quality and Reduce Resource Waste? Not Rewarding Environmentally Harmful Activities

We can improve environmental quality and help phase in full-cost pricing by removing environmentally harmful government subsidies and tax breaks.

Government subsidies and tax breaks can accelerate resource development, depletion, and degradation. We currently give depletion allowances and tax breaks to mining, oil, and coal companies for getting minerals and oil out of the ground. Taxpayers subsidize the cost of irrigation water for farmers and help to provide subsidies and low-cost loans to buy fishing boats.

One way to encourage a shift to full-cost pricing is to *phase out* environmentally harmful subsidies and tax breaks. They cost the world's governments about $1.9 trillion (U.S.) a year, according to studies by Norman Myers and other analysts, and create a huge economic incentive for environmental destruction that would not otherwise take place.

On paper, phasing out such subsidies may seem like a great idea. But it involves political decisions that often are opposed successfully by powerful interests receiving the subsidies and tax breaks. They want to keep, and if possible increase, these benefits and often oppose subsidies and tax breaks for more environmentally beneficial competitors. For example, the fossil fuel and nuclear power industries in Canada, in the United States, and in most developed countries have received huge government subsidies compared to those for less harmful competing alternatives, such as conservation and wind power. Removing these harmful subsidies and tax breaks would level the economic playing field and promote the use of the cheapest and least environmentally harmful energy alternatives.

How Can Green Taxes and Fees and Tax Shifting Improve Environmental Quality and Reduce Resource Waste? Making Polluters and Consumers Pay the Full Price

Taxes and fees on pollution and resource use can take us closer to full-cost pricing, and shifting taxes from wages and profits to pollution and waste helps make this feasible.

Another way to discourage pollution and resource waste is to *use green taxes or effluent fees* to help internalize many of the harmful environmental costs of production and consumption. Higher fees can also be charged for extracting lumber and minerals from public lands, using water provided by government-financed projects, and using public lands for livestock grazing.

Taxes can be levied on a per-unit basis on the release of pollution and hazardous or nuclear waste produced, and on the use of fossil fuels, timber, and minerals. Figure 26-9 lists advantages and disadvantages of using green taxes and fees.

CONSIDER, DISCUSS, OR DEBATE

Do advantages of green taxes and fees outweigh the disadvantages?

To many analysts, the tax system in most countries is backwards. It can *discourage* what we want more of—jobs, income, and profit-driven innovation—and *encourage* what we want less of—pollution, resource waste, and environmental degradation. A more environmentally sustainable economic system would *lower* taxes on labour, income, and wealth and *raise* taxes on environmentally harmful activities.

With such a tax shift, for example, a tax on coal would include the increased health costs of breathing polluted air, damages from acid deposition, and estimated costs from climate change. Then taxes on wages and wealth could be reduced by the amount produced by the coal tax.

Shifting more of the tax burden from wages and profits to pollution and waste has a number of advantages (Figure 26-10). Some 2 500 economists, including eight Nobel Prize winners, have endorsed the concept of tax shifting. According to N. Gregory Mankiw, who chaired the U.S. President's Council of Economic Advisers: "Cutting income taxes while increasing gasoline taxes would lead to more rapid economic growth, less traffic congestion, safer roads, and reduced risk of global warming—all without jeopardizing long-term fiscal solvency. This may be the closest thing to a free lunch that economics has to offer." Such taxes would also stimulate the production and use of more

Trade-Offs

Environmental Taxes and Fees

Advantages	Disadvantages
Helps bring about full-cost pricing	Penalizes low-income groups unless safety nets are provided
Provides incentive for businesses to do better to save money	Hard to determine optimum level for taxes and fees
Can change behaviour of polluters and consumers if taxes and fees are set at a high enough level	Need to frequently readjust levels, which is technically and politically difficult
Easily administered by existing tax agencies	Governments may see this as a way of increasing general revenue instead of using funds to improve environmental quality and reduce taxes on income, payroll, and profits
Fairly easy to detect cheaters	

FIGURE 26-9 Trade-offs: advantages and disadvantages of using environmental or green taxes and fees to reduce pollution and resource waste. Pick the single advantage and disadvantage that you think are the most important.

Solutions

- Decreases depletion and degradation of natural resources
- Improves environmental quality by full-cost pricing
- Encourages pollution prevention and waste reduction
- Stimulates creativity in solving environmental problems to avoid paying pollution taxes and thereby increases profits
- Rewards recycling and reuse
- Relies more on marketplace rather than regulation for environmental protection
- Provides jobs
- Can stimulate sustainable economic development
- Allows cuts in income, payroll, and sales taxes

FIGURE 26-10 Solutions: advantages of taxing wages and profits less and pollution and waste more. Pick the two advantages that you think are the most important.

fuel-efficient motor vehicles and reduce dependence on imported oil.

Economists also point out that successful implementation of green taxes would require such a tax shift. It would have to be phased in over 15 to 20 years to allow businesses to plan for the future and depreciate existing capital investments over their useful lives. And because consumption taxes place a larger burden on the poor and lower middle class than do income taxes, governments would need to provide safety nets in the form of lifeline payments or credits for essentials such as food, fuel, and housing.

Nine western European countries have begun trial versions of such tax shifting, known as *environmental tax reform*. So far only a small amount of revenue has been shifted by taxes on emissions of CO_2 and toxic metals, garbage production, and vehicles entering congested cities. But such experience shows that this idea works.

CONSIDER, DISCUSS, OR DEBATE

Do you favour shifting taxes on wages and profits to pollution and waste? Explain.

How Can Environmental Laws and Regulations Improve Environmental Quality and Reduce Resource Waste? Encouraging Innovation

Environmental laws and regulations work best if they motivate companies to find innovative ways to control and prevent pollution and reduce resource waste.

Most economists agree that government intervention in the marketplace is needed to control or prevent pollution, reduce resource waste, and encourage full-cost pricing.

Regulation is a widely used form of government intervention. It involves enacting and enforcing laws that set pollution standards, regulate harmful activities such as releasing toxic chemicals into the environment, and require that certain irreplaceable or slowly replenished resources be protected from unsustainable use.

Many environmentalists and business leaders agree that *innovation-friendly regulations* can motivate companies to develop eco-friendly products and processes that can increase profits and competitiveness in national and international markets. But they also agree that some overly costly pollution-control regulations discourage innovation. Some regulations are too prescriptive, for example, mandating specific technologies. Some set compliance deadlines that are too short to allow companies to find innovative solutions, and they discourage risk taking and experimentation.

Consider the contrast between the United States and Sweden concerning their regulation of the pulp and paper industries. In the 1970s, strict U.S. regulations with short compliance deadlines forced companies to adopt the best available end-of-pipe water pollution treatment systems, which were costly.

Meanwhile, in Sweden the government started with slightly less strict standards and longer compliance deadlines but clearly indicated that tougher standards would follow. This more flexible and innovation-friendly approach gave companies time to focus on redesigning their production processes instead of relying mostly on waste treatment. It also spurred them to look for innovative ways to prevent pollution and improve resource productivity to meet stricter future standards. They developed processes for pulping and chlorine-free bleaching that met the emission standards, lowered operating costs, and gained a competitive advantage in international markets.

Experience shows that an innovation-friendly regulatory process emphasizes pollution prevention and waste reduction and requires industry and environmental interests to work together in developing realistic standards and timetables. It sets goals, but frees industries to meet them in any way that works, and establishes standards strict enough to promote real innovation, allowing enough time for it. It also uses market incentives such as emissions and resource-use charges and tradable pollution and resource-use permits to encourage compliance and innovation.

Finally, pollution-control regulations have to be designed to improve environmental quality while not being too costly. Recall that the marginal cost for removing a specific pollutant from gases or wastewater being discharged rises with each additional unit of that pollutant that is removed (Figure 26-7, p. 644).

There are problems with the regulatory approach. One is that ecological economists, health scientists, and business leaders often disagree in their estimates of the harmful costs of pollution. Even scientists in the same field often have different estimates of such costs because they lack data and hold different assumptions.

Also, many regulations are geared toward achieving optimum levels of pollution over a large area such as a whole province. Some critics raise environmental justice questions about who benefits and who suffers from such regulations. Levels may be optimum for the province, but not for the people living near or downwind or downriver from a polluting power plant, incinerator, or factory. They are being exposed to much higher levels of pollution than are the majority of people in the province.

In addition, assigning monetary values to lost lives, ecosystems, and ecological services is difficult and controversial, and varies widely because of lack of data and different assumptions and value judgments. But assigning little or no value to such things means they will not be counted at all in determining optimum pollution levels.

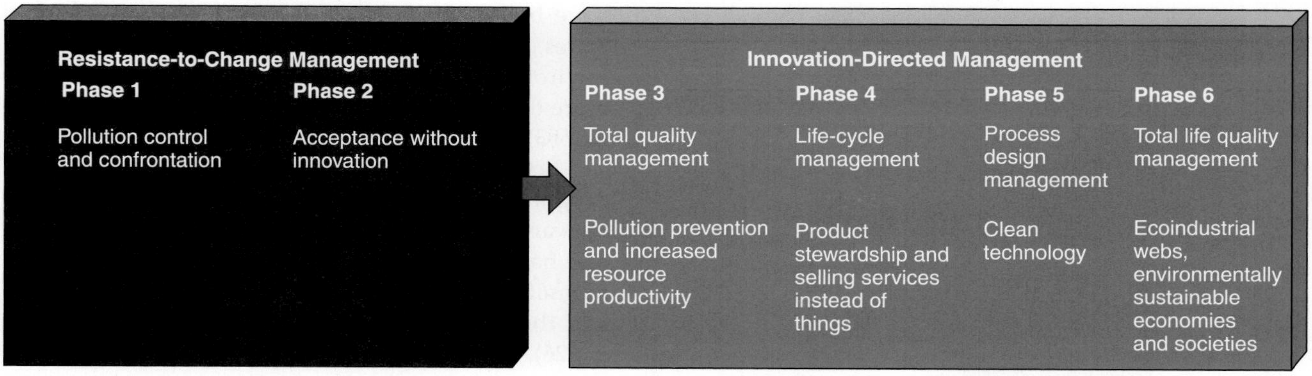

FIGURE 26-11 Solutions: evolution of environmental management.

Figure 26-11 shows the evolution of several phases of environmental management through regulation. The period between 1970 and 1985 can be viewed as the *resistance-to-change management era*, during which many companies and government regulators developed an adversarial relationship, and companies resented and actively resisted environmental regulations (Figure 26-11, left). In addition, many government regulators thought they had to prescribe ways for reluctant companies to clean up their pollution emissions. Most companies responded by hiring outside environmental consultants (who usually favoured end-of-pipe pollution-control solutions) and by using lawyers to oppose or find legal loopholes in the regulations. They also lobbied elected officials to have environmental laws and regulations overthrown, weakened, or changed to allow for easy compliance.

By 1985, most company managers accepted environmental regulations and continued to rely mostly on pollution control. However, they placed little emphasis on trying to find innovative solutions to pollution and resource waste problems because the regulations were too strict and the market rewards too low.

In the 1990s, a growing number of company managers began to realize that environmental improvement is an economic and competitive opportunity instead of a cost to be resisted. This was the beginning of the *innovative management era*, which environmental and business visionaries project will go through several phases over the next 40–50 years (Figure 26-11).

During this time, increasing numbers of consumers were buying green products. Some firms also recognized that their shareholder value depends in part on having a good environmental record. A growing number of firms began looking for innovative and profitable ways to reduce resource use, pollution, and waste (Figure 24-6, p. 590 and Individuals Matter, p. 591). As a result, the environment is becoming an important component of business strategic planning. Many corporations now routinely issue environmental and sustainability reports to their shareholders.

Should We Rely More on Tradable Pollution and Resource-Use Permits? The Marketplace Can Work

The government can set a limit on pollution emissions or use of a resource, give pollution or resource use permits to users, and allow them to trade their permits in the marketplace.

A market approach is for the government to *grant tradable pollution and resource-use permits*. The government sets a limit or cap on total emissions of a pollutant or use of a resource such as a fishery. Then it issues or auctions permits that allocate the total among manufacturers or users. A permit holder not using its entire allocation can use it as a credit against future expansion, use it in another part of its operation, or sell it to other companies.

This approach has been used in the United States to reduce the emissions of sulphur dioxide and several other air pollutants, as discussed on p. 499. Tradable rights can also be established among countries to help preserve biodiversity and reduce emissions of greenhouse gases and other pollutants with harmful regional or global effects.

Figure 26-12 lists advantages and disadvantages of using tradable pollution and resource-use permits. The effectiveness of such programs depends on how high or low the initial cap is set and the rate at which the cap is reduced.

CONSIDER, DISCUSS, OR DEBATE

Do the advantages of using tradable pollution and resource-use permits to reduce pollution and resource waste outweigh the disadvantages?

Trade-Offs

Tradable Environmental Permits

Advantages	Disadvantages
Flexible	Big polluters and resource wasters can buy their way out
Easy to administer	May not reduce pollution at dirtiest plants
Encourages pollution prevention and waste reduction	Can exclude small companies from buying permits
Can guarantee achievement of caps	Caps can be too low
	Caps must be gradually reduced to encourage innovation
Permit prices determined by market transactions	Determining caps is difficult
	Must decide who gets permits and why
Confronts ethical problem of how much pollution or resource waste is acceptable	Administrative costs high with many participants
	Emissions and resource wastes must be monitored
	Self-monitoring can promote cheating
Confronts problem of how permits should be fairly distributed	Sets bad example by selling legal rights to pollute or waste resources

FIGURE 26-12 **Trade-offs:** advantages and disadvantages of using tradable pollution and resource-use permits to reduce pollution and resource waste. Pick the single advantage and disadvantage that you think are the most important.

How Can Eco-Labelling Improve Environmental Quality and Reduce Resource Waste? Informing Consumers

Labelling environmentally beneficial goods and resources extracted by more sustainable methods can help consumers decide what goods and services to buy.

We can use *product eco-labelling* to encourage companies to develop green products and services and to help consumers select more environmentally beneficial products and services. Eco-labelling programs

have been developed in Europe, Japan, the United States, and Canada—where, for example, the Canadian Environmental Choice labelling program has certified more than 300 categories of products; see Figure 26-13 (p. 653).

Eco-labels are also being used to identify fish caught by sustainable methods (certified by the Marine Stewardship Council) and to certify timber produced and harvested by sustainable methods (evaluated by organizations such as the Forest Stewardship Council and the Canadian Standards Association; Solutions, p. 226).

CONSIDER, DISCUSS, OR DEBATE

Given a choice between a green product and a less expensive but not environmentally beneficial version of the same product, which would you buy? Explain.

26-6 REDUCING POVERTY TO IMPROVE ENVIRONMENTAL QUALITY AND HUMAN WELL-BEING

How Is the World's Wealth Distributed? Flowing Up to the Rich

Since 1960, most of the financial benefits of global economic growth have flowed up to the rich rather than down to the poor.

Poverty is usually defined as the inability to meet one's basic economic needs. According to the World Bank, about half of humanity is trying to live on less than $3 (U.S.) a day and one of every seven people on the planet is struggling to survive on an income of roughly $1.25 (U.S.) per day.

Poverty has numerous harmful health and environmental effects (Figures 1-10, p. 12, and 19-18, p. 470) and has been identified as one of the five major causes of the environmental problems we face (Figure 1-9, p. 12).

Most neoclassical economists believe a growing economy can help the poor by creating more jobs, enabling more of the increased wealth to reach workers, and providing greater tax revenues that can be used to help the poor help themselves. Economists call this the *trickle-down* effect.

However, since 1960, most of the benefits of global economic growth as measured by income have flowed up to the rich rather than down to the poor (Figure 26-14, p. 653). Since 1980, growth of this *wealth gap* has increased. According to Ismail Serageldin, the planet's richest three people have more wealth than the combined GDP of the world's 47 poorest countries and their 600 million people. In Vandana Shiva's words, "Resources move from the poor to the rich,

| Germany: Blue Angel (1978) | United States: Green Seal (1989) | The Nordic Countries: Nordic Swan (1989) | European Union: Eco-label (1992) |

FIGURE 26-13 Solutions: symbols used in some of the *eco-labelling* programs that evaluate green or environmentally favourable products.

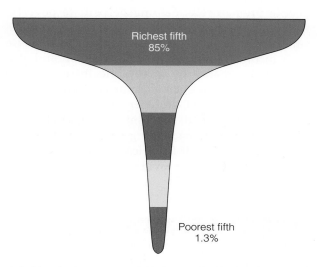

FIGURE 26-14 Data on the *global distribution of income* show that most of the world's income has flowed up; the richest 20% of the world's population receive more of the world's income than all of the remaining 80%. Each horizontal band in this diagram represents one-fifth of the world's population. This upward flow of global income has accelerated since 1960 and especially since 1980. This trend can increase environmental degradation by increasing average per capita consumption by the richest 20% of the population and causing the poorest 20% of the world's people to use renewable resources faster than they are replenished in order to survive. (Data from UN Development Programme and Ismail Serageldin, "World Poverty and Hunger—A Challenge for Science," *Science* 296 (2002): 54–58)

and pollution moves from the rich to the poor." South African President Thabo Mbeki told delegates at the 2003 Johannesburg World Summit on Sustainable Development, "A global human society based on poverty for many and prosperity for a few, characterized by islands of wealth, surrounded by a sea of poverty, is unsustainable."

These trends do not mean that economic growth causes poverty. Instead, they mean that for a variety of reasons rich nations and individuals have devoted only a small fraction of their wealth to helping reduce poverty and its harmful effects on the environment and human well-being.

Poverty is also sustained by corruption, absence of property rights, insufficient legal protection, and inability of many poor people to borrow money to grow crops or start a small business.

Case Study: What Is the Role of the World Bank in Economic Development? Controversy Over Big Loans

The World Bank makes loans to developing countries for their economic development, but a number of these loans have had harmful environmental and social effects.

The World Bank is the major player in global economic development. It was formed in 1945 after World War II to provide loans for rebuilding Europe and Japan. In the 1950s, the focus shifted to providing loans to aid the economic development of developing countries, provided mostly by private investors in the 150 countries that jointly own the bank. Investors hope to make a profit on the funds they put up, mostly from interest paid on the loans. The United States provides more of the investment capital than any other country and the presidents of the bank have all been Americans.

DID YOU KNOW

Canada was a founding member of the World Bank and has contributed more than $12 billion in loans since 1945.

A number of World Bank loans for large-scale dams, roads into tropical forests, and mining operations have been environmentally destructive and controversial. Critics accuse the bank of making loans for large-scale projects without evaluating the long-term environmental and social impacts and without requiring adequate safeguards to help reduce or eliminate harmful environmental and social impacts. Critics also call for the bank to focus more on making moderate and small-scale loans that benefit the poor directly.

Another problem is that to make enough money to pay the interest on their loans, many developing countries sell their mineral, timber, and other resources to developed countries at low prices. This depletes their natural capital and can eventually leave them without enough resources to support future economic development. Also, interest payments can deplete national budgets, leaving little for health, education, and other important programs.

In recent years, environmentalists and representatives of the poor have staged large-scale protests against such policies. In response, the bank has begun trying to carry out more detailed reviews of the environmental and social impacts of its loans. But it remains to be seen how such reviews will affect the bank's lending policies.

How Can We Reduce Poverty? Help the Poor Help Themselves

We can sharply cut poverty by forgiving the international debts of the poorest countries and greatly increasing international aid and small individual loans to help the poor help themselves.

Analysts point out that reducing poverty requires the governments of most developing countries to make policy changes. One is to shift more of the national budget to help the rural and urban poor work their way out of poverty. Another is to give villages and the urban poor title to common lands and to crops and trees they plant.

Encouraging sustainable forms of economic development can help reduce global poverty but analysts say that by itself this is not enough. Analysts suggest that one way to help reduce global poverty is to forgive at least 60% of the $2.4 trillion (U.S.) debt that developing countries owe to developed countries and international lending agencies and all of the $422 billion (U.S.) debt of the poorest and most heavily indebted countries on the condition that the money saved on the debt interest be spent on meeting basic human needs. Developing countries have been paying more than $300 billion per year in interest to developed countries to service this debt. The International Monetary Fund and the World Bank have gradually been expanding the Heavily Indebted Poor Country (HIPC) Initiative they started in 1996. As of 2012, debt reduction packages were approved for 36 countries and $76 billion was directed toward their debt relief. The goal is to ensure that no poor country faces a debt burden that it cannot manage (http://www.imf.org/external/np/exr/facts/hipc.htm).

Critics say that many countries relieved of some debt will take on more debt, and they want assurances that most of the savings from debt relief are passed on to the poor in the form of titles to land, education, jobs, and better health care.

Developed countries can increase nonmilitary government and private aid to developing countries, with mechanisms to ensure that most of the aid goes directly to the poor to help them become more self-reliant and to help provide social safety nets such as welfare, unemployment payments, and pension benefits that are available in most developed countries. Developed countries also need to mount a massive global effort to combat malnutrition and the infectious diseases that kill millions of people prematurely, helping perpetuate poverty. Another approach is for lending agencies to make small loans to poor people who want to increase their income (Solutions, p. 655). They should also make investments in small-scale infrastructure that help the poor such as solar-cell power facilities in villages, small-scale irrigation projects, and farm-to-market roads. Lending agencies can also make investments in helping sustain and restore the resource bases of fisheries, forests, and small-scale agriculture that provide more than half of the world's jobs.

CONSIDER, DISCUSS, OR DEBATE

If you were in charge of the World Bank or the International Monetary Fund, how would you direct aid to developing countries? Make a list of the kinds of projects that you think would do the most good.

Developed countries can help developing countries create more environmentally sustainable economies, or eco-economies. According to Robert B. Shapiro, former CEO of Monsanto, "If emerging economies have to relive the entire industrial revolution with all its waste, its energy use, and its pollution, I think it's all over."

Finally, there is a need for both developed countries and developing countries to stabilize their populations. Many analysts also call for encouraging the political and social empowerment of the poor, especially women. This can be done by doing more decision making at the local level and integrating human rights with sustainable development.

According to the United Nations Development Programme (UNDP), it would cost more than $50 billion a year to provide universal access to basic services such as education, health, nutrition, family planning, safe water, and sanitation. The UNDP notes that this is less than 0.1% of the world's annual income and is only a fraction of what the world devotes each year to military spending (Figure 26-15, p. 655).

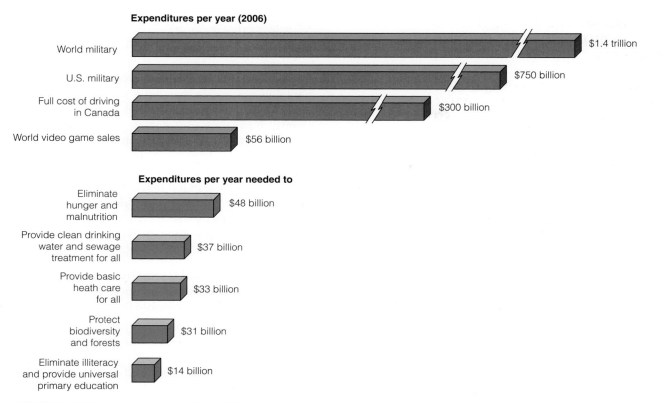

Expenditures per year (2006)

World military — $1.4 trillion

U.S. military — $750 billion

Full cost of driving in Canada — $300 billion

World video game sales — $56 billion

Expenditures per year needed to

Eliminate hunger and malnutrition — $48 billion

Provide clean drinking water and sewage treatment for all — $37 billion

Provide basic heath care for all — $33 billion

Protect biodiversity and forests — $31 billion

Eliminate illiteracy and provide universal primary education — $14 billion

FIGURE 26-15 What should our priorities be? (Data from United Nations, World Health Organization, Transport Canada, and Victoria Transport Policy Institute)

SOLUTIONS

Microloans to the Poor

Most of the world's poor want to earn more, become more self-reliant, and have a better life. But they have no credit record. Also, they have few if any assets they can use for collateral to secure a loan to buy seeds and fertilizer for farming or tools and materials for a small business.

For almost three decades, an innovative tool called *microlending* or *microfinance* has helped deal with this problem. For example, since economist Muhammad Yunus started it in 1976, the Grameen (Village) Bank in Bangladesh has provided more than $4 billion in microloans (varying from $50 to $500) to several million mostly poor, rural, and landless women in 40 000 villages. About 94% of the loans are to women who start their own small businesses as dressmakers, weavers, bookbinders, peanut fryers, or vendors.

To stimulate repayment and provide support, the Grameen Bank organizes microborrowers into five-member "solidarity" groups. If one member of the group misses a weekly payment or defaults on the loan, the other members of the group must make the payments.

The Grameen Bank's experience has shown that microlending is both successful and profitable. For example, less than 3% of microloan repayments to the Grameen Bank are late, and the repayment rate on its loans is 90–95%, much higher than the repayment rate for conventional loans by commercial banks throughout most of the world.

About half of Grameen's borrowers move above the poverty line within five years, and domestic violence, divorce, and birth rates are lower among most borrowers.

Microloans to the poor by the Grameen Bank are being used to

develop day-care centres, health clinics, reforestation projects, drinking water supply projects, literacy programs, and group insurance programs. People also use them to bring small-scale solar and wind power systems to rural villages.

Grameen's model has inspired the development of microcredit projects in more than 58 countries that have reached 133 million people (including dependants), and the number is growing rapidly.

Critical Thinking

Why do you think there has been little use of microloans by international development and lending agencies such as the World Bank and the International Monetary Fund? How might this situation be changed?

26-7 MAKING THE TRANSITION TO MORE ENVIRONMENTALLY SUSTAINABLE ECONOMIES

How Can We Make a Transition to an Eco-Economy? Imitate Nature and Use Full-Cost Pricing

An eco-economy imitates nature's four principles of sustainability and environmental economic strategies.

On page 641, we listed environmental economic strategies that have been discussed at length in this chapter. Eco-economies will increasingly employ these strategies—environmentally sensitive economic indicators, full-cost pricing, tax shifting, and eco-labelling, among many others.

An eco-economy mimics the processes that sustain the Earth's natural systems (Figure 9-14, p. 191). Paul Hawken and several other business leaders and economists have suggested ways for using these guidelines and various economic tools for making the transition to more environmentally sustainable eco-economies over the next several decades. They echo what has been discussed in this chapter and are summarized in Figure 26-16. Hawken's simple golden rule for an eco-economy is this: *Leave the world better than you found it, take no more than you need, try not to harm life or the environment, and make amends if you do.*

As we make the transition to more environmentally sustainable economies during this century, Lester R. Brown projects that some environmentally harmful businesses will decline and become *sunset businesses,* and others that are more environmentally sustainable—*eco-friendly businesses*—will grow in importance. Figure 26-17 (p. 657) lists some of both types. The right side of this figure might give you some ideas for a career choice. Forward-looking owners and investors in sunset businesses will use their profits and capital to invest in emerging eco-friendly businesses.

Case Study: How Are Germany and the Netherlands Working to Achieve More Environmentally Sustainable Economies? Leading the Way

Germany and the Netherlands have dedicated themselves to making their economies more environmentally sustainable for economic and ecological reasons.

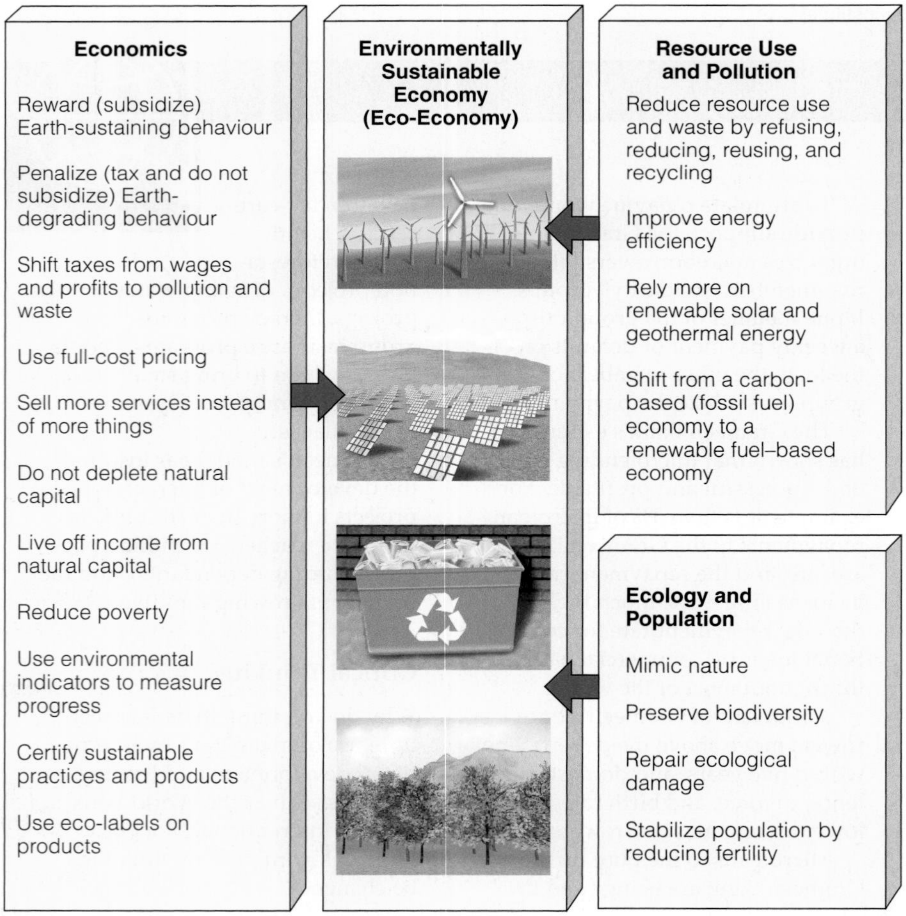

Economics

Reward (subsidize) Earth-sustaining behaviour

Penalize (tax and do not subsidize) Earth-degrading behaviour

Shift taxes from wages and profits to pollution and waste

Use full-cost pricing

Sell more services instead of more things

Do not deplete natural capital

Live off income from natural capital

Reduce poverty

Use environmental indicators to measure progress

Certify sustainable practices and products

Use eco-labels on products

Environmentally Sustainable Economy (Eco-Economy)

Resource Use and Pollution

Reduce resource use and waste by refusing, reducing, reusing, and recycling

Improve energy efficiency

Rely more on renewable solar and geothermal energy

Shift from a carbon-based (fossil fuel) economy to a renewable fuel–based economy

Ecology and Population

Mimic nature

Preserve biodiversity

Repair ecological damage

Stabilize population by reducing fertility

FIGURE 26-16 Solutions: principles for shifting to more environmentally sustainable economies or eco-economies during this century.

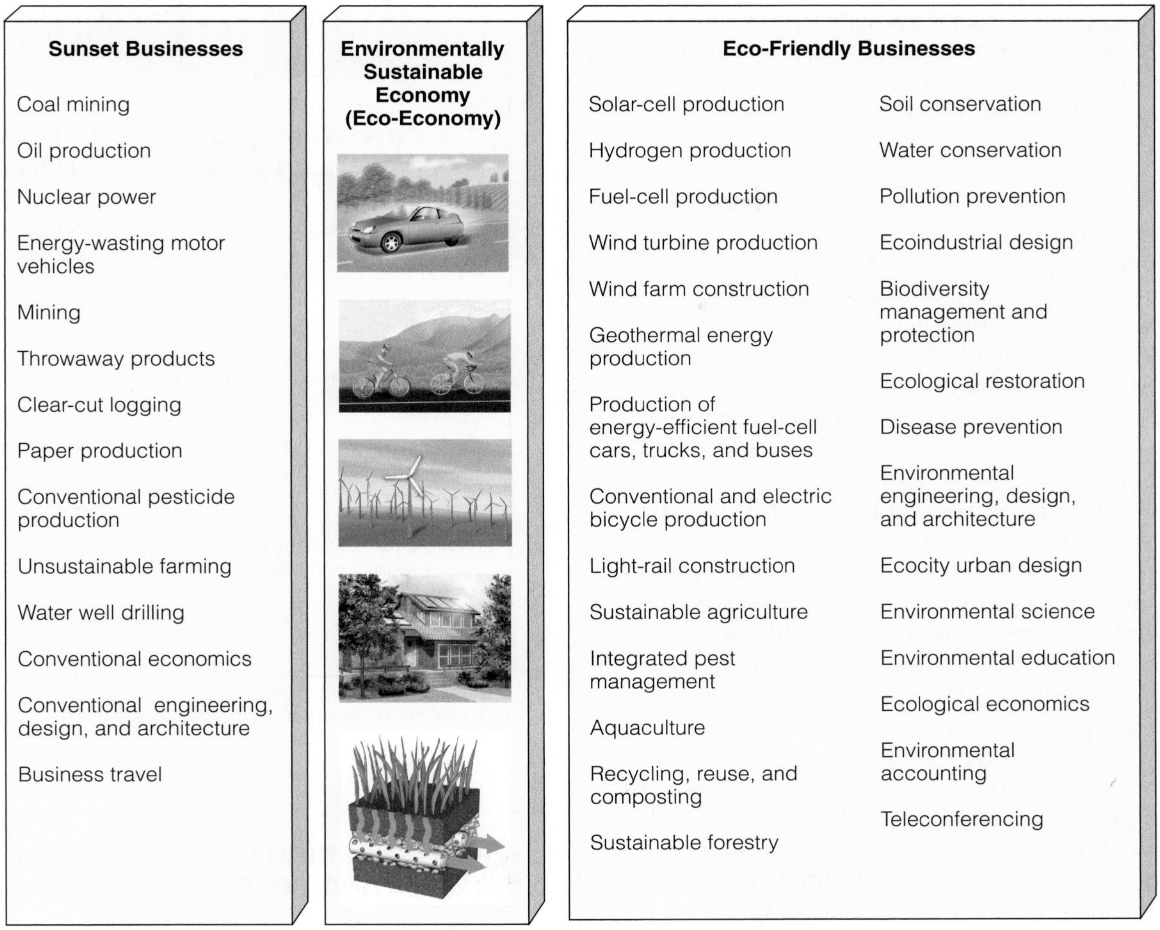

Sunset Businesses	Environmentally Sustainable Economy (Eco-Economy)	Eco-Friendly Businesses	
Coal mining		Solar-cell production	Soil conservation
Oil production		Hydrogen production	Water conservation
Nuclear power		Fuel-cell production	Pollution prevention
Energy-wasting motor vehicles		Wind turbine production	Ecoindustrial design
Mining		Wind farm construction	Biodiversity management and protection
Throwaway products		Geothermal energy production	
Clear-cut logging			Ecological restoration
Paper production		Production of energy-efficient fuel-cell cars, trucks, and buses	Disease prevention
Conventional pesticide production		Conventional and electric bicycle production	Environmental engineering, design, and architecture
Unsustainable farming		Light-rail construction	Ecocity urban design
Water well drilling		Sustainable agriculture	Environmental science
Conventional economics		Integrated pest management	Environmental education
Conventional engineering, design, and architecture		Aquaculture	Ecological economics
Business travel		Recycling, reuse, and composting	Environmental accounting
		Sustainable forestry	Teleconferencing

FIGURE 26-17 The projected decline of environmentally harmful, or *sunset*, businesses and rise of more environmentally sustainable, or *eco-friendly*, businesses during this century. As this transition takes place, jobs will decrease in sunset businesses (left) and increase in eco-friendly businesses (right). (Data from Lester R. Brown, Earth Policy Institute)

Germany and the Netherlands are working to make their economies more environmentally sustainable. In Germany, sales of environmental protection goods and services—already more than $600 billion (U.S.) per year—are projected to rise.

Mostly because of stricter air pollution regulations, German companies have developed some of the world's cleanest and most efficient gas turbines and invented the world's first steel mill that uses no coal. Germany sells these and other improved environmental technologies globally. Germany is also one of the world's leading manufacturers of wind turbines.

In 1977, the German government started the Blue Angel *eco-labelling* program to inform consumers about products that cause the least environmental harm (Figure 26-13). Most international companies use the German market to test and evaluate green products.

German car companies, as part of a recycling revolution, are required to pick up and recycle all domestic cars they make, and such *take-back* requirements are being extended to almost all products to reduce use of energy and virgin raw materials. Germany is selling these recycling technologies to other countries.

Germany's government has supported research and development aimed at making it the world's leader in solar-cell and wind turbine technology and hydrogen fuel.

Finally, Germany provides more than $1 billion per year in green foreign aid to developing countries, much of it designed to stimulate demand for German technologies and products.

In 1989, the Netherlands—a tiny country with about 16 million people—began implementing a National Environmental Policy Plan, or Green Plan, as a result of widespread public alarm over declining environmental quality. The goal is to slash production of many types of pollution by 70–90% and achieve the world's first environmentally sustainable economy, ideally within a few decades.

The government began by identifying eight major areas for improvement: climate change, acid deposition, eutrophication, toxic chemicals, waste disposal, groundwater depletion, unsustainable use of renewable and nonrenewable resources, and local nuisances (mostly noise and odour pollution).

Then the government formed task forces consisting of people in industry, government, and citizens' groups for each of the eight areas, asking each task force to agree on targets and timetables for drastically reducing pollution. Each group was free to pursue whatever policies or technologies it wanted, but if a group could not agree, the government would impose its own targets and timetables and stiff penalties for industries not meeting certain pollution reduction goals.

Each task force focused on four general themes: (1) life-cycle management (Figure 26-11, right); (2) energy efficiency, with the government committing $385 million (U.S.) per year to energy conservation programs; (3) environmentally sustainable technologies, also supported by a government program; and (4) improving public awareness through a massive government-sponsored public education program.

Many of the country's leading industrialists like the Green Plan because they can make investments in pollution prevention and pollution control with less financial risk and a high degree of certainty about long-term environmental policy. And they are free to deal with the problems in ways that make the most sense for their businesses. Industrial leaders have also learned that creating more efficient and environmentally sound products and processes often reduces costs and increases profits as they are sold at home and abroad.

The Netherlands' plan is the first attempt by any country to foster a national debate on the issue of environmental sustainability and to encourage innovative solutions to environmental problems. Is the plan working? There is a long way to go, but the news is encouraging. Most of the target groups have met or exceeded their goals on schedule. A huge amount of environmental research by the government and private sector has taken place. This has led to an increase in organic agriculture, greater reliance on bicycles in some cities, and more ecologically sound new housing developments.

Shifting to eco-economies over the next several decades will require bold leadership by business leaders and elected officials and bottom-up political pressure from concerned citizens (Figure 26-18). Forward-looking investors, corporate executives, and political leaders are recognizing that *the environmental revolution is also an economic revolution.*

What Can You Do?

Promoting Eco-Economies from the Ground Up

- Buy green or environmentally favourable products.

- Do a lifestyle makeover based on products, services, and activities that solve environmental problems.

- When investing in the stock market, buy the shares of eco-friendly companies.

- Make charitable contributions to groups and organizations that are working to solve environmental problems.

- Vote for politicians and political parties that support a pro-environment agenda.

- Persuade your family and friends to do all of the above.

FIGURE 26-18 What can you do? Ways to encourage the shift to eco-economies at the grassroots level.

26-8 CHECKING OUR PROGRESS AT ERADICATING POVERTY

How Well Are We Proceeding toward Millennium Goal 1? Mixed Progress

Target 1A appears to have been met.

The eight Millennium Development Goals were introduced in Chapter 1 and so far have been addressed in Chapters 9, 10, 13, 14, 15, 19, 21, and 25. Goal 1—aimed at eradicating poverty and hunger—is extremely important. Poverty and hunger lie at the root of so many other problems, including child mortality, maternal health, resistance to disease, access to education, and living in slums. Here we will deal with Targets A and B, which address *poverty* (Figure 26-19). Target C addresses hunger and is covered in Chapter 14.

Target 1A is *to halve, between 1990 and 2015, the proportion of people whose income is less than one dollar per day.* Figure 26-19 shows the three indicators that are being used to assess progress toward this target. Note that although "one dollar per day" has long been used as a standard of extreme poverty, the World Bank and the UN have switched to using "$1.25 per day" as their new standard. The term *PPP* in Indicator 1.1 refers to *purchasing power parity.* In other words, since costs and

Millennium Development Goal 1:

Eradicate Extreme Poverty and Hunger

Target 1A: Halve, between 1990 and 2015, the proportion of people whose income is less than one dollar per day.

1.1 Proportion of population below $1 (PPP) per day.

1.2 Poverty gap ratio.

1.3 Share of poorest quintile in national consumption.

Target 1B: Achieve full and productive employment and decent work for all, including women and young people.

1.4 Growth rate of GDP per person employed.

1.5 Employment-to-population ratio.

1.6 Proportion of employed people living below $1 (PPP) per day.

1.7 Proportion of own-account and contributing family workers in total employment.

FIGURE 26-19 Eradicating poverty: Millennium Development Goal 1 takes aim at poverty and hunger through specific targets and indicators. Targets 1A and 1B focus on poverty and are considered here. Target 1C, concerning hunger, is addressed in Chapter 14. (Courtesy of the UNDP)

currencies vary greatly among countries, adjustments have been made that reflect realistic costs such as the price to buy a standard basket of basic goods in the currency of that country. The *poverty gap ratio* is an indicator derived by multiplying the incidence of poverty with the depth of poverty in a given country. The final indicator for this target compares the *poorest quintile* (the poorest one-fifth of the population) in each country.

The newest *Millennium Development Goals Report* (2012) focuses on delivering one particular message of progress. Research done by the World Bank shows that, in 2010, the percentage of people living in extreme poverty at $1.25 per day or less has fallen to half its 1990 value. If this continues to be true, then Target 1A has already been met—ahead of the 2015 deadline!

Target 1B is *to achieve full and productive employment and decent work for all, including women and young people.* This target recognizes that plentiful jobs of at least a certain level will be required to effectively reduce poverty. The jobs should be physically safe for the worker, as well as not vulnerable to ending suddenly and plunging the worker into poverty. The jobs should pay well enough to avoid the trap of "working poverty," where a person is working but earning so little that he or she is still poor. Social changes should be facilitated to enable women to take their places in the job market. If a number of people from the same household could earn income, even small amounts, it is much more likely that family could escape poverty.

The indicators for tracking this target are listed in Figure 26-19. The newest *Millennium Development Goals Report* (2012) indicates that the number of workers who are living on $1.25 per day or less ("the working poor") has declined from 689 million to 456 million. In percentage terms, this is a reduction from 26.4% of the workforce in 2000 to 14.8% in 2011. Still, the ideal of achieving Target B—"full and productive employment and decent work for all"—seems a long way off. The report brings out the fact that women are more likely than men to be in *vulnerable* employment—jobs that are apt to end, likely with little warning. Youths still tend to have few opportunities in most developing countries.

You can track progress in these areas by monitoring UN websites such as http://www.mdgmonitor.org/. Topics such as debt forgiveness, which affect poverty but depend on global cooperation, are dealt with under Goal 8 (p. 681).

Converting the economy of the 21st century into one that is environmentally sustainable represents the greatest investment opportunity in history.

LESTER R. BROWN AND CHRISTOPHER FLAVIN

CHAPTER REVIEW

1. Review the Key Questions for this chapter on p. 639. Describe the disagreements among some economists over economic growth versus economic development **(Core Case Study)**. Explain why the sustainability revolution is also an economic revolution. Describe how each picture in Figure 26-1 could be an important part of a sustainable economy.

2. What is an *economic system*? Distinguish among *natural capital, human capital (human resources),* and *manufactured capital (manufactured resources).* What is a *pure free-market economic system*? Describe the interactions among demand, supply, and market prices in a market economic system. Explain why and how governments intervene in market economic systems. What is a *high-throughput economy*?

3. Compare how neoclassical economists and ecological and environmental economists view economic systems. List eight strategies that ecological and economic economists would use to make the transition to more sustainable eco-economies.

4. Describe ways in which economists can estimate the economic values of natural goods and services. Why are such values not included in the market prices of goods and services? Define *discount rate* and discuss the controversy over how to assign such rates.

5. Describe how economists can estimate the optimal levels for pollution control and resource use. Define *cost-benefit analysis* and discuss its advantages and limitations.

6. What is the *genuine progress indicator* and how does it differ from the gross domestic product economic indicator? What are the *Human Development Index* and the *Canadian Index of Well-Being*? What is *full-cost pricing* and what are some benefits of using it to determine the market values of goods and services? Give three reasons why it is not widely used. What are the advantages of providing consumers with eco-labels on the goods and services they buy?

7. Describe the benefits of using government subsidies and tax breaks to encourage a more environmentally sustainable economy. Describe the proposal to tax pollution and wastes instead of wages and profits. What are the major advantages and disadvantages of using green taxes? What are the requirements for implementing green taxes? Describe tradable pollution and resource-use permits. What are the major advantages and disadvantages of this approach?

8. What steps have Germany and the Netherlands taken to ensure that their economies will be more sustainable? How do we know that they are succeeding? How do they profit from their success? What innovative programs have they initiated?

9. What is a *matter recycling and reuse economy*? What is a *low-throughput (low-waste) economy*? List six ways to shift to more environmentally sustainable economies. Name five new businesses and careers that would be important in such eco-economies. Describe connections between more environmentally sustainable economies (**Core Case Study**) and the four *scientific principles of sustainability*.

10. What is *poverty* and how is it related to population growth and environmental degradation? List three ways in which governments can help to reduce poverty. What are the advantages of making microloans to the poor? Describe the type of jobs that economies must provide if people are to escape poverty.

CRITICAL THINKING

1. Should we attempt to maximize economic growth by producing and consuming more and more economic goods and services? Explain the consequences of this approach. What are the alternatives?

2. According to one definition, *sustainable development* involves meeting the needs of the present human generation without compromising the ability of future generations to meet their needs, as discussed in Chapter 1. What do you believe are the needs referred to in this definition? Compare this definition with the definition of environmentally sustainable economic development given in Figure 26-5.

3. Suppose that over the next 20 years the current harmful environmental and health costs of goods and services are internalized so that their market prices reflect their total costs. What harmful and beneficial effects might such full-cost pricing have on your lifestyle?

4. Explain why you agree or disagree with the proposals that various analysts have made for sharply reducing poverty, as discussed on page 654. Which two of these proposals do you believe are the most important?

5. Explain why you agree or disagree with each of the major principles for shifting to a more environmentally sustainable economy listed in Figure 26-16. Which three do you believe are the most important?

6. Congratulations! You are in charge of the world. List your five most important actions for shifting to eco-economies over the next 50 years.

PROJECTS

1. Make a list of the economic goods you commonly use, and then identify those that meet your basic needs and those that satisfy your wants. Identify any economic wants you **(a)** would be willing to give up, **(b)** believe you should give up but are unwilling to, and **(c)** hope to give up in the future. Relate the results of this analysis to your personal impact on the environment. Compare your results with those of your classmates.

2. Pick one of the suggestions listed under "Eco-Friendly Businesses" in Figure 26-17 and develop a business plan for a company that would provide the service you selected. For example, assume you'll go into the business of ecological restoration and describe **(a)** your service, **(b)** your customers, **(c)** your mission statement, and **(d)** your strategy for promoting the business.

3. Pick a federal or provincial regulation (such as a water pollution law or regulation) and examine how it affects businesses and other organizations. Determine whether it is an innovation-friendly regulation and explain why or why not. If not, how could it be made more innovation-friendly?

4. Interview officials at a company in your town or region to get their views on one or more environmental regulations affecting their industry. Describe the effects of that regulation on the company and the company's approach toward dealing with it.

5. Use the library or the Internet to learn more about the economic theories of *Milton Friedman, Robert Samuelson, Herman Daly,* and *Robert Costanza.*

6. Use the Internet to research companies that sell green products. Make a list of the products you would consider buying. Share your list with classmates and determine which of your chosen products has the greatest consumer appeal.

7. Reread the section on economic, environmental, and social indicators (pp. 645–646). As a class, decide which is the best indicator for measuring global sustainable development. Modify your chosen indicator as needed to improve its usefulness.

27 Politics, Environment, and Sustainability

Ontario's Environmental Watchdog

Environmental groups in Ontario had long campaigned for a vehicle that would hold the provincial government accountable for the actions it took—or chose not to take—on matters affecting the environment. In 1993, following years of consultation, the Ontario government finally passed the *Environmental Bill of Rights (EBR)*. The EBR, which came into effect in February 1994, recognizes the importance of protecting our natural environment. Moreover, it informs the public about government activities and provides a mechanism through which the public can both influence and respond to government decisions about the environment.

The right of the public to defend the environment is enshrined in the EBR. The EBR recognizes this right in practical terms by (1) making it easier for citizens to use the court system to defend the environment, (2) increasing the protections afforded to employees who engage in whistle-blowing in defence of the environment, and (3) making the government's environment-related decisions more transparent.

The *Environmental Commissioner of Ontario (ECO)*, an independent officer of the legislature, is responsible for monitoring government compliance with the EBR and for advising the public as to its rights under the EBR. Those rights are spelled out on the ECO's website (http://www.eco.on.ca), which also provides information about ECO-sponsored programs, key environmental decisions made by the Ontario government, and environmental issues of concern to citizens (Figure 27-1A).

The third and current Environmental Commissioner of Ontario is Gord Miller (Figure 27-1B). Before assuming

(continued)

FIGURE 27-1A The ECO provides information about how to use the Environmental Bill of Rights and about current environmental issues.

FIGURE 27-1B Ontario's third ECO, Gord Miller. (http://www.eco.on.ca)

the post, the former professor and environmentalist managed a district office of the Ministry of the Environment. Since 2000, Miller and his staff have been busy educating the public about the EBR, ensuring that the Ontario government complies with its requirements, and assisting citizens who are seeking investigations and reviews of environmentally significant government decisions.

Do other provinces have the equivalent of an environmental commissioner? Should they? How could you make use of a document such as the Environmental Bill of Rights (ECO, 2003)?

Politics is the art of making good decisions on insufficient evidence.

LORD KENNET

CHAPTER PURPOSE AND QUESTIONS

Chapter 27 discusses how we can use politics to promote environmental quality and sustainability. The chapter addresses the following questions:

27-1 What changes have taken place in environmental awareness and focus?

27-2 What is democracy and how do democratic governments work?

27-3 What principles can guide us in making environmental policy decisions?

27-4 What is environmental law and how does it evolve?

27-5 What are the roles of major environmental groups?

27-6 Should we expand the concept of national and global security?

27-7 What progress are we making at creating a global partnership for development?

27-1 ENVIRONMENTAL AND POLITICAL CHALLENGES FOR THIS CENTURY

What Changes in Environmental Awareness and Focus Have Taken Place? Some Major Shifts

There have been seven shifts in the way we view and deal with environmental problems.

This chapter examines the strengths and weaknesses of political systems in dealing with environmental problems. Before doing this we need to understand the nature of the environmental problems we face in terms of nations and the international community of nations.

Since the 1970s, there have been seven shifts in the types and focus of the environmental problems we face. One is increasing concern about *the harmful effects of human activities on biodiversity and other forms of natural capital* that support all life and economies. This is leading to increased emphasis on protecting and restoring entire ecosystems instead of focusing primarily on keeping individual species from becoming prematurely extinct. To be effective this will require international cooperative efforts.

A second is a *shift from local to regional and global concerns* about emissions of air and water pollutants that can be transported from one region or country to another. One example is a significant increase in emissions of sulphur and nitrogen compounds, especially in Asia, that can blanket large regions with smog and harmful and acid-forming chemicals. Another example is rising levels of carbon dioxide in the atmosphere from burning fossil fuels and clearing forests that can affect regional and global climate patterns. A third example is rising levels of nitrogen compounds in the atmosphere and aquatic systems because of emissions of gaseous nitrogen compounds by power plants and motor vehicles and rapidly growing runoff of nitrogen fertilizers from cropland and urban land into rivers, lakes, and coastal waters.

A third shift involves *growing concern over the threat of climate change and its potential to disrupt ecological, economic, and political systems*. Many analysts consider this threat and the related problem of biodiversity loss to be the two most important environmental problems we face.

A fourth shift is a *growing awareness of the pollution problems of developing countries*—especially those in the heavily populated urban areas of China, India, Mexico, and Brazil—that are undergoing rapid industrialization and economic growth. Many people in these countries now have some of the world's highest levels of exposure to tiny particles in indoor and outdoor air, lead (mostly from burning leaded gasoline), and exposure to infectious organisms in drinking water. A fifth and related shift is a *growing awareness of the harmful effects of poverty on the environment and human health* (pp. 12, 481, and 652).

Sixth is *increasing concern about possible effects of trace amounts of some synthetic organic (carbon-based) chemicals on human health and wildlife*. Examples are pesticides, plastics, industrial chemicals, drugs, and food additives. We know little about the potentially harmful environmental and health effects of trace amounts of such chemicals.

So far our approach has been to assume that such chemicals are innocent until shown to be harmful. Now there is a shift, led by the European Union, to have nations and the international community assume that such chemicals are potentially harmful until shown to be harmless. This leads to increased emphasis on preventing pollutants from reaching the environment instead of trying to clean them up after they have been dispersed into the environment.

The seventh shift involves *relying more on the international community to deal with environmental problems in an increasingly globalized world and economy.* So far we have not been very effective in bringing about this important shift.

CONSIDER, DISCUSS, OR DEBATE

Which of these seven shifts described in this section do you think is the most important? Explain.

27-2 DEALING WITH ENVIRONMENTAL PROBLEMS IN DEMOCRACIES

What Is a Democracy, and How Do Democratic Governments Work? Government By and For the People

In a democracy, people elect others to govern, and can freely express their opinions and beliefs.

Democracy is government by the people through elected officials and representatives. In a *constitutional democracy*, a constitution provides the basis of government authority, limits government power by mandating free elections, and guarantees free speech.

Political institutions in constitutional democracies are designed to allow gradual change to ensure economic and political stability. In Canada, for example, rapid and destabilizing change is curbed by a system of checks and balances that distributes power among the three branches of government—*legislative, executive,* and *judicial*—and among federal, provincial, and local governments.

In passing laws, developing budgets, and formulating regulations, elected and appointed government officials must deal with pressure from many competing *special-interest groups.* Each group advocates passing laws, providing subsidies or tax breaks, or establishing regulations favourable to its cause and weakening or repealing laws, subsidies, taxes, and regulations unfavourable to its position.

Some special-interest groups, such as corporations, are *profit-making organizations,* and others are nonprofit *nongovernmental organizations (NGOs).* Examples of NGOs are labour unions and major and grassroots environmental organizations.

What Factors Hinder the Ability of Democracies to Deal with Environmental Problems? A Short-Term Outlook

Democracies are designed to deal mostly with short-term, isolated problems.

The deliberate design of democracies to promote stability is highly desirable. But several related features of democratic governments hinder their ability to deal with environmental problems. One is a tendency to react to short-term, isolated environmental problems, instead of regarding them as parts of a whole and acting to prevent them from occurring. Many important environmental problems such as climate change, biodiversity loss, and long-lived hazardous waste have long-range effects, are related to one another, and require integrated long-term solutions emphasizing prevention.

But because elections are held every few years, most politicians seeking re-election are compelled to focus on short-term, isolated problems rather than on complex, interrelated, time-consuming, and long-term problems.

Most politicians will no longer be in office when harmful long-term effects from environmental problems appear. And there is no powerful political constituency representing future generations or long-term environmental sustainability.

Another problem is that many elected officials must spend much of their time dealing with short-term rather than long-term issues. Finally, too many political leaders do not understand how the Earth's natural systems work and how they support all life, economies, and societies. This lack of ecological literacy is dangerous in these times when we are moving through treacherous ecological waters at an increasing speed.

27-3 DEVELOPING, INFLUENCING, AND IMPLEMENTING ENVIRONMENTAL POLICY

What Principles Can Guide Us in Making Environmental Policy Decisions? Principles Are Important

Several principles can guide us in making environmental decisions.

An **environmental policy** consists of laws, rules, and regulations related to an environmental problem that are developed, implemented, and enforced by a particular government agency. Analysts have suggested that legislators and individuals evaluating existing or proposed environmental policy should be guided by several principles:

- *The humility principle*: Our understanding of nature and of the consequences of our actions is quite limited.

- *The reversibility principle*: Try not to do something that cannot be reversed later if the decision turns out to be wrong. For example, most biologists believe the current large-scale destruction and degradation of forests, wetlands, wild species, and other components of the Earth's biodiversity is irreversible on a human time scale.

- *The precautionary principle*: When much evidence indicates that an activity threatens human health or the environment, take measures to prevent or reduce harm, even if some of the cause-and-effect relationships are not fully established scientifically. In such cases, it is better to be safe than sorry.

- *The prevention principle*: Whenever possible, make decisions that help prevent a problem from occurring or becoming worse.

- *The polluter pays principle*: Develop regulations and use economic tools such as full-cost pricing to ensure that polluters bear the cost of the pollutants and wastes they produce.

- *The integrative principle*: Make decisions that involve integrated solutions to environmental and other problems.

- *The public participation principle*: Citizens should have open access to environmental data and information and the right to participate in developing, criticizing, and modifying environmental policies.

- *The human-rights principle*: All people have a right to an environment that does not harm their health and well-being.

- *The environmental justice principle*: Establish environmental policy so that no group of people bears an unfair share of the harmful environmental risks from industrial, municipal, and commercial operations or from the execution of environmental laws, regulations, and policies. **Environmental justice**, as discussed in Chapter 26, means that every person is entitled to protection from environmental hazards regardless of race, gender, age, national origin, income, social class, or any other factor.

How Can Individuals Affect Environmental Policy? All Politics Is Local

Most improvements in environmental quality are the result of millions of citizens putting pressure on elected officials and of individuals developing innovative solutions to environmental problems.

A major theme of this book is that *individuals matter*. History shows that significant social change usually comes from the *bottom up* when individuals join with others to bring about change. Without grassroots political action by millions of individual citizens and organized groups, the air you breathe and the water you drink today would be much more polluted, and much more of the Earth's biodiversity would have disappeared. Figure 27-2 lists ways you can influence and change government policies in constitutional democracies.

In developed countries, many people devote much of their lives to acquiring more things instead of participating in building more just and sustainable communities. In Canada, only a small percentage of

What Can You Do?

Influencing Environmental Policy

- Become informed on issues.

- Run for office (especially at local level).

- Make your views known at public hearings.

- Make your views known to elected representatives.

- Contribute money and time to candidates for office.

- Vote.

- Form or join nongovernment organizations (NGOs) seeking change.

- Submit an article or a letter to a newspaper.

FIGURE 27-2 What can you do? Ways you can influence environmental policy.

people vote or participate in political campaigns and elections.

In addition, an increasing number of citizens are too busy, tired, distracted, or cynical to participate in helping make their communities better places to live. Instead of becoming involved in their communities and helping develop environmental policies, many believe they can perform their environmental duty by recycling, buying environmentally friendly products, planting a tree, composting, eating organic food, buying shade-grown coffee, driving a fuel-efficient vehicle, and perhaps mailing a cheque to an environmental organization.

These are important and responsible activities that help the environment. But in order to influence environmental policy, people need to actively work together to improve communities and neighbourhoods, as the citizens of North Bay, Ontario (p. 633) and Curitiba, Brazil (p. 614) have done. These and other cases have demonstrated the validity of the insight of Aldo Leopold: "All ethics rest upon a single premise: that the individual is a member of a community of interdependent parts." Thus what we do at the local level has global implications—much like dropping a pebble in a lake and watching the resulting ripples spread outward. This is the meaning of the slogan, "Think globally and act locally."

CONSIDER, DISCUSS, OR DEBATE

Study Figure 27-2 carefully. Which, if any, of these things do you do? Under what circumstances would you be motivated to take on activities that you don't already engage in?

Case Study: What Is Environmental Leadership? An Option for Each of Us

Environmental leaders provide vision, focus, resources, and other types of support to people who want to make changes to environmental policies, and each of us can play a leadership role.

Leaders are persons whom other people choose to follow because of their vision, credibility, courage, or charisma. Good leaders help people to focus their energy, to set goals, and to pursue those goals efficiently. And leaders often provide the resources and moral support that people need to keep going when their goals seem to be slipping away. So if a group wants to influence environmental policy, an energetic leader is indispensable.

Sometimes political leaders are well positioned to serve as environmental leaders. Pierre Trudeau (Figure 27-3) was not particularly known for advancing environmental policies during his time as prime minister (1968–79 and 1980–84), but his attractions to wilderness, to the outdoors, to canoeing, and to the Far North were well known and he is remembered as a friend of the environment. Brian Mulroney (Figure 27-4) was not always popular as prime minister (1984–93)

FIGURE 27-4 Prime Minister Brian Mulroney's environmental record—from his willingness to challenge the U.S. government on the issue of acid rain to his participation in the 1992 Rio Earth Summit and many other environmental conferences—has been praised by Green Party leader Elizabeth May.

but he rose to the occasion to defend Canada against transboundary acid precipitation in the mid-1980s; he orchestrated some debt-for-nature swaps in the early 1990s; and he was an active supporter and participant at key UN conferences during his time in office. Elizabeth May (Figure 27-5) is a true environmental

FIGURE 27-3 Although environmental policy is not a key feature of Prime Minister Pierre Elliott Trudeau political legacy, his passion for the natural world set a positive example for all Canadians.

FIGURE 27-5 Elizabeth May has been an environmental activist as well as a politician. She is currently the leader of the Green Party of Canada.

advocate who has been an author of influential books, an activist for important causes including cleaning up the Sydney Tar Ponds and protecting South Moresby Island, and a leader of environmental groups including the Sierra Club of Canada; she is currently the leader of the Green Party in Canada (elected 2006).

Prime Minister Stephen Harper (elected 2006; Figure 27-6) has yet to fully demonstrate his legacy as an environmental leader; however, many Canadians feel that his time in office so far indicates the environment is not one of his priorities. Soon after Harper was elected in 2006, his government abandoned Canada's commitments to the greenhouse gas targets of the Kyoto Protocol, much to the dismay of many Canadians (Fitzpatrick, 2011; Suzuki, 2007). Harper's resulting Clean Air Act was criticized for postponing greenhouse gas targets until 2050. At the 2007 Commonwealth Summit held in Uganda, and again at the 2007 UN Climate Conference in Bali, Canada and the U.S. blocked climate change agreements until GHG targets were considerably weakened. Many environmental organizations are upset with how the Harper government has handled endangered species (EcoJustice, 2012), hazardous materials such as asbestos and mercury (Sierra Club, 2012), and ideas that are contrary to its environmental policies (Scoffield and Ditchburn, 2012).

On the other hand, as mentioned on p. 510, carbon dioxide emissions are declining in Canada recently (either due to Harper's policies or due to a sluggish economy). The Conservative government claims to be strongly committed to protecting the environment. Its 2011 platform (http://media.conservative.ca/media/ConservativePlatform2011_EN.pdf) describes expanding parks, protecting the Arctic, cracking down on polluters, and supporting clean energy (though it says little about greenhouse gas emissions). It will be easiest to judge the environmental impact of Stephen Harper's government in retrospect.

A number of politicians outside Canada would likely be seen as environmental leaders by Canadians. Gro Harlem Brundtland was the prime minister of Norway for 10 years (1981; 1986–89; 1990–96) but achieved worldwide recognition as Chair of the World Commission of Environment and Development ("the Brundtland Commission"), where she championed the principle of sustainable development and publicized her cause in the famous 1987 book *Our Common Future*. She has since held key positions including Director General of the World Health Organization and Special Envoy on Climate Change for the UN. Tony Blair, while prime minister of the United Kingdom (1997–2007), called for nations of the world to reduce carbon dioxide emissions by 60% before 2050 and to work together to protect the environment; he thought that environmental degradation and climate change were the most urgent challenges for the current generation to solve.

George Bush Senior might be seen as an unlikely environmental leader to some, but just as negotiations between U.S. President Ronald Reagan and Canadian Prime Minister Brian Mulroney over transboundary acid precipitation seemed to reach an impasse in the late 1980s, George Bush Senior was elected U.S. president (1989–93) and swiftly made changes to the U.S. Clean Air Act that helped to save the situation. George W. Bush, on the other hand, is likely to be remembered as the U.S. president (2001–9) who did the most to oppose environmental initiatives (p. 30).

Barack Obama (elected 2009; Figure 27-6) has yet to demonstrate his full potential as an environmental leader, but he made it clear during his election campaign that he was concerned about climate change, willing to make significant greenhouse gas reductions, and planning to create millions of new "green" jobs. Upon gaining office, Obama directed funding to energy-efficiency projects, renewable energy initiatives, "green" job training, and vehicle-efficiency programs.

AP Photo-Haraz N. Ghanbari/The Canadian Press

FIGURE 27-6 Environmental leadership: North Americans are watching to see how well the environmental agendas of Canadian Prime Minister Stephen Harper and U.S. President Barack Obama mesh.

He has protected wilderness and strengthened the U.S. Endangered Species Act. He has injected billions of dollars into science, appointed environmental experts in high positions, given assurances of cooperation to world leaders—even those who had been enemies of President George W. Bush. Many people are watching to see if Obama will live up to his potential to be an extremely influential environmental leader.

Much of our environmental leadership does not come from politicians. Quite frankly, many politicians did not appear to be environmentally aware until a large proportion of the voting public became educated and concerned about environmental issues. We can thank people like David Suzuki (p. 3) for being a tireless leader, educator, and advocate for all things environmental in Canada and in the world. David Schindler (p. 337) has been an active researcher and vocal spokesperson on topics concerning aquatic ecosystems; he has been described as the world's greatest living freshwater ecologist. Mark Jaccard, a professor of environmental economics at Simon Fraser University, has been described as Canada's leading authority on climate change and is having a large impact on this aspect of environmental thinking. Maude Barlow is an environmental activist, the author of many books, the national chairperson of the Council of Canadians, and a leading spokesperson at national and global levels concerning the world's water crisis (Chapter 15).

Outside of Canada, many non-politicians would be recognized as environmental leaders by Canadians. Jacques Cousteau (1910–97) was a French naval officer, a co-inventor of the aqualung, a filmmaker, and a roving scientist with his own research ship who educated the world about the beauty, mystery, and fragility of the sea. Lester Brown is a prolific American writer and thinker who has written more than 50 books on the environment and founded key environmental organizations such as the Worldwatch Institute and the Earth Policy Institute. He has been described as one of the world's most widely published and most influential thinkers about environmental topics.

There may be many other people in your immediate life, or in your circle of awareness, that you would consider to be environmental leaders. And where do you fit in as an environmental leader? What are you doing to influence and lead others toward improving the environment? What could you do? How could you best use your particular talents, motivations, and opportunities?

Each of us can provide leadership on environmental or other issues in three ways. One is to *lead by example*, using our own lifestyles and beliefs to demonstrate that change is possible and beneficial.

A second approach is to *work within existing economic and political systems to bring about environmental improvement*. We can influence political decisions by campaigning and voting for candidates and by communicating with elected officials. We can also send a message to companies making harmful environment products or policies by *voting with our wallets* and letting them know what we have done. You would be surprised at how few consumer complaints it takes for a company to change its ways because of a fear of having a bad public image. We can join an influential environmental group. We can also work within the system by choosing environmental careers (Individuals Matter, p. 675).

A third form of environmental leadership is to *run for a local office*. Look in the mirror. Maybe you are one who can make a difference as an office holder.

A fourth form involves *proposing and working for better solutions to environmental problems*. Leadership is more than being against something. It also involves coming up with alternatives and getting people to work together to achieve them, especially in today's often-hostile political climate.

CONSIDER, DISCUSS, OR DEBATE

Whom do you consider to be the best examples of environmental leaders on global, national, and local levels? Are there things you could do to influence your peers? Suggest ways in which you practise environmental leadership within the context of your college or university.

How Can Organizations Change to Foster Better Policy Making? Be Nimble, Flexible, and Adaptive in a Rapidly Changing World

To achieve more sustainable environmental policies, most organizations will be more effective if they shift from hierarchical to network models.

Businesses, governments, and all organizations are entering a new era in which to thrive and survive, most must shift from rigid, slow-acting, top-down hierarchical organizations to something more flexible that can adapt quickly to changing conditions. This new organizational model is that of a *network* instead of that of a *hierarchy*.

In a hierarchy consisting of a pyramid of increasingly powerful layers of decision makers, information takes a long route to the top, and decisions take time to filter down. People in such organizations are used more as information transmitters than as innovators of new ideas. The result is a lack of good information at the top, a rigid set of controls and rules, and too little innovation. In today's rapidly changing and increasingly globalized and interconnected world, such hierarchical structures are rapidly going the way of dinosaurs.

Hierarchies are necessary for the stable functioning of some parts of governments and for some businesses. But many organizations are shifting to a flatter, leaner, and more adaptable network structure without as many middle and senior managers. In such organizations, information flows rapidly to all members of the network, not unlike the way energy and matter flow through food webs in ecosystems. It is one way of achieving more organizational sustainability by copying nature. More open and democratic information flow makes it much easier to adapt to changing conditions, and it promotes cooperation and innovation. Some analysts say that the European Union is slowly emerging as an example of a new and more flexible network form of government.

In the network model, leaders still have a vital role. Their job is to develop vision, values, and objectives for their organizations. Then they must promote feedback from employees, encourage innovation and adaptation, and establish employee performance goals.

An important aspect of emerging network organizations is their use of **adaptive management** strategies (Figure 11-29, p. 243) to cope with new information and changing conditions, to learn from experience, and to modify plans quickly as needed. This approach uses the basic techniques of science (Figure 3-2, p. 35) and systems analysis (Figure 4-35, p. 91) to develop computer models for examining alternative plans and projecting possible outcomes or scenarios. The primary goal is to anticipate problems rather than simply react to them.

Plans should be flexible and easy to change in response to new information, unexpected developments, and changing conditions. Progress toward goals is regularly monitored and evaluated, and this information is used as feedback to adapt the plan as needed. Any group seeking to influence environmental or other policies will need to adopt such organizational structures and strategies.

> **CONSIDER, DISCUSS, OR DEBATE**
>
> Identify a hierarchical system within your college, university, or community. How would you go about converting it into a network system?

27-4 ENVIRONMENTAL LAW

What Is Environmental Law, and How Does It Evolve? A Mix of Legislation and Tradition

The body of environmental laws is constantly evolving through legislation and lawsuits.

Environmental law is a body of statements defining what is reasonable environmental behaviour for individuals and groups according to the larger community, and attempting to balance competing social and private interests. It includes statutory laws, administrative laws, and common laws.

Statutory laws are those developed and passed by legislative bodies such as federal and provincial governments. **Administrative laws** consist of administrative rules and regulations, executive orders, and enforcement decisions related to the implementation and interpretation of statutory laws. **Common law** is a body of unwritten rules and principles derived from thousands of past legal decisions along with commonly accepted practices, or *norms*, within a society. Most of it consists of *case law*, a body of legal opinions derived from past court decisions. The body of laws is continuously evolving, as almost every major environmental regulation is challenged in court.

Most environmental lawsuits are **civil suits**—those brought to settle disputes or damages between one party and another. Many common law cases are settled using the legal principle of *nuisance*. A nuisance occurs when people use their property in a way that causes annoyance or injury to others. For example, a homeowner may bring a nuisance suit against a nearby factory because of the noise it generates.

In such a civil suit, the **plaintiff,** the party bringing the charge, seeks to collect damages for injuries to health or for economic loss from the **defendant,** the party being charged. The plaintiff may also seek an *injunction*, by which the defendant would be required to stop whatever action is causing the harm. An individual or a clearly identified group may bring such a suit. A **class action suit** is a civil suit filed by a group, often a public interest or environmental group, on behalf of a larger number of citizens who allege similar damages but who need not be listed and represented individually.

Using the principles of common law, the court may side with the plaintiff if it finds that the loss of sleep, health problems, or other damage from the noise is greater than the cost of eliminating or reducing the noise. Short of closing the factory, often the court tries to find a reasonable or balanced solution to the problem. For example, it may order the factory to reduce noise to certain levels or to eliminate it during certain periods, such as at night.

Another principle used in common law cases is *negligence*, in which a party causes damage by knowingly acting in an unlawful or unreasonable manner. For example, a company may be found negligent if it fails to handle hazardous waste in a way required by a statutory law. A court may also find a company negligent if it fails to do something a reasonable person would do, such as testing waste for certain harmful chemicals before dumping it into a sewer, landfill, or river. Generally, negligence is harder to prove than nuisance.

What Factors Hinder the Effectiveness of Environmental Lawsuits? Mostly Money and Time

Environmental lawsuits are expensive and difficult to win.

Several factors limit the effectiveness of environmental lawsuits. *First*, any person bringing the suit must establish that she or he has the legal right or *legal standing* to do so in a particular court. To have such a right, plaintiffs must show that they have personally suffered health or financial losses from some alleged environmental activity.

Second, bringing any lawsuit is expensive—too much so for most individuals. Large organizations, on the other hand, can often afford to defend themselves in court for months or years.

Third, unlike public interest law firms, corporations can reduce their taxes by deducting their legal expenses—in effect having the public pay for part of their legal fees. In other words, the legal playing field is uneven and in financial terms is stacked against individuals and groups of private citizens filing environmental lawsuits.

Fourth, to stop a nuisance or to collect damages from a nuisance or an act of negligence, plaintiffs must establish they have been harmed in some significant way and that the defendant caused the harm. Doing this can be difficult and costly. Suppose a company (the defendant) is charged with causing cancer in individuals by polluting a river. If hundreds of other industries and cities dump waste into that river, establishing that the defendant is the culprit is very difficult and requires expensive investigation, scientific research, and expert testimony. In addition, it is hard to establish that a particular chemical caused the plaintiffs' cancers.

Fifth, there may be *statutes of limitations*, laws that limit how long a plaintiff can take to sue after a particular event occurs. These statutes often make it essentially impossible for victims of cancer, which may take 10–20 years to develop, to file or win a negligence suit.

Sixth, the court, or series of courts if the case is appealed, may take years to reach a decision. During that time, a defendant may continue the allegedly damaging action unless the court issues a temporary injunction against it until the case is decided.

Finally, some corporations may take aggressive court action against citizens who publicly criticize them. These actions are often intended to discourage individuals and activist groups from opposing projects they believe are environmentally harmful. Win or lose, corporations and developers generally save money by filing such suits. Unlike the people they are suing, they can count legal and liability insurance costs as business expenses and write them off on their taxes. In other words, they get all taxpayers to pay much of the cost of lawsuits against a few taxpayers who are exercising their rights as citizens.

Because of the numerous difficulties just discussed, an increasing number of environmental lawsuits are being settled out of court. Some are settled privately and others by *mediation*, in which a neutral party tries to resolve the dispute in a way that is acceptable to both parties. Mediation is much less costly and time consuming and may provide a more satisfactory resolution of a dispute than going to court. But a settlement drawn up by mediation is not legally binding unless the terms of the agreement make it so. Thus months of mediation can result in an agreement that polluters may ignore.

CONSIDER, DISCUSS, OR DEBATE

People found guilty of breaking environmental laws are often required to pay fines. Do you think serious violators of these laws should be punished with prison sentences instead? Explain.

Case Study: What Are Some Major Environmental Laws in Canada?

Canadian environmental laws set pollution standards, screen toxic substances, evaluate environmental impacts, encourage resource conservation, and protect various ecosystems and species from harm.

Concerned citizens have persuaded the Canadian government to enact a number of important federal environmental and resource protection laws (Table 27-1) that seek to protect environmental quality by using various approaches. One is to set standards for pollution levels (as in the Canada Water Act). Another is to screen new substances for safety (as in the Canadian Environmental Protection Act).

A third type of legislation encourages resource conservation (the Fisheries Act). A fourth type sets aside or protects various ecosystems, resources, and species (the Species at Risk Act).

A fifth approach is to require evaluation of the environmental impact of an activity proposed by a federal agency, as in the Canadian Environmental Assessment Act or CEAA passed in 1992. Under CEAA, an environmental impact statement (EIS) must be developed for every major federal project likely to have an important effect on environmental quality. The EIS must describe why the proposed project is needed, its short-term and long-term beneficial and harmful environmental impacts, ways to lessen harmful impacts, and an evaluation of alternatives. An EIS typically takes 6–9 months to develop and is often hundreds of pages long. The documents must be published and are open to public comment.

Table 27-1 Some Canadian Environmental Laws in Brief

Act	Function
Alternative Fuels Act (1995)	Directs government to update its fleet of vehicles until 75% of vehicles are using alternative fuels (not gasoline or diesel)
Arctic Waters Pollution Prevention Act (1985)	Controls pollution related to shipping through Arctic waters
Canada National Marine Conservation Areas Act (2002)	Describes how national marine conservation areas will be established and managed
Canada Oil and Gas Operations Act (1985)	Establishes how exploration and drilling for oil and gas shall be carried out in northern Canada
Canada Water Act (1970)	Establishes a framework for federal–provincial cooperation in the management of freshwater resources
Canada Wildlife Act (1985)	Regulates the conservation of wildlife under federal control and facilitates research, planning, and conservation practices
Canadian Environmental Assessment Act (1992)	Establishes the procedures for conducting environmental impact assessments, including public participation, for projects involving the federal government
Canadian Environmental Protection Act (1999)	Controls toxic substances and provides national environmental quality guidelines
Clean Air Act (2006)	Controls air pollutants including greenhouse gases. The legislation consists of amendments to other acts such as the Canadian Environmental Protection Act (1999), the Motor Vehicle Consumption Standards Act (1985), and the Energy Efficiency Act (1992)
Department of the Environment Act (1985)	Establishes the Department of the Environment, the Minister of the Environment, and the mandate of preserving environmental quality and handling international environmental issues
Energy Efficiency Act (1992)	Allows the government to control the energy efficiency of energy-using products and the use of energy-alternative sources
Environmental Violations Administrative Monetary Penalties Act (2009)	Establishes a fair and consistent monetary penalty system to aid the enforcement of environmental acts such as the Canada National Marine Conservation Areas Act, the Canada National Parks Act, the Canada Water Act, and the Canada Wildlife Act
Federal Sustainable Development Act (2008)	Requires the government to create and implement a federal sustainable development strategy, and an advisory council, to ensure that the ecologically efficient use of natural, social, and economic resources is an integral part of government decision making
Fisheries Act (1985)	Regulates management of the fisheries industry, protects fish habitat, and outlines the powers of fisheries officers
Migratory Birds Convention Act (1994)	Protects migratory bird species, establishes sanctuaries, and prohibits the possession of unlicensed migratory birds
Motor Vehicle Fuel Consumption Standards Act (1985)	Allows Canada to control the fuel consumption standards of motor vehicles
National Parks Act (1988)	Empowers the federal government to preserve areas that reflect Canada's national and cultural heritage
National Roundtable on the Environment and the Economy Act (1993)	Promotes principles and practices of sustainable development
Oceans Act (1996)	Establishes marine protected areas and outlines an oceans management strategy that incorporates the ideas of sustainable development and the precautionary principle
Species at Risk Act (2002)	Protects and supports the recovery of species that are at risk
Tobacco Act (1997)	Regulates tobacco products and educates the public about the hazards of smoking
Wild Animal and Plant Protection and Regulation of International and Interprovincial Trade Act (1992)	Allows Canada to control the import and export of endangered species identified by the CITES Convention (p. 262)

Source: Department of Justice Canada, http://laws.justice.gc.ca/en.

CEAA does not prohibit environmentally harmful government projects but it requires federal agencies to take environmental consequences into account in making decisions and exposes proposed projects and their likely harmful effects to public scrutiny. A number of other countries—including the United States, Sweden, France, New Zealand, and Australia—have passed laws similar to CEAA.

Environmentalists have used EISs to block harmful projects or get them modified to reduce their environmental impacts. Many agree that CEAA has helped federal agencies to evaluate and reduce the harmful environmental impacts of their projects and activities.

Critics say EISs are costly and can unnecessarily delay projects by requiring too much analysis (paralysis by analysis). Proponents say analysis is needed to make government agencies think more seriously about the impact of proposed projects and to examine alternatives.

27-5 ENVIRONMENTAL GROUPS AND THEIR OPPONENTS

What Are the Roles of Major Environmental Groups? Watchdogs and Agents of Change

Environmental groups monitor environmental activities, work to pass and strengthen environmental laws, and work with corporations to find solutions to environmental problems.

The spearhead of the global conservation and environmental movement consists of more than 100 000 non-profit NGOs working at the international, national, state, and local levels—up from about 2 000 in 1970. The growing influence of these organizations is one of the most important changes affecting environmental decisions and policies.

NGOs range from grassroots groups with just a few members to global organizations like the 5-million-member World Wide Fund for Nature (called the World Wildlife Fund in North America) with offices in 70 countries. Other international groups with large memberships include Greenpeace, the Nature Conservancy (Solutions, p. 241), Grameen Bank (Solutions, p. 655), and Conservation International.

Using e-mail and the Internet, environmental NGOs have organized themselves into an array of powerful international networks. Examples include the Pesticide Action, Climate Action, International Rivers, Women's Environment and Development, and Biodiversity Action Networks. They collaborate across borders, gathering environmental information, monitoring environmental change, and acting quickly. They monitor the environmental activities of governments, corporations, and international agencies such as the World Bank and the World Trade Organization (WTO). They expose corruption and violations of national and international environmental agreements, such as CITES, which prohibits international trade of endangered species. Groups such as Conservation International and the Nature Conservancy have brokered debt-for-nature swaps where developing countries agree to protect ecologically important areas in exchange for reduction of their international debt. NGOs are also watchdogs for environmental accountability at the local level.

In Canada and the United States, more than 8 million citizens belong to over 30 000 NGOs dealing with environmental issues. They range from small grassroots groups to large heavily funded groups, led by chief executive officers and staffed by expert lawyers, scientists, economists, lobbyists, and fundraisers. The largest of these are the World Wildlife Fund, Sierra Club, National Wildlife Federation, Audubon Society, Greenpeace, Friends of the Earth, Natural Resources Defense Council, Wilderness Society, and Ducks Unlimited.

The large groups have become powerful and important forces within the political system, by working individually and together in coalitions to help persuade government to pass and strengthen environmental laws and to fight off attempts to weaken or repeal them.

However, these large environmental groups must guard against being subverted by the political system they work to improve. This is a risk because these groups rely heavily on corporate donations, and many of them have corporate executives as board members, trustees, or council members.

The *good news* is that instead of acting as adversaries, some industries and environmental groups are working together to find solutions to environmental problems. For example, Environmental Defense Fund has worked with McDonald's to redesign its packaging system to eliminate polyethylene foam clamshell hamburger containers. It has also worked with General Motors to help remove high-pollution cars from the road and with various multinational corporations to set targets for reducing their carbon dioxide emissions. The World Resources Institute is collaborating with leading businesses to build a market among corporations for electrical power produced from renewable energy resources.

Some environmental groups have shifted some resources from demonstrating and litigating to publicizing research on innovative solutions to environmental problems. For example, to promote the use of chlorine-free paper, Greenpeace Germany printed a magazine using such paper and encouraged readers to demand that magazine publishers switch to chlorine-free paper. Shortly thereafter, several major magazines made that shift.

What Are the Roles of Grassroots Environmental Groups? Citizen Action from the Bottom Up

Thousands of citizens' groups throughout the world are working to improve environmental quality.

The base of the environmental movement throughout the world consists of thousands of grassroots citizens' groups organized to improve environmental quality, often at the local level. According to political analyst Konrad von Moltke (1941–2005), "There isn't a government in the world that would have done anything for the environment if it weren't for the citizen groups." Table 27-2 lists some of the groups that are operating in Canada.

These groups carry out a number of environmental roles. One is to work with individuals and communities to oppose harmful projects such as landfills, waste incinerators, nuclear waste dumps, clear-cutting of forests, and various development projects. They have also pressured government officials to take action when group members have been victims of environmental harm or of environmental injustice because of the unequal distribution of environmental risks.

Grassroots groups have also formed land trusts and other local organizations to save wetlands, forests, farmland, and ranchland from development. They have helped restore degraded rivers and wetlands, and have converted abandoned urban lots into community gardens and parks. Some groups are coalitions of workers and environmentalists who aim to improve worker safety and health.

International examples of grassroots NGOs are Kenya's Green Belt Movement, in which citizens plant trees on public and private land; India's long-standing Chipko movement, where villagers protect trees by hugging them and thus placing themselves between the trees and axes and chainsaws; and Sri Lanka's Sarvodaya Shramadana movement, which has developed wells for drinking water, gardening, and other small-scale improvement projects in 12 000 villages.

Taken together, a loosely connected network of grassroots NGOs working for bottom-up political, social, economic, and environmental change can be viewed as an emerging citizen-based *global sustainability movement*. These millions of citizens are becoming informed and empowered by access to the World Wide Web, cell phones, e-mail, faxes, GIS

Table 27-2 A Selection of Environmental Groups Operating in Canada	
Group	**Mandate**
Canadian Environmental Law Association http://www.cela.ca	Advocates for comprehensive environmental laws, standards, and policies throughout Canada
David Suzuki Foundation http://www.davidsuzuki.org	Uses science and education to promote sustainable communities throughout the world
Friends of the Environment Foundation http://www.fef.td.com	Funds the efforts of Canadian environmentalists
Friends of Laurier Woods http://www.laurierwoods.com	Works to preserve the Laurier Woods ecosystem in its natural state
Greenpeace Canada http://www.greenpeace.org/canada	Uses nonviolent, creative confrontation to expose global environmental problems
Nature Conservancy Canada http://www.natureconservancy.ca	Works to preserve natural habitats
Ontario Nature http://www.ontarionature.org	Uses research, education, and conservation to protect and restore natural habitats
Pembina Institute http://www.pembina.org	Promotes sustainable energy solutions as an independent, nonprofit environmental policy research and education organization
Pollution Probe http://www.pollutionprobe.org	Uses education and research to promote positive environmental change
Sierra Club Canada http://www.sierraclub.ca	Works to protect our communities and the planet
Sustainable Calgary http://www.sustainablecalgary.ca	Supports community-level actions and initiatives designed to move Calgary toward a sustainable future
World Wildlife Fund Canada http://www.wwf.ca	Works to stop the degradation of the planet's natural environment and to build a future in which humans live in harmony with nature

mapping programs, and other components of the global communications web.

As Jeremy Rifkin puts it, "We are rapidly moving from geopolitics to biosphere politics." According to Rifkin, the Internet, coupled with our better understanding of how the Earth sustains itself, will allow us, for the first time in human history, to really think globally and act locally.

The late John W. Gardner, former U.S. cabinet official and founder of the environmental group Common Cause, suggested using the following rules for effective political action by grassroots organizations:

- Have a full-time continuing organization.

- Limit the number of targets and hit them hard. Groups dilute their effectiveness by taking on too many issues.

- Organize for action, not just for study, discussion, or education.

- Form alliances with other organizations on a particular issue.

- Communicate positions in an accurate, concise, and moving way.

- Persuade and use positive reinforcement.

- Concentrate efforts mostly at the regional and local levels.

Some grassroots environmental groups use non-violent and nondestructive tactics of protest marches, pickets, road blocks, tree sitting, confronting illegal whaling ships, street theatre, and other devices for generating publicity to help educate and sway members of the public to their causes. Many of these tactics are borrowed from Mahatma Gandhi's nonviolent civil disobedience strategies, used to help win India's independence from Great Britain, and in the U.S. civil-rights movement. Some find the tactics of these groups controversial while others admire them for standing up for their beliefs in nonviolent ways.

SPOTLIGHT

Earth Hour: Uniting People to Protect the Planet

Earth Hour began in Australia on March 31, 2007, when 2.2 million residents of Sydney demonstrated that they were willing to turn off non-essential lights and appliances for an hour to show their support for climate change action.

In 2008, the plan was to take Earth Hour to the rest of Australia. However, the City of Toronto, Canada, also signed up and it wasn't long before 35 countries and almost 400 cities and towns were part of the event. People voluntarily turned down lights in their homes and the same was also done on famous public buildings. It said something compelling to the world: that the climate challenges facing our planet are so significant that change needs to be global.

Earth Hour 2009 (March 28) was bigger again, kick-starting the world's first global election, calling on citizens of the world to show their vote for Earth over Global Warming. Ten times as many cities were officially involved, in 88 different countries. NGOs, politicians and celebrities vigorously promoted the event while making good use of the public attention. When the hour of darkness came, it was more effective and more significant than ever.

In the newspapers the next day, various columnists tried to calculate how much energy was actually saved by the event, but that wasn't the point. People had learned that their symbolic gesture of turning off the lights was a display of what can be achieved when everybody does their part for the environment. This awareness was carried into the 2009 United Nations Climate Change Conference later that year. The vote that people clearly had made by switching off their lights for an hour was a global voice in the ears of the decision makers.

With the invitation to 'switch off' extended to everyone and being fuelled by social media, Earth Hour quickly became an annual global event scheduled towards the end of March—closely coinciding with the equinox to ensure most cities are in darkness as it rolled out around the Earth.

Jump ahead to 2012, and Earth Hour had expanded to include more than 7000 cities and towns in 152 countries and territories all over the world. Social media was again the driving force behind the campaign, encouraging people to go "Beyond the Hour." Around 200,000 people accepted "I Will If You Will" challenges from celebrity ambassadors, politicians, organisations and members of the public. With the power of social networks used to promote the campaign, Earth Hour is working towards an interconnected global community committed to creating a more sustainable planet.

To learn more about past Earth Hours, and to anticipate the next ones go to earthhour.org. plus web pages you will discover.

Critical Thinking

Analyze why the Earth Hour program (http://www.earthhour.org) has been successful at uniting the actions of millions of people throughout the world. Is it likely that people will make large steps to deal with energy issues without first gaining awareness and taking smaller steps such as turning off nonessential lights?

Courtesy of the WWF

Much more controversial are those environmental groups that break into labs to free animals used to test drugs or that destroy property such as bulldozers and SUVs. Most environmentalists oppose such tactics because they involve illegal and destructive acts, give other environmentalists a bad name, and play into the hands of environmentalists' political opponents.

CONSIDER, DISCUSS, OR DEBATE

Do you support the use of confrontational (but nonviolent) tactics by environmental groups and individuals? What are the advantages and disadvantages of this approach?

Case Study: Environmental Action by Students—Making a Difference

Many student environmental groups work with faculty and administrators to bring about environmental improvements in their schools and local communities.

In recent years, students, faculty, and administrators across Canada have been working together to create sustainable campuses.

At Queen's University in Kingston, Ontario, the student-run Science 44 Housing Cooperative features hot water solar pas and long-term plans for environmental retrofits. McGill University's EcoResidence, which was renovated with recycled materials, uses greenhouses to generate solar energy and rooftop-collected rainwater that is filtered for use by students living in the residence. Each year, students at Red River College in Winnipeg, Manitoba, produce 10–20 metric tons of compost using organic waste collected from the campus. At Mount Allison University in Sackville, New Brunswick, the inhabitants of *Carriage House Sustainable Residence* grow much of their own food in the Sackville community garden, participate in an organic food co-op, and engage in vermicomposting.

At Nipissing University in North Bay, Ontario, the student-run Environmental Action Committee focuses on environmental issues and practises recycling and other green activities. In conjunction with administration and faculty, students helped to design *Eco-Village*, a student residence that opened in 2007. The students are living in an experiment as they make alterations to their housing and habits and monitor the energy savings. If you have a sustainable-campus story to tell, please e-mail Dr. Dave Hackett at daveh@nipissingu.ca.

How Successful Have Environmental Groups and Their Opponents Been? Achievements and Setbacks

Environmental groups throughout the world have helped educate the public and business and political leaders about environmental issues and pass environmental laws, but in the United States an organized movement has undermined many of these efforts.

Since 1970, a variety of environmental groups throughout the world have helped increase understanding of

---

INDIVIDUALS MATTER

Environmental Careers

One thing you could do is have an environmental career. In Canada and most other developed countries, the *green job market* is one of the fastest-growing segments of the economy.

Many employers are actively seeking environmentally educated graduates. They are especially interested in people with scientific and engineering backgrounds and double majors (business and ecology, for example) or double minors. Other possibilities are majors in business administration and environmental law.

Throughout this book, we have exposed you to various career possibilities in this exciting and challenging field. They include environmental engineering, sustainable forestry and range management, parks and recreation management, air and water quality control, solid waste and hazardous waste management, recycling, urban and rural land-use planning, computer modelling, ecological restoration, and soil, water, fishery, and wildlife conservation and management.

Environmental careers can also be found in education, environmental planning, environmental management, environmental health, toxicology, geology, ecology, conservation biology, chemistry, climatology, population dynamics and regulation (demography), law, risk analysis, risk management, accounting, environmental journalism, design and architecture, energy conservation and analysis, renewable-energy technologies, hydrology, consulting, public relations, activism and lobbying, economics, diplomacy, development and marketing, publishing (environmental magazines and books), and teaching and law enforcement (pollution detection and enforcement teams).

Critical Thinking

Have you considered an environmental career? Visit http://www.goodworkcanada.ca and other green job sites to explore your options.

environmental issues by the general public and some business and government leaders. They have also gained public support for an array of environmental and resource-use laws. In addition, they have helped individuals and groups deal with environmental problems.

An interesting contradiction exists in the United States. Polls show that more than 80% of the U.S. public strongly supports environmental laws and regulations and do not want them weakened. But polls also show that less than 10% of the U.S. public views the environment as one of the nation's most pressing problems. As a result, environmental concerns often do not get transferred to the ballot box. As one political scientist put it, "Environmental concerns are like the Florida Everglades, a mile wide but only a few inches deep." And since 1980 a well-organized and well-funded movement has undermined much of the improvement in environmental understanding and support for environmental concerns in the United States.

One problem is that the focus of environmental issues has shifted from easy-to-see dirty smokestacks and burning rivers to more complex and controversial environmental problems that are less visible, are harder to understand and solve, and have long-range harmful effects. Examples are climate change,

wasted energy, ozone depletion, biodiversity loss, nonpoint-source water pollution, and unseen groundwater pollution. Explaining such complex issues to the public and mobilizing support for often controversial, long-range solutions to such problems can be difficult.

Another problem is that many environmentalists have brought mostly bad news. History shows that bearers of bad news are not received well, and opponents of environmentalists have used this to undermine environmental concerns.

History also shows that people are moved to bring about change mostly by an inspiring, positive vision of what the world could be like, one that provides hope for the future. So far, environmentalists with a variety of beliefs and goals have not worked together to develop broad, compelling, and positive visions that can be used as road maps for a more sustainable future for humans and other species.

Instead of using confrontation, some people are working to mediate environmental disputes by getting each side to listen to one another's concerns, try to find areas of agreement, and work together to find solutions (Solutions, below). This approach is being used successfully in places such as the Netherlands (pp. 657–658), the Great Lakes (p. 550), Curitiba, Brazil (p. 614), and North Bay, Ontario (p. 633).

SOLUTIONS

How Can We Improve Environmental Laws and Regulations? Time for a Checkup

Environmentalists agree that some government laws and regulations go too far and that bureaucrats sometimes develop and impose unfair and excessively costly regulations. They argue that the solution is to stop regulatory abuse, not to throw out or seriously weaken the body of laws and regulations that help protect the public good.

According to environmental economist William Ashworth,

Government regulation did not fall out of the sky; it was erected, piece-by-piece, as an attempt to deal with the damage caused by unrestrained property rights and the unregulated free-market system…. We do not need to deconstruct regulation, but to reconstruct it.

To accomplish this, a growing number of analysts urge environmentalists to take a hard look at existing environmental laws and regulations. Which laws or parts of laws have worked, and why? Which have failed, and why? Which government bureaucracies concerned with developing and enforcing environmental and resource regulations have abused their power or have not been responsive enough to the needs of ordinary people? How can such abuses be corrected? What existing environmental laws (or parts of such laws) and regulations should be repealed or modified?

What environmental problems lend themselves to market-based

approaches (free-market environmentalism), and which ones do not? What roles should pollution prevention, waste reduction, and the precautionary principle play in environmental legislation and regulation?

These are important issues that environmentalists, business leaders, elected officials, and government regulators need to address with a cooperative, problem-solving spirit.

Critical Thinking

Identify an environmental law in Canada that you believe needs to be improved. How would you improve it?

Solutions: Should We Expand the Concept of National and Global Security? The Big Three

Many analysts believe that environmental security is as important as military and economic security.

Countries are legitimately concerned with *military security* and *economic security*. However, ecologists point out that all economies are supported by the Earth's natural capital. According to environmental expert Norman Myers,

If a nation's environmental foundations are degraded or depleted, its economy may well decline, its social fabric deteriorate, and its political structure become destabilized as growing numbers of people seek to sustain themselves from declining resource stocks. Thus, national security is no longer about fighting forces and weaponry alone. It relates increasingly to watersheds, croplands, forests, genetic resources, climate, and other factors that, taken together, are as crucial to a nation's security as are military factors.

Proponents of this view call for all countries to make environmental security a major focus of diplomacy and government policy at all levels. This would be implemented by having a council of advisers made up of highly qualified experts in environmental, economic, and military security who integrate all three security concerns in making major decisions.

> **CONSIDER, DISCUSS, OR DEBATE**
>
> Do you believe that environmental security is just as important as economic and military security? Explain.

FIGURE 27-7 Canadian industrialist and diplomat Maurice Strong headed the Canadian International Development Agency (CIDA) and held a variety of UN posts. He is best known to environmentalists as the chair of the 1992 Rio Earth Summit. At this historic convention, governments from around the world set unprecedented environmental goals.

What Is the Role of International Environmental Organizations? Major Players

International environmental organizations gather and evaluate environmental data, help develop environmental treaties, and provide funds and loans for sustainable economic development.

A diverse array of international environmental organizations helps shape and set environmental policy. Perhaps the most influential is the United Nations, with a large family of organizations such as the UN Environment Programme (UNEP), the World Health Organization (WHO), the United Nations Development Programme (UNDP), and the Food and Agriculture Organization (FAO). Canada's Maurice Strong (Figure 27-7) has held many important UN posts and has served as an adviser to many Canadian and UN politicians. Recently, he was senior adviser to the 2012 Rio+20 Summit (http://www.mauricestrong. net). See the Spotlight below on Rio+20.

Other organizations that make or influence environmental decisions are the World Bank, the Global Environment Facility (GEF), and the World Conservation Union (IUCN). These organizations have played important roles in

- Expanding understanding of environmental issues
- Gathering and evaluating environmental data
- Helping develop and monitor international environmental treaties
- Providing funds and loans for sustainable economic development and reducing poverty
- Helping more than 100 nations develop environmental laws and institutions

Despite their often limited funding, these diverse organizations have made important contributions to global and national environmental progress since 1970.

Since the 1972 UN Conference on the Human Environment in Stockholm, Sweden, progress has been made in addressing environmental issues at the global level. Political scientist Keith Caldwell credits the Stockholm conference with forcing many governments to develop domestic environmental programs and legitimizing not harming the biosphere as an object of national and international concern and policy. It also created the United Nations Environment Programme (UNEP) to help develop the global environmental agenda. But the UNEP is a small and underfunded agency. Figure 27-8 lists some of the good and bad news about international efforts to deal with global environmental problems such as poverty, climate change, biodiversity loss, and ocean pollution. Carefully study this figure.

The primary focus of the international community on environmental problems has been the development of various international environmental laws and nonbinding policy declarations called *conventions*. Over 500 international environmental treaties and agreements—known as *multilateral environmental agreements* (MEAs)—have been developed, two-thirds of them signed in recent decades.

To date, the Montreal and Copenhagen Protocols for protecting the ozone layer are two of the most successful examples of how the global community can work together to deal with a serious global environmental challenge (p. 535). Figure 27-9 lists some major problems with MEAs and solutions to these problems.

During the past 30 years, James Gustave (Gus) Speth has either created or run many of the world's most important environmental organizations, including the Natural Resources Defense Council, the White House Council on Environmental Quality, and the United Nations Development Programme, and is now dean of Yale University's School of Forestry and Environmental Studies. In 1994, he wrote the book *Red Sky at Morning*, summarizing his insider view of global environmental efforts. He gives a failing grade to almost every one.

Speth says that "in general, the issue with major treaties is not weak enforcement or weak compliance; the issue is weak treaties. These agreements are easy for governments to slight because their impressive goals are not followed by clear requirements, targets, and timetables … and [there is] an unwillingness to commit financial resources for real incentives." He says that "international law is still far too dominated by the outmoded concept that only governments get to play" instead of following a principle in the 1992 Rio convention that "environmental issues are best handled with the participation of all concerned citizens."

Trade-Offs

Global Efforts on Environmental Problems

Good News

Environmental protection agencies in 150 nations

Over 500 international environmental treaties and agreements

UN Environment Programme (UNEP) created in 1972 to negotiate and monitor international environmental treaties

1992 Rio Earth Summit adopted key principles for dealing with global environmental problems

2002 Johannesburg Earth Summit attempted to implement policies and goals of 1992 Rio summit and find ways to reduce poverty

2012 Rio+20 Summit united governments, the private sector, and civil society in greater cooperation toward achieving sustainable development

The 8 MDGs, designed to achieve specified goals by 2015, showed how rapid progress could be made through organized global cooperation

Bad News

Most international environmental treaties lack criteria for monitoring and evaluating their effectiveness

1992 Rio Earth Summit led to nonbinding agreements without enough funding to implement them

2002 Johannesburg Earth Summit failed to provide adequate goals, deadlines, and funding for dealing with global environmental problems such as climate change, biodiversity loss, and poverty

2009 Copenhagen Conference failed to make concrete progress toward dealing with climate change

FIGURE 27-8 Trade-offs: good and bad news about international efforts to deal with global environmental problems. Pick the single piece of good news and the single piece of bad news that you think are the most important.

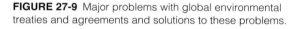

Solutions

International Environmental Treaties

Problems

Take a long time to develop and are weakened by requiring full consensus

Poorly monitored and enforced

Lack of funding for monitoring and enforcement

Treaties are not integrated with one another

Solutions

Do not require full consensus among regulating parties

Establish procedures for monitoring and enforcement

Increase funding for monitoring and enforcement

Harmonize or integrate existing agreements

FIGURE 27-9 Major problems with global environmental treaties and agreements and solutions to these problems.

Speth and several other national and international environmental leaders call for establishing a World Environment Organization (WEO) to help develop and oversee global environmental policies. He says it is strange that we have the World Trade Organization (WTO), the World Health Organization (WHO), and a number of other similar organizations but no World Environmental Organization (WEO). He asks us to imagine what might have happened with global environmental policies if the developed nations "had put as much energy into a WEO as they have put into the WTO."

Can We Develop More Environmentally Sustainable Political and Economic Systems in the Next Few Decades? Establishing a New Partnership

We need to work together to find and implement innovative solutions to local, national, and global environmental, economic, and social problems.

Environmentalists call for people from all political persuasions and walks of life to work together to develop a positive vision for a transition to more environmentally sustainable societies and economies throughout the world.

A major goal would be to promote the development of creative experiments at local levels—such as the one in Curitiba, Brazil (p. 614)—that could be spread to other areas over the next few decades. A second goal is to get citizens, business leaders, and

---

SPOTLIGHT

RIO+20: Two Decades After the Rio Earth Summit

The UN Rio+20 Summit on Sustainable Development took place from June 13 to 22, 2012, in Rio de Janeiro, Brazil. This summit was the follow-up to the 1992 UN Conference on Environment and Development, often called "the Earth Summit," held 20 years earlier in Rio de Janeiro.

The purpose of the Rio+20 Summit was to secure renewed commitment for sustainable development, to assess the progress that had been made over the past 20 years, and to move ahead with increased support and cooperation from a broader base of participants representing governments, the private sector, and civil society. The two main areas of focus were developing green economies to support sustainable development and poverty eradication, and creating institutional frameworks to advance sustainable development.

According to UN Secretary-General Ban Ki-moon, the Rio+20 Summit was a great success. It was the largest UN conference ever held, involving participation from more than 40 000 people including politicians, business leaders, academics, civil leaders, journalists, and the public. Over 100 governments were represented at the head-of-state level. More than $513 billion (U.S.) was committed to support sustainable development of energy, forests, agriculture, disaster relief, and other focal areas. More than 700 voluntary commitments were made by participants, promising actions that will support sustainable development.

As a result of the summit, a political forum on sustainable development was established, and participants agreed to create a set of sustainable development goals (SDGs) to pursue. Visions of the future are outlined in the Rio+20 outcome document entitled *The Future We Want*. The document is 49 pages of ideas arising from the summit, arranged in the form of 283 points (http://www.uncsd2012.org/rio20/thefuturewewant.html). It calls for actions and outlines how green economies can be used for sustainable development. In the words of Secretary-General Ban Ki-moon, "Rio+20 was not an end but a new beginning—a milestone on an essential journey towards 2032 and beyond.... I want a world where not only my children, your children and grandchildren can live free from threats, where men and women can live together with the same opportunities and dignity. That is the future we want" (2012).

RIO+20
United Nations Conference on Sustainable Development

Courtesy of the UN

elected officials to cooperate in trying to find and implement innovative solutions to local, national, and global environmental, economic, and social problems.

Some progress is being made in developing reliable indicator to help gauge and guide the sustainable development of nations. The World Economic Forum, The Yale Center for Environmental Law and Policy, and the Center for International Earth Science Information Network (CIESIN) at Columbia University developed and used an *Environmental Sustainability Index (ESI)* between 1999 and 2005. It measured the overall environmental progress of 142 countries using 21 core indicators, including urban air quality, resource use, and environmental regulation. Canada and the Nordic countries consistently held the top rankings because they were highly developed countries with plentiful natural resources, low population densities, and strong economies; they were in excellent positions to be sustainable.

Since 2006, the same group has switched to publishing an *Environmental Performance Index (EPI)* that ranks countries on performance indicators that cover various aspects of environmental health. This provides a numerical evaluation of how close countries are to established environmental goals; the change was made to better reflect progress toward the targets outlined by the Millennium Development Goals. In 2006, Canada was ranked number 8 with an EPI of 84%. Our EPI ranking and score have declined since then. In 2012, Canada was ranked number 37 with an EPI of 58.4%. In comparison, Switzerland was ranked number 1 with an EPI of 76.7% and the United States was ranked number 49 with an EPI of 56.6%.

CONSIDER, DISCUSS, OR DEBATE

What can Canada and other countries do to improve the rankings and values that result from these EPI indicators? Visit http://epi.yale.edu/ and study the country profiles of Switzerland, Canada, and the United States. Can you see, in a general way, why these three countries were ranked in that order?

Proponents of making progress toward the Millennium Development Goals and sustainable development, and using tools such as the EPI for monitoring progress, recognize that making a cultural shift to more environmentally sustainable societies over the next few decades will be controversial, and like all significant change it will not be predictable, orderly, or painless.

According to business leader Paul Hawken, making this change means

thinking big and long into the future. It also means doing something now. It means electing people who really want to make things work, and who can imagine a better world. It means writing to companies and telling them what you think. It means never forgetting that the cash register is the daily voting booth in democratic capitalism.

Several guidelines have been suggested for fostering cooperation instead of confrontation as we deal with important environmental problems. First, recognize that business is not the enemy. Businesses are here to make money for their investors and shareholders. So why not reward them and encourage new environmental innovations by shifting government subsidies from Earth-degrading activities to Earth-sustaining activities and by shifting taxes from income and wealth to pollution and resource waste? Environmentalists and leaders of corporations could thus become partners in a joint quest for environmental and economic sustainability.

Second, shift the emphasis for dealing with environmental problems to preventing or minimizing them. Third, use well-designed and carefully monitored marketplace solutions to prevent most environmental problems instead of relying primarily on laws, regulations, and litigation in dealing with environmental problems.

Fourth, cooperate and innovate to find win-win solutions to environmental problems instead of using confrontational tactics to come up with less effective I-win-you-lose solutions in which the Earth always ends up losing.

Fifth, stop exaggerating. People on both sides of thorny environmental issues should take a vow not to exaggerate or distort their positions in attempts to play win-lose environmental games. They should recognize that there are trade-offs in any environmental decision—as presented throughout this book—and work together to find balanced win-win solutions that are implemented in a flexible and adaptive manner.

In working to make the Earth a better place to live, we should be guided by historian Arnold Toynbee's observation, "If you make the world ever so little better, you will have done splendidly, and your life will have been worthwhile," and by George Bernard Shaw's reminder that "indifference is the essence of inhumanity."

In the end, it all comes back to each of us taking responsibility. We all have to decide whether we want to be part of the problem or part of the solution to the environmental challenges we face.

As the wagon driver said when they came to a long, hard hill, "Them that's going on with us, get out and push. Them that ain't, get out of the way."
ROBERT FULGHUM

CHECKING OUR PROGRESS AT CREATING A GLOBAL PARTNERSHIP FOR DEVELOPMENT

How Well Are We Progressing with Millennium Goal 8? We Need to Increase Our Efforts

Our progress at meeting the development-related goals of Target 8 has been limited by lack of funding and cooperation; developed nations need to step up their efforts if the Millennium Development Goals are to be met.

The eight Millennium Development Goals were introduced in Chapter 1 and so far have been addressed in Chapters 9, 10, 13, 14, 15, 19, 21, 24, and 26. Goal 8—aimed at creating a global partnership for development—has six targets that are briefly outlined below and in Figure 27-10. The 16 related indicators can be seen online at http://www.mdgmonitor.org/goal8.cfm/.

Some of the Goal 8 targets may seem to be simply "economics," but clearly governments of the world must be involved to promote global cooperation and to design solutions that would not happen if left to free market forces alone.

Target 8A is *to develop further an open, rule-based, predictable, non-discriminatory trading and financial system.*

- Some progress has been made at improving market access for developing nations.

- However, developed nations still subsidize their own agriculture with three times more funding than they spend on aid for developing nations. This creates difficulties for developing nations.

Target 8B is *to address the special needs of the least developed countries.*

- The UN aims to discourage developed countries from subsidizing their own agriculture, to remove tariffs for exports of least developed countries, and to prioritize access to world markets for least developed countries.

Target 8C *addresses the special needs of landlocked developing countries and small-island developing states.*

- Landlocked developing nations are flagged as vulnerable in that they may have to move their goods to market through other countries that can impose tariffs on those goods. Small-island developing states may be isolated from markets, and they may face the threat of rising expenses from sea-level rise associated with global warming. The UN is promoting trade advantages to help both of these groups.

Target 8D is *to deal comprehensively with debt problems of developing countries through national and international measures to make debt sustainable in the long term.*

- There has been progress at reducing debt through debt cancellations and through the economic growth of some developing nations. By 2008, 23 of 42 heavily indebted nations significantly improved their balance of debts; however, many such countries must still spend more on debt payments than they can spend on health or education.

Target 8E is *to provide, in cooperation with pharmaceutical companies, access to affordable essential drugs in developing countries.*

- The involvement of pharmaceutical companies with this target has helped to initiate actions and mobilize funding for securing drugs and treatments to help deal with HIV/AIDS, malaria, and tuberculosis in developing countries. As discussed on pp. 468 and 473, drugs and treatments are expensive and access for those in need is far from universal.

Target 8F is *to make available, in cooperation with the private sector, the benefits of new technologies, especially information and communications.*

- There has been rapid progress in gaining telephone and cell phone access in developing countries. The availability of Internet access has accelerated and now 63% of Internet users live in developing countries. Technologies that allow for better communication, and rapid exchange of information, are of key strategic importance to developing nations that are trying to catch up with the rest of the world.

One of the main themes of the 2012 MDG report (UN, 2012) and the MDG Gap Task Force Report

Millennium Development Goal 8:

Develop a Global Partnership for Development

Target 8A: Develop further an open, rule-based, predictable, non-discriminatory trading and financial system.

Target 8B: Address the special needs of the least developed countries.

Target 8C: Address the special needs of landlocked developing countries and small island developing states.

Target 8D: Deal comprehensively with debt problems of developing countries through national and international measures to make debt sustainable in the long term.

Target 8E: In cooperation with pharmaceutical companies, provide access to affordable essential drugs in developing countries.

Target 8F: In cooperation with the private sector, make available the benefits of new technologies, especially information and communications.

FIGURE 27-10 Working together to ensure the future: Millennium Development Goal 8 aims to build and coordinate a global partnership to solve problems of environmental sustainability that are particularly related to developing nations. (Courtesy of the UNDP)

(UN, 2008) is that more funding is required in order to meet the targets of Goal 8 and the other seven goals. Specifically, 22 countries—16 European Union countries plus 6 more countries (Australia, Canada, Japan, New Zealand, Switzerland, and the United States)—are supposed to provide 0.7% of their Gross National Income (GNI) every year to help developing countries overcome their problems and become environmentally sustainable. Only 5 countries have reached or exceeded the full amount of their Official Development Assistance (ODA) in 2011. These countries are Sweden, Luxembourg, Norway, Denmark, and the Netherlands. Consequently, in 2011 the net aid disbursements received by the UN amounted to 0.31% of the developed countries' combined income, rather than the 0.7% that had been promised. This shortfall of income, combined with effects stemming from the 2008–9 economic slow-down and rising prices, caused some limitations for UN programs.

Luckily, some money can come from other sources, such as NGOs, private industry, and debt relief. However, the UN's firm message is that countries need to deliver on their ODAs every year if the eight Millennium Development Goals are to succeed on time.

CHAPTER REVIEW

1. Review the Key Questions for this chapter on p. 663. What is the purpose of the Environmental Bill of Rights **(Core Case Study)**? What is the function of the Environmental Commissioner? Why is it important that citizens be empowered and assisted in bringing environmental complaints before government?

2. Describe seven shifts that have occurred since the 1970s in the way we view and attempt to deal with environmental problems.

3. What key roles can governments play in improving environmental quality? What is *politics*? What is *environmental policy*? What is a *democracy*? Describe two features of democratic governments that hinder their ability to deal with environmental problems. Explain nine principles that decision makers can use in making environmental policy.

4. Describe four ways in which individuals in democracies can help to develop or change environmental policy. What does it mean to say that we should *think globally and act locally*? Give an example of such an action. What are four ways to provide environmental leadership? Name, in your opinion, some good examples of environmental leaders.

5. What is *environmental law*? Distinguish among a *statutory law*, an *administrative law*, and a *common law*. What is a *civil suit*? What are the *plaintiff* and the *defendant* in a lawsuit? List six reasons why it is difficult to win an environmental lawsuit. What are *negligence* and *mediation*? List five general types of Canadian environmental laws. What is an *environmental impact statement*?

6. Describe the roles of grassroots and mainstream environmental organizations, and give an example of each type of organization. How important are the actions of individuals? How can students get involved in environmental issues at local, regional, national, international, and global levels?

7. In terms of political and environmental activities at an international level, distinguish among a *conference*, a *convention*, and a *multilateral environmental agreement (MEA)*.

8. Explain the importance of environmental security relative to economic security and military security. Describe some examples of international efforts to deal with global environmental problems, mentioning the groups involved and the names of specific meetings. List three general problems with global environmental treaties and agreements.

9. How can we develop environmentally sustainable political and economic systems locally, nationally, and globally? What is the *Environmental Sustainability Index*, and would this be a good indicator to guide us in the right direction? List five guidelines that can help us foster a high level of cooperation so that diverse groups can work together to accomplish their common goals.

10. Describe the development problems that the UN is trying to address with the targets of Goal 8. How are these targets supposed to be funded? How should the UN deal with countries that do not pay their Official Development Assistance commitments?

CRITICAL THINKING

1. What are the greatest strengths and weaknesses of the system of government with respect to **(a)** protecting the environment and **(b)** ensuring environmental justice for all? What three major changes, if any, would you make in this system?

2. Explain why you agree or disagree with the nine principles recommended by some analysts for use in making environmental policy decisions listed on pp. 664–665.

3. Rate the last six prime ministers on a scale of 1–10 in terms of their ability to act as environmental leaders.

4. Suppose a political candidate ran on a platform calling for the federal government to phase in a tax

on gasoline so that, over 5–10 years, the price of gasoline would triple. The candidate argues that this tax increase is necessary to encourage oil and gasoline conservation, reduce air pollution, slow global warming, and enhance future economic, environmental, and military security. The candidate also says the tax revenue would be used to reduce taxes on wages and profits and to provide an economic safety net for the poor and lower middle class. Would you vote for this candidate who wants to greatly increase the price of gasoline? Explain.

5. Some people say: "Most people will not become involved in making the world a better place so why should I?" "Individuals cannot make a difference."

"People will act only when there is a crisis, and by then it will be too late." Do you have any of these attitudes? Compare your response with those of other members of your class. Some analysts say that these are merely excuses or rationalizations some people use to avoid getting involved, and as such, are forms of intellectual dishonesty and civic and ethical laziness. Do you agree with this assessment?

6. Congratulations! You are in charge of formulating environmental policy in the country where you live. List the three most important components of your policy. Compare your views with those of other members of your class and see if you can agree on a consensus policy.

PROJECTS

1. Polls have identified five categories of citizens in terms of their concern over environmental quality: (1) those involved in a wide range of environmental activities, (2) those who do not want to get involved but are willing to pay more for a cleaner environment, (3) those who are not involved because they disagree with many environmental laws and regulations, (4) those who are concerned but do not believe individual action will make much difference, and (5) those who strongly oppose the environmental movement. To which group do you belong? Compare the results of members in your class and determine the percentage in each category. As a class, conduct a similar poll on your campus.

2. Pick a Canadian environmental law. Use the library or the Internet to evaluate the law's major strengths and weaknesses. Decide whether the law should be weakened, strengthened, or abolished, and explain why. List the three most important ways you believe the law should be improved.

3. Try to interview (a) someone from an industry who is seeking to weaken a specific environmental law, (b) someone from an environmental group who would like to strengthen the law, and (c) someone from government who must make decisions about the law. Compare their views and perspectives, and come to a conclusion about what should be done. If you cannot get interviews, set up a mock discussion pa with class members taking each of these roles.

4. What student environmental groups, if any, are active at your school? How many people actively participate in them? Pick one of these groups and find out what environmentally beneficial things they have done. What actions taken by this group do you agree or disagree with? Why?

5. Use the library or the Internet to learn about and evaluate the effectiveness of a particular national or international environmental group. What is your chosen group's mission? How successful has the group been in fulfilling its mission? To what do you attribute its success or failure?

6. Use the Internet and the local phonebook to identify environmental or conservation groups in your area. Contact them for information on their activities and their achievements and report this information to your class.

7. Use the library or Internet to research the lives and accomplishments of a selection of the following people: Maude Barlow, Tony Blair, Lester Brown, Gro Harlem Brundtland, George Bush Senior, George W. Bush, Jacques Cousteau, Stephen Harper, Mark Jaccard, Elizabeth May, Brian Mulroney, Barack Obama, David Schindler, Maurice Strong, David Suzuki, and Pierre Trudeau. Assess their significance as environmental leaders. Compare them to other environmental leaders of your choice.

8. Visit websites about the Environmental Bill of Rights. Find out how you could use the bill to lodge an environmental complaint. Write a brief report or make a chart summarizing where some of the environmental hot spots are, what the issues at those locations are, and how each case is progressing.

Environmental Worldviews, Ethics, and Sustainability

CASE STUDY   Biosphere 2: A Lesson in Humility

In 1991, eight scientists (four men and four women) were sealed into Biosphere 2, a $200 million (U.S.) facility designed to be a self-sustaining life-support system (Figure 28-1) and to increase our understanding of the Earth's life-support system: Biosphere 1.

The 1.3-hectare (3.2-acre) sealed system of interconnected domes was built in the desert near Tucson, Arizona. It had a tropical rain forest, savanna, desert, lakes, streams, freshwater and saltwater wetlands, and a mini-ocean with a coral reef.

The facility was stocked with more than 4 000 species of organisms. Sunlight and external natural gas–powered generators provided energy. The Biospherians were to be isolated for two years and to raise their own food using intensive organic agriculture, breathe air recirculated by plants, and drink water cleansed by natural recycling processes.

From the beginning there were many unexpected problems. The life-support system began unravelling. Large amounts of oxygen disappeared when soil organisms converted it to carbon dioxide. Additional oxygen had to be pumped in from the outside to keep the Biospherians from suffocating.

The nitrogen and carbon recycling systems also failed to function properly. Levels of nitrous oxide rose high enough to threaten the occupants with brain damage and had to be controlled by outside intervention. Carbon dioxide skyrocketed to levels that threatened to poison the humans and spurred the growth of weedy vines that choked out food crops. Plant nutrients leached from the soil and polluted the water systems.

Tropical birds died after the first freeze. An Arizona ant species got into the enclosure, proliferated, and killed off most of the system's introduced insect species. After the majority of the introduced insect species became extinct, the facility was overrun with cockroaches and katydids. All together, 19 of the Biosphere's 25 small animal species became extinct. Before the two-year period was up, all plant-pollinating insects became extinct, thereby dooming to extinction most of the plant species.

Despite many problems, the facility's waste and wastewater were recycled, and the Biospherians were able to produce 80% of their food supply.

Scientists Joel Cohen and David Tilman, who evaluated the project, concluded, "No one yet knows how to engineer systems that provide humans with life-supporting services that natural ecosystems provide for free."

Columbia University took over Biosphere 2 as a research facility for a few years, but abandoned it in 2003. Since 2007, the University of Arizona has been using the site to conduct biological research and to provide environmental education.

FIGURE 28-1 Biosphere 2, constructed near Tucson, Arizona, was designed to be a self-sustaining life-support system for eight people sealed into the facility. The experiment failed because of a breakdown in its nutrient recycling systems.

The main ingredients of an environmental ethic are caring about the planet and all of its inhabitants, allowing unselfishness to control the immediate self-interest that harms others, and living each day so as to leave the lightest possible footprints on the planet.

ROBERT CAHN

CHAPTER PURPOSE AND QUESTIONS

The purpose of this chapter is to compare different values and beliefs about the environment, and to consider how people with different worldviews can work together to solve our common environmental problems. The chapter addresses the following questions:

28-1   What is an environmental worldview?

28-2   What are some life-centred and Earth-centred environmental worldviews?

28-3   How can we live more sustainably through our environmental literacy?

28-1 ENVIRONMENTAL WORLDVIEWS IN INDUSTRIAL SOCIETIES

What Is an Environmental Worldview? Beliefs and Values

Your environmental worldview is how you think the world works, what you believe your role in it should be, and what you believe is right and wrong in terms of environmental behaviour.

People disagree about how serious our environmental problems are and what we should do about them. The conflicts arise mostly out of differing **environmental worldviews:** how people think the world works, what they believe their role in it should be, and what they believe is right and wrong in terms of environmental behaviour **(environmental ethics).**

People with widely differing environmental worldviews can take the same data, be logically consistent, and arrive at quite different conclusions because they start with different assumptions, beliefs, and values.

Figure 28-2 shows some different types of environmental worldviews. Most can be characterized as *human-centred, Earth-centred*, or some combination of both. As you move from the centre of Figure 28-2 to the outside rings, the worldviews become less human-centred and more Earth-centred and devoted to sustaining the Earth's natural systems (ecosystems), life forms (biodiversity), and life-support system (biosphere) for the benefit of humans and other forms of life.

How Do We Decide What Is Right and Wrong Environmental Behaviour? A Search for Ethical Principles

Several philosophies can help us decide what is right and wrong environmental behaviour.

There are several major moral philosophical systems that deal with the concepts of what constitutes right and wrong environmental (or other) behaviour.

One is *universalism*, developed by philosophers such as Plato (427–347 B.C.) and Immanuel Kant (1724–1804). According to this view, there are basic principles of ethics, or rules of right and wrong, that are universal and unchanging. Some believe that God or other sources of wisdom have provided ethical guidelines. Others believe that these rules can be discovered through reason, experience, and knowledge.

Another philosophy is *utilitarianism*, developed by Jeremy Bentham (1748–1832) and John Stuart Mill (1806–73). It says that an action is right if it produces the greatest satisfaction or pleasure for the greatest number of people. Critics contend that this assumes that we can somehow quantitatively measure happiness and compare it among different people.

A related moral philosophy is *consequentialism*, which proposes that whether an act is morally right or wrong depends on its consequences. In effect, we determine correct moral conduct *solely* by conducting a cost-benefit analysis of the consequences of our actions. Thus an action is morally right if its consequences as a whole are more favourable than unfavourable.

Another philosophy of right and wrong is *relativism*, promoted by ancient Greek teachers called Sophists who disagreed with Plato's universalist ethics. It asserts that moral values of right and wrong are relative to cultures, eras, or situations and there are no absolute principles of right and wrong.

According to the philosophy of *rationalism*, we can develop principles of right and wrong by using logic to analyze ideas and arguments. This philosophy based on the power of reason was developed by philosophers such as René Descartes (1596–1650), Benedict De Spinoza (1632–77), and Gottfried W. Leibniz (1646–1716).

According to *nihilism*, often associated with Friedrich Nietzsche (1844–1900), the concepts of values and moral beliefs are useless because nothing can be known or communicated. There is no purpose or meaning to life except the struggle to survive in which "might is right."

Because this is not a philosophy textbook, the brief summaries of several moral philosophies just given are necessarily superficial and incomplete. There are many complex arguments involved in evaluating these and other moral philosophies that you can explore by studying philosophy.

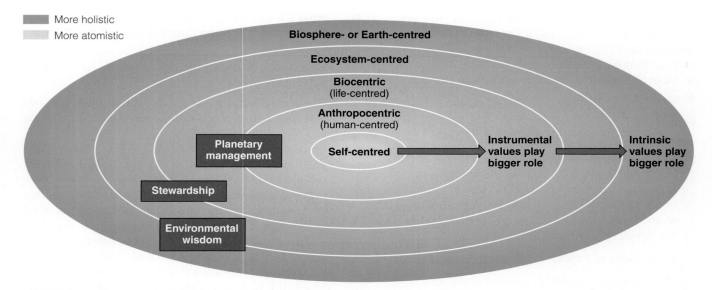

Biosphere- or Earth-centred

Ecosystem-centred

Biocentric
(life-centred)

Anthropocentric
(human-centred)

Self-centred

Planetary
management

Stewardship

Environmental
wisdom

Instrumental
values play
bigger role

Intrinsic
values play
bigger role

FIGURE 28-2 Environmental worldviews lie on a continuum running from more self- and human-centred (centre) to biosphere- or Earth-centred (outer rings). (Diagram developed by Scott Spoolman)

What Is the Difference between Instrumental and Intrinsic Values? Usefulness vs. Existence

Life forms have value because of their usefulness to us or to the biosphere or merely because they exist.

What we value largely determines how we act. Environmental philosophers normally divide values into two types. One type, called **instrumental** or **utilitarian,** values life forms because of their usefulness to us or to the biosphere. The concept of preserving natural capital and biodiversity because they sustain life and support economies is an instrumental value based mostly on the usefulness of these natural goods and services to us.

A second type, called **intrinsic** or **inherent,** values a form of life just because it exists, regardless of whether it has any usefulness to us.

As worldviews go from being human-centred to more Earth-centred (moving out from the centre of Figure 28-2) instrumental values play a lesser role, and intrinsic values become more important. The view that a wild species, an ecosystem, biodiversity, or the biosphere has value only because of its usefulness to us is called an **anthropocentric** (human-centred) instrumental value.

In contrast, the view that these forms of life are valuable simply because they exist, independently of their use to human beings, is called a **biocentric** (life-centred) intrinsic value. According to a *biocentric worldview,* all species and ecosystems and the biosphere have both intrinsic and instrumental value, we are just one of many species, and we have an ethical responsibility not to impair the long-term sustainability and adaptability of the Earth's natural systems for all life.

What Are the Major Human-Centred Environmental Worldviews? Managers and Stewards

In the human-centred view, we are the planet's most important species and should become managers or stewards of the Earth.

Some people in today's industrial consumer societies have a **planetary management worldview**. According to this human-centred environmental worldview, we are the planet's most important and dominant species and we can and should manage the Earth mostly for our own benefit. Other species and parts of nature are seen as having only *instrumental value* based on how useful they are to us. This is a form of utilitarianism.

Figure 28-3 (left, p. 687) summarizes the four major beliefs or assumptions of this environmental worldview. Here are three variations of this environmental worldview:

- The *no-problem school.* We can solve any environmental, population, or resource problems with more economic growth and development, better management, and better technology.

- The *free-market school.* The best way to manage the planet for human benefit is through a free-market global economy with minimal government interference and regulations. All public property resources should be converted to private property resources and the global marketplace, governed by pure free-market competition, should decide essentially everything.

- The *spaceship-Earth school.* The Earth is like a spaceship: a complex machine that we can

Environmental Worldviews

Planetary Management

- As the planet's most important species, we are in charge of the Earth.

- Because of our ingenuity and technology, we will not run out of resources.

- The potential for economic growth is essentially unlimited.

- Our success depends on how well we manage the Earth's life-support systems, mostly for our benefit.

Stewardship

- We are the planet's most important species, but we have an ethical responsibility to care for the rest of nature.

- We will probably not run out of resources, but they should not be wasted.

- We should encourage environmentally beneficial forms of economic growth and discourage environmentally harmful forms.

- Our success depends on how well we manage the Earth's life-support systems for our benefit and for the rest of nature.

Environmental Wisdom

- Nature exists for all species, and we are not in charge of the Earth.

- Resources are limited, should not be wasted, and are not all for us.

- We should encourage Earth-sustaining forms of economic growth and discourage Earth-degrading forms.

- Our success depends on learning how nature sustains itself and integrating such lessons from nature into the ways we think and act.

FIGURE 28-3 Comparison of environmental worldviews. Which of these environmental worldviews comes closer to your own environmental worldview?

understand, dominate, change, and manage to prevent environmental overload and provide a good life for everyone. This **spaceship-Earth worldview** developed as a result of photographs taken from space showing the Earth as a finite planet, or an island in space (Figure 5-1, p. 94). This led many people to see that the Earth is our only home and we had better treat it with care.

Another anthropocentric environmental worldview is the stewardship worldview. According to this increasingly popular view, we have an ethical responsibility to be caring and responsible managers, or *stewards,* of the Earth. We can and should make the world a better place for our species and others through love, care, knowledge, and technology. Figure 28-3 (centre) summarizes the major beliefs of this worldview.

According to the stewardship view, as we use the Earth's natural capital, we are borrowing from the Earth and from future generations, and we have an ethical responsibility to pay the debt by leaving the Earth in at least as good a condition as we enjoy.

In thinking about our responsibility toward future generations, some analysts believe we should consider the wisdom of the 18th-century Iroquois Confederation of Native Americans: *In our every deliberation, we must consider the impact of our decisions on the next seven generations.*

28-2 LIFE-CENTRED AND EARTH-CENTRED ENVIRONMENTAL WORLDVIEWS

Can We Manage the Planet? Look at Biosphere 2

Some analysts doubt that we can effectively manage the planet.

Some people believe any human-centred worldview will eventually fail because it wrongly assumes we now have or can gain enough knowledge to become effective managers or stewards of the Earth.

According to these analysts, the unregulated global free-market approach will not work because it is based on increased losses or degradation of the Earth's natural capital and focuses on short-term economic benefits regardless of the harmful long-term environmental and social consequences.

The image of the Earth as an island or ship in space has played an important role in raising global environmental awareness. But critics argue that thinking of the Earth as a spaceship that we can manage is an oversimplified and misleading way to view an incredibly complex and ever-changing planet. This view was supported by the failure of Biosphere 2 (p. 684).

These critics point out that we do not even know how many species live on the Earth, much less what their roles are and how they interact with one another and their nonliving environment. We have only an inkling of what goes on in a handful of soil, a meadow, a pond, or any other part of the Earth.

As biologist David Ehrenfeld puts it, "In no important instance have we been able to demonstrate comprehensive successful management of the world, nor do we understand it well enough to manage it even in theory." According to environmental educator David Orr, "On balance, I think, we are becoming more ignorant because we are losing cultural knowledge about how to inhabit our places on the planet sustainably, while impoverishing the genetic knowledge accumulated through millions of years of evolution."

What Are Life-Centred and Eco-Centred Worldviews? Deciding What to Protect and Sustain

Some believe we should focus on protecting species from premature extinction and others on not destroying or degrading ecosystems, biodiversity, and the Earth's life support systems.

People disagree over how far we should extend our ethical concerns for various forms or levels of life (Figure 28-4). Some critics believe that human-centred environmental worldviews should be expanded to recognize the *inherent* or *intrinsic value* of all forms of life regardless of their potential or actual use to us.

Most people with a life-centred worldview believe we have an ethical responsibility to avoid causing the premature extinction of species through our activities, for three reasons. *First*, each species is a unique storehouse of genetic information that should be respected and protected because it exists (intrinsic value). *Second*, each species is a potential economic good for human use (instrumental value). *Third*, populations of species are capable through evolution and speciation of adapting to changing environmental conditions.

Trying to decide whether all or only some species should be protected from premature extinction resulting from human activities is a difficult and controversial ethical problem. It is hard to know where to draw the line and be ethically consistent.

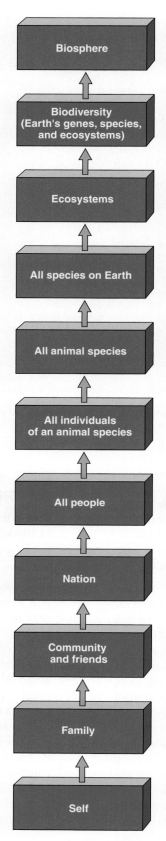

FIGURE 28-4 Levels of ethical concern. People disagree over how far we should extend our ethical concerns on this scale. How far up this scale would you extend your own ethical concerns?

Here are three of the issues involved: *First*, should all species be protected from premature extinction because of their intrinsic value, or should only certain ones be preserved because of their known or potential instrumental value to us or to their ecosystems?

Second, should all insect and bacterial species be protected, or should we attempt to exterminate those that eat our crops, harm us, or transmit disease organisms?

Third, should we emphasize protecting keystone and foundation species over other species that play lesser roles in ecosystems?

Some people believe we must go beyond focusing on species. They believe we have an ethical responsibility not to degrade the Earth's ecosystems, biodiversity, and biosphere for this and future generations of humans and other species. In other words, they have an *Earth-centred*, or *ecocentric*, environmental worldview, devoted to preserving the Earth's biodiversity and the functioning of its life-support systems for all forms of life.

Why should we care about the Earth's biodiversity? According to the late environmentalist and systems expert Donella Meadows,

> Biodiversity contains the accumulated wisdom of nature and the key to its future. If you wanted to destroy a society, you would burn its libraries and kill its intellectuals. You would destroy its knowledge. Nature's knowledge is contained in the DNA within living cells. The variety of genetic information is the driving engine of evolution and the source of adaptability.

What Is the Environmental Wisdom Worldview? Learning to Work with the Earth

According to this view we are not in charge, should not waste the Earth's finite resources, and should live more sustainably by mimicking the ways in which the Earth has sustained itself for billions of years.

As we move out from the centre of Figure 28-2, we see life-centred and then Earth-centred worldviews. One Earth-centred worldview is called the **environmental wisdom worldview** (see Individuals Matter, below). Its major beliefs are summarized in Figure 28-3 (right). In many respects, it is the opposite of the planetary management worldview (Figure 28-3, left).

According to this worldview, because we are not in charge of the biosphere, we should learn how it has maintained itself over billions of years and use what we learn to sustain ourselves and the biosphere into the future (Figure 9-14, p. 191).

This worldview includes the belief that the Earth does not need us managing it in order to go on, whereas we do need the Earth in order to survive. According to this view, we cannot save the Earth because it does not need saving. What we need to save is the existence of our own species and other species that may become extinct because of our activities.

Sustainability expert Lester W. Milbrath asks us to try this thought experiment: "Imagine that, suddenly, all the humans disappeared, but all the buildings, roads, shopping malls, factories, automobiles, and other artifacts of modern civilization were left behind. What then? After three or four centuries, buildings would have crumbled, vehicles would have rusted and fallen apart, and plants would have recolonized fields, roads, parking lots, even buildings. Water, air,

and soil would gradually clear up; some endangered species would flourish. Nature would thrive splendidly without us."

Others say we do not need to be biocentrists or ecocentrists to value life and the Earth. They point out that the human-centred stewardship environmental worldview also calls for us to value individuals, species, and the Earth's life-support systems as part of our responsibility as the Earth's caretakers.

What Is the Deep Ecology Environmental Worldview? Thinking Deeply about Our Responsibilities

The beliefs of deep ecology call for us to think more deeply about our obligations toward both human and nonhuman life.

A related ecocentric environmental worldview is the *deep ecology worldview*, which consists of eight premises developed in 1972 by Norwegian philosopher Arne Naess, in conjunction with philosopher George Sessions and sociologist Bill Devall. *First*, each nonhuman form of life on the Earth has inherent value, independent of its value to humans. *Second*, the fundamental interdependence and diversity of life forms contribute to the flourishing of human and nonhuman life on Earth.

INDIVIDUALS MATTER

Aldo Leopold

Aldo Leopold (1887–1948) was a forester, a writer, a conservationist, and a professor who made his mark on the world in several ways. In 1933, while a professor at the University of Wisconsin, he was one of the first people to apply the science of ecology to **wildlife management.** He was a founder of the Wilderness Society in 1935. Through his writings and lectures, he became known as one of the leaders of the conservation and environmental movements of the 20th century.

One of Leopold's greatest contributions was his idea of *land ethics,* a philosophy that humans were a part of nature that should love and respect land and its biotic community, rather than trying to dominate nature. His

book *A Sand County Almanac* (1949) is considered an environmental classic and we think it should be read by every student of the environment. Moreover, it is an entertaining and enlightening read. Here are some of Leopold's words that illustrate his land ethic:

All ethics so far evolved rest upon a single premise: that the individual is a member of a community of interdependent parts.

That land is a community is a basic concept of ecology, but that land is to be loved and respected is an extension of ethics.

The land ethics changes the role of Homo sapiens *from conqueror of the land-community to plain member and citizen of it.*

We abuse land because we regard it as a commodity belonging to us. When we see land as a community to which we belong, we may begin to use it with love and respect.

Anything is right when it tends to preserve the integrity, stability, and beauty of the biotic community. It is wrong when it tends otherwise.

Leopold's ideas had a huge impact on many individuals and groups that followed him, and his ideas form the basis for many beliefs of the environmental wisdom worldview. Leopold is considered by many to be one of the founders of environmental ethics.

Environmental Worldviews, Ethics, and Sustainability **689**

Third, humans have no right to reduce this interdependence and diversity except to satisfy vital needs. *Fourth,* present human interference with the nonhuman world is excessive, and the situation is worsening rapidly. *Fifth,* because of the damage caused by this interference, it would be better for humans, and much better for nonhumans, if there were a substantial decrease in the human population.

Sixth, basic economic and technological policies must therefore be changed. *Seventh,* the predominant ideology must change such that measurements of the *quality of life* focus on the overall health of the environment and all living things, rather than on the material wealth of individuals and societies. *Eighth,* those who subscribe to these points have an obligation directly or indirectly to try to implement the necessary changes.

Naess also described some lifestyle guidelines compatible with the basic beliefs of deep ecology. They include appreciating all forms of life, consuming less, emphasizing satisfaction of vital needs rather than wants, working to improve the standard of living for the world's poor, working to eliminate injustice toward fellow humans or other species, and acting nonviolently.

Deep ecology is not an ecoreligion, nor is it antireligious or antihuman, as some of its critics have claimed. It is a set of beliefs that would have us think more deeply about the inherent value of all life on the Earth and about our obligations toward all life.

What Is the Ecofeminist Environmental Worldview? Give Women a Fair Chance

Women should have the same rights as men and be treated as equal partners in our joint quest to develop more environmentally sustainable and just societies.

French writer Françoise d'Eaubonne coined the term *ecofeminism* in 1974. It includes a spectrum of views on the relationships of women to the Earth and to male-dominated societies (patriarchies). Most ecofeminists agree that we need a life-centred or Earth-centred environmental worldview. However, they believe a main cause of our environmental problems is not just human centredness, but specifically male centredness (*androcentrism*).

Many ecofeminists argue that the rise of male-dominated societies and environmental worldviews since the advent of agriculture is primarily responsible for our violence against nature and for the oppression of women and minorities as well. To such ecofeminists, our shift from hunter-gatherer to agricultural and industrial societies changed our view of nature from that of a nurturing mother to that of a foe to be conquered.

Ecofeminists note that women earn less than 10% of all wages, own less than 1% of all property, and in most societies have far fewer rights than men. These analysts also argue that to become primary players in the male power-and-domination game, most women are forced to emphasize the characteristics deemed masculine and become "honorary men."

Some ecofeminists suggest that oppression by men has driven women closer to nature and made them more compassionate and nurturing. As oppressed members of society, they argue, many women have more experience in dealing with interpersonal conflicts, bringing people together, acting as caregivers, and identifying emotionally with injustice, pain, and suffering. Thus women with such qualities are in a better position to help lead as we struggle to develop more environmentally sustainable and just societies. Such societies would be based on cooperation, rather than confrontation and domination, and on finding *win-win* solutions to our environmental and human problems instead of *win-lose* solutions often associated with our current male-dominated societies.

Ecofeminists argue that women should be treated as equal partners with men. They do not want just a fair share of the patriarchal pie or to be given token roles or co-opted into the male power game. They want to work with men to bake an entirely new pie. They hope to heal the rift between humans and nature and end oppression based on sex, race, class, and cultural and religious beliefs.

Ecofeminists are not alone in calling for us to encourage the rise of *life-centred people* who emphasize the best human characteristics: gentleness, caring, compassion, nonviolence, cooperation, and love.

CONSIDER, DISCUSS, OR DEBATE

Which one of the following comes closest to your environmental worldview: planetary management, stewardship, environmental wisdom, deep ecology, or ecofeminist? What are the advantages and disadvantages of each worldview?

Which Worldview Is More Likely to Prove Correct? Catastrophe vs. Continuing Growth

Using images of economic or ecological collapse can deter us from preventing or slowing the spread of environmental degradation.

The planetary management, stewardship, and environmental wisdom worldviews differ over whether there are physical and biological limits to economic growth, beyond which ecological and economic collapse are likely to occur. This argument has been going on since Thomas Malthus published his book *The Principles of Political Economy* in 1836.

In 2000, conservation biologist Carlos Davidson proposed a way to bridge the gap between differing worldviews and to help motivate the political changes needed to halt or slow the spread of environmental degradation.

Davidson disagrees with the view of some economists that technology will allow continuing economic growth without causing serious environmental damage. However, he also disagrees with the view that continuing economic growth based on consuming and degrading natural capital will lead to ecological and economic crashes.

Instead of crashes, he suggests the metaphor of a gradually unravelling tapestry to describe the effects of environmental degradation. He asks us to think of nature as a diverse tapestry—an incredible variety of biomes, aquatic systems, and ecosystems.

The tapestry is losing threads, more in some areas than in others, and is even torn in some places, but it is unlikely to simply fall apart. However, he believes that degradation in parts of the Earth's ecological tapestry is occurring; is likely to increase because of problems such as climate change and biodiversity; and must be prevented and slowed by using the pollution prevention and precautionary principles.

However, Davidson believes that using catastrophe metaphors such as "ecological collapse" and "going over a cliff" can hinder these efforts. He argues that repeated predictions of catastrophe, like the boy who cried wolf, will be heard at first, but later ignored. As a result, people will lose motivation to prevent more tears in nature's tapestry or to look more deeply at the causes of the damage.

> **CONSIDER, DISCUSS, OR DEBATE**
>
> Evaluate the effectiveness of the "unravelling tapestry" and "ecological collapse" metaphors. Which metaphor do you think best describes our current situation, and which is the most likely to stimulate positive change?

28-3 LIVING MORE SUSTAINABLY

What Are the Main Components of Environmental Literacy? Understanding and Caring About How the Earth Works and Sustains Itself

Environmentally literate citizens and leaders are needed to build more environmentally sustainable and just societies.

Most environmentalists believe that learning how to live more sustainably requires a foundation of environmental education. They cite some of the key goals of environmental literacy:

- *Develop respect or reverence for all life.*
- *Understand as much as we can about how the Earth works and sustains itself, and use such knowledge to guide our lives, communities, and societies.*

- *Look for connections within the biosphere and between our actions and the biosphere.*
- *Use critical thinking skills to become seekers of environmental wisdom instead of overfilled vessels of environmental information.*
- *Understand and evaluate our environmental worldview and see this as a lifelong process.*
- *Learn how to evaluate the beneficial and harmful environmental consequences of our lifestyle and professional choices, today and in the future.*
- *Foster a desire to make the world a better place and act on this desire.*

Specifically, an ecologically literate person should have a basic comprehension of:

- Concepts such as environmental sustainability, natural capital, exponential growth, carrying capacity, and risks and risk analysis
- Environmental history (to help keep us from repeating past mistakes)
- The laws of thermodynamics and the law of conservation of matter
- Basic principles of ecology
- Ways to sustain biodiversity
- Sustainable agriculture and forestry
- Sustainable cities
- Sustainable water use
- Nonrenewable and renewable energy resources
- Soil and mineral resources
- Pollution prevention and waste reduction
- Environmentally sustainable economic and political systems
- Environmental ethics

According to environmental educator Mitchell Thomashow, four basic questions should be at the heart of environmental literacy.

First, where do the things I consume come from? *Second,* what do I know about the place where I live? *Third,* how am I connected to the Earth and other living things? *Fourth,* what is my purpose and responsibility as a human being?

How we answer these questions determines our *ecological identity.* What are your answers to these four questions?

Figure 28-5 summarizes guidelines and strategies for achieving more sustainable societies that have been discussed throughout this book.

> **CONSIDER, DISCUSS, OR DEBATE**
>
> Study the guidelines and strategies summarized in Figure 28-5. Pick the single guideline and the single strategy that you think are the most important. Explain your choices.

Developing Environmentally Sustainable Societies

Guidelines		Strategies

Leave the world in as good a shape as—or better than—we found it

Do not degrade or deplete the Earth's natural capital, and live off the natural income it provides

Copy nature

Sustain biodiversity

Eliminate poverty

Develop eco-economies

Build sustainable communities

Do not use renewable resources faster than nature can replace them

Use sustainable agriculture

Take no more than we need

Do not reduce biodiversity

Try not to harm life, air, water, soil

Depend more on locally available renewable energy from the sun, wind, flowing water, and sustainable biomass

Emphasize pollution prevention and waste reduction

Do not change the world's climate

Help maintain the Earth's capacity for self-repair

Do not waste matter and energy resources

Recycle, reuse, and compost 60–80% of matter resources

Do not overshoot the Earth's carrying capacity

Repair past ecological damage

Maintain a human population size such that needs are met without threatening life-support systems

Emphasize ecological restoration

FIGURE 28-5 Solutions: guidelines and strategies for achieving more sustainable societies.

How Can We Learn from the Earth? Seeking Environmental Wisdom

In addition to formal learning, we need to learn by experiencing nature directly.

Formal environmental education is important, but is it enough? Many analysts say no and urge us to take the time to escape the cultural and technological body armour we use to insulate ourselves from nature and to experience nature directly.

They suggest we kindle a sense of awe, wonder, mystery, and humility by standing under the stars, sitting in a forest or taking in the majesty and power of an ocean.

We might pick up a handful of soil and try to sense the teeming microscopic life within it that keeps us alive. We might look at a tree, mountain, rock, or bee and try to sense how it is a part of us and we a part of it as interdependent participants in the Earth's life-sustaining recycling processes.

Many psychologists believe that consciously or unconsciously we spend much of our lives in a search for roots: something to anchor us in a bewildering and frightening sea of change. As philosopher Simone Weil observed, "To be rooted is perhaps the most important and least recognized need of the human soul."

Earth-focused philosophers say that to be rooted, each of us needs to find a *sense of place*: a stream, a mountain, a yard, or any piece of the Earth we feel at one with—a place we know, experience emotionally, and love. When we become part of that place, it becomes a part of us. Then we are driven to defend it from harm and to help heal its wounds.

This might lead us to recognize that the healing of the Earth and the healing of the human spirit are one and the same. We might discover and tap into what Aldo Leopold calls "the green fire that burns in our hearts" and use this as a force for respecting and working with the Earth and with one another.

CONSIDER, DISCUSS, OR DEBATE

Think of something in your own life that has engendered a sense of place. Has it made you more sensitive to environmental problems? Explain.

How Can We Live More Simply? Escaping from Affluenza

Some people are voluntarily adopting lifestyles in which they enjoy life more by consuming less.

Many analysts urge us to *learn how to live more simply.* Seeking happiness through the pursuit of material things is considered folly by almost every major religion and philosophy. Yet it is preached incessantly by modern advertising that encourages us to buy more and more things. Some affluent people in developed countries are adopting a lifestyle of *voluntary simplicity*, doing and enjoying more with less by learning to live more simply. Voluntary simplicity is based on Mahatma Gandhi's *principle of enoughness:* "The Earth provides enough to satisfy every person's need but not every person's greed.... When we take more than we need, we are simply taking from each other, borrowing from the future, or destroying the environment and other species."

What Are Our Basic Needs?

Obviously, each of us has a basic need for enough food, clean air, clean water, shelter, and clothing to keep us alive and in good health. According to various psychologists and other social scientists, each of us also has other basic needs:

• A secure and meaningful livelihood to provide our basic material needs

• Good physical and mental health

• The opportunity to learn and give expression to our intellectual, mechanical, and artistic talents

• A nurturing family and friends and a peaceful and secure community that help us develop our capacity for caring and loving relationships while giving us the freedom to make personal choices

• A clean and healthy environment that is vibrant with biological and cultural diversity

• A sense of belonging to and caring for a particular place and community

• An assurance that our children and grandchildren will be able to meet these same basic needs

A difficult but fundamental question is asking how much of the stuff we are all urged to buy helps us meet our basic needs. Indeed, psychologists point out that many people buy things in the hope or belief that these objects will somehow compensate for inadequacies in the basic needs listed here.

Critical Thinking

1. What basic needs, if any, would you add to or remove from the list given here?

2. Which of the basic needs listed here (or additional ones you would add) do you feel are being met for you? What are your plans for trying to fulfill any of your unfulfilled needs? Relate these plans to your environmental worldview.

Most of the world's major religions have similar teachings. For example, "Why do you spend your money for that which is not bread, and your labour for that which does not satisfy?" (Christianity: Old Testament, Isaiah 55:2). "Eat and drink, but waste not by excess" (Islam: Koran 7.31). "One should abstain from acquisitiveness" (Hinduism: Acarangastura 2.119). "He who knows he has enough is rich" (Taoism: Tao Te Ching, Chapter 33).

Implementing these principles means asking ourselves, "How much is enough?" The answer is not easy because people in affluent societies are conditioned to want more and more, and they often think of such wants as vital needs (Spotlight, above).

Voluntary simplicity is a form of *environmentally ethical consumption*. It begins by asking a series of questions before buying anything: Do I really need this, or do I merely want it? Can I buy it secondhand (reuse)? Can I borrow, rent, lease, or share it? Can I build it myself?

The decision to buy something triggers another set of questions: Is the product produced in an environmentally sustainable manner? Did the workers who produced it get fair wages for their work, and did they have safe and healthful working conditions? Is it designed to last as long as possible? Is it easy to repair, upgrade, reuse, and recycle?

Figure 28-6 (p. 694) summarizes some ethical guidelines proposed by various ethicists and philosophers for living more sustainably or simply on the Earth. In the words of biologist David Suzuki, "Family, friends, community—these are the sources of the greatest love and joy we experience as humans. . . . None of these pleasures requires us to consume things from the Earth, yet each is deeply fulfilling."

CONSIDER, DISCUSS, OR DEBATE

Does money buy happiness? Think of the most contented people you know. What are their personal traits? Is the pursuit of material things important to them?

How Can We Be More Effective as Environmental Citizens? Avoid Mental Traps and Despair, Be Adaptable, and Enjoy Life

We can help make the world a better place by not falling into mental traps that lead to denial and inaction, and by using our empowering feelings of hope to energize our actions.

When we first encounter an environmental problem, our initial response often is to find someone or something to blame, such as greedy industrialists or uncaring politicians. It is the fault of such villains, and we are the victims. This response can lead to despair, denial, apathy, and inaction because we feel powerless to stop or influence these forces.

Upon closer examination we may realize that we all make some direct or indirect contributions to the environmental problems we face. Yet, we do not want to feel guilty or bad about the environmental harm our lifestyles may be inflicting. Thus we try not to think about it much—another path to denial and inaction.

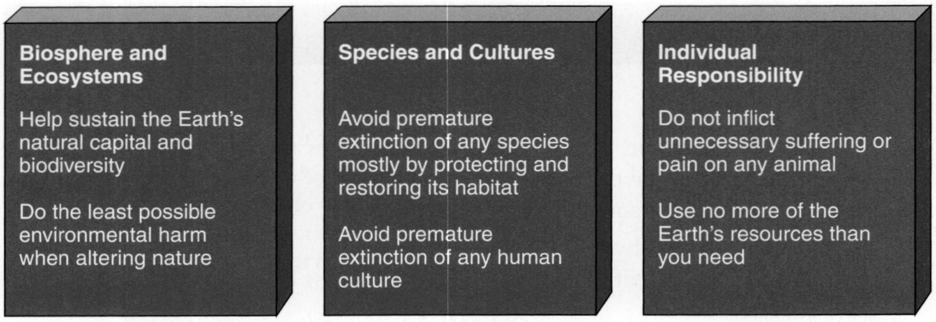

| Biosphere and Ecosystems | Species and Cultures | Individual Responsibility |

Biosphere and Ecosystems	**Species and Cultures**	**Individual Responsibility**
Help sustain the Earth's natural capital and biodiversity Do the least possible environmental harm when altering nature	Avoid premature extinction of any species mostly by protecting and restoring its habitat Avoid premature extinction of any human culture	Do not inflict unnecessary suffering or pain on any animal Use no more of the Earth's resources than you need

FIGURE 28-6 Solutions: some ethical guidelines for living more sustainably.

According to primatologist Jane Goodall, "The greatest danger to our future is apathy. . . . Can we overcome apathy? Yes, but only if we have hope. . . . Technology alone is not enough. We must engage with our hearts also."

Analysts suggest that we move beyond blame, guilt, fear, denial, and apathy by recognizing and avoiding common mental traps that lead to denial, indifference, and inaction. These traps include *gloom-and-doom pessimism* (it is hopeless), *blind technological optimism* (science and technofixes will save us), *fatalism* (we have no control over our actions and the future), *extrapolation to infinity* (if I cannot change the entire world quickly, I will not try to change any of it), *paralysis by analysis* (searching for the perfect world-view, philosophy, solutions, and scientific information before doing anything), and *faith in simple, easy answers*.

We will all accomplish more if we keep our empowering feelings of hope burning brightly, rather than allowing ourselves to be immobilized by feelings of despair. If we set realistic goals for ourselves, we will increase our chances of success. And this success in turn will give us the confidence we need to pursue and achieve other goals.

Recognizing that there is no single correct or best solution to the environmental problems we face is also important. Indeed, one of nature's most important lessons is that preserving diversity—in this case, being flexible and adaptable in trying a variety of solutions to our problems—is the best way to adapt to the Earth's and life's largely unpredictable, ever-changing conditions.

Finally, we should have fun and take time to enjoy life. Laugh every day and enjoy nature, beauty, friendship, and love. This empowers us to become good Earth citizens who practise *good Earthkeeping*.

What Are the Major Components of the Environmental Revolution? A Call for Greatness

The message of environmentalism is one of hope, a positive vision of the future, and a call for greatness in dealing with the environmental challenges we face.

The **environmental revolution** that many environmentalists call for us to bring about during this century would have several components:

- A *biodiversity protection revolution* devoted to protecting and sustaining the genes, species, natural systems, and chemical and biological processes that make up the Earth's biodiversity.

- An *efficiency revolution*, that minimizes the wasting of matter and energy resources.

- A *solar-hydrogen revolution* based on decreasing our dependence on carbon-based nonrenewable fossil fuels and increasing our dependence on forms of renewable solar energy that can be used to produce hydrogen fuel from water.

- A *pollution prevention revolution* that reduces pollution and environmental degradation from harmful chemicals, preventing their release into the environment by recycling or reusing them, and learning to live without them.

- A *sufficiency revolution*, dedicated to meeting the basic needs of all people on the planet while affluent societies learn to live more sustainably by living with less.

- A *demographic revolution* based on empowering people to make fertility choices that will bring the size and growth rate of the human population into balance with the Earth's ability to support humans and other species more sustainably.

- An *economic and political revolution* in which we use economic systems to reward environmentally beneficial behaviour and to discourage environmentally harmful behaviour.

Opponents of such cultural changes like to paint environmentalists as messengers of gloom, doom, and hopelessness. But *the message of environmentalism is not gloom and doom, fear, and catastrophe. It is a message of hope, and of willingness to take proactive steps toward a brighter future.*

We should rejoice in our environmental accomplishments, and learn from our past successes. Then we should ask ourselves, "*Where do we go from here, and how should we get there?*" How can past environmental advances be transferred to developing countries? How can humans make the cultural transition to more environmentally sustainable societies based on learning from and working with nature?

As you have read in this book, we have an incredible array of technological and economic solutions to the environmental problems we face. The challenge for all of us is to implement such solutions by converting environmental wisdom and beliefs into political action.

This requires becoming involved in making the world a better place. As Gandhi said many years ago, "We must become the change we want to see." This requires understanding that *individuals matter.* Virtually all of the environmental progress we have made during the last few decades occurred because individuals banded together to insist that we can do better.

This journey begins in your own community because in the final analysis *all sustainability is local.* We help to make the world more sustainable by working to make our local communities more sustainable. This begins with your own lifestyle. This is the meaning of the motto, "Think globally, act locally."

Throughout this book we have used various figures to list things that you can do to act as a responsible environmental citizen. We suggest that you review such actions by looking at Figures 11-31 (p. 246), 12-22 (p. 273), 14-32 (p. 332), 15-27 (p. 360), 18-38 (p. 449), 20-31 (p. 504), 21-21 (p. 529), 21-28 (p. 535), 22-22 (p. 567), 24-5 (p. 589), 24-8 (p. 593), 24-24 (p. 606), and 27-2 (p. 665) and the more general list in Figure 28-5 (p. 692).

As you review these ideas, we suggest you mark off the things you are doing. Then try to pick out two or three of the items in each list that you believe are the most important things to do and combine them into a master list. Each week try to carry out at least one of these actions until you have worked through your entire list.

CONSIDER, DISCUSS, OR DEBATE

What are you currently doing to make the world a more sustainable place? Would you like to do more? What do you do to keep yourself motivated?

What Is the Earth Charter? Four Ethical Guidelines

Respect and care for life and biodiversity and build more sustainable, just, democratic, and peaceful societies for present and future generations.

In March 2000, the Earth Charter was finalized. More than 100 000 people in 51 countries and 25 global leaders in environment, business, politics, religion, and education took part in creating this charter. It is a document creating an ethical and moral framework to guide the conduct of people and nations toward each other and the Earth. Here are its four guiding principles:

1. Respect Earth and life in all its diversity.
2. Care for life with understanding, love, and compassion.
3. Build societies that are free, just, participatory, sustainable, and peaceful.
4. Secure Earth's bounty and beauty for present and future generations.

It is an incredibly exciting time to be alive as we struggle to implement such ideals by entering into a new relationship with the Earth that keeps us all alive and supports our economies. The transition to a more sustainable world will not be easy but it can be done if enough of us care.

Envision the Earth's life-sustaining processes as a beautiful and diverse web of interrelationships—a kaleidoscope of patterns, rhythms, and connections whose very complexity and multitude of possibilities remind us that cooperation, sharing, honesty, humility, and love should be the guidelines for our behaviour toward one another and the Earth.

Bear in mind that not everybody is as lucky as we in the developed nations are. Canadians in particular can feel good about living in a land with abundant space, plentiful resources, high technology, and a strong economy. We need to consider what more we can do to help people in the developing world solve their problems and live sustainably, too. Ensuring the success of the eight Millennium Development Goals (Figure 1-16, p. 17) would be a solid step in the right direction.

When there is no dream, the people perish.
PROVERBS 29:18

CHAPTER REVIEW

1. Review the Key Questions for this chapter on p. 685. Describe the Biosphere 2 project **(Core Case Study)** and the major lessons learned from this project.

2. What is an *environmental worldview*? What are *environmental ethics*? Distinguish among the following environmental worldviews: *planetary management, stewardship, environmental wisdom,* and *deep ecology.*

3. List three issues involved in deciding which species to protect from premature extinction as a result of our

activities. Discuss the controversy over whether we can effectively manage the Earth.

4. List seven goals for a person seeking environmental literacy. List four questions that lie at the heart of environmental literacy.

5. Describe three ways in which we can learn from the Earth. What does it mean to find a *sense of place*?

6. Describe the relationship between owning things and being happy. What is *voluntary simplicity*? What are three examples of basic needs? What are five examples of more qualitative needs?

7. The environmental revolution can be broken down into seven smaller revolutions. What are they?

8. Describe three traps that lead to denial, indifference, and inaction concerning the environmental problems we face. How can we escape these traps and focus our energies on the problems at hand?

9. What are the four basic principles of the Earth Charter? What connections can be made between the range of views about how to manage the Earth and the eight challenges that are posed to us in the form of the Millennium Development Goals?

10. Describe connections between lessons learned through Biosphere 2 (**Core Case Study**) and the four *scientific principles of sustainability*.

CRITICAL THINKING

1. Some analysts argue that the problems with Biosphere 2 resulted mostly from inadequate design and that a better team of scientists and engineers could make it work. Explain why you agree or disagree with this view.

2. This chapter has summarized a number of different environmental worldviews. Analyze them and find the beliefs you agree with, as a description your own environmental worldview. Which of your beliefs were added or modified as a result of taking this course? Compare your answer with those of your classmates.

3. Explain why you agree or disagree with the following ideas: **(a)** Everyone has the right to have as many children as he or she wants. **(b)** Each member of the human species has a right to use as many resources as he or she wants. **(c)** Individuals should have the right to do anything they want with land they own. **(d)** Nature should be used, not preserved. **(e)** Species exist to be used by humans. **(f)** All forms of life have an intrinsic value and therefore have a right to exist. **(g)** All organisms are interconnected and interdependent. **(h)** We have no right to harm and kill animals by using them for furs and to test for toxic chemicals, pharmaceutical drugs, or cosmetics. Are your answers consistent with the beliefs of your environmental worldview that you described in question 2?

4. Theologian Thomas Berry calls the industrial consumer society built on the human-centred, planetary management environmental worldview the "supreme pathology of all history." He says, "We can break the mountains apart; we can drain the rivers and flood the valleys. We can turn the most luxuriant forests into throwaway paper products. We can tear apart the great grass cover of the western plains, and pour toxic chemicals into the soil and pesticides onto the fields, until the soil is dead and blows away in the wind. We can pollute the air with acids, the rivers with sewage, the seas with oil. ... We can invent computers capable of processing ten million calculations per second. And why? To increase the volume and speed with which we move natural resources through the consumer economy to the junk pile or the waste heap. . . . If, in these activities, the topography of the planet is damaged, if the environment is made inhospitable for a multitude of living species, then so be it. We are, supposedly, creating a technological wonderworld. . . . But our supposed progress . . . is bringing us to a wasteworld instead of a wonderworld." Explain why you agree or disagree with this assessment.

5. Some analysts believe learning environmental wisdom by experiencing the Earth and forming an emotional bond with its life forms and processes is unscientific, mystical nonsense based on a romanticized view of nature. They believe better scientific understanding of how the Earth works and improved technology are the best ways to achieve sustainability. Do you agree or disagree? Explain.

6. Try to answer the following fundamental ecological questions about the community where you live. Where does your water come from? Where does the energy you use come from? What kinds of soils are under your feet? What types of wildlife are your neighbours? Where does your food come from? Where does your waste go?

7. How do you feel about **(a)** engaging in factory farming, **(b)** driving an off-road motorized vehicle in a desert, grassland, or forest, **(c)** using throwaway paper towels, tissues, napkins, and plates, **(d)** wearing furs, and **(e)** having tropical fish, birds, snakes, or other wild animals as pets? Are your answers consistent with the beliefs of your environmental worldview that you described in question 2?

8. Review your experience with the mental traps described on p. 693. Which of these traps have you fallen into? Were you aware you had been ensnared by any of them? Do you plan to free yourself from these traps? How?

PROJECTS

1. Use a combination of the major existing societal, economic, and environmental trends, possible new trends, and your imagination to construct three different scenarios of what the world might be like in 2060. Identify the scenario you favour, and outline a strategy for achieving this alternative future. Compare your scenarios and strategies with those of your classmates.

2. Make an environmental audit of your school. Rate each of the following items on a scale of 1 through 10, with 10 being the highest rating. What proportion of each of the major types of matter resources used are recycled, reused, or composted? What priority does your school give to buying recycled materials? How much does your school emphasize energy efficiency, use of renewable forms of solar energy, and environmental design in developing new buildings and renovating existing ones? Does it use ecologically sound planning in deciding how its grounds and buildings are managed and used? Does your school limit the use of toxic chemicals in its buildings and on its grounds? What proportion of its food purchases comes from nearby farmers? What proportion of the food it purchases is grown by sustainable or organic agriculture? Average the number assigned to each category to come up with an overall environmental rating of your school. Compare your ratings with those of other members of your class and come up with a list of the five most important things that need to be done to improve the environmental rating of your school. Share your findings with school officials.

3. Does your school's curriculum provide *all* graduates with the basic elements of environmental literacy? To what extent are the funds in its financial endowments invested in enterprises that are working to develop or encourage environmental sustainability? Over the past 20 years, what important roles have its graduates played in making the world a better and more sustainable place to live? Using such information, rate your school on a 1–10 scale in terms of its contributions to environmental awareness and sustainability. Develop a detailed plan illustrating how your school could become better at achieving such goals, and present this information to school officials, alumni, parents, and financial backers.

4. If you knew you were going to die from a cancer caused by environmental toxins, and you had an opportunity to address everyone in the world for five minutes, what would you say? Write out your five-minute speech and compare it with those of other members of your class.

5. Write an essay in which you identify key environmental experiences that have influenced your life and thus helped form your current ecological identity. Examples may include **(a)** fond childhood memories of special places where you connected with the Earth through emotional experiences, **(b)** places you knew and cherished that have been polluted, developed, or destroyed, **(c)** key events that forced you to think about environmental values or worldviews, **(d)** people or educational experiences that influenced your understanding of and concern about environmental problems and challenges, and **(e)** direct experience and contemplation of wild places. Share your experiences with other members of your class.

6. Are developed and developing countries sufficiently motivated to build a more sustainable planet? Are short-term economic goals more important to most countries than the environmental well-being of future generations? Discuss with other members of your class.

ECOLOGICAL FOOTPRINT ANALYSIS

Working with classmates, conduct an ecological footprint analysis of your campus. Work with a partner or in small groups to research and investigate an area of your school, such as material resources recycling/composting; water use; food service practices; energy use; building management and energy conservation; transportation (both on- and off-campus trips); grounds maintenance; and institutional environmental awareness and education. Depending on your school and its location, you may be able to add more areas to your investigation. You may decide to study the campus as a whole, or you may decide to break down the campus into smaller research areas, such as dorms, library, administration buildings, classrooms and classroom buildings, grounds, or other areas.

1. After deciding on your group's research area, conduct your analysis. As part of your analysis, develop a list of questions that will help to determine the ecological impact related to your chosen topic. Each question item in the audit could have a range of responses on a scale of 1 (poor) to 10 (excellent).

2. Analyze your results, and share them with the class to determine what can be done to shrink the ecological footprint of your school.

3. Arrange a meeting with school officials to share your action plan with them.

APPENDIX 1

Units of Measure

LENGTH

Metric
1 kilometre (km) = 1 000 metres (m)
1 metre (m) = 100 centimetres (cm)
1 metre (m) = 1 000 millimetres (mm)
1 centimetre (cm) = 0.01 metre (m)
1 millimetre (mm) = 0.001 metre (m)

English
1 foot (ft) = 12 inches (in)
1 yard (yd) = 3 feet (ft)
1 mile (mi) = 5 280 feet (ft)
1 nautical mile = 1.15 miles (mi)

Metric–English
1 kilometre (km) = 0.621 mile (mi)
1 metre (m) = 39.4 inches (in)
1 inch (in) = 2.54 centimetres (cm)
1 foot (ft) = 0.305 metre (m)
1 yard (yd) = 0.914 metre (m)
1 nautical mile = 1.85 kilometres (km)

AREA

Metric
1 square kilometre (km²) = 1 000 000 square metres (m²)
1 square metre (m²) = 1 000 000 square millimetres (mm²)
1 hectare (ha) = 10 000 square metres (m²)
1 hectare (ha) = 0.01 square kilometre (km²)

English
1 square foot (ft²) = 144 square inches (in²)
1 square yard (yd²) = 9 square feet (ft²)
1 square mile (mi²) = 27 880 000 square feet (ft²)
1 acre (ac) = 43 560 square feet (ft²)

Metric–English
1 hectare (ha) = 2.471 acres (ac)
1 square kilometre (km²) = 0.386 square mile (mi²)
1 square metre (m²) = 1.196 square yards (yd²)
1 square metre (m²) = 10.76 square feet (ft²)
1 square centimetre (cm²) = 0.155 square inch (in²)

VOLUME

Metric
1 cubic kilometre (km³) = 1 000 000 000 cubic metres (m³)
1 cubic metre (m³) = 1 000 000 cubic centimetres (cm³)
1 litre (L) = 1 000 millilitres (mL) = 1 000 cubic centimetres (cm³)
1 millilitre (mL) = 0.001 litre (L)
1 millilitre (mL) = 1 cubic centimetre (cm³)

English
1 gallon (gal) = 4 quarts (qt)
1 quart (qt) = 2 pints (pt)

Metric–English
1 litre (L) = 0.265 gallon (gal)
1 litre (L) = 1.06 quarts (qt)
1 litre (L) = 0.0353 cubic foot (ft³)
1 cubic metre (m³) = 35.3 cubic feet (ft³)
1 cubic metre (m³) = 1.30 cubic yards (yd³)
1 cubic kilometre (km³) = 0.24 cubic mile (mi³)
1 barrel (bbl) = 159 litres (L)
1 barrel (bbl) = 42 U.S. gallons (gal)

MASS

Metric
1 kilogram (kg) = 1 000 grams (g)
1 gram (g) = 1 000 milligrams (mg)
1 gram (g) = 1 000 000 micrograms (μg)
1 milligram (mg) = 0.001 gram (g)
1 microgram (μg) = 0.000001 gram (g)
1 metric ton (mt) = 1 000 kilograms (kg)

English
1 ton (t) = 2 000 pounds (lb)
1 pound (lb) = 16 ounces (oz)

Metric–English
1 metric ton (mt) = 2 200 pounds (lb) = 1.1 tons (t)
1 kilogram (kg) = 2.20 pounds (lb)
1 pound (lb) = 454 grams (g)
1 gram (g) = 0.035 ounce (oz)

ENERGY AND POWER

Metric
1 kilojoule (kJ) = 1 000 joules (J)
1 kilocalorie (kcal) = 1 000 calories (cal)
1 calorie (cal) = 4 184 joules (J)

Metric–English
1 kilojoule (kJ) = 0.949 British thermal unit (Btu)
1 kilojoule (kJ) = 0.000278 kilowatt-hour (kW-h)
1 kilocalorie (kcal) = 3.97 British thermal units (Btu)
1 kilocalorie (kcal) = 0.00116 kilowatt-hour (kW-h)
1 kilowatt-hour (kW-h) = 860 kilocalories (kcal)
1 kilowatt-hour (kW-h) = 3 400 British thermal units (Btu)
1 quad (Q) = 1 050 000 000 000 000 kilojoules (kJ)
1 quad (Q) = 2 930 000 000 000 kilowatt-hours (kW-h)

TEMPERATURE CONVERSIONS

Fahrenheit (°F) to Celsius (°C):
$$°C = (°F - 32.0) \div 1.80$$
Celsius (°C) to Fahrenheit (°F):
$$°F = (°C \times 1.80) + 32.0$$

APPENDIX 2

Major Events in Environmental History

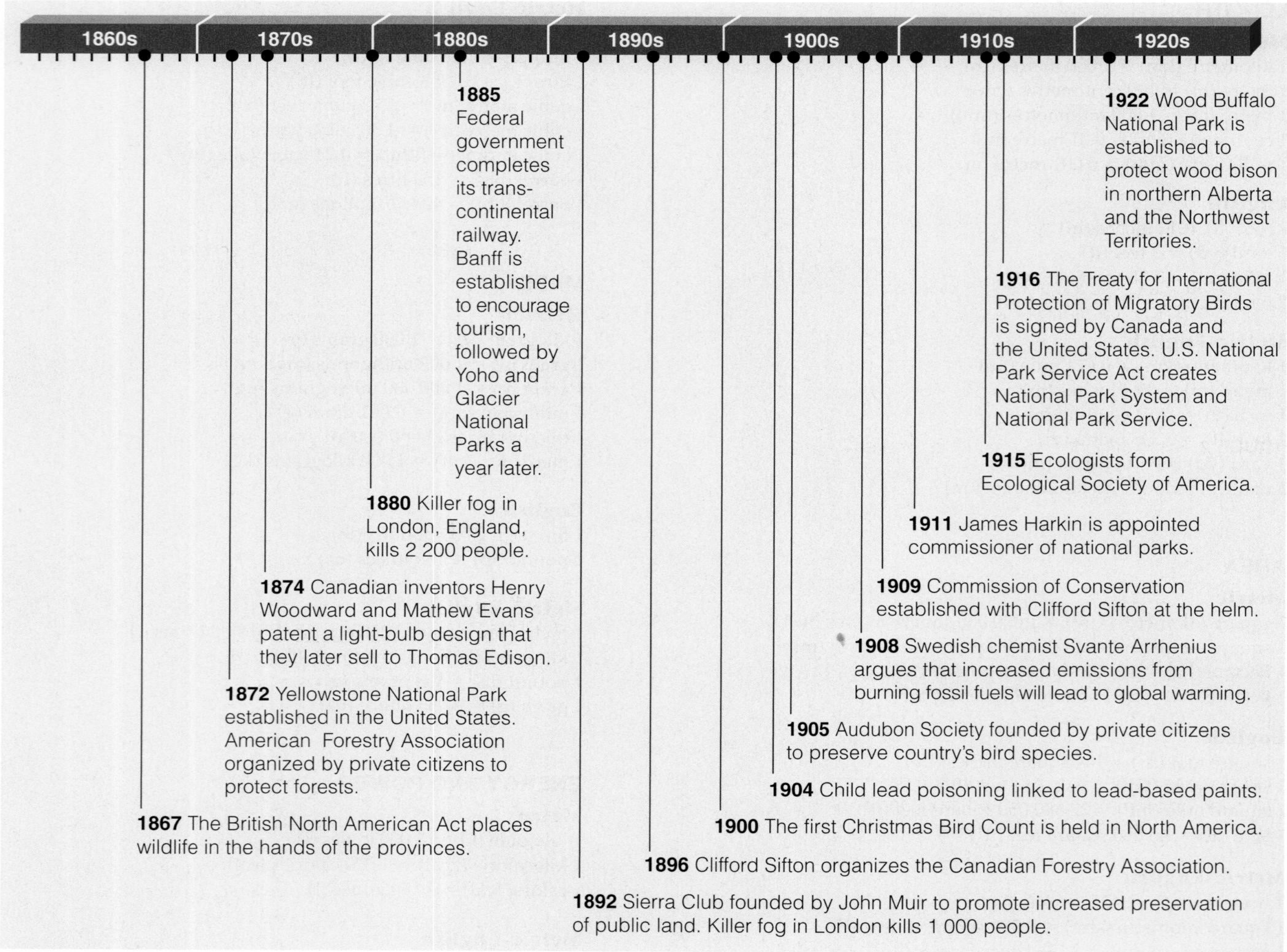

FIGURE 1 Key events in environmental history, 1867–1922.

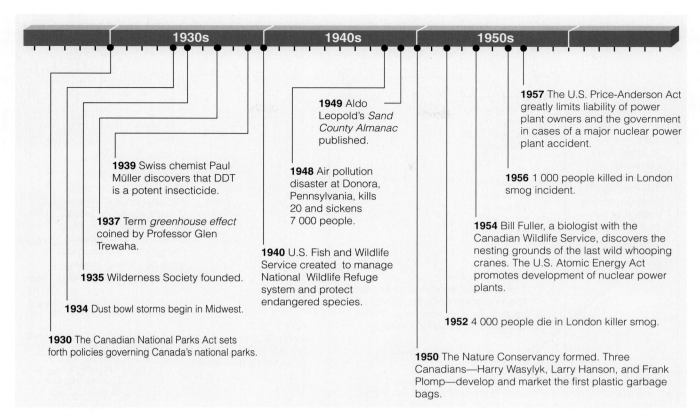

FIGURE 2 Some important conservation and environmental events, 1930–57.

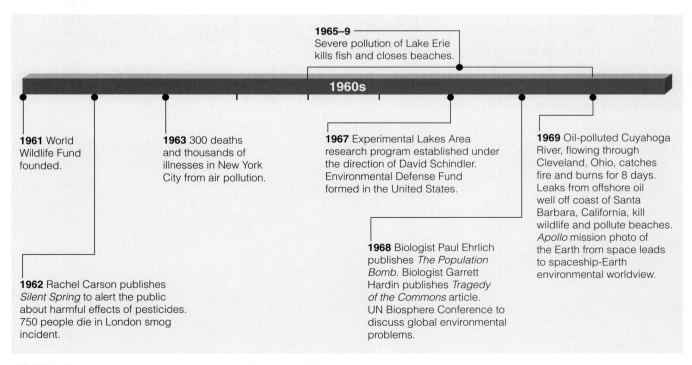

FIGURE 3 Some important environmental events during the 1960s.

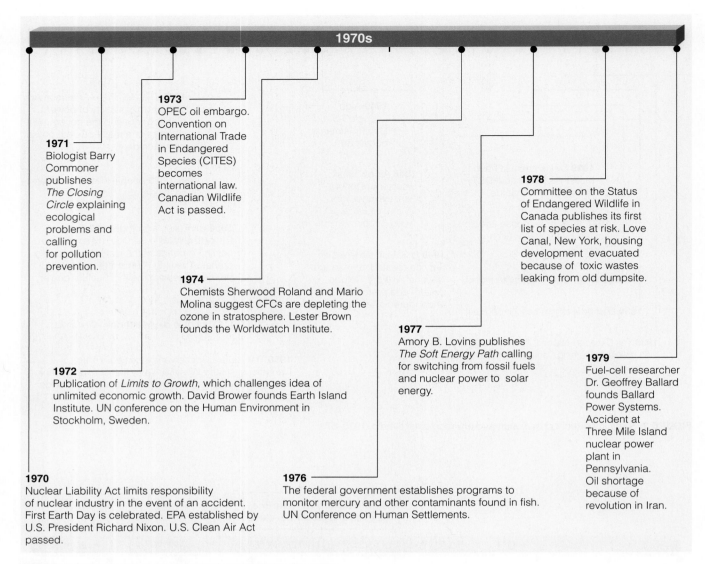

1970s

1971
Biologist Barry Commoner publishes *The Closing Circle* explaining ecological problems and calling for pollution prevention.

1973
OPEC oil embargo. Convention on International Trade in Endangered Species (CITES) becomes international law. Canadian Wildlife Act is passed.

1974
Chemists Sherwood Roland and Mario Molina suggest CFCs are depleting the ozone in stratosphere. Lester Brown founds the Worldwatch Institute.

1978
Committee on the Status of Endangered Wildlife in Canada publishes its first list of species at risk. Love Canal, New York, housing development evacuated because of toxic wastes leaking from old dumpsite.

1972
Publication of *Limits to Growth*, which challenges idea of unlimited economic growth. David Brower founds Earth Island Institute. UN conference on the Human Environment in Stockholm, Sweden.

1977
Amory B. Lovins publishes *The Soft Energy Path* calling for switching from fossil fuels and nuclear power to solar energy.

1979
Fuel-cell researcher Dr. Geoffrey Ballard founds Ballard Power Systems. Accident at Three Mile Island nuclear power plant in Pennsylvania. Oil shortage because of revolution in Iran.

1970
Nuclear Liability Act limits responsibility of nuclear industry in the event of an accident. First Earth Day is celebrated. EPA established by U.S. President Richard Nixon. U.S. Clean Air Act passed.

1976
The federal government establishes programs to monitor mercury and other contaminants found in fish. UN Conference on Human Settlements.

FIGURE 4 Some important environmental events during the 1970s.

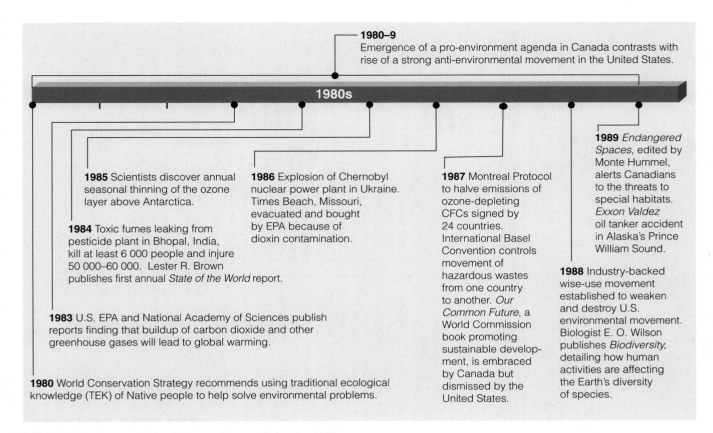

1980–9
Emergence of a pro-environment agenda in Canada contrasts with rise of a strong anti-environmental movement in the United States.

1980s

1985 Scientists discover annual seasonal thinning of the ozone layer above Antarctica.

1984 Toxic fumes leaking from pesticide plant in Bhopal, India, kill at least 6 000 people and injure 50 000–60 000. Lester R. Brown publishes first annual *State of the World* report.

1983 U.S. EPA and National Academy of Sciences publish reports finding that buildup of carbon dioxide and other greenhouse gases will lead to global warming.

1980 World Conservation Strategy recommends using traditional ecological knowledge (TEK) of Native people to help solve environmental problems.

1986 Explosion of Chernobyl nuclear power plant in Ukraine. Times Beach, Missouri, evacuated and bought by EPA because of dioxin contamination.

1987 Montreal Protocol to halve emissions of ozone-depleting CFCs signed by 24 countries. International Basel Convention controls movement of hazardous wastes from one country to another. *Our Common Future*, a World Commission book promoting sustainable development, is embraced by Canada but dismissed by the United States.

1988 Industry-backed wise-use movement established to weaken and destroy U.S. environmental movement. Biologist E. O. Wilson publishes *Biodiversity*, detailing how human activities are affecting the Earth's diversity of species.

1989 *Endangered Spaces*, edited by Monte Hummel, alerts Canadians to the threats to special habitats. *Exxon Valdez* oil tanker accident in Alaska's Prince William Sound.

FIGURE 5 Some important environmental events during the 1980s.

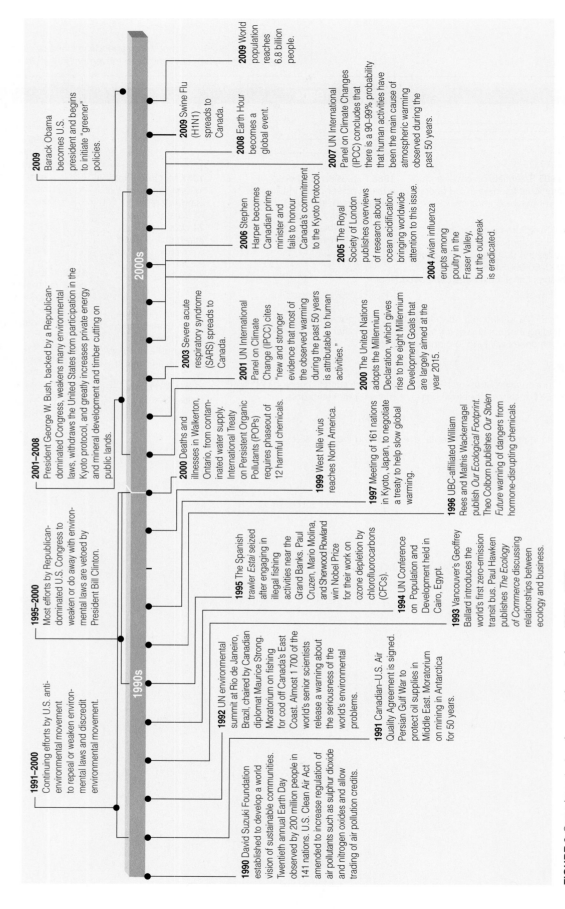

FIGURE 6 Some important environmental events from 1990 to 2009.

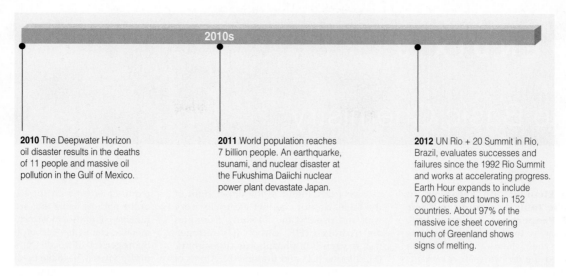

2010 The Deepwater Horizon oil disaster results in the deaths of 11 people and massive oil pollution in the Gulf of Mexico.

2011 World population reaches 7 billion people. An earthquarke, tsunami, and nuclear disaster at the Fukushima Daiichi nuclear power plant devastate Japan.

2012 UN Rio + 20 Summit in Rio, Brazil, evaluates successes and failures since the 1992 Rio Summit and works at accelerating progress. Earth Hour expands to include 7 000 cities and towns in 152 countries. About 97% of the massive ice sheet covering much of Greenland shows signs of melting.

FIGURE 7 Some important environmental events from 2010 to present.

APPENDIX 3

Some Basic Chemistry

How Can Elements Be Arranged in the Periodic Table According to Their Chemical Properties? Chemists have developed a way to classify the elements according to their chemical behaviour, in what is called the *periodic table of elements* (Figure 1). Each of the horizontal rows in the table is called a *period*. Each vertical column lists elements with similar chemical properties and is called a *group*.

The partial periodic table in Figure 1 shows how the elements can be classified as *metals, nonmetals,* and *metalloids*. Most of the elements found to the left and at the bottom of the table are *metals,* which usually conduct electricity and heat and are shiny. Examples are sodium (Na), calcium (Ca), aluminum (Al), iron (Fe), lead (Pb), and mercury (Hg). Atoms of such metals achieve a more stable state by losing one or more of their electrons to form positively charged ions such as Na^+, Ca^{2+}, and Al^{3+}.

Nonmetals, found in the upper right of the table, do not conduct electricity very well and usually are not shiny. Examples are hydrogen (H),* carbon (C), nitrogen (N), oxygen (O), phosphorus (P), sulphur (S), chlorine (Cl), and fluorine (F). Atoms of some nonmetals such as chlorine, oxygen, and sulphur tend to gain one or more electrons lost by metallic atoms to form negatively charged ions such as O^{2-}, S^{2-}, and Cl^-. Atoms of nonmetals can also combine with one another to form molecules in which they share one or more pairs of their electrons.

The elements arranged in a diagonal staircase pattern between the metals and nonmetals have a mixture of metallic and nonmetallic properties and are called *metalloids*. Figure 1 also identifies the elements

---

*Hydrogen, a nonmetal, is placed by itself above the centre of the table because it does not fit very well into any of the groups.

required as *nutrients* for all or some forms of life and elements that are moderately or highly toxic to all or most forms of life. Six non-metallic elements—carbon (C), oxygen (O), hydrogen (H), nitrogen (N), sulphur (S), and phosphorus (P)—make up about 99% of the atoms of all living things.

What Are Ionic and Covalent Bonds? Sodium chloride (NaCl) consists of a three-dimensional network of oppositely charged ions (Na^- and Cl^+) held together by the forces of attraction between opposite charges (Figure 2). The strong forces of attraction between such oppositely charged ions are called *ionic bonds*. Because ionic compounds consist of ions formed from atoms of metallic (positive ions) and nonmetallic (negative ions) elements, they can be described as *metal-nonmetal compounds*.

Figure 3 shows the chemical formulas and shapes of the molecules for several

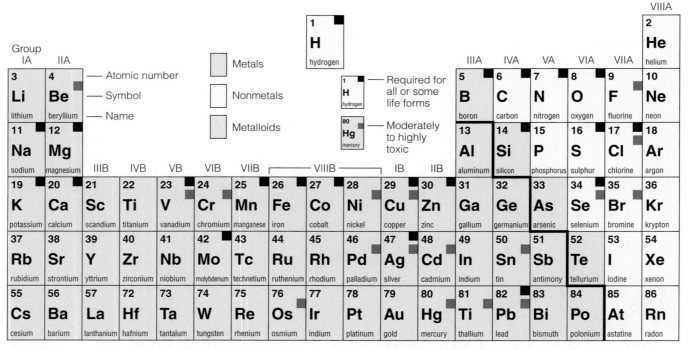

FIGURE 1 Abbreviated *periodic table of elements*. Elements in the same vertical column, called a *group*, have similar chemical properties. To simplify matters at this introductory level, only 72 of the 115 known elements are shown.

common covalent compounds, formed when atoms of one or more nonmetallic elements (Figure 1) combine with one another. The bonds between the atoms in such molecules are called *covalent bonds* and form when the atoms in the molecule share one or more pairs of their electrons. Because they are formed from atoms of nonmetallic elements, molecular or covalent compounds can be described as *nonmetal compounds*.

What Are Hydrogen Bonds? Ionic and covalent bonds form between the ions or atoms *within* a compound. There are also weaker forces of attraction *between* the molecules of covalent compounds (such as water) resulting from an unequal sharing of electrons by two atoms.

For example, an oxygen atom has a much greater attraction for electrons than does a hydrogen atom. Thus, in a water molecule, the electrons shared between the oxygen atom and its two hydrogen atoms are pulled closer to the oxygen atom, but not actually transferred to the oxygen atom. As a result, the oxygen atom in a water molecule has a slightly negative partial charge, and its two hydrogen atoms have a slightly positive partial charge (Figure 4, top).

The slightly positive hydrogen atoms in one water molecule are then attracted to the slightly negative oxygen atoms in another water molecule. These forces of attraction *between* water molecules are called *hydrogen bonds* (Figure 4, top). Hydrogen bonds also form between other covalent molecules or portions of such molecules containing hydrogen and nonmetallic atoms with a strong ability to attract electrons.

Nucleic acids are made by linking hundreds to thousands of four different types of monomers, called *nucleotides*. Each nucleotide consists of **(1)** a phosphate group, **(2)** a sugar molecule containing five carbon atoms (deoxyribose in DNA molecules and ribose in RNA molecules), and **(3)** one of four different nucleotide bases (represented by A, G, C, and T, the first letter in each of their names) (Figure 5).

In the cells of living organisms, these nucleotide units combine in different numbers and sequences to form *nucleic acids* such as various types of DNA and RNA. Hydrogen bonds formed between parts of the four nucleotides in DNA hold two DNA strands together like a spiral staircase, forming a double helix (Figure 6). DNA molecules can unwind and replicate themselves.

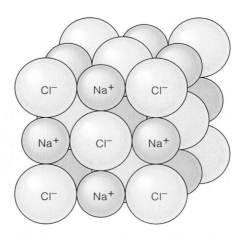

FIGURE 2 A solid crystal of an *ionic compound* such as sodium chloride consists of a three-dimensional array of oppositely charged ions held together by *ionic bonds* resulting from the strong forces of attraction between opposite electrical charges. They are formed when an electron is transferred from a metallic atom such as sodium (Na) to a nonmetallic element such as chlorine (Cl). Such compounds tend to exist as solids at normal room temperature and atmospheric pressure.

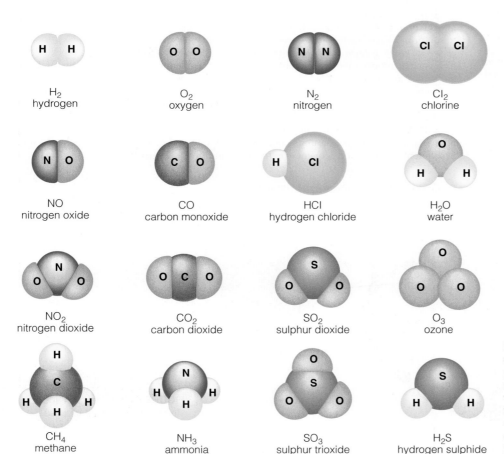

H_2
hydrogen

O_2
oxygen

N_2
nitrogen

Cl_2
chlorine

NO
nitrogen oxide

CO
carbon monoxide

HCl
hydrogen chloride

H_2O
water

NO_2
nitrogen dioxide

CO_2
carbon dioxide

SO_2
sulphur dioxide

O_3
ozone

CH_4
methane

NH_3
ammonia

SO_3
sulphur trioxide

H_2S
hydrogen sulphide

FIGURE 3 Chemical formulas and shapes for some molecular compounds formed when atoms of one or more nonmetallic elements combine with one another. The bonds between the atoms in such molecules are called *covalent bonds*. Molecular compounds tend to exist as gases or liquids at normal room temperature and atmospheric pressure.

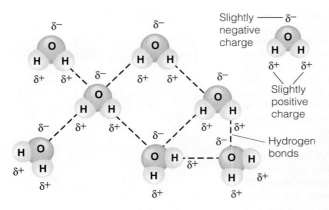

Slightly —— δ− negative charge

Slightly positive charge

Hydrogen bonds

FIGURE 4 *Hydrogen bonds.* Slightly unequal sharing of electrons in the water molecule creates a molecule with a slightly negatively charged end and a slightly positively charged end. Because of this electrical polarity, hydrogen atoms of one water molecule are attracted to oxygen atoms of another water molecule. These forces of attraction *between* water molecules are called *hydrogen bonds*.

FOUR TYPES OF LARGE ORGANIC COMPOUNDS ARE THE MOLECULAR BUILDING BLOCKS OF LIFE

Larger and more complex organic compounds, called *polymers*, consist of a number of basic structural or molecular units (*monomers*) linked by chemical bonds, somewhat like rail cars linked in a freight train. Four types of macromolecules—complex carbohydrates, proteins, nucleic acids, and lipids—are molecular building blocks of life.

Complex carbohydrates consist of two or more monomers of *simple sugars* (such as glucose, Figure 5) linked together. One example is the starches that plants use to store energy and also to provide energy for animals that feed on plants. Another is cellulose, the Earth's most abundant organic compound, which is found in the cell walls of bark, leaves, stems, and roots.

Proteins are large polymer molecules formed by linking together long chains of monomers called *amino acids* (Figure 6).

Living organisms use about 20 different amino acid molecules to build a variety of proteins, which play different roles. Some help to store energy. Some are components of the *immune system* that protects the body against diseases and harmful substances by forming antibodies that make invading agents harmless. Others are *hormones* that are used as chemical messengers in the bloodstreams of animals to turn various bodily functions on or off. In animals, proteins are also components of hair, skin, muscle, and tendons. In addition, some proteins act as *enzymes* that catalyze or speed up certain chemical reactions.

Nucleic acids are large polymer molecules made by linking hundreds to thousands of four types of monomers called *nucleotides*. Two nucleic acids—DNA (deoxyribonucleic acid) and RNA (ribonucleic acid)—participate in the building of proteins and carry hereditary information used to pass traits from parent to offspring. Each nucleotide consists of a *phosphate group*, a *sugar molecule* containing five carbon atoms (deoxyribose in DNA molecules and ribose in RNA molecules), and one of four different *nucleotide bases* (represented by A, G, C, and T, the first letter in each of their names, or A, G, C, and U in RNA) (Figure 7). In the cells of living organisms, these nucleotide units combine in different numbers and sequences to form

nucleic acids such as various types of RNA and DNA (Figure 8).

Hydrogen bonds formed between parts of the four nucleotides in DNA hold two DNA strands together like a spiral staircase, forming a double helix (Figure 8). DNA molecules can unwind and replicate themselves.

The total weight of the DNA needed to reproduce all of the world's people is only about 50 milligrams—the weight of a small match. If the DNA coiled in your body were unwound, it would stretch about 960 million kilometres (600 million miles)—more than six times the distance between the sun and the Earth.

The different molecules of DNA that make up the millions of species found on the Earth are like a vast and diverse genetic library. Each species is a unique book in that library. The *genome* of a species is made up of the entire sequence of DNA "letters" or base pairs that combine to "spell out" the chromosomes in typical members of each species. In 2002, scientists were able to map out the genome for the human species by analyzing the 3.1 billion base sequences in human DNA.

Lipids, a fourth building block of life, are a chemically diverse group of large organic compounds that do not dissolve in water. Examples are *fats and oils* for storing energy (Figure 9), *waxes* for structure, and *steroids* for producing hormones.

Figure 10 shows the relative sizes of simple and complex molecules, cells, and multicelled organisms.

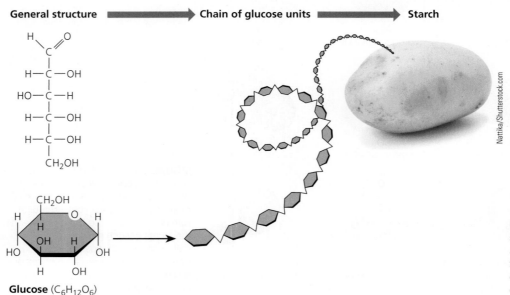

General structure ⟶ **Chain of glucose units** ⟶ **Starch**

Glucose ($C_6H_{12}O_6$)

Nattika/Shutterstock.com

FIGURE 5 Straight-chain and ring structural formulas of glucose, a simple sugar that can be used to build long chains of complex carbohydrates such as starch and cellulose.

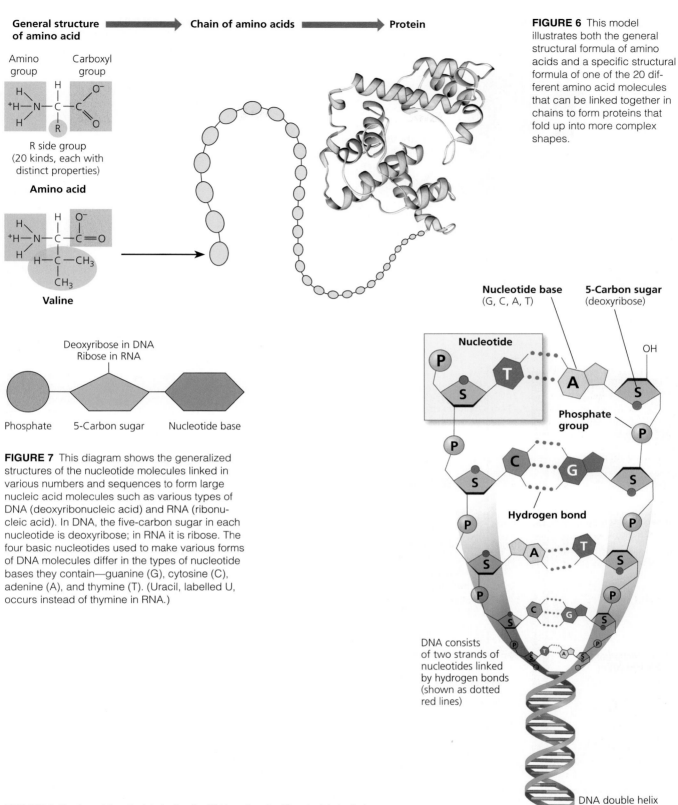

General structure of amino acid ➡ **Chain of amino acids** ➡ **Protein**

Amino group · Carboxyl group

Amino acid

R side group (20 kinds, each with distinct properties)

Valine

FIGURE 6 This model illustrates both the general structural formula of amino acids and a specific structural formula of one of the 20 different amino acid molecules that can be linked together in chains to form proteins that fold up into more complex shapes.

Deoxyribose in DNA
Ribose in RNA

Phosphate · 5-Carbon sugar · Nucleotide base

FIGURE 7 This diagram shows the generalized structures of the nucleotide molecules linked in various numbers and sequences to form large nucleic acid molecules such as various types of DNA (deoxyribonucleic acid) and RNA (ribonucleic acid). In DNA, the five-carbon sugar in each nucleotide is deoxyribose; in RNA it is ribose. The four basic nucleotides used to make various forms of DNA molecules differ in the types of nucleotide bases they contain—guanine (G), cytosine (C), adenine (A), and thymine (T). (Uracil, labelled U, occurs instead of thymine in RNA.)

Nucleotide base (G, C, A, T) · 5-Carbon sugar (deoxyribose)

Nucleotide

Phosphate group

Hydrogen bond

DNA consists of two strands of nucleotides linked by hydrogen bonds (shown as dotted red lines)

DNA double helix

FIGURE 8 Portion of the double helix of a DNA molecule. The double helix is composed of two spiral (helical) strands of nucleotides. Each nucleotide contains a unit of phosphate (P), deoxyribose (S), and one of four nucleotide bases: guanine (G), cytosine (C), adenine (A), and thymine (T). The two strands are held together by hydrogen bonds formed between various pairs of the nucleotide bases. Guanine (G) bonds with cytosine (C), and adenine (A) with thymine (T).

Fatty acid
(lipid)

Fat molecule
(triglyceride)

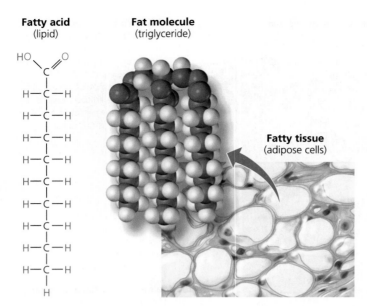

Fatty tissue
(adipose cells)

FIGURE 9 The structural formula of fatty acid that is one form of lipid (left) is shown here. Fatty acids are converted into more complex fat molecules (centre) that are stored in adipose cells (right).

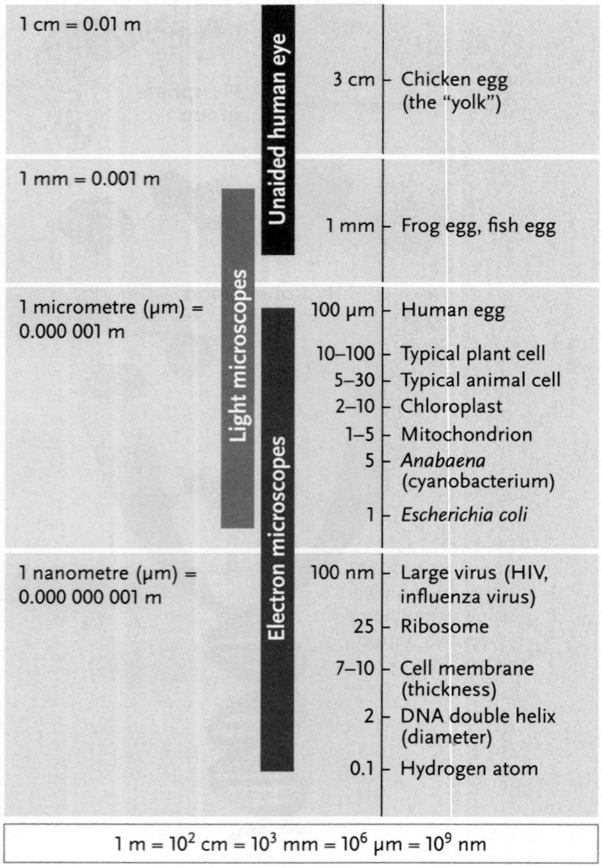

1 cm = 0.01 m		
	3 cm	Chicken egg (the "yolk")
1 mm = 0.001 m		
	1 mm	Frog egg, fish egg
1 micrometre (μm) = 0.000 001 m	100 μm	Human egg
	10–100	Typical plant cell
	5–30	Typical animal cell
	2–10	Chloroplast
	1–5	Mitochondrion
	5	*Anabaena* (cyanobacterium)
	1	*Escherichia coli*
1 nanometre (μm) = 0.000 000 001 m	100 nm	Large virus (HIV, influenza virus)
	25	Ribosome
	7–10	Cell membrane (thickness)
	2	DNA double helix (diameter)
	0.1	Hydrogen atom

Unaided human eye

Light microscopes

Electron microscopes

$$1 \text{ m} = 10^2 \text{ cm} = 10^3 \text{ mm} = 10^6 \text{ μm} = 10^9 \text{ nm}$$

FIGURE 10 This chart compares the relative size of simple molecules, complex molecules, cells, and multicellular organisms. This scale is exponential, not linear. Each unit of measure is ten times larger than the unit preceding it. (From RUSSELL/WOLFE/HERTZ/STARR. *Biology*, 2E. © 2013 Nelson Education Ltd. Reproduced by permission. www.cengage.com/permissions)

How Can Species Be Classified? Biologists classify species into different *kingdoms,* on the basis of similarities and differences in characteristics such as their **(1)** modes of nutrition, **(2)** cell structure, **(3)** appearance, and **(4)** developmental features.

In this book, the Earth's organisms are classified into six kingdoms: *eubacteria, archaebacteria, protists, fungi, plants,* and *animals.* Most bacteria, fungi, and protists are *microorganisms:* organisms so small they cannot be seen with the naked eye.

Eubacteria consist of all single-celled prokaryotic (Figure 4-3, left, p. 62) bacteria except archaebacteria. Examples are various cyanobacteria and bacteria such as *Staphylococcus* and *Streptococcus.*

Archaebacteria are single-celled bacteria that are evolutionarily closer to eukaryotic cells than to eubacteria. Examples are **(1)** methanogens that live in anaerobic sediments of lakes and swamps and in animal guts, **(2)** halophiles that live in extremely salty water, and **(3)** thermophiles that live in hot springs, hydrothermal vents, and acidic soil.

Protists (Protista) are mostly single-celled eukaryotic organisms such as diatoms, dinoflagellates, amoebas, golden brown and yellow-green algae, and protozoans. Some protists cause human diseases such as malaria and sleeping sickness.

Fungi are mostly many-celled, sometimes microscopic, eukaryotic organisms such as mushrooms, moulds, mildews, and yeasts. Many fungi are decomposers. Other fungi kill various plants and cause huge losses of crops and valuable trees.

Plants (Plantae) are many-celled eukaryotic organisms such as mosses, liverworts, frens, conifers, and flowering plants (whose flowers produce seeds that perpetuate the species).

Some plants such as corn and marigolds are *annuals,* which complete their life cycles in one growing season; others are *perennials,* which can live for more than two years, such as roses, grapes, elms, and magnolias.

Animals (Animalia) are also many-celled eukaryotic organisms. Most, called *invertebrates,* have no backbones. They include sponges, jellyfish, worms, arthropods (insects, shrimp, and spiders), mollusks (snails, clams, and octopuses), and echinoderms (sea urchins and sea stars). Insects play roles that are vital to our existence (p. 60). *Vertebrates* (animals with backbones and a brain protected by skull bones) include fishes (sharks and tuna), amphibians (frogs and salamanders), reptiles (crocodiles and snakes), birds (eagles and robins), and mammals (bats, elephants, whales, and humans).

How Are Species Named? Within each kingdom, biologists have created subcategories based on anatomical, physiological, and behavioural characteristics. Kingdoms are divided into *phyla,* which are divided into subgroups called *classes.* Classes are subdivided into *orders,* which are further divided into *families.* Families consist of *genera* (singular, *genus*), and each genus contains one or more *species.* Note that the word *species* is both singular and plural. Figure 1 shows this detailed taxonomic classification for the current human species.

Most people call a species by its common name, such as robin or grizzly bear. Biologists use scientific names (derived from Latin) consisting of two parts (printed in italics or underlined) to describe a species. The first word is the capitalized name (or abbreviation) for the genus to which the organism belongs. This is followed by a lowercase name that distinguishes the species from other members of the same genus. For example, the scientific name of the robin is *Turdus migratorius* (Latin for "migratory thrush"), and the grizzly bear goes by the scientific name *Ursus horribilis* (Latin for "horrible bear").

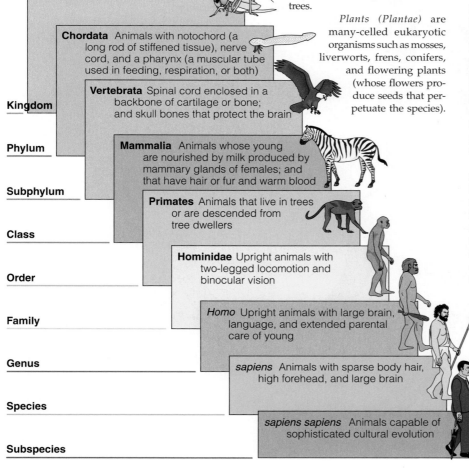

Animalia Many-celled eukaryotic organisms

Chordata Animals with notochord (a long rod of stiffened tissue), nerve cord, and a pharynx (a muscular tube used in feeding, respiration, or both)

Vertebrata Spinal cord enclosed in a backbone of cartilage or bone; and skull bones that protect the brain

Mammalia Animals whose young are nourished by milk produced by mammary glands of females; and that have hair or fur and warm blood

Primates Animals that live in trees or are descended from tree dwellers

Hominidae Upright animals with two-legged locomotion and binocular vision

Homo Upright animals with large brain, language, and extended parental care of young

sapiens Animals with sparse body hair, high forehead, and large brain

sapiens sapiens Animals capable of sophisticated cultural evolution

Kingdom
Phylum
Subphylum
Class
Order
Family
Genus
Species
Subspecies

FIGURE 1 Taxonomic classification of the human subspecies, *Homo sapiens sapiens,* that exists today.

APPENDIX 5

Evolution and Time

The relationship between the evolution of life on Earth and geological time is shown in Figure 1. Evidence indicates that microorganisms (mostly bacteria and, later, protists) that lived in water dominated the early span of biological evolution on Earth, from about 3.7 billion years ago to about 1 billion years ago. Then plants and animals began evolving in the seas. Fossil and DNA evidence suggests that plants began moving onto land about 780 million years ago, and animals began invading the land about 370 million years ago. Humans evolved a very short time ago compared to the history of life on Earth, yet we have already had a major impact on the planet. Some of our actions are causing the premature extinction of other species (see Chapters 11 and 12).

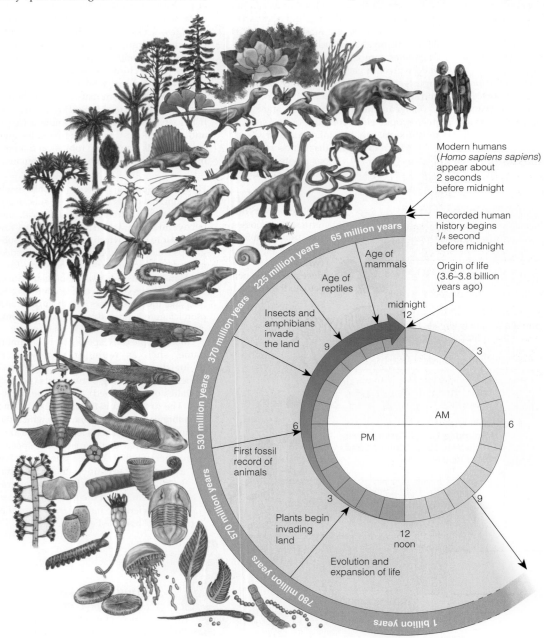

Modern humans
(*Homo sapiens sapiens*)
appear about
2 seconds
before midnight

Recorded human
history begins
¼ second
before midnight

Origin of life
(3.6–3.8 billion
years ago)

Age of
mammals

Age of
reptiles

65 million years

225 million years

370 million years

530 million years

570 million years

780 million years

1 billion years

Insects and
amphibians
invade
the land

First fossil
record of
animals

Plants begin
invading
land

Evolution and
expansion of life

midnight
12

9

6

3

3

6

9

AM

PM

12
noon

FIGURE 1 Natural capital: greatly simplified overview of the evolution of life on Earth, which was preceded by about 1 billion years of chemical evolution. The information is presented in the form of a clock to illustrate the relative timing of events, including the brief time that modern humans have lived on the planet.

APPENDIX 6

Brief History of the Age of Oil

Some milestones in the Age of Oil:

- **1859:** First oil well is drilled in North America.
- **1864:** Exports of North American oil begin.
- **1869:** Internal combustion engine is invented in Germany.
- **1903:** Henry Ford's automobile assembly line makes affordable mass-produced automobiles a reality.
- **1905:** Oil supplies 10% of North American energy.
- **1930:** Because of an oil glut, oil sells for 10¢ a barrel.
- **1953:** U.S. oil companies account for about half of the world's oil production and the United States is the world's leading oil exporter.
- **1960:** OPEC formed so developing countries, with most of the world's known oil and projected oil reserves, can get a higher price for their oil.
- **1973:** United States uses 30% of the world's oil, imports 36% of this oil, and has only 5% of the world's proven oil reserves.
- **1973–4:** OPEC reduces oil imports to the West and bans oil exports to the United States because of its support for Israel in the 18-day Yom Kippur War with Egypt and Syria. World oil prices rise sharply (Figure 17-11, p. 391) and lead to double-digit inflation in North America and a global economic recession.
- **1979:** Iran's Islamic Revolution shuts down most of Iran's oil production and reduces world oil production.

- **1981:** Iran–Iraq war pushes global oil prices to a historic high.
- **1983:** Facing an oil glut, OPEC cuts its oil prices.
- **August 1990–June 1991:** United States and its allies fight the Persian Gulf War to oust Iraqi invaders of Kuwait and to protect Western access to Saudi Arabian and Kuwaiti oil supplies.
- **March 2003:** United States and some allies, primarily the United Kingdom, engage Iraq in the Second Gulf War, overthrow Iraqi dictator Saddam Hussein, and gain control of Iraqi oil fields. The repercussions of these actions are still unfolding.
- **2004:** OPEC has 67% of world oil reserves and produces 40% of the world's oil. United States has only 2.9% of oil reserves, uses 26% of the world's oil production, and imports 55% of its oil.
- **2006:** Some oil experts claim that the peak of conventional oil supplies occurs this year.
- **2010–30:** Production of oil from the world's conventional oil reserves is expected to decline. Oil prices expected to increase gradually as the demand for oil increasingly exceeds the supply—unless the world decreases demand by wasting less energy and shifting to other sources of energy.
- **2010–48:** Development of Alberta's oil sands expected to continue to increase Canada's oil reserves. Domestic U.S. oil reserves projected to be 80% depleted.
- **2042–83:** A gradual decline in dependence on oil is expected.

Index

Non-native (exotic) species, **160**, 258
  effect of on fish populations, 281–82
  extinction threats from, 255–57
  in Great Lakes, 294–95
Nonpersistent pollutants, **51**
Nonpoint sources, **10**, **543**
Nonrenewable energy resources, 382–415
  coal, **401**–3
  fossil fuels, 383–84. *See also* Fossil fuels
  natural gas, **398**–99
  oil, 388–89
Nonrenewable mineral resources, **370**–71
  depletion time of, **378**
  as energy resource, 370
  environmental effects of, 372–75
  finding, removing, and processing, 371–72
  life cycle of, 373–75
  substitutes for, 380
Nonreplenishable aquifers, 339
Nonthreshold dose-response model, 457*f*
Nontransmissible diseases, **462**
Nonuse values, 218, 646
No-problem school, 686
North America
  environmental history of, 25–31
  See also Canada; Mexico; United States
North American bison, extinction of, 21
North American Free Trade Agreement
    (NAFTA), 351
North American Waterfowl Management Plan,
    269, 296
North Bay, Ontario, 633–34
Northwest Atlantic Fisheries Organization
    (NAFO), 290
Northwest Game Act, 27
Nosko, Peter, 494
NPP. *See* Net primary productivity
Nuclear changes, **51**–54
Nuclear energy, 403–15
  advantages and disadvantages of, 407–8
  breeder nuclear fission, **414**
  vs. coal, 408*f*
    expense of, 413
  future of, 414–15
  nuclear fission reactors, 403–4, 403*f*
  nuclear fuel cells, 406–7
  nuclear fusion, 53, 414
Nuclear fission reactors, 403–4, 403*f*
Nuclear fission, **52**–53, 53*f*
Nuclear fuel cycle, 406–8, 406*f*
Nuclear fusion, **53**, 53*f*, 414
Nuclear power plants
  case study: Chernobyl, 382
  decommissioned, 413
  energy efficiency of, 420, 421
  radioactive waste from, 411–13
  vulnerability of to attack, 408
Nuclei, 45*f*
Nucleic acids, 44, A10
Nucleotides, 45*f*
Nucleus, 41–42
Nutrient cycles, **80**
Nutritional deficiencies, 315
Nutritional mutualism, 169–70

O

Obaid, Thorya, 209
Obama, Barack, 31, 667*f*
Obesity, 317
Ocean Acidification, 519

Ocean bottoms, loss and degradation of, 281
Ocean currents, effect of on climate, 118
Ocean drilling, 557
Ocean fisheries, 301
Ocean pollution, 554–56
Oceans
  carbon dioxide storage in, 517–18, 526
  dumping of wastes in, 556
  pollution in, 554–58, 555*f*
  oil pollution in, 556–58
  research on, 142
  role of, in carbon cycle, 83
  See also Saltwater life zones
Oceans Act, 671*t*
Ogallala Aquifer, 350
O horizon, 77
Oil, 388–95
  advantages and disadvantages of, 393–95
  Age of Oil, A15
  Arctic National Wildlife Refuge, drilling
    in, 392
  crude, **388**–89
  drilling, 389
  growing demand for, 391–93
  refining, 389*f*
  U.S. consumption of, 391
  usefulness of heavy, 395–98
Oil industry, 388
Oil pollution, in oceans, 556–58
Oil prices, 391*f*
Oil sand, **395**–98
Oil shale, 398*f*
Oil-soluble toxins, 455
Oil spills, 558–59
Oil supply
  countries with greatest, 389
  time until depletion of, 390–91
Oil tanker accidents, 556–57
Olah, George A., 441
Old-growth forests, **220**
Oligotrophic lake, **151**
Omnivores, **70**
One Planet perspective, 10
Ontario
  air quality in, 480
  Environmental Bill of Rights (EBR), 662
Ontario Breeding Bird Atlas, 275, 275*f*
Ontario Herpetofaunal Atlas, 275
Open dumps, **599**
Open net-cages, 292
Open nuclear fuel cycle, 407
Open-pit mining, **371**, 372*f*
Open sea, 143, **148**
Optimum levels, of pollution, 643–44
Optimum sustained yield (OSY), 288
Option value, 646
Oral rehydration therapy, 469
Orders, **60**
Ore, **370**
Organic compounds, **44**
Organic farming, 300
Organic fertilizer, **314**
Organic matter, 586
Organic solar cells, 431–33
Organisms, **60**
  in aquatic life zones, 140
  classification of, 60
  consumers, **70**
  eukaryotic, **60**
  genetically modified, **104**–5

knowledge of past, 95
  in open sea, 143
  producers, **68**
  prokaryotic, **60**
  tolerance limits of, 66
Organization of Petroleum Exporting
    Countries (OPEC), 389
Organizational hierarchies, 668–69
Orr, David, 688
Osoyoos, British Columbia, 125
Our Common Future (The Brundtland Report),
    29, 31
Outdoor air pollution, 478–83, 500–1, 504
Output pollution control, **11**
Outputs, 38
Overburden, **371**
Overconsumption, 13
Overfishing, 281–82, 293–94, **328**
  Grand Banks, 290
  ways to reduce, 288–89
Overgrazing, **324**
Overnutrition, **317**
Overshoots, population, 183, 183*f*
Overweight, 317
Oxpeckers, 170*f*
Oxygen (O), 40, 478
  in aquatic life zones, 142
  in atmosphere, 94
Oxygen-demanding wastes, 542*t*
Oxygen sag curve, 545
Ozone, 41, 94
  as air pollutant, 482*t*, 483*f*
  hydrogen and, 445
  in stratosphere, 478
Ozone-depleting compounds (ODCs), 532
Ozone depletion, 530–35, 532*f*
  causes of, 530–32
  characteristics of, 513*t*
  effect on Earth's poles, 532–33
  human protection and, 535
  ozone protection, 535–36
  UV radiation and, 533
Ozone layer, protection of, 535–36

P

Packaging, reducing, 587–89
Paine, Robert, 164
Pakistan, population growth in, 201
Pandas, 259
Pandemic, 465
Pangaea, 103*f*
Paper products, 586
Paper recycling, 230, 595–96
Paper, tree-free, 230
Paracelsus, 453, 455
Para-dichlorobenzene, 496*f*
Parasites, 462
Parasitism, **169**–71
Parent material, 78
Parks Canada, 235–36
Parts per million (ppm), 50
Passenger pigeons, 249, 250–51
Passive data collection, 88
Passive solar heating system, **429**, 429*f*, 430*f*
Pastures, **322**
Pathogens, 462, 463*f*
Paty, Alma Hale, 380
Pay-as-you-throw (PAUT) system, 595
Peatland, 154
Peer review, 36–37

factors governing changes in, 180–81
predators and, 185
Portland, Oregon, 629
Positive externalities, 647
Positive feedback loop, **39**
Possibility, 453
Postindustrial stage, 207
Potash, 377
Potential energy, 46
Poverty
environmental problems and, 12–13, 12*f*
reduction of, 652–55, 653*f*
Poverty gap ratio, 659
Poverty reduction, environmental quality and, 652–55
Power towers, 431
Prairie Farm Rehabilitation Program, 28
Prairie potholes, 154
Prairies, **125**, 128*f*
Precautionary principle, **176**, 289, **462**, 523, 665
Precious stones, 377
Precipitation, 81
annual, 126*f*
in Canada, 306*f*, 341*f*
changes, from global warming, 544
as limiting factor, 66
seasonal changes in, 116
Pre-Columbian era, 25
Predation, **164**–69
Predators, 166
control of, 260
role of, in controlling population size, 185
sharks, 166–67
Preindustrial stage, 207
Premature death
from air pollution, 498
causes of, 13
Preservationist movement, 27
Prevailing winds, 116
Preventable deaths, from overnutrition, 317
Prevention principle, 665
Prey species, 166, 168*f*
Price inelasticity, 640
Primary pollutants, **479**
Primary productivity, in ecosystems, 75–76
Primary sewage treatment, 560, 561*f*
Primary succession, **171**
Pimm, Stuart, 103
Principle of enoughness, 692
Principles of Political Economy (Malthus), 690
Principles of sustainability, 16–17
Private goods, 640
Private ownership
of free-access resources, 7
of water resources, 345
Probability, 453
Producers, **68**
Product eco-labelling, 652
Productive forest, 227
Product stewardship policies, 598
Profit, 639
Profit-making organizations, 664
Profundal zone, 149
Project FeederWatch, 274, 274*f*
Prokaryotic organisms, **60**, 62*f*
Proof, 37
Proteins, 44
Protists, A13, 462
Protons, **41**
Public lands, in Canada, 219–20

Public participation principle, 665
Public services, 640
Purchasing power parity (PPP), 658
Pure free-market economic system, **639**
Purple loosestrife, 283, 283*f*, 284
Purse-seine fishing, 326
Pyramid of energy flow, **74**, 74*f*
Pyrethrum, 571

Q

Queen's University, 675

R

Radiation, 52*f*
electromagnetic, **46–47**
hormesis, 458
infrared, 65
ionizing, **47**, 51
nonionizing, **47**
ultraviolet, 94, 484, 530–35
Radiation-measuring equipment, 371
Radioactive decay, 51
Radioactive isotopes, **51**
Radioactive substances, 480*f*
Radioactive wastes
in Canada, 405*f*
from nuclear energy, 400, 411
in water, 542*t*
Radioisotopes, **51**
Radon gas, 496*f*, 497, 497*f*
Rail systems, 622
Rainfall, flooding and, 356–57
Rain shadow effect, **121**, 121*f*
Ramsar Convention, 296
Ramsar sites, 237–39, 38*f*
Random dispersion, 180
Range, **63**
Range of tolerance, **65–66**, 68*f*
Rangelands, 301
meat production on, 322–23
sustainable management of, 324–25
Rapid rail, 626–27*f*
Rationalism, 685
Ray, G. Carleton, 279
Reagan, Ronald, 29, 291, 502
Realized niche, **98**
Reasoning
deductive, **37**
inductive, 36–37
Reconciliation ecology, **271**–75, 630
definition of, **271**
implementation of, 264–65
public participation, 275
Recycling, 593–98
wood and paper, 230
composting, 594
definition of, **593**
plastics, 595–96, 596*f*
product life cycle, 596, 597*f*
solid waste and, 594–95, 595*f*
types of, 593
wastepaper and, 595–96
Red River, 357
Red tides, 109
Redwood sorrel, 171
Rees, William, 9
Refillable containers, 592
Refineries, 389*f*
Refuse-derived fuel incinerators, 599

Regulations
on free-access resources, 7
to improve environmental quality, 648–52
Relativism, 685
Reliable runoff, **338**, 339
Remedial Action Plans (RAPs), 551
Remote sensing, 88
Renewable energy, 428–33
biomass, 437–42
geothermal energy, 442–43
hydropower, 433–34
to reduce global warming, 523
solar energy, 428–33
wind power, 434–37
Renewable resources, **6**, 7*f*
environmental degradation of, **7**
overharvesting of, 190
sustainable yield, **7**
Renewable water, 343
Replacement-level fertility, **198**, 202
Reproducibility, 36
Reproductive isolation, **102**
Reproductive patterns, 186–88
asexual reproduction, 186
competitive, 186
definition of, **186**
K-selected species, 186, 186*f*
opportunistic, 186–88
r-selected species, 186, 186*f*
sexual reproduction, 186
survivorship curves, 187
types of, 186–87
Reproductive time lags, 183
Research
field, 87
laboratory, 88
Reservoirs, 346–48
pollution of, 545–46
Resilience, **175**
Resource consumption, relationship between environmental problems and, 13
Resource exchange webs, 589
Resource management, market prices and, 643–44
Resource partitioning, 164–65, 165*f*
Resource productivity, **46**
Resource productivity revolution, 589
Resources, **6**, 7*f*, 641*f*
common-property, **7**
definition of, **6**
ecological footprint and, 8, 8*f*
garbage, 586–87
main types of, 7*f*
perpetual, 6
renewable, 6–7
solid waste, 585, 586*f*
waste, 585–87
Resource-use permits, 650
Respiratory disease, 13, 490, 498, 498*f*, 499*f*
Respiratory system, 498*f*
air pollution and, 498
Reusable shopping bags, 592
Reuse, 592–93, 595*f*, 597–98
Reverse osmosis, 352
Reversibility principle, 664
Rhinoceros horns, 259
Rice, 301
Richter scale, **368**
Rio+20 Summit on Sustainable Development, 677
Riparian zones, 324*f*

CHAPTERS DEALING WITH THE U.N. MILLENNIUM DEVELOPMENT GOALS

Symbol	Goal	Textbook Chapter
1 ERADICATE EXTREME POVERTY AND HUNGER	Goal 1: Eradicate Extreme Hunger and Poverty	1, 14, 26, 28
2 ACHIEVE UNIVERSAL PRIMARY EDUCATION	Goal 2: Achieve Universal Primary Education	1, 10, 28
3 PROMOTE GENDER EQUALITY AND EMPOWER WOMEN	Goal 3: Promote Gender Equality and Empower Women	1, 10, 28
4 REDUCE CHILD MORTALITY	Goal 4: Reduce Child Mortality	1, 10, 28
5 IMPROVE MATERNAL HEALTH	Goal 5: Improve Maternal Health	1, 10, 28
6 COMBAT HIV/AIDS, MALARIA AND OTHER DISEASES	Goal 6: Combat HIV/AIDS, Malaria and Other diseases	1, 19, 28
7 ENSURE ENVIRONMENTAL SUSTAINABILITY	Goal 7: Ensure Environmental Sustainability	1, 9, 13, 15, 21, 25, 28
8 GLOBAL PARTNERSHIP FOR DEVELOPMENT	Goal 8: Develop a Global Partnership for Development	1, 27, 28